INSTRUCTOR'S SOLUTIONS MANUAL
SINGLE VARIABLE

MARK WOODARD
Furman University

CALCULUS
EARLY TRANSCENDENTALS
SECOND EDITION

William Briggs
University of Colorado at Denver

Lyle Cochran
Whitworth University

Bernard Gillett
University of Colorado at Boulder

with the assistance of
Eric Schulz
Walla Walla Community College

PEARSON

Boston   Columbus   Indianapolis   New York   San Francisco   Upper Saddle River
Amsterdam   Cape Town   Dubai   London   Madrid   Milan   Munich   Paris   Montreal   Toronto
Delhi   Mexico City   São Paulo   Sydney   Hong Kong   Seoul   Singapore   Taipei   Tokyo

Copyright © 2015, 2011 Pearson Education, Inc.
Publishing as Pearson, 75 Arlington Street, Boston, MA 02116.

ISBN-13: 978-0-321-95422-0
ISBN-10: 0-321-95422-X

1 2 3 4 5 6 CRK 17 16 15 14 13

www.pearsonhighered.com

PEARSON

Contents

Chapter 1

Functions

1.1 Review of Functions

1.1.1 A function is a rule which assigns each domain element to a unique range element. The independent variable is associated with the domain, while the dependent variable is associated with the range.

1.1.2 The independent variable belongs to the domain, while the dependent variable belongs to the range.

1.1.3 The vertical line test is used to determine whether a given graph represents a function. (Specifically, it tests whether the variable associated with the vertical axis is a function of the variable associated with the horizontal axis.) If every vertical line which intersects the graph does so in exactly one point, then the given graph represents a function. If any vertical line $x = a$ intersects the curve in more than one point, then there is more than one range value for the domain value $x = a$, so the given curve does not represent a function.

1.1.4 $f(2) = \frac{1}{2^3+1} = \frac{1}{9}$. $f(y^2) = \frac{1}{(y^2)^3+1} = \frac{1}{y^6+1}$.

1.1.5 Item i. is true while item ii. isn't necessarily true. In the definition of function, item i. is stipulated. However, item ii. need not be true – for example, the function $f(x) = x^2$ has two different domain values associated with the one range value 4, because $f(2) = f(-2) = 4$.

1.1.6 $(f \circ g)(x) = f(g(x)) = f(x^3 - 2) = \sqrt{x^3 - 2}$
$(g \circ f)(x) = g(f(x)) = g(\sqrt{x}) = x^{3/2} - 2$.
$(f \circ f)(x) = f(f(x)) = f(\sqrt{x}) = \sqrt{\sqrt{x}} = \sqrt[4]{x}$.
$(g \circ g)(x) = g(g(x)) = g(x^3 - 2) = (x^3 - 2)^3 - 2 = x^9 - 6x^6 + 12x^3 - 10$

1.1.7 $f(g(2)) = f(-2) = f(2) = 2$. The fact that $f(-2) = f(2)$ follows from the fact that f is an even function.
  $g(f(-2)) = g(f(2)) = g(2) = -2$.

1.1.8 The domain of $f \circ g$ is the subset of the domain of g whose range is in the domain of f. Thus, we need to look for elements x in the domain of g so that $g(x)$ is in the domain of f.

1.1.9 When f is an even function, we have $f(-x) = f(x)$ for all x in the domain of f, which ensures that the graph of the function is symmetric about the y-axis.

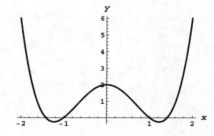

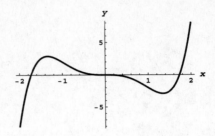

1.1.10 When f is an odd function, we have $f(-x) = -f(x)$ for all x in the domain of f, which ensures that the graph of the function is symmetric about the origin.

1.1.11 Graph A does not represent a function, while graph B does. Note that graph A fails the vertical line test, while graph B passes it.

1.1.12 Graph A does not represent a function, while graph B does. Note that graph A fails the vertical line test, while graph B passes it.

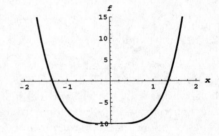

1.1.13 The domain of this function is the set of a real numbers. The range is $[-10, \infty)$.

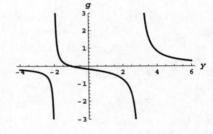

1.1.14 The domain of this function is $(-\infty, -2) \cup (-2, 3) \cup (3, \infty)$. The range is the set of all real numbers.

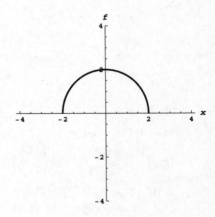

1.1.15 The domain of this function is $[-2, 2]$. The range is $[0, 2]$.

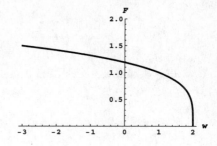

1.1.16 The domain of this function is $(-\infty, 2]$. The range is $[0, \infty)$.

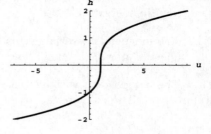

1.1.17 The domain and the range for this function are both the set of all real numbers.

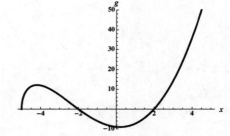

1.1.18 The domain of this function is $[-5, \infty)$. The range is approximately $[-9.03, \infty)$.

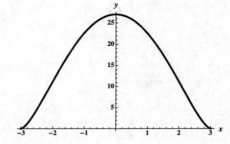

1.1.19 The domain of this function is $[-3, 3]$. The range is $[0, 27]$.

1.1.20 The domain of this function is $(-\infty, \infty)]$. The range is $(0, 1]$.

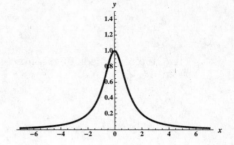

1.1.21 The independent variable t is elapsed time and the dependent variable d is distance above the ground. The domain in context is $[0, 8]$

1.1.22 The independent variable t is elapsed time and the dependent variable d is distance above the water. The domain in context is $[0, 2]$

1.1.23 The independent variable h is the height of the water in the tank and the dependent variable V is the volume of water in the tank. The domain in context is $[0, 50]$

1.1.24 The independent variable r is the radius of the balloon and the dependent variable V is the volume of the balloon. The domain in context is $[0, \sqrt[3]{3/(4\pi)}]$

1.1.25 $f(10) = 96$

1.1.26 $f(p^2) = (p^2)^2 - 4 = p^4 - 4$

1.1.27 $g(1/z) = (1/z)^3 = \frac{1}{z^3}$

1.1.28 $F(y^4) = \frac{1}{y^4 - 3}$

1.1.29 $F(g(y)) = F(y^3) = \frac{1}{y^3 - 3}$

1.1.30 $f(g(w)) = f(w^3) = (w^3)^2 - 4 = w^6 - 4$

1.1.31 $g(f(u)) = g(u^2 - 4) = (u^2 - 4)^3$

1.1.32 $\frac{f(2+h) - f(2)}{h} = \frac{(2+h)^2 - 4 - 0}{h} = \frac{4 + 4h + h^2 - 4}{h} = \frac{4h + h^2}{h} = 4 + h$

1.1.33 $F(F(x)) = F\left(\frac{1}{x-3}\right) = \frac{1}{\frac{1}{x-3} - 3} = \frac{1}{\frac{1}{x-3} - \frac{3(x-3)}{x-3}} = \frac{1}{\frac{10 - 3x}{x-3}} = \frac{x - 3}{10 - 3x}$

1.1.34 $g(F(f(x))) = g(F(x^2 - 4)) = g\left(\frac{1}{x^2 - 4 - 3}\right) = \left(\frac{1}{x^2 - 7}\right)^3$

1.1.35 $f(\sqrt{x+4}) = (\sqrt{x+4})^2 - 4 = x + 4 - 4 = x$.

1.1.36 $F((3x+1)/x) = \frac{1}{\frac{3x+1}{x} - 3} = \frac{1}{\frac{3x+1-3x}{x}} = \frac{x}{3x + 1 - 3x} = x$.

1.1.37 $g(x) = x^3 - 5$ and $f(x) = x^{10}$. The domain of h is the set of all real numbers.

1.1.38 $g(x) = x^6 + x^2 + 1$ and $f(x) = \frac{2}{x^2}$. The domain of h is the set of all real numbers.

1.1.39 $g(x) = x^4 + 2$ and $f(x) = \sqrt{x}$. The domain of h is the set of all real numbers.

1.1.40 $g(x) = x^3 - 1$ and $f(x) = \frac{1}{\sqrt{x}}$. The domain of h is the set of all real numbers for which $x^3 - 1 > 0$, which corresponds to the set $(1, \infty)$.

1.1.41 $(f \circ g)(x) = f(g(x)) = f(x^2 - 4) = |x^2 - 4|$. The domain of this function is the set of all real numbers.

1.1.42 $(g \circ f)(x) = g(f(x)) = g(|x|) = |x|^2 - 4 = x^2 - 4$. The domain of this function is the set of all real numbers.

1.1.43 $(f \circ G)(x) = f(G(x)) = f\left(\frac{1}{x-2}\right) = \left|\frac{1}{x-2}\right|$. The domain of this function is the set of all real numbers except for the number 2.

1.1.44 $(f \circ g \circ G)(x) = f(g(G(x))) = f\left(g\left(\frac{1}{x-2}\right)\right) = f\left(\left(\frac{1}{x-2}\right)^2 - 4\right) = \left|\left(\frac{1}{x-2}\right)^2 - 4\right|$. The domain of this function is the set of all real numbers except for the number 2.

1.1.45 $(G \circ g \circ f)(x) = G(g(f(x))) = G(g(|x|)) = G(x^2 - 4) = \frac{1}{x^2 - 4 - 2} = \frac{1}{x^2 - 6}$. The domain of this function is the set of all real numbers except for the numbers $\pm\sqrt{6}$.

1.1.46 $(F \circ g \circ g)(x) = F(g(g(x))) = F(g(x^2 - 4)) = F((x^2 - 4)^2 - 4) = \sqrt{(x^2 - 4)^2 - 4} = \sqrt{x^4 - 8x^2 + 12}$. The domain of this function consists of the numbers x so that $x^4 - 8x^2 + 12 \geq 0$. Because $x^4 - 8x^2 + 12 = (x^2 - 6) \cdot (x^2 - 2)$, we see that this expression is zero for $x = \pm\sqrt{6}$ and $x = \pm\sqrt{2}$, By looking between these points, we see that the expression is greater than or equal to zero for the set $(-\infty, -\sqrt{6}] \cup [-\sqrt{2}, \sqrt{2}] \cup [\sqrt{2}, \infty)$.

1.1.47 $(g \circ g)(x) = g(g(x)) = g(x^2 - 4) = (x^2 - 4)^2 - 4 = x^4 - 8x^2 + 16 - 4 = x^4 - 8x^2 + 12$. The domain is the set of all real numbers.

1.1.48 $(G \circ G)(x) = G(G(x)) = G(1/(x-2)) = \frac{1}{\frac{1}{x-2} - 2} = \frac{1}{\frac{1 - 2(x-2)}{x-2}} = \frac{x-2}{1 - 2x + 4} = \frac{x-2}{5 - 2x}$. Then $G \circ G$ is defined except where the denominator vanishes, so its domain is the set of all real numbers except for $x = \frac{5}{2}$.

1.1.49 Because $(x^2 + 3) - 3 = x^2$, we may choose $f(x) = x - 3$.

1.1.50 Because the reciprocal of $x^2 + 3$ is $\frac{1}{x^2 + 3}$, we may choose $f(x) = \frac{1}{x}$.

1.1.51 Because $(x^2 + 3)^2 = x^4 + 6x^2 + 9$, we may choose $f(x) = x^2$.

1.1.52 Because $(x^2 + 3)^2 = x^4 + 6x^2 + 9$, and the given expression is 11 more than this, we may choose $f(x) = x^2 + 11$.

1.1.53 Because $(x^2)^2 + 3 = x^4 + 3$, this expression results from squaring x^2 and adding 3 to it. Thus we may choose $f(x) = x^2$.

1.1.54 Because $x^{2/3} + 3 = (\sqrt[3]{x})^2 + 3$, we may choose $f(x) = \sqrt[3]{x}$.

1.1.55

    a. $(f \circ g)(2) = f(g(2)) = f(2) = 4$.

    b. $g(f(2)) = g(4) = 1$.

    c. $f(g(4)) = f(1) = 3$.

    d. $g(f(5)) = g(6) = 3$.

    e. $f(f(8)) = f(8) = 8$.

    f. $g(f(g(5))) = g(f(2)) = g(4) = 1$.

1.1.56

    a. $h(g(0)) = h(0) = -1$.

    b. $g(f(4)) = g(-1) = -1$.

    c. $h(h(0)) = h(-1) = 0$.

    d. $g(h(f(4))) = g(h(-1)) = g(0) = 0$.

    e. $f(f(f(1))) = f(f(0)) = f(1) = 0$.

    f. $h(h(h(0))) = h(h(-1)) = h(0) = -1$.

    g. $f(h(g(2))) = f(h(3)) = f(0) = 1$.

    h. $g(f(h(4))) = g(f(4)) = g(-1) = -1$.

    i. $g(g(g(1))) = g(g(2)) = g(3) = 4$.

    j. $f(f(h(3))) = f(f(0)) = f(1) = 0$.

1.1.57 $\frac{f(x+h) - f(x)}{h} = \frac{(x+h)^2 - x^2}{h} = \frac{(x^2 + 2hx + h^2) - x^2}{h} = \frac{h(2x+h)}{h} = 2x + h$.

1.1.58 $\frac{f(x+h) - f(x)}{h} = \frac{4(x+h) - 3 - (4x - 3)}{h} = \frac{4x + 4h - 3 - 4x + 3}{h} = \frac{4h}{h} = 4$.

1.1.59 $\frac{f(x+h)-f(x)}{h} = \frac{\frac{2}{x+h}-\frac{2}{x}}{h} = \frac{\frac{2x-2(x+h)}{x(x+h)}}{h} = \frac{2x-2x-2h}{h(x)(x+h)} = -\frac{2h}{h(x)(x+h)} = -\frac{2}{(x)(x+h)}.$

1.1.60 $\frac{f(x+h)-f(x)}{h} = \frac{2(x+h)^2-3(x+h)+1-(2x^2-3x+1)}{h} = \frac{2x^2+4xh+2h^2-3x-3h+1-2x^2+3x-1}{h} =$
$\frac{4xh+2h^2-3h}{h} = \frac{h(4x+2h-3)}{h} = 4x + 2h - 3.$

1.1.61 $\frac{f(x+h)-f(x)}{h} = \frac{\frac{x+h}{x+h+1}-\frac{x}{x+1}}{h} = \frac{\frac{(x+h)(x+1)-x(x+h+1)}{(x+1)(x+h+1)}}{h} = \frac{x^2+x+hx+h-x^2-xh-x}{h(x+1)(x+h+1)} =$
$\frac{h}{h(x+1)(x+h+1)} = \frac{1}{(x+1)(x+h+1)}$

1.1.62 $\frac{f(x)-f(a)}{x-a} = \frac{x^4-a^4}{x-a} = \frac{(x^2-a^2)(x^2+a^2)}{x-a} = \frac{(x-a)(x+a)(x^2+a^2)}{x-a} = (x+a)(x^2+a^2).$

1.1.63 $\frac{f(x)-f(a)}{x-a} = \frac{x^3-2x-(a^3-2a)}{x-a} = \frac{(x^3-a^3)-2(x-a)}{x-a} = \frac{(x-a)(x^2+ax+a^2)-2(x-a)}{x-a} =$
$\frac{(x-a)(x^2+ax+a^2-2)}{x-a} = x^2 + ax + a^2 - 2.$

1.1.64 $\frac{f(x)-f(a)}{x-a} = \frac{4-4x-x^2-(4-4a-a^2)}{x-a} = \frac{-4(x-a)-(x^2-a^2)}{x-a} = \frac{-4(x-a)-(x-a)(x+a)}{x-a} =$
$\frac{(x-a)(-4-(x+a))}{x-a} = -4 - x - a.$

1.1.65 $\frac{f(x)-f(a)}{x-a} = \frac{\frac{-4}{x^2}-\frac{-4}{a^2}}{x-a} = \frac{\frac{-4a^2+4x^2}{a^2x^2}}{x-a} = \frac{4(x^2-a^2)}{(x-a)a^2x^2} = \frac{4(x-a)(x+a)}{(x-a)a^2x^2} = \frac{4(x+a)}{a^2x^2}.$

1.1.66 $\frac{f(x)-f(a)}{x-a} = \frac{\frac{1}{x}-x^2-(\frac{1}{a}-a^2)}{x-a} = \frac{\frac{1}{x}-\frac{1}{a}}{x-a} - \frac{x^2-a^2}{x-a} = \frac{\frac{a-x}{ax}}{x-a} - \frac{(x-a)(x+a)}{x-a} = -\frac{1}{ax} - (x+a).$

1.1.67

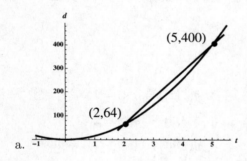

a.

b. The slope of the secant line is given by $\frac{400-64}{5-2} = \frac{336}{3} = 112$ feet per second. The object falls at an average rate of 112 feet per second over the interval $2 \le t \le 5$.

1.1.68

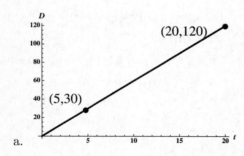

a.

b. The slope of the secant line is given by $\frac{120-30}{20-5} = \frac{90}{15} = 6$ degrees per second. The second hand moves at an average rate of 6 degrees per second over the interval $5 \le t \le 20$.

1.1.69

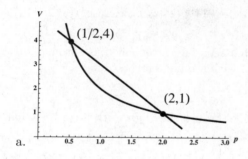

a.

b. The slope of the secant line is given by $\frac{1-4}{2-(1/2)} = -\frac{3}{3/2} = -2$ cubic cm per atmosphere. The volume decreases at an average rate of 2 cubic cm per atmosphere over the interval $0.5 \le p \le 2$.

1.1.70

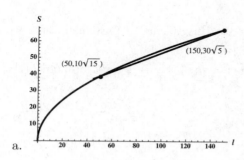

a.

b. The slope of the secant line is given by $\frac{30\sqrt{5}-10\sqrt{15}}{150-50} \approx .2835$ mph per foot. The speed of the car changes with an average rate of about .2835 mph per foot over the interval $50 \le l \le 150$.

1.1.71 This function is symmetric about the y-axis, because $f(-x) = (-x)^4 + 5(-x)^2 - 12 = x^4 + 5x^2 - 12 = f(x)$.

1.1.72 This function is symmetric about the origin, because $f(-x) = 3(-x)^5 + 2(-x)^3 - (-x) = -3x^5 - 2x^3 + x = -(3x^5 + 2x^3 - x) = f(x)$.

1.1.73 This function has none of the indicated symmetries. For example, note that $f(-2) = -26$, while $f(2) = 22$, so f is not symmetric about either the origin or about the y-axis, and is not symmetric about the x-axis because it is a function.

1.1.74 This function is symmetric about the y-axis. Note that $f(-x) = 2|-x| = 2|x| = f(x)$.

1.1.75 This curve (which is not a function) is symmetric about the x-axis, the y-axis, and the origin. Note that replacing either x by $-x$ or y by $-y$ (or both) yields the same equation. This is due to the fact that $(-x)^{2/3} = ((-x)^2)^{1/3} = (x^2)^{1/3} = x^{2/3}$, and a similar fact holds for the term involving y.

1.1.76 This function is symmetric about the origin. Writing the function as $y = f(x) = x^{3/5}$, we see that $f(-x) = (-x)^{3/5} = -(x)^{3/5} = -f(x)$.

1.1.77 This function is symmetric about the origin. Note that $f(-x) = (-x)|(-x)| = -x|x| = -f(x)$.

1.1.78 This curve (which is not a function) is symmetric about the x-axis, the y-axis, and the origin. Note that replacing either x by $-x$ or y by $-y$ (or both) yields the same equation. This is due to the fact that $|-x| = |x|$ and $|-y| = |y|$.

1.1.79 Function A is symmetric about the y-axis, so is even. Function B is symmetric about the origin, so is odd. Function C is also symmetric about the y-axis, so is even.

1.1.80 Function A is symmetric about the y-axis, so is even. Function B is symmetric about the origin, so is odd. Function C is also symmetric about the origin, so is odd.

1.1.81

a. True. A real number z corresponds to the domain element $z/2 + 19$, because $f(z/2 + 19) = 2(z/2 + 19) - 38 = z + 38 - 38 = z$.

b. False. The definition of function does not require that each range element comes from a unique domain element, rather that each domain element is paired with a unique range element.

c. True. $f(1/x) = \frac{1}{1/x} = x$, and $\frac{1}{f(x)} = \frac{1}{1/x} = x$.

d. False. For example, suppose that f is the straight line through the origin with slope 1, so that $f(x) = x$. Then $f(f(x)) = f(x) = x$, while $(f(x))^2 = x^2$.

e. False. For example, let $f(x) = x + 2$ and $g(x) = 2x - 1$. Then $f(g(x)) = f(2x - 1) = 2x - 1 + 2 = 2x + 1$, while $g(f(x)) = g(x + 2) = 2(x + 2) - 1 = 2x + 3$.

f. True. This is the definition of $f \circ g$.

g. True. If f is even, then $f(-z) = f(z)$ for all z, so this is true in particular for $z = ax$. So if $g(x) = cf(ax)$, then $g(-x) = cf(-ax) = cf(ax) = g(x)$, so g is even.

h. False. For example, $f(x) = x$ is an odd function, but $h(x) = x + 1$ isn't, because $h(2) = 3$, while $h(-2) = -1$ which isn't $-h(2)$.

i. True. If $f(-x) = -f(x) = f(x)$, then in particular $-f(x) = f(x)$, so $0 = 2f(x)$, so $f(x) = 0$ for all x.

1.1.82

If n is odd, then $n = 2k + 1$ for some integer k, and $(x)^n = (x)^{2k+1} = x(x)^{2k}$, which is less than 0 when $x < 0$ and greater than 0 when $x > 0$. For any number P (positive or negative) the number $\sqrt[n]{P}$ is a real number when n is odd, and $f(\sqrt[n]{P}) = P$. So the range of f in this case is the set of all real numbers.

If n is even, then $n = 2k$ for some integer k, and $x^n = (x^2)^k$. Thus $g(-x) = g(x) = (x^2)^k \geq 0$ for all x. Also, for any nonnegative number M, we have $g(\sqrt[n]{M}) = M$, so the range of g in this case is the set of all nonnegative numbers.

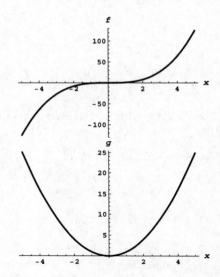

1.1.83

We will make heavy use of the fact that $|x|$ is x if $x > 0$, and is $-x$ if $x < 0$. In the first quadrant where x and y are both positive, this equation becomes $x - y = 1$ which is a straight line with slope 1 and y-intercept -1. In the second quadrant where x is negative and y is positive, this equation becomes $-x - y = 1$, which is a straight line with slope -1 and y-intercept -1. In the third quadrant where both x and y are negative, we obtain the equation $-x - (-y) = 1$, or $y = x + 1$, and in the fourth quadrant, we obtain $x + y = 1$. Graphing these lines and restricting them to the appropriate quadrants yields the following curve:

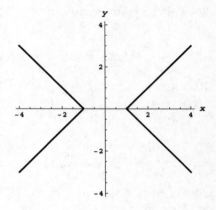

1.1.84

a. No. For example $f(x) = x^2 + 3$ is an even function, but $f(0)$ is not 0.

b. Yes. because $f(-x) = -f(x)$, and because $-0 = 0$, we must have $f(-0) = f(0) = -f(0)$, so $f(0) = -f(0)$, and the only number which is its own additive inverse is 0, so $f(0) = 0$.

1.1.85 Because the composition of f with itself has first degree, f has first degree as well, so let $f(x) = ax+b$. Then $(f \circ f)(x) = f(ax + b) = a(ax + b) + b = a^2x + (ab + b)$. Equating coefficients, we see that $a^2 = 9$ and $ab + b = -8$. If $a = 3$, we get that $b = -2$, while if $a = -3$ we have $b = 4$. So the two possible answers are $f(x) = 3x - 2$ and $f(x) = -3x + 4$.

1.1.86 Since the square of a linear function is a quadratic, we let $f(x) = ax+b$. Then $f(x)^2 = a^2x^2+2abx+b^2$. Equating coefficients yields that $a = \pm 3$ and $b = \pm 2$. However, a quick check shows that the middle term is correct only when one of these is positive and one is negative. So the two possible such functions f are $f(x) = 3x - 2$ and $f(x) = -3x + 2$.

1.1.87 Let $f(x) = ax^2 + bx + c$. Then $(f \circ f)(x) = f(ax^2 + bx + c) = a(ax^2 + bx + c)^2 + b(ax^2 + bx + c) + c$. Expanding this expression yields $a^3x^4 + 2a^2bx^3 + 2a^2cx^2 + ab^2x^2 + 2abcx + ac^2 + abx^2 + b^2x + bc + c$, which simplifies to $a^3x^4 + 2a^2bx^3 + (2a^2c + ab^2 + ab)x^2 + (2abc + b^2)x + (ac^2 + bc + c)$. Equating coefficients yields $a^3 = 1$, so $a = 1$. Then $2a^2b = 0$, so $b = 0$. It then follows that $c = -6$, so the original function was $f(x) = x^2 - 6$.

1.1.88 Because the square of a quadratic is a quartic, we let $f(x) = ax^2 + bx + c$. Then the square of f is $c^2 + 2bcx + b^2x^2 + 2acx^2 + 2abx^3 + a^2x^4$. By equating coefficients, we see that $a^2 = 1$ and so $a = \pm 1$. Because the coefficient on x^3 must be 0, we have that $b = 0$. And the constant term reveals that $c = \pm 6$. A quick check shows that the only possible solutions are thus $f(x) = x^2 - 6$ and $f(x) = -x^2 + 6$.

1.1.89 $\dfrac{f(x+h)-f(x)}{h} = \dfrac{\sqrt{x+h}-\sqrt{x}}{h} = \dfrac{\sqrt{x+h}-\sqrt{x}}{h} \cdot \dfrac{\sqrt{x+h}+\sqrt{x}}{\sqrt{x+h}+\sqrt{x}} = \dfrac{(x+h)-x}{h(\sqrt{x+h}+\sqrt{x})} = \dfrac{1}{\sqrt{x+h}+\sqrt{x}}.$

$\dfrac{f(x)-f(a)}{x-a} = \dfrac{\sqrt{x}-\sqrt{a}}{x-a} = \dfrac{\sqrt{x}-\sqrt{a}}{x-a} \cdot \dfrac{\sqrt{x}+\sqrt{a}}{\sqrt{x}+\sqrt{a}} = \dfrac{x-a}{(x-a)(\sqrt{x}+\sqrt{a})} = \dfrac{1}{\sqrt{x}+\sqrt{a}}.$

1.1.90 $\dfrac{f(x+h)-f(x)}{h} = \dfrac{\sqrt{1-2(x+h)}-\sqrt{1-2x}}{h} = \dfrac{\sqrt{1-2(x+h)}-\sqrt{1-2x}}{h} \cdot \dfrac{\sqrt{1-2(x+h)}+\sqrt{1-2x}}{\sqrt{1-2(x+h)}+\sqrt{1-2x}} =$

$\dfrac{1-2(x+h)-(1-2x)}{h(\sqrt{1-2(x+h)}+\sqrt{1-2x})} = -\dfrac{2}{\sqrt{1-2(x+h)}+\sqrt{1-2x}}.$

$\dfrac{f(x)-f(a)}{x-a} = \dfrac{\sqrt{1-2x}-\sqrt{1-2a}}{x-a} = \dfrac{\sqrt{1-2x}-\sqrt{1-2a}}{x-a} \cdot \dfrac{\sqrt{1-2x}+\sqrt{1-2a}}{\sqrt{1-2x}+\sqrt{1-2a}} = \dfrac{(1-2x)-(1-2a)}{(x-a)(\sqrt{1-2x}+\sqrt{1-2a})} =$

$\dfrac{(-2)(x-a)}{(x-a)(\sqrt{1-2x}+\sqrt{1-2a})} = -\dfrac{2}{(\sqrt{1-2x}+\sqrt{1-2a})}.$

1.1.91 $\dfrac{f(x+h)-f(x)}{h} = \dfrac{\frac{-3}{\sqrt{x+h}}-\frac{-3}{\sqrt{x}}}{h} = \dfrac{-3(\sqrt{x}-\sqrt{x+h})}{h\sqrt{x}\sqrt{x+h}} = \dfrac{-3(\sqrt{x}-\sqrt{x+h})}{h\sqrt{x}\sqrt{x+h}} \cdot \dfrac{\sqrt{x}+\sqrt{x+h}}{\sqrt{x}+\sqrt{x+h}} =$

$\dfrac{-3(x-(x+h))}{h\sqrt{x}\sqrt{x+h}(\sqrt{x}+\sqrt{x+h})} = \dfrac{3}{\sqrt{x}\sqrt{x+h}(\sqrt{x}+\sqrt{x+h})}.$

$\dfrac{f(x)-f(a)}{x-a} = \dfrac{\frac{-3}{\sqrt{x}}-\frac{-3}{\sqrt{a}}}{x-a} = \dfrac{-3\left(\frac{\sqrt{a}-\sqrt{x}}{\sqrt{a}\sqrt{x}}\right)}{x-a} = \dfrac{(-3)(\sqrt{a}-\sqrt{x})}{(x-a)\sqrt{a}\sqrt{x}} \cdot \dfrac{\sqrt{a}+\sqrt{x}}{\sqrt{a}+\sqrt{x}} = \dfrac{(3)(x-a)}{(x-a)(\sqrt{a}\sqrt{x})(\sqrt{a}+\sqrt{x})} = \dfrac{3}{\sqrt{ax}(\sqrt{a}+\sqrt{x})}.$

1.1.92 $\dfrac{f(x+h)-f(x)}{h} = \dfrac{\sqrt{(x+h)^2+1}-\sqrt{x^2+1}}{h} = \dfrac{\sqrt{(x+h)^2+1}-\sqrt{x^2+1}}{h} \cdot \dfrac{\sqrt{(x+h)^2+1}+\sqrt{x^2+1}}{\sqrt{(x+h)^2+1}+\sqrt{x^2+1}} =$

$\dfrac{(x+h)^2+1-(x^2+1)}{h(\sqrt{(x+h)^2+1}+\sqrt{x^2+1})} = \dfrac{x^2+2hx+h^2-x^2}{h(\sqrt{(x+h)^2+1}+\sqrt{x^2+1})} = \dfrac{2x+h}{\sqrt{(x+h)^2+1}+\sqrt{x^2+1}}.$

$\dfrac{f(x)-f(a)}{x-a} = \dfrac{\sqrt{x^2+1}-\sqrt{a^2+1}}{x-a} = \dfrac{\sqrt{x^2+1}-\sqrt{a^2+1}}{x-a} \cdot \dfrac{\sqrt{x^2+1}+\sqrt{a^2+1}}{\sqrt{x^2+1}+\sqrt{a^2+1}} = \dfrac{x^2+1-(a^2+1)}{(x-a)(\sqrt{x^2+1}+\sqrt{a^2+1})} =$

$\dfrac{(x-a)(x+a)}{(x-a)(\sqrt{x^2+1}+\sqrt{a^2+1})} = \dfrac{x+a}{\sqrt{x^2+1}+\sqrt{a^2+1}}.$

1.1.93

a. The formula for the height of the rocket is valid from $t = 0$ until the rocket hits the ground, which is the positive solution to $-16t^2 + 96t + 80 = 0$, which the quadratic formula reveals is $t = 3 + \sqrt{14}$. Thus, the domain is $[0, 3 + \sqrt{14}]$.

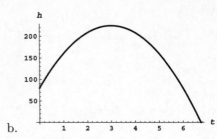

b. The maximum appears to occur at $t = 3$. The height at that time would be 224.

1.1.94

a. $d(0) = (10 - (2.2) \cdot 0)^2 = 100$.

b. The tank is first empty when $d(t) = 0$, which is when $10 - (2.2)t = 0$, or $t = 50/11$.

c. An appropriate domain would $[0, 50/11]$.

1.1.95 This would not necessarily have either kind of symmetry. For example, $f(x) = x^2$ is an even function and $g(x) = x^3$ is odd, but the sum of these two is neither even nor odd.

1.1.96 This would be an odd function, so it would be symmetric about the origin. Suppose f is even and g is odd. Then $(f \cdot g)(-x) = f(-x)g(-x) = f(x) \cdot (-g(x)) = -(f \cdot g)(x)$.

1.1.97 This would be an odd function, so it would be symmetric about the origin. Suppose f is even and g is odd. Then $\frac{f}{g}(-x) = \frac{f(-x)}{g(-x)} = \frac{f(x)}{-g(x)} = -\frac{f}{g}(x)$.

1.1.98 This would be an even function, so it would be symmetric about the y-axis. Suppose f is even and g is odd. Then $f(g(-x)) = f(-g(x)) = f(g(x))$.

1.1.99 This would be an even function, so it would be symmetric about the y-axis. Suppose f is even and g is even. Then $f(g(-x)) = f(g(x))$, because $g(-x) = g(x)$.

1.1.100 This would be an odd function, so it would be symmetric about the origin. Suppose f is odd and g is odd. Then $f(g(-x)) = f(-g(x)) = -f(g(x))$.

1.1.101 This would be an even function, so it would be symmetric about the y-axis. Suppose f is even and g is odd. Then $g(f(-x)) = g(f(x))$, because $f(-x) = f(x)$.

1.1.102

a. $f(g(-1)) = f(-g(1)) = f(3) = 3$

b. $g(f(-4)) = g(f(4)) = g(-4) = -g(4) = 2$

c. $f(g(-3)) = f(-g(3)) = f(4) = -4$

d. $f(g(-2)) = f(-g(2)) = f(1) = 2$

e. $g(g(-1)) = g(-g(1)) = g(3) = -4$

f. $f(g(0) - 1) = f(-1) = f(1) = 2$

g. $f(g(g(-2))) = f(g(-g(2))) = f(g(1)) = f(-3) = 3$

h. $g(f(f(-4))) = g(f(-4)) = g(-4) = 2$

i. $g(g(g(-1))) = g(g(-g(1))) = g(g(3)) = g(-4) = 2$

1.1.103

a. $f(g(-2)) = f(-g(2)) = f(-2) = 4$

b. $g(f(-2)) = g(f(2)) = g(4) = 1$

c. $f(g(-4)) = f(-g(4)) = f(-1) = 3$

d. $g(f(5) - 8) = g(-2) = -g(2) = -2$

e. $g(g(-7)) = g(-g(7)) = g(-4) = -1$

f. $f(1 - f(8)) = f(-7) = 7$

1.2 Representing Functions

1.2.1 Functions can be defined and represented by a formula, through a graph, via a table, and by using words.

1.2.2 The domain of every polynomial is the set of all real numbers.

1.2.3 The domain of a rational function $\frac{p(x)}{q(x)}$ is the set of all real numbers for which $q(x) \neq 0$.

1.2.4 A piecewise linear function is one which is linear over intervals in the domain.

1.2.5

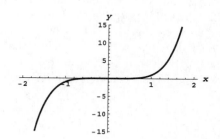

1.2.6

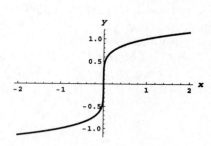

1.2.7 Compared to the graph of $f(x)$, the graph of $f(x+2)$ will be shifted 2 units to the left.

1.2.8 Compared to the graph of $f(x)$, the graph of $-3f(x)$ will be scaled vertically by a factor of 3 and flipped about the x axis.

1.2.9 Compared to the graph of $f(x)$, the graph of $f(3x)$ will be scaled horizontally by a factor of 3.

1.2.10 To produce the graph of $y = 4(x+3)^2 + 6$ from the graph of x^2, one must

1. shift the graph horizontally by 3 units to left

2. scale the graph vertically by a factor of 4

3. shift the graph vertically up 6 units.

1.2.11 The slope of the line shown is $m = \frac{-3-(-1)}{3-0} = -2/3$. The y-intercept is $b = -1$. Thus the function is given by $f(x) = (-2/3)x - 1$.

1.2.12 The slope of the line shown is $m = \frac{1-(5)}{5-0} = -4/5$. The y-intercept is $b = 5$. Thus the function is given by $f(x) = (-4/5)x + 5$.

1.2.13

The slope is given by $\frac{5-3}{2-1} = 2$, so the equation of the line is $y - 3 = 2(x - 1)$, which can be written as $y = 2x - 2 + 3$, or $y = 2x + 1$.

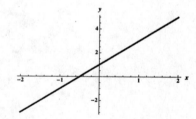

1.2.14

The slope is given by $\frac{0-(-3)}{5-2} = 1$, so the equation of the line is $y - 0 = 1(x - 5)$, or $y = x - 5$.

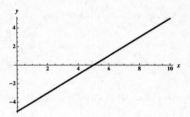

1.2.15 Using price as the independent variable p and the average number of units sold per day as the dependent variable d, we have the ordered pairs $(250, 12)$ and $(200, 15)$. The slope of the line determined by these points is $m = \frac{15-12}{200-250} = \frac{3}{-50}$. Thus the demand function has the form $d(p) = (-3/50)p + b$ for some constant b. Using the point $(200, 15)$, we find that $15 = (-3/50) \cdot 200 + b$, so $b = 27$. Thus the demand function is $d = (-3/50)p + 27$. While the domain of this linear function is the set of all real numbers, the formula is only likely to be valid for some subset of the interval $(0, 450)$, because outside of that interval either $p \leq 0$ or $d \leq 0$.

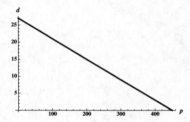

1.2.16 The profit is given by $p = f(n) = 8n - 175$. The break-even point is when $p = 0$, which occurs when $n = 175/8 = 21.875$, so they need to sell at least 22 tickets to not have a negative profit.

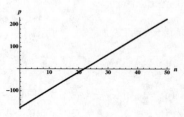

1.2.17 The slope is given by the rate of growth, which is 24. When $t = 0$ (years past 2015), the population is 500, so the point $(0, 500)$ satisfies our linear function. Thus the population is given by $p(t) = 24t + 500$. In 2030, we have $t = 15$, so the population will be approximately $p(15) = 360 + 500 = 860$.

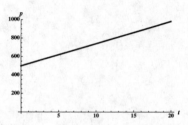

1.2.18 The cost per mile is the slope of the desired line, and the intercept is the fixed cost of 3.5. Thus, the cost per mile is given by $c(m) = 2.5m + 3.5$. When $m = 9$, we have $c(9) = (2.5)(9) + 3.5 = 22.5 + 3.5 = 26$ dollars.

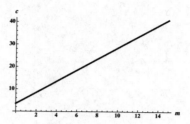

1.2.19 For $x < 0$, the graph is a line with slope 1 and y- intercept 3, while for $x > 0$, it is a line with slope $-1/2$ and y-intercept 3. Note that both of these lines contain the point $(0, 3)$. The function shown can thus be written

$$f(x) = \begin{cases} x + 3 & \text{if } x < 0; \\ -\frac{1}{2}x + 3 & \text{if } x \geq 0. \end{cases}$$

1.2.20 For $x < 3$, the graph is a line with slope 1 and y- intercept 1, while for $x > 3$, it is a line with slope $-1/3$. The portion to the right thus is represented by $y = (-1/3)x + b$, but because it contains the point $(6, 1)$, we must have $1 = (-1/3)(6) + b$ so $b = 3$. The function shown can thus be written

$$f(x) = \begin{cases} x + 1 & \text{if } x < 3; \\ (-1/3)x + 3 & \text{if } x \geq 3. \end{cases}$$

Note that at $x = 3$ the value of the function is 2, as indicated by our formula.

1.2.21

The cost is given by

$$c(t) = \begin{cases} 0.05t & \text{for } 0 \leq t \leq 60 \\ 1.2 + 0.03t & \text{for } 60 < t \leq 120 \end{cases}.$$

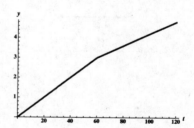

1.2.22

The cost is given by

$$c(m) = \begin{cases} 3.5 + 2.5m & \text{for } 0 \leq m \leq 5 \\ 8.5 + 1.5m & \text{for } m > 5 \end{cases}.$$

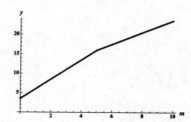

1.2.23

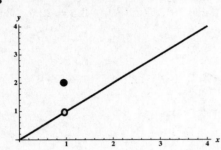

1.2.24

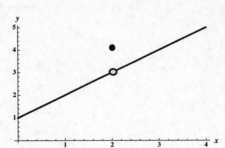

1.2.25

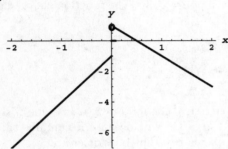

1.2.26

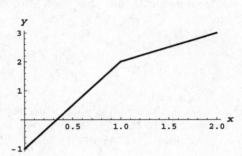

1.2.27

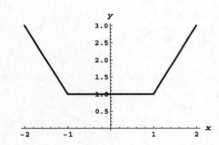

1.2.28

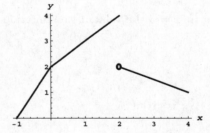

1.2.29

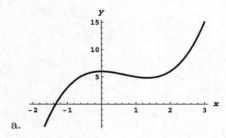

a.

b. The function is a polynomial, so its domain is the set of all real numbers.

c. It has one peak near its y-intercept of $(0, 6)$ and one valley between $x = 1$ and $x = 2$. Its x-intercept is near $x = -4/3$.

1.2.30

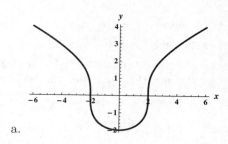

a.

b. The function's domain is the set of all real numbers.

c. It has a valley at the y-intercept of $(0, -2)$, and is very steep at $x = -2$ and $x = 2$ which are the x-intercepts. It is symmetric about the y-axis.

1.2.31

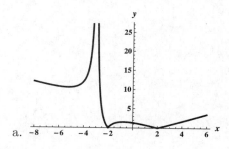

a.

b. The domain of the function is the set of all real numbers except -3.

c. There is a valley near $x = -5.2$ and a peak near $x = -0.8$. The x-intercepts are at -2 and 2, where the curve does not appear to be smooth. There is a vertical asymptote at $x = -3$. The function is never below the x-axis. The y-intercept is $(0, 4/3)$.

1.2.32

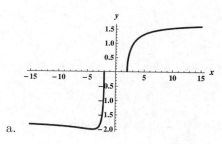

a.

b. The domain of the function is $(-\infty, -2] \cup [2, \infty)$

c. x-intercepts are at -2 and 2. Because 0 isn't in the domain, there is no y-intercept. The function has a valley at $x = -4$.

1.2.33

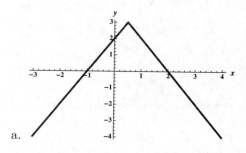

a.

b. The domain of the function is $(-\infty, \infty)$

c. The function has a maximum of 3 at $x = 1/2$, and a y-intercept of 2.

1.2.34

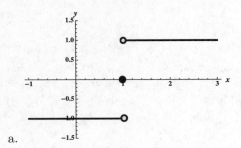

a.

b. The domain of the function is $(-\infty, \infty)$

c. The function contains a jump at $x = 1$. The maximum value of the function is 1 and the minimum value is -1.

1.2.35 The slope of this line is constantly 2, so the slope function is $s(x) = 2$.

1.2.36 The function can be written as $|x| = \begin{cases} -x & \text{if } x \leq 0 \\ x & \text{if } x > 0 \end{cases}$.

The slope function is $s(x) = \begin{cases} -1 & \text{if } x < 0 \\ 1 & \text{if } x > 0 \end{cases}$.

1.2.37 The slope function is given by $s(x) = \begin{cases} 1 & \text{if } x < 0; \\ -1/2 & \text{if } x > 0. \end{cases}$

1.2.38 The slope function is given by $s(x) = \begin{cases} 1 & \text{if } x < 3; \\ -1/3 & \text{if } x > 3. \end{cases}$

1.2.39

a. Because the area under consideration is that of a rectangle with base 2 and height 6, $A(2) = 12$.

b. Because the area under consideration is that of a rectangle with base 6 and height 6, $A(6) = 36$.

c. Because the area under consideration is that of a rectangle with base x and height 6, $A(x) = 6x$.

1.2.40

a. Because the area under consideration is that of a triangle with base 2 and height 1, $A(2) = 1$.

b. Because the area under consideration is that of a triangle with base 6 and height 3, the $A(6) = 9$.

c. Because $A(x)$ represents the area of a triangle with base x and height $(1/2)x$, the formula for $A(x)$ is $\frac{1}{2} \cdot x \cdot \frac{x}{2} = \frac{x^2}{4}$.

1.2.41

a. Because the area under consideration is that of a trapezoid with base 2 and heights 8 and 4, we have $A(2) = 2 \cdot \frac{8+4}{2} = 12$.

b. Note that $A(3)$ represents the area of a trapezoid with base 3 and heights 8 and 2, so $A(3) = 3 \cdot \frac{8+2}{2} = 15$. So $A(6) = 15 + (A(6) - A(3))$, and $A(6) - A(3)$ represents the area of a triangle with base 3 and height 2. Thus $A(6) = 15 + 6 = 21$.

c. For x between 0 and 3, $A(x)$ represents the area of a trapezoid with base x, and heights 8 and $8 - 2x$. Thus the area is $x \cdot \frac{8+8-2x}{2} = 8x - x^2$. For $x > 3$, $A(x) = A(3) + A(x) - A(3) = 15 + 2(x-3) = 2x + 9$. Thus

$$A(x) = \begin{cases} 8x - x^2 & \text{if } 0 \leq x \leq 3; \\ 2x + 9 & \text{if } x > 3. \end{cases}$$

1.2.42

a. Because the area under consideration is that of trapezoid with base 2 and heights 3 and 1, we have $A(2) = 2 \cdot \frac{3+1}{2} = 4$.

b. Note that $A(6) = A(2) + (A(6) - A(2)$, and that $A(6) - A(2)$ represents a trapezoid with base $6 - 2 = 4$ and heights 1 and 5. The area is thus $4 + \left(4 \cdot \frac{1+5}{2}\right) = 4 + 12 = 16$.

c. For x between 0 and 2, $A(x)$ represents the area of a trapezoid with base x, and heights 3 and $3 - x$. Thus the area is $x \cdot \frac{3+3-x}{2} = 3x - \frac{x^2}{2}$. For $x > 2$, $A(x) = A(2) + A(x) - A(2) = 4 + (A(x) - A(2))$. Note that $A(x) - A(2)$ represents the area of a trapezoid with base $x - 2$ and heights 1 and $x - 1$. Thus $A(x) = 4 + (x - 2) \cdot \frac{1+x-1}{2} = 4 + (x-2)\left(\frac{x}{2}\right) = \frac{x^2}{2} - x + 4$. Thus

$$A(x) = \begin{cases} 3x - \frac{x^2}{2} & \text{if } 0 \leq x \leq 2; \\ \frac{x^2}{2} - x + 4 & \text{if } x > 2. \end{cases}$$

1.2.43 $f(x) = |x - 2| + 3$, because the graph of f is obtained from that of $|x|$ by shifting 2 units to the right and 3 units up.

$g(x) = -|x + 2| - 1$, because the graph of g is obtained from the graph of $|x|$ by shifting 2 units to the left, then reflecting about the x-axis, and then shifting 1 unit down.

1.2.44

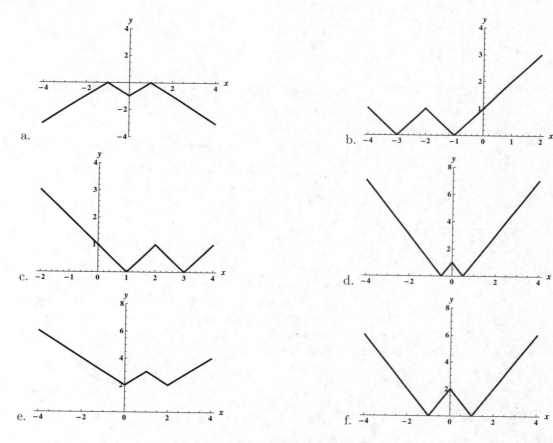

1.2.45

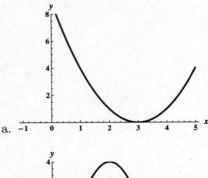 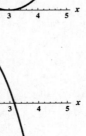 

a.

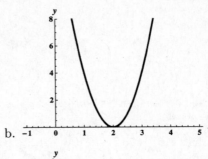

b.

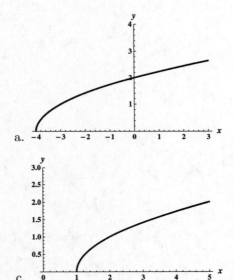

c.

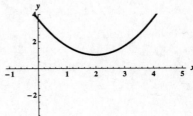

d.

1.2.46

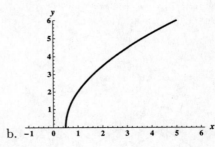

a.

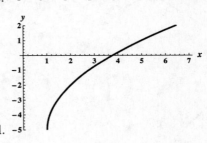

b.

c.

d.

1.2.47   The graph is obtained by shifting the graph of x^2 two units to the right and one unit up.

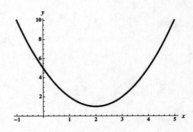

1.2.48 Write $x^2 - 2x + 3$ as $(x^2 - 2x + 1) + 2 = (x-1)^2 + 2$. The graph is obtained by shifting the graph of x^2 one unit to the right and two units up.

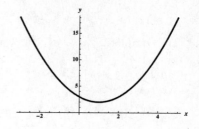

1.2.49 This function is $-3 \cdot f(x)$ where $f(x) = x^2$

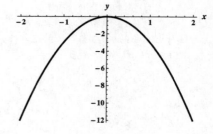

1.2.50 This function is $2 \cdot f(x) - 1$ where $f(x) = x^3$

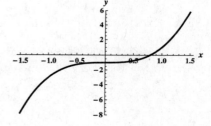

1.2.51 This function is $2 \cdot f(x+3)$ where $f(x) = x^2$

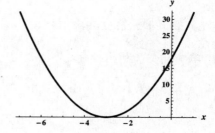

1.2.52 By completing the square, we have that $p(x) = (x^2 + 3x + (9/4)) - (29/4) = (x + (3/2))^2 - (29/4)$. So it is $f(x + (3/2)) - (29/4)$ where $f(x) = x^2$.

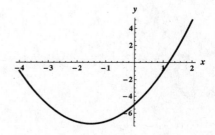

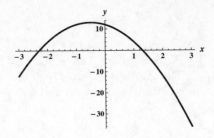

1.2.53 By completing the square, we have that $h(x) = -4(x^2 + x - 3) = -4\left(x^2 + x + \frac{1}{4} - \frac{1}{4} - 3\right) = -4(x + (1/2))^2 + 13$. So it is $-4f(x + (1/2)) + 13$ where $f(x) = x^2$.

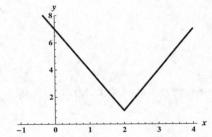

1.2.54 Because $|3x-6|+1 = 3|x-2|+1$, this is $3f(x-2)+1$ where $f(x) = |x|$.

1.2.55

    a. True. A polynomial $p(x)$ can be written as the ratio of polynomials $\frac{p(x)}{1}$, so it is a rational function. However, a rational function like $\frac{1}{x}$ is not a polynomial.

    b. False. For example, if $f(x) = 2x$, then $(f \circ f)(x) = f(f(x)) = f(2x) = 4x$ is linear, not quadratic.

    c. True. In fact, if f is degree m and g is degree n, then the degree of the composition of f and g is $m \cdot n$, regardless of the order they are composed.

    d. False. The graph would be shifted two units to the left.

1.2.56 The points of intersection are found by solving $x^2 + 2 = x + 4$. This yields the quadratic equation $x^2 - x - 2 = 0$ or $(x - 2)(x + 1) = 0$. So the x-values of the points of intersection are 2 and -1. The actual points of intersection are $(2, 6)$ and $(-1, 3)$.

1.2.57 The points of intersection are found by solving $x^2 = -x^2 + 8x$. This yields the quadratic equation $2x^2 - 8x = 0$ or $(2x)(x - 4) = 0$. So the x-values of the points of intersection are 0 and 4. The actual points of intersection are $(0, 0)$ and $(4, 16)$.

1.2.58 $y = x + 1$, because the y value is always 1 more than the x value.

1.2.59 $y = \sqrt{x} - 1$, because the y value is always 1 less than the square root of the x value.

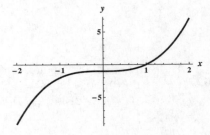

1.2.60 $y = x^3 - 1$. The domain is $(-\infty, \infty)$.

1.2.61 The car moving north has gone $30t$ miles after t hours and the car moving east has gone $60t$ miles. Using the Pythagorean theorem, we have $s(t) = \sqrt{(30t)^2 + (60t)^2} = \sqrt{900t^2 + 3600t^2} = \sqrt{4500t^2} = 30\sqrt{5}t$ miles. The context domain could be $[0, 4]$.

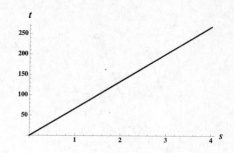

1.2.62 $y = \frac{50}{x}$. Theoretically the domain is $(0, \infty)$, but the world record for the "hour ride" is just short of 50 miles.

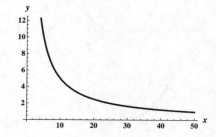

1.2.63 $y = \frac{3200}{x}$. Note that $\frac{x \text{ dollars per gallon}}{32 \text{ miles per gallon}} \cdot y$ miles would represent the numbers of dollars, so this must be 100. So we have $\frac{xy}{32} = 100$, or $y = \frac{3200}{x}$. We certainly have $x > 0$, and a reasonable upper bound to imagine for x is $5 (let's hope), so the context domain is $(0, 5]$.

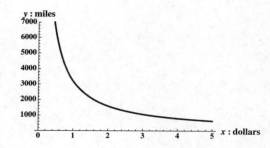

1.2.64

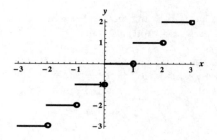

1.2.65

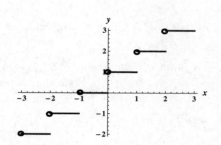

1.2.66

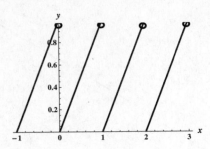

1.2.67

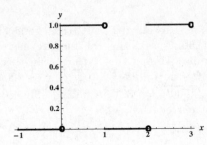

1.2.68

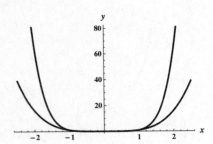

1.2.69

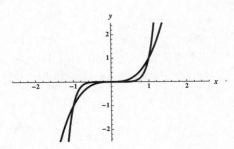

1.2.70

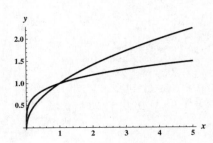

1.2.71

a. The zeros of f are the points where the graph crosses the x-axis, so these are points A, D, F, and I.

b. The only high point, or peak, of f occurs at point E, because it appears that the graph has larger and larger y values as x increases past point I and decreases past point A.

c. The only low points, or valleys, of f are at points B and H, again assuming that the graph of f continues its apparent behavior for larger values of x.

d. Past point H, the graph is rising, and is rising faster and faster as x increases. It is also rising between points B and E, but not as quickly as it is past point H. So the marked point at which it is rising most rapidly is I.

e. Before point B, the graph is falling, and falls more and more rapidly as x becomes more and more negative. It is also falling between points E and H, but not as rapidly as it is before point B. So the marked point at which it is falling most rapidly is A.

1.2.72

a. The zeros of g appear to be at $x = 0$, $x = 1$, $x = 1.6$, and $x \approx 3.15$.

b. The two peaks of g appear to be at $x \approx 0.5$ and $x \approx 2.6$, with corresponding points $\approx (0.5, 0.4)$ and $\approx (2.6, 3.4)$.

c. The only valley of g is at $\approx (1.3, -0.2)$.

d. Moving right from $x \approx 1.3$, the graph is rising more and more rapidly until about $x = 2$, at which point it starts rising less rapidly (because, by $x \approx 2.6$, it is not rising at all). So the coordinates of the point at which it is rising most rapidly are approximately $(2.1, g(2)) \approx (2.1, 2)$. Note that while the curve is also rising between $x = 0$ and $x \approx 0.5$, it is not rising as rapidly as it is near $x = 2$.

e. To the right of $x \approx 2.6$, the curve is falling, and falling more and more rapidly as x increases. So the point at which it is falling most rapidly in the interval $[0, 3]$ is at $x = 3$, which has the approximate coordinates $(3, 1.4)$. Note that while the curve is also falling between $x \approx 0.5$ and $x \approx 1.3$, it is not falling as rapidly as it is near $x = 3$.

1.2.73

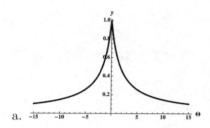

a.

b. This appears to have a maximum when $\theta = 0$. Our vision is sharpest when we look straight ahead.

c. For $|\theta| \leq .19°$. We have an extremely narrow range where our eyesight is sharp.

1.2.74

a. $f(.75) = \frac{.75^2}{1 - 2(.75)(.25)} = .9$. There is a 90% chance that the server will win from deuce if they win 75% of their service points.

b. $f(.25) = \frac{.25^2}{1 - 2(.25)(.75)} = .1$. There is a 10% chance that the server will win from deuce if they win 25% of their service points.

1.2.75

a. Using the points $(1986, 1875)$ and $(2000, 6471)$ we see that the slope is about 328.3. At $t = 0$, the value of p is 1875. Therefore a line which reasonably approximates the data is $p(t) = 328.3t + 1875$.

b. Using this line, we have that $p(9) = 4830$.

1.2.76

a. We know that the points $(32, 0)$ and $(212, 100)$ are on our line. The slope of our line is thus $\frac{100 - 0}{212 - 32} = \frac{100}{180} = \frac{5}{9}$. The function $f(F)$ thus has the form $C = (5/9)F + b$, and using the point $(32, 0)$ we see that $0 = (5/9)32 + b$, so $b = -(160/9)$. Thus $C = (5/9)F - (160/9)$

b. Solving the system of equations $C = (5/9)F - (160/9)$ and $C = F$, we have that $F = (5/9)F - (160/9)$, so $(4/9)F = -160/9$, so $F = -40$ when $C = -40$.

1.2.77

a. Because you are paying \$350 per month, the amount paid after m months is $y = 350m + 1200$.

b. After 4 years (48 months) you have paid $350 \cdot 48 + 1200 = 18000$ dollars. If you then buy the car for \$10,000, you will have paid a total of \$28,000 for the car instead of \$25,000. So you should buy the car instead of leasing it.

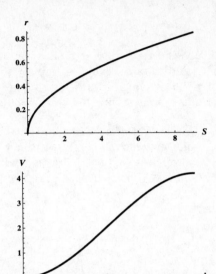

Because $S = 4\pi r^2$, we have that $r^2 = \frac{S}{4\pi}$, so $|r| =$

1.2.78 $\frac{\sqrt{S}}{2\sqrt{\pi}}$, but because r is positive, we can write $r =$
$\frac{\sqrt{S}}{2\sqrt{\pi}}$.

1.2.79 The function makes sense for $0 \le h \le 2$.

1.2.80

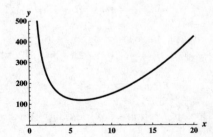

a. Note that the island, the point P on shore, and the point down shore x units from P form a right triangle. By the Pythagorean theorem, the length of the hypotenuse is $\sqrt{40000 + x^2}$. So Kelly must row this distance and then jog $600-x$ meters to get home. So her total distance $d(x) = \sqrt{40000 + x^2} + (600 - x)$.

b. Because distance is rate times time, we have that time is distance divided by rate. Thus $T(x) = \frac{\sqrt{40000+x^2}}{2} + \frac{600-x}{4}$.

c. By inspection, it looks as though she should head to a point about 115 meters down shore from P. This would lead to a time of about 236.6 seconds.

1.2.81

a. The volume of the box is $x^2 h$, but because the box has volume 125 cubic feet, we have that $x^2 h = 125$, so $h = \frac{125}{x^2}$. The surface area of the box is given by x^2 (the area of the base) plus $4 \cdot hx$, because each side has area hx. Thus $S = x^2 + 4hx = x^2 + \frac{4 \cdot 125 \cdot x}{x^2} = x^2 + \frac{500}{x}$.

b. By inspection, it looks like the value of x which minimizes the surface area is about 6.3.

1.2.82 Let $f(x) = a_n x^n +$ smaller degree terms and let $g(x) = b_m x^m +$ some smaller degree terms.

a. The largest degree term in $f \cdot f$ is $a_n x^n \cdot a_n x^n = a_n^2 x^{n+n}$, so the degree of this polynomial is $n+n = 2n$.

b. The largest degree term in $f \circ f$ is $a_n \cdot (a_n x^n)^n$, so the degree is n^2.

c. The largest degree term in $f \cdot g$ is $a_n b_m x^{m+n}$, so the degree of the product is $m + n$.

d. The largest degree term in $f \circ g$ is $a_n \cdot (b_m x^m)^n$, so the degree is mn.

1.2.83 Suppose that the parabola f crosses the x-axis at a and b, with $a < b$. Then a and b are roots of the polynomial, so $(x - a)$ and $(x - b)$ are factors. Thus the polynomial must be $f(x) = c(x - a)(x - b)$ for some non-zero real number c. So $f(x) = cx^2 - c(a + b)x + abc$. Because the vertex always occurs at the x value which is $\frac{-\text{coefficient on x}}{2 \cdot \text{coefficient on } x^2}$ we have that the vertex occurs at $\frac{c(a+b)}{2c} = \frac{a+b}{2}$, which is halfway between a and b.

1.2.84

a. We complete the square to rewrite the function f. Write $f(x) = ax^2 + bx + c$ as $f(x) = a(x^2 + \frac{b}{a}x + \frac{c}{a})$. Completing the square yields

$$a\left(\left(x^2 + \frac{b}{a}x + \frac{b^2}{4a}\right) + \left(\frac{c}{a} - \frac{b^2}{4a}\right)\right) = a\left(x + \frac{b}{2a}\right)^2 + \left(c - \frac{b^2}{4}\right).$$

Thus the graph of f is obtained from the graph of x^2 by shifting $\frac{b}{2a}$ units to the left (and then doing some scaling and vertical shifting) – moving the vertex from 0 to $-\frac{b}{2a}$. The vertex is therefore $\left(\frac{-b}{2a}, c - \frac{b^2}{4}\right)$.

b. We know that the graph of f touches the x-axis twice if the equation $ax^2 + bx + c = 0$ has two real solutions. By the quadratic formula, we know that this occurs exactly when the discriminant $b^2 - 4ac$ is positive. So the condition we seek is for $b^2 - 4ac > 0$, or $b^2 > 4ac$.

1.2.85

b.

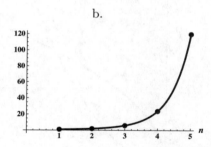

a.

n	1	2	3	4	5
$n!$	1	2	6	24	120

c. Using trial and error and a calculator yields that 10! is more than a million, but 9! isn't.

1.2.86

a.

n	1	2	3	4	5	6	7	8	9	10
$S(n)$	1	3	6	10	15	21	28	36	45	55

b. The domain of this function consists of the positive integers. The range is a subset of the set of positive integers.

c. Using trial and error and a calculator yields that $S(n) > 1000$ for the first time for $n = 45$.

1.2.87

a.

n	1	2	3	4	5	6	7	8	9	10
$T(n)$	1	5	14	30	55	91	140	204	285	385

b. The domain of this function consists of the positive integers.

c. Using trial and error and a calculator yields that $T(n) > 1000$ for the first time for $n = 14$.

1.3   Inverse, Exponential and Logarithmic Functions

1.3.1 $D = \mathbb{R}, R = (0, \infty)$.

1.3.2 $f(x) = 2x + 1$ is one-to-one on all of $\mathbb{R}$. If $f(a) = f(b)$, then $2a + 1 = 2b + 1$, so it must follow that $a = b$.

1.3.3 If a function f is not one-to-one, then there are domain values $x_1 \neq x_2$ with $f(x_1) = f(x_2)$. If f^{-1} were to exist, then $f^{-1}(f(x_1)) = f^{-1}(f(x_2))$ which would imply that $x_1 = x_2$, a contradiction.

1.3.4

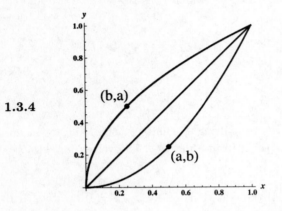

Recall that the graph of $f^{-1}(x)$ is obtained from the graph of $f(x)$ by reflecting across the line $y = x$. Thus, if (a, b) is on the graph of $y = f(x)$, then (b, a) must be on the graph of $y = f^{-1}(x)$.

1.3.5

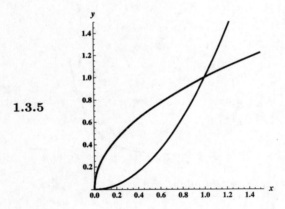

1.3.6 To find the inverse of $y = 3x - 4$, we write $x = 3y - 4$ and solve for y. We have $x + 4 = 3y$, so $y = \frac{x+4}{3}$. Thus $f^{-1}(x) = \frac{x+4}{3}$.

1.3.7 $\log_b x$ represents the power to which b must be raised in order to obtain x. So, $b^{\log_b x} = x$.

1.3.8 The properties are related in that each can be used to derive the other. Assume $b^{x+y} = b^x b^y$, for all real numbers x and y. Then applying this rule to the numbers $\log_b x$ and $\log_b y$ gives $b^{\log_b x + \log_b y} = b^{\log_b x} b^{\log_b y} = xy$. Taking logs of the leftmost and rightmost sides of this equation yields $\log_b x + \log_b y = \log_b(xy)$.

   Now assume that $\log_b(xy) = \log_b x + \log_b y$ for all positive numbers x and y. Applying this rule to the product $b^x b^y$, we have $\log_b(b^x b^y) = \log_b b^x + \log_b b^y = x + y$. Now looking at the leftmost and rightmost sides of this equality and applying the definition of logarithm yields $b^{x+y} = b^x b^y$, as was desired.

1.3.9 Because the domain of b^x is $\mathbb{R}$ and the range of b^x is $(0, \infty)$, and because $\log_b x$ is the inverse of b^x, the domain of $\log_b x$ is $(0, \infty)$ and the range is $\mathbb{R}$.

1.3.10 Let $2^5 = z$. Then $\ln(2^5) = \ln(z)$, so $\ln(z) = 5\ln(2)$. Taking the exponential function of both sides gives $z = e^{5\ln(2)}$. Therefore, $2^5 = e^{5\ln(2)}$.

1.3.11 f is one-to-one on $(-\infty, -1]$, on $[-1, 1]$, and on $[1, \infty)$.

1.3.12 f is one-to-one on $(-\infty, -2]$, on $[-2, 0]$, on $[0, 2]$, and on $[2, \infty)$.

1.3.13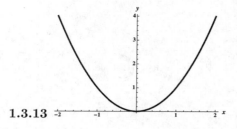

1.3.14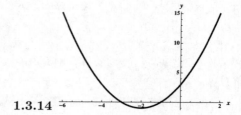

1.3.15 f is one-to-one on $\mathbb{R}$, so it has an inverse on $\mathbb{R}$.

1.3.16 f is one-to-one on $[-1/2, \infty)$, so it has an inverse on that set. (Alternatively, it is one-to-one on the interval $(-\infty, -1/2]$, so that interval could be used as well.)

1.3.17 f is one-to-one on its domain, which is $(-\infty, 5) \cup (5, \infty)$, so it has an inverse on that set.

1.3.18 f is one-to-one on the set $(-\infty, 6]$, so it has an inverse on that set. (Alternatively, it is one-to-one on the interval $[6, \infty)$, so that interval could be used as well.)

1.3.19 f is one-to-one on the interval $(0, \infty)$, so it has an inverse on that interval. (Alternatively, it is one-to-one on the interval $(-\infty, 0)$, so that interval could be used as well.)

1.3.20 Note that f can be written as $f(x) = x^2 - 2x + 8 = x^2 - 2x + 1 + 7 = (x - 1)^2 + 7$. It is one-to-one on the interval $(1, \infty)$, so it has an inverse on that interval. (Alternatively, it is one-to-one on the interval $(-\infty, 1)$, so that interval could be used as well.)

1.3.21

    a. Switching x and y, we have $x = 2y$, so $y = \frac{1}{2}x$. Thus $y = f^{-1}(x) = \frac{1}{2}x$.

    b. $f(f^{-1}(x)) = f\left(\frac{1}{2}x\right) = 2\left(\frac{1}{2}x\right) = x$. Also, $f^{-1}(f(x)) = f^{-1}(2x) = \frac{1}{2} \cdot (2x) = x$.

1.3.22

    a. Switching x and y yields $x = \frac{y}{4} + 1$. Solving for y gives $y = 4(x - 1)$, so $f^{-1}(x) = 4x - 4$.

    b. $f(f^{-1}(x)) = f(4x - 4) = \frac{4x - 4}{4} + 1 = x - 1 + 1 = x$. Also, $f^{-1}(f(x)) = f^{-1}\left(\frac{x}{4} + 1\right) = 4\left(\frac{x}{4} + 1\right) - 4 = x$.

1.3.23

    a. Switching x and y, we have $x = 6 - 4y$. Solving for y in terms of x we have $4y = 6 - x$, so $y = f^{-1}(x) = \frac{6-x}{4}$.

    b. $f(f^{-1}(x)) = f\left(\frac{6-x}{4}\right) = 6 - 4 \cdot \left(\frac{6-x}{4}\right) = 6 - (6 - x) = x$.
       $f^{-1}(f(x)) = f^{-1}(6 - 4x) = \frac{6 - (6 - 4x)}{4} = \frac{4x}{4} = x$.

1.3.24

    a. Switching x and y, we have $x = 3y^3$. Solving for y in terms of x we have $y = \sqrt[3]{x/3}$, so $y = f^{-1}(x) = \sqrt[3]{x/3}$.

    b. $f(f^{-1}(x)) = f(\sqrt[3]{x/3}) = 3(\sqrt[3]{x/3})^3 = 3(x/3) = x$.
       $f^{-1}(f(x)) = f^{-1}(3x^3) = \sqrt[3]{3x^3/3} = \sqrt[3]{x^3} = x$.

1.3.25

a. Switching x and y, we have $x = 3y + 5$. Solving for y in terms of x we have $y = \frac{x-5}{3}$, so $y = f^{-1}(x) = \frac{x-5}{3}$.

b. $f(f^{-1}(x)) = f\left(\frac{x-5}{3}\right) = 3\left(\frac{x-5}{3}\right) + 5 = (x - 5) + 5 = x$.
$f^{-1}(f(x)) = f^{-1}(3x + 5) = \frac{(3x+5)-5}{3} = \frac{3x}{3} = x$.

1.3.26

a. Switching x and y, we have $x = y^2 + 4$. Solving for y in terms of x we have $y^2 = x - 4$, so $|y| = \sqrt{x - 4}$. But because we are given that the domain of f is $\{x : x \geq 0\}$, we know that the range of f^{-1} is also non-negative. So $y = f^{-1}(x) = \sqrt{x - 4}$.

b. $f(f^{-1}(x)) = f(\sqrt{x - 4}) = (\sqrt{x - 4})^2 + 4 = x - 4 + 4 = x$.
$f^{-1}(f(x)) = f^{-1}(x^2 + 4) = \sqrt{x^2 + 4 - 4} = \sqrt{x^2} = |x| = x$, because $x \geq 0$.

1.3.27

a. Switching x and y, we have $x = \sqrt{y + 2}$. Solving for y in terms of x we have $y = f^{-1}(x) = x^2 - 2$. Note that because the range of f is $[0, \infty)$, that is also the domain of f^{-1}.

b. $f(f^{-1}(x)) = f(x^2 - 2) = \sqrt{x^2 - 2 + 2} = |x| = x$, because x is in the domain of f^{-1} and so is nonnegative.
$f^{-1}(f(x)) = f^{-1}(\sqrt{x + 2}) = \sqrt{x + 2}^2 - 2 = x + 2 - 2 = x$.

1.3.28

a. Switching x and y, we have $x = \frac{2}{y^2+1}$. Solving for y in terms of x we have $y^2 + 1 = \frac{2}{x}$. Thus $y^2 = \frac{2}{x} - 1$, so $|y| = \sqrt{\frac{2}{x} - 1}$. Note that the domain of f is $[0, \infty)$ and that this is therefore the range of f^{-1}, so we must have $f^{-1}(x) = \sqrt{\frac{2}{x} - 1}$.

b. $f(f^{-1}(x)) = f\left(\sqrt{\frac{2}{x} - 1}\right) = \frac{2}{\sqrt{\frac{2}{x}-1}^2 + 1} = \frac{2}{\frac{2}{x}} = x$.

$f^{-1}(f(x)) = f^{-1}\left(\frac{2}{x^2+1}\right) = \sqrt{\frac{2}{\frac{2}{x^2+1}} - 1} = \sqrt{x^2 + 1 - 1} = |x| = x$,

because x is in the domain of f and is thus nonnegative.

1.3.29 First note that because the expression is symmetric, switching x and y doesn't change the expression. Solving for y gives $|y| = \sqrt{1 - x^2}$. To get the four one-to-one functions, we restrict the domain and choose either the upper part or lower part of the circle as follows:

a. $f_1(x) = \sqrt{1 - x^2}$, $0 \leq x \leq 1$
$f_2(x) = \sqrt{1 - x^2}$, $-1 \leq x \leq 0$
$f_3(x) = -\sqrt{1 - x^2}$, $-1 \leq x \leq 0$
$f_4(x) = -\sqrt{1 - x^2}$, $0 \leq x \leq 1$

b. Reflecting these functions across the line $y = x$ yields the following:
$f_1^{-1}(x) = \sqrt{1 - x^2}$, $0 \leq x \leq 1$
$f_2^{-1}(x) = -\sqrt{1 - x^2}$, $0 \leq x \leq 1$
$f_3^{-1}(x) = -\sqrt{1 - x^2}$, $-1 \leq x \leq 0$
$f_4^{-1}(x) = \sqrt{1 - x^2}$, $-1 \leq x \leq 0$

1.3.30 First note that because the expression is symmetric, switching x and y doesn't change the expression. Solving for y gives $|y| = \sqrt{2|x|}$. To get the four one-to-one functions, we restrict the domain and choose either the upper part or lower part of the parabola as follows:

a. $f_1(x) = \sqrt{2x},\ x \geq 0$

   $f_2(x) = \sqrt{-2x},\ x \leq 0$

   $f_3(x) = -\sqrt{-2x},\ x \leq 0$

   $f_4(x) = -\sqrt{2x},\ x \geq 0$

b. Reflecting these functions across the line $y = x$ yields the following:

   $f_1^{-1}(x) = x^2/2,\ x \geq 0$

   $f_2^{-1}(x) = -x^2/2,\ x \geq 0$

   $f_3^{-1}(x) = -x^2/2,\ x \leq 0$

   $f_4^{-1}(x) = x^2/2,\ x \leq 0$

1.3.31 Switching x and y gives $x = 8 - 4y$. Solving this for y yields $y = f^{-1}(x) = \frac{8-x}{4}$.

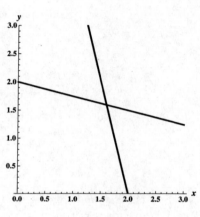

1.3.32 Switching x and y gives $x = 4y - 12$. Solving this for y yields $y = f^{-1}(x) = \frac{x}{4} + 3$.

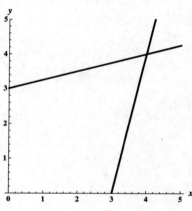

1.3.33 Switching x and y gives $x = \sqrt{y}$. Solving this for y yields $y = f^{-1}(x) = x^2$, but note that the range of f is $[0, \infty)$ so that is the domain of f^{-1}.

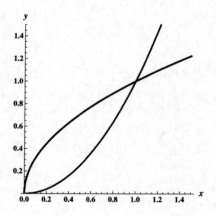

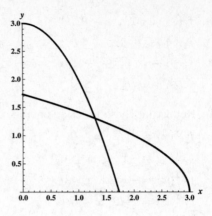

1.3.34 Switching x and y gives $x = \sqrt{3-y}$. Solving this for y yields $y = f^{-1}(x) = 3 - x^2$, but note that the range of f is $[0, \infty)$ so that is the domain of f^{-1}.

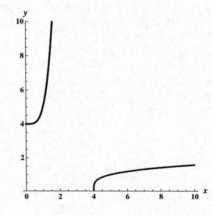

1.3.35 Switching x and y gives $x = y^4 + 4$. Solving this for y yields $y = f^{-1}(x) = \sqrt[4]{x-4}$.

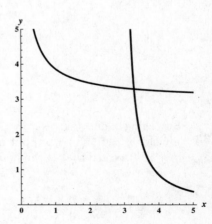

1.3.36 Switching x and y gives $x = \frac{6}{y^2-9}$. Solving yields $y^2 - 9 = \frac{6}{x}$, or $|y| = \sqrt{(6/x) + 9}$, but because the domain of f is positive, the range of f^{-1} must be positive as well, so we have $f^{-1}(x) = \sqrt{(6/x) + 9}$.

1.3.37 Begin by completing the square: $f(x) = x^2 - 2x + 6 = (x^2 - 2x + 1) + 5 = (x - 1)^2 + 5$. Switching x and y yields $x = (y - 1)^2 + 5$. Solving for y gives $|y - 1| = \sqrt{x - 5}$. Choosing the principal square root (because the original given interval has x positive) gives $y = f^{-1}(x) = \sqrt{x - 5} + 1$, $x \geq 5$.

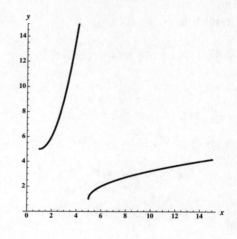

1.3.38 Begin by completing the square: $f(x) = -x^2 - 4x - 3 = -(x^2 + 4x + 3) = -(x^2 + 4x + 4 - 1) = -((x + 2)^2 - 1) = 1 - (x + 2)^2$. Switching x and y yields $x = 1 - (y + 2)^2$, and solving for y gives $|y + 2| = \sqrt{1 - x}$. Since the given domain of f was negative, the range of f^{-1} must be negative, so we must have $y + 2 = -\sqrt{1 - x}$, so the inverse function is $f^{-1}(x) = -\sqrt{1 - x} - 2$.

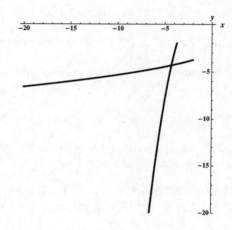

1.3.39

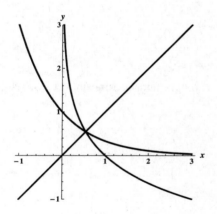

1.3.40

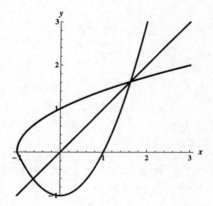

1.3.41 If $\log_{10} x = 3$, then $10^3 = x$, so $x = 1000$.

1.3.42 If $\log_5 x = -1$, then $5^{-1} = x$, so $x = 1/5$.

1.3.43 If $\log_8 x = 1/3$, then $x = 8^{1/3} = 2$.

1.3.44 If $\log_b 125 = 3$, then $b^3 = 125$, so $b = 5$ because $5^3 = 125$.

1.3.45 If $\ln x = -1$, then $e^{-1} = x$, so $x = \frac{1}{e}$.

1.3.46 If $\ln y = 3$, then $y = e^3$.

1.3.47 $\log_b\left(\frac{x}{y}\right) = \log_b x - \log_b y = .36 - .56 = -0.2$.

1.3.48 $\log_b x^2 = 2\log_b x = 2(.36) = 0.72$.

1.3.49 $\log_b xz = \log_b x + \log_b z = .36 + .83 = 1.19$.

1.3.50 $\log_b \frac{\sqrt{xy}}{z} = \log_b(xy)^{1/2} - \log_b z = \frac{1}{2}(\log_b x + \log_b y) - \log_b z = (.36)/2 + (.56)/2 - .83 = -.37$.

1.3.51 $\log_b \frac{\sqrt{x}}{\sqrt[3]{z}} = \log_b x^{1/2} - \log_b z^{1/3} = (1/2)\log_b x - (1/3)\log_b z = (.36)/2 - (.83)/3 = -.09\overline{6}$.

1.3.52 $\log_b \frac{b^2 x^{5/2}}{\sqrt{y}} = \log_b b^2 x^{5/2} - \log_b y^{1/2} = \log_b b^2 + (5/2)\log_b x - (1/2)\log_b y = 2 + (5/2)(.36) - (1/2)(.56) = 2.62$.

1.3.53 Since $7^x = 21$, we have that $\ln 7^x = \ln 21$, so $x\ln 7 = \ln 21$, and $x = \frac{\ln 21}{\ln 7}$.

1.3.54 Since $2^x = 55$, we have that $\ln 2^x = \ln 55$, so $x\ln 2 = \ln 55$, and $x = \frac{\ln 55}{\ln 2}$.

1.3.55 Since $3^{3x-4} = 15$, we have that $\ln 3^{3x-4} = \ln 15$, so $(3x-4)\ln 3 = \ln 15$. Thus, $3x - 4 = \frac{\ln 15}{\ln 3}$, so $x = \frac{(\ln 15)/(\ln 3) + 4}{3} = \frac{\ln 15 + 4\ln 3}{3\ln 3} = \frac{\ln 5 + \ln 3 + 4\ln 3}{3\ln 3} = \frac{\ln 5}{3\ln 3} + \frac{5}{3}$.

1.3.56 Since $5^{3x} = 29$, we have that $\ln 5^{3x} = \ln 29$, so $(3x)\ln 5 = \ln 29$. Solving for x gives $x = \frac{\ln 29}{3\ln 5}$.

1.3.57 We are seeking t so that $50 = 100e^{-t/650}$. This occurs when $e^{-t/650} = \frac{1}{2}$, which is when $-\frac{t}{650} = \ln(1/2)$, so $t = 650\ln 2 \approx 451$ years.

1.3.58 In 2010 (when $t = 0$), the population is $P(0) = 100$. So we are seeking t so that $200 = 100e^{t/50}$, or $e^{t/50} = 2$. Taking the natural logarithm of both sides yields $\frac{t}{50} = \ln 2$, or $t = 50\ln 2 \approx 35$ years.

1.3.59 $\log_2 15 = \frac{\ln 15}{\ln 2} \approx 3.9069$.

1.3.60 $\log_3 30 = \frac{\ln 30}{\ln 3} \approx 3.0959$.

1.3.61 $\log_4 40 = \frac{\ln 40}{\ln 4} \approx 2.6610$.

1.3.62 $\log_6 60 = \frac{\ln 60}{\ln 6} \approx 2.2851$.

1.3.63 Let $2^x = z$. Then $\ln 2^x = \ln z$, so $x\ln 2 = \ln z$. Taking the exponential function of both sides gives $z = e^{x\ln 2}$.

1.3.64 Let $3^{\sin x} = z$. Then $\ln 3^{\sin x} = \ln z$, so $(\sin x)\ln 3 = \ln z$. Taking the exponential function of both sides gives $z = e^{(\sin x)\ln 3}$.

1.3.65 Let $z = \ln |x|$. Then $e^z = |x|$. Taking logarithms with base 5 of both sides gives $\log_5 e^z = \log_5 |x|$, so $z \cdot \log_5 e = \log_5 |x|$, and thus $z = \frac{\log_5 |x|}{\log_5 e}$.

1.3.66 Using the change of base formula, $\log_2(x^2 + 1) = \frac{\ln(x^2+1)}{\ln 2}$.

1.3.67 Let $z = a^{1/\ln a}$. Then $\ln z = \ln\left(a^{1/\ln a}\right) = \frac{1}{\ln a} \cdot \ln a = 1$. Thus $z = e$.

1.3.68 Let $z = a^{1/\log a}$. Then $\log z = \log\left(a^{1/\log a}\right) = \frac{1}{\log a} \cdot \log a = 1$. Thus $z = 10$.

1.3.69

a. False. For example, $3 = 3^1$, but $1 \neq \sqrt[3]{3}$.

b. False. For example, suppose $x = y = b = 2$. Then the left-hand side of the equation is equal to 1, but the right-hand side is 0.

c. False. $\log_5 4^6 = 6\log_5 4 > 4\log_5 6$.

d. True. This follows because 10^x and $\log_{10}$ are inverses of each other.

e. False. $\ln 2^e = e \ln 2 < 2$.

f. False. For example $f(0) = 1$, but the alleged inverse function evaluated at 1 is not 0 (rather, it has value $1/2$.)

g. True. f is its own inverse because $f(f(x)) = f(1/x) = \frac{1}{1/x} = x$.

1.3.70

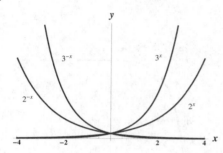

1.3.71

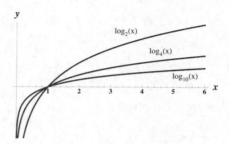

1.3.72

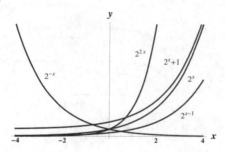

1.3.73

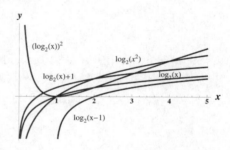

1.3.74 Since $e^x = x^{123}$, we have $x = \ln(x^{123})$, so $x = 123\ln x$. Consider the function $f(x) = x - 123\ln x$. Plotting this function using a computer or calculator reveals a graph which crosses the x axis twice, near $x = 1$ and near $x = 826$. (Try graphing it using the domain $(0, 900)$). Using a calculator and some trial and error reveals that the roots of f are approximately 1.0082 and 826.1659.

1.3.75 Note that f is one-to-one, so there is only one inverse. Switching x and y gives $x = (y + 1)^3$. Then $\sqrt[3]{x} = y + 1$, so $y = f^{-1}(x) = \sqrt[3]{x} - 1$. The domain of f^{-1} is $\mathbb{R}$.

1.3.76 Note that to get a one-to-one function, we should restrict the domain to either $[4, \infty)$ or $(-\infty, 4]$. Switching x and y yields $x = (y - 4)^2$, so $\sqrt{x} = |y - 4|$. So $y = 4 \pm \sqrt{x}$. So the inverse of f when the domain of f is restricted to $[4, \infty)$ is $f^{-1}(x) = 4 + \sqrt{x}$, while if the domain of f is restricted to $(-\infty, 4]$ the inverse is $f^{-1}(x) = 4 - \sqrt{x}$. In either case, the domain of f^{-1} is $[0, \infty)$.

1.3.77 Note that to get a one-to-one function, we should restrict the domain to either $[0, \infty)$ or $(-\infty, 0]$. Switching x and y yields $x = \frac{2}{y^2 + 2}$, so $y^2 + 2 = (2/x)$. So $y = \pm\sqrt{(2/x) - 2}$. So the inverse of f when the domain of f is restricted to $[0, \infty)$ is $f^{-1}(x) = \sqrt{(2/x) - 2}$, while if the domain of f is restricted to $(-\infty, 0]$ the inverse is $f^{-1}(x) = -\sqrt{(2/x) - 2}$. In either case, the domain of f^{-1} is $(0, 1]$.

1.3.78 Note that f is one-to-one. Switching x and y yields $x = \frac{2y}{y+2}$, so $x(y + 2) = 2y$. Thus $xy + 2x = 2y$, so $2x = 2y - xy = y(2 - x)$. Thus, $y = \frac{2x}{2-x}$. The domain of $f^{-1}(x) = \frac{2x}{2-x}$ is $(-\infty, 2) \cup (2, \infty)$.

1.3.79

a. $p(0) = 150(2^{0/12}) = 150$.

b. At a given time t, let the population be $z = 150(2^{t/12})$. Then 12 hours later, the time is $12 + t$, and the population is $150(2^{(t+12)/12}) = 150(2^{(t/12)+1}) = 150(2^{t/12} \cdot 2) = 2z$.

c. Since 4 days is 96 hours, we have $p(96) = 150(2^{96/12}) = 150(2^8) = 38{,}400$.

d. We can find the time to triple by solving $450 = 150(2^{t/12})$, which is equivalent to $3 = 2^{t/12}$. By taking logs of both sides we have $\ln 3 = \frac{t}{12} \cdot \ln 2$, so $t = \frac{12 \ln 3}{\ln 2} \approx 19.0$ hours.

e. The population will reach 10,000 when $10{,}000 = 150(2^{12/t})$, which is equivalent to $\frac{200}{3} = 2^{t/12}$. By taking logs of both sides we have $\ln(200/3) = \frac{t}{12} \ln 2$, so $= \frac{12 \cdot \ln(200/3)}{\ln 2} \approx 72.7$ hours.

1.3.80

a.   The relevant graph is:

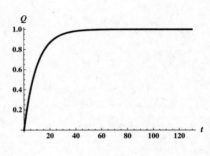

b. Varying a while holding c constant scales the curve vertically. It appears that the steady-state charge is equal to a.

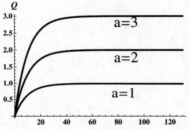

c. Varying c while holding a constant scales the curve horizontally. It appears that the steady-state charge does not vary with c.

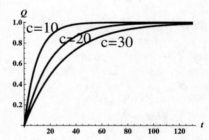

d. As t grows large, the term $ae^{-t/c}$ approaches zero for any fixed c and a. So the steady-state charge for $a - ae^{-t/c}$ is a.

1.3.81

a. No. The function takes on the values from 0 to 64 as t varies from 0 to 2, and then takes on the values from 64 to 0 as t varies from 2 to 4, so h is not one-to-one.

b. Solving for h in terms of t we have $h = 64t - 16t^2$, so (completing the square) we have $h - 64 = -16(t^2 - 4t + 4)$. Thus, $h - 64 = -16(t - 2)^2$, and $(t - 2)^2 = \frac{64-h}{16}$. Therefore $|t - 2| = \frac{\sqrt{64-h}}{4}$. When the ball is on the way up we know that $t < 2$, so the inverse of f is $f^{-1}(h) = 2 - \frac{\sqrt{64-h}}{4}$.

c. Using the work from the previous part of this problem, we have that when the ball is on the way down (when $t > 2$) we have that the inverse of f is $f^{-1}(h) = 2 + \frac{\sqrt{64-h}}{4}$.

d. On the way up, the ball is at a height of 30 ft at $2 - \frac{\sqrt{64-30}}{4} \approx 0.542$ seconds.

e. On the way down, the ball is at a height of 10 ft at $2 + \frac{\sqrt{64-10}}{4} \approx 3.837$ seconds.

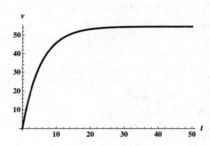

1.3.82 The terminal velocity for $k = 11$ is $\frac{600}{11}$.

1.3.83 Using the change of base formula, we have $\log_{1/b} x = \frac{\ln x}{\ln 1/b} = \frac{\ln x}{\ln 1 - \ln b} = \frac{\ln x}{-\ln b} = -\frac{\ln x}{\ln b} = -\log_b x$.

1.3.84

a. Given $x = b^p$, we have $p = \log_b x$, and given $y = b^q$, we have $q = \log_b y$.

b. $xy = b^p b^q = b^{p+q}$.

c. $\log_b xy = \log_b b^{p+q} = p + q = \log_b x + \log_b y$.

1.3.85 Using the same notation as in the previous problem, we have:
$\frac{x}{y} = \frac{b^p}{b^q} = b^{p-q}$. Thus $\log_b \frac{x}{y} = \log_b b^{p-q} = p - q = \log_b x - \log_b y$.

1.3.86

a. Given $x = b^p$, we have $p = \log_b x$.

b. $x^y = (b^p)^y = b^{yp}$.

c. $\log_b x^y = \log_b b^{yp} = yp = y \log_b x$.

1.3.87

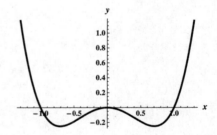

a. f is one-to-one on $(-\infty, -\sqrt{2}/2]$, on $[-\sqrt{2}/2, 0]$, on $[0, \sqrt{2}/2]$, and on $[\sqrt{2}/2, \infty)$.

b. If $u = x^2$, then our function becomes $y = u^2 - u$. Completing the square gives $y + (1/4) = u^2 - u + (1/4) = (u - (1/2))^2$. Thus $|u - (1/2)| = \sqrt{y + (1/4)}$, so $u = (1/2) \pm \sqrt{y + (1/4)}$, with the "+" applying for $u = x^2 > (1/2)$ and the "−" applying when $u = x^2 < (1/2)$. Now letting $u = x^2$, we have $x^2 = (1/2) \pm \sqrt{y + (1/4)}$, so $x = \pm\sqrt{(1/2) \pm \sqrt{y + (1/4)}}$. Now switching the x and y gives the following inverses:

Domain of f	$(-\infty, -\sqrt{2}/2]$	$[-\sqrt{2}/2, 0]$	$[0, \sqrt{2}/2]$	$[\sqrt{2}/2, \infty)$
Range of f	$[-1/4, \infty)$	$[-1/4, 0]$	$[-1/4, 0]$	$[-1/4, \infty)$
Inverse of f	$-\sqrt{(1/2) + \sqrt{x + (1/4)}}$	$-\sqrt{(1/2) - \sqrt{x + (1/4)}}$	$\sqrt{(1/2) - \sqrt{x + (1/4)}}$	$\sqrt{(1/2) + \sqrt{x + (1/4)}}$

1.3.88

a. $f(x) = g(h(x)) = g(x^3) = 2x^3 + 3$. To find the inverse of f, we switch x and y to obtain $x = 2y^3 + 3$, so that $y^3 = \frac{x-3}{2}$, so $f^{-1}(x) = \sqrt[3]{\frac{x-3}{2}}$. Note that $g^{-1}(x) = \frac{x-3}{2}$, and $h^{-1}(x) = \sqrt[3]{x}$, and so $f^{-1}(x) = h^{-1}(g^{-1}(x))$.

b. $f(x) = g(h(x)) = g(\sqrt{x}) = (\sqrt{x})^2 + 1 = x + 1$. so the inverse of f is $f^{-1}(x) = x - 1$. Note that $g^{-1}(x) = \sqrt{x-1}$, and $h^{-1}(x) = x^2$, and so $f^{-1}(x) = h^{-1}(g^{-1}(x))$.

c. If h and g are one-to-one, then their inverses exist, and $f^{-1}(x) = h^{-1}(g^{-1}(x))$, because $f(f^{-1}(x)) = g(h(h^{-1}(g^{-1}(x)))) = g(g^{-1}(x)) = x$ and likewise, $f^{-1}(f(x)) = h^{-1}(g^{-1}(g(h(x)))) = h^{-1}(h(x)) = x$.

1.3.89 Let $y = x^3 + 2x$. This function is one-to-one, so it has an inverse. Making the suggested substitution yields $y = (z - 2/(3z))^3 + 2(z - 2/(3z))$. Expanding gives $y = z^3 - 2z + 4/(3z) - 8/(27z^3) + 2z - 4/(3z) = z^3 - 8/(27z^3)$. Thus we have $y = z^3 - 8/(27z^3)$, so $27z^3 y = 27(z^3)^2 - 8$, or $27(z^3)^2 - 27y(z^3) - 8 = 0$. Applying the quadratic formula gives $z^3 = \frac{y}{2} \pm \frac{\sqrt{3}\sqrt{32+27y^2}}{18}$ We will take the "+" part and finish solving to obtain:

$$z = \sqrt[3]{\frac{y}{2} + \frac{\sqrt{3}\sqrt{32+27y^2}}{18}}$$

Now

$$x = z - (2/(3z)) = \frac{3z^2 - 2}{3z} = \frac{3\left(\sqrt[3]{\frac{y}{2} + \frac{\sqrt{3}\sqrt{32+27y^2}}{18}}\right)^2 - 2}{3\sqrt[3]{\frac{y}{2} + \frac{\sqrt{3}\sqrt{32+27y^2}}{18}}}.$$

So the inverse function $f^{-1}(x)$ is now obtained by switching y and x.

1.3.90 The given function is one-to-one, so it has an inverse. Let $y = x^3 + 4x - 1$, so $y + 1 = x^3 + 4x$. Making the suggested substitution yields $y + 1 = (z - 4/(3z))^3 + 4(z - 4/(3z))$. Expanding gives $y + 1 = z^3 - 4z + 16/(3z) - 64/(27z^3) + 4z - 16/(3z) = z^3 - 64/(27z^3)$. Thus we have $y + 1 = z^3 - 64/(27z^3)$, so $27z^3(y + 1) = 27(z^3)^2 - 64$, or $27(z^3)^2 - 27(y+1)(z^3) - 64 = 0$. Applying the quadratic formula gives $z^3 = \frac{y+1}{2} \pm \frac{\sqrt{3}\sqrt{256+27(y+1)^2}}{18}$ We will take the "+" part and finish solving to obtain:

$$z = \sqrt[3]{\frac{y+1}{2} + \frac{\sqrt{3}\sqrt{256+27(1+y)^2}}{18}}$$

Now

$$x = z - (4/(3z)) = \frac{3z^2 - 4}{3z} = \frac{3\left(\sqrt[3]{\frac{y+1}{2} + \frac{\sqrt{3}\sqrt{256+27(y+1)^2}}{18}}\right)^2 - 4}{3\sqrt[3]{\frac{y+1}{2} + \frac{\sqrt{3}\sqrt{256+27(y+1)^2}}{18}}}.$$

So the inverse function $f^{-1}(x)$ is now obtained by switching y and x.

1.3.91 Using the change of base formulas $\log_b c = \frac{\ln c}{\ln b}$ and $\log_c b = \frac{\ln b}{\ln c}$ we have

$$(\log_b c) \cdot (\log_c b) = \frac{\ln c}{\ln b} \cdot \frac{\ln b}{\ln c} = 1.$$

1.4 Trigonometric Functions and Their Inverses

1.4.1 Let O be the length of the side opposite the angle x, let A be length of the side adjacent to the angle x, and let H be the length of the hypotenuse. Then $\sin x = \frac{O}{H}$, $\cos x = \frac{A}{H}$, $\tan x = \frac{O}{A}$, $\csc x = \frac{H}{O}$, $\sec x = \frac{H}{A}$, and $\cot x = \frac{A}{O}$.

1.4.2 We consider the angle formed by the positive x axis and the ray from the origin through the point $P(x, y)$. A positive angle is one for which the rotation from the positive x axis to the other ray is counterclockwise. We then define the six trigonometric functions as follows: let $r = \sqrt{x^2 + y^2}$. Then $\sin\theta = \frac{y}{r}$, $\cos\theta = \frac{x}{r}$, $\tan\theta = \frac{y}{x}$, $\csc\theta = \frac{r}{y}$, $\sec\theta = \frac{r}{x}$, and $\cot\theta = \frac{x}{y}$.

1.4.3 The radian measure of an angle θ is the length of the arc s on the unit circle associated with θ.

1.4.4 The period of a function is the smallest positive real number k so that $f(x + k) = f(x)$ for all x in the domain of the function. The sine, cosine, secant, and cosecant function all have period 2π. The tangent and cotangent functions have period π.

1.4.5 $\sin^2 x + \cos^2 x = 1$, $1 + \cot^2 x = \csc^2 x$, and $\tan^2 x + 1 = \sec^2 x$.

1.4.6 $\csc x = \frac{1}{\sin x}$, $\sec x = \frac{1}{\cos x}$, $\tan x = \frac{\sin x}{\cos x}$, and $\cot x = \frac{\cos x}{\sin x}$.

1.4.7 The tangent function is undefined where $\cos x = 0$, which is at all real numbers of the form $\frac{\pi}{2} + k\pi$, k an integer.

1.4.8 $\sec x$ is defined wherever $\cos x \neq 0$, which is $\{x \colon x \neq \frac{\pi}{2} + k\pi, k \text{ an integer}\}$.

1.4.9 The sine function is not one-to-one over its whole domain, so in order to define an inverse, it must be restricted to an interval on which it is one-to-one.

1.4.10 In order to define an inverse for the cosine function, we restricted the domain to $[0, \pi]$ in order to get a one-to-one function. Because the range of the inverse of a function is the domain of the function, we have that the values of $\cos^{-1} x$ lie in the interval $[0, \pi]$.

1.4.11 $\tan(\tan^{-1}(x)) = x$ for all real numbers x. (Note that the domain of the inverse tangent is $\mathbb{R}$). However, it is not always true that $\tan^{-1}(\tan x) = x$. For example, $\tan 27\pi = 0$, and $\tan^{-1}(0) = 0$. Thus $\tan^{-1}(\tan(27\pi)) \neq 27\pi$.

1.4.12

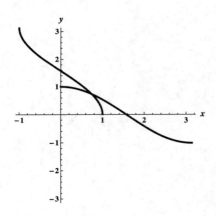

1.4.13 The numbers $\pm\pi/2$ are not in the range of $\tan^{-1} x$. The range is $(-\pi/2, \pi/2)$. However, it is true that as x increases without bound, the values of $\tan^{-1} x$ get close to $\pi/2$, and as x decreases without bound, the values of $\tan^{-1} x$ get close to $-\pi/2$.

1.4.14 The domain of $\sec^{-1} x$ is $\{x \colon |x| \geq 1\}$. The range is $[0, \pi/2) \cup (\pi/2, \pi]$.

1.4.15

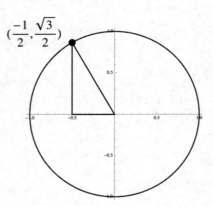

The point on the unit circle associated with $2\pi/3$ is $(-1/2, \sqrt{3}/2)$, so $\cos(2\pi/3) = -1/2$.

1.4.16 The point on the unit circle associated with $2\pi/3$ is $(-1/2, \sqrt{3}/2)$, so $\sin(2\pi/3) = \sqrt{3}/2$. See the picture from the previous problem.

1.4.17

The point on the unit circle associated with $-3\pi/4$ is $(-\sqrt{2}/2, -\sqrt{2}/2)$, so $\tan(-3\pi/4) = 1$.

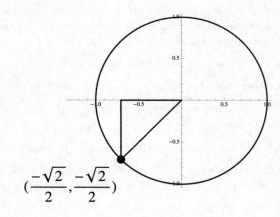

$$\left(\frac{-\sqrt{2}}{2}, \frac{-\sqrt{2}}{2}\right)$$

1.4.18

The point on the unit circle associated with $15\pi/4$ is $(\sqrt{2}/2, -\sqrt{2}/2)$, so $\tan(15\pi/4) = -1$.

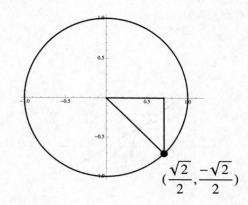

$$\left(\frac{\sqrt{2}}{2}, \frac{-\sqrt{2}}{2}\right)$$

1.4.19

The point on the unit circle associated with $-13\pi/3$ is $(1/2, -\sqrt{3}/2)$, so $\cot(-13\pi/3) = -1/\sqrt{3} = -\sqrt{3}/3$.

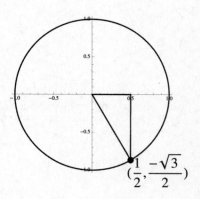

$$\left(\frac{1}{2}, \frac{-\sqrt{3}}{2}\right)$$

1.4.20

The point on the unit circle associated with $7\pi/6$ is $(-\sqrt{3}/2, -1/2)$, so $\sec(7\pi/6) = -2/\sqrt{3} = -2\sqrt{3}/3$.

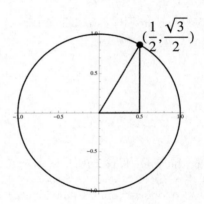

$(\dfrac{-\sqrt{3}}{2}, \dfrac{-1}{2})$

1.4.21

The point on the unit circle associated with $-17\pi/3$ is $(1/2, \sqrt{3}/2)$, so $\cot(-17\pi/3) = 1/\sqrt{3} = \sqrt{3}/3$.

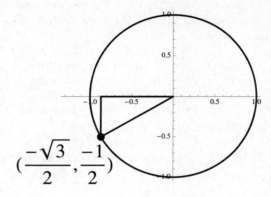

$(\dfrac{1}{2}, \dfrac{\sqrt{3}}{2})$

1.4.22

The point on the unit circle associated with $16\pi/3$ is $(-1/2, -\sqrt{3}/2)$, so $\sin(16\pi/3) = -\sqrt{3}/2$.

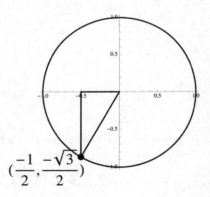

$(\dfrac{-1}{2}, \dfrac{-\sqrt{3}}{2})$

1.4.23 Because the point on the unit circle associated with $\theta = 0$ is the point $(1, 0)$, we have $\cos 0 = 1$.

1.4.24 Because $-\pi/2$ corresponds to a quarter circle clockwise revolution, the point on the unit circle associated with $-\pi/2$ is the point $(0, -1)$. Thus $\sin(-\pi/2) = -1$.

1.4.25 Because $-\pi$ corresponds to a half circle clockwise revolution, the point on the unit circle associated with $-\pi$ is the point $(-1, 0)$. Thus $\cos(-\pi) = -1$.

1.4.26 Because 3π corresponds to one and a half counterclockwise revolutions, the point on the unit circle associated with 3π is $(-1, 0)$, so $\tan 3\pi = \frac{0}{-1} = 0$.

1.4.27 Because $5\pi/2$ corresponds to one and a quarter counterclockwise revolutions, the point on the unit circle associated with $5\pi/2$ is the same as the point associated with $\pi/2$, which is $(0,1)$. Thus $\sec 5\pi/2$ is undefined.

1.4.28 Because π corresponds to one half circle counterclockwise revolution, the point on the unit circle associated with π is $(-1,0)$. Thus $\cot \pi$ is undefined.

1.4.29 From our definitions of the trigonometric functions via a point $P(x,y)$ on a circle of radius $r = \sqrt{x^2 + y^2}$, we have $\sec \theta = \frac{r}{x} = \frac{1}{x/r} = \frac{1}{\cos \theta}$.

1.4.30 From our definitions of the trigonometric functions via a point $P(x,y)$ on a circle of radius $r = \sqrt{x^2 + y^2}$, we have $\tan \theta = \frac{y}{x} = \frac{y/r}{x/r} = \frac{\sin \theta}{\cos \theta}$.

1.4.31 We have already established that $\sin^2 \theta + \cos^2 \theta = 1$. Dividing both sides by $\cos^2 \theta$ gives $\tan^2 \theta + 1 = \sec^2 \theta$.

1.4.32 We have already established that $\sin^2 \theta + \cos^2 \theta = 1$. We can write this as $\frac{\sin \theta}{(1/\sin \theta)} + \frac{\cos \theta}{(1/\cos \theta)} = 1$, or $\frac{\sin \theta}{\csc \theta} + \frac{\cos \theta}{\sec \theta} = 1$.

1.4.33

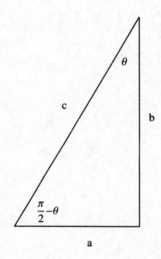

Using the triangle pictured, we see that $\sec(\pi/2 - \theta) = \frac{c}{a} = \csc \theta$.

This also follows from the sum identity $\cos(a+b) = \cos a \cos b - \sin a \sin b$ as follows: $\sec(\pi/2 - \theta) = \frac{1}{\cos(\pi/2 + (-\theta))} = \frac{1}{\cos(\pi/2)\cos(-\theta) - \sin(\pi/2)\sin(-\theta)} = \frac{1}{0 - (-\sin(\theta))} = \csc(\theta)$.

1.4.34 Using the trig identity for the cosine of a sum (mentioned in the previous solution) we have:

$$\sec(x + \pi) = \frac{1}{\cos(x + \pi)} = \frac{1}{\cos(x)\cos(\pi) - \sin(x)\sin(\pi)} = \frac{1}{\cos(x) \cdot (-1) - \sin(x) \cdot 0} = \frac{1}{-\cos(x)} = -\sec x.$$

1.4.35 Using the fact that $\frac{\pi}{12} = \frac{\pi/6}{2}$ and the half-angle identity for cosine:

$$\cos^2(\pi/12) = \frac{1 + \cos(\pi/6)}{2} = \frac{1 + \sqrt{3}/2}{2} = \frac{2 + \sqrt{3}}{4}.$$

Thus, $\cos(\pi/12) = \sqrt{\frac{2+\sqrt{3}}{4}}$.

1.4.36 Using the fact that $\frac{3\pi}{8} = \frac{3\pi/4}{2}$ and the half-angle identities for sine and cosine, we have:

$$\cos^2(3\pi/8) = \frac{1 + \cos(3\pi/4)}{2} = \frac{1 + (-\sqrt{2}/2)}{2} = \frac{2 - \sqrt{2}}{4},$$

and using the fact that $3\pi/8$ is in the first quadrant (and thus has positive value for cosine) we deduce that $\cos(3\pi/8) = \sqrt{2 - \sqrt{2}}/2$. A similar calculation using the sine function results in $\sin(3\pi/8) = \sqrt{2 + \sqrt{2}}/2$. Thus $\tan(3\pi/8) = \sqrt{\frac{2+\sqrt{2}}{2-\sqrt{2}}}$, which simplifies as

$$\sqrt{\frac{2 + \sqrt{2}}{2 - \sqrt{2}} \cdot \frac{2 + \sqrt{2}}{2 + \sqrt{2}}} = \sqrt{\frac{(2 + \sqrt{2})^2}{2}} = \frac{2 + \sqrt{2}}{\sqrt{2}} = 1 + \sqrt{2}.$$

1.4.37 First note that $\tan x = 1$ when $\sin x = \cos x$. Using our knowledge of the values of the standard angles between 0 and 2π, we recognize that the sine function and the cosine function are equal at $\pi/4$. Then, because we recall that the period of the tangent function is π, we know that $\tan(\pi/4 + k\pi) = \tan(\pi/4) = 1$ for every integer value of k. Thus the solution set is $\{\pi/4 + k\pi, \text{where } k \text{ is an integer}\}$.

1.4.38 Given that $2\theta \cos(\theta) + \theta = 0$, we have $\theta(2 \cos(\theta) + 1) = 0$. Which means that either $\theta = 0$, or $2 \cos(\theta) + 1 = 0$. The latter leads to the equation $\cos \theta = -1/2$, which occurs at $\theta = 2\pi/3$ and $\theta = 4\pi/3$. Using the fact that the cosine function has period 2π the entire solution set is thus

$$\{0\} \cup \{2\pi/3 + 2k\pi, \text{where } k \text{ is an integer}\} \cup \{4\pi/3 + 2l\pi, \text{where } l \text{ is an integer}\}.$$

1.4.39 Given that $\sin^2 \theta = \frac{1}{4}$, we have $|\sin \theta| = \frac{1}{2}$, so $\sin \theta = \frac{1}{2}$ or $\sin \theta = -\frac{1}{2}$. It follows that $\theta = \pi/6, 5\pi/6, 7\pi/6, 11\pi/6$.

1.4.40 Given that $\cos^2 \theta = \frac{1}{2}$, we have $|\cos \theta| = \frac{1}{\sqrt{2}} = \frac{\sqrt{2}}{2}$. Thus $\cos \theta = \frac{\sqrt{2}}{2}$ or $\cos \theta = -\frac{\sqrt{2}}{2}$. We have $\theta = \pi/4, 3\pi/4, 5\pi/4, 7\pi/4$.

1.4.41 The equation $\sqrt{2} \sin(x) - 1 = 0$ can be written as $\sin x = \frac{1}{\sqrt{2}} = \frac{\sqrt{2}}{2}$. Standard solutions to this equation occur at $x = \pi/4$ and $x = 3\pi/4$. Because the sine function has period 2π the set of all solutions can be written as:

$$\{\pi/4 + 2k\pi, \text{where } k \text{ is an integer}\} \cup \{3\pi/4 + 2l\pi, \text{where } l \text{ is an integer}\}.$$

1.4.42 Let $u = 3x$. Note that because $0 \le x < 2\pi$, we have $0 \le u < 6\pi$. Because $\sin u = \sqrt{2}/2$ for $u = \pi/4$, $3\pi/4, 9\pi/4, 11\pi/4, 17\pi/4$, and $19\pi/4$, we must have that $\sin 3x = \sqrt{2}/2$ for $3x = \pi/4, 3\pi/4, 9\pi/4, 11\pi/4$, $17\pi/4$, and $19\pi/4$, which translates into

$$x = \pi/12, \pi/4, 3\pi/4, 11\pi/12, 17\pi/12, \text{and } 19\pi/12.$$

1.4.43 As in the previous problem, let $u = 3x$. Then we are interested in the solutions to $\cos u = \sin u$, for $0 \le u < 6\pi$.

This would occur for $u = 3x = \pi/4, 5\pi/4, 9\pi/4, 13\pi/4, 17\pi/4$, and $21\pi/4$. Thus there are solutions for the original equation at

$$x = \pi/12, 5\pi/12, 3\pi/4, 13\pi/12, 17\pi/12, \text{and } 7\pi/4.$$

1.4.44 $\sin^2(\theta) - 1 = 0$ wherever $\sin^2(\theta) = 1$, which is wherever $\sin(\theta) = \pm 1$. This occurs for $\theta = \pi/2 + k\pi$, where k is an integer.

1.4.45 If $\sin \theta \cos \theta = 0$, then either $\sin \theta = 0$ or $\cos \theta = 0$. This occurs for $\theta = 0, \pi/2, \pi, 3\pi/2$.

1.4.46 If $\tan^2 2\theta = 1$, then $\sin^2 2\theta = \cos^2 2\theta$, so we have either $\sin 2\theta = \cos 2\theta$ or $\sin 2\theta = -\cos 2\theta$. This occurs for $2\theta = \pi/4, 3\pi/4, 5\pi/4, 7\pi/4$ for $0 \le 2\theta \le 2\pi$, so the corresponding values for θ are $\pi/8, 3\pi/8, 5\pi/8$, $7\pi/8$, $0 \le \theta \le \pi$.

1.4.47 Let $z = \sin^{-1}(1)$. Then $\sin z = 1$, and because $\sin \pi/2 = 1$, and $\pi/2$ is in the desired interval, $z = \pi/2$.

1.4.48 Let $z = \cos^{-1}(-1)$. Then $\cos z = -1$, and because $\cos \pi = -1$ and π is in the desired interval, $z = \pi$.

1.4.49 Let $z = \tan^{-1}(1)$. Then $\tan z = 1$, so $\frac{\sin z}{\cos z} = 1$, so $\sin z = \cos z$. Because $\cos \pi/4 = \sin \pi/4$, and $\pi/4$ is in the desired interval, $z = \pi/4$.

1.4.50 Let $z = \cos^{-1}(-\sqrt{2}/2)$. Then $\cos z = -\sqrt{2}/2$. Because $\cos 3\pi/4 = -\sqrt{2}/2$ and $3\pi/4$ is in the desired interval, we have $z = 3\pi/4$. (Note that $\cos(-\pi/4)$ is also equal to $-\sqrt{2}/2$, but $-\pi/4$ isn't in the desired interval $[0, \pi]$.)

1.4.51 $\sin^{-1}(\sqrt{3}/2) = \pi/3$, because $\sin(\pi/3) = \sqrt{3}/2$.

1.4.52 $\cos^{-1}(2)$ does not exist, because 2 is not in the domain of the inverse cosine function (because 2 is not in the range of the cosine function.)

1.4.53 $\cos^{-1}(-1/2) = 2\pi/3$, because $\cos(2\pi/3) = -1/2$.

1.4.54 $\sin^{-1}(-1) = -\pi/2$, because $\sin(-\pi/2) = -1$.

1.4.55 $\cos(\cos^{-1}(-1)) = \cos(\pi) = -1$.

1.4.56 $\cos^{-1}(\cos(7\pi/6)) = \cos^{-1}(-\sqrt{3}/2) = 5\pi/6$. Note that the range of the inverse cosine function is $[0, \pi]$.

1.4.57

$$\cos(\sin^{-1}(x)) = \frac{\text{side adjacent to } \sin^{-1}(x)}{\text{hypotenuse}} = \frac{\sqrt{1 - x^2}}{1} = \sqrt{1 - x^2}.$$

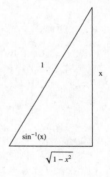

1.4.58

$$\cos(\sin^{-1}(x/3)) = \frac{\text{side adjacent to } \sin^{-1}(x/3)}{\text{hypotenuse}} = \frac{\sqrt{9 - x^2}}{3}.$$

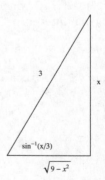

1.4.59

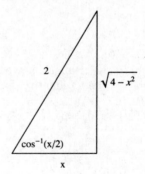

$$\sin(\cos^{-1}(x/2)) = \frac{\text{side opposite of } \cos^{-1}(x/2)}{\text{hypotenuse}} = \frac{\sqrt{4-x^2}}{2}.$$

1.4.60

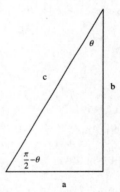

Note (from the triangle pictured) that $\cos\theta = \frac{b}{c} = \sin(\frac{\pi}{2} - \theta)$. Thus $\sin^{-1}(\cos\theta) = \sin^{-1}(\sin(\frac{\pi}{2} - \theta)) = \frac{\pi}{2} - \theta$.

1.4.61

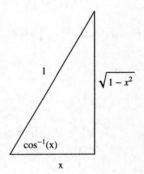

Using the identity given, we have $\sin(2\cos^{-1}(x)) = 2\sin(\cos^{-1}(x))\cos(\cos^{-1}(x)) = 2x\sin(\cos^{-1}(x)) = 2x\sqrt{1-x^2}$.

1.4.62

First note that $\cos(\sin^{-1}(\theta)) = \sqrt{1 - \theta^2}$, as indicated in the triangle shown.

Using the identity given, we have $\cos(2\sin^{-1}(x)) = \cos^2((\sin^{-1}(x)) - \sin^2(\sin^{-1}(x)) = (\sqrt{1 - x^2})^2 - x^2 = 1 - 2x^2$.

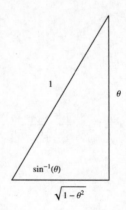

1.4.63

Let $\theta = \cos^{-1}(x)$, and note from the diagram that it then follows that $\cos^{-1}(-x) = \pi - \theta$. So $\cos^{-1}(x) + \cos^{-1}(-x) = \theta + \pi - \theta = \pi$.

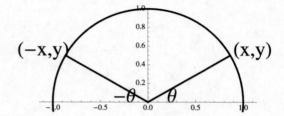

1.4.64 Let $\theta = \sin^{-1}(y)$. Then $\sin\theta = y$, and $\sin(-\theta) = -\sin(\theta) = -y$ (because the sine function is an odd function) and it then follows that $-\theta = \sin^{-1}(-y)$. Therefore, $\sin^{-1}(y) + \sin^{-1}(-y) = \theta + -\theta = 0$. It would be instructive for the reader to draw his or her own diagram like that in the previous solution.

1.4.65 The graphs appear to be identical: so $\sin^{-1} x = \pi/2 - \cos^{-1}(x)$.

1.4.66 The graphs appear to be identical: so $\tan^{-1} x = \pi/2 - \cot^{-1}(x)$.

1.4.67 $\tan^{-1}(\sqrt{3}) = \tan^{-1}\left(\frac{\sqrt{3}/2}{1/2}\right) = \pi/3$, because $\sin(\pi/3) = \sqrt{3}/2$ and $\cos(\pi/3) = 1/2$.

1.4.68 $\cot^{-1}(-1/\sqrt{3}) = \cot^{-1}\left(-\frac{1/2}{\sqrt{3}/2}\right) = 2\pi/3$, because $\sin(2\pi/3) = \sqrt{3}/2$ and $\cos(2\pi/3) = -1/2$.

1.4.69 $\sec^{-1}(2) = \sec^{-1}\left(\frac{1}{1/2}\right) = \pi/3$, because $\sec(\pi/3) = \frac{1}{\cos(\pi/3)} = \frac{1}{1/2} = 2$.

1.4.70 $\csc^{-1}(-1) = \sin^{-1}(-1) = -\pi/2$.

1.4.71 $\tan^{-1}(\tan(\pi/4)) = \tan^{-1}(1) = \pi/4$.

1.4.72 $\tan^{-1}(\tan(3\pi/4)) = \tan^{-1}(-1) = -\pi/4$.

1.4.73 Let $\csc^{-1}(\sec 2) = z$. Then $\csc z = \sec 2$, so $\sin z = \cos 2$. Now by applying the result of problem 60, we see that $z = \sin^{-1}(\cos 2) = \pi/2 - 2 = \frac{\pi - 4}{2}$.

1.4.74 $\tan(\tan^{-1}(1)) = \tan(\pi/4) = 1$.

1.4.75

$$\cos(\tan^{-1}(x)) = \frac{\text{side adjacent to } \tan^{-1}(x)}{\text{hypotenuse}} = \frac{1}{\sqrt{1+x^2}}.$$

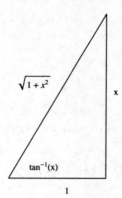

1.4.76

$$\tan(\cos^{-1}(x)) = \frac{\text{side opposite of } \cos^{-1}(x)}{\text{side adjacent to } \cos^{-1}(x)} = \frac{\sqrt{1-x^2}}{x}.$$

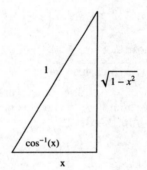

1.4.77

$$\cos(\sec^{-1}(x)) = \frac{\text{side adjacent to } \sec^{-1} x}{\text{hypotenuse}} = \frac{1}{x}.$$

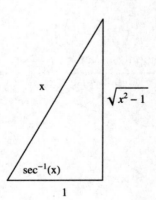

1.4.78

$$\cot(\tan^{-1} 2x) = \frac{\text{side adjacent to } \tan^{-1} 2x}{\text{side opposite of } \tan^{-1} 2x} = \frac{1}{2x}.$$

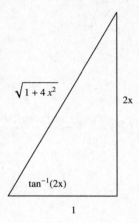

1.4.79

Assume $x > 0$. Then $\sin\left(\sec^{-1}\left(\dfrac{\sqrt{x^2 + 16}}{4}\right)\right) =$

$\dfrac{\text{side opposite of } \sec^{-1}\left(\frac{\sqrt{x^2+16}}{4}\right)}{\text{hypotenuse}} = \dfrac{|x|}{\sqrt{x^2 + 16}}.$

Note: If $x < 0$, then the expression results in a positive number, hence the necessary absolute value sign in the result.

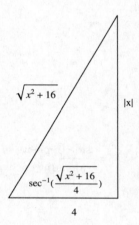

1.4.80

$\cos\left(\tan^{-1}\left(\dfrac{x}{\sqrt{9 - x^2}}\right)\right) =$

$\dfrac{\text{side adjacent to } \tan^{-1}\left(\frac{x}{\sqrt{9-x^2}}\right)}{\text{hypotenuse}} = \dfrac{\sqrt{9 - x^2}}{3}.$

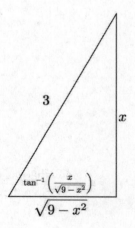

1.4.81 Because $\sin\theta = \frac{x}{6}$, $\theta = \sin^{-1}(x/6)$. Also, $\theta = \tan^{-1}\left(\frac{x}{\sqrt{36-x^2}}\right) = \sec^{-1}\left(\frac{6}{\sqrt{36-x^2}}\right)$.

1.4.82

First note that $\tan(\psi) = \frac{2x}{\sqrt{144-9x^2}}$, so $\psi = \tan^{-1}\left(\frac{2x}{\sqrt{144-9x^2}}\right)$. Also, $\sin(\theta+\psi) = \frac{3x}{12} = \frac{x}{4}$, so $\theta + \psi = \sin^{-1}(x/4)$. Therefore, $\theta = \sin^{-1}(x/4) - \psi = \sin^{-1}(x/4) - \tan^{-1}(2x/\sqrt{144-9x^2})$.

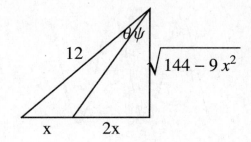

1.4.83

a. False. For example, $\sin(\pi/2 + \pi/2) = \sin(\pi) = 0 \neq \sin(\pi/2) + \sin(\pi/2) = 1 + 1 = 2$.

b. False. That equation has zero solutions, because the range of the cosine function is $[-1,1]$.

c. False. It has infinitely many solutions of the form $\pi/6 + 2k\pi$, where k is an integer (among others.)

d. False. It has period $\frac{2\pi}{\pi/12} = 24$.

e. True. The others have a range of either $[-1,1]$ or $(-\infty,-1] \cup [1,\infty)$.

f. False. For example, suppose $x = .5$. Then $\sin^{-1}(x) = \pi/6$ and $\cos^{-1}(x) = \pi/3$, so that $\frac{\sin^{-1}(x)}{\cos^{-1}(x)} = \frac{\pi/6}{\pi/3} = .5$. However, note that $\tan^{-1}(.5) \neq .5$,

g. True. Note that the range of the inverse cosine function is $[0,\pi]$.

h. False. For example, if $x = .5$, we would have $\sin^{-1}(.5) = \pi/6 \neq 1/\sin(.5)$.

1.4.84 If $\sin\theta = -4/5$, then the Pythagorean identity gives $|\cos\theta| = 3/5$. But if $\pi < \theta < 3\pi/2$, then the cosine of θ is negative, so $\cos\theta = -3/5$. Thus $\tan\theta = 4/3$, $\cot\theta = 3/4$, $\sec\theta = -5/3$, and $\csc\theta = -5/4$.

1.4.85 If $\cos\theta = 5/13$, then the Pythagorean identity gives $|\sin\theta| = 12/13$. But if $0 < \theta < \pi/2$, then the sine of θ is positive, so $\sin\theta = 12/13$. Thus $\tan\theta = 12/5$, $\cot\theta = 5/12$, $\sec\theta = 13/5$, and $\csc\theta = 13/12$.

1.4.86 If $\sec\theta = 5/3$, then $\cos\theta = 3/5$, and the Pythagorean identity gives $|\sin\theta| = 4/5$. But if $3\pi/2 < \theta < 2\pi$, then the sine of θ is negative, so $\sin\theta = -4/5$. Thus $\tan\theta = -4/3$, $\cot\theta = -3/4$, and $\csc\theta = -5/4$.

1.4.87 If $\csc\theta = 13/12$, then $\sin\theta = 12/13$, and the Pythagorean identity gives $|\cos\theta| = 5/13$. But if $0 < \theta < \pi/2$, then the cosine of θ is positive, so $\cos\theta = 5/13$. Thus $\tan\theta = 12/5$, $\cot\theta = 5/12$, and $\sec\theta = 13/5$.

1.4.88 The amplitude is 2, and the period is $\frac{2\pi}{2} = \pi$.

1.4.89 The amplitude is 3, and the period is $\frac{2\pi}{1/3} = 6\pi$.

1.4.90 The amplitude is 2.5, and the period is $\frac{2\pi}{1/2} = 4\pi$.

1.4.91 The amplitude is 3.6, and the period is $\frac{2\pi}{\pi/24} = 48$.

1.4.92

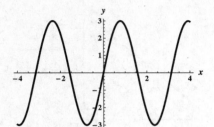

1.4.93

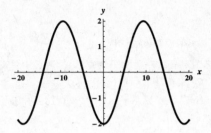

1.4.94

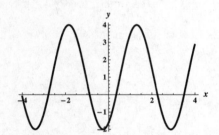

1.4.95

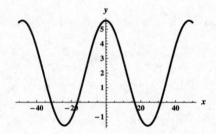

1.4.96

It is helpful to imagine first shifting the function horizontally so that the x intercept is where it should be, then stretching the function horizontally to obtain the correct period, and then stretching the function vertically to obtain the correct amplitude. Because the old x-intercept is at $x = 0$ and the new one should be at $x = 3$ (halfway between where the maximum and the minimum occur), we need to shift the function 3 units to the right. Then to get the right period, we need to multiply (before applying the sine function) by $\pi/6$ so that the new period is $\frac{2\pi}{\pi/6} = 12$. Finally, to get the right amplitude and to get the max and min at the right spots, we need to multiply on the outside by 4. Thus, the desired function is:

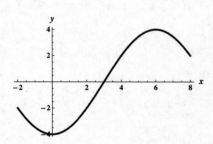

$$f(x) = 4\sin((\pi/6)(x - 3)) = 4\sin((\pi/6)x - \pi/2).$$

1.4.97

It is helpful to imagine first shifting the function horizontally so that the x intercept is where it should be, then stretching the function horizontally to obtain the correct period, and then stretching the function vertically to obtain the correct amplitude, and then shifting the whole graph up. Because the old x-intercept is at $x = 0$ and the new one should be at $x = 9$ (halfway between where the maximum and the minimum occur), we need to shift the function 9 units to the right. Then to get the right period, we need to multiply (before applying the sine function) by $\pi/12$ so that the new period is $\frac{2\pi}{\pi/12} = 24$. Finally, to get the right amplitude and to get the max and min at the right spots, we need to multiply on the outside by 3, and then shift the whole thing up 13 units. Thus, the desired function is:

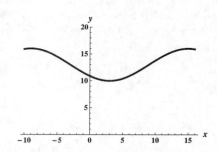

$$f(x) = 3\sin((\pi/12)(x-9)) + 13 = 3\sin((\pi/12)x - 3\pi/4) + 13.$$

1.4.98 Let C be the point on the end line so that segment $\overline{AC}$ is perpendicular to the endline. Then the distance $G_1C = 38.\overline{3}$, $G_2C = 15$, and $AC = 69$ and $BC = 84$, where all lengths are in feet. Thus

$$m(\angle G_1AG_2) = m(\angle G_1AC) - m(\angle G_2AC) = \tan^{-1}\left(\frac{38.\overline{3}}{69}\right) - \tan^{-1}\left(\frac{15}{69}\right) \approx 16.79°,$$

while

$$m(\angle G_1BG_2) = m(\angle G_1BC) - m(\angle G_2BC) = \tan^{-1}\left(\frac{38.\overline{3}}{84}\right) - \tan^{-1}\left(\frac{15}{84}\right) \approx 14.4°.$$

The kicking angle was not improved by the penalty.

1.4.99 Let C be the circumference of the earth. Then the first rope has radius $r_1 = \frac{C}{2\pi}$. The circle generated by the longer rope has circumference $C + 38$, so its radius is $r_2 = \frac{C+38}{2\pi} = \frac{C}{2\pi} + \frac{38}{2\pi} \approx r_1 + 6$, so the radius of the bigger circle is about 6 feet more than the smaller circle.

1.4.100

a. The period of this function is $\frac{2\pi}{2\pi/365} = 365$.

b. Because the maximum for the regular sine function is 1, and this function is scaled vertically by a factor of 2.8 and shifted 12 units up, the maximum for this function is $(2.8)(1) + 12 = 14.8$. Similarly, the minimum is $(2.8)(-1) + 12 = 9.2$. Because of the horizontal shift, the point at $t = 81$ is the midpoint between where the max and min occur. Thus the max occurs at $81 + (365/4) \approx 172$ and the min occurs approximately $(365/2)$ days later at about $t = 355$.

c. The solstices occur halfway between these points, at 81 and $81 + (365/2) \approx 264$.

1.4.101 We are seeking a function with amplitude 10 and period 1.5, and value 10 at time 0, so it should have the form $10\cos(kt)$, where $\frac{2\pi}{k} = 1.5$. Solving for k yields $k = \frac{4\pi}{3}$, so the desired function is $d(t) = 10\cos(4\pi t/3)$.

1.4.102

a. Because $\tan\theta = \frac{50}{d}$, we have $d = \frac{50}{\tan\theta}$.

b. Because $\sin\theta = \frac{50}{L}$, we have $L = \frac{50}{\sin\theta}$.

1.4.103 Let L be the line segment connecting the tops of the ladders and let M be the horizontal line segment between the walls h feet above the ground. Now note that the triangle formed by the ladders and L is equilateral, because the angle between the ladders is 60 degrees, and the other two angles must be equal and add to 120, so they are 60 degrees as well. Now we can see that the triangle formed by L, M and the right wall is similar to the triangle formed by the left ladder, the left wall, and the ground, because they are both right triangles with one angle of 75 degrees and one of 15 degrees. Thus $M = h$ is the distance between the walls.

1.4.104

Let the corner point P divide the pole into two pieces, L_1 (which spans the 3-ft hallway) and L_2 (which spans the 4-ft hallway.) Then $L = L_1 + L_2$. Now $L_2 = \frac{4}{\sin\theta}$, and $\frac{3}{L_1} = \cos\theta$ (see diagram.) Thus $L = L_1 + L_2 = \frac{3}{\cos\theta} + \frac{4}{\sin\theta}$. When $L = 10$, $\theta \approx .9273$.

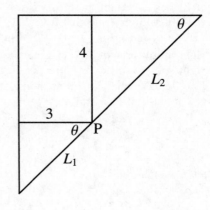

1.4.105

To find $s(t)$ note that we are seeking a periodic function with period 365, and with amplitude 87.5 (which is half of the number of minutes between 7:25 and 4:30). We need to shift the function 4 days plus one fourth of 365, which is about 95 days so that the max and min occur at $t = 4$ days and at half a year later. Also, to get the right value for the maximum and minimum, we need to multiply by negative one and add 117.5 (which represents 30 minutes plus half the amplitude, because $s = 0$ corresponds to 4:00 AM.) Thus we have

$$s(t) = 117.5 - 87.5\sin\left(\frac{\pi}{182.5}(t - 95)\right).$$

A similar analysis leads to the formula

$$S(t) = 844.5 + 87.5\sin\left(\frac{\pi}{182.5}(t - 67)\right).$$

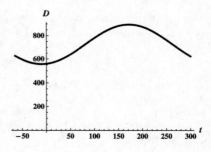

The graph pictured shows $D(t) = S(t) - s(t)$, the length of day function, which has its max at the summer solstice which is about the 172nd day of the year, and its min at the winter solstice.

1.4.106 Let θ_1 be the viewing angle to the bottom of the television. Then $\theta_1 = \tan^{-1}\left(\frac{3}{x}\right)$. Now $\tan(\theta + \theta_1) = \frac{10}{x}$, so $\theta + \theta_1 = \tan^{-1}\left(\frac{10}{x}\right)$, so $\theta = \tan^{-1}\left(\frac{10}{x}\right) - \theta_1 = \tan^{-1}\left(\frac{10}{x}\right) - \tan^{-1}\left(\frac{3}{x}\right)$.

1.4.107 The area of the entire circle is πr^2. The ratio $\frac{\theta}{2\pi}$ represents the proportion of the area swept out by a central angle θ. Thus the area of a sector of a circle is this same proportion of the entire area, so it is $\frac{\theta}{2\pi} \cdot \pi r^2 = \frac{r^2\theta}{2}$.

1.4.108 Using the given diagram, drop a perpendicular from the point $(b\cos\theta, b\sin\theta)$ to the x axis, and consider the right triangle thus formed whose hypotenuse has length c. By the Pythagorean theorem, $(b\sin\theta)^2 + (a - b\cos\theta)^2 = c^2$. Expanding the binomial gives $b^2\sin^2\theta + a^2 - 2ab\cos\theta + b^2\cos^2\theta = c^2$. Now because $b^2\sin^2\theta + b^2\cos^2\theta = b^2$, this reduces to $a^2 + b^2 - 2ab\cos\theta = c^2$.

1.4.109 Note that $\sin A = \frac{h}{c}$ and $\sin C = \frac{h}{a}$, so $h = c\sin A = a\sin C$. Thus

$$\frac{\sin A}{a} = \frac{\sin C}{c}.$$

Now drop a perpendicular from the vertex A to the line determined by $\overline{BC}$, and let h_2 be the length of this perpendicular. Then $\sin C = \frac{h_2}{b}$ and $\sin B = \frac{h_2}{C}$, so $h_2 = b\sin C = c\sin B$. Thus

$$\frac{\sin C}{c} = \frac{\sin B}{b}.$$

Putting the two displayed equations together gives

$$\frac{\sin A}{a} = \frac{\sin B}{b} = \frac{\sin C}{c}.$$

Chapter One Review

1

    a. True. For example, $f(x) = x^2$ is such a function.

    b. False. For example, $\cos(\pi/2 + \pi/2) = \cos(\pi) = -1 \neq \cos(\pi/2) + \cos(\pi/2) = 0 + 0 = 0$.

    c. False. Consider $f(1 + 1) = f(2) = 2m + b \neq f(1) + f(1) = (m + b) + (m + b) = 2m + 2b$. (At least these aren't equal when $b \neq 0$.)

    d. True. $f(f(x)) = f(1 - x) = 1 - (1 - x) = x$.

    e. False. This set is the union of the disjoint intervals $(-\infty, -7)$ and $(1, \infty)$.

    f. False. For example, if $x = y = 10$, then $\log_{10} xy = \log_{10} 100 = 2$, but $\log_{10} 10 \cdot \log_{10} 10 = 1 \cdot 1 = 1$.

    g. True. $\sin^{-1}(\sin(2\pi)) = \sin^{-1}(0) = 0$.

2

    a. Because the quantity under the radical must be non-zero, the domain of f is $[0, \infty)$. The range is also $[0, \infty)$.

    b. The domain is $(-\infty, 2) \cup (2, \infty)$. The range is $(-\infty, 0) \cup (0, \infty)$. (Note that if 0 were in the range then $\frac{1}{y-2} = 0$ for some value of y, but this expression has no real solutions.)

    c. Because h can be written $h(z) = \sqrt{(z-3)(z+1)}$, we see that the domain is $(-\infty, -1] \cup [3, \infty)$. The range is $[0, \infty)$. (Note that as z gets large, $h(z)$ gets large as well.)

3

a. This line has slope $\frac{2-(-3)}{4-2} = 5/2$. Therefore the equation of the line is $y - 2 = \frac{5}{2}(x - 4)$, so $y = \frac{5}{2}x - 8$.

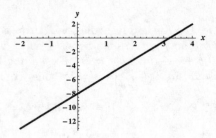

b. This line has the form $y = (3/4)x + b$, and because $(-4, 0)$ is on the line, $0 = (3/4)(-4) + b$, so $b = 3$. Thus the equation of the line is given by $y = (3/4)x + 3$.

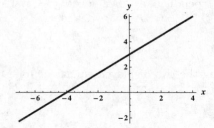

c. This line has slope $\frac{0-(-2)}{4-0} = \frac{1}{2}$, and the y-intercept is given to be -2, so the equation of this line is $y = (1/2)x - 2$.

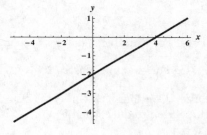

4

The function is a piecewise step function which jumps up by one every half-hour step.

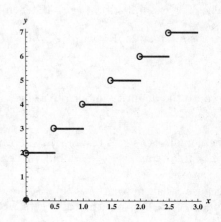

5

Because $|x| = \begin{cases} -x & \text{if } x < 0; \\ x & \text{if } x \geq 0, \end{cases}$

we have

$2(x - |x|) = \begin{cases} 2(x - (-x)) = 4x & \text{if } x < 0; \\ 2(x - x) = 0 & \text{if } x \geq 0. \end{cases}$

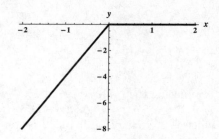

6 Because the trip is 500 miles in a car that gets 35 miles per gallon, $\frac{500}{35} = \frac{100}{7}$ represents the number of gallons required for the trip. If we multiply this times the number of dollars per gallon we will get the cost. Thus $C = f(p) = \frac{100}{7}p$ dollars.

7

a.   This is a straight line with slope 2/3 and y-intercept 10/3.

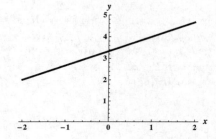

b.   Completing the square gives $y = (x^2 + 2x + 1) - 4$, or $y = (x+1)^2 - 4$, so this is the standard parabola shifted one unit to the left and down 4 units.

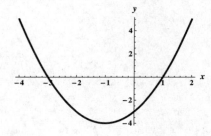

c.   Completing the square, we have $x^2 + 2x + 1 + y^2 + 4y + 4 = -1 + 1 + 4$, so we have $(x+1)^2 + (y+2)^2 = 4$, a circle of radius 2 centered at $(-1, -2)$.

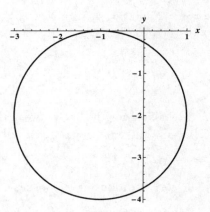

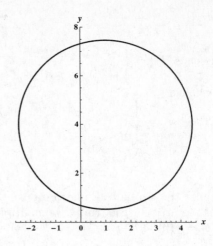

d. Completing the square, we have $x^2 - 2x + 1 + y^2 - 8y + 16 = -5 + 1 + 16$, or $(x-1)^2 + (y-4)^2 = 12$, which is a circle of radius $\sqrt{12}$ centered at $(1, 4)$.

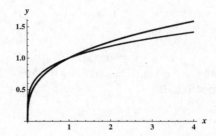

8 To solve $x^{1/3} = x^{1/4}$ we raise each side to the 12th power, yielding $x^4 = x^3$. This gives $x^4 - x^3 = 0$, or $x^3(x-1) = 0$, so the only solutions are $x = 0$ and $x = 1$ (which can be easily verified as solutions.) Between 0 and 1, $x^{1/4} > x^{1/3}$, but for $x > 1$, $x^{1/3} > x^{1/4}$.

9 The domain of $x^{1/7}$ is the set of all real numbers, as is its range. The domain of $x^{1/4}$ is the set of non-negative real numbers, as is its range.

10

Completing the square in the second equation, we have $x^2 + y^2 - 7y + \frac{49}{4} = -8 + \frac{49}{4}$, which can be written as $x^2 + (y - (7/2))^2 = \frac{17}{4}$. Thus we have a circle of radius $\sqrt{17}/2$ centered at $(0, 7/2)$, along with the standard parabola. These intersect when $y = 7y - y^2 - 8$, which occurs for $y^2 - 6y + 8 = 0$, so for $y = 2$ and $y = 4$, with corresponding x values of ± 2 and $\pm\sqrt{2}$.

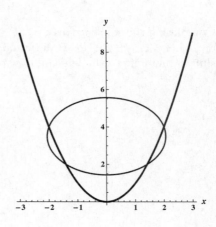

11 We are looking for the line between the points $(0, 212)$ and $(6000, 200)$. The slope is $\frac{212-200}{0-6000} = -\frac{12}{6000} = -\frac{1}{500}$. Because the intercept is given, we deduce that the line is $B = f(a) = -\frac{1}{500}a + 212$.

12

a. The cost of producing x books is $C(x) = 1000 + 2.5x$.

b. The revenue generated by selling x books is $R(x) = 7x$.

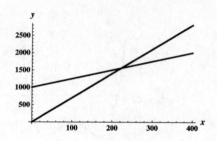

The break-even point is where $R(x) = C(x)$. This
c. is where $7x = 1000 + 2.5x$, or $4.5x = 1000$. So
$x = \frac{1000}{4.5} \approx 222$.

13

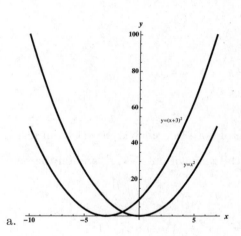

a.

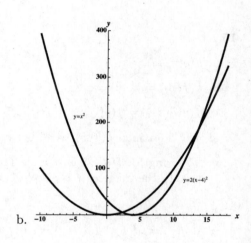

b.

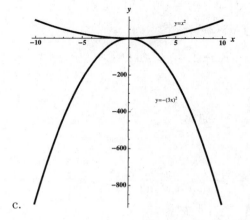

c.

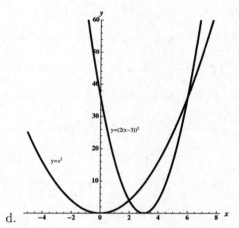

d.

14

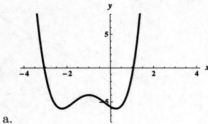

a.

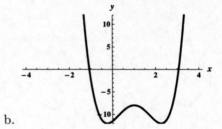

b.

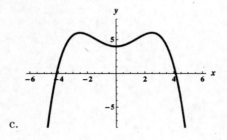

c.

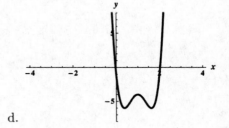

d.

15

a. $h(g(\pi/2)) = h(1) = 1$

b. $h(f(x)) = h(x^3) = x^{3/2}$.

c. $f(g(h(x))) = f(g(\sqrt{x})) = f(\sin(\sqrt{x})) = (\sin(\sqrt{x}))^3$.

d The domain of $g(f(x))$ is $\mathbb{R}$, because the domain of both functions is the set of all real numbers.

e. The range of $f(g(x))$ is $[-1, 1]$. This is because the range of g is $[-1, 1]$, and on the restricted domain $[-1, 1]$, the range of f is also $[-1, 1]$.

16

a. If $g(x) = x^2 + 1$ and $f(x) = \sin x$, then $f(g(x)) = f(x^2 + 1) = \sin(x^2 + 1)$.

b. If $g(x) = x^2 - 4$ and $f(x) = x^{-3}$ then $f(g(x)) = f(x^2 - 4) = (x^2 - 4)^{-3}$.

c. If $g(x) = \cos 2x$ and $f(x) = e^x$, then $f(g(x)) = f(\cos 2x) = e^{\cos 2x}$.

17 $\frac{f(x+h)-f(x)}{h} = \frac{(x+h)^2-2(x+h)-(x^2-2x)}{h} = \frac{x^2+2hx+h^2-2x-2h-x^2+2x}{h} = \frac{2hx+h^2-2h}{h} = 2x + h - 2$.

$\frac{f(x)-f(a)}{x-a} = \frac{x^2-2x-(a^2-2a)}{x-a} = \frac{(x^2-a^2)-2(x-a)}{x-a} = \frac{(x-a)(x+a)-2(x-a)}{x-a} = x + a - 2$.

18 $\frac{f(x+h)-f(x)}{h} = \frac{4-5(x+h)-(4-5x)}{h} = \frac{4-5x-5h-4+5x}{h} = -\frac{5h}{h} = -5$.

$\frac{f(x)-f(a)}{x-a} = \frac{4-5x-(4-5a)}{x-a} = -\frac{5(x-a)}{x-a} = -5$.

19 $\frac{f(x+h)-f(x)}{h} = \frac{(x+h)^2+2-(x^3+2)}{h} = \frac{x^2+3x^2h+3xh^2+h^3+2-x^3-2}{h} = \frac{h(3x^2+3xh+h^2)}{h} = 3x^2 + 3xh + h^2$.

$\frac{f(x)-f(a)}{x-a} = \frac{x^3+2-(a^3+2)}{x-a} = \frac{x^3-a^3}{x-a} = \frac{(x-a)(x^2+ax+a^2)}{x-a} = x^2 + ax + a^2$.

20 $\frac{f(x+h)-f(x)}{h} = \frac{\frac{7}{x+h+3}-\frac{7}{x+3}}{h} = \frac{\frac{7x+21-(7x+7h+21)}{(x+3)(x+h+3)}}{h} = -\frac{7h}{(h)(x+3)(x+h+3)} = -\frac{7}{(x+3)(x+h+3)}$.

$\frac{f(x)-f(a)}{x-a} = \frac{\frac{7}{x+3}-\frac{7}{a+3}}{x-a} = \frac{\frac{7a+21-(7x+21)}{(x+3)(a+3)}}{x-a} = -\frac{7(x-a)}{(x-a)(x+3)(a+3)} = -\frac{7}{(x+3)(a+3)}$.

21

  a. Because $f(-x) = \cos -3x = \cos 3x = f(x)$, this is an even function, and is symmetric about the y-axis.

  b. Because $f(-x) = 3(-x)^4 - 3(-x)^2 + 1 = 3x^4 - 3x^2 + 1 = f(x)$, this is an even function, and is symmetric about the y-axis.

  c. Because replacing x by $-x$ and/or replacing y by $-y$ gives the same equation, this represents a curve which is symmetric about the y-axis and about the origin and about the x-axis.

22 We have $8 = e^{4k}$, and so $\ln 8 = 4k$, so $k = \frac{\ln 8}{4}$.

23 If $\log x^2 + 3\log x = \log 32$, then $\log(x^2 \cdot x^3) = \log(32)$, so $x^5 = 32$ and $x = 2$. The answer does not depend on the base of the log.

24

The functions are as labelled.

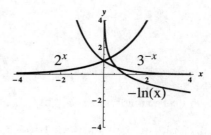

25

By graphing, it is clear that this function is not one-to-one on its whole domain, but it is one-to-one on the interval $(-\infty, 0]$, on the interval $[0, 2]$, and on the interval $[2, \infty)$, so it would have an inverse if we restricted it to any of these particular intervals.

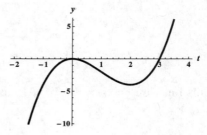

26

This function is a stretched version of the sine function, it is one-to-one on the interval $[-3\pi/2, 3\pi/2]$ (and on other intervals as well ...)

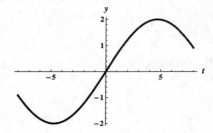

27

Completing the square gives $f(x) = x^2 - 4x + 4 + 1 = (x-2)^2 + 1$. Switching the x and y and solving for y yields $(y-2)^2 = x - 1$, so $|y - 2| = \sqrt{x-1}$, and thus $y = f^{-1}(x) = 2 + \sqrt{x-1}$ (we choose the "+" rather than the "−" because the domain of f is $x > 2$, so the range of f^{-1} must also consist of numbers greater than 2.)

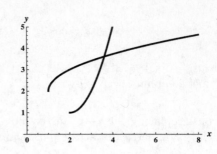

28   If $y = 1/x^2$, then switching x and y gives $x = 1/y^2$, so $y = f^{-1}(x) = 1/\sqrt{x}$.

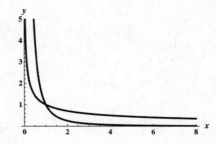

29

a. A 135 degree angle measures $135 \cdot (\pi/180)$ radians, which is $3\pi/4$ radians.

b. A $4\pi/5$ radian angle measues $4\pi/5 \cdot (180/\pi)$ degrees, which is 144 degrees.

c. Because the length of the arc is the measure of the subtended angle (in radians) times the radius, this arc would be $4\pi/3 \cdot 10 = \frac{40\pi}{3}$ units long.

30

a.   This function has period $\frac{2\pi}{1/2} = 4\pi$ and amplitude 4.

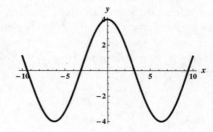

b.   This function has period $\frac{2\pi}{2\pi/3} = 3$ and amplitude 2.

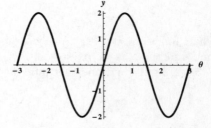

c. This function has period $\frac{2\pi}{2} = \pi$ and amplitude 1. Compared to the ordinary cosine function it is compressed horizontally, flipped about the x-axis, and shifted $\pi/4$ units to the right.

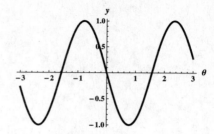

31

a. We need to scale the ordinary cosine function so that its period is 6, and then shift it 3 units to the right, and multiply it by 2. So the function we seek is $y = 2\cos((\pi/3)(t-3)) = -2\cos(\pi t/3)$.

b. We need to scale the ordinary cosine function so that its period is 24, and then shift it to the right 6 units. We then need to change the amplitude to be half the difference between the maximum and minimum, which would be 5. Then finally we need to shift the whole thing up by 15 units. The function we seek is thus $y = 15 + 5\cos((\pi/12)(t-6)) = 15 + 5\sin(\pi t/12)$.

32 The pictured function has a period of π, an amplitude of 2, and a maximum of 3 and a minimum of -1. It can be described by $y = 1 + 2\cos(2(x - \pi/2))$.

33

a. $-\sin x$ is pictured in F.

b. $\cos 2x$ is pictured in E.

c. $\tan(x/2)$ is pictured in D.

d. $-\sec x$ is pictured in B.

e. $\cot 2x$ is pictured in C.

f. $\sin^2 x$ is pictured in A.

34 If $\sec x = 2$, then $\cos x = \frac{1}{2}$. This occurs for $x = -\pi/3$ and $x = \pi/3$, so the intersection points are $(-\pi/3, 2)$ and $(\pi/3, 2)$.

35 $\sin x = -\frac{1}{2}$ for $x = 7\pi/6$ and for $x = 11\pi/6$, so the intersection points are $(7\pi/6, -1/2)$ and $(11\pi/6, -1/2)$.

36 Because $\sin(\pi/3) = \sqrt{3}/2$, $\sin^{-1}(\sqrt{3}/2) = \pi/3$.

37 Because $\cos(\pi/6) = \sqrt{3}/2$, $\cos^{-1}(\sqrt{3}/2) = \pi/6$.

38 Because $\cos(2\pi/3) = -1/2$, $\cos^{-1}(-1/2) = 2\pi/3$.

39 Because $\sin(-\pi/2) = -1$, $\sin^{-1}(-1) = -\pi/2$.

40 $\cos(\cos^{-1}(-1)) = \cos(\pi) = -1$.

41 $\sin(\sin^{-1}(x)) = x$, for all x in the domain of the inverse sine function.

42 $\cos^{-1}(\sin 3\pi) = \cos^{-1}(0) = \pi/2$.

43 If $\theta = \sin^{-1}(12/13)$, then $0 < \theta < \pi/2$, and $\sin\theta = 12/13$. Then (using the Pythagorean identity) we can deduce that $\cos\theta = 5/13$. It must follow that $\tan\theta = 12/5$, $\cot\theta = 5/12$, $\sec\theta = 13/5$, and $\csc\theta = 13/12$.

44

$$\cos(\tan^{-1}(x)) = \frac{\text{side adjacent to } \tan^{-1}(x)}{\text{hypotenuse}} = \frac{1}{\sqrt{1+x^2}}.$$

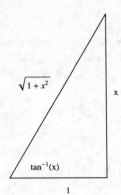

45

$$\sin(\cos^{-1}(x/2)) = \frac{\text{side opposite of } \cos^{-1}(x/2)}{\text{hypotenuse}} = \frac{\sqrt{4-x^2}}{2}.$$

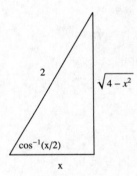

46

$$\tan(\sec^{-1}(x/2)) = \frac{\text{side opposite of } \sec^{-1}(x/2)}{\text{side adjacent to } \sec^{-1}(x/2)} = \frac{\sqrt{x^2-4}}{2}.$$

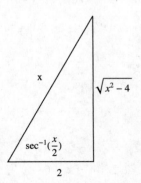

47

Note that

$$\tan\theta = \frac{a}{b} = \cot(\pi/2 - \theta).$$

Thus, $\cot^{-1}(\tan\theta) = \cot^{-1}(\cot(\pi/2 - \theta)) = \pi/2 - \theta$.

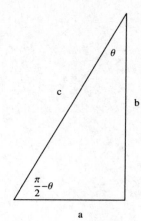

48

(Using the figure from the previous solution) Note that

$$\sec\theta = \frac{c}{b} = \csc(\pi/2 - \theta).$$

Thus, $\csc^{-1}(\sec\theta) = \csc^{-1}(\csc(\pi/2 - \theta)) = \pi/2 - \theta$.

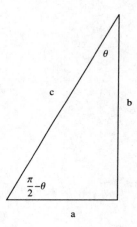

49 Let $\theta = \sin^{-1}(x)$. Then $\sin\theta = x$ and note that then $\sin(-\theta) = -\sin\theta = -x$, so $-\theta = \sin^{-1}(-x)$. Then $\sin^{-1}(x) + \sin^{-1}(-x) = \theta + -\theta = 0$.

50 Using the hint, we have $\sin(2\cos^{-1}(x)) = 2\sin(\cos^{-1}(x))\cos(\cos^{-1}(x)) = 2x\sqrt{1 - x^2}$.

51 Using the hint, we have $\cos(2\sin^{-1}(x)) = \cos^2(\sin^{-1}(x)) - \sin^2(\sin^{-1}(x)) = (\sqrt{1 - x^2})^2 - x^2 = 1 - 2x^2$.

52 Let N be the north pole, and C the center of the given circle, and consider the angle CNP. This angle measures $\frac{\pi - \varphi}{2}$. (Note that the triangle CNP is isosceles.) Now consider the triangle NOX where O is the origin and X is the point $(x, 0)$. Using triangle NOX, we have $\tan\left(\frac{\pi - \varphi}{2}\right) = \frac{x}{2R}$, so $x = 2R\tan\left(\frac{\pi - \varphi}{2}\right)$.

Chapter 2

Limits

2.1 The Idea of Limits

2.1.1 The average velocity of the object between time $t = a$ and $t = b$ is the change in position divided by the elapsed time: $v_{av} = \frac{s(b)-s(a)}{b-a}$.

2.1.2 In order to compute the instantaneous velocity of the object at time $t = a$, we compute the average velocity over smaller and smaller time intervals of the form $[a, t]$, using the formula: $v_{av} = \frac{s(t)-s(a)}{t-a}$. We let t approach a. If the quantity $\frac{s(t)-s(a)}{t-a}$ approaches a limit as $t \to a$, then that limit is called the instantaneous velocity of the object at time $t = a$.

2.1.3 The slope of the secant line between points $(a, f(a))$ and $(b, f(b))$ is the ratio of the differences $f(b) - f(a)$ and $b - a$. Thus $m_{sec} = \frac{f(b)-f(a)}{b-a}$.

2.1.4 In order to compute the slope of the tangent line to the graph of $y = f(t)$ at $(a, f(a))$, we compute the slope of the secant line over smaller and smaller time intervals of the form $[a, t]$. Thus we consider $\frac{f(t)-f(a)}{t-a}$ and let $t \to a$. If this quantity approaches a limit, then that limit is the slope of the tangent line to the curve $y = f(t)$ at $t = a$.

2.1.5 Both problems involve the same mathematics, namely finding the limit as $t \to a$ of a quotient of differences of the form $\frac{g(t)-g(a)}{t-a}$ for some function g.

2.1.6

Because $f(x) = x^2$ is an even function, $f(-a) = f(a)$ for all a. Thus the slope of the secant line between the points $(a, f(a))$ and $(-a, f(-a))$ is $m_{sec} = \frac{f(-a)-f(a)}{-a-a} = \frac{0}{-2a} = 0$. The slope of the tangent line at $x = 0$ is also zero.

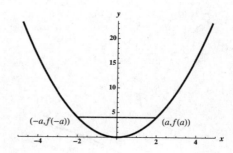

2.1.7 The average velocity is $\frac{s(3)-s(2)}{3-2} = 156 - 136 = 20$.

2.1.8 The average velocity is $\frac{s(4)-s(1)}{4-1} = \frac{144-84}{3} = \frac{60}{3} = 20$.

2.1.9

a. Over $[1,4]$, we have $v_{\text{av}} = \frac{s(4)-s(1)}{4-1} = \frac{256-112}{3} = 48$.

b. Over $[1,3]$, we have $v_{\text{av}} = \frac{s(3)-s(1)}{3-1} = \frac{240-112}{2} = 64$.

c. Over $[1,2]$, we have $v_{\text{av}} = \frac{s(2)-s(1)}{2-1} = \frac{192-112}{1} = 80$.

d. Over $[1,1+h]$, we have $v_{\text{av}} = \frac{s(1+h)-s(1)}{1+h-1} = \frac{-16(1+h)^2+128(1+h)-(112)}{h} = \frac{-16h^2-32h+128h}{h} = \frac{h(-16h+96)}{h} = 96-16h = 16(6-h)$.

2.1.10

a. Over $[0,3]$, we have $v_{\text{av}} = \frac{s(3)-s(0)}{3-0} = \frac{65.9-20}{3} = 15.3$.

b. Over $[0,2]$, we have $v_{\text{av}} = \frac{s(2)-s(0)}{2-0} = \frac{60.4-20}{2} = 20.2$.

c. Over $[0,1]$, we have $v_{\text{av}} = \frac{s(1)-s(0)}{1-0} = \frac{45.1-20}{1} = 25.1$.

d. Over $[0,h]$, we have $v_{\text{av}} = \frac{s(h)-s(0)}{h-0} = \frac{-4.9h^2+30h+20-20}{h} = \frac{(h)(-4.9h+30)}{h} = -4.9h+30$.

2.1.11

a. $\frac{s(2)-s(0)}{2-0} = \frac{72-0}{2} = 36$.

b. $\frac{s(1.5)-s(0)}{1.5-0} = \frac{66-0}{1.5} = 44$.

c. $\frac{s(1)-s(0)}{1-0} = \frac{52-0}{1} = 52$.

d. $\frac{s(.5)-s(0)}{.5-0} = \frac{30-0}{.5} = 60$.

2.1.12

a. $\frac{s(2.5)-s(.5)}{2.5-.5} = \frac{150-46}{2} = 52$.

b. $\frac{s(2)-s(.5)}{2-.5} = \frac{136-46}{1.5} = 60$.

c. $\frac{s(1.5)-s(.5)}{1.5-.5} = \frac{114-46}{1} = 68$.

d. $\frac{s(1)-s(.5)}{1-.5} = \frac{84-46}{.5} = 76$.

2.1.13

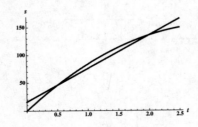

The slope of the secant line is given by $\frac{s(2)-s(.5)}{2-.5} = \frac{136-46}{1.5} = 60$. This represents the average velocity of the object over the time interval $[.5, 2]$.

2.1.14

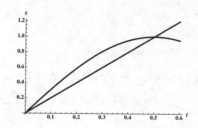

The slope of the secant line is given by $\frac{s(.5)-s(0)}{.5-0} = \frac{1}{.5} = 2$. This represents the average velocity of the object over the time interval $[0, .5]$.

2.1.15

Time Interval	$[1, 2]$	$[1, 1.5]$	$[1, 1.1]$	$[1, 1.01]$	$[1, 1.001]$
Average Velocity	80	88	94.4	95.84	95.984

The instantaneous velocity appears to be 96 ft/s.

2.1.16

Time Interval	$[2, 3]$	$[2, 2.25]$	$[2, 2.1]$	$[2, 2.01]$	$[2, 2.001]$
Average Velocity	5.5	9.175	9.91	10.351	10.395

The instantaneous velocity appears to be 10.4 m/s.

2.1.17 $\frac{s(1.01)-s(1)}{.01} = 47.84$, while $\frac{s(1.001)-s(1)}{.001} = 47.984$ and $\frac{s(1.0001)-s(1)}{.0001} = 47.9984$. It appears that the instantaneous velocity at $t = 1$ is approximately 48.

2.1.18 $\frac{s(2.01)-s(2)}{.01} = -4.16$, while $\frac{s(2.001)-s(2)}{.001} = -4.016$ and $\frac{s(2.0001)-s(2)}{.0001} = -4.0016$. It appears that the instantaneous velocity at $t = 2$ is approximately -4.

2.1.19

Time Interval	$[2, 3]$	$[2.9, 3]$	$[2.99, 3]$	$[2.999, 3]$	$[2.9999, 3]$	$[2.99999, 3]$
Average Velocity	20	5.6	4.16	4.016	4.002	4.0002

The instantaneous velocity appears to be 4 ft/s.

2.1.20

Time Interval	$[\pi/2, \pi]$	$[\pi/2, \pi/2 + .1]$	$[\pi/2, \pi/2 + .01]$	$[\pi/2, \pi/2 + .001]$	$[\pi/2, \pi/2 + .0001]$
Average Velocity	-1.90986	$-.149875$	$-.0149999$	$-.0015$	$-.00015$

The instantaneous velocity appears to be 0 ft/s.

2.1.21

Time Interval	$[3, 3.1]$	$[3, 3.01]$	$[3, 3.001]$	$[3, 3.0001]$
Average Velocity	-17.6	-16.16	-16.016	-16.002

The instantaneous velocity appears to be -16 ft/s.

2.1.22

Time Interval	$[\pi/2, \pi/2 + .1]$	$[\pi/2, \pi/2 + .01]$	$[\pi/2, \pi/2 + .001]$	$[\pi/2, \pi/2 + .0001]$
Average Velocity	-19.9667	-19.9997	-20.0000	-20.0000

The instantaneous velocity appears to be -20 ft/s.

2.1.23

Time Interval	$[0, 0.1]$	$[0, 0.01]$	$[0, 0.001]$	$[0, 0.0001]$
Average Velocity	79.468	79.995	80.000	80.0000

The instantaneous velocity appears to be 80 ft/s.

2.1.24

Time Interval	$[0, 1]$	$[0, 0.1]$	$[0, 0.01]$	$[0, 0.001]$
Average Velocity	-10	-18.1818	-19.802	-19.98

The instantaneous velocity appears to be -20 ft/s.

2.1.25

x Interval	$[2, 2.1]$	$[2, 2.01]$	$[2, 2.001]$	$[2, 2.0001]$
Slope of Secant Line	8.2	8.02	8.002	8.0002

The slope of the tangent line appears to be 8.

2.1.26

x Interval	$[\pi/2, \pi/2 + .1]$	$[\pi/2, \pi/2 + .01]$	$[\pi/2, \pi/2 + .001]$	$[\pi/2, \pi/2 + .0001]$
Slope of Secant Line	-2.995	-2.99995	-3.0000	-3.0000

The slope of the tangent line appears to be -3.

2.1.27

x Interval	$[0, 0.1]$	$[0, 0.01]$	$[0, 0.001]$	$[0, 0.0001]$
Slope of the Secant Line	1.05171	1.00502	1.0005	1.00005

The slope of the tangent line appears to be 1.

2.1.28

x Interval	$[1, 1.1]$	$[1, 1.01]$	$[1, 1.001]$	$[1, 1.0001]$
Slope of the Secant Line	2.31	2.0301	2.003	2.0003

The slope of the tangent line appears to be 2.

2.1.29

    a. Note that the graph is a parabola with vertex $(2, -1)$.

    b. At $(2, -1)$ the function has tangent line with slope 0.

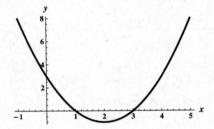

    c.

x Interval	$[2, 2.1]$	$[2, 2.01]$	$[2, 2.001]$	$[2, 2.0001]$
Slope of the Secant Line	.1	.01	.001	.0001

The slope of the tangent line at $(2, -1)$ appears to be 0.

2.1.30

    a. Note that the graph is a parabola with vertex $(0, 4)$.

    b. At $(0, 4)$ the function has a tangent line with slope 0.

    c. This is true for this function – because the function is symmetric about the y-axis and we are taking pairs of points symmetrically about the y axis. Thus $f(0 + h) = 4 - (0 + h)^2 = 4 - (-h)^2 = f(0 - h)$. So the slope of any such secant line is $\frac{4 - h^2 - (4 - h^2)}{h - (-h)} = \frac{0}{2h} = 0$.

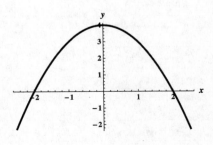

2.1.31

a. Note that the graph is a parabola with vertex $(4, 448)$.

b. At $(4, 448)$ the function has tangent line with slope 0, so $a = 4$.

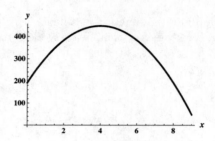

c.

x Interval	$[4, 4.1]$	$[4, 4.01]$	$[4, 4.001]$	$[4, 4.0001]$
Slope of the Secant Line	-1.6	$-.16$	$-.016$	$-.0016$

The slopes of the secant lines appear to be approaching zero.

d. On the interval $[0, 4)$ the instantaneous velocity of the projectile is positive.

e. On the interval $(4, 9]$ the instantaneous velocity of the projectile is negative.

2.1.32

a. The rock strikes the water when $s(t) = 96$. This occurs when $16t^2 = 96$, or $t^2 = 6$, whose only positive solution is $t = \sqrt{6} \approx 2.45$ seconds.

b.

t Interval	$[\sqrt{6} - .1, \sqrt{6}]$	$[\sqrt{6} - .01, \sqrt{6}]$	$[\sqrt{6} - .001, \sqrt{6}]$	$[\sqrt{6} - .0001, \sqrt{6}]$
Average Velocity	76.7837	78.2237	78.3677	78.3821

When the rock strikes the water, its instantaneous velocity is about 78.38 ft/s.

2.1.33 For line AD, we have

$$m_{AD} = \frac{y_D - y_A}{x_D - x_A} = \frac{f(\pi) - f(\pi/2)}{\pi - (\pi/2)} = \frac{1}{\pi/2} \approx .63662.$$

For line AC, we have

$$m_{AC} = \frac{y_C - y_A}{x_C - x_A} = \frac{f(\pi/2 + .5) - f(\pi/2)}{(\pi/2 + .5) - (\pi/2)} = -\frac{\cos(\pi/2 + .5)}{.5} \approx .958851.$$

For line AB, we have

$$m_{AB} = \frac{y_B - y_A}{x_B - x_A} = \frac{f(\pi/2 + .05) - f(\pi/2)}{(\pi/2 + .05) - (\pi/2)} = -\frac{\cos(\pi/2 + .05)}{.05} \approx .999583.$$

Computing one more slope of a secant line:

$$m_{\text{sec}} = \frac{f(\pi/2 + .01) - f(\pi/2)}{(\pi/2 + .01) - (\pi/2)} = -\frac{\cos(\pi/2 + .01)}{.01} \approx .999983.$$

Conjecture: The slope of the tangent line to the graph of f at $x = \pi/2$ is 1.

2.2   Definition of a Limit

2.2.1 Suppose the function f is defined for all x near a except possibly at a. If $f(x)$ is arbitrarily close to a number L whenever x is sufficiently close to (but not equal to) a, then we write $\lim\limits_{x \to a} f(x) = L$.

2.2.2 False. For example, consider the function $f(x) = \begin{cases} x^2 & \text{if } x \neq 0 \\ 4 & \text{if } x = 0. \end{cases}$

Then $\lim\limits_{x \to 0} f(x) = 0$, but $f(0) = 4$.

2.2.3 Suppose the function f is defined for all x near a but greater than a. If $f(x)$ is arbitrarily close to L for x sufficiently close to (but strictly greater than) a, then we write $\lim\limits_{x \to a^+} f(x) = L$.

2.2.4 Suppose the function f is defined for all x near a but less than a. If $f(x)$ is arbitrarily close to L for x sufficiently close to (but strictly less than) a, then we write $\lim\limits_{x \to a^-} f(x) = L$.

2.2.5 It must be true that $L = M$.

2.2.6 Because graphing utilities generally just plot a sampling of points and "connect the dots," they can sometimes mislead the user investigating the subtleties of limits.

2.2.7

   a. $h(2) = 5$.

   b. $\lim\limits_{x \to 2} h(x) = 3$.

   c. $h(4)$ does not exist.

   d. $\lim\limits_{x \to 4} f(x) = 1$.

   e. $\lim\limits_{x \to 5} h(x) = 2$.

2.2.8

   a. $g(0) = 0$.

   b. $\lim\limits_{x \to 0} g(x) = 1$.

   c. $g(1) = 2$.

   d. $\lim\limits_{x \to 1} g(x) = 2$.

2.2.9

   a. $f(1) = -1$.

   b. $\lim\limits_{x \to 1} f(x) = 1$.

   c. $f(0) = 2$.

   d. $\lim\limits_{x \to 0} f(x) = 2$.

2.2.10

   a. $f(2) = 2$.

   b. $\lim\limits_{x \to 2} f(x) = 4$.

   c. $\lim\limits_{x \to 4} f(x) = 4$.

   d. $\lim\limits_{x \to 5} f(x) = 2$.

2.2.11

a.

x	1.9	1.99	1.999	1.9999	2	2.0001	2.001	2.01	2.1
$f(x) = \frac{x^2-4}{x-2}$	3.9	3.99	3.999	3.9999	undefined	4.0001	4.001	4.01	4.1

   b. $\lim\limits_{x \to 2} f(x) = 4$.

2.2.12

a.

x	.9	.99	.999	.9999	1	1.0001	1.001	1.01	1.1
$f(x) = \frac{x^3-1}{x-1}$	2.71	2.9701	2.997	2.9997	undefined	3.0003	3.003	3.0301	3.31

   b. $\lim\limits_{x \to 1} \dfrac{x^3 - 1}{x - 1} = 3$

2.2.13

a.

t	8.9	8.99	8.999	9	9.001	9.01	9.1
$g(t) = \frac{t-9}{\sqrt{t}-3}$	5.98329	5.99833	5.99983	undefined	6.00017	6.00167	6.01662

b. $\lim\limits_{t \to 9} \dfrac{t-9}{\sqrt{t}-3} = 6.$

2.2.14

a.

x	.01	.001	.0001	.00001
$f(x) = (1+x)^{1/x}$	2.70481	2.71692	2.71815	2.71827

x	$-.01$	$-.001$	$-.0001$	$-.00001$
$f(x) = (1+x)^{1/x}$	2.732	2.71964	2.71842	2.71830

b. $\lim\limits_{x \to 0} (1+x)^{1/x} \approx 2.718.$

c. $\lim\limits_{x \to 0} (1+x)^{1/x} = e.$

2.2.15

a.

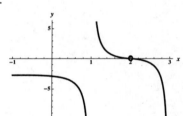

b.

x	1.99	1.999	1.9999	2.0001	2.001	2.01
$f(x)$	.00217	.00014	.0000109	$-.0000109$	$-.00014$	$-.00217$

From both the graph and the table, the limit appears to be 0.

2.2.16

a.

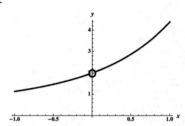

b.

x	-0.1	-0.01	-0.001	0.001	0.01	0.1
$f(x)$	1.8731	1.98673	1.9987	2.0013	2.0134	2.1403

From both the graph and the table, the limit appears to be 2.

2.2.17

a.

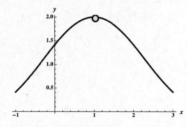

b.

x	0.9	0.99	0.999	1.001	1.01	1.1
$f(x)$	1.993342	1.999933	1.999999	1.999999	1.999933	1.993342

From both the graph and the table, the limit appears to be 2.

2.2.18

a.

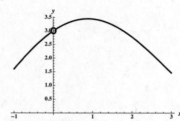

b.

x	-0.1	-0.01	-0.001	0.001	0.01	0.1
$f(x)$	2.8951	2.99	2.999	3.001	3.0099	3.0949

From both the graph and the table, the limit appears to be 3.

2.2.19

x	4.9	4.99	4.999	4.9999	5	5.0001	5.001	5.01	5.1
$f(x) = \frac{x^2-25}{x-5}$	9.9	9.99	9.999	9.9999	undefined	10.0001	10.001	10.01	10.1

$\displaystyle\lim_{x \to 5^+} \frac{x^2-25}{x-5} = 10,\ \lim_{x \to 5^-} \frac{x^2-25}{x-5} = 10$, and thus $\displaystyle\lim_{x \to 5} \frac{x^2-25}{x-5} = 10$.

2.2.20

x	99.9	99.99	99.999	99.9999	100	100.0001	100.001	100.01	100.1
$f(x) = \frac{x-100}{\sqrt{x}-10}$	19.995	19.9995	19.99995	≈ 20	undefined	≈ 20	20.0005	20.00005	20.005

$\displaystyle\lim_{x \to 100^+} \frac{x-100}{\sqrt{x}-10} = 20,\ \lim_{x \to 100^-} \frac{x-100}{\sqrt{x}-10} = 20$, and thus $\displaystyle\lim_{x \to 100} \frac{x-100}{\sqrt{x}-10} = 20$.

2.2.21

a. $f(1) = 0$.   b. $\displaystyle\lim_{x \to 1^-} f(x) = 1$.   c. $\displaystyle\lim_{x \to 1^+} f(x) = 0$.

d. $\displaystyle\lim_{x \to 1} f(x)$ does not exist, since the two one-sided limits aren't equal.

2.2.22

a. $g(2) = 3$.

b. $\lim\limits_{x \to 2^-} g(x) = 2$.

c. $\lim\limits_{x \to 2^+} g(x) = 3$.

d. $\lim\limits_{x \to 2} g(x)$ does not exist.

e. $g(3) = 2$.

f. $\lim\limits_{x \to 3^-} g(x) = 3$.

g. $\lim\limits_{x \to 3^+} g(x) = 2$.

h. $g(4) = 3$.

i. $\lim\limits_{x \to 4} g(x) = 3$.

2.2.23

a. $f(1) = 3$.

b. $\lim\limits_{x \to 1^-} f(x) = 2$.

c. $\lim\limits_{x \to 1^+} f(x) = 2$.

d. $\lim\limits_{x \to 1} f(x) = 2$.

e. $f(3) = 2$.

f. $\lim\limits_{x \to 3^-} f(x) = 4$.

g. $\lim\limits_{x \to 3^+} f(x) = 1$.

h. $\lim\limits_{x \to 3} f(x)$ does not exist.

i. $f(2) = 3$.

j. $\lim\limits_{x \to 2^-} f(x) = 3$.

k. $\lim\limits_{x \to 2^+} f(x) = 3$.

l. $\lim\limits_{x \to 2} f(x) = 3$.

2.2.24

a. $g(-1) = 3$.

b. $\lim\limits_{x \to -1^-} g(x) = 2$.

c. $\lim\limits_{x \to -1^+} g(x) = 2$.

d. $\lim\limits_{x \to -1} g(x) = 2$.

e. $g(1) = 2$.

f. $\lim\limits_{x \to 1} g(x)$ does not exist.

g. $\lim\limits_{x \to 3} g(x) = 4$.

h. $g(5) = 5$.

i. $\lim\limits_{x \to 5^-} g(x) = 5$.

2.2.25

a.

x	$\frac{2}{\pi}$	$\frac{2}{3\pi}$	$\frac{2}{5\pi}$	$\frac{2}{7\pi}$	$\frac{2}{9\pi}$	$\frac{2}{11\pi}$
$f(x) = \sin(1/x)$	1	-1	1	-1	1	-1

If $x_n = \frac{2}{(2n+1)\pi}$, then $f(x_n) = (-1)^n$ where n is a non-negative integer.

b. As $x \to 0$, $1/x \to \infty$. So the values of $f(x)$ oscillate dramatically between -1 and 1.

c. $\lim\limits_{x \to 0} \sin(1/x)$ does not exist.

2.2.26

a.

x	$\frac{12}{\pi}$	$\frac{12}{3\pi}$	$\frac{12}{5\pi}$	$\frac{12}{7\pi}$	$\frac{12}{9\pi}$	$\frac{12}{11\pi}$
$f(x) = \tan(3/x)$	1	-1	1	-1	1	-1

We have alternating 1's and -1's.

b. $\tan 3x$ alternates between 1 and -1 infinitely many times on $(0, h)$ for any $h > 0$.

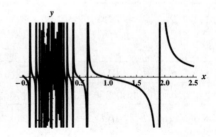

c. $\lim\limits_{x \to 0} \tan(3/x)$ does not exist.

2.2.27

a. False. In fact $\lim\limits_{x \to 3} \dfrac{x^2 - 9}{x - 3} = \lim\limits_{x \to 3} (x + 3) = 6$.

b. False. For example, if $f(x) = \begin{cases} x^2 & \text{if } x \neq 0; \\ 5 & \text{if } x = 0 \end{cases}$ and if $a = 0$ then $f(a) = 5$ but $\lim\limits_{x \to a} f(x) = 0$.

c. False. For example, the limit in part a of this problem exists, even though the corresponding function is undefined at $a = 3$.

d. False. It is true that the limit of $\sqrt{x}$ as x approaches zero from the right is zero, but because the domain of $\sqrt{x}$ does not include any numbers to the left of zero, the two-sided limit doesn't exist.

e. True. Note that $\lim\limits_{x \to \pi/2} \cos x = 0$ and $\lim\limits_{x \to \pi/2} \sin x = 1$, so $\lim\limits_{x \to \pi/2} \dfrac{\cos x}{\sin x} = \dfrac{0}{1} = 0$.

2.2.28

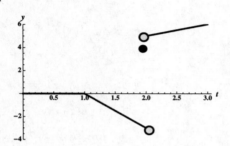

2.2.29

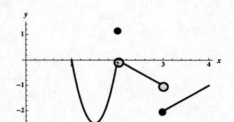

2.2.30

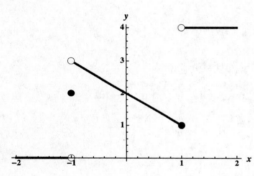

2.2.31

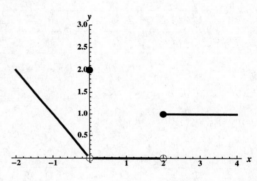

2.2.32

h	.01	.001	.0001	$-.0001$	$-.001$	$-.01$
$(1+2h)^{1/h}$	7.24465	7.37431	7.38758	7.39053	7.40387	7.54037

$\lim\limits_{h \to 0} (1+2h)^{1/h} \approx 7.39.$

2.2.33

h	.01	.001	.0001	$-.0001$	$-.001$	$-.01$
$(1+3h)^{2/h}$	369.356	399.821	403.066	403.792	407.083	442.235

$\lim\limits_{h \to 0} (1+3h)^{2/h} \approx 403.4.$

2.2.34

h	.01	.001	.0001	$-.0001$	$-.001$	$-.01$
$\frac{2^h - 1}{h}$	.695555	.693387	.693171	.693123	.692907	.69075

$\lim\limits_{h \to 0} \dfrac{2^h - 1}{h} \approx .6931.$

2.2.35

h	.01	.001	.0001	$-.0001$	$-.001$	$-.01$
$\frac{\ln(1+h)}{h}$	.995033	.9995	.99995	1.00005	1.0005	1.00503

$$\lim_{h \to 0} \frac{\ln(1+h)}{h} = 1.$$

2.2.36

a. Note that $f(x) = \frac{|x|}{x}$ is undefined at 0, and $\lim_{x \to 0^-} f(x) = -1$ and $\lim_{x \to 0^+} f(x) = 1$.

b. $\lim_{x \to 0} f(x)$ does not exist, since the two one-side limits aren't equal.

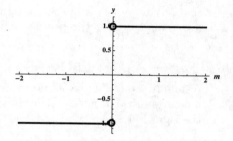

2.2.37

a. $\lim_{x \to -1^-} \lfloor x \rfloor = -2$, $\lim_{x \to -1^+} \lfloor x \rfloor = -1$, $\lim_{x \to 2^-} \lfloor x \rfloor = 1$, $\lim_{x \to 2^+} \lfloor x \rfloor = 2$.

b. $\lim_{x \to 2.3^-} \lfloor x \rfloor = 2$, $\lim_{x \to 2.3^+} \lfloor x \rfloor = 2$, $\lim_{x \to 2.3} \lfloor x \rfloor = 2$.

c. In general, for an integer a, $\lim_{x \to a^-} \lfloor x \rfloor = a - 1$ and $\lim_{x \to a^+} \lfloor x \rfloor = a$.

d. In general, if a is not an integer, $\lim_{x \to a^-} \lfloor x \rfloor = \lim_{x \to a^+} \lfloor x \rfloor = \lfloor a \rfloor$.

e. $\lim_{x \to a} \lfloor x \rfloor$ exists and is equal to $\lfloor a \rfloor$ for non-integers a.

2.2.38

a. Note that the graph is piecewise constant.

b. $\lim_{x \to 2^-} \lceil x \rceil = 2$, $\lim_{x \to 1^+} \lceil x \rceil = 2$, $\lim_{x \to 1.5} \lceil x \rceil = 2$.

c. $\lim_{x \to a} \lceil x \rceil$ exists and is equal to $\lceil a \rceil$ for non-integers a.

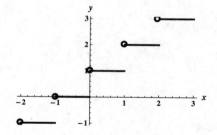

2.2.39 By zooming in closely, you should be able to convince yourself that the answer is 0.

2.2.40 By zooming in closely, you should be able to convince yourself that the answer is 2.

2.2.41 By zooming in closely, you should be able to convince yourself that the answer is 16.

2.2.42 By zooming in closely, you should be able to convince yourself that the answer is 1.

2.2.43

    a. Note that the function is piecewise constant.

    b. $\lim\limits_{w\to 3.3} f(w) = .95$.

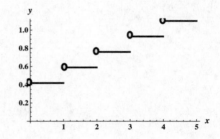

    c. $\lim\limits_{w\to 1^+} f(w) = .61$ corresponds to the fact that for any piece of mail that weighs slightly over 1 ounce, the postage will cost 61 cents. $\lim\limits_{w\to 1^-} f(w) = .44$ corresponds to the fact that for any piece of mail that weighs slightly less than 1 ounce, the postage will cost 44 cents.

    d. $\lim\limits_{w\to 4} f(w)$ does not exist because the two corresponding one-side limits don't exist. (The limit from the left is .95, while the limit from the right is 1.12.)

2.2.44

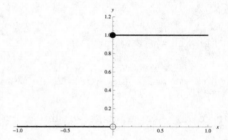

    a. Note that H is piecewise constant.

    b. $\lim\limits_{x\to 0^-} H(x) = 0$, $\lim\limits_{x\to 0^+} H(x) = 1$, and so $\lim\limits_{x\to 0} H(x)$ does not exist.

2.2.45

    a. Because of the symmetry about the y axis, we must have $\lim\limits_{x\to -2^+} f(x) = 8$.

    b. Because of the symmetry about the y axis, we must have $\lim\limits_{x\to -2^-} f(x) = 5$.

2.2.46

    a. Because of the symmetry about the origin, we must have $\lim\limits_{x\to -2^+} g(x) = -8$.

    b. Because of the symmetry about the origin, we must have $\lim\limits_{x\to -2^-} g(x) = -5$.

2.2.47

    a.

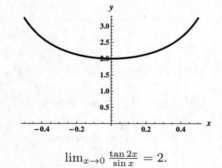

$$\lim\nolimits_{x\to 0} \frac{\tan 2x}{\sin x} = 2.$$

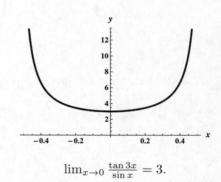

$$\lim\nolimits_{x\to 0} \frac{\tan 3x}{\sin x} = 3.$$

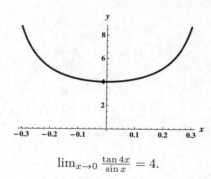

$\lim_{x \to 0} \frac{\tan 4x}{\sin x} = 4.$

b. It appears that $\lim_{x \to 0} \frac{\tan(px)}{\sin x} = p$.

2.2.48

a.

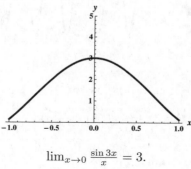

$\lim_{x \to 0} \frac{\sin x}{x} = 1.$

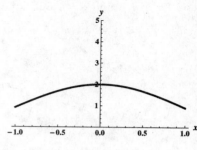

$\lim_{x \to 0} \frac{\sin 2x}{x} = 2.$

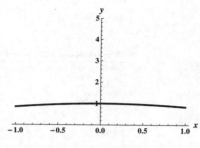

$\lim_{x \to 0} \frac{\sin 3x}{x} = 3.$

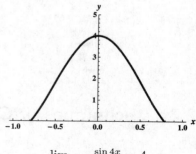

$\lim_{x \to 0} \frac{\sin 4x}{x} = 4.$

b. It appears that $\lim_{x \to 0} \frac{\sin(px)}{x} = p$.

2.2.49

For $p = 8$ and $q = 2$, it appears that the limit is 4.

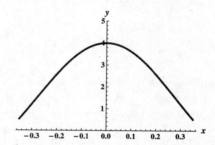

For $p = 12$ and $q = 3$, it appears that the limit is 4.

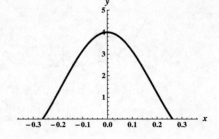

For $p = 4$ and $q = 16$, it appears that the limit is 1/4.

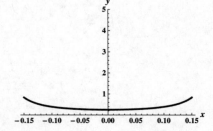

For $p = 100$ and $q = 50$, it appears that the limit is 2.

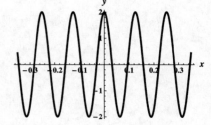

Conjecture: $\displaystyle\lim_{x\to 0}\frac{\sin px}{\sin qx} = \frac{p}{q}$.

2.3   Techniques of Computing Limits

2.3.1 If $f(x) = a_n x^n + a_{n-1}x^{n-1} + \cdots + a_1 x + a_0$, then $\lim_{x\to a} f(x) = \lim_{x\to a}(a_n x^n + a_{n-1}x^{n-1} + \cdots + a_1 x + a_0)$
$= a_n(\lim_{x\to a} x)^n + a_{n-1}(\lim_{x\to a} x)^{n-1} + \cdots + a_1 \lim_{x\to a} x + \lim_{x\to a} a_0$
$= a_n a^n + a_{n-1}a^{n-1} + \cdots + a_1 a + a_0$.

2.3.2 If $f(x)$ is a polynomial, then $\displaystyle\lim_{x\to a^-} f(x) = \lim_{x\to a^+} f(x) = f(a)$.

2.3.3 For a rational function $r(x)$, we have $\displaystyle\lim_{x\to a} r(x) = r(a)$ exactly for those numbers a which are in the domain of r.

2.3.4 If $f(x) = g(x)$ for $x \neq 3$, and $\displaystyle\lim_{x\to 3} g(x) = 4$, then $\displaystyle\lim_{x\to 3} f(x) = 4$ as well.

2.3.5 Because $\frac{x^2 - 7x + 12}{x - 3} = \frac{(x-3)(x-4)}{x-3} = x - 4$ (for $x \neq 3$), we can see that the graphs of these two functions are the same except that one is undefined at $x = 3$ and the other is a straight line that is defined everywhere. Thus the function $\frac{x^2 - 7x + 12}{x-3}$ is a straight line except that it has a "hole" at $(3, -1)$. The two functions have the same limit as $x \to 3$, namely $\displaystyle\lim_{x\to 3}\frac{x^2 - 7x + 12}{x - 3} = \lim_{x\to 3}(x - 4) = -1$.

2.3.6 $\lim\limits_{x \to 2} f(x)^{2/3} = \left(\lim\limits_{x \to 2} f(x)\right)^{2/3} = (-8)^{2/3} = (-2)^2 = 4.$

2.3.7 If p and q are polynomials then $\lim\limits_{x \to 0} \dfrac{p(x)}{q(x)} = \dfrac{\lim\limits_{x \to 0} p(x)}{\lim\limits_{x \to 0} q(x)} = \dfrac{p(0)}{q(0)}.$ Because this quantity is given to be equal to 10, we have $\frac{p(0)}{2} = 10,$ so $p(0) = 20.$

2.3.8 By a direct application of the squeeze theorem, $\lim\limits_{x \to 2} g(x) = 5.$

2.3.9 $\lim\limits_{x \to 5} \sqrt{x^2 - 9} = \sqrt{\lim\limits_{x \to 5} (x^2 - 9)} = \sqrt{16} = 4.$

2.3.10 $\lim\limits_{x \to 3^-} f(x) = \lim\limits_{x \to 3^-} 4 = 4,$ and $\lim\limits_{x \to 3^+} f(x) = \lim\limits_{x \to 3^+} (x + 2) = 5.$

2.3.11 $\lim\limits_{x \to 4} (3x - 7) = 3 \lim\limits_{x \to 4} x - 7 = 3 \cdot 4 - 7 = 5.$

2.3.12 $\lim\limits_{x \to 1} (-2x + 5) = -2 \lim\limits_{x \to 1} x + 5 = -2 \cdot 1 + 5 = 3.$

2.3.13 $\lim\limits_{x \to -9} (5x) = 5 \lim\limits_{x \to -9} x = 5 \cdot -9 = -45.$

2.3.14 $\lim\limits_{x \to 2} (-3x) = -3 \lim\limits_{x \to 2} x = -3 \cdot 2 = -6.$

2.3.15 $\lim\limits_{x \to 6} 4 = 4.$

2.3.16 $\lim\limits_{x \to -5} \pi = \pi.$

2.3.17 $\lim\limits_{x \to 1} 4f(x) = 4 \lim\limits_{x \to 1} f(x) = 4 \cdot 8 = 32.$ This follows from the Constant Multiple Law.

2.3.18 $\lim\limits_{x \to 1} \dfrac{f(x)}{h(x)} = \dfrac{\lim\limits_{x \to 1} f(x)}{\lim\limits_{x \to 1} h(x)} = \dfrac{8}{2} = 4.$ This follows from the Quotient Law.

2.3.19 $\lim\limits_{x \to 1} (f(x) - g(x)) = \lim\limits_{x \to 1} f(x) - \lim\limits_{x \to 1} g(x) = 8 - 3 = 5.$ This follows from the Difference Law.

2.3.20 $\lim\limits_{x \to 1} f(x)h(x) = \lim\limits_{x \to 1} f(x) \cdot \lim\limits_{x \to 1} h(x) = 8 \cdot 2 = 16.$ This follows from the Product Law.

2.3.21 $\lim\limits_{x \to 1} \dfrac{f(x)g(x)}{h(x)} = \dfrac{\lim\limits_{x \to 1} (f(x)g(x))}{\lim\limits_{x \to 1} h(x)} = \dfrac{\lim\limits_{x \to 1} f(x) \cdot \lim\limits_{x \to 1} g(x)}{\lim\limits_{x \to 1} h(x)} = \dfrac{8 \cdot 3}{2} = 12.$ This follows from the Quotient and Product Laws.

2.3.22 $\lim\limits_{x \to 1} \dfrac{f(x)}{g(x) - h(x)} = \dfrac{\lim\limits_{x \to 1} f(x)}{\lim\limits_{x \to 1} [g(x) - h(x)]} = \dfrac{\lim\limits_{x \to 1} f(x)}{\lim\limits_{x \to 1} g(x) - \lim\limits_{x \to 1} h(x)} = \dfrac{8}{3 - 2} = 8.$ This follows from the Quotient and Difference Laws.

2.3.23 $\lim\limits_{x \to 1} (h(x))^5 = \left(\lim\limits_{x \to 1} h(x)\right)^5 = (2)^5 = 32.$ This follows from the Power Law.

2.3.24 $\lim\limits_{x \to 1} \sqrt[3]{f(x)g(x) + 3} = \sqrt[3]{\lim\limits_{x \to 1} (f(x)g(x) + 3)} = \sqrt[3]{\lim\limits_{x \to 1} f(x) \cdot \lim\limits_{x \to 1} g(x) + \lim\limits_{x \to 1} 3} = \sqrt[3]{8 \cdot 3 + 3} = \sqrt[3]{27} = 3.$ This follows form the Root, Product, Sum and Constant Laws.

2.3.25 $\lim\limits_{x \to 1} (2x^3 - 3x^2 + 4x + 5) = \lim\limits_{x \to 1} 2x^3 - \lim\limits_{x \to 1} 3x^2 + \lim\limits_{x \to 1} 4x + \lim\limits_{x \to 1} 5 = 2(\lim\limits_{x \to 1} x)^3 - 3(\lim\limits_{x \to 1} x)^2 + 4(\lim\limits_{x \to 1} x) + 5 = 2(1)^3 - 3(1)^2 + 4 \cdot 1 + 5 = 8.$

2.3.26 $\lim\limits_{t\to-2}(t^2+5t+7)=\lim\limits_{t\to-2}t^2+\lim\limits_{t\to-2}5t+\lim\limits_{t\to-2}7=\left(\lim\limits_{t\to-2}t\right)^2+5\lim\limits_{t\to-2}t+7=(-2)^2+5\cdot(-2)+7=1.$

2.3.27 $\lim\limits_{x\to1}\dfrac{5x^2+6x+1}{8x-4}=\dfrac{\lim\limits_{x\to1}(5x^2+6x+1)}{\lim\limits_{x\to1}(8x-4)}=\dfrac{5(\lim\limits_{x\to1}x)^2+6\lim\limits_{x\to1}x+\lim\limits_{x\to1}1}{8\lim\limits_{x\to1}x-\lim\limits_{x\to1}4}=\dfrac{5(1)^2+6\cdot1+1}{8\cdot1-4}=3.$

2.3.28 $\lim\limits_{t\to3}\sqrt[3]{t^2-10}=\sqrt[3]{\lim\limits_{t\to3}(t^2-10)}=\sqrt[3]{\lim\limits_{t\to3}t^2-\lim\limits_{t\to3}10}=\sqrt[3]{\left(\lim\limits_{t\to3}t\right)^2-10}=\sqrt[3]{(3)^2-10}=-1.$

2.3.29 $\lim\limits_{b\to2}\dfrac{3b}{\sqrt{4b+1}-1}=\dfrac{\lim\limits_{b\to2}3b}{\lim\limits_{b\to2}(\sqrt{4b+1}-1)}=\dfrac{3\lim\limits_{b\to2}b}{\lim\limits_{b\to2}\sqrt{4b+1}-\lim\limits_{b\to2}1}=\dfrac{3\cdot2}{\sqrt{\lim\limits_{b\to2}(4b+1)}-1}=\dfrac{6}{3-1}=3.$

2.3.30 $\lim\limits_{x\to2}(x^2-x)^5=\left(\lim\limits_{x\to2}(x^2-x)\right)^5=\left(\lim\limits_{x\to2}x^2-\lim\limits_{x\to2}x\right)^5=(4-2)^5=32.$

2.3.31 $\lim\limits_{x\to3}\dfrac{-5x}{\sqrt{4x-3}}=\dfrac{\lim\limits_{x\to3}-5x}{\lim\limits_{x\to3}\sqrt{4x-3}}=\dfrac{-5\lim\limits_{x\to3}x}{\sqrt{\lim\limits_{x\to3}(4x-3)}}=\dfrac{-5\cdot3}{\sqrt{4\lim\limits_{x\to3}x-\lim\limits_{x\to3}3}}=\dfrac{-15}{\sqrt{4\cdot3-3}}=-5.$

2.3.32 $\lim\limits_{h\to0}\dfrac{3}{\sqrt{16+3h}+4}=\dfrac{\lim\limits_{h\to0}3}{\lim\limits_{h\to0}(\sqrt{16+3h}+4)}=\dfrac{3}{\sqrt{\lim\limits_{h\to0}(16+3h)}+\lim\limits_{h\to0}4}=\dfrac{3}{\sqrt{\lim\limits_{h\to0}16+\lim\limits_{h\to0}3h}+4}=$
$\dfrac{3}{\sqrt{16+3\cdot0}+4}=\dfrac{3}{4+4}=\dfrac{3}{8}.$

2.3.33

    a. $\lim\limits_{x\to-1^-}f(x)=\lim\limits_{x\to-1^-}(x^2+1)=(-1)^2+1=2.$

    b. $\lim\limits_{x\to-1^+}f(x)=\lim\limits_{x\to-1^+}\sqrt{x+1}=\sqrt{-1+1}=0.$

    c. $\lim\limits_{x\to-1}f(x)$ does not exist.

2.3.34

    a. $\lim\limits_{x\to-5^-}f(x)=\lim\limits_{x\to-5^-}0=0.$
                    b. $\lim\limits_{x\to-5^+}f(x)=\lim\limits_{x\to-5^+}\sqrt{25-x^2}=\sqrt{25-25}=0.$

    c. $\lim\limits_{x\to-5}f(x)=0.$
                         d. $\lim\limits_{x\to5^-}f(x)=\lim\limits_{x\to5^-}\sqrt{25-x^2}=\sqrt{25-25}=0.$

    e. $\lim\limits_{x\to5^+}f(x)=\lim\limits_{x\to5^+}3x=15.$
                        f. $\lim\limits_{x\to5}f(x)$ does not exist.

2.3.35

    a. $\lim\limits_{x\to2^+}\sqrt{x-2}=\sqrt{2-2}=0.$

    b. The domain of $f(x)=\sqrt{x-2}$ is $[2,\infty)$. Thus, any question about this function that involves numbers less than 2 doesn't make any sense, because those numbers aren't in the domain of f.

2.3.36

    a. Note that the domain of $f(x)=\sqrt{\frac{x-3}{2-x}}$ is $(2,3]$. $\lim\limits_{x\to3^-}\sqrt{\dfrac{x-3}{2-x}}=0.$

    b. Because the numbers to the right of 3 aren't in the domain of this function, the limit as $x\to3^+$ of this function doesn't make any sense.

2.3.37 Using the definition of $|x|$ given, we have $\lim\limits_{x\to 0^-} |x| = \lim\limits_{x\to 0^-} (-x) = -0 = 0$. Also, $\lim\limits_{x\to 0^+} |x| = \lim\limits_{x\to 0^+} x = 0$. Because the two one-sided limits are both 0, we also have $\lim\limits_{x\to 0} |x| = 0$.

2.3.38

If $a > 0$, then for x near a, $|x| = x$. So in this case, $\lim\limits_{x\to a} |x| = \lim\limits_{x\to a} x = a = |a|$.

If $a < 0$, then for x near a, $|x| = -x$. So in this case, $\lim\limits_{x\to a} |x| = \lim\limits_{x\to a} (-x) = -a = |a|$, (because $a < 0$).

If $a = 0$, we have already seen in a previous problem that $\lim\limits_{x\to 0} |x| = 0 = |0|$.

Thus in all cases, $\lim\limits_{x\to a} |x| = |a|$.

2.3.39 $\lim\limits_{x\to 1} \dfrac{x^2 - 1}{x - 1} = \lim\limits_{x\to 1} \dfrac{(x+1)(x-1)}{x-1} = \lim\limits_{x\to 1} (x+1) = 2.$

2.3.40 $\lim\limits_{x\to 3} \dfrac{x^2 - 2x - 3}{x - 3} = \lim\limits_{x\to 3} \dfrac{(x-3)(x+1)}{x-3} = \lim\limits_{x\to 3} (x+1) = 4.$

2.3.41 $\lim\limits_{x\to 4} \dfrac{x^2 - 16}{4 - x} = \lim\limits_{x\to 4} \dfrac{(x+4)(x-4)}{-(x-4)} = \lim\limits_{x\to 4} [-(x+4)] = -8.$

2.3.42 $\lim\limits_{t\to 2} \dfrac{3t^2 - 7t + 2}{2 - t} = \lim\limits_{t\to 2} \dfrac{(t-2)(3t-1)}{-(t-2)} = \lim\limits_{t\to 2} [-(3t-1)] = -5.$

2.3.43 $\lim\limits_{x\to b} \dfrac{(x-b)^{50} - x + b}{x - b} = \lim\limits_{x\to b} \dfrac{(x-b)^{50} - (x-b)}{x-b} = \lim\limits_{x\to b} \dfrac{(x-b)((x-b)^{49} - 1)}{x-b} =$
$\lim\limits_{x\to b} [(x-b)^{49} - 1] = -1.$

2.3.44 $\lim\limits_{x\to -b} \dfrac{(x+b)^7 + (x+b)^{10}}{4(x+b)} = \lim\limits_{x\to -b} \dfrac{(x+b)((x+b)^6 + (x+b)^9)}{4(x+b)} = \lim\limits_{x\to -b} \dfrac{(x+b)^6 + (x+b)^9}{4} = \dfrac{0}{4} = 0.$

2.3.45 $\lim\limits_{x\to -1} \dfrac{(2x-1)^2 - 9}{x + 1} = \lim\limits_{x\to -1} \dfrac{(2x-1-3)(2x-1+3)}{x+1} = \lim\limits_{x\to -1} \dfrac{2(x-2)2(x+1)}{x+1} = \lim\limits_{x\to -1} 4(x-2) =$
$4 \cdot (-3) = -12.$

2.3.46 $\lim\limits_{h\to 0} \dfrac{\frac{1}{5+h} - \frac{1}{5}}{h} = \lim\limits_{h\to 0} \dfrac{\left(\frac{1}{5+h} - \frac{1}{5}\right) \cdot 5 \cdot (5+h)}{h \cdot 5 \cdot (5+h)} = \lim\limits_{h\to 0} \dfrac{5 - (5+h)}{5h(5+h)} = \lim\limits_{h\to 0} \dfrac{-h}{5h(5+h)} =$
$\lim\limits_{h\to 0} \dfrac{-1}{5(5+h)} = \dfrac{-1}{25}.$

2.3.47 $\lim\limits_{x\to 9} \dfrac{\sqrt{x} - 3}{x - 9} = \lim\limits_{x\to 9} \dfrac{(\sqrt{x} - 3)(\sqrt{x} + 3)}{(x-9)(\sqrt{x} + 3)} = \lim\limits_{x\to 9} \dfrac{x - 9}{(x-9)(\sqrt{x} + 3)} = \lim\limits_{x\to 9} \dfrac{1}{\sqrt{x} + 3} = \dfrac{1}{6}.$

2.3.48 Expanding gives

$$\lim\limits_{t\to 3} \left(4t - \dfrac{2}{t-3}\right)(6 + t - t^2) = \lim\limits_{t\to 3} \left(4t(6 + t - t^2) - \dfrac{2(6 + t - t^2)}{t-3}\right) = \lim\limits_{t\to 3} \left(4t(6 + t - t^2) - \dfrac{2(3-t)(2+t)}{t-3}\right).$$

Now because $t - 3 = -(3 - t)$, we have

$$\lim\limits_{t\to 3} \left(4t(6 + t - t^2) + 2(2+t)\right) = 12(6 + 3 - 9) + 2(2 + 3) = 10.$$

2.3.49 $\lim\limits_{x\to a} \dfrac{x - a}{\sqrt{x} - \sqrt{a}} = \lim\limits_{x\to a} \dfrac{x - a}{\sqrt{x} - \sqrt{a}} \cdot \dfrac{\sqrt{x} + \sqrt{a}}{\sqrt{x} + \sqrt{a}} = \lim\limits_{x\to a} \dfrac{(x-a)(\sqrt{x} + \sqrt{a})}{x - a} = \lim\limits_{x\to a} (\sqrt{x} + \sqrt{a}) = 2\sqrt{a}.$

2.3.50 $\lim\limits_{x\to a} \dfrac{x^2 - a^2}{\sqrt{x} - \sqrt{a}} = \lim\limits_{x\to a} \dfrac{x^2 - a^2}{\sqrt{x} - \sqrt{a}} \cdot \dfrac{\sqrt{x} + \sqrt{a}}{\sqrt{x} + \sqrt{a}} = \lim\limits_{x\to a} \dfrac{(x-a)(x+a)(\sqrt{x} + \sqrt{a})}{x - a} =$
$(a + a)(\sqrt{a} + \sqrt{a}) = 4a^{3/2}.$

2.3.51 $\lim\limits_{h\to 0}\dfrac{\sqrt{16+h}-4}{h}=\lim\limits_{h\to 0}\dfrac{(\sqrt{16+h}-4)(\sqrt{16+h}+4)}{h(\sqrt{16+h}+4)}=\lim\limits_{h\to 0}\dfrac{(16+h)-16}{h(\sqrt{16+h}+4)}=\lim\limits_{h\to 0}\dfrac{h}{h(\sqrt{16+h}+4)}$

$=\lim\limits_{h\to 0}\dfrac{1}{(\sqrt{16+h}+4)}=\dfrac{1}{8}.$

2.3.52 Note that $x^3-a^3=(x-a)(x^2+ax+a^2)$, and thus as long as $x\neq a$, we have

$$\frac{x^3-a^3}{x-a}=x^2+ax+a^2.$$

Thus,

$$\lim_{x\to a}\frac{x^3-a^3}{x-a}=\lim_{x\to a}(x^2+ax+a^2)=a^2+a^2+a^2=3a^2.$$

2.3.53

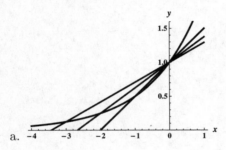

a.

b. The slope of the secant line between $(0,1)$ and $(x,2^x)$ is $\frac{2^x-1}{x}$.

c.

x	-1	$-.1$	$-.01$	$-.001$	$-.0001$	$-.00001$
$\frac{2^x-1}{x}$	.5	.66967	.69075	.692907	.693123	.693145

It appears that $\lim_{x\to 0^-}\frac{2^x-1}{x}\approx 0.693$.

2.3.54

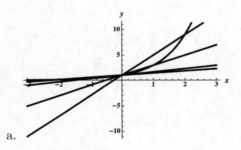

a.

b. The slope of the secant line between $(0,1)$ and $(x,3^x)$ is $\frac{3^x-1}{x}$.

c.

x	$-.1$	$-.01$	$-.001$	$-.0001$	$.0001$	$.001$	$.01$	$.1$
$\frac{3^x-1}{x}$	1.04042	1.0926	1.09801	1.09855	1.09867	1.09922	1.10467	1.16123

It appears that $\lim\limits_{x\to 0}\dfrac{3^x-1}{x}\approx 1.099$.

2.3.55

a. The statement we are trying to prove can be stated in cases as follows: For $x>0$, $-x\le x\sin(1/x)\le x$, and for $x<0$, $x\le x\sin(1/x)\le -x$.

Now for all $x\neq 0$, note that $-1\le \sin(1/x)\le 1$ (because the range of the sine function is $[-1,1]$). We will consider the two cases $x>0$ and $x<0$ separately, but in each case, we will multiply this inequality through by x, switching the inequalities for the $x<0$ case.

For $x > 0$ we have $-x \le x\sin(1/x) \le x$, and for $x < 0$ we have $-x \ge x\sin(1/x) \ge x$, which are exactly the statements we are trying to prove.

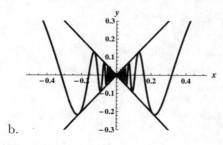

c. Because $\lim\limits_{x \to 0} -|x| = \lim\limits_{x \to 0} |x| = 0$, and because $-|x| \le x\sin(1/x) \le |x|$, the Squeeze Theorem assures us that $\lim\limits_{x \to 0}[x\sin(1/x)] = 0$ as well.

b.

2.3.56

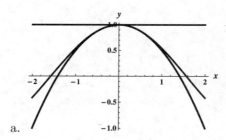

b. Note that $\lim\limits_{x \to 0}\left[1 - \dfrac{x^2}{2}\right] = 1 = \lim\limits_{x \to 0} 1$. So because $1 - \dfrac{x^2}{2} \le \cos x \le 1$, the squeeze theorem assures us that $\lim\limits_{x \to 0} \cos x = 1$ as well.

a.

2.3.57

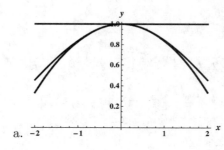

b. Note that $\lim\limits_{x \to 0}\left[1 - \dfrac{x^2}{6}\right] = 1 = \lim\limits_{x \to 0} 1$. So because $1 - \dfrac{x^2}{6} \le \dfrac{\sin x}{x} \le 1$, the squeeze theorem assures us that $\lim\limits_{x \to 0} \dfrac{\sin x}{x} = 1$ as well.

a.

2.3.58

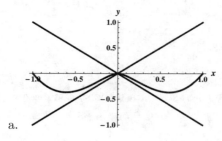

b. Note that $\lim\limits_{x \to 0}(-|x|) = 0 = \lim\limits_{x \to 0} |x|$. So because $-|x| \le x^2 \ln x^2 \le |x|$, the squeeze theorem assures us that $\lim\limits_{x \to 0}(x^2 \ln x^2) = 0$ as well.

a.

2.3.59

a. False. For example, if $f(x) = \begin{cases} x & \text{if } x \ne 1; \\ 4 & \text{if } x = 1, \end{cases}$ then $\lim\limits_{x \to 1} f(x) = 1$ but $f(1) = 4$.

b. False. For example, if $f(x) = \begin{cases} x+1 & \text{if } x \le 1; \\ x-6 & \text{if } x > 1, \end{cases}$ then $\lim\limits_{x \to 1^-} f(x) = 2$ but $\lim\limits_{x \to 1^+} f(x) = -5$.

c. False. For example, if $f(x) = \begin{cases} x & \text{if } x \ne 1; \\ 4 & \text{if } x = 1, \end{cases}$ and $g(x) = 1$, then f and g both have limit 1 as $x \to 1$, but $f(1) = 4 \ne g(1)$.

d. False. For example $\lim\limits_{x \to 2} \dfrac{x^2 - 4}{x - 2}$ exists and is equal to 4.

e. False. For example, it would be possible for the domain of f to be $[1, \infty)$, so that the one-sided limit exists but the two-sided limit doesn't even make sense. This would be true, for example, if $f(x) = x - 1$.

2.3.60 $\lim\limits_{h \to 0} \dfrac{100}{(10h - 1)^{11} + 2} = \dfrac{100}{(-1)^{11} + 2} = \dfrac{100}{1} = 100$.

2.3.61 $\lim\limits_{x \to 2}(5x - 6)^{3/2} = (5 \cdot 2 - 6)^{3/2} = 4^{3/2} = 2^3 = 8$.

2.3.62 $\lim\limits_{x \to 3} \dfrac{\frac{1}{x^2 + 2x} - \frac{1}{15}}{x - 3} = \lim\limits_{x \to 3} \dfrac{\frac{15 - (x^2 + 2x)}{15(x^2 + 2x)}}{x - 3} = \lim\limits_{x \to 3} \dfrac{15 - (x^2 + 2x)}{15(x^2 + 2x)(x - 3)} = \lim\limits_{x \to 3} \dfrac{15 - 2x - x^2}{15(x^2 + 2x)(x - 3)} =$
$\lim\limits_{x \to 3} \dfrac{(3 - x)(5 + x)}{15(x^2 + 2x)(x - 3)} = \lim\limits_{x \to 3} \dfrac{-(5 + x)}{15(x^2 + 2x)} = \dfrac{-8}{225}$.

2.3.63 $\lim\limits_{x \to 1} \dfrac{\sqrt{10x - 9} - 1}{x - 1} = \lim\limits_{x \to 1} \dfrac{(\sqrt{10x - 9} - 1)(\sqrt{10x - 9} + 1)}{(x - 1)(\sqrt{10x - 9} + 1)} = \lim\limits_{x \to 1} \dfrac{(10x - 9) - 1}{(x - 1)(\sqrt{10x - 9} + 1)} =$
$\lim\limits_{x \to 1} \dfrac{10(x - 1)}{(x - 1)(\sqrt{10x - 9} + 1)} = \lim\limits_{x \to 1} \dfrac{10}{(\sqrt{10x - 9} + 1)} = \dfrac{10}{2} = 5$.

2.3.64 $\lim\limits_{x \to 2} \left(\dfrac{1}{x - 2} - \dfrac{2}{x^2 - 2x} \right) = \lim\limits_{x \to 2} \left(\dfrac{x}{x(x - 2)} - \dfrac{2}{x(x - 2)} \right) = \lim\limits_{x \to 2} \left(\dfrac{x - 2}{x(x - 2)} \right) = \lim\limits_{x \to 2} \dfrac{1}{x} = \dfrac{1}{2}$.

2.3.65 $\lim\limits_{h \to 0} \dfrac{(5 + h)^2 - 25}{h} = \lim\limits_{h \to 0} \dfrac{25 + 10h + h^2 - 25}{h} = \lim\limits_{h \to 0} \dfrac{h(10 + h)}{h} = \lim\limits_{h \to 0}(10 + h) = 10$.

2.3.66 $\lim\limits_{x \to c} \dfrac{x^2 - 2cx + c^2}{x - c} = \lim\limits_{x \to c} \dfrac{(x - c)^2}{x - c} = \lim\limits_{x \to c} x - c = c - c = 0$.

2.3.67 We have

$$\lim\limits_{w \to -k} \dfrac{w^2 + 5kw + 4k^2}{w^2 + kw} = \lim\limits_{w \to -k} \dfrac{(w + 4k)(w + k)}{(w)(w + k)} = \lim\limits_{w \to -k} \dfrac{w + 4k}{w} = \dfrac{-k + 4k}{-k} = -3.$$

If $k = 0$, we have $\lim\limits_{w \to -k} \dfrac{w^2 + 5kw + 4k^2}{w^2 + kw} = \lim\limits_{w \to 0} \dfrac{w^2}{w^2} = 1$.

2.3.68 In order for $\lim\limits_{x \to 2} f(x)$ to exist, we need the two one-sided limits to exist and be equal. We have $\lim\limits_{x \to 2^-} f(x) = \lim\limits_{x \to 2^-}(3x + b) = 6 + b$, and $\lim\limits_{x \to 2^+} f(x) = \lim\limits_{x \to 2^+}(x - 2) = 0$. So we need $6 + b = 0$, so we require that $b = -6$. Then $\lim\limits_{x \to 2} f(x) = 0$.

2.3.69 In order for $\lim\limits_{x \to -1} g(x)$ to exist, we need the two one-sided limits to exist and be equal. We have $\lim\limits_{x \to -1^-} g(x) = \lim\limits_{x \to -1^-}(x^2 - 5x) = 6$, and $\lim\limits_{x \to -1^+} g(x) = \lim\limits_{x \to -1^+}(ax^3 - 7) = -a - 7$. So we need $-a - 7 = 6$, so we require that $a = -13$. Then $\lim\limits_{x \to -1} f(x) = 6$.

2.3.70 $\lim\limits_{x \to 2} \dfrac{x^5 - 32}{x - 2} = \lim\limits_{x \to 2} \dfrac{(x-2)(x^4 + 2x^3 + 4x^2 + 8x + 16)}{x - 2} = \lim\limits_{x \to 2}(x^4 + 2x^3 + 4x^2 + 8x + 16) = 16 + 16 + 16 + 16 + 16 = 80.$

2.3.71 $\lim\limits_{x \to 1} \dfrac{x^6 - 1}{x - 1} = \lim\limits_{x \to 1} \dfrac{(x-1)(x^5 + x^4 + x^3 + x^2 + x + 1)}{x - 1} = \lim\limits_{x \to 1}(x^5 + x^4 + x^3 + x^2 + x + 1) = 6.$

2.3.72 $\lim\limits_{x \to -1} \dfrac{x^7 + 1}{x + 1} = \lim\limits_{x \to -1} \dfrac{(x+1)(x^6 - x^5 + x^4 - x^3 + x^2 - x + 1)}{x + 1} = \lim\limits_{x \to -1}(x^6 - x^5 + x^4 - x^3 + x^2 - x + 1) = 7.$

2.3.73 $\lim\limits_{x \to a} \dfrac{x^5 - a^5}{x - a} = \lim\limits_{x \to a} \dfrac{(x-a)(x^4 + ax^3 + a^2x^2 + a^3x + a^4)}{x - a} = \lim\limits_{x \to a}(x^4 + ax^3 + a^2x^2 + a^3x + a^4) = 5a^4.$

2.3.74 $\lim\limits_{x \to a} \dfrac{x^n - a^n}{x - a} = \lim\limits_{x \to a} \dfrac{(x-a)(x^{n-1} + ax^{n-2} + \cdots + a^{n-2}x + a^{n-1})}{x - a} = \lim\limits_{x \to a}(x^{n-1} + ax^{n-2} + \cdots + a^{n-2}x + a^{n-1}) = na^{n-1}.$

2.3.75 $\lim\limits_{x \to 1} \dfrac{\sqrt[3]{x} - 1}{x - 1} = \lim\limits_{x \to 1} \dfrac{\sqrt[3]{x} - 1}{(\sqrt[3]{x} - 1)(\sqrt[3]{x^2} + \sqrt[3]{x} + 1)} = \lim\limits_{x \to 1} \dfrac{1}{\sqrt[3]{x^2} + \sqrt[3]{x} + 1} = \dfrac{1}{3}.$

2.3.76 $\lim\limits_{x \to 16} \dfrac{\sqrt[4]{x} - 2}{x - 16} = \lim\limits_{x \to 16} \dfrac{\sqrt[4]{x} - 2}{(\sqrt[4]{x} - 2)(\sqrt[4]{x^3} + 2\sqrt[4]{x^2} + 4\sqrt[4]{x} + 8)} = \lim\limits_{x \to 16} \dfrac{1}{\sqrt[4]{x^3} + 2\sqrt[4]{x^2} + 4\sqrt[4]{x} + 8} = \dfrac{1}{32}.$

2.3.77 $\lim\limits_{x \to 1} \dfrac{x - 1}{\sqrt{x} - 1} = \lim\limits_{x \to 1} \dfrac{(x-1)(\sqrt{x} + 1)}{(\sqrt{x} - 1)(\sqrt{x} + 1)} = \lim\limits_{x \to 1} \dfrac{(x-1)(\sqrt{x} + 1)}{x - 1} = \lim\limits_{x \to 1}(\sqrt{x} + 1) = 2.$

2.3.78 $\lim\limits_{x \to 1} \dfrac{x - 1}{\sqrt{4x + 5} - 3} = \lim\limits_{x \to 1} \dfrac{(x-1)(\sqrt{4x+5} + 3)}{(\sqrt{4x+5} - 3)(\sqrt{4x+5} + 3)} = \lim\limits_{x \to 1} \dfrac{(x-1)(\sqrt{4x+5} + 3)}{4x + 5 - 9} = $
$\lim\limits_{x \to 1} \dfrac{(x-1)(\sqrt{4x+5} + 3)}{4(x - 1)} = \lim\limits_{x \to 1} \dfrac{(\sqrt{4x+5} + 3)}{4} = \dfrac{6}{4} = \dfrac{3}{2}.$

2.3.79 $\lim\limits_{x \to 4} \dfrac{3(x-4)\sqrt{x+5}}{3 - \sqrt{x+5}} = \lim\limits_{x \to 4} \dfrac{3(x-4)(\sqrt{x+5})(3 + \sqrt{x+5})}{(3 - \sqrt{x+5})(3 + \sqrt{x+5})} = \lim\limits_{x \to 4} \dfrac{3(x-4)(\sqrt{x+5})(3 + \sqrt{x+5})}{9 - (x+5)} = $
$\lim\limits_{x \to 4} \dfrac{3(x-4)(\sqrt{x+5})(3 + \sqrt{x+5})}{-(x-4)} = \lim\limits_{x \to 4}[-3(\sqrt{x+5})(3 + \sqrt{x+5})] = (-3)(3)(3 + 3) = -54.$

2.3.80 Assume $c \neq 0$. $\lim\limits_{x \to 0} \dfrac{x}{\sqrt{cx + 1} - 1} = \lim\limits_{x \to 0} \dfrac{x(\sqrt{cx+1} + 1)}{(\sqrt{cx+1} - 1)(\sqrt{cx+1} + 1)} = \lim\limits_{x \to 0} \dfrac{x(\sqrt{cx+1} + 1)}{(cx+1) - 1} = $
$\lim\limits_{x \to 0} \dfrac{x(\sqrt{cx+1} + 1)}{cx} = \lim\limits_{x \to 0} \dfrac{(\sqrt{cx+1} + 1)}{c} = \dfrac{2}{c}.$

2.3.81 Let $f(x) = x - 1$ and $g(x) = \dfrac{5}{x-1}$. Then $\lim\limits_{x \to 1} f(x) = 0$, $\lim\limits_{x \to 1} f(x)g(x) = \lim\limits_{x \to 1} \dfrac{5(x-1)}{x - 1} = \lim\limits_{x \to 1} 5 = 5.$

2.3.82 Let $f(x) = x^2 - 1$. Then $\lim\limits_{x \to 1} \dfrac{f(x)}{x - 1} = \lim\limits_{x \to 1} \dfrac{x^2 - 1}{x - 1} = \lim\limits_{x \to 1}(x + 1) = 2.$

2.3.83 Let $p(x) = x^2 + 2x - 8$. Then $\lim\limits_{x \to 2} \dfrac{p(x)}{x - 2} = \lim\limits_{x \to 2} \dfrac{(x-2)(x+4)}{x - 2} = \lim\limits_{x \to 2}(x + 4) = 6.$

The constants are unique. We know that 2 must be a root of p (otherwise the given limit couldn't exist), so it must have the form $p(x) = (x - 2)q(x)$, and q must be a degree 1 polynomial with leading coefficient 1 (otherwise p wouldn't have leading coefficient 1.) So we have $p(x) = (x - 2)(x + d)$, but because $\lim\limits_{x \to 2} \dfrac{p(x)}{x - 2} = \lim\limits_{x \to 2}(x + d) = 2 + d = 6$, we are forced to realize that $d = 4$. Therefore, we have deduced that the only possibility for p is $p(x) = (x - 2)(x + 4) = x^2 + 2x - 8$.

2.3.84

a. $L(c/2) = L_0 \sqrt{1 - \dfrac{(c/2)^2}{c^2}} = L_0 \sqrt{1 - (1/4)} = \sqrt{3}L_0/2.$

b. $L(3c/4) = L_0\sqrt{1 - (1/c^2)(3c/4)^2} = L_0\sqrt{1 - (9/16)} = \sqrt{7}L_0/4.$

c. It appears that that the observed length L of the ship decreases as the ship speed increases.

d. $\lim\limits_{x \to c^-} L_0\sqrt{1 - (v^2/c^2)} = L_0 \cdot 0 = 0.$ As the speed of the ship approaches the speed of light, the observed length of the ship shrinks to 0.

2.3.85 $\lim\limits_{S \to 0^+} r(S) = \lim\limits_{S \to 0^+} (1/2)\left(\sqrt{100 + \dfrac{2S}{\pi}} - 10\right) = 0.$

The radius of the circular cylinder approaches zero as the surface area approaches zero.

2.3.86 $\lim\limits_{t \to 200^-} d(t) = \lim\limits_{t \to 200^-} (3 - 0.015t)^2 = (3 - (0.015)(200))^2 = (3 - 3)^2 = 0.$ As time approaches 200 seconds, the depth of the water in the tank is approaching 0.

2.3.87 $\lim\limits_{x \to 10} E(x) = \lim\limits_{x \to 10} \dfrac{4.35}{x\sqrt{x^2 + 0.01}} = \dfrac{4.35}{10\sqrt{100.01}} \approx .0435$ N/C.

2.3.88 Because $\lim\limits_{x \to 1} f(x) = 4$, we know that f is near 4 when x is near 1 (but not equal to 1). It follows that $\lim\limits_{x \to -1} f(x^2) = 4$ as well, because when x is near but not equal to -1, x^2 is near 1 but not equal to 1. Thus $f(x^2)$ is near 4 when x is near -1.

2.3.89

a. As $x \to 0^+$, $(1 - x) \to 1^-$. So $\lim\limits_{x \to 0^+} g(x) = \lim\limits_{(1-x) \to 1^-} f(1 - x) = \lim\limits_{z \to 1^-} f(z) = 6.$ (Where $z = 1 - x$.)

b. As $x \to 0^-$, $(1 - x) \to 1^+$. So $\lim\limits_{x \to 0^-} g(x) = \lim\limits_{(1-x) \to 1^+} f(1 - x) = \lim\limits_{z \to 1^+} f(z) = 4.$ (Where $z = 1 - x$.)

2.3.90

a. Suppose $0 < \theta < \pi/2$. Note that $\sin\theta > 0$, so $|\sin\theta| = \sin\theta$. Also, $\sin\theta = \frac{|AC|}{1}$, so $|AC| = |\sin\theta|$.

Now suppose that $-\pi/2 < \theta < 0$. Then $\sin\theta$ is negative, so $|\sin\theta| = -\sin\theta$. We have $\sin\theta = \frac{-|AC|}{1}$, so $|AC| = -\sin\theta = |\sin\theta|$.

b. Suppose $0 < \theta < \pi/2$. Because AB is the hypotenuse of triangle ABC, we know that $|AB| > |AC|$. We have $|\sin\theta| = |AC| < |AB| <$ the length of arc $AB = \theta = |\theta|$.

If $-\pi/2 < \theta < 0$, we can make a similar argument. We have

$$|\sin\theta| = |AC| < |AB| < \text{ the length of arc } AB = -\theta = |\theta|.$$

c. If $0 < \theta < \pi/2$, we have $\sin\theta = |\sin\theta| < |\theta|$, and because $\sin\theta$ is positive, we have $-|\theta| \leq 0 < \sin\theta$. Putting these together gives $-|\theta| < \sin\theta < |\theta|$.

If $-\pi/2 < \theta < 0$, then $|\sin\theta| = -\sin\theta$. From the previous part, we have $|\sin\theta| = -\sin\theta < |\theta|$. Therefore, $-|\theta| < \sin\theta$. Now because $\sin\theta$ is negative on this interval, we have $\sin\theta < 0 \leq |\theta|$. Putting these together gives $-|\theta| < \sin\theta < |\theta|$.

d. If $0 < \theta < \pi/2$, we have

$$0 \leq 1 - \cos\theta = |OB| - |OC| = |BC| < |AB| < \text{ the length of arc } AB = \theta = |\theta|.$$

For $-\pi/2 < \theta < 0$, we have

$$0 \leq 1 - \cos\theta = |OB| - |OC| = |BC| < |AB| < \text{ the length of arc } AB = -\theta = |\theta|.$$

2.3.91 $\lim\limits_{x \to a} p(x) = \lim\limits_{x \to a} (a_n x^n + a_{n-1} x^{n-1} + \cdots + a_1 x + a_0) = \lim\limits_{x \to a} (a_n x^n) + \lim\limits_{x \to a} (a_{n-1} x^{n-1}) + \cdots + \lim\limits_{x \to a} (a_1 x) + \lim\limits_{x \to a} a_0 = a_n \lim\limits_{x \to a} x^n + a_{n-1} \lim\limits_{x \to a} x^{n-1} + \cdots + a_1 \lim\limits_{x \to a} x + a_0 = a_n (\lim\limits_{x \to a} x)^n + a_{n-1} (\lim\limits_{x \to a} x)^{n-1} + \cdots + a_1 (\lim\limits_{x \to a} x) + a_0 = a_n a^n + a_{n-1} a^{n-1} + \cdots + a_1 a + a_0 = p(a).$

2.4 Infinite Limits

2.4.1

$\lim\limits_{x \to a^+} f(x) = -\infty$ means that when x is very close to (but a little bigger than) a, the corresponding values for $f(x)$ are negative numbers whose absolute value is very large.

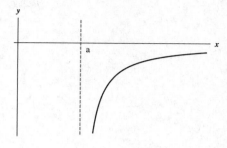

2.4.2

$\lim\limits_{x \to a} f(x) = \infty$ means that when x is close to (but not equal to) a, the corresponding values for $f(x)$ are very large positive numbers.

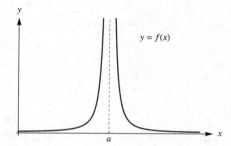

2.4.3 A vertical asymptote for a function f is a vertical line $x = a$ so that one or more of the following are true: $\lim\limits_{x \to a^-} f(x) = \pm\infty$, $\lim\limits_{x \to a^+} f(x) = \pm\infty$.

2.4.4 No. For example, if $f(x) = x^2 - 4$ and $g(x) = x - 2$ and $a = 2$, we would have $\lim\limits_{x \to 2} \dfrac{f(x)}{g(x)} = 4$, even though $g(2) = 0$.

2.4.5 Because the numerator is approaching a non-zero constant while the denominator is approaching zero, the quotient of these numbers is getting big – at least the absolute value of the quotient is getting big. The quotient is actually always negative, because a number near 100 divided by a negative number is always negative. Thus $\lim\limits_{x \to 2} \dfrac{f(x)}{g(x)} = -\infty$.

2.4.6 Using the same sort of reasoning as in the last problem – as $x \to 3$ the numerator is fixed at 1, but the denominator is getting small, so the quotient is getting big. It remains to investigate the sign of the quotient. As $x \to 3^-$, the quantity $x - 3$ is negative, so the quotient of the positive number 1 and this small negative number is negative. On the other hand, as $x \to 3^+$, the quantity $x - 3$ is positive, so the quotient of 1 and this number is positive. Thus: $\lim\limits_{x \to 3^-} \dfrac{1}{x - 3} = -\infty$, and $\lim\limits_{x \to 3^+} \dfrac{1}{x - 3} = \infty$.

2.4.7

x	$\frac{x+1}{(x-1)^2}$	x	$\frac{x+1}{(x-1)^2}$
1.1	210	.9	190
1.01	20,100	.99	19,900
1.001	2,001,000	.999	1,999,000
1.0001	200,010,000	.9999	199,990,000

From the data given, it appears that $\lim\limits_{x \to 1} f(x) = \infty$.

2.4.8 $\lim\limits_{x \to 3} f(x) = \infty$, and $\lim\limits_{x \to -1} f(x) = -\infty$.

2.4.9

a. $\lim\limits_{x \to 1^-} f(x) = \infty$.

b. $\lim\limits_{x \to 1^+} f(x) = \infty$.

c. $\lim\limits_{x \to 1} f(x) = \infty$.

d. $\lim\limits_{x \to 2^-} f(x) = \infty$.

e. $\lim\limits_{x \to 2^+} f(x) = -\infty$.

f. $\lim\limits_{x \to 2} f(x)$ does not exist.

2.4.10

a. $\lim\limits_{x \to 2^-} g(x) = \infty$.

b. $\lim\limits_{x \to 2^+} g(x) = -\infty$.

c. $\lim\limits_{x \to 2} g(x)$ does not exist.

d. $\lim\limits_{x \to 4^-} g(x) = -\infty$.

e. $\lim\limits_{x \to 4^+} g(x) = -\infty$.

f. $\lim\limits_{x \to 4} g(x) = -\infty$.

2.4.11

a. $\lim\limits_{x \to -2^-} h(x) = -\infty$.

b. $\lim\limits_{x \to -2^+} h(x) = -\infty$.

c. $\lim\limits_{x \to -2} h(x) = -\infty$.

d. $\lim\limits_{x \to 3^-} h(x) = \infty$.

e. $\lim\limits_{x \to 3^+} h(x) = -\infty$.

f. $\lim\limits_{x \to 3} h(x)$ does not exist.

2.4.12

a. $\lim\limits_{x \to -2^-} p(x) = -\infty$.

b. $\lim\limits_{x \to -2^+} p(x) = -\infty$.

c. $\lim\limits_{x \to -2} p(x) = -\infty$.

d. $\lim\limits_{x \to 3^-} p(x) = -\infty$.

e. $\lim\limits_{x \to 3^+} p(x) = -\infty$.

f. $\lim\limits_{x \to 3} p(x) = -\infty$.

2.4.13

a. $\lim\limits_{x \to 0^-} \dfrac{1}{x^2 - x} = \infty$.

b. $\lim\limits_{x \to 0^+} \dfrac{1}{x^2 - x} = -\infty$.

c. $\lim\limits_{x \to 1^-} \dfrac{1}{x^2 - x} = -\infty$.

d. $\lim\limits_{x \to 1^+} \dfrac{1}{x^2 - x} = \infty$.

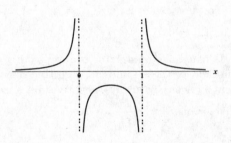

2.4.14

a. $\lim\limits_{x \to -2^+} \dfrac{e^{-x}}{x(x + 2)^2} = -\infty$.

b. $\lim\limits_{x \to -2} \dfrac{e^{-x}}{x(x + 2)^2} = -\infty$.

c. $\lim\limits_{x \to 0^-} \dfrac{e^{-x}}{x(x + 2)^2} = -\infty$.

d. $\lim\limits_{x \to 0^+} \dfrac{e^{-x}}{x(x + 2)^2} = \infty$.

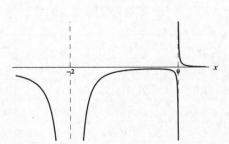

2.4.15

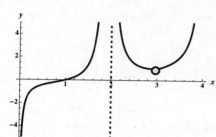

2.4.16

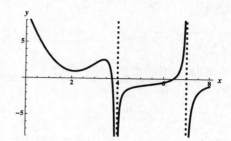

2.4.17

a. $\displaystyle\lim_{x\to 2^+}\frac{1}{x-2}=\infty.$

b. $\displaystyle\lim_{x\to 2^-}\frac{1}{x-2}=-\infty.$

c. $\displaystyle\lim_{x\to 2}\frac{1}{x-2}$ does not exist.

2.4.18

a. $\displaystyle\lim_{x\to 3^+}\frac{2}{(x-3)^3}=\infty.$

b. $\displaystyle\lim_{x\to 3^-}\frac{2}{(x-3)^3}=-\infty.$

c. $\displaystyle\lim_{x\to 3}\frac{2}{(x-3)^3}$ does not exist.

2.4.19

a. $\displaystyle\lim_{x\to 4^+}\frac{x-5}{(x-4)^2}=-\infty.$

b. $\displaystyle\lim_{x\to 4^-}\frac{x-5}{(x-4)^2}=-\infty.$

c. $\displaystyle\lim_{x\to 4}\frac{x-5}{(x-4)^2}=-\infty.$

2.4.20

a. $\displaystyle\lim_{x\to 1^+}\frac{x-2}{(x-1)^3}=-\infty.$

b. $\displaystyle\lim_{x\to 1^-}\frac{x-2}{(x-1)^3}=\infty.$

c. $\displaystyle\lim_{x\to 1}\frac{x-2}{(x-1)^3}$ does not exist.

2.4.21

a. $\displaystyle\lim_{x\to 3^+}\frac{(x-1)(x-2)}{(x-3)}=\infty.$

b. $\displaystyle\lim_{x\to 3^-}\frac{(x-1)(x-2)}{(x-3)}=-\infty.$

c. $\displaystyle\lim_{x\to 3}\frac{(x-1)(x-2)}{(x-3)}$ does not exist.

2.4.22

a. $\displaystyle\lim_{x\to -2^+}\frac{(x-4)}{x(x+2)}=\infty.$

b. $\displaystyle\lim_{x\to -2^-}\frac{(x-4)}{x(x+2)}=-\infty.$

c. $\displaystyle\lim_{x\to -2}\frac{(x-4)}{x(x+2)}$ does not exist.

2.4.23

a. $\displaystyle\lim_{x\to 2^+}\frac{x^2-4x+3}{(x-2)^2}=-\infty.$

b. $\displaystyle\lim_{x\to 2^-}\frac{x^2-4x+3}{(x-2)^2}=-\infty.$

c. $\displaystyle\lim_{x\to 2}\frac{x^2-4x+3}{(x-2)^2}=-\infty.$

2.4.24

a. $\displaystyle\lim_{x\to -2^+}\frac{x^3-5x^2+6x}{x^4-4x^2}=\lim_{x\to -2^+}\frac{x(x-2)(x-3)}{x^2(x-2)(x+2)}=\lim_{x\to -2^+}\frac{x-3}{x(x+2)}=\infty.$

b. $\displaystyle\lim_{x\to -2^-}\frac{x^3-5x^2+6x}{x^4-4x^2}=\lim_{x\to -2^-}\frac{x(x-2)(x-3)}{x^2(x-2)(x+2)}=\lim_{x\to -2^-}\frac{x-3}{x(x+2)}=-\infty.$

c. Because the two one-sided limits differ, $\displaystyle\lim_{x\to -2}\frac{x^3-5x^2+6x}{x^4-4x^2}$ does not exist.

d. $\lim_{x \to 2} \dfrac{x^3 - 5x^2 + 6x}{x^4 - 4x^2} = \lim_{x \to 2} \dfrac{x - 3}{x(x + 2)} = \dfrac{-1}{8}$.

2.4.25 $\lim_{x \to 0} \dfrac{x^3 - 5x^2}{x^2} = \lim_{x \to 0} \dfrac{x^2(x - 5)}{x^2} = \lim_{x \to 0}(x - 5) = -5$.

2.4.26 $\lim_{t \to 5} \dfrac{4t^2 - 100}{t - 5} = \lim_{t \to 5} \dfrac{4(t - 5)(t + 5)}{t - 5} = \lim_{t \to 5}[4(t + 5)] = 40$.

2.4.27 $\lim_{x \to 1^+} \dfrac{x^2 - 5x + 6}{x - 1} = \lim_{x \to 1^+} \dfrac{(x - 2)(x - 3)}{x - 1} = \infty$. (Note that as $x \to 1^+$, the numerator is near 2, while the denominator is near zero, but is positive. So the quotient is positive and large.)

2.4.28 $\lim_{z \to 4} \dfrac{z - 5}{(z^2 - 10z + 24)^2} = \lim_{z \to 4} \dfrac{z - 5}{(z - 4)^2(z - 6)^2} = -\infty$. (Note that as $z \to 4$, the numerator is near -1 while the denominator is near zero but is positive. So the quotient is negative with large absolute value.)

2.4.29

a. $\lim_{x \to 5} \dfrac{x - 5}{x^2 - 25} = \lim_{x \to 5} \dfrac{1}{x + 5} = \dfrac{1}{10}$, so there isn't a vertical asymptote at $x = 5$.

b. $\lim_{x \to -5^-} \dfrac{x - 5}{x^2 - 25} = \lim_{x \to -5^-} \dfrac{1}{x + 5} = -\infty$, so there is a vertical asymptote at $x = -5$.

c. $\lim_{x \to -5^+} \dfrac{x - 5}{x^2 - 25} = \lim_{x \to -5^+} \dfrac{1}{x + 5} = \infty$. This also implies that $x = -5$ is a vertical asymptote, as we already noted in part b.

2.4.30

a. $\lim_{x \to 7^-} \dfrac{x + 7}{x^4 - 49x^2} = \lim_{x \to 7^-} \dfrac{x + 7}{x^2(x + 7)(x - 7)} = \lim_{x \to 7^-} \dfrac{1}{x^2(x - 7)} = -\infty$, so there is a vertical asymptote at $x = 7$.

b. $\lim_{x \to 7^+} \dfrac{x + 7}{x^4 - 49x^2} = \lim_{x \to 7^+} \dfrac{x + 7}{x^2(x + 7)(x - 7)} = \lim_{x \to 7^+} \dfrac{1}{x^2(x - 7)} = \infty$. This also implies that there is a vertical asymptote at $x = 7$, as we already noted in part a.

c. $\lim_{x \to -7} \dfrac{x + 7}{x^4 - 49x^2} = \lim_{x \to -7} \dfrac{x + 7}{x^2(x + 7)(x - 7)} = \lim_{x \to -7} \dfrac{1}{x^2(x - 7)} = \dfrac{1}{-686}$. So there is not a vertical asymptote at $x = 7$.

d. $\lim_{x \to 0} \dfrac{x + 7}{x^4 - 49x^2} = \lim_{x \to 0} \dfrac{x + 7}{x^2(x + 7)(x - 7)} = \lim_{x \to 0} \dfrac{1}{x^2(x - 7)} = -\infty$. So there is a vertical asymptote at $x = 0$.

2.4.31 $f(x) = \dfrac{x^2 - 9x + 14}{x^2 - 5x + 6} = \dfrac{(x - 2)(x - 7)}{(x - 2)(x - 3)}$. Note that $x = 3$ is a vertical asymptote, while $x = 2$ appears to be a candidate but isn't one. We have $\lim_{x \to 3^+} f(x) = \lim_{x \to 3^+} \dfrac{x - 7}{x - 3} = -\infty$ and $\lim_{x \to 3^-} f(x) = \lim_{x \to 3^-} \dfrac{x - 7}{x - 3} = \infty$, and thus $\lim_{x \to 3} f(x)$ doesn't exist. Note that $\lim_{x \to 2} f(x) = 5$.

2.4.32 $f(x) = \dfrac{\cos x}{x(x + 2)}$ has vertical asymptotes at $x = 0$ and at $x = -2$. Note that $\cos x$ is near 1 when x is near 0, and $\cos x$ is near $-.4$ when x is near -2. Thus, $\lim_{x \to 0^+} f(x) = +\infty$, $\lim_{x \to 0^-} f(x) = -\infty$, $\lim_{x \to -2^+} f(x) = \infty$, and $\lim_{x \to -2^-} f(x) = -\infty$.

2.4.33 $f(x) = \dfrac{x + 1}{x^3 - 4x^2 + 4x} = \dfrac{x + 1}{x(x - 2)^2}$. There are vertical asymptotes at $x = 0$ and $x = 2$. We have $\lim_{x \to 0^-} f(x) = \lim_{x \to 0^-} \dfrac{x + 1}{x(x - 2)^2} = -\infty$, while $\lim_{x \to 0^+} f(x) = \lim_{x \to 0^+} \dfrac{x + 1}{x(x - 2)^2} = \infty$, and thus $\lim_{x \to 0} f(x)$ doesn't exist.

Also we have $\lim_{x \to 2^-} f(x) = \lim_{x \to 2^-} \dfrac{x + 1}{x(x - 2)^2} = \infty$, while $\lim_{x \to 2^+} f(x) = \lim_{x \to 2^+} \dfrac{x + 1}{x(x - 2)^2} = \infty$, and thus $\lim_{x \to 2} f(x) = \infty$ as well.

2.4.34 $g(x) = \frac{x^3 - 10x^2 + 16x}{x^2 - 8x} = \frac{x(x-2)(x-8)}{x(x-8)}$. This function has no vertical asymptotes.

2.4.35 $\lim\limits_{\theta \to 0^+} \csc\theta = \lim\limits_{\theta \to 0^+} \frac{1}{\sin\theta} = \infty$.

2.4.36 $\lim\limits_{x \to 0^-} \csc x = \lim\limits_{x \to 0^-} \frac{1}{\sin x} = -\infty$.

2.4.37 $\lim\limits_{x \to 0^+} -10\cot x = \lim\limits_{x \to 0^+} \frac{-10\cos x}{\sin x} = -\infty$. (Note that as $x \to 0^+$, the numerator is near -10 and the denominator is near zero, but is positive. Thus the quotient is a negative number whose absolute value is large.)

2.4.38 $\lim\limits_{\theta \to (\pi/2)^+} \frac{1}{3}\tan\theta = \lim\limits_{\theta \to (\pi/2)^+} \frac{\sin\theta}{3\cos\theta} = -\infty$. (Note that as $\theta \to (\pi/2)^+$, the numerator is near 1 and the denominator is near 0, but is negative. Thus the quotient is a negative number whose absolute value is large.)

2.4.39

   a. $\lim\limits_{x \to (\pi/2)^+} \tan x = -\infty$.

   b. $\lim\limits_{x \to (\pi/2)^-} \tan x = \infty$.

   c. $\lim\limits_{x \to (-\pi/2)^+} \tan x = -\infty$.

   d. $\lim\limits_{x \to (-\pi/2)^-} \tan x = \infty$.

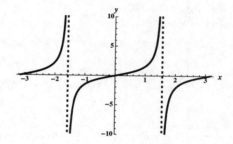

2.4.40

   a. $\lim\limits_{x \to (\pi/2)^+} \sec x \tan x = \infty$.

   b. $\lim\limits_{x \to (\pi/2)^-} \sec x \tan x = \infty$.

   c. $\lim\limits_{x \to (-\pi/2)^+} \sec x \tan x = -\infty$.

   d. $\lim\limits_{x \to (-\pi/2)^-} \sec x \tan x = -\infty$.

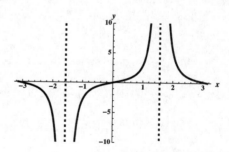

2.4.41

  a. False. $\lim\limits_{x \to 1^-} f(x) = \lim\limits_{x \to 1^+} f(x) = \lim\limits_{x \to 1} f(x) = \lim\limits_{x \to 1} \frac{(x-1)(x-6)}{(x-1)(x+1)} = \frac{-5}{2}$.

  b. True. For example, $\lim\limits_{x \to -1^+} f(x) = \lim\limits_{x \to -1^+} \frac{(x-1)(x-6)}{(x-1)(x+1)} = -\infty$.

  c. False. For example $g(x) = \frac{1}{x-1}$ has $\lim\limits_{x \to 1^+} g(x) = \infty$, but $\lim\limits_{x \to 1^-} g(x) = -\infty$.

2.4.42

One such function is $f(x) = \frac{x^2-4x+3}{x^2-3x+2} = \frac{(x-1)(x-3)}{(x-1)(x-2)}$.

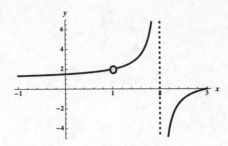

2.4.43 One example is $f(x) = \frac{1}{x-6}$.

2.4.44

function	a	b	c	d	e	f
graph	D	C	F	B	A	E

2.4.45 $f(x) = \frac{x^2-3x+2}{x^{10}-x^9} = \frac{(x-2)(x-1)}{x^9(x-1)}$. f has a vertical asymptote at $x = 0$, because $\lim\limits_{x\to 0^+} f(x) = -\infty$ (and $\lim\limits_{x\to 0^-} f(x) = \infty$.) Note that $\lim\limits_{x\to 1} f(x) = -1$, so there isn't a vertical asymptote at $x = 1$.

2.4.46 $g(x) = 2 - \ln x^2$ has a vertical asymptote at $x = 0$, because $\lim\limits_{x\to 0}(2 - \ln x^2) = \infty$.

2.4.47 $h(x) = \frac{e^x}{(x+1)^3}$ has a vertical asymptote at $x = -1$, because $\lim\limits_{x\to -1^+} \frac{e^x}{(x+1)^3} = \infty$ (and $\lim\limits_{x\to -1^-} h(x) = -\infty$.)

2.4.48 $p(x) = \sec(\pi x/2) = \frac{1}{\cos(\pi x/2)}$ has a vertical asymptote on $(-2, 2)$ at $x = \pm 1$.

2.4.49 $g(\theta) = \tan(\pi\theta/10) = \frac{\sin(\pi\theta/10)}{\cos(\pi\theta/10)}$ has a vertical asymptote at each $\theta = 10n + 5$ where n is an integer. This is due to the fact that $\cos(\pi\theta/10) = 0$ when $\pi\theta/10 = \pi/2 + n\pi$ where n is an integer, which is the same as $\{\theta : \theta = 10n + 5, n \text{ an integer}\}$. Note that at all of these numbers which make the denominator zero, the numerator isn't zero.

2.4.50 $q(s) = \frac{\pi}{s - \sin s}$ has a vertical asymptote at $s = 0$. Note that this is the only number where $\sin s = s$.

2.4.51 $f(x) = \frac{1}{\sqrt{x}\sec x} = \frac{\cos x}{\sqrt{x}}$ has a vertical asymptote at $x = 0$.

2.4.52 $g(x) = e^{1/x}$ has a vertical asymptote at $x = 0$, because $\lim\limits_{x\to 0^+} e^{1/x} = \infty$. (Note that as $x \to 0^+$, $1/x \to \infty$, so $e^{1/x} \to \infty$ as well.)

2.4.53

a. Note that the numerator of the given expression factors as $(x - 3)(x - 4)$. So if $a = 3$ or if $a = 4$ the limit would be a finite number. In fact, $\lim\limits_{x\to 3} \frac{(x-3)(x-4)}{x-3} = -1$ and $\lim\limits_{x\to 4} \frac{(x-3)(x-4)}{x-4} = 1$.

b. For any number other than 3 or 4, the limit would be either $\pm\infty$. Because $x - a$ is always positive as $x \to a^+$, the limit would be $+\infty$ exactly when the numerator is positive, which is for a in the set $(-\infty, 3) \cup (4, \infty)$.

c. The limit would be $-\infty$ for a in the set $(3, 4)$.

2.4.54

a. The slope of the secant line is given by $\frac{f(h)-f(0)}{h} = \frac{h^{1/3}}{h} = h^{-2/3}$.

b. $\lim\limits_{h \to 0} \frac{1}{\sqrt[3]{h^2}} = \infty$. This tells us that the slope of the tangent line is infinite – which means that the tangent line at $(0,0)$ is vertical.

2.4.55

a. The slope of the secant line is $\frac{f(h)-f(0)}{h} = \frac{h^{2/3}}{h} = h^{-1/3}$.

b. $\lim\limits_{h \to 0^+} \frac{1}{h^{1/3}} = \infty$, and $\lim\limits_{h \to 0^-} \frac{1}{h^{1/3}} = -\infty$. The tangent line is infinitely steep at the origin (i.e., it is a vertical line.)

2.5   Limits at Infinity

2.5.1

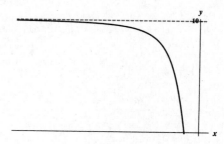

As $x < 0$ becomes large in absolute value, the corresponding values of f level off near 10.

2.5.2 A horizontal asymptote is a horizontal line $y = L$ so that either $\lim\limits_{x \to \infty} f(x) = L$ or $\lim\limits_{x \to -\infty} f(x) = L$ (or both.)

2.5.3 If $f(x) \to 100,000$ as $x \to \infty$ and $g(x) \to \infty$ as $x \to \infty$, then the ratio $\frac{f(x)}{g(x)} \to 0$ as $x \to \infty$. (Because *eventually* the values of f are small compared to the values of g.)

2.5.4 As $x \to \infty$, we note that $e^{-2x} \to 0$, while as $x \to -\infty$, we have $e^{-2x} \to \infty$.

2.5.5 $\lim\limits_{x \to \infty} (-2x^3) = -\infty$, and $\lim\limits_{x \to -\infty} (-2x^3) = \infty$.

2.5.6 The line $y = 0$ may be a horizontal asymptote, the line $y = a$ where $a \neq 0$ may be a horizontal asymptote, and the limit at $\pm\infty$ may not exist either with or without a slant asymptote.

2.5.7 $\lim\limits_{x \to \infty} e^x = \infty$, $\lim\limits_{x \to -\infty} e^x = 0$, and $\lim\limits_{x \to \infty} e^{-x} = 0$.

2.5.8

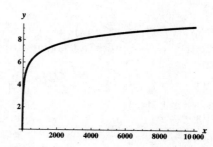

As $x \to \infty$, $\ln x \to \infty$. (Albeit somewhat slowly.)

2.5.9 $\lim\limits_{x\to\infty} (3 + 10/x^2) = 3 + \lim\limits_{x\to\infty} (10/x^2) = 3 + 0 = 3.$

2.5.10 $\lim\limits_{x\to\infty} (5 + 1/x + 10/x^2) = 5 + \lim\limits_{x\to\infty} (1/x) + \lim\limits_{x\to\infty} (10/x^2) = 5 + 0 + 0 = 5.$

2.5.11 $\lim\limits_{\theta\to\infty} \dfrac{\cos\theta}{\theta^2} = 0.$ Note that $-1 \le \cos\theta \le 1$, so $-\frac{1}{\theta^2} \le \frac{\cos\theta}{\theta^2} \le \frac{1}{\theta^2}$. The result now follows from the squeeze theorem.

2.5.12 $\lim\limits_{x\to\infty} \dfrac{3 + 2x + 4x^2}{x^2} = \lim\limits_{x\to\infty} \dfrac{3}{x^2} + \lim\limits_{x\to\infty} \dfrac{2x}{x^2} + \lim\limits_{x\to\infty} \dfrac{4x^2}{x^2} = 0 + \lim\limits_{x\to\infty} \dfrac{2}{x} + \lim\limits_{x\to\infty} 4 = 0 + 0 + 4 = 4.$

2.5.13 $\lim\limits_{x\to\infty} \dfrac{\cos x^5}{\sqrt{x}} = 0.$ Note that $-1 \le \cos x^5 \le 1$, so $\frac{-1}{\sqrt{x}} \le \frac{\cos x^5}{\sqrt{x}} \le \frac{1}{\sqrt{x}}$. Because $\lim\limits_{x\to\infty} \dfrac{1}{\sqrt{x}} = \lim\limits_{x\to\infty} \dfrac{-1}{\sqrt{x}} = 0$, we have $\lim\limits_{x\to\infty} \dfrac{\cos x^5}{\sqrt{x}} = 0$ by the squeeze theorem.

2.5.14 $\lim\limits_{x\to-\infty} \left(5 + \dfrac{100}{x} + \dfrac{\sin^4(x^3)}{x^2} \right) = 5 + 0 + 0 = 5.$ For this last limit, note that $0 \le \sin^4(x^3) \le 1$, so $0 \le \frac{\sin^4(x^3)}{x^2} \le \frac{1}{x^2}$. The result now follows from the squeeze theorem.

2.5.15 $\lim\limits_{x\to\infty} x^{12} = \infty.$ Note that x^{12} is positive when $x > 0$.

2.5.16 $\lim\limits_{x\to-\infty} 3x^{11} = -\infty.$ Note that x^{11} is negative when $x < 0$.

2.5.17 $\lim\limits_{x\to\infty} x^{-6} = \lim\limits_{x\to\infty} \dfrac{1}{x^6} = 0.$

2.5.18 $\lim\limits_{x\to-\infty} x^{-11} = \lim\limits_{x\to-\infty} \dfrac{1}{x^{11}} = 0.$

2.5.19 $\lim\limits_{x\to\infty} (3x^{12} - 9x^7) = \infty.$

2.5.20 $\lim\limits_{x\to-\infty} (3x^7 + x^2) = -\infty.$

2.5.21 $\lim\limits_{x\to-\infty} (-3x^{16} + 2) = -\infty.$

2.5.22 $\lim\limits_{x\to-\infty} 2x^{-8} = \lim\limits_{x\to-\infty} \dfrac{2}{x^8} = 0.$

2.5.23 $\lim\limits_{x\to\infty} (-12x^{-5}) = \lim\limits_{x\to\infty} -\dfrac{12}{x^5} = 0.$

2.5.24 $\lim\limits_{x\to-\infty} (2x^{-8} + 4x^3) = 0 + \lim\limits_{x\to-\infty} 4x^3 = -\infty.$

2.5.25 $\lim\limits_{x\to\infty} \dfrac{4x}{20x+1} = \lim\limits_{x\to\infty} \dfrac{4x}{20x+1} \cdot \dfrac{1/x}{1/x} = \lim\limits_{x\to\infty} \dfrac{4}{20 + 1/x} = \dfrac{4}{20} = \dfrac{1}{5}.$ Thus, the line $y = \frac{1}{5}$ is a horizontal asymptote.

$\lim\limits_{x\to-\infty} \dfrac{4x}{20x+1} = \lim\limits_{x\to-\infty} \dfrac{4x}{20x+1} \cdot \dfrac{1/x}{1/x} = \lim\limits_{x\to-\infty} \dfrac{4}{20 + 1/x} = \dfrac{4}{20} = \dfrac{1}{5}.$ This shows that the curve is also asymptotic to the asymptote in the negative direction.

2.5.26 $\lim\limits_{x\to\infty} \dfrac{3x^2 - 7}{x^2 + 5x} = \lim\limits_{x\to\infty} \dfrac{3x^2 - 7}{x^2 + 5x} \cdot \dfrac{1/x^2}{1/x^2} = \lim\limits_{x\to\infty} \dfrac{3 - (7/x^2)}{1 + (5/x)} = \dfrac{3 - 0}{1 + 0} = 3.$ Thus, the line $y = 3$ is a horizontal asymptote.

$\lim\limits_{x\to-\infty} \dfrac{3x^2 - 7}{x^2 + 5x} = \lim\limits_{x\to-\infty} \dfrac{3x^2 - 7}{x^2 + 5x} \cdot \dfrac{1/x^2}{1/x^2} = \lim\limits_{x\to-\infty} \dfrac{3 - (7/x^2)}{1 + (5/x)} = \dfrac{3 - 0}{1 + 0} = 3.$ Thus, the curve is also asymptotic to the asymptote in the negative direction.

2.5.27 $\lim\limits_{x\to\infty} \dfrac{(6x^2 - 9x + 8)}{(3x^2 + 2)} \cdot \dfrac{1/x^2}{1/x^2} = \lim\limits_{x\to\infty} \dfrac{6 - 9/x + 8/x^2}{3 + 2/x^2} = \dfrac{6 - 0 + 0}{3 + 0} = 2.$ Similarly $\lim\limits_{x\to-\infty} f(x) = 2.$ The line $y = 2$ is a horizontal asymptote.

2.5.28 $\lim\limits_{x\to\infty} \dfrac{(4x^2 - 7)}{(8x^2 + 5x + 2)} \cdot \dfrac{1/x^2}{1/x^2} = \lim\limits_{x\to\infty} \dfrac{4 - 7/x^2}{8 + 5/x + 2/x^2} = \dfrac{4 - 0}{8 + 0 + 0} = \dfrac{1}{2}.$ Similarly $\lim\limits_{x\to-\infty} f(x) = \dfrac{1}{2}.$ The line $y = \frac{1}{2}$ is a horizontal asymptote.

2.5.29 $\lim\limits_{x\to\infty} \dfrac{3x^3 - 7}{x^4 + 5x^2} = \lim\limits_{x\to\infty} \dfrac{3x^3 - 7}{x^4 + 5x^2} \cdot \dfrac{3/x^4}{1/x^4} = \lim\limits_{x\to\infty} \dfrac{1/x - (7/x^4)}{1 + (5/x^2)} = \dfrac{0 - 0}{1 + 0} = 0.$ Thus, the line $y = 0$ (the x-axis) is a horizontal asymptote.

$\lim\limits_{x\to-\infty} \dfrac{3x^3 - 7}{x^4 + 5x^2} = \lim\limits_{x\to-\infty} \dfrac{3x^3 - 7}{x^4 + 5x^2} \cdot \dfrac{3/x^4}{1/x^4} = \lim\limits_{x\to-\infty} \dfrac{1/x - (7/x^4)}{1 + (5/x^2)} = \dfrac{0 - 0}{1 + 0} = 0.$ Thus, the curve is asymptotic to the x-axis in the negative direction as well.

2.5.30 $\lim\limits_{x\to\infty} \dfrac{x^4 + 7}{x^5 + x^2 - x} = \lim\limits_{x\to\infty} \dfrac{x^4 + 7}{x^5 + x^2 - x} \cdot \dfrac{1/x^5}{1/x^5} = \lim\limits_{x\to\infty} \dfrac{(1/x) + (7/x^5)}{1 + (1/x^3) - (1/x^4)} = \dfrac{0 + 0}{1 + 0 - 0} = 0.$ Thus, the line $y = 0$ (the x-axis) is a horizontal asymptote.

$\lim\limits_{x\to-\infty} \dfrac{x^4 + 7}{x^5 + x^2 - x} = \lim\limits_{x\to-\infty} \dfrac{x^4 + 7}{x^5 + x^2 - x} \cdot \dfrac{1/x^5}{1/x^5} = \lim\limits_{x\to-\infty} \dfrac{(1/x) + (7/x^5)}{1 + (1/x^3) - (1/x^4)} = \dfrac{0 + 0}{1 + 0 - 0} = 0.$ Thus, the curve is asymptotic to the x-axis in the negative direction as well.

2.5.31 $\lim\limits_{x\to\infty} \dfrac{(2x + 1)}{(3x^4 - 2)} \cdot \dfrac{1/x^4}{1/x^4} = \lim\limits_{x\to\infty} \dfrac{2/x^3 + 1/x^4}{3 - 2/x^4} = \dfrac{0 + 0}{3 - 0} = 0.$ Similarly $\lim\limits_{x\to-\infty} f(x) = 0.$ The line $y = 0$ is a horizontal asymptote.

2.5.32 $\lim\limits_{x\to\infty} \dfrac{(12x^8 - 3)}{(3x^8 - 2x^7)} \cdot \dfrac{1/x^8}{1/x^8} = \lim\limits_{x\to\infty} \dfrac{12 - 3/x^8}{3 - 2/x} = \dfrac{12 - 0}{3 - 0} = 4.$ Similarly $\lim\limits_{x\to-\infty} f(x) = 4.$ The line $y = 4$ is a horizontal asymptote.

2.5.33 $\lim\limits_{x\to\infty} \dfrac{(40x^5 + x^2)}{(16x^4 - 2x)} \cdot \dfrac{1/x^4}{1/x^4} = \lim\limits_{x\to\infty} \dfrac{40x + 1/x^2}{16 - 2/x^3} = \infty.$ Similarly $\lim\limits_{x\to-\infty} f(x) = -\infty.$ There are no horizontal asymptotes.

2.5.34 $\lim\limits_{x\to\infty} \dfrac{(-x^3 + 1)}{(2x + 8)} \cdot \dfrac{1/x}{1/x} = \lim\limits_{x\to\infty} \dfrac{-x^2 + 1/x}{2 + 8/x} = -\infty.$ Similarly $\lim\limits_{x\to-\infty} f(x) = -\infty.$ There are no horizontal asymptotes.

2.5.35

a. $f(x) = \frac{x^2 - 3}{x + 6} = x - 6 + \frac{33}{x + 6}.$ The oblique asymptote of f is $y = x - 6.$

b. Because $\lim\limits_{x\to-6^+} f(x) = \infty,$ there is a vertical asymptote at $x = -6.$ Note also that $\lim\limits_{x\to-6^-} f(x) = -\infty.$

c.

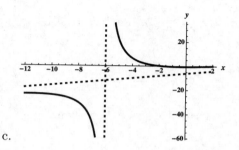

2.5.36

a. $f(x) = \frac{x^2 - 1}{x + 2} = x - 2 + \frac{3}{x + 2}.$ The oblique asymptote of f is $y = x - 2.$

Because $\lim\limits_{x \to -2^+} f(x) = \infty$, there is a verti-

b. cal asymptote at $x = -2$. Note also that $\lim\limits_{x \to -2^-} f(x) = -\infty$.

c.

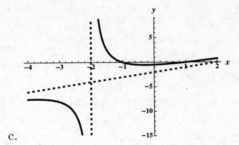

2.5.37

a. $f(x) = \frac{x^2 - 2x + 5}{3x - 2} = (1/3)x - 4/9 + \frac{37}{9(3x-2)}$. The oblique asymptote of f is $y = (1/3)x - 4/9$.

Because $\lim\limits_{x \to (2/3)^+} f(x) = \infty$, there is a verti-

b. cal asymptote at $x = 2/3$. Note also that $\lim\limits_{x \to (2/3)^-} f(x) = -\infty$.

c.

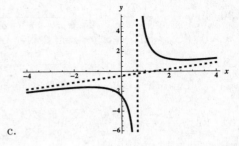

2.5.38

a. $f(x) = \frac{3x^2 - 2x + 7}{2x - 5} = (3/2)x + 11/4 + \frac{83}{4(2x-5)}$. The oblique asymptote of f is $y = (3/2)x + 11/4$.

Because $\lim\limits_{x \to (5/2)^+} f(x) = \infty$, there is a verti-

b. cal asymptote at $x = 5/2$. Note also that $\lim\limits_{x \to (5/2)^-} f(x) = -\infty$.

c.

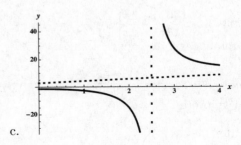

2.5.39

a. $f(x) = \frac{4x^3 + 4x^2 + 7x + 4}{1 + x^2} = 4x + 4 + \frac{3x}{1 + x^2}$. The oblique asymptote of f is $y = 4x + 4$.

b. There are no vertical asymptotes.

c.

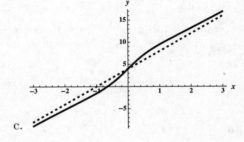

2.5.40

a. $f(x) = \frac{3x^2 - 2x + 5}{3x + 4} = x - 2 + \frac{13}{3x+4}$. The oblique asymptote of f is $y = x - 2$.

b. Because $\lim\limits_{x \to (-4/3)^+} f(x) = \infty$, there is a vertical asymptote at $x = -4/3$. Note also that $\lim\limits_{x \to (-4/3)^-} f(x) = -\infty$.

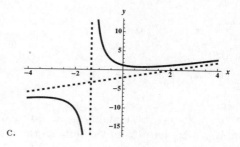

c.

2.5.41 First note that $\sqrt{x^6} = x^3$ if $x > 0$, but $\sqrt{x^6} = -x^3$ if $x < 0$. We have $\lim\limits_{x \to \infty} \frac{4x^3 + 1}{(2x^3 + \sqrt{16x^6 + 1})} \cdot \frac{1/x^3}{1/x^3} =$
$\lim\limits_{x \to \infty} \frac{4 + 1/x^3}{2 + \sqrt{16 + 1/x^6}} = \frac{4 + 0}{2 + \sqrt{16 + 0}} = \frac{2}{3}$.

However, $\lim\limits_{x \to -\infty} \frac{4x^3 + 1}{(2x^3 + \sqrt{16x^6 + 1})} \cdot \frac{1/x^3}{1/x^3} = \lim\limits_{x \to -\infty} \frac{4 + 1/x^3}{2 - \sqrt{16 + 1/x^6}} = \frac{4 + 0}{2 - \sqrt{16 + 0}} = \frac{4}{-2} = -2$.

So $y = \frac{2}{3}$ is a horizontal asymptote (as $x \to \infty$) and $y = -2$ is a horizontal asymptote (as $x \to -\infty$).

2.5.42 First note that $\sqrt{x^2} = x$ for $x > 0$, while $\sqrt{x^2} = -x$ for $x < 0$. Then $\lim\limits_{x \to \infty} f(x)$ can be written as

$$\lim\limits_{x \to \infty} \frac{\sqrt{x^2 + 1}}{2x + 1} \cdot \frac{1/\sqrt{x^2}}{1/x} = \lim\limits_{x \to \infty} \frac{\sqrt{1 + 1/x^2}}{2 + 1/x} = \frac{1}{2}.$$

However, $\lim\limits_{x \to -\infty} f(x)$ can be written as

$$\lim\limits_{x \to -\infty} \frac{\sqrt{x^2 + 1}}{2x + 1} \cdot \frac{1/\sqrt{x^2}}{-1/x} = \lim\limits_{x \to -\infty} \frac{\sqrt{1 + 1/x^2}}{-2 - 1/x} = -\frac{1}{2}.$$

2.5.43 First note that $\sqrt[3]{x^6} = x^2$ and $\sqrt{x^4} = x^2$ for all x (even when $x < 0$.) We have $\lim\limits_{x \to \infty} \frac{\sqrt[3]{x^6 + 8}}{(4x^2 + \sqrt{3x^4 + 1})} \cdot$
$\frac{1/x^2}{1/x^2} = \lim\limits_{x \to \infty} \frac{\sqrt[3]{1 + 8/x^6}}{4 + \sqrt{3 + 1/x^4}} = \frac{1}{4 + \sqrt{3 + 0}} = \frac{1}{4\sqrt{3}}$.

The calculation as $x \to -\infty$ is similar. So $y = \frac{1}{4\sqrt{3}}$ is a horizontal asymptote.

2.5.44 First note that $\sqrt{x^2} = x$ for $x > 0$ and $\sqrt{x^2} = -x$ for $x < 0$.
We have

$$\lim\limits_{x \to \infty} 4x(3x - \sqrt{9x^2 + 1}) = \lim\limits_{x \to \infty} \frac{4x(3x - \sqrt{9x^2 + 1})(3x + \sqrt{9x^2 + 1})}{3x + \sqrt{9x^2 + 1}}$$

$$= \lim\limits_{x \to \infty} \frac{(4x)(-1)}{(3x + \sqrt{9x^2 + 1})} \cdot \frac{1/x}{1/x}$$

$$= \lim\limits_{x \to \infty} -\frac{4}{3 + \sqrt{9 + 1/x^2}} = -\frac{4}{6} = -\frac{2}{3}.$$

Moreover, as $x \to -\infty$ we have

$$\lim_{x \to -\infty} 4x(3x - \sqrt{9x^2 + 1}) = \lim_{x \to -\infty} \frac{4x(3x - \sqrt{9x^2 + 1})(3x + \sqrt{9x^2 + 1})}{3x + \sqrt{9x^2 + 1}}$$

$$= \lim_{x \to -\infty} \frac{(4x)(-1)}{(3x + \sqrt{9x^2 + 1})} \cdot \frac{1/x}{1/x}$$

$$= \lim_{x \to -\infty} -\frac{4}{3 - \sqrt{9 + 1/x^2}} = \infty.$$

Note that this last equality is due to the fact that the numerator is the constant -4 and the denominator is approaching zero (from the left) so the quotient is positive and is getting large.

So $y = -\frac{2}{3}$ is the only horizontal asymptote.

2.5.45

$$\lim_{x \to \infty} (-3e^{-x}) = -3 \cdot 0 = 0. \quad \lim_{x \to -\infty} (-3e^{-x}) = -\infty.$$

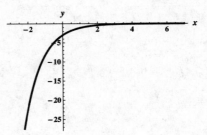

2.5.46

$$\lim_{x \to \infty} 2^x = \infty. \quad \lim_{x \to -\infty} 2^x = 0.$$

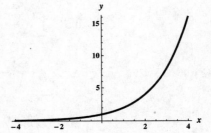

2.5.47

$$\lim_{x \to \infty} (1 - \ln x) = -\infty. \quad \lim_{x \to 0^+} (1 - \ln x) = \infty.$$

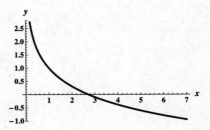

2.5.48

$$\lim_{x \to \infty} |\ln x| = \infty. \quad \lim_{x \to 0^+} |\ln x| = \infty.$$

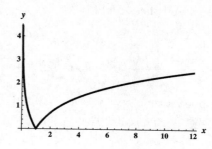

2.5.49

$y = \sin x$ has no asymptotes. $\lim_{x \to \infty} \sin x$ and $\lim_{x \to -\infty} \sin x$ do not exist.

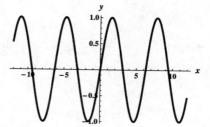

2.5.50

$$\lim_{x \to \infty} \frac{50}{e^{2x}} = 0. \quad \lim_{x \to -\infty} \frac{50}{e^{2x}} = \infty.$$

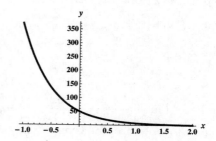

2.5.51

a. False. For example, the function $y = \frac{\sin x}{x}$ on the domain $[1, \infty)$ has a horizontal asymptote of $y = 0$, and it crosses the x-axis infinitely many times.

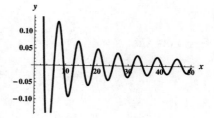

b. False. If f is a rational function, and if $\lim_{x \to \infty} f(x) = L \neq 0$, then the degree of the polynomial in the numerator must equal the degree of the polynomial in the denominator. In this case, both $\lim_{x \to \infty} f(x)$ and $\lim_{x \to -\infty} f(x) = \frac{a_n}{b_n}$ where a_n is the leading coefficient of the polynomial in the numerator and b_n is the leading coefficient of the polynomial in the denominator. In the case where $\lim_{x \to \infty} f(x) = 0$, then the degree of the numerator is strictly less than the degree of the denominator. This case holds for $\lim_{x \to -\infty} f(x) = 0$ as well.

c. True. There are only two directions which might lead to horizontal asymptotes: there could be one as $x \to \infty$ and there could be one as $x \to -\infty$, and those are the only possibilities.

2.5.52

a. $\lim\limits_{x \to \infty} \dfrac{x^2 - 4x + 3}{x - 1} = \infty$, and $\lim\limits_{x \to -\infty} \dfrac{x^2 - 4x + 3}{x - 1} = -\infty$. There are no horizontal asymptotes.

b. It appears that $x = 1$ is a candidate to be a vertical asymptote, but note that $f(x) = \frac{x^2 - 4x + 3}{x - 1} = \frac{(x-1)(x-3)}{x-1}$. Thus $\lim\limits_{x \to 1} f(x) = \lim\limits_{x \to 1}(x - 3) = -2$. So f has no vertical asymptotes.

2.5.53

a. $\lim\limits_{x \to \infty} \dfrac{2x^3 + 10x^2 + 12x}{x^3 + 2x^2} \cdot \dfrac{(1/x^3)}{(1/x^3)} = \lim\limits_{x \to \infty} \dfrac{2 + 10/x + 12/x^2}{1 + 2/x} = 2$. Similarly, $\lim\limits_{x \to -\infty} f(x) = 2$. Thus, $y = 2$ is a horizontal asymptote.

b. Note that $f(x) = \frac{2x(x+2)(x+3)}{x^2(x+2)}$. So $\lim\limits_{x \to 0^+} f(x) = \lim\limits_{x \to 0^+} \dfrac{2(x+3)}{x} = \infty$, and similarly, $\lim\limits_{x \to 0^-} f(x) = -\infty$. There is a vertical asymptote at $x = 0$. Note that there is no asymptote at $x = -2$ because $\lim\limits_{x \to -2} f(x) = -1$.

2.5.54

a. We have $\lim\limits_{x \to \infty} \dfrac{\sqrt{16x^4 + 64x^2} + x^2}{2x^2 - 4} \cdot \dfrac{(1/x^2)}{(1/x^2)} = \lim\limits_{x \to \infty} \dfrac{\sqrt{16 + 64/x^2} + 1}{2 - 4/x^2} = \dfrac{5}{2}$. Similarly, $\lim\limits_{x \to -\infty} f(x) = \dfrac{5}{2}$. So $y = \frac{5}{2}$ is a horizontal asymptote.

b. $\lim\limits_{x \to \sqrt{2}^+} f(x) = \lim\limits_{x \to -\sqrt{2}^-} f(x) = \infty$, and $\lim\limits_{x \to \sqrt{2}^-} f(x) = \lim\limits_{x \to -\sqrt{2}^+} f(x) = -\infty$ so there are vertical asymptotes at $x = \pm\sqrt{2}$.

2.5.55

a. We have $\lim\limits_{x \to \infty} \dfrac{3x^4 + 3x^3 - 36x^2}{x^4 - 25x^2 + 144} \cdot \dfrac{(1/x^4)}{(1/x^4)} = \lim\limits_{x \to \infty} \dfrac{3 + 3/x - 36/x^2}{1 - 25/x^2 + 144/x^4} = 3$. Similarly, $\lim\limits_{x \to -\infty} f(x) = 3$. So $y = 3$ is a horizontal asymptote.

b. Note that $f(x) = \frac{3x^2(x+4)(x-3)}{(x+4)(x-4)(x+3)(x-3)}$. Thus, $\lim\limits_{x \to -3^+} f(x) = -\infty$ and $\lim\limits_{x \to -3^-} f(x) = \infty$. Also, $\lim\limits_{x \to 4^-} f(x) = -\infty$ and $\lim\limits_{x \to 4^+} f(x) = \infty$. Thus there are vertical asymptotes at $x = -3$ and $x = 4$.

2.5.56

a. First note that

$$f(x) = 16x^2(4x^2 - \sqrt{16x^4 + 1}) \cdot \frac{4x^2 + \sqrt{16x^4 + 1}}{4x^2 + \sqrt{16x^4 + 1}} = -\frac{16x^2}{4x^2 + \sqrt{16x^4 + 1}}.$$

We have $\lim\limits_{x \to \infty} -\dfrac{16x^2}{4x^2 + \sqrt{16x^4 + 1}} \cdot \dfrac{(1/x^2)}{(1/x^2)} = \lim\limits_{x \to \infty} -\dfrac{16}{4 + \sqrt{16 + 1/x^4}} = -2$. Similarly, the limit as $x \to -\infty$ of $f(x)$ is -2 as well. so $y = -2$ is a horizontal asymptote.

b. f has no vertical asymptotes.

2.5.57

a. $\lim\limits_{x \to \infty} \dfrac{x^2 - 9}{x^2 - 3x} \cdot \dfrac{(1/x^2)}{(1/x^2)} = \lim\limits_{x \to \infty} \dfrac{1 - 9/x^2}{1 - 3/x} = 1$. A similar result holds as $x \to -\infty$. So $y = 1$ is a horizontal asymptote.

b. Because $\displaystyle\lim_{x\to 0^+} f(x) = \lim_{x\to 0^+} \frac{x+3}{x} = \infty$ and $\displaystyle\lim_{x\to 0^-} f(x) = -\infty$, there is a vertical asymptote at $x = 0$.

2.5.58

a. $\displaystyle\lim_{x\to\infty} \frac{x-1}{x^{2/3}-1} \cdot \frac{1/x^{2/3}}{1/x^{2/3}} = \lim_{x\to\infty} \frac{x^{1/3}-1/x^{2/3}}{1-1/x^{2/3}} = \infty$. Similarly, $\displaystyle\lim_{x\to-\infty} f(x) = -\infty$. So there are no horizontal asymptotes.

b. There is a vertical asymptote at $x = -1$. The easiest way to see this is to factor the denominator as the difference of squares, and the numerator as the difference of cubes. We have

$$f(x) = \frac{x-1}{x^{2/3}-1} = \frac{(x^{1/3}-1)(x^{2/3}+x^{1/3}+1)}{(x^{1/3}+1)(x^{1/3}-1)}.$$

Thus,

$$\lim_{x\to-1^+} f(x) = \lim_{x\to-1^+} \frac{x^{2/3}+x^{1/3}+1}{x^{1/3}+1} = \infty.$$

Similarly, $\displaystyle\lim_{x\to-1^-} f(x) = -\infty$.

2.5.59

a. First note that $f(x) = \frac{\sqrt{x^2+2x+6}-3}{x-1} \cdot \frac{\sqrt{x^2+2x+6}+3}{\sqrt{x^2+2x+6}+3} = \frac{x^2+2x+6-9}{(x-1)(\sqrt{x^2+2x+6}+3)} = \frac{(x-1)(x+3)}{(x-1)(\sqrt{x^2+2x+6}+3)}$.
Thus

$$\lim_{x\to\infty} f(x) = \lim_{x\to\infty} \frac{x+3}{\sqrt{x^2+2x+6}+3} \cdot \frac{1/x}{1/x} = \lim_{x\to\infty} \frac{1+3/x}{\sqrt{1+2/x+6/x^2}+3/x} = 1.$$

Using the fact that $\sqrt{x^2} = -x$ for $x < 0$, we have $\displaystyle\lim_{x\to-\infty} f(x) = -1$. Thus the lines $y = 1$ and $y = -1$ are horizontal asymptotes.

b. f has no vertical asymptotes.

2.5.60

a. Note that when x is large $|1-x^2| = x^2 - 1$. We have $\displaystyle\lim_{x\to\infty} \frac{|1-x^2|}{x^2+x} = \lim_{x\to\infty} \frac{x^2-1}{x^2+x} = 1$. Likewise $\displaystyle\lim_{x\to-\infty} \frac{|1-x^2|}{x^2+x} = \lim_{x\to-\infty} \frac{x^2-1}{x^2+x} = 1$. So there is a horizontal asymptote at $y = 1$.

b. Note that when x is near 0, we have $|1-x^2| = 1-x^2 = (1-x)(1+x)$. So $\displaystyle\lim_{x\to 0^+} f(x) = \lim_{x\to 0^+} \frac{1-x}{x} = \infty$.
Similarly, $\displaystyle\lim_{x\to 0^-} f(x) = -\infty$. There is a vertical asymptote at $x = 0$.

2.5.61

a. Note that when $x > 1$, we have $|x| = x$ and $|x-1| = x-1$. Thus

$$f(x) = (\sqrt{x} - \sqrt{x-1}) \cdot \frac{\sqrt{x}+\sqrt{x-1}}{\sqrt{x}+\sqrt{x-1}} = \frac{1}{\sqrt{x}+\sqrt{x-1}}.$$

Thus $\displaystyle\lim_{x\to\infty} f(x) = 0$.

When $x < 0$, we have $|x| = -x$ and $|x-1| = 1-x$. Thus

$$f(x) = (\sqrt{-x} - \sqrt{1-x}) \cdot \frac{\sqrt{-x}+\sqrt{1-x}}{\sqrt{-x}+\sqrt{1-x}} = -\frac{1}{\sqrt{-x}+\sqrt{1-x}}.$$

Thus, $\displaystyle\lim_{x\to-\infty} f(x) = 0$. There is a horizontal asymptote at $y = 0$.

b. f has no vertical asymptotes.

2.5.62

a. $\displaystyle\lim_{x\to \pi/2^-} \tan x = \infty$ and $\displaystyle\lim_{x\to \pi/2^+} \tan x = -\infty$. These are infinite limits.

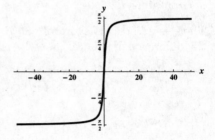

b. $\displaystyle\lim_{x\to\infty} \tan^{-1}(x) = \pi/2$ and $\displaystyle\lim_{x\to-\infty} \tan^{-1}(x) = -\pi/2$.

2.5.63

a. $\displaystyle\lim_{x\to\infty} \sec^{-1} x = \pi/2$.

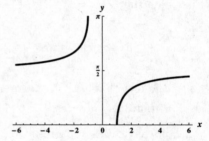

b. $\displaystyle\lim_{x\to-\infty} \sec^{-1} x = \pi/2$.

2.5.64

a. $\displaystyle\lim_{x\to\infty} \frac{e^x + e^{-x}}{2} = \infty$.

$\displaystyle\lim_{x\to-\infty} \frac{e^x + e^{-x}}{2} = \infty$.

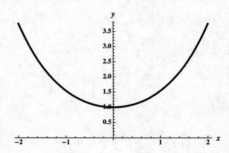

b. $\cosh(0) = \frac{e^0 + e^0}{2} = \frac{1+1}{2} = 1$.

2.5.65

a. $\displaystyle\lim_{x\to\infty} \frac{e^x - e^{-x}}{2} = \infty$.

$\displaystyle\lim_{x\to-\infty} \frac{e^x - e^{-x}}{2} = -\infty$.

b. $\sinh(0) = \frac{e^0 - e^0}{2} = \frac{1-1}{2} = 0$.

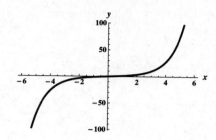

2.5.66

One possible such graph is:

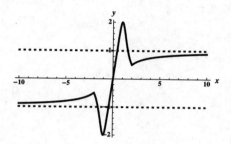

2.5.67

One possible such graph is:

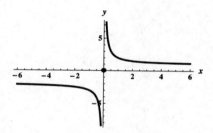

2.5.68 $\displaystyle\lim_{x\to 0^+} e^{1/x} = \infty.$ $\displaystyle\lim_{x\to\infty} e^{1/x} = 1.$ $\displaystyle\lim_{x\to -\infty} e^{1/x} = 1.$
There is a vertical asymptote at $x = 0$ and a horizontal asymptote at $y = 1$.

2.5.69 $\displaystyle\lim_{x\to 0^+} \frac{\cos x + 2\sqrt{x}}{\sqrt{x}} = \infty.$ $\displaystyle\lim_{x\to\infty} \frac{\cos x + 2\sqrt{x}}{\sqrt{x}} = \lim_{x\to\infty}\left(2 + \frac{\cos x}{\sqrt{x}}\right) = 2.$
There is a vertical asymptote at $x = 0$ and a horizontal asymptote at $y = 2$.

2.5.70 $\displaystyle\lim_{t\to\infty} p(t) = \lim_{t\to\infty}\frac{2500}{t+1} = 0.$ The steady state exists. The steady state value is 0.

2.5.71 $\displaystyle\lim_{t\to\infty} p(t) = \lim_{t\to\infty}\frac{3500t}{t+1} = 3500.$ The steady state exists. The steady state value is 3500.

2.5.72 $\displaystyle\lim_{t\to\infty} m(t) = \lim_{t\to\infty} 200(1 - 2^{-t}) = 200.$ The steady state exists. The steady state value is 200.

2.5.73 $\displaystyle\lim_{t\to\infty} v(t) = \lim_{t\to\infty} 1000e^{0.065t} = \infty.$ The steady state does not exist.

2.5.74 $\displaystyle\lim_{t\to\infty} p(t) = \lim_{t\to\infty}\frac{1500}{3 + 2e^{-.1t}} = \frac{1500}{3} = 500.$ The steady state exists. The steady state value is 500.

2.5.75 $\lim\limits_{t\to\infty} a(t) = \lim\limits_{t\to\infty} 2\left(\dfrac{t+\sin t}{t}\right) = \lim\limits_{t\to\infty} 2\left(1+\dfrac{\sin t}{t}\right) = 2$. The steady state exists. The steady state value is 2.

2.5.76 $\lim\limits_{n\to\infty} f(n) = \lim\limits_{n\to\infty} \dfrac{4}{n} = 0$.

2.5.77 $\lim\limits_{n\to\infty} f(n) = \lim\limits_{n\to\infty} \dfrac{n-1}{n} = \lim\limits_{n\to\infty} [1 - (1/n)] = 1$.

2.5.78 $\lim\limits_{n\to\infty} f(n) = \lim\limits_{n\to\infty} \dfrac{n^2}{n+1} = \lim\limits_{n\to\infty} \dfrac{n}{1 + 1/n} = \infty$, so the limit does not exist.

2.5.79 $\lim\limits_{n\to\infty} f(n) = \lim\limits_{n\to\infty} \dfrac{n+1}{n^2} = \lim\limits_{n\to\infty} [1/n + 1/n^2] = 0$.

2.5.80

   a. Suppose $m = n$.

$$\lim_{x\to\pm\infty} f(x) = \lim_{x\to\pm\infty} \frac{p(x)}{q(x)} \cdot \frac{1/x^n}{1/x^n}$$
$$= \lim_{x\to\pm\infty} \frac{a_n + a_{n-1}/x + \cdots + a_1/x^{n-1} + a_0/x^n}{b_n + b_{n-1}/x + \cdots + b_1/x^{n-1} + b_0/x^n}$$
$$= \frac{a_n}{b_n}.$$

   b. Suppose $m < n$.

$$\lim_{x\to\pm\infty} f(x) = \lim_{x\to\pm\infty} \frac{p(x)}{q(x)} \cdot \frac{1/x^n}{1/x^n}$$
$$= \lim_{x\to\pm\infty} \frac{a_n/x^{n-m} + a_{n-1}/x^{n-m+1} + \cdots + a_1/x^{n-1} + a_0/x^n}{b_n + b_{n-1}/x + \cdots + b_1/x^{n-1} + b_0/x^n}$$
$$= \frac{0}{b_n} = 0.$$

2.5.81 No. If $m = n$, there will be a horizontal asymptote, and if $m = n + 1$, there will be an oblique asymptote.

2.5.82

   a. $\lim\limits_{x\to\infty} \dfrac{e^x + e^{2x}}{e^{2x} + e^{3x}} = \lim\limits_{x\to\infty} \dfrac{e^x + e^{2x}}{e^{2x} + e^{3x}} \cdot \dfrac{1/e^{3x}}{1/e^{3x}} = \lim\limits_{x\to\infty} \dfrac{(1/e^{2x}) + (1/e^x)}{(1/e^x) + 1} = \dfrac{0+0}{0+1} = 0$.

   b. $\lim\limits_{x\to-\infty} \dfrac{e^x + e^{2x}}{e^{2x} + e^{3x}} = \lim\limits_{x\to-\infty} \dfrac{e^x + e^{2x}}{e^{2x} + e^{3x}} \cdot \dfrac{1/e^{2x}}{1/e^{2x}} = \lim\limits_{x\to-\infty} \dfrac{e^{-x} + 1}{1 + e^x} = \infty$.

   c. The line $y = 0$ is a horizontal asympotote.

   d.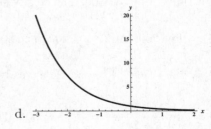

2.5.83 $\lim\limits_{x\to\infty} \dfrac{2e^x + 3e^{2x}}{e^{2x} + e^{3x}} = \lim\limits_{x\to\infty} \dfrac{2e^x + 3e^{2x}}{e^{2x} + e^{3x}} \cdot \dfrac{1/e^{3x}}{1/e^{3x}} = \lim\limits_{x\to\infty} \dfrac{2/e^x + 3/e^x}{1/e^x + 1} = \dfrac{0+0}{0+1} = 0.$ Thus the line $y = 0$ is a horizontal asymptote.

$$\lim_{x\to-\infty} \dfrac{2e^x + 3e^{2x}}{e^{2x} + e^{3x}} = \lim_{x\to-\infty} \dfrac{2e^x + 3e^{2x}}{e^{2x} + e^{3x}} \cdot \dfrac{1/e^{2x}}{1/e^{2x}} = \lim_{x\to-\infty} \dfrac{2e^{-x} + 3}{1 + e^x} = \infty.$$

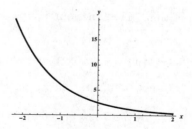

2.5.84 $\lim\limits_{x\to\infty} \dfrac{3e^x + e^{-x}}{e^x + e^{-x}} = \lim\limits_{x\to\infty} \dfrac{3e^x + e^{-x}}{e^x + e^{-x}} \cdot \dfrac{1/e^x}{1/e^x} = \lim\limits_{x\to\infty} \dfrac{3 + e^{-2x}}{1 + e^{-2x}} = \dfrac{3+0}{1+0} = 3.$ Thus the line $y = 3$ is a horizontal asymptote.

$\lim\limits_{x\to-\infty} \dfrac{3e^x + e^{-x}}{e^x + e^{-x}} = \lim\limits_{x\to-\infty} \dfrac{3e^x + e^{-x}}{e^x + e^{-x}} \cdot \dfrac{e^x}{e^x} = \lim\limits_{x\to-\infty} \dfrac{3e^{2x} + 1}{e^{2x} + 1} = \dfrac{0+1}{0+1} = 1.$ Thus the line $y = 1$ is a horizontal asymptote.

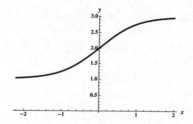

2.5.85 The numerator of f is defined for $-3 < x < 3$. The denominator is defined everywhere, but is zero when $2e^x = e^{-x}$. Simplifying gives $2e^{2x} = 1$, or $e^{2x} = 1/2$. This has the solution $x = (-\ln 2)/2 \approx -0.347$, which lies in the domain of the numerator. So the domain of f is $\{x : -3 < x < 3, x \neq (-\ln 2)/2\}$, and any questions about horizontal asymptotes are moot. As $x \to 3^-$ or as $x \to -3^+$, the numerator approaches $-\infty$, which follows because $\lim_{t\to 0^+} \ln t = -\infty$, and the denominator is approaching a positive constant as $x \to 3^-$ and a negative constant as $x \to -3^+$. Thus $\lim_{x\to 3^-} f(x) = -\infty$ and $\lim_{x\to -3^+} f(x) = \infty$, and there are vertical asymptotes at $x = 3$ and $x = -3$.

As $x \to -(\ln 2)/2$, the numerator is nonzero because $9 - x^2$ is not approaching 1. Thus, there is a vertical asymptote at $x = -(\ln 2)/2$. A graph of the function, with the vertical asymptotes shown in gray, verifies this analysis. Note that the vertical asymptotes at ± 3 require a different viewing window.

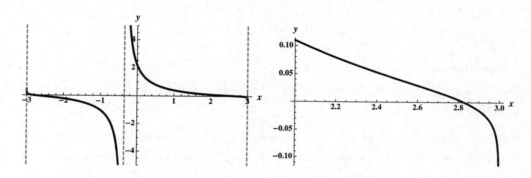

2.6   Continuity

2.6.1

a. $a(t)$ is a continuous function during the time period from when she jumps from the plane and when she touches down on the ground, because her position is changing continuously with time.

b. $n(t)$ is not a continuous function of time. The function "jumps" at the times when a quarter must be added.

c. $T(t)$ is a continuous function, because temperature varies continuously with time.

d. $p(t)$ is not continuous – it jumps by whole numbers when a player scores a point.

2.6.2 In order for f to be continuous at $x = a$, the following conditions must hold:

- f must be defined at a (i.e. a must be in the domain of f),

- $\lim\limits_{x \to a} f(x)$ must exist, and

- $\lim\limits_{x \to a} f(x)$ must equal $f(a)$.

2.6.3 A function f is continuous on an interval I if it is continuous at all points in the interior of I, and it must be continuous from the right at the left endpoint (if the left endpoint is included in I) and it must be continuous from the left at the right endpoint (if the right endpoint is included in I.)

2.6.4 The words "hole" and "break" are not mathematically precise, so a strict mathematical definition can not be based on them.

2.6.5

a. A function f is continuous from the left at $x = a$ if a is in the domain of f, and $\lim\limits_{x \to a^-} f(x) = f(a)$.

b. A function f is continuous from the right at $x = a$ if a is in the domain of f, and $\lim\limits_{x \to a^+} f(x) = f(a)$.

2.6.6 A rational function is discontinuous at each point not in its domain.

2.6.7 The domain of $f(x) = \frac{e^x}{x}$ is $(-\infty, 0) \cup (0, \infty)$, and f is continuous everywhere on this domain.

2.6.8 The Intermediate Value Theorem says that if f is continuous on $[a, b]$ and if L is strictly between $f(a)$ and $f(b)$, then there must be a domain value c (with $a < c < b$) where $f(c) = L$. This means that a continuous function assumes all the intermediate values between the values at the endpoints of an interval.

2.6.9 f is discontinuous at $x = 1$, at $x = 2$, and at $x = 3$. At $x = 1$, $f(1)$ does not exist (so the first condition is violated). At $x = 2$, $f(2)$ exists and $\lim\limits_{x \to 2} f(x)$ exists, but $\lim\limits_{x \to 2} f(x) \neq f(2)$ (so condition 3 is violated). At $x = 3$, $\lim\limits_{x \to 3} f(x)$ does not exist (so condition 2 is violated).

2.6.10 f is discontinuous at $x = 1$, at $x = 2$, and at $x = 3$. At $x = 1$, $\lim\limits_{x \to 1} f(x) \neq f(1)$ (so condition 3 is violated). At $x = 2$, $\lim\limits_{x \to 2} f(x)$ does not exist (so condition 2 is violated). At $x = 3$, $f(3)$ does not exist (so condition 1 is violated).

2.6.11 f is discontinuous at $x = 1$, at $x = 2$, and at $x = 3$. At $x = 1$, $\lim\limits_{x \to 1} f(x)$ does not exist, and $f(1)$ does not exist (so conditions 1 and 2 are violated). At $x = 2$, $\lim\limits_{x \to 2} f(x)$ does not exist (so condition 2 is violated). At $x = 3$, $f(3)$ does not exist (so condition 1 is violated).

2.6.12 f is discontinuous at $x = 2$, at $x = 3$, and at $x = 4$. At $x = 2$, $\lim\limits_{x \to 2} f(x)$ does not exist (so condition 2 is violated). At $x = 3$, $f(3)$ does not exist and $\lim\limits_{x \to 3} f(x)$ does not exist (so conditions 1 and 2 are violated). At $x = 4$, $\lim\limits_{x \to 4} f(x) \neq f(4)$ (so condition 3 is violated).

2.6.13 The function is defined at 5, in fact $f(5) = \frac{50+15+1}{25+25} = \frac{66}{50} = \frac{33}{25}$. Also, $\lim\limits_{x \to 5} f(x) = \lim\limits_{x \to 5} \frac{2x^2 + 3x + 1}{x^2 + 5x} = \frac{33}{25} = f(5)$. The function is continuous at $a = 5$.

2.6.14 The number -5 is not in the domain of f, because the denominator is equal to 0 when $x = -5$. Thus, the function is not continuous at -5.

2.6.15 f is discontinuous at 1, because 1 is not in the domain of f.

2.6.16 g is discontinuous at 3 because 3 is not in the domain of g.

2.6.17 f is discontinuous at 1, because $\lim\limits_{x \to 1} f(x) \neq f(1)$. In fact, $f(1) = 3$, but $\lim\limits_{x \to 1} f(x) = 2$.

2.6.18 f is continuous at 3, because $\lim\limits_{x \to 3} f(x) = f(3)$. In fact, $f(3) = 2$ and $\lim\limits_{x \to 3} f(x) = \lim\limits_{x \to 3} \frac{(x-3)(x-1)}{x-3} = \lim\limits_{x \to 3}(x-1) = 2$.

2.6.19 f is discontinuous at 4, because 4 is not in the domain of f.

2.6.20 f is discontinuous at -1 because $\lim\limits_{x \to -1} f(x) = \lim\limits_{x \to -1} \frac{x(x+1)}{x+1} = \lim\limits_{x \to -1} x = -1 \neq f(-1) = 2$.

2.6.21 Because f is a polynomial, it is continuous on all of $\mathbb{R}$.

2.6.22 Because g is a rational function, it is continuous on its domain, which is all of $\mathbb{R}$. (Because $x^2 + x + 1$ has no real roots.)

2.6.23 Because f is a rational function, it is continuous on its domain. Its domain is $(-\infty, -3) \cup (-3, 3) \cup (3, \infty)$.

2.6.24 Because s is a rational function, it is continuous on its domain. Its domain is $(-\infty, -1) \cup (-1, 1) \cup (1, \infty)$.

2.6.25 Because f is a rational function, it is continuous on its domain. Its domain is $(-\infty, -2) \cup (-2, 2) \cup (2, \infty)$.

2.6.26 Because f is a rational function, it is continuous on its domain. Its domain is $(-\infty, -2) \cup (-2, 2) \cup (2, \infty)$.

2.6.27 Because $f(x) = \left(x^8 - 3x^6 - 1\right)^{40}$ is a polynomial, it is continuous everywhere, including at 0. Thus $\lim\limits_{x \to 0} f(x) = f(0) = (-1)^{40} = 1$.

2.6.28 Because $f(x) = \left(\frac{3}{2x^5 - 4x^2 - 50}\right)^4$ is a rational function, it is continuous at all points in its domain, including at $x = 2$. So $\lim\limits_{x \to 2} f(x) = f(2) = \frac{81}{16}$.

2.6.29 Because $f(x) = \left(\frac{x+5}{x+2}\right)^4$ is a rational function, it is continuous at all points in its domain, including at $x = 1$. Thus $\lim\limits_{x \to 1} f(x) = f(1) = 16$.

2.6.30 $\displaystyle\lim_{x\to\infty}\left(\frac{2x+1}{x}\right)^3 = \lim_{x\to\infty}(2+(1/x))^3 = 2^3 = 8.$

2.6.31 Because $x^3 - 2x^2 - 8x = x(x^2 - 2x - 8) = x(x-4)(x+2)$, we have (as long as $x \neq 4$)

$$\sqrt{\frac{x^3 - 2x^2 - 8x}{x - 4}} = \sqrt{x(x+2)}.$$

Thus, $\displaystyle\lim_{x\to 4}\sqrt{\frac{x^3 - 2x^2 - 8x}{x-4}} = \lim_{x\to 4}\sqrt{x(x+2)} = \sqrt{24}$, using Theorem 2.12 and the fact that the square root is a continuous function.

2.6.32 Note that $t - 4 = (\sqrt{t} - 2)(\sqrt{t} + 2)$, so for $t \neq 4$, we have

$$\frac{t-4}{\sqrt{t}-2} = \sqrt{t} + 2.$$

Thus, $\displaystyle\lim_{t\to 4}\frac{t-4}{\sqrt{t}-2} = \lim_{t\to 4}(\sqrt{t}+2) = 4.$ Then using Theorem 2.12 and the fact that the tangent function is continuous at 4, we have $\displaystyle\lim_{t\to 4}\tan\left(\frac{t-4}{\sqrt{t}-2}\right) = \tan\left(\lim_{t\to 4}\frac{t-4}{\sqrt{t}-2}\right) = \tan 4.$

2.6.33 Recall that $\displaystyle\lim_{x\to 0}\frac{\sin x}{x} = 1$. Now noting that the function $f(x) = \ln 2x$ is continuous at 1, we have by Theorem 2.12 that $\displaystyle\lim_{x\to 0}\ln\left(\frac{2\sin x}{x}\right) = \ln\left(2\left(\lim_{x\to 0}\frac{\sin x}{x}\right)\right) = \ln(2\cdot 1) = \ln 2.$

2.6.34 First note that

$$\lim_{x\to 0}\frac{x}{\sqrt{16x+1}-1} = \lim_{x\to 0}\frac{x}{(\sqrt{16x+1}-1)}\cdot\frac{(\sqrt{16x+1}+1)}{(\sqrt{16x+1}+1)} = \lim_{x\to 0}\frac{x(\sqrt{16x+1}+1)}{16x} = \frac{2}{16} = \frac{1}{8}.$$

Then because $f(x) = x^{1/3}$ is continuous at $1/8$, we have $\displaystyle\lim_{x\to 0}\left(\frac{x}{\sqrt{16x+1}-1}\right)^{1/3} = \left(\frac{1}{8}\right)^{1/3} = \frac{1}{2}$, by Theorem 2.12.

2.6.35 f is continuous on $[0,1)$, on $(1,2)$, on $(2,3]$, and on $(3,4]$.

2.6.36 f is continuous on $[0,1)$, on $(1,2]$, on $(2,3)$, and on $(3,4]$.

2.6.37 f is continuous on $[0,1)$, on $(1,2)$, on $[2,3)$, and on $(3,5]$.

2.6.38 f is continuous on $[0,2]$, on $(2,3)$, on $(3,4)$, and on $(4,5]$.

2.6.39

    a. f is defined at 1. We have $f(1) = 1^2 + (3)(1) = 4$. To see whether or not $\displaystyle\lim_{x\to 1}f(x)$ exists, we investigate the two one-sided limits. $\displaystyle\lim_{x\to 1^-}f(x) = \lim_{x\to 1^-}2x = 2$, and $\displaystyle\lim_{x\to 1^+}f(x) = \lim_{x\to 1^+}(x^2+3x) = 4$, so $\displaystyle\lim_{x\to 1}f(x)$ does not exist. Thus f is discontinuous at $x = 1$.

    b. f is continuous from the right, because $\displaystyle\lim_{x\to 1^+}f(x) = 4 = f(1)$.

    c. f is continuous on $(-\infty, 1)$ and on $[1, \infty)$.

2.6.40

    a. f is defined at 0, in fact $f(0) = 1$. However, $\lim_{x\to 0^-}f(x) = \lim_{x\to 0^-}(x^3 + 4x + 1) = 1$, while $\lim_{x\to 0^+}f(x) = \lim_{x\to 0^+}2x^3 = 0$. So $\lim_{x\to 0}f(x)$ does not exist.

b. f is continuous from the left at 0, because $\lim_{x \to 0^-} f(x) = f(0) = 1$.

c. f is continuous on $(-\infty, 0]$ and on $(0, \infty)$.

2.6.41 f is continuous on $(-\infty, -\sqrt{8}]$ and on $[\sqrt{8}, \infty)$.

2.6.42 g is continuous on $(-\infty, -1]$ and on $[1, \infty)$.

2.6.43 Because f is the composition of two functions which are continuous everywhere, it is continuous everywhere.

2.6.44 f is continuous on $(-\infty, -1]$ and on $[1, \infty)$.

2.6.45 Because f is the composition of two functions which are continuous everywhere, it is continuous everywhere.

2.6.46 f is continuous on $[1, \infty)$.

2.6.47 $\lim_{x \to 2} \sqrt{\dfrac{4x + 10}{2x - 2}} = \sqrt{\dfrac{18}{2}} = 3$.

2.6.48 $\lim_{x \to -1} \left(x^2 - 4 + \sqrt[3]{x^2 - 9} \right) = (-1)^2 - 4 + \sqrt[3]{(-1)^2 - 9} = -3 + \sqrt[3]{-8} = -3 + -2 = -5$.

2.6.49 $\lim_{x \to 3} \sqrt{x^2 + 7} = \sqrt{9 + 7} = 4$.

2.6.50 $\lim_{t \to 2} \dfrac{t^2 + 5}{1 + \sqrt{t^2 + 5}} = \dfrac{9}{1 + \sqrt{9}} = \dfrac{9}{4}$.

2.6.51 $f(x) = \csc x$ isn't defined at $x = k\pi$ where k is an integer, so it isn't continuous at those points. So it is continuous on intervals of the form $(k\pi, (k+1)\pi)$ where k is an integer. $\lim_{x \to \pi/4} \csc x = \sqrt{2}$. $\lim_{x \to 2\pi^-} \csc x = -\infty$.

2.6.52 f is defined on $[0, \infty)$, and it is continuous there, because it is the composition of continuous functions defined on that interval.
$\lim_{x \to 4} f(x) = e^2$. $\lim_{x \to 0} f(x)$ does not exist—but $\lim_{x \to 0^+} f(x) = e^0 = 1$, because f is continuous from the right.

2.6.53 f isn't defined for any number of the form $\pi/2 + k\pi$ where k is an integer, so it isn't continuous there. It is continuous on intervals of the form $(\pi/2 + k\pi, \pi/2 + (k+1)\pi)$, where k is an integer.
$\lim_{x \to \pi/2^-} f(x) = \infty$. $\lim_{x \to 4\pi/3} f(x) = \dfrac{1 - \sqrt{3}/2}{-1/2} = \sqrt{3} - 2$.

2.6.54 The domain of f is $(0, 1]$, and f is continuous on this interval because it is the quotient of two continuous functions and the function in the denominator isn't zero on that interval.
$\lim_{x \to 1^-} f(x) = \lim_{x \to 1^-} \dfrac{\ln x}{\sin^{-1}(x)} = \dfrac{\ln 1}{\sin^{-1}(1)} = \dfrac{0}{\pi/2} = 0$.

2.6.55 This function is continuous on its domain, which is $(-\infty, 0) \cup (0, \infty)$.
$\lim_{x \to 0^-} f(x) = \lim_{x \to 0^-} \dfrac{e^x}{1 - e^x} = \infty$, while $\lim_{x \to 0^+} f(x) = \lim_{x \to 0^+} \dfrac{e^x}{1 - e^x} = -\infty$.

2.6.56 This function is continuous on its domain, which is $(-\infty, 0) \cup (0, \infty)$.
$\lim_{x \to 0} f(x) = \lim_{x \to 0} \dfrac{e^{2x} - 1}{e^x - 1} = \lim_{x \to 0} \dfrac{(e^x + 1)(e^x - 1)}{e^x - 1} = \lim_{x \to 0} (e^x + 1) = 2$.

2.6.57

a. Because A is a continuous function of r on $[0, .08]$, and because $A(0) = 5000$ and $A(.08) \approx 11098.2$, (and 7000 is an intermediate value between these two numbers) the Intermediate Value Theorem guarantees a value of r between 0 and .08 where $A(r) = 7000$.

b. Solving $5000(1 + (r/12))^{120} = 7000$ for r, we see that $(1 + (r/12))^{120} = 7/5$, so $1 + r/12 = \sqrt[120]{7/5}$, so $r = 12(\sqrt[120]{7/5} - 1) \approx 0.034$.

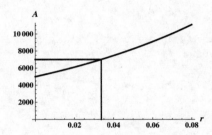

2.6.58

a. Because m is a continuous function of r on $[.06, .08]$, and because $m(.06) \approx 899.33$ and $m(.08) \approx 1100.65$, (and 1000 is an intermediate value between these two numbers) the Intermediate Value Theorem guarantees a value of r between .06 and .08 where $m(r) = 1000$.

b. Using a computer algebra system, we see that the required interest rate is about .0702.

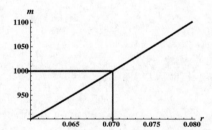

2.6.59

a. Note that $f(x) = 2x^3 + x - 2$ is continuous everywhere, so in particular it is continuous on $[-1, 1]$. Note that $f(-1) = -5 < 0$ and $f(1) = 1 > 0$. Because 0 is an intermediate value between $f(-1)$ and $f(1)$, the Intermediate Value Theorem guarantees a number c between -1 and 1 where $f(c) = 0$.

b. Using a graphing calculator and a computer algebra system, we see that the root of f is about 0.835.

c.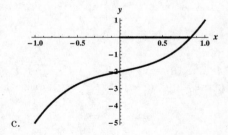

2.6.60

a. Note that $f(x) = \sqrt{x^4 + 25x^3 + 10} - 5$ is continuous on its domain, so in particular it is continuous on $[0, 1]$. Note that $f(0) = \sqrt{10} - 5 < 0$ and $f(1) = 6 - 5 = 1 > 0$. Because 0 is an intermediate value between $f(0)$ and $f(1)$, the Intermediate Value Theorem guarantees a number c between 0 and 1 where $f(c) = 0$.

b. Using a graphing calculator and a computer algebra system, we see the root of $f(x)$ is at about .834.

c.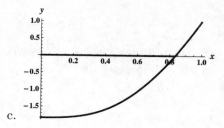

2.6.61

a. Note that $f(x) = x^3 - 5x^2 + 2x$ is continuous everywhere, so in particular it is continuous on $[-1, 5]$. Note that $f(-1) = -8 < -1$ and $f(5) = 10 > -1$. Because -1 is an intermediate value between $f(-1)$ and $f(5)$, the Intermediate Value Theorem guarantees a number c between -1 and 5 where $f(c) = -1$.

b. Using a graphing calculator and a computer algebra system, we see that there are actually three different values of c between -1 and 5 for which $f(c) = -1$. They are $c \approx -0.285$, $c \approx 0.778$, and $c \approx 4.507$.

c.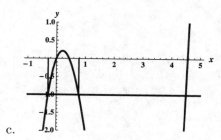

2.6.62

a. Note that $f(x) = -x^5 - 4x^2 + 2\sqrt{x} + 5$ is continuous on its domain, so in particular it is continuous on $[0, 3]$. Note that $f(0) = 5 > 0$ and $f(3) \approx -270.5 < 0$. Because 0 is an intermediate value between $f(0)$ and $f(3)$, the Intermediate Value Theorem guarantees a number c between 0 and 3 where $f(c) = 0$.

b. Using a graphing calculator and a computer algebra system, we see that the value of c guaranteed by the theorem is about 1.141.

c.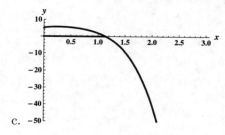

2.6.63

a. Note that $f(x) = e^x + x$ is continuous on its domain, so in particular it is continuous on $[-1, 0]$. Note that $f(-1) = \frac{1}{e} - 1 < 0$ and $f(0) = 1 > 0$. Because 0 is an intermediate value between $f(-1)$ and $f(0)$, the Intermediate Value Theorem guarantees a number c between -1 and 0 where $f(c) = 0$.

b. Using a graphing calculator and a computer algebra system, we see that the value of c guaranteed by the theorem is about -0.567.

c.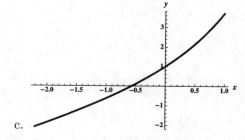

2.6.64

a. Note that $f(x) = x \ln x - 1$ is continuous on its domain, so in particular it is continuous on $[1, e]$. Note that $f(1) = \ln 1 - 1 = -1 < 0$ and $f(e) = e - 1 > 0$. Because 0 is an intermediate value between $f(1)$ and $f(e)$, the Intermediate Value Theorem guarantees a number c between 1 and e where $f(c) = 0$.

b. Using a graphing calculator and a computer algebra system, we see that the value of c guaranteed by the theorem is about 1.76322.

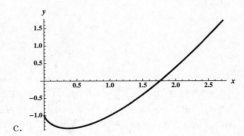

c.

2.6.65

a. True. If f is right continuous at a, then $f(a)$ exists and the limit from the right at a exists and is equal to $f(a)$. Because it is left continuous, the limit from the left exists — so we now know that the limit as $x \to a$ of $f(x)$ exists, because the two one-sided limits are both equal to $f(a)$.

b. True. If $\lim_{x \to a} f(x) = f(a)$, then $\lim_{x \to a^+} f(x) = f(a)$ and $\lim_{x \to a^-} f(x) = f(a)$.

c. False. The statement would be true if f were continuous. However, if f isn't continuous, then the statement doesn't hold. For example, suppose that $f(x) = \begin{cases} 0 & \text{if } 0 \leq x < 1; \\ 1 & \text{if } 1 \leq x \leq 2, \end{cases}$ Note that $f(0) = 0$ and $f(2) = 1$, but there is no number c between 0 and 2 where $f(c) = 1/2$.

d. False. Consider $f(x) = x^2$ and $a = -1$ and $b = 1$. Then f is continuous on $[a, b]$, but $\frac{f(1) + f(-1)}{2} = 1$, and there is no c on (a, b) with $f(c) = 1$.

2.6.66 Let $f(x) = |x|$.

For values of a other than 0, it is clear that $\lim_{x \to a} |x| = |a|$ because f is defined to be either the polynomial x (for values greater than 0) or the polynomial $-x$ (for values less than 0.) For the value of $a = 0$, we have $\lim_{x \to 0^+} f(x) = \lim_{x \to 0^+} x = 0 = f(0)$. Also, $\lim_{x \to 0^-} f(x) = \lim_{x \to 0^-} (-x) = -0 = 0$. Thus $\lim_{x \to 0} f(x) = f(0)$, so f is continuous at 0.

2.6.67 Because $f(x) = x^3 + 3x - 18$ is a polynomial, it is continuous on $(-\infty, \infty)$, and because the absolute value function is continuous everywhere, $|f(x)|$ is continuous everywhere.

2.6.68 Let $f(x) = \frac{x+4}{x^2-4}$. Then f is continuous on $(-\infty, -2) \cup (-2, 2) \cup (2, \infty)$. So $g(x) = |f(x)|$ is also continuous on this set.

2.6.69 Let $f(x) = \frac{1}{\sqrt{x}-4}$. Then f is continuous on $[0, 16) \cup (16, \infty)$. So $h(x) = |f(x)|$ is continuous on this set as well.

2.6.70 Because $x^2 + 2x + 5$ is a polynomial, it is continuous everywhere, as is $|x^2 + 2x + 5|$. So $h(x) = |x^2 + 2x + 5| + \sqrt{x}$ is continuous on its domain, namely $[0, \infty)$.

2.6.71 $\lim_{x \to \pi} \frac{\cos^2 x + 3\cos x + 2}{\cos x + 1} = \lim_{x \to \pi} \frac{(\cos x + 1)(\cos x + 2)}{\cos x + 1} = \lim_{x \to \pi} (\cos x + 2) = 1.$

2.6.72 $\lim_{x \to 3\pi/2} \frac{\sin^2 x + 6\sin x + 5}{\sin^2 x - 1} = \lim_{x \to 3\pi/2} \frac{(\sin x + 5)(\sin x + 1)}{(\sin x - 1)(\sin x + 1)} = \lim_{x \to 3\pi/2} \frac{\sin x + 5}{\sin x - 1} = \frac{4}{-2} = -2.$

2.6.73 $\displaystyle\lim_{x\to\pi/2}\frac{\sin x-1}{\sqrt{\sin x}-1}=\lim_{x\to\pi/2}(\sqrt{\sin x}+1)=2.$

2.6.74 $\displaystyle\lim_{\theta\to0}\frac{\frac{1}{2+\sin\theta}-\frac12}{\sin\theta}\cdot\frac{(2)(2+\sin\theta)}{(2)(2+\sin\theta)}=\lim_{\theta\to0}\frac{2-(2+\sin\theta)}{(\sin\theta)(2)(2+\sin\theta)}=\lim_{\theta\to0}-\frac{1}{2(2+\sin\theta)}=-\frac14.$

2.6.75 $\displaystyle\lim_{x\to0}\frac{\cos x-1}{\sin^2 x}=\lim_{x\to0}\frac{\cos x-1}{1-\cos^2 x}=\lim_{x\to0}\frac{\cos x-1}{(1-\cos x)(1+\cos x)}=\lim_{x\to0}-\frac{1}{1+\cos x}=-\frac12.$

2.6.76 $\displaystyle\lim_{x\to0^+}\frac{1-\cos^2 x}{\sin x}=\lim_{x\to0^+}\frac{\sin^2 x}{\sin x}=\lim_{x\to0^+}\sin x=0.$

2.6.77 Recall that $-\pi/2\le\tan^{-1}x\le\pi/2$. Thus for $x>0$, $-\frac{\pi/2}{x}\le\frac{\tan^{-1}x}{x}\le\frac{\pi/2}{x}$. Thus $\displaystyle\lim_{x\to\infty}\frac{\tan^{-1}(x)}{x}=0$ by the Squeeze Theorem.

2.6.78 Recall that $-1\le\cos t\le1$, and that $e^{3t}>0$ for all t. Thus $-\frac{1}{e^{3t}}\le\frac{\cos t}{e^{3t}}\le\frac{1}{e^{3t}}$. Thus $\displaystyle\lim_{t\to\infty}\frac{\cos t}{e^{3t}}=0$ by the Squeeze Theorem.

2.6.79 $\displaystyle\lim_{x\to1^-}\frac{x}{\ln x}=-\infty.$

2.6.80 $\displaystyle\lim_{x\to0^+}\frac{x}{\ln x}=0.$

2.6.81

The graph shown isn't drawn correctly at the integers. At an integer a, the value of the function is 0, whereas the graph shown appears to take on all the values from 0 to 1.
Note that in the correct graph, $\displaystyle\lim_{x\to a^-}f(x)=1$ and $\displaystyle\lim_{x\to a^+}f(x)=0$ for every integer a.

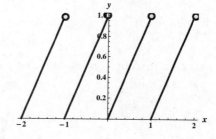

2.6.82

The graph as drawn on most graphing calculators appears to be continuous at $x=0$, but it isn't, of course (because the function isn't defined at $x=0$). A better drawing would show the "hole" in the graph at $(0,1)$.

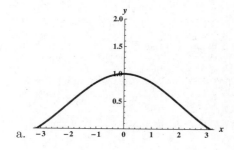

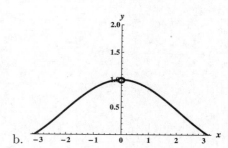

c. It appears that $\displaystyle\lim_{x\to0}\frac{\sin x}{x}=1.$

2.6.83 With slight modifications, we can use the examples from the previous two problems.

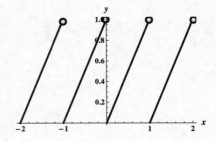

a. The function $y = x - \lfloor x \rfloor$ is defined at $x = 1$ but isn't continuous there.

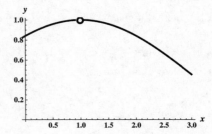

b. The function $y = \frac{\sin(x-1)}{x-1}$ has a limit at $x = 1$, but isn't defined there, so isn't continuous there.

2.6.84 In order for this function to be continuous at $x = -1$, we require $\lim\limits_{x \to -1} f(x) = f(-1) = a$. So the value of a must be equal to the value of $\lim\limits_{x \to -1} \dfrac{x^2 + 3x + 2}{x + 1} = \lim\limits_{x \to -1} \dfrac{(x+2)(x+1)}{x+1} = \lim\limits_{x \to -1} (x+2) = 1$. Thus we must have $a = 1$.

2.6.85

a. In order for g to be continuous from the left at $x = 1$, we must have $\lim\limits_{x \to 1^-} g(x) = g(1) = a$. We have $\lim\limits_{x \to 1^-} g(x) = \lim\limits_{x \to 1^-} (x^2 + x) = 2$. So we must have $a = 2$.

b. In order for g to be continuous from the right at $x = 1$, we must have $\lim\limits_{x \to 1^+} g(x) = g(1) = a$. We have $\lim\limits_{x \to 1^+} g(x) = \lim\limits_{x \to 1^+} (3x + 5) = 8$. So we must have $a = 8$.

c. Because the limit from the left and the limit from the right at $x = 1$ don't agree, there is no value of a which will make the function continuous at $x = 1$.

2.6.86 $\lim\limits_{x \to 0^-} \dfrac{2e^x + 5e^{3x}}{e^{2x} - e^{3x}} = \lim\limits_{x \to 0^-} \dfrac{2e^x + 5e^{3x}}{e^{2x}(1 - e^x)} = \infty.$

$\lim\limits_{x \to 0^+} \dfrac{2e^x + 5e^{3x}}{e^{2x} - e^{3x}} = \lim\limits_{x \to 0^+} \dfrac{2e^x + 5e^{3x}}{e^{2x}(1 - e^x)} = -\infty.$

$\lim\limits_{x \to -\infty} \dfrac{2e^x + 5e^{3x}}{e^{2x} - e^{3x}} = \lim\limits_{x \to -\infty} \dfrac{2e^x + 5e^{3x}}{e^{2x} - e^{3x}} \cdot \dfrac{e^{-2x}}{e^{-2x}} = \lim\limits_{x \to -\infty} \dfrac{2e^{-x} + 5e^x}{1 - e^x} = \infty.$

$\lim\limits_{x \to \infty} \dfrac{2e^x + 5e^{3x}}{e^{2x} - e^{3x}} = \lim\limits_{x \to \infty} \dfrac{2e^x + 5e^{3x}}{e^{2x} - e^{3x}} \cdot \dfrac{e^{-3x}}{e^{-3x}} = \lim\limits_{x \to \infty} \dfrac{2e^{-2x} + 5}{e^{-x} - 1} = -5.$

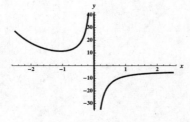

There is a vertical asymptote at $x = 0$, and the line $y = -5$ is a horizontal asymptote.

2.6.87 $\displaystyle\lim_{x \to 0} \frac{2e^x + 10e^{-x}}{e^x + e^{-x}} = \frac{12}{2} = 6.$

$\displaystyle\lim_{x \to -\infty} \frac{2e^x + 10e^{-x}}{e^x + e^{-x}} = \lim_{x \to -\infty} \frac{2e^x + 10e^{-x}}{e^x + e^{-x}} \cdot \frac{e^x}{e^x} = \lim_{x \to -\infty} \frac{2e^{2x} + 10}{e^{2x} + 1} = \frac{10}{1} = 10.$

$\displaystyle\lim_{x \to \infty} \frac{2e^x + 10e^{-x}}{e^x + e^{-x}} = \lim_{x \to \infty} \frac{2e^x + 10e^{-x}}{e^x + e^{-x}} \cdot \frac{e^{-x}}{e^{-x}} = \lim_{x \to \infty} \frac{2 + 10e^{-2x}}{1 + e^{-2x}} = \frac{2}{1} = 2.$

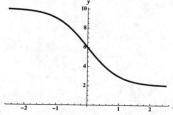

There are no vertical asymptotes. The lines $y = 2$ and $y = 10$ are horizontal asymptotes.

2.6.88 Let $f(x) = x^3 + 10x^2 - 100x + 50$. Note that $f(-20) < 0$, $f(-5) > 0$, $f(5) < 0$, and $f(10) > 0$. Because the given polynomial is continuous everywhere, the Intermediate Value Theorem guarantees us a root on $(-20, -5)$, at least one on $(-5, 5)$, and at least one on $(5, 10)$. Because there can be at most 3 roots and there are at least 3 roots, there must be exactly 3 roots. The roots are $x_1 \approx -16.32$, $x_2 \approx 0.53$ and $x_3 \approx 5.79$.

2.6.89 Let $f(x) = 70x^3 - 87x^2 + 32x - 3$. Note that $f(0) < 0$, $f(.2) > 0$, $f(.55) < 0$, and $f(1) > 0$. Because the given polynomial is continuous everywhere, the Intermediate Value Theorem guarantees us a root on $(0, .2)$, at least one on $(.2, .55)$, and at least one on $(.55, 1)$. Because there can be at most 3 roots and there are at least 3 roots, there must be exactly 3 roots. The roots are $x_1 = 1/7$, $x_2 = 1/2$ and $x_3 = 3/5$.

2.6.90 The function is continuous on $(0, 15]$, on $(15, 30]$, on $(30, 45]$, and on $(45, 60]$.

2.6.91

a. Note that $A(.01) \approx 2615.55$ and $A(.1) \approx 3984.36$. By the Intermediate Value Theorem, there must be a number r_0 between $.01$ and $.1$ so that $A(r_0) = 3500$.

b. The desired value is $r_0 \approx 0.0728$ or 7.28%.

2.6.92

a. We have $f(0) = 0$, $f(2) = 3$, $g(0) = 3$ and $g(2) = 0$.

b. $h(t) = f(t) - g(t)$, $h(0) = -3$ and $h(2) = 3$.

c. By the Intermediate Value Theorem, because h is a continuous function and 0 is an intermediate value between -3 and 3, there must be a time c between 0 and 2 where $h(c) = 0$. At this point $f(c) = g(c)$, and at that time, the distance from the car is the same on both days, so the hiker is passing over the exact same point at that time.

2.6.93 We can argue essentially like the previous problem, or we can imagine an identical twin to the original monk, who takes an identical version of the original monk's journey up the winding path while the monk is taking the return journey down. Because they must pass somewhere on the path, that point is the one we are looking for.

2.6.94

a. Because $|-1| = 1$, $|g(x)| = 1$, for all x.

b. The function g isn't continuous at $x = 0$, because $\lim\limits_{x \to 0^+} g(x) = 1 \neq -1 = \lim\limits_{x \to 0^-} g(x)$.

c. This constant function is continuous everywhere, in particular at $x = 0$.

d. This example shows that in general, the continuity of $|g|$ does not imply the continuity of g.

2.6.95 The discontinuity is not removable, because $\lim\limits_{x \to a} f(x)$ does not exist. The discontinuity pictured is a jump discontinuity.

2.6.96 The discontinuity is not removable, because $\lim\limits_{x \to a} f(x)$ does not exist. The discontinuity pictured is an infinite discontinuity.

2.6.97 Note that $\lim\limits_{x \to 2} \dfrac{x^2 - 7x + 10}{x - 2} = \lim\limits_{x \to 2} \dfrac{(x-2)(x-5)}{x-2} = \lim\limits_{x \to 2}(x - 5) = -3$. Because this limit exists, the discontinuity is removable.

2.6.98 Note that $\lim\limits_{x \to 1} \dfrac{x^2 - 1}{1 - x} = \lim\limits_{x \to 1} \dfrac{(x-1)(x+1)}{1-x} = \lim\limits_{x \to 1}[-(x+1)] = -2$. Because this limit exists, the discontinuity is removable.

2.6.99

a. Note that $-1 \leq \sin(1/x) \leq 1$ for all $x \neq 0$, so $-x \leq x\sin(1/x) \leq x$ (for $x > 0$. For $x < 0$ we would have $x \leq x\sin(1/x) \leq -x$.) Because both $x \to 0$ and $-x \to 0$ as $x \to 0$, the Squeeze Theorem tells us that $\lim\limits_{x \to 0} x\sin(1/x) = 0$ as well. Because this limit exists, the discontinuity is removable.

b. Note that as $x \to 0^+$, $1/x \to \infty$, and thus $\lim\limits_{x \to 0^+} \sin(1/x)$ does not exist. So the discontinuity is not removable.

2.6.100 This is a jump discontinuity, because $\lim\limits_{x \to 2^+} f(x) = 1$ and $\lim\limits_{x \to 2^-} f(x) = -1$.

2.6.101 Note that $h(x) = \frac{x^3 - 4x^2 + 4x}{x(x-1)} = \frac{x(x-2)^2}{x(x-1)}$. Thus $\lim\limits_{x \to 0} h(x) = -4$, and the discontinuity at $x = 0$ is removable. However, $\lim\limits_{x \to 1} h(x)$ does not exist, and the discontinuity at $x = 1$ is not removable (it is infinite.)

2.6.102 Because g is continuous at a, as $x \to a$, $g(x) \to g(a)$. Because f is continuous at $g(a)$, as $z \to g(a)$, $f(z) \to f(g(a))$. Let $z = g(x)$, and suppose $x \to a$. Then $g(x) = z \to g(a)$, so $f(z) = f(g(x)) \to f(g(a))$, as desired.

2.6.103

a. Consider $g(x) = x + 1$ and $f(x) = \frac{|x-1|}{x-1}$. Note that both g and f are continuous at $x = 0$. However $f(g(x)) = f(x+1) = \frac{|x|}{x}$ is not continuous at 0.

b. The previous theorem says that the composition of f and g is continuous at a if g is continuous at a and f is continuous at $g(a)$. It does not say that if g and f are both continuous at a that the composition is continuous at a.

2.6.104 The Intermediate Value Theorem requires that our function be continuous on the given interval. In this example, the function f is not continuous on $[-2, 2]$ because it isn't continuous at 0.

2.6.105

a. Using the hint, we have

$$\sin x = \sin(a + (x - a)) = \sin a \cos(x - a) + \sin(x - a)\cos a.$$

Note that as $x \to a$, we have that $\cos(x - a) \to 1$ and $\sin(x - a) \to 0$.

So,

$$\lim\limits_{x \to a} \sin x = \lim\limits_{x \to a} \sin(a + (x - a)) = \lim\limits_{x \to a}(\sin a \cos(x - a) + \sin(x - a)\cos a) = (\sin a) \cdot 1 + 0 \cdot \cos a = \sin a.$$

b. Using the hint, we have

$$\cos x = \cos(a + (x - a)) = \cos a \cos(x - a) - \sin a \sin(x - a).$$

So,

$$\lim_{x \to a} \cos x = \lim_{x \to a} \cos(a + (x - a)) = \lim_{x \to a} ((\cos a) \cos(x - a) - (\sin a) \sin(x - a)) = (\cos a) \cdot 1 - (\sin a) \cdot 0 = \cos a.$$

2.7 Precise Definitions of Limits

2.7.1 Note that all the numbers in the interval $(1, 3)$ are within 1 unit of the number 2. So $|x - 2| < 1$ is true for all numbers in that interval. In fact, $\{x : 0 < |x - 2| < 1\}$ is exactly the set $(1, 3)$ with $x \neq 2$.

2.7.2 Note that all the numbers in the interval $(2, 6)$ are within 2 units of the number 4. So $|f(x) - 4| < \epsilon$ for $\epsilon = 2$ (or any number greater than 2).

2.7.3

$(3, 8)$ has center 5.5, so it is not symmetric about the number 5.

$(1, 9)$ and $(4, 6)$ and $(4.5, 5.5)$ are symmetric about the number 5.

2.7.4 No. At $x = a$, we would have $|x - a| = 0$, not $|x - a| > 0$, so a is not included in the given set.

2.7.5 $\lim_{x \to a} f(x) = L$ if for any arbitrarily small positive number ϵ, there exists a number δ, so that $f(x)$ is within ϵ units of L for any number x within δ units of a (but not including a itself).

2.7.6 The set of all x for which $|f(x) - L| < \epsilon$ is the set of numbers so that the value of the function f at those numbers is within ϵ units of L.

2.7.7 We are given that $|f(x) - 5| < .1$ for values of x in the interval $(0, 5)$, so we need to ensure that the set of x values we are allowing fall in this interval.

Note that the number 0 is two units away from the number 2 and the number 5 is three units away from the number 2. In order to be sure that we are talking about numbers in the interval $(0, 5)$ when we write $|x - 2| < \delta$, we would need to have $\delta = 2$ (or a number less than 2). In fact, the set of numbers for which $|x - 2| < 2$ is the interval $(0, 4)$ which is a subset of $(0, 5)$.

If we were to allow δ to be any number greater than 2, then the set of all x so that $|x - 2| < \delta$ would include numbers less than 0, and those numbers aren't on the interval $(0, 5)$.

2.7.8

$\lim_{x \to a} f(x) = \infty$, if for any $N > 0$, there exists $\delta > 0$
so that if $0 < |x - a| < \delta$ then $f(x) > N$.

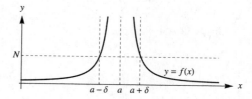

2.7.9

a. In order for f to be within 2 units of 5, it appears that we need x to be within 1 unit of 2. So $\delta = 1$.

b. In order for f to be within 1 unit of 5, it appears that we would need x to be within 1/2 unit of 2. So $\delta = .5$.

2.7.10

a. In order for f to be within 1 unit of 4, it appears that we would need x to be within 1 unit of 2. So $\delta = 1$.

b. In order for f to be within 1/2 unit of 4, it appears that we would need x to be within 1/2 unit of 2. So $\delta = 1/2$.

2.7.11

    a. In order for f to be within 3 units of 6, it appears that we would need x to be within 2 units of 3. So $\delta = 2$.

    b. In order for f to be within 1 unit of 6, it appears that we would need x to be within 1/2 unit of 3. So $\delta = 1/2$.

2.7.12

    a. In order for f to be within 1 unit of 5, it appears that we would need x to be within 3 units of 4. So $\delta = 3$.

    b. In order for f to be within 1/2 unit of 5, it appears that we would need x to be within 2 units of 4. So $\delta = 2$.

2.7.13

    a. If $\epsilon = 1$, we need $|x^3 + 3 - 3| < 1$. So we need $|x| < \sqrt[3]{1} = 1$ in order for this to happen. Thus $\delta = 1$ will suffice.

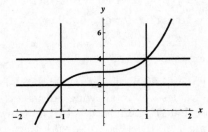

    b. If $\epsilon = .5$, we need $|x^3 + 3 - 3| < .5$. So we need $|x| < \sqrt[3]{.5}$ in order for this to happen. Thus $\delta = \sqrt[3]{.5} \approx .79$ will suffice.

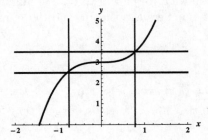

2.7.14

    a. By looking at the graph, it appears that for $\epsilon = 1$, we would need δ to be about .4 or less.

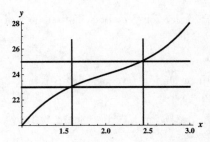

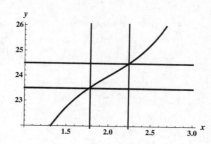

b. By looking at the graph, it appears that for $\epsilon = .5$, we would need δ to be about .2 or less.

2.7.15

a. For $\epsilon = 1$, the required value of δ would also be 1. A larger value of δ would work to the right of 2, but this is the largest one that would work to the left of 2.

b. For $\epsilon = 1/2$, the required value of δ would also be 1/2.

c. It appears that for a given value of ϵ, it would be wise to take $\delta = \min(\epsilon, 2)$. This assures that the desired inequality is met on both sides of 2.

2.7.16

a. For $\epsilon = 2$, the required value of δ would be 1 (or smaller). This is the largest value of δ that works on either side.

b. For $\epsilon = 1$, the required value of δ would be 1/2 (or smaller). This is the largest value of δ that works on the right of 4.

c. It appears that for a given value of ϵ, the corresponding value of $\delta = \min(5/2, \epsilon/2)$.

2.7.17

a. For $\epsilon = 2$, it appears that a value of $\delta = 1$ (or smaller) would work.

b. For $\epsilon = 1$, it appears that a value of $\delta = 1/2$ (or smaller) would work.

c. For an arbitrary ϵ, a value of $\delta = \epsilon/2$ or smaller appears to suffice.

2.7.18

a. For $\epsilon = 1/2$, it appears that a value of $\delta = 1$ (or smaller) would work.

b. For $\epsilon = 1/4$, it appears that a value of $\delta = 1/2$ (or smaller) would work.

c. For an arbitrary ϵ, a value of 2ϵ or smaller appears to suffice.

2.7.19 For any $\epsilon > 0$, let $\delta = \epsilon/8$. Then if $0 < |x - 1| < \delta$, we would have $|x - 1| < \epsilon/8$. Then $|8x - 8| < \epsilon$, so $|(8x + 5) - 13| < \epsilon$. This last inequality has the form $|f(x) - L| < \epsilon$, which is what we were attempting to show. Thus, $\lim_{x \to 1}(8x + 5) = 13$.

2.7.20 For any $\epsilon > 0$, let $\delta = \epsilon/2$. Then if $0 < |x - 3| < \delta$, we would have $|x - 3| < \epsilon/2$. Then $|2x - 6| < \epsilon$, so $|-2x + 6| < \epsilon$, so $|(-2x + 8) - 2| < \epsilon$. This last inequality has the form $|f(x) - L| < \epsilon$, which is what we were attempting to show. Thus, $\lim_{x \to 3}(-2x + 8) = 2$.

2.7.21 First note that if $x \neq 4$, $f(x) = \frac{x^2 - 16}{x - 4} = x + 4$.

Now if $\epsilon > 0$ is given, let $\delta = \epsilon$. Now suppose $0 < |x - 4| < \delta$. Then $x \neq 4$, so the function $f(x)$ can be described by $x + 4$. Also, because $|x - 4| < \delta$, we have $|x - 4| < \epsilon$. Thus $|(x + 4) - 8| < \epsilon$. This last inequality has the form $|f(x) - L| < \epsilon$, which is what we were attempting to show. Thus, $\lim_{x \to 4} \frac{x^2 - 16}{x - 4} = 8$.

2.7.22 First note that if $x \neq 3$, $f(x) = \frac{x^2-7x+12}{x-3} = \frac{(x-4)(x-3)}{x-3} = x-4$.

Now if $\epsilon > 0$ is given, let $\delta = \epsilon$. Now suppose $0 < |x-3| < \delta$. Then $x \neq 3$, so the function $f(x)$ can be described by $x-4$. Also, because $|x-3| < \delta$, we have $|x-3| < \epsilon$. Thus $|(x-4)-(-1)| < \epsilon$. This last inequality has the form $|f(x) - L| < \epsilon$, which is what we were attempting to show. Thus, $\lim_{x \to 3} f(x) = -1$.

2.7.23 Let $\epsilon > 0$ be given. Let $\delta = \sqrt{\epsilon}$. Then if $0 < |x-0| < \delta$, we would have $|x| < \sqrt{\epsilon}$. But then $|x^2| < \epsilon$, which has the form $|f(x) - L| < \epsilon$. Thus, $\lim_{x \to 0} f(x) = 0$.

2.7.24 Let $\epsilon > 0$ be given. Let $\delta = \sqrt{\epsilon}$. Then if $0 < |x-3| < \delta$, we would have $|x-3| < \sqrt{\epsilon}$. But then $|(x-3)^2| < \epsilon$, which has the form $|f(x) - L| < \epsilon$. Thus, $\lim_{x \to 3} f(x) = 0$.

2.7.25 Let $\epsilon > 0$ be given.

Because $\lim_{x \to a} f(x) = L$, we know that there exists a $\delta_1 > 0$ so that $|f(x) - L| < \epsilon/2$ when $0 < |x-a| < \delta_1$. Also, because $\lim_{x \to a} g(x) = M$, there exists a $\delta_2 > 0$ so that $|g(x) - M| < \epsilon/2$ when $0 < |x-a| < \delta_2$.

Now let $\delta = \min(\delta_1, \delta_2)$.

Then if $0 < |x-a| < \delta$, we would have $|f(x) - g(x) - (L-M)| = |(f(x) - L) + (M - g(x))| \leq |f(x) - L| + |M - g(x)| = |f(x) - L| + |g(x) - M| \leq \epsilon/2 + \epsilon/2 = \epsilon$. Note that the key inequality in this sentence follows from the triangle inequality.

2.7.26 First note that the theorem is trivially true if $c = 0$. So assume $c \neq 0$.

Let $\epsilon > 0$ be given. Because $\lim_{x \to a} f(x) = L$, there exists a $\delta > 0$ so that if $0 < |x-a| < \delta$, we have $|f(x) - L| < \epsilon/|c|$. But then $|c||f(x) - L| = |cf(x) - cL| < \epsilon$, as desired. Thus, $\lim_{x \to a} cf(x) = cL$.

2.7.27

a. Let $\epsilon > 0$ be given. It won't end up mattering what δ is, so let $\delta = 1$. Note that the statement $|f(x) - L| < \epsilon$ amounts to $|c - c| < \epsilon$, which is true for any positive number ϵ, without any restrictions on x. So $\lim_{x \to a} c = c$.

b. Let $\epsilon > 0$ be given. Let $\delta = \epsilon$. Note that the statement $|f(x) - L| < \epsilon$ has the form $|x - a| < \epsilon$, which follows whenever $0 < |x - a| < \delta$ (because $\delta = \epsilon$). Thus $\lim_{x \to a} x = a$.

2.7.28 First note that if $m = 0$, this follows from exercise 27a. So assume $m \neq 0$.

Let $\epsilon > 0$ be given. Let $\delta = \epsilon/|m|$. Now if $0 < |x-a| < \delta$, we would have $|x-a| < \epsilon/|m|$, so $|mx - ma| < \epsilon$. This can be written as $|(mx+b) - (ma+b)| < \epsilon$, which has the form $|f(x) - L| < \epsilon$. Thus, $\lim_{x \to a} f(x) = f(a)$, which implies that f is continuous at $x = a$ by the definition of continuity at a point. Because a is an arbitrary number, f must be continuous at all real numbers.

2.7.29 Let $N > 0$ be given. Let $\delta = 1/\sqrt{N}$. Then if $0 < |x-4| < \delta$, we have $|x-4| < 1/\sqrt{N}$. Taking the reciprocal of both sides, we have $\frac{1}{|x-4|} > \sqrt{N}$, and squaring both sides of this inequality yields $\frac{1}{(x-4)^2} > N$. Thus $\lim_{x \to 4} f(x) = \infty$.

2.7.30 Let $N > 0$ be given. Let $\delta = 1/\sqrt[4]{N}$. Then if $0 < |x-(-1)| < \delta$, we have $|x+1| < 1/\sqrt[4]{N}$. Taking the reciprocal of both sides, we have $\frac{1}{|x+1|} > \sqrt[4]{N}$, and raising both sides to the 4th power yields $\frac{1}{(x+1)^4} > N$. Thus $\lim_{x \to -1} f(x) = \infty$.

2.7.31 Let $N > 1$ be given. Let $\delta = 1/\sqrt{N-1}$. Suppose that $0 < |x-0| < \delta$. Then $|x| < 1/\sqrt{N-1}$, and taking the reciprocal of both sides, we see that $1/|x| > \sqrt{N-1}$. Then squaring both sides yields $\frac{1}{x^2} > N-1$, so $\frac{1}{x^2} + 1 > N$. Thus $\lim_{x \to 0} f(x) = \infty$.

2.7.32 Let $N > 0$ be given. Let $\delta = 1/\sqrt[4]{N+1}$. Then if $0 < |x-0| < \delta$, we would have $|x| < 1/\sqrt[4]{N+1}$. Taking the reciprocal of both sides yields $\frac{1}{|x|} > \sqrt[4]{N+1}$, and then raising both sides to the 4th power gives $\frac{1}{x^4} > N+1$, so $\frac{1}{x^4} - 1 > N$. Now because $-1 \leq \sin x \leq 1$, we can surmise that $\frac{1}{x^4} - \sin x > N$ as well, because $\frac{1}{x^4} - \sin x \geq \frac{1}{x^4} - 1$. Hence $\lim_{x \to 0} \left(\frac{1}{x^4} - \sin x \right) = \infty$.

2.7.33

   a. False. In fact, if the statement is true for a specific value of δ_1, then it would be true for any value of $\delta < \delta_1$. This is because if $0 < |x - a| < \delta$, it would automatically follow that $0 < |x - a| < \delta_1$.

   b. False. This statement is not equivalent to the definition – note that it says "for an arbitrary δ there exists an ϵ" rather than "for an arbitrary ϵ there exists a δ."

   c. True. This is the definition of $\lim\limits_{x \to a} f(x) = L$.

   d. True. Both inequalities describe the set of x's which are within δ units of a.

2.7.34

   a. We want it to be true that $|f(x) - 2| < .25$. So we need $|x^2 - 2x + 3 - 2| = |x^2 - 2x + 1| = (x-1)^2 < .25$. Therefore we need $|x - 1| < \sqrt{.25} = .5$. Thus we should let $\delta = .5$.

   b. We want it to be true that $|f(x) - 2| < \epsilon$. So we need $|x^2 - 2x + 3 - 2| = |x^2 - 2x + 1| = (x-1)^2 < \epsilon$. Therefore we need $|x - 1| < \sqrt{\epsilon}$. Thus we should let $\delta = \sqrt{\epsilon}$.

2.7.35 Assume $|x - 3| < 1$, as indicated in the hint. Then $2 < x < 4$, so $\frac{1}{4} < \frac{1}{x} < \frac{1}{2}$, and thus $\left|\frac{1}{x}\right| < \frac{1}{2}$. Also note that the expression $\left|\frac{1}{x} - \frac{1}{3}\right|$ can be written as $\left|\frac{x-3}{3x}\right|$.

Now let $\epsilon > 0$ be given. Let $\delta = \min(6\epsilon, 1)$. Now assume that $0 < |x - 3| < \delta$. Then

$$|f(x) - L| = \left|\frac{x-3}{3x}\right| < \left|\frac{x-3}{6}\right| < \frac{6\epsilon}{6} = \epsilon.$$

Thus we have established that $\left|\frac{1}{x} - \frac{1}{3}\right| < \epsilon$ whenever $0 < |x - 3| < \delta$.

2.7.36 Note that for $x \neq 4$, the expression $\frac{x-4}{\sqrt{x}-2} = \frac{x-4}{\sqrt{x}-2} \cdot \frac{\sqrt{x}+2}{\sqrt{x}+2} = \sqrt{x} + 2$. Also note that if $|x - 4| < 1$, then x is between 3 and 5, so $\sqrt{x} > 0$. Then it follows that $\sqrt{x} + 2 > 2$, and therefore $\frac{1}{\sqrt{x}+2} < \frac{1}{2}$. We will use this fact below.

Let $\epsilon > 0$ be given. Let $\delta = \min(2\epsilon, 1)$. Suppose that $0 < |x - 4| < \delta$, so $|x - 4| < 2\epsilon$. We have

$$|f(x) - L| = |\sqrt{x} + 2 - 4| = |\sqrt{x} - 2| = \left|\frac{x-4}{\sqrt{x}+2}\right|$$

$$< \frac{|x-4|}{2} < \frac{2\epsilon}{2} = \epsilon.$$

2.7.37 Assume $|x - (1/10)| < (1/20)$, as indicated in the hint. Then $1/20 < x < 3/20$, so $\frac{20}{3} < \frac{1}{x} < \frac{20}{1}$, and thus $\left|\frac{1}{x}\right| < 20$.

Also note that the expression $\left|\frac{1}{x} - 10\right|$ can be written as $\left|\frac{10x-1}{x}\right|$.

Let $\epsilon > 0$ be given. Let $\delta = \min(\epsilon/200, 1/20)$. Now assume that $0 < |x - (1/10)| < \delta$. Then

$$|f(x) - L| = \left|\frac{10x-1}{x}\right| < |(10x - 1) \cdot 20|$$

$$\leq |x - (1/10)| \cdot 200 < \frac{\epsilon}{200} \cdot 200 = \epsilon.$$

Thus we have established that $\left|\frac{1}{x} - 10\right| < \epsilon$ whenever $0 < |x - (1/10)| < \delta$.

2.7.38 Note that if $|x - 5| < 1$, then $4 < x < 6$, so that $9 < x + 5 < 11$, so $|x + 5| < 11$. Note also that $16 < x^2 < 36$, so $\frac{1}{x^2} < \frac{1}{16}$.

Let $\epsilon > 0$ be given. Let $\delta = \min(1, \frac{400}{11}\epsilon)$. Assume that $0 < |x - 5| < \delta$. Then

$$|f(x) - L| = \left|\frac{1}{x^2} - \frac{1}{25}\right| = \frac{|x+5||x-5|}{25x^2}$$

$$< \frac{11|x-5|}{25x^2} < \frac{11}{25 \cdot 16}|x - 5| < \frac{11}{400}\frac{400\epsilon}{11} = \epsilon.$$

2.7.39 Because we are approaching a from the right, we are only considering values of x which are close to, but a little larger than a. The numbers x to the right of a which are within δ units of a satisfy $0 < x - a < \delta$.

2.7.40 Because we are approaching a from the left, we are only considering values of x which are close to, but a little smaller than a. The numbers x to the left of a which are within δ units of a satisfy $0 < a - x < \delta$.

2.7.41

   a. Let $\epsilon > 0$ be given. let $\delta = \epsilon/2$. Suppose that $0 < x < \delta$. Then $0 < x < \epsilon/2$ and

$$|f(x) - L| = |2x - 4 - (-4)| = |2x| = 2|x|$$
$$= 2x < \epsilon.$$

   b. Let $\epsilon > 0$ be given. let $\delta = \epsilon/3$. Suppose that $0 < 0 - x < \delta$. Then $-\delta < x < 0$ and $-\epsilon/3 < x < 0$, so $\epsilon > -3x$. We have

$$|f(x) - L| = |3x - 4 - (-4)| = |3x| = 3|x|$$
$$= -3x < \epsilon.$$

   c. Let $\epsilon > 0$ be given. Let $\delta = \epsilon/3$. Because $\epsilon/3 < \epsilon/2$, we can argue that $|f(x) - L| < \epsilon$ whenever $0 < |x| < \delta$ exactly as in the previous two parts of this problem.

2.7.42

   a. This statement holds for $\delta = 2$ (or any number less than 2).

   b. This statement holds for $\delta = 2$ (or any number less than 2).

   c. This statement holds for $\delta = 1$ (or any number less than 1).

   d. This statement holds for $\delta = .5$ (or any number less than 0.5).

2.7.43 Let $\epsilon > 0$ be given, and let $\delta = \epsilon^2$. Suppose that $0 < x < \delta$, which means that $x < \epsilon^2$, so that $\sqrt{x} < \epsilon$. Then we have

$$|f(x) - L| = |\sqrt{x} - 0| = \sqrt{x} < \epsilon.$$

as desired.

2.7.44

a. Suppose that $\lim_{x \to a^-} f(x) = L$ and $\lim_{x \to a^+} f(x) = L$. Let $\epsilon > 0$ be given. There exists a number δ_1 so that $|f(x) - L| < \epsilon$ whenever $0 < x - a < \delta_1$, and there exists a number δ_2 so that $|f(x) - L| < \epsilon$ whenever $0 < a - x < \delta_2$. Let $\delta = \min(\delta_1, \delta_2)$. It immediately follows that $|f(x) - L| < \epsilon$ whenever $0 < |x - a| < \delta$, as desired.

b. Suppose $\lim_{x \to a} f(x) = L$, and let $\epsilon > 0$ be given. We know that a δ exists so that $|f(x) - L| < \epsilon$ whenever $0 < |x - a| < \delta$. In particular, it must be the case that $|f(x) - L| < \epsilon$ whenever $0 < x - a < \delta$ and also that $|f(x) - L| < \epsilon$ whenever $0 < a - x < \delta$. Thus $\lim_{x \to a^+} f(x) = L$ and $\lim_{x \to a^-} f(x) = L$.

2.7.45

a. We say that $\lim_{x \to a^+} f(x) = \infty$ if for each positive number N, there exists $\delta > 0$ such that

$$f(x) > N \quad \text{whenever} \quad a < x < a + \delta.$$

b. We say that $\lim_{x \to a^-} f(x) = -\infty$ if for each negative number N, there exists $\delta > 0$ such that

$$f(x) < N \quad \text{whenever} \quad a - \delta < x < a.$$

c. We say that $\lim_{x \to a^-} f(x) = \infty$ if for each positive number N, there exists $\delta > 0$ such that

$$f(x) > N \quad \text{whenever} \quad a - \delta < x < a.$$

2.7.46 Let $N < 0$ be given. Let $\delta = -1/N$, and suppose that $1 < x < 1 + \delta$. Then $1 < x < \frac{N-1}{N}$, so $\frac{1-N}{N} < -x < -1$, and therefore $1 + \frac{1-N}{N} < 1 - x < 0$, which can be written as $\frac{1}{N} < 1 - x < 0$. Taking reciprocals yields the inequality $N > \frac{1}{1-x}$, as desired.

2.7.47 Let $N > 0$ be given. Let $\delta = 1/N$, and suppose that $1 - \delta < x < 1$. Then $\frac{N-1}{N} < x < 1$, so $\frac{1-N}{N} > -x > -1$, and therefore $1 + \frac{1-N}{N} > 1 - x > 0$, which can be written as $\frac{1}{N} > 1 - x > 0$. Taking reciprocals yields the inequality $N < \frac{1}{1-x}$, as desired.

2.7.48 Let $M < 0$ be given. Let $\delta = \sqrt{-2/M}$. Suppose that $0 < |x - 1| < \delta$. Then $(x - 1)^2 < -2/M$, so $\frac{1}{(x-1)^2} > \frac{M}{-2}$, and $\frac{-2}{(x-1)^2} < M$, as desired.

2.7.49 Let $M < 0$ be given. Let $\delta = \sqrt[4]{-10/M}$. Suppose that $0 < |x + 2| < \delta$. Then $(x + 2)^4 < -10/M$, so $\frac{1}{(x+2)^4} > \frac{M}{-10}$, and $\frac{-10}{(x+2)^4} < M$, as desired.

2.7.50 Let $\epsilon > 0$ be given. Let $N = \frac{10}{\epsilon}$. Suppose that $x > N$. Then $x > \frac{10}{\epsilon}$ so $0 < \frac{10}{x} < \epsilon$. Thus, $|\frac{10}{x} - 0| < \epsilon$, as desired.

2.7.51 Let $\epsilon > 0$ be given. Let $N = 1/\epsilon$. Suppose that $x > N$. Then $\frac{1}{x} < \epsilon$, and so $|f(x) - L| = |2 + \frac{1}{x} - 2| < \epsilon$.

2.7.52 Let $M > 0$ be given. Let $N = 100M$. Suppose that $x > N$. Then $x > 100M$, so $\frac{x}{100} > M$, as desired.

2.7.53 Let $M > 0$ be given. Let $N = M - 1$. Suppose that $x > N$. Then $x > M - 1$, so $x + 1 > M$, and thus $\frac{x^2 + x}{x} > M$, as desired.

2.7.54 Let $\epsilon > 0$ be given. Because $\lim_{x \to a} f(x) = L$, there exists a number δ_1 so that $|f(x) - L| < \epsilon$ whenever $0 < |x - a| < \delta_1$. And because $\lim_{x \to a} h(x) = L$, there exists a number δ_2 so that $|h(x) - L| < \epsilon$ whenever $0 < |x - a| < \delta_2$. Let $\delta = \min(\delta_1, \delta_2)$, and suppose that $0 < |x - a| < \delta$. Because $f(x) \le g(x) \le h(x)$ for x near a, we also have that $f(x) - L \le g(x) - L \le h(x) - L$. Now whenever x is within δ units of a (but $x \ne a$), we also note that $-\epsilon < f(x) - L \le g(x) - L \le h(x) - L < \epsilon$. Therefore $|g(x) - L| < \epsilon$, as desired.

2.7.55 Let $\epsilon > 0$ be given. Let $N = \lfloor (1/\epsilon) \rfloor + 1$. By assumption, there exists an integer $M > 0$ so that $|f(x) - L| < 1/N$ whenever $|x - a| < 1/M$. Let $\delta = 1/M$.

Now assume $0 < |x - a| < \delta$. Then $|x - a| < 1/M$, and thus $|f(x) - L| < 1/N$. But then

$$|f(x) - L| < \frac{1}{\lfloor (1/\epsilon) \rfloor + 1} < \epsilon,$$

as desired.

2.7.56 Suppose that $\epsilon = 1$. Then no matter what δ is, there are numbers in the set $0 < |x - 2| < \delta$ so that $|f(x) - 2| > \epsilon$. For example, when x is only slightly greater than 2, the value of $|f(x) - 2|$ will be 2 or more.

2.7.57 Let $f(x) = \frac{|x|}{x}$ and suppose $\lim_{x \to 0} f(x)$ does exist and is equal to L. Let $\epsilon = 1/2$. There must be a value of δ so that when $0 < |x| < \delta$, $|f(x) - L| < 1/2$. Now consider the numbers $\delta/3$ and $-\delta/3$, both of which are within δ of 0. We have $f(\delta/3) = 1$ and $f(-\delta/3) = -1$. However, it is impossible for both $|1 - L| < 1/2$ and $|-1 - L| < 1/2$, because the former implies that $1/2 < L < 3/2$ and the latter implies that $-3/2 < L < -1/2$. Thus $\lim_{x \to 0} f(x)$ does not exist.

2.7.58 Suppose that $\lim_{x \to a} f(x)$ exists and is equal to L. Let $\epsilon = 1/2$. By the definition of limit, there must be a number δ so that $|f(x) - L| < \frac{1}{2}$ whenever $0 < |x - a| < \delta$. Now in every set of the form $(a, a + \delta)$ there are both rational and irrational numbers, so there will be value of f equal to both 0 and 1. Thus we have $|0 - L| < 1/2$, which means that L lies in the interval $(-1/2, 1/2)$, and we have $|1 - L| < 1/2$, which means that L lies in the interval $(1/2, 3/2)$. Because these both can't be true, we have a contradiction.

2.7.59 Because f is continuous at a, we know that $\lim_{x \to a} f(x)$ exists and is equal to $f(a) > 0$. Let $\epsilon = f(a)/3$. Then there is a number $\delta > 0$ so that $|f(x) - f(a)| < f(a)/3$ whenever $|x - a| < \delta$. Then whenever x lies in the interval $(a - \delta, a + \delta)$ we have $-f(a)/3 \leq f(x) - f(a) \leq f(a)/3$, so $2f(a)/3 \leq f(x) \leq 4f(a)/3$, so f is positive in this interval.

Chapter Two Review

1

a. False. Because $\lim_{x \to 1} \frac{x - 1}{x^2 - 1} = \lim_{x \to 1} \frac{1}{x + 1} = \frac{1}{2}$, f doesn't have a vertical asymptote at $x = 1$.

b. False. In general, these methods are too imprecise to produce accurate results.

c. False. For example, the function $f(x) = \begin{cases} 2x & \text{if } x < 0; \\ 1 & \text{if } x = 0; \\ 4x & \text{if } x > 0 \end{cases}$ has a limit of 0 as $x \to 0$, but $f(0) = 1$.

d. True. When we say that a limit exists, we are saying that there is a real number L that the function is approaching. If the limit of the function is ∞, it is still the case that there is no real number that the function is approaching. (There is no real number called "infinity.")

e. False. It could be the case that $\lim_{x \to a^-} f(x) = 1$ and $\lim_{x \to a^+} f(x) = 2$.

f. False.

g. False. For example, the function $f(x) = \begin{cases} 2 & \text{if } 0 < x < 1; \\ 3 & \text{if } 1 \leq x < 2, \end{cases}$ is continuous on $(0, 1)$, and on $[1, 2)$, but isn't continuous on $(0, 2)$.

h. True. $\lim_{x \to a} f(x) = f(a)$ if and only if f is continuous at a.

2

a. $f(-1) = 1$

b. $\lim_{x \to -1^-} f(x) = 3$.

c. $\lim_{x \to -1^+} f(x) = 1$.

d. $\lim_{x \to -1} f(x)$ does not exist.

e. $f(1) = 5$.

f. $\lim_{x \to 1} f(x) = 5$.

g. $\lim_{x \to 2} f(x) = 4$.

h. $\lim_{x \to 3^-} f(x) = 3$.

i. $\lim_{x \to 3^+} f(x) = 5$.

j. $\lim_{x \to 3} f(x)$ does not exist.

3 This function is discontinuous at $x = -1$, at $x = 1$, and at $x = 3$. At $x = -1$ it is discontinuous because $\lim_{x \to -1} f(x)$ does not exist. At $x = 1$, it is discontinuous because $\lim_{x \to 1} f(x) \neq f(1)$. At $x = 3$, it is discontinuous because $f(3)$ does not exist, and because $\lim_{x \to 3} f(x)$ does not exist.

4

a. The graph drawn by most graphing calculators and computer algebra systems doesn't show the discontinuities where $\sin \theta = 0$.

b. It appears to be equal to 2

c. Using a trigonometric identity, $\lim_{\theta \to 0} \dfrac{\sin 2\theta}{\sin \theta} = \lim_{\theta \to 0} \dfrac{2 \sin \theta \cos \theta}{\sin \theta}$. This can then be seen to be $\lim_{\theta \to 0} 2 \cos \theta = 2$.

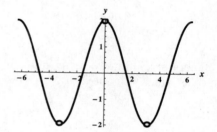

True graph, showing discontinuities where $\sin \theta = 0$.

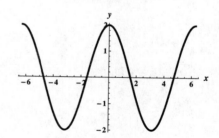

Graph shown without discontinuities.

5

a.

x	$.9\pi/4$	$.99\pi/4$	$.999\pi/4$	$.9999\pi/4$
$f(x)$	1.4098	1.4142	1.4142	1.4142

x	$1.1\pi/4$	$1.01\pi/4$	$1.001\pi/4$	$1.0001\pi/4$
$f(x)$	1.4098	1.4142	1.4142	1.4142

The limit appears to be approximately 1.4142.

b. $\lim_{x \to \pi/4} \dfrac{\cos 2x}{\cos x - \sin x} = \lim_{x \to \pi/4} \dfrac{\cos^2 x - \sin^2 x}{\cos x - \sin x} = \lim_{x \to \pi/4} (\cos x + \sin x) = \sqrt{2}$.

6

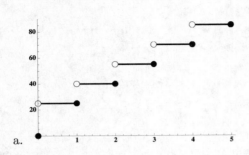

b. $\displaystyle\lim_{t\to 2.9} f(t) = 55.$

c. $\displaystyle\lim_{t\to 3^-} f(t) = 55$ and $\displaystyle\lim_{t\to 3^+} f(t) = 70.$

d. The cost of the rental jumps by \$15 exactly at $t = 3$. A rental lasting slightly less than 3 days cost \$55 and rentals lasting slightly more than 3 days cost \$70.

e. The function f is continuous everywhere except at the integers. The cost of the rental jumps by \$15 at each integer.

7

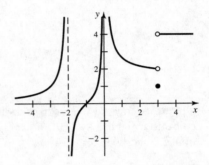

There are infinitely many different correct functions which you could draw. One of them is:

8 $\displaystyle\lim_{x\to 1000} 18\pi^2 = 18\pi^2.$

9 $\displaystyle\lim_{x\to 1} \sqrt{5x + 6} = \sqrt{11}.$

10

$$\lim_{h\to 0} \frac{\sqrt{5x + 5h} - \sqrt{5x}}{h} \cdot \frac{\sqrt{5x + 5h} + \sqrt{5x}}{\sqrt{5x + 5h} + \sqrt{5x}} = \lim_{h\to 0} \frac{(5x + 5h) - 5x}{h(\sqrt{5x + 5h} + \sqrt{5x})} = \lim_{h\to 0} \frac{5}{\sqrt{5x + 5h} + \sqrt{5x}} = \frac{5}{2\sqrt{5x}}.$$

11 $\displaystyle\lim_{x\to 1} \frac{x^3 - 7x^2 + 12x}{4 - x} = \frac{1 - 7 + 12}{4 - 1} = \frac{6}{3} = 2.$

12 $\displaystyle\lim_{x\to 4} \frac{x^3 - 7x^2 + 12x}{4 - x} = \lim_{x\to 4} \frac{x(x - 3)(x - 4)}{4 - x} = \lim_{x\to 4} x(3 - x) = -4.$

13 $\displaystyle\lim_{x\to 1} \frac{1 - x^2}{x^2 - 8x + 7} = \lim_{x\to 1} \frac{(1 - x)(1 + x)}{(x - 7)(x - 1)} = \lim_{x\to 1} \frac{-(x + 1)}{x - 7} = \frac{1}{3}.$

14 $\displaystyle\lim_{x\to 3} \frac{\sqrt{3x + 16} - 5}{x - 3} \cdot \frac{\sqrt{3x + 16} + 5}{\sqrt{3x + 16} + 5} = \lim_{x\to 3} \frac{3(x - 3)}{(x - 3)(\sqrt{3x + 16} + 5)} = \lim_{x\to 3} \frac{3}{\sqrt{3x + 16} + 5} = \frac{3}{10}.$

15

$$\lim_{x\to 3}\frac{1}{x-3}\left(\frac{1}{\sqrt{x+1}}-\frac{1}{2}\right)=\lim_{x\to 3}\frac{2-\sqrt{x+1}}{2(x-3)\sqrt{x+1}}\cdot\frac{(2+\sqrt{x+1})}{(2+\sqrt{x+1})}$$

$$=\lim_{x\to 3}\frac{4-(x+1)}{2(x-3)(\sqrt{x+1})(2+\sqrt{x+1})}$$

$$=\lim_{x\to 3}\frac{-(x-3)}{2(x-3)(\sqrt{x+1})(2+\sqrt{x+1})}$$

$$=\lim_{x\to 3}-\frac{1}{2\sqrt{x+1}(2+\sqrt{x+1})}=-\frac{1}{16}.$$

16 $\displaystyle\lim_{t\to 1/3}\frac{t-\frac{1}{3}}{(3t-1)^2}=\lim_{t\to 1/3}\frac{3t-1}{3(3t-1)^2}=\lim_{t\to 1/3}\frac{1}{3(3t-1)}$, which does not exist.

17 $\displaystyle\lim_{x\to 3}\frac{x^4-81}{x-3}=\lim_{x\to 3}\frac{(x-3)(x+3)(x^2+9)}{x-3}=\lim_{x\to 3}(x+3)(x^2+9)=108.$

18 Note that $\frac{p^5-1}{p-1}=p^4+p^3+p^2+p+1$. (Use long division.)

$\displaystyle\lim_{p\to 1}\frac{p^5-1}{p-1}=\lim_{p\to 1}(p^4+p^3+p^2+p+1)=5.$

19 $\displaystyle\lim_{x\to 81}\frac{\sqrt[4]{x}-3}{x-81}=\lim_{x\to 81}\frac{\sqrt[4]{x}-3}{(\sqrt{x}+9)(\sqrt[4]{x}+3)(\sqrt[4]{x}-3)}=\lim_{x\to 81}\frac{1}{(\sqrt{x}+9)(\sqrt[4]{x}+3)}=\frac{1}{108}.$

20 $\displaystyle\lim_{\theta\to\pi/4}\frac{\sin^2\theta-\cos^2\theta}{\sin\theta-\cos\theta}=\lim_{\theta\to\pi/4}\frac{(\sin\theta-\cos\theta)(\sin\theta+\cos\theta)}{\sin\theta-\cos\theta}=\lim_{\theta\to\pi/4}(\sin\theta+\cos\theta)=\sqrt{2}.$

21 $\displaystyle\lim_{x\to\pi/2}\frac{\frac{1}{\sqrt{\sin x}}-1}{x+\pi/2}=\frac{0}{\pi}=0.$

22 The domain of $f(x)=\sqrt{\frac{x-1}{x-3}}$ is $(-\infty,1]$ and $(3,\infty)$, so $\displaystyle\lim_{x\to 1^+}f(x)$ doesn't exist.

However, we have $\displaystyle\lim_{x\to 1^-}f(x)=0.$

23

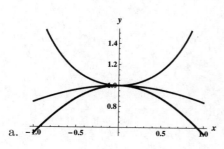

a.

b. Because $\displaystyle\lim_{x\to 0}\cos x=\lim_{x\to 0}\frac{1}{\cos x}=1$, the squeeze theorem assures us that $\displaystyle\lim_{x\to 0}\frac{\sin x}{x}=1$ as well.

24 Note that $\displaystyle\lim_{x\to 0}(\sin^2 x+1)=1$. Thus if $1\le g(x)\le\sin^2 x+1$, the squeeze theorem assures us that $\displaystyle\lim_{x\to 0}g(x)=1$ as well.

25 $\displaystyle\lim_{x\to 5}\frac{x-7}{x(x-5)^2}=-\infty.$

26 $\displaystyle\lim_{x\to -5^+}\frac{x-5}{x+5}=-\infty.$

27 $\lim\limits_{x\to 3^-} \dfrac{x-4}{x^2-3x} = \lim\limits_{x\to 3^-} \dfrac{x-4}{x(x-3)} = \infty.$

28 $\lim\limits_{x\to 0^+} \dfrac{u-1}{\sin u} = -\infty.$

29 $\lim\limits_{x\to 0^-} \dfrac{2}{\tan x} = -\infty.$

30

First note that $f(x) = \frac{x^2-5x+6}{x^2-2x} = \frac{(x-3)(x-2)}{x(x-2)}$.

a. $\lim\limits_{x\to 0^-} f(x) = \lim\limits_{x\to 0^-} \dfrac{(x-3)(x-2)}{x(x-2)} = \infty.$

   $\lim\limits_{x\to 0^+} f(x) = \lim\limits_{x\to 0^+} \dfrac{(x-3)(x-2)}{x(x-2)} = -\infty.$

   $\lim\limits_{x\to 2^-} f(x) = \lim\limits_{x\to 2^-} \dfrac{x-3}{x} = -\dfrac{1}{2}.$

   $\lim\limits_{x\to 2^+} f(x) = \lim\limits_{x\to 2^+} \dfrac{x-3}{x} = -\dfrac{1}{2}.$

b. By the above calculations and the definition of vertical asymptote, f has a vertical asymptote at $x = 0$.

c. Note that the actual graph has a "hole" at the point $(2, -1/2)$, because $x = 2$ isn't in the domain, but $\lim\limits_{x\to 2} f(x) = -1/2$.

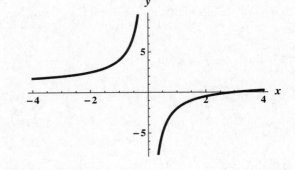

31 $\lim\limits_{x\to\infty} \dfrac{2x-3}{4x+10} = \lim\limits_{x\to\infty} \dfrac{2-(3/x)}{4+(10/x)} = \dfrac{2}{4} = \dfrac{1}{2}.$

32 $\lim\limits_{x\to\infty} \dfrac{x^4-1}{x^5+2} = \lim\limits_{x\to\infty} \dfrac{(1/x)-(1/x^5)}{1+(2/x^5)} = \dfrac{0-0}{1+0} = 0.$

33 $\lim\limits_{x\to-\infty} (-3x^3+5) = \infty.$

34 $\lim\limits_{z\to\infty} \left(e^{-2z} + \dfrac{2}{z}\right) = 0 + 0 = 0.$

35 $\lim\limits_{x\to\infty} (3\tan^{-1} x + 2) = \dfrac{3\pi}{2} + 2.$

36 $\lim\limits_{r\to\infty} \dfrac{1}{\ln r + 1} = 0.$

37 $\lim\limits_{x\to\infty} \dfrac{4x^3+1}{1-x^3} = \lim\limits_{x\to\infty} \dfrac{4+(1/x^3)}{(1/x^3)-1} = \dfrac{4+0}{0-1} = -4.$ A similar result holds as $x \to -\infty$. Thus, $y = -4$ is a horizontal asymptote as $x \to \infty$ and as $x \to -\infty$.

38 First note that $\sqrt{\frac{1}{x^2}} = \left|\frac{1}{x}\right| = \begin{cases} \frac{1}{x} & \text{if } x > 0; \\[4pt] -\frac{1}{x} & \text{if } x < 0. \end{cases}$

$\lim\limits_{x\to\infty} \dfrac{x+1}{\sqrt{9x^2+x}} = \lim\limits_{x\to\infty} \dfrac{1+(1/x)}{\sqrt{9+\frac{1}{x}}} = \dfrac{1}{3}.$

On the other hand, $\lim\limits_{x\to-\infty} \dfrac{x+1}{\sqrt{9x^2+x}} = \lim\limits_{x\to\infty} \dfrac{1+(1/x)}{-\sqrt{9+\frac{1}{x}}} = -\dfrac{1}{3}.$

So $y = \frac{1}{3}$ is a horizontal asymptote as $x \to \infty$, and $y = -\frac{1}{3}$ is a horizontal asymptote as $x \to -\infty$.

39 $\lim\limits_{x \to \infty} (1 - e^{-2x}) = 1$, while $\lim\limits_{x \to -\infty} (1 - e^{-2x}) = -\infty$.

$y = 1$ is a horizontal asymptote as $x \to \infty$.

40 $\lim\limits_{x \to \infty} \dfrac{1}{\ln x^2} = 0$, and $\lim\limits_{x \to -\infty} \dfrac{1}{\ln x^2} = 0$, so $y = 0$ is a horizontal asymptote as $x \to \infty$ and as $x \to -\infty$.

41 Recall that $\tan^{-1} x = 0$ only for $x = 0$. The only vertical asymptote is $x = 0$.

$\lim\limits_{x \to \infty} \dfrac{1}{\tan^{-1} x} = \dfrac{1}{\pi/2} = \dfrac{2}{\pi}$.

$\lim\limits_{x \to -\infty} \dfrac{1}{\tan^{-1} x} = \dfrac{1}{-\pi/2} = -\dfrac{2}{\pi}$. So $y = \frac{2}{\pi}$ is a horizontal asymptote as $x \to \infty$ and $y = -\frac{2}{\pi}$ is a horizontal asymptote as $x \to -\infty$.

42 Note that $f(x) = \dfrac{2x^2 + 6}{2x^2 + 3x - 2} = \dfrac{2(x^2 + 3)}{(2x - 1)(x + 2)}$.

We have $\lim\limits_{x \to \infty} f(x) = \lim\limits_{x \to \infty} \dfrac{2 + 6/x^2}{2 + 3/x - 2/x^2} = 1$. A similar result holds as $x \to -\infty$.

$\lim\limits_{x \to 1/2^-} f(x) = -\infty$. $\lim\limits_{x \to 1/2^+} f(x) = \infty$.

$\lim\limits_{x \to -2^-} f(x) = \infty$. $\lim\limits_{x \to -2^+} f(x) = -\infty$.

Thus, $y = 1$ is a horizontal asymptote as $x \to \infty$ and as $x \to -\infty$. Also, $x = \frac{1}{2}$ and $x = -2$ are vertical asymptotes.

43 $\lim\limits_{x \to \infty} \dfrac{3x^2 + 2x - 1}{4x + 1} = \lim\limits_{x \to \infty} \dfrac{3x^2 + 2x - 1}{4x + 1} \cdot \dfrac{1/x}{1/x} = \lim\limits_{x \to \infty} \dfrac{3x + 2 - 1/x}{4 + 1/x} = \infty$.

$\lim\limits_{x \to -\infty} \dfrac{3x^2 + 2x - 1}{4x + 1} = \lim\limits_{x \to -\infty} \dfrac{3x^2 + 2x - 1}{4x + 1} \cdot \dfrac{1/x}{1/x} = \lim\limits_{x \to -\infty} \dfrac{3x + 2 - 1/x}{4 + 1/x} = -\infty$.

By long division, we can write $f(x)$ as $f(x) = \frac{3x}{4} + \frac{5}{16} + \frac{-21/16}{4x+1}$, so the line $y = \frac{3x}{4} + \frac{5}{16}$ is the slant asymptote.

44 $\lim\limits_{x \to \infty} \dfrac{9x^2 + 4}{(2x - 1)^2} = \lim\limits_{x \to \infty} \dfrac{9x^2 + 4}{4x^2 - 4x + 1} \cdot \dfrac{1/x^2}{1/x^2} = \lim\limits_{x \to \infty} \dfrac{9 + 4/x^2}{4 - 4/x + 1/x^2} = \dfrac{9}{4}$.

$\lim\limits_{x \to -\infty} \dfrac{9x^2 + 4}{(2x - 1)^2} = \lim\limits_{x \to -\infty} \dfrac{9x^2 + 4}{4x^2 - 4x + 1} \cdot \dfrac{1/x^2}{1/x^2} = \lim\limits_{x \to -\infty} \dfrac{9 + 4/x^2}{4 - 4/x + 1/x^2} = \dfrac{9}{4}$. Because there is a horizontal asymptote, there is not a slant asymptote.

45 $\lim\limits_{x \to \infty} \dfrac{1 + x - 2x^2 - x^3}{x^2 + 1} = \lim\limits_{x \to \infty} \dfrac{1 + x - 2x^2 - x^3}{x^2 + 1} \cdot \dfrac{1/x^2}{1/x^2} = \lim\limits_{x \to \infty} \dfrac{1/x^2 + 1/x - 2 - x}{1 + 1/x^2} = -\infty$.

$\lim\limits_{x \to -\infty} \dfrac{1 + x - 2x^2 - x^3}{x^2 + 1} = \lim\limits_{x \to -\infty} \dfrac{1 + x - 2x^2 - x^3}{x^2 + 1} \cdot \dfrac{1/x^2}{1/x^2} = \lim\limits_{x \to -\infty} \dfrac{1/x^2 + 1/x - 2 - x}{1 + 1/x^2} = \infty$.

By long division, we can write $f(x)$ as $f(x) = -x - 2 + \frac{2x+3}{x^2+1}$, so the line $y = -x - 2$ is the slant asymptote.

46 $\lim\limits_{x \to \infty} \dfrac{x(x + 2)^3}{3x^2 - 4x} = \lim\limits_{x \to \infty} \dfrac{x^4 + 6x^3 + 12x^2 + 8x}{3x^2 - 4x} \cdot \dfrac{1/x^2}{1/x^2} = \lim\limits_{x \to \infty} \dfrac{x^2 + 6x + 12 + 8/x}{3 - 4/x} = \infty$.

$\lim\limits_{x \to -\infty} \dfrac{x(x + 2)^3}{3x^2 - 4x} = \lim\limits_{x \to -\infty} \dfrac{x^4 + 6x^3 + 12x^2 + 8x}{3x^2 - 4x} \cdot \dfrac{1/x^2}{1/x^2} = \lim\limits_{x \to -\infty} \dfrac{x^2 + 6x + 12 + 8/x}{3 - 4/x} = \infty$.

Because the degree of the numerator of this rational function is two more than the degree of the denominator, there is no slant asymptote.

47 f is discontinuous at 5, because $f(5)$ does not exist, and also because $\lim\limits_{x \to 5} f(x)$ does not exist

48 g is discontinuous at 4 because $\lim\limits_{x \to 4} g(x) = \lim\limits_{x \to 4} \dfrac{(x + 4)(x - 4)}{x - 4} = 8 \neq g(4)$.

49 h is not continuous at 3 because $\lim\limits_{x \to 3^-} h(x)$ does not exist, so $\lim\limits_{x \to 3} h(x)$ does not exist.

50 g is continuous at 4 because $\lim\limits_{x\to 4} g(x) = \lim\limits_{x\to 4} \dfrac{(x+4)(x-4)}{x-4} = 8 = g(4)$.

51 The domain of f is $(-\infty, -\sqrt{5}]$ and $[\sqrt{5}, \infty)$, and f is continuous on that domain.

52 The domain of g is $[2, \infty)$, and it is continuous from the right at $x = 2$.

53 The domain of h is $(-\infty, -5)$, $(-5, 0)$, $(0, 5)$, $(5, \infty)$, and like all rational functions, it is continuous on its domain.

54 g is the composition of two functions which are defined and continuous on $(-\infty, \infty)$, so g is continuous on that interval as well.

55 In order for g to be left continuous at 1, it is necessary that $\lim\limits_{x\to 1^-} g(x) = g(1)$, which means that $a = 3$. In order for g to be right continuous at 1, it is necessary that $\lim\limits_{x\to 1^+} g(x) = g(1)$, which means that $a + b = 3 + b = 3$, so $b = 0$.

56

    a. Because the domain of h is $(-\infty, -3]$ and $[3, \infty)$, there is no way that h can be left continuous at 3.

    b. h is right continuous at 3, because $\lim\limits_{x\to 3^+} h(x) = 0 = h(3)$.

57

One such possible graph is pictured to the right.

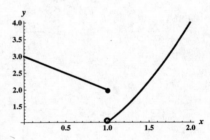

58   a. Consider the function $f(x) = x^5 + 7x + 5$. f is continuous everywhere, and $f(-1) = -3 < 0$ while $f(0) = 5 > 0$. Therefore, 0 is an intermediate value between $f(-1)$ and $f(0)$. By the IVT, there must a number c between 0 and 1 so that $f(c) = 0$.

    b. Using a computer algebra system, one can find that $c \approx -0.691671$ is a root.

59

    a. Note that $m(0) = 0$ and $m(5) \approx 38.34$ and $m(15) \approx 21.2$. Thus, 30 is an intermediate value between both $m(0)$ and $m(5)$, and $m(5)$ and $m(15)$. Note also that m is a continuous function. By the IVT, there must be a number c_1 between 0 and 5 with $m(c_1) = 30$, and a number c_2 between 5 and 15 with $m(c_2) = 30$.

    b. A little trial and error leads $c_1 \approx 2.4$ and $c_2 \approx 10.8$.

    c. No. The graph of the function on a graphing calculator suggests that it peaks at about 38.5

60 Let $\epsilon > 0$ be given. Let $\delta = \epsilon/5$. Now suppose that $0 < |x - 1| < \delta$.
Then

$$|f(x) - L| = |(5x - 2) - 3| = |5x - 5|$$
$$= 5|x - 1| < 5 \cdot \frac{\epsilon}{5} = \epsilon.$$

61 Let $\epsilon > 0$ be given. Let $\delta = \epsilon$. Now suppose that $0 < |x - 5| < \delta$.
Then

$$|f(x) - L| = \left| \frac{x^2 - 25}{x - 5} - 10 \right| = \left| \frac{(x - 5)(x + 5)}{x - 5} - 10 \right| = |x + 5 - 10|$$
$$= |x - 5| < \epsilon.$$

62

a. Assume $L > 0$. (If $L = 0$, the result follows immediately because that would imply that the function f is the constant function 0, and then $f(x)g(x)$ is also the constant function 0.) Assume that δ_1 is a number so that $|f(x)| \le L$ for $|x - a| < \delta_1$.

Let $\epsilon > 0$ be given. Because $\lim\limits_{x \to a} g(x) = 0$, we know that there exists a number $\delta_2 > 0$ so that $|g(x)| < \epsilon/L$ whenever $0 < |x - a| < \delta_2$. Let $\delta = \min(\delta_1, \delta_2)$.
Then

$$|f(x)g(x) - 0| = |f(x)||g(x)| < L \cdot \frac{\epsilon}{L} = \epsilon,$$

whenever $0 < |x - a| < \delta$.

b. Let $f(x) = \frac{x^2}{x - 2}$. Then

$$\lim_{x \to 2} f(x)(x - 2) = \lim_{x \to 2} \frac{x^2(x - 2)}{x - 2} = \lim_{x \to 2} x^2 = 4 \ne 0.$$

This doesn't violate the previous result because the given function f is not bounded near $x = 2$.

c. Because $|H(x)| \le 1$ for all x, the result follows directly from part a) of this problem (using $L = 1$, $a = 0$, $f(x) = H(x)$, and $g(x) = x$).

63 Let $N > 0$ be given. Let $\delta = 1/\sqrt[4]{N}$. Suppose that $0 < |x - 2| < \delta$. Then $|x - 2| < \frac{1}{\sqrt[4]{N}}$, so $\frac{1}{|x-2|} > \sqrt[4]{N}$, and $\frac{1}{(x-2)^4} > N$, as desired.

Chapter 3

Derivatives

3.1 Introducing the Derivative

3.1.1 The secant line through the points $(a, f(a))$ and $(x, f(x))$ for x near a, of the graph of f, is given by $m_{\text{sec}} = \frac{f(x)-f(a)}{x-a}$. As x approaches a, we obtain the limit $m_{\text{tan}} = \lim\limits_{x \to a} \frac{f(x) - f(a)}{x - a} = \lim\limits_{x \to a} m_{\text{sec}}$.

3.1.2 The slope of the secant line through the points $(a, f(a))$ and $(x, f(x))$ for x near a, of the graph of f, is given by $m_{\text{sec}} = \frac{f(x)-f(a)}{x-a}$. So the slope is the change of f divided by the length of the interval $[a, x]$ over which the change occurs, that is, the average rate of change of f over $[a, x]$.

3.1.3 The average rate of change of f over $[a, x]$ is the slope of the secant line $m_{\text{sec}} = \frac{f(x)-f(a)}{x-a}$. As x approaches a, the length of the interval $x - a$ goes to zero, and in the limit we obtain the instantaneous rate of change of f at a given by $m_{\text{tan}} = \lim\limits_{x \to a} \frac{f(x) - f(a)}{x - a}$.

3.1.4 f' is the derivative of f. It represents the slope function of f.

3.1.5 $f'(a)$ is the value of the derivative of f at a. Also, $f'(a)$ is the slope of the tangent line to the graph of f at $(a, f(a))$. Furthermore, $f'(a)$ is the instantaneous rate of change of f at a.

3.1.6 The slope of the tangent line, the instantaneous rate of change, and the value of the derivative of a function at a given point are all the same.

3.1.7 $\frac{dy}{dx}$ is the limit of $\frac{\Delta y}{\Delta x}$ and is the rate of change of y with respect to x.

3.1.8 The derivative of f with respect to x can be written as $f'(x)$ or $\frac{df}{dx}$ or $D_x(f)$ or $\frac{d}{dx}(f)$.

3.1.9

a. $m_{\text{tan}} = \lim\limits_{x \to 3} \dfrac{x^2 - 5 - 4}{x - 3} = \lim\limits_{x \to 3} \dfrac{x^2 - 9}{x - 3} = \lim\limits_{x \to 3} \dfrac{(x - 3)(x + 3)}{x - 3} = \lim\limits_{x \to 3}(x + 3) = 6.$

b. Using the point-slope form of the equation of a line, we obtain $y - 4 = 6(x - 3)$, or $y = 6x - 14$.

c.

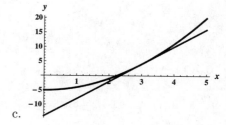

135

3.1.10

a. $m_{\tan} \ = \ \lim\limits_{x \to 1} \dfrac{-3x^2 - 5x + 1 - (-7)}{x - 1} \ =$

$\lim\limits_{x \to 1} \dfrac{-3x^2 - 5x + 8}{x - 1} \ = \ \lim\limits_{x \to 1} \dfrac{-(3x + 8)(x - 1)}{x - 1} \ =$

$\lim\limits_{x \to 1} (-3x - 8) = -11.$

b. Using the point-slope form of the equation of a line,
we get $y + 7 = -11(x - 1)$, or $y = -11x + 4$.

c.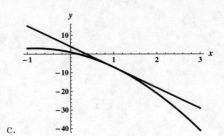

3.1.11

a. $m_{\tan} \ = \ \lim\limits_{x \to 1} \dfrac{-5x + 1 + 4}{x - 1} \ = \ \lim\limits_{x \to 1} \dfrac{-5x + 5}{x - 1} \ =$

$\lim\limits_{x \to 1} -5\left(\dfrac{x - 1}{x - 1}\right) = -5.$

b. Using the point-slope form of the equation of a line,
we get $y + 4 = -5(x - 1)$ which equals $y = -5x + 1$,
the function itself.

c.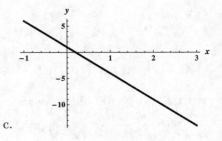

3.1.12

a. $m_{\tan} = \lim\limits_{x \to 1} \dfrac{5 - 5}{x - 1} = 0.$

b. $y - 5 = 0(x - 1)$, or $y = 5$.

c.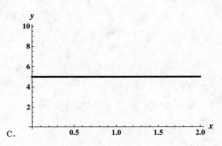

3.1.13

a. $m_{\tan} = \lim\limits_{x \to -1} \dfrac{\frac{1}{x} + 1}{x + 1} = \lim\limits_{x \to -1} \dfrac{\frac{1 + x}{x}}{x + 1} = \lim\limits_{x \to -1} \dfrac{1}{x} = -1.$

b. $y - (-1) = -1(x + 1)$, or $y = -x - 2$.

c.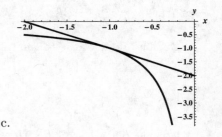

3.1.14

a. $m_{\tan} \ = \ \lim\limits_{x \to -1} \dfrac{\frac{4}{x^2} - 4}{x + 1} \ = \ \lim\limits_{x \to -1} \dfrac{4(1 - x)(x + 1)}{x^2(x + 1)} \ =$

$\lim\limits_{x \to -1} \dfrac{4(1 - x)}{x^2} = 8.$

b. $y - 4 = 8(x + 1)$, or $y = 8x + 12$.

c.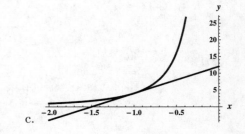

3.1.15

a. $m_{\tan} = \lim\limits_{h \to 0} \dfrac{2(0+h) + 1 - 1}{h} = \lim\limits_{h \to 0} \dfrac{2h}{h} = 2.$

b. $y - 1 = 2x$, or $y = 2x + 1$.

3.1.16

a. $m_{\tan} = \lim\limits_{h \to 0} \dfrac{3(1+h)^2 - 4(1+h) + 1}{h} = \lim\limits_{h \to 0} \dfrac{3 + 6h + 3h^2 - 4 - 4h + 1}{h} = \lim\limits_{h \to 0} \dfrac{3h^2 + 2h}{h} =$
   $\lim\limits_{h \to 0}(3h + 2) = 2.$

b. $y + 1 = 2(x - 1)$, or $y = 2x - 3$.

3.1.17

a. $m_{\tan} = \lim\limits_{h \to 0} \dfrac{-7(-1+h) - 7}{h} = \lim\limits_{h \to 0} -\dfrac{7h}{h} = \lim\limits_{h \to 0} -7 = -7.$

b. $y - 7 = -7(x + 1)$ or $y = -7x$.

3.1.18

a. $m_{\tan} = \lim\limits_{h \to 0} \dfrac{8 - 2h^2 - 8}{h} = \lim\limits_{h \to 0} -\dfrac{2h^2}{h} = \lim\limits_{h \to 0} -2h = 0.$

b. $y - 8 = 0(x - 0)$ or $y = 8$.

3.1.19

a. $m_{\tan} = \lim\limits_{h \to 0} \dfrac{(2+h)^2 - 4 - 0}{h} = \lim\limits_{h \to 0} \dfrac{4 + 4h + h^2 - 4}{h} = \lim\limits_{h \to 0}(4 + h) = 4.$

b. $y - 0 = 4(x - 2)$, or $y = 4x - 8$.

3.1.20

a. $m_{\tan} = \lim\limits_{h \to 0} \dfrac{\frac{1}{1+h} - 1}{h} = \lim\limits_{h \to 0} \dfrac{1 - (1+h)}{(1+h)h} = \lim\limits_{h \to 0} \dfrac{-1}{1+h} = -1.$

b. $y - 1 = -1(x - 1)$, or $y = -x + 2$.

3.1.21

a. $m_{\tan} = \lim\limits_{h \to 0} \dfrac{(1+h)^3 - 1}{h} = \lim\limits_{h \to 0} \dfrac{1 + 3h + 3h^2 + h^3 - 1}{h} = \lim\limits_{h \to 0} \dfrac{h(3 + 3h + h^2)}{h} = \lim\limits_{h \to 0}(3 + 3h + h^2) = 3.$

b. $y - 1 = 3(x - 1)$, or $y = 3x - 2$.

3.1.22

a. $m_{\tan} = \lim\limits_{h \to 0} \dfrac{\frac{1}{2h+1} - 1}{h} = \lim\limits_{h \to 0} \dfrac{\frac{1-2h-1}{2h+1}}{h} = \lim\limits_{h \to 0} -\dfrac{2h}{h(2h+1)} = \lim\limits_{h \to 0} -\dfrac{2}{2h+1} = -2.$

b. $y - 1 = -2x$, or $y = -2x + 1$.

3.1.23

a. $m_{\tan} = \lim\limits_{h \to 0} \dfrac{\frac{1}{3-2(h-1)} - \frac{1}{5}}{h} = \lim\limits_{h \to 0} \dfrac{\frac{5-(3-2h+2)}{15-10(h-1)}}{h} = \lim\limits_{h \to 0} \dfrac{2}{15 - 10(h-1)} = \dfrac{2}{25}.$

b. $y - \frac{1}{5} = \frac{2}{25}(x + 1)$, or $y = \frac{2}{25}x + \frac{7}{25}$.

3.1.24

a. $m_{\tan} = \lim\limits_{h \to 0} \dfrac{\sqrt{h + 2 - 1} - 1}{h} = \lim\limits_{h \to 0} \dfrac{(\sqrt{h + 1} - 1)(\sqrt{h + 1} + 1)}{h(\sqrt{h + 1} + 1)} = \lim\limits_{h \to 0} \dfrac{h + 1 - 1}{h(\sqrt{h + 1} + 1)} =$
$\lim\limits_{h \to 0} \dfrac{1}{\sqrt{h + 1} + 1} = \dfrac{1}{2}.$

b. $y - 1 = \frac{1}{2}(x - 2)$, or $y = \frac{1}{2}x$.

3.1.25

a. $m_{\tan} = \lim\limits_{h \to 0} \dfrac{\sqrt{1 + h + 3} - 2}{h} = \lim\limits_{h \to 0} \dfrac{\sqrt{4 + h} - 2}{h} \cdot \dfrac{\sqrt{4 + h} + 2}{\sqrt{4 + h} + 2} = \lim\limits_{h \to 0} \dfrac{4 + h - 4}{h(\sqrt{4 + h} + 2)} =$
$\lim\limits_{h \to 0} \dfrac{1}{\sqrt{4 + h} + 2} = \dfrac{1}{4}.$

b. $y - 2 = \frac{1}{4}(x - 1)$, or $y = \frac{1}{4}x + \frac{7}{4}$.

3.1.26

a. $m_{\tan} = \lim\limits_{h \to 0} \dfrac{\frac{-2+h}{-2+h+1} - 2}{h} = \lim\limits_{h \to 0} \dfrac{-2 + h - 2(-2 + h + 1)}{(h)(-2 + h + 1)} = \lim\limits_{h \to 0} -\dfrac{1}{-2 + h + 1} = 1.$

b. $y - 2 = (x - -2)$ or $y = x + 4$.

3.1.27

a. $f'(-3) = \lim\limits_{h \to 0} \dfrac{8(-3 + h) + 24}{h} = \lim\limits_{h \to 0} \dfrac{8h}{h} = 8.$

b. $y - (-24) = 8(x + 3)$, or $y = 8x$.

3.1.28

a. $f'(3) = \lim\limits_{h \to 0} \dfrac{(3 + h)^2 - 9}{h} = \lim\limits_{h \to 0} \dfrac{(9 + 6h + h^2) - 9}{h} = \lim\limits_{h \to 0} \dfrac{6h + h^2}{h} = 6.$

b. $y - 9 = 6(x - 3)$, or $y = 6x - 9$.

3.1.29

a. $f'(-2) = \lim\limits_{h \to 0} \dfrac{4(-2 + h)^2 + 2(-2 + h) - 12}{h} = \lim\limits_{h \to 0} \dfrac{16 - 16h + 4h^2 - 4 + 2h - 12}{h} =$
$\lim\limits_{h \to 0} \dfrac{-14h + 4h^2}{h} = -14.$

b. $y - 12 = -14(x + 2)$, or $y = -14x - 16$.

3.1.30

a. $f'(10) = \lim\limits_{h \to 0} \dfrac{2(10 + h)^3 - 2000}{h} = \lim\limits_{h \to 0} \dfrac{2(1000 + 300h + 30h^2 + h^3) - 2000}{h} =$
$\lim\limits_{h \to 0} (600 + 60h + 2h^2) = 600.$

b. $y - 2000 = 600(x - 10)$, or $y = 600x - 4000$.

3.1.31

a. $f'\left(\dfrac{1}{4}\right) = \lim\limits_{h \to 0} \dfrac{\frac{1}{\sqrt{\frac{1}{4}+h}} - 2}{h} = \lim\limits_{h \to 0} \dfrac{1 - 2\sqrt{\frac{1}{4} + h}}{h\sqrt{\frac{1}{4} + h}} = \lim\limits_{h \to 0} \dfrac{\left(1 - 2\sqrt{\frac{1}{4} + h}\right)\left(1 + 2\sqrt{\frac{1}{4} + h}\right)}{h\sqrt{\frac{1}{4} + h}\left(1 + 2\sqrt{\frac{1}{4} + h}\right)} =$
$\lim\limits_{h \to 0} \dfrac{1 - 4\left(\frac{1}{4} + h\right)}{h\sqrt{\frac{1}{4} + h}\left(1 + 2\sqrt{\frac{1}{4} + h}\right)} = \lim\limits_{h \to 0} -\dfrac{4}{\sqrt{\frac{1}{4} + h}\left(1 + 2\sqrt{\frac{1}{4} + h}\right)} = -4.$

b. $y - 2 = -4\left(x - \frac{1}{4}\right)$, or $y = -4x + 3$.

3.1.32

a. $f'(1) = \lim\limits_{h \to 0} \dfrac{\frac{1}{(1+h)^2} - 1}{h} = \lim\limits_{h \to 0} \dfrac{1 - (1+h)^2}{h(1+h)^2} = \lim\limits_{h \to 0} \dfrac{1 - 1 - 2h - h^2}{h(1+h)^2} = \lim\limits_{h \to 0} \dfrac{-2 - h}{(1+h)^2} = -2.$

b. $y - 1 = -2(x - 1)$, or $y = -2x + 3$.

3.1.33

a. $f'(4) = \lim\limits_{h \to 0} \dfrac{\sqrt{2(4+h) + 1} - 3}{h} = \lim\limits_{h \to 0} \dfrac{\sqrt{9 + 2h} - 3}{h} \cdot \dfrac{\sqrt{9 + 2h} + 3}{\sqrt{9 + 2h} + 3} = \lim\limits_{h \to 0} \dfrac{9 + 2h - 9}{h(\sqrt{9 + 2h} + 3)} =$
$\lim\limits_{h \to 0} \dfrac{2}{\sqrt{9 + 2h} + 3} = \dfrac{1}{3}.$

b. $y - 3 = \frac{1}{3}(x - 4)$, or $y = \frac{1}{3}x + \frac{5}{3}$.

3.1.34

a. $f'(12) = \lim\limits_{h \to 0} \dfrac{\sqrt{3(12 + h)} - 6}{h} = \lim\limits_{h \to 0} \dfrac{\sqrt{36 + 3h} - 6}{h} \cdot \dfrac{\sqrt{36 + 3h} + 6}{\sqrt{36 + 3h} + 6} = \lim\limits_{h \to 0} \dfrac{36 + 3h - 36}{h(\sqrt{36 + 3h} + 6)} =$
$\lim\limits_{h \to 0} \dfrac{3}{\sqrt{36 + 3h} + 6} = \dfrac{1}{4}.$

b. $y - 6 = \frac{1}{4}(x - 12)$, or $y = \frac{1}{4}x + 3$.

3.1.35

a. $f'(5) = \lim\limits_{h \to 0} \dfrac{\frac{1}{5 + h + 5} - \frac{1}{10}}{h} = \lim\limits_{h \to 0} \dfrac{10 - (10 + h)}{10h(10 + h)} = \lim\limits_{h \to 0} \dfrac{-1}{10(10 + h)} = -\dfrac{1}{100}.$

b. $y - \frac{1}{10} = -\frac{1}{100}(x - 5)$, or $y = -\frac{1}{100}x + \frac{3}{20}$.

3.1.36

a. $f'(2) = \lim\limits_{h \to 0} \dfrac{\frac{1}{3(2 + h) - 1} - \frac{1}{5}}{h} = \lim\limits_{h \to 0} \dfrac{5 - (3(2 + h) - 1)}{h(3(2 + h) - 1)5} = \lim\limits_{h \to 0} -\dfrac{3h}{h(5 + 3h)5} = \lim\limits_{h \to 0} -\dfrac{3}{(5 + 3h)5} = -\dfrac{3}{25}.$

b. $y - \frac{1}{5} = -\frac{3}{25}(x - 2)$, or $y = -\frac{3}{25}x + \frac{11}{25}$.

3.1.37

a.

$$
\begin{aligned}
f'(x) &= \lim\limits_{h \to 0} \dfrac{3(x + h)^2 + 2(x + h) - 10 - (3x^2 + 2x - 10)}{h} \\
&= \lim\limits_{h \to 0} \dfrac{3x^2 + 6xh + 3h^2 + 2x + 2h - 10 - 3x^2 - 2x + 10}{h} \\
&= \lim\limits_{h \to 0} \dfrac{6xh + 2h + 3h^2}{h} = \lim\limits_{h \to 0}(6x + 2 + 3h) = 6x + 2.
\end{aligned}
$$

b. We have $f'(1) = 8$, and the tangent line is given by $y + 5 = 8(x - 1)$, or $y = 8x - 13$.

c.

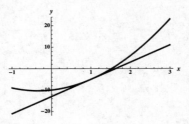

3.1.38

a. $f'(x) = \lim\limits_{h \to 0} \dfrac{3(x + h)^2 - 3x^2}{h} = \lim\limits_{h \to 0} \dfrac{3x^2 + 6xh + 3h^2 - 3x^2}{h} = \lim\limits_{h \to 0} (6x + 3h) = 6x.$

b. We have $f'(0) = 0$, and the tangent line is given by $y - 0 = 0(x - 0)$, so $y = 0$.

c.

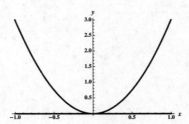

3.1.39

a. $f'(x) = \lim\limits_{h \to 0} \dfrac{5(x + h)^2 - 6(x + h) + 1 - (5x^2 - 6x + 1)}{h} =$
$\lim\limits_{h \to 0} \dfrac{5x^2 + 10xh + 5h^2 - 6x - 6h - 5x^2 + 6x}{h} = \lim\limits_{h \to 0} \dfrac{10xh + 5h^2 - 6h}{h} = \lim\limits_{h \to 0} (10x + 5h - 6) = 10x - 6.$

b. We have $f'(2) = 14$, so the tangent line is given by $y - 9 = 14(x - 2)$, or $y = 14x - 19$.

c.

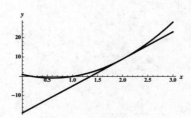

3.1.40

a. $f'(x) = \lim\limits_{h \to 0} \dfrac{1 - (x + h)^2 - (1 - x^2)}{h} = \lim\limits_{h \to 0} \dfrac{1 - (x^2 + 2xh + h^2) - 1 + x^2}{h} = \lim\limits_{h \to 0} \dfrac{-2xh - h^2}{h} =$
$\lim\limits_{h \to 0} (-2x - h) = -2x.$

b. We have $f'(-1) = 2$, so the tangent line is given by $y = 2x + 2$.

c.

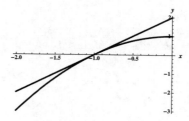

3.1.41

a. $\dfrac{d}{dx}\left(ax^2 + bx + c\right) =$

$$\lim_{h \to 0} \frac{a(x+h)^2 + b(x+h) + c - \left(ax^2 + bx + c\right)}{h} = \lim_{h \to 0} \frac{ax^2 + 2axh + ah^2 + bx + bh + c - ax^2 - bx - c}{h}$$

$$= \lim_{h \to 0} \frac{2axh + ah^2 + bh}{h} = \lim_{h \to 0}\left(2ax + ah + b\right) = 2ax + b.$$

b. With $a = 4, b = -3, c = 10$ we have $\frac{d}{dx}(4x^2 - 3x + 10) = 2 \cdot 4 \cdot x + (-3) = 8x - 3$.

c. From part (b), $f'(1) = 8 \cdot 1 - 3 = 5$.

3.1.42

a. $\dfrac{d}{dx}\sqrt{ax + b} = \lim_{h \to 0} \dfrac{\sqrt{a(x+h) + b} - \sqrt{ax + b}}{h} =$

$$\lim_{h \to 0} \frac{\left(\sqrt{a(x+h) + b} - \sqrt{ax + b}\right)\left(\sqrt{a(x+h) + b} + \sqrt{ax + b}\right)}{h\left(\sqrt{a(x+h) + b} + \sqrt{ax + b}\right)} =$$

$$\lim_{h \to 0} \frac{a(x+h) + b - (ax + b)}{h\left(\sqrt{a(x+h) + b} + \sqrt{ax + b}\right)} = \lim_{h \to 0} \frac{ax + ah + b - ax - b}{h\left(\sqrt{a(x+h) + b} + \sqrt{ax + b}\right)} =$$

$$\lim_{h \to 0} \frac{a}{\sqrt{a(x+h) + b} + \sqrt{ax + b}} = \frac{a}{2\sqrt{ax + b}}, \text{ provided } ax + b > 0.$$

b. With $a = 5, b = 9$, we have $\frac{d}{dx}\sqrt{5x + 9} = \frac{5}{2\sqrt{5x+9}}$.

c. From part (b), $f'(-1) = \frac{5}{2\sqrt{-5+9}} = \frac{5}{2\sqrt{4}} = \frac{5}{4}$.

3.1.43 $m_{\tan} = \lim_{h \to 0} \dfrac{\frac{1}{1+h+1} - \frac{1}{2}}{h} = \lim_{h \to 0} \dfrac{2 - (2+h)}{h(2+h)2} = \lim_{h \to 0} \dfrac{-1}{(2+h)2} = -\dfrac{1}{4}$.

3.1.44 $m_{\tan} = \lim_{h \to 0} \dfrac{2 + h - (2+h)^2 - (2 - 4)}{h} = \lim_{h \to 0} \dfrac{2 + h - 4 - 4h - h^2 + 2}{h} = \lim_{h \to 0} \dfrac{-3h - h^2}{h} =$
$\lim_{h \to 0}(-3 - h) = -3$.

3.1.45 $m_{\tan} = \lim_{h \to 0} \dfrac{2\sqrt{25 + h} - 1 - (2\sqrt{25} - 1)}{h} = \lim_{h \to 0} \dfrac{2(\sqrt{25 + h} - \sqrt{25})}{h} =$
$\lim_{h \to 0} \dfrac{2(\sqrt{25 + h} - \sqrt{25})(\sqrt{25 + h} + \sqrt{25})}{h(\sqrt{25 + h} + \sqrt{25})} = \lim_{h \to 0} \dfrac{2(25 + h - 25)}{h(\sqrt{25 + h} + \sqrt{25})} = \lim_{h \to 0} \dfrac{2}{\sqrt{25 + h} + \sqrt{25}} = \dfrac{1}{5}$.

3.1.46 $m_{\tan} = \lim_{h \to 0} \dfrac{\pi(3 + h)^2 - 9\pi}{h} = \lim_{h \to 0} \dfrac{\pi(9 + 6h + h^2) - 9\pi}{h} = \lim_{h \to 0} \dfrac{6\pi h + \pi h^2}{h} = \lim_{h \to 0}(6\pi + \pi h) = 6\pi$.

3.1.47

a. True. Because the graph is a line, any secant line has the same graph as the function and thus the same slope.

b. False. For example, take $f(x) = x^2$, $P = (0,0)$ and $Q = (1,1)$. Then the secant line has slope $m_{\text{sec}} = \frac{1-0}{1-0} = 1$, but the the graph has a horizontal tangent at P so $m_{\text{tan}} = 0$ and $m_{\text{sec}} > m_{\text{tan}}$.

c. True. $m_{\text{sec}} = \frac{(x+h)^2 - x^2}{h} = \frac{2xh + h^2}{h} = 2x + h$, while $m_{\text{tan}} = \lim_{h \to 0}(2x+h) = 2x$. Because we assume that $h > 0$, we have $m_{\text{sec}} = 2x + h > 2x = m_{\text{tan}}$.

3.1.48 $m_{\text{tan}} = \lim_{h \to 0} \dfrac{m(x+h) + b - (mx + b)}{h} = \lim_{h \to 0} \dfrac{mh}{h} = m$. Thus the derivative has the same value as the slope of the line and the graph and formula of the tangent line are the same as those of the function, namely $mx + b$.

3.1.49

a.

$$f'(x) = \lim_{h \to 0} \frac{\sqrt{3(x+h)+1} - \sqrt{3x+1}}{h}$$

$$= \lim_{h \to 0} \frac{\sqrt{3(x+h)+1} - \sqrt{3x+1}}{h} \cdot \frac{\sqrt{3x+3h+1} + \sqrt{3x+1}}{\sqrt{3x+3h+1} + \sqrt{3x+1}}$$

$$= \lim_{h \to 0} \frac{3x + 3h + 1 - 3x - 1}{h(\sqrt{3x+3h+1} + \sqrt{3x+1})} = \lim_{h \to 0} \frac{3}{\sqrt{3x+3h+1} + \sqrt{3x+1}} = \frac{3}{2\sqrt{3x+1}}.$$

b. We have $f'(8) = \frac{3}{10}$. Using the point-slope form, we get that the tangent line has equation $y - 5 = \frac{3}{10}(x - 8)$, which can be written as $y = \frac{3}{10}x + \frac{13}{5}$.

3.1.50

a.

$$f'(x) = \lim_{h \to 0} \frac{\sqrt{x+h+2} - \sqrt{x+2}}{h}$$

$$= \lim_{h \to 0} \frac{\sqrt{x+h+2} - \sqrt{x+2}}{h} \cdot \frac{\sqrt{x+h+2} + \sqrt{x+2}}{\sqrt{x+h+2} + \sqrt{x+2}}$$

$$= \lim_{h \to 0} \frac{x + h + 2 - x - 2}{h(\sqrt{x+h+2} + \sqrt{x+2})} = \lim_{h \to 0} \frac{1}{\sqrt{x+h+2} + \sqrt{x+2}} = \frac{1}{2\sqrt{x+2}}.$$

b. We have $f'(7) = \frac{1}{6}$. Using the point-slope form, we get that the tangent line has equation $y - 3 = \frac{1}{6}(x - 7)$, or $y = \frac{1}{6}x + \frac{11}{6}$.

3.1.51

a. $f'(x) = \lim_{h \to 0} \dfrac{\frac{2}{3(x+h)+1} - \frac{2}{3x+1}}{h} = \lim_{h \to 0} \dfrac{6x + 2 - (6x + 6h + 2)}{h(3x+1)(3x+3h+1)} = \lim_{h \to 0} \dfrac{-6h}{h(3x+1)(3x+3h+1)} =$

$-\dfrac{6}{(3x+1)^2}.$

b. We have $f'(-1) = -\frac{3}{2}$. Using the point-slope form, we get that the tangent line has equation $y + 1 = -\frac{3}{2}(x + 1)$, which can be written as $y = -\frac{3}{2}x - \frac{5}{2}$.

3.1.52

a. $f'(x) = \lim\limits_{h \to 0} \dfrac{\frac{1}{x+h} - \frac{1}{x}}{h} = \lim\limits_{h \to 0} \dfrac{x - x - h}{h(x+h)x} = \lim\limits_{h \to 0} \dfrac{-1}{x^2 + xh} = -\dfrac{1}{x^2}.$

b. We have $f'(-5) = -\frac{1}{25}$. Using the point-slope form, we get that the tangent line has equation $y + \frac{1}{5} = -\frac{1}{25}(x+5)$, which can be written as $y = \frac{-1}{25}x - \frac{2}{5}$.

3.1.53

a. At C and D, the slope of the tangent line (and thus of the curve) is negative.

b. At A, B, and E, the slope of the curve is positive.

c. The graph is in its steepest ascent at A followed by B. At E it barely increases, at D it slightly decreases and at C it is decreasing the most, so the points in decreasing order of slope are A, B, E, D, C.

3.1.54

a. The graph of the function has negative slope to the right of the vertical axis so the slope is negative at D and E.

b. The graph of the function has positive slope to the left of the vertical axis so the slope is positive at A, B, C.

c. The slope at D and E is negative, with a slightly larger absolute value at D. The slope at A and C is about equal and positive, and the slope is steepest at B. So the order is B, A, C, E, D, where A and C could be switched.

3.1.55

a. From the graph we approximate the derivative by the slope of a secant line: For example we see that $E(6) = 250\,\text{kWh}$ and $E(18) = 350\,\text{kWh}$, so the power after 10 hours is approximately the slope of the secant line through these points, so $P(10) \approx m_{sec} = \frac{E(18)-E(6)}{18-6} = \frac{350\,\text{kWh}-250\,\text{kWh}}{12\text{h}} \approx 8.3\,\text{kW}$. Similarly, after 20 hours, using 18 hours and 25 hours, that $P(20) \approx m_{sec} = \frac{E(22)-E(18)}{22-18} = \frac{325\,\text{kWh}-350\,\text{kWh}}{4\text{h}} \approx -6.25\text{kW}$.

b. The power is zero where the graph of $E(t)$ has a horizontal tangent line, which happens approximately at $t = 6$ hours and $t = 18$ hours.

c. The power has a maximum where the graph of $E(t)$ has the steepest increase, which is approximately at $t = 12$ hours.

3.1.56

a. The average rate of growth is the slope of the secant line between $t = 20$ and $t = 30$ so $m_{sec} = \frac{528,000-304,744}{30-20} \approx 22,326$, which means that the average population growth is a bit over 22,000 people per year (Census data only provide estimates; there is no use in calculating more accurately).

b. Drawing the secant line from part a) and the approximate tangent line for 1975 (corresponding to $t = 25$), we see that they have about the same slope.

c. The average is given by $m_{sec} = \frac{1,563,282-852,737}{50-40} \approx 71,055$, so Las Vegas is growing at a rate of approximately 71,100 people per year. This is an underestimate of the growth rate in 2000 as the slope of the graph keeps increasing.

3.1.57 Consider $a = 2$ and $f(x) = \frac{1}{x+1}$.

Then $f'(2) = \lim\limits_{x \to 2} \dfrac{\frac{1}{x+1} - \frac{1}{3}}{x-2}$ as desired.

We have $f'(2) = \lim\limits_{x \to 2} \dfrac{\frac{1}{x+1} - \frac{1}{3}}{x-2} = \lim\limits_{x \to 2} \dfrac{3-(x+1)}{(x-2)3(x+1)} = \lim\limits_{x \to 2} \dfrac{-(x-2)}{(x-2)3(x+1)} = \lim\limits_{x \to 2} \dfrac{-1}{3(x+1)} = -\dfrac{1}{9}.$

3.1.58 Consider $a = 2$ and $f(x) = \sqrt{x}$.

Then $f'(2) = \lim\limits_{h \to 0} \dfrac{\sqrt{2+h} - \sqrt{2}}{h}$, as desired.

We have

$$f'(2) = \lim_{h \to 0} \frac{\sqrt{2+h} - \sqrt{2}}{h} = \lim_{h \to 0} \frac{\left(\sqrt{2+h} - \sqrt{2}\right)\left(\sqrt{2+h} + \sqrt{2}\right)}{h\left(\sqrt{2+h} + \sqrt{2}\right)}$$

$$= \lim_{h \to 0} \frac{2 + h - 2}{h\left(\sqrt{2+h} + \sqrt{2}\right)} = \lim_{h \to 0} \frac{1}{\sqrt{2+h} + \sqrt{2}} = \frac{1}{2\sqrt{2}}.$$

3.1.59 Consider $a = 2$ and $f(x) = x^4$.

Then $f'(2) = \lim\limits_{h \to 0} \dfrac{(2+h)^4 - 16}{h}$ as desired.

We have

$$f'(2) = \lim_{h \to 0} \frac{(2+h)^4 - 16}{h} = \lim_{h \to 0} \frac{16 + 32h + 24h^2 + 8h^3 + h^4 - 16}{h}$$

$$= \lim_{h \to 0} \frac{h\left(32 + 24h + 8h^2 + h^3\right)}{h} = \lim_{h \to 0} \left(32 + 24h + 8h^2 + h^3\right) = 32.$$

3.1.60 Consider $a = 1$ and $f(x) = 3x^2 + 4x$.

Then $f'(1) = \lim\limits_{x \to 1} \dfrac{3x^2 + 4x - 7}{x - 1}$, as desired.

We have $f'(1) = \lim\limits_{x \to 1} \dfrac{3x^2 + 4x - 7}{x - 1} = \lim\limits_{x \to 1} \dfrac{(x-1)(3x+7)}{x - 1} = \lim\limits_{x \to 1} (3x + 7) = 10.$

3.1.61 It is not differentiable at $x = 2$. The denominator of f is zero when $x = 2$, so f is not defined at $x = 2$, and is therefore not differentiable there.

3.1.62

    a. $f'(x) = 2x$ b. $f'(x) = 3x^2$

    c. $f'(x) = 4x^3$ d. $f'(x) = nx^{n-1}$.

3.1.63 In order for f to be differentiable at $x = 1$, it would need to be continuous there. Thus, $\lim\limits_{x \to 1^-} f(x) = \lim\limits_{x \to 1^-} 2x^2 = 2 = \lim\limits_{x \to 1^+} f(x) = \lim\limits_{x \to 1^+} ax - 2 = a - 2$, so the only possible value for a is 4. Now checking the differentiability at 1, we have (from the left)

$$\lim_{x \to 1^-} \frac{f(x) - f(1)}{x - 1} = \lim_{x \to 1^-} \frac{2x^2 - 2}{x - 1} = \lim_{x \to 1^-} 2(x + 1) = 4.$$

Also, from the right we have

$$\lim_{x \to 1^+} \frac{f(x) - f(1)}{x - 1} = \lim_{x \to 1^+} \frac{4x - 2 - 2}{x - 1} = \lim_{x \to 1^+} 4 = 4,$$

so f is differentiable at 1 for $a = 4$.

3.1.64

    a. $f'(4) = \lim\limits_{x \to 4} \dfrac{\sqrt{x} - \sqrt{4}}{x - 4} = \lim\limits_{x \to 4} \dfrac{\sqrt{x} - 2}{(\sqrt{x} - 2)(\sqrt{x} + 2)} = \lim\limits_{x \to 4} \dfrac{1}{\sqrt{x} + 2} = \dfrac{1}{4}.$

b. For $|h|$ near zero we have $f'(4) \approx \frac{f(4+h)-f(4)}{h} = \frac{\sqrt{4+h}-2}{h}$.

c.

h	$\frac{\sqrt{4+h}-2}{h}$	Error	h	$\frac{\sqrt{4+h}-2}{h}$	Error
0.1	0.248457	−0.001543	−0.1	0.251582	.001582
0.01	0.249844	−0.000156	−0.01	0.250156	.000156
0.001	0.249984	−0.000016	−0.001	0.250016	.000016
0.0001	0.249998	−0.000002	−0.0001	0.250002	.000002

d. The error approaches zero as h approaches zero.

3.1.65

a. Note that the slope generated by the centered difference quotient is $\frac{f(4.5)-f(3.5)}{2(.5)} = \sqrt{4.5} - \sqrt{3.5} \approx$ 0.250492. The centered difference quotient line is very close to the tangent line, which closely approximates the function near the point of tangency.

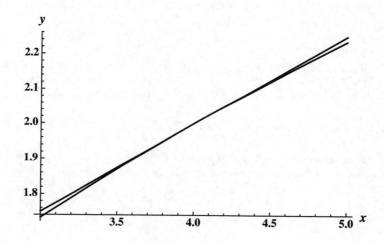

b.

h	Approximation	Error
0.1	0.25002	2.0×10^{-5}
0.01	$\approx .25000$	2.0×10^{-7}
0.001	$\approx .25000$	2.0×10^{-9}

c. The centered difference quotient is symmetric about zero, so using the corresponding negative values yields the same results.

d. The centered difference quotient appears to be more accurate than the approximation in the previous problem.

3.1.66

a. $\frac{f(2.5)-f(2)}{2.5-2} = \frac{81-55}{.5} = 52.$

b. $\frac{f(2.5)-f(1.5)}{2(0.5)} = 81 - 33 = 48.$

3.1.67

a. Forward:

$$\frac{\text{erf}(1.05) - \text{erf}(1)}{.05} = \frac{.862436 - .842701}{.05} = 0.3947.$$

Centered:

$$\frac{\text{erf}(1.05) - \text{erf}(.95)}{2(.05)} = \frac{.862436 - .820891}{0.1} = 0.41545.$$

b. Forward:

$$0.3947 - \frac{2}{e\sqrt{\pi}} \approx -0.0204075.$$

Centered:

$$0.41545 - \frac{2}{e\sqrt{\pi}} \approx 0.000342503.$$

3.2   Working with Derivatives

3.2.1 $f(x)$ refers to the value of the function at x, while $f'(x)$ refers to the slope of the graph. If the function is positive and increasing, such as $f(x) = x^2$ for $x = 2$, then $f(x) > 0$ and $f'(x) > 0$. But if the function is positive and decreasing, such as $f(x) = x^2$ for $x = -2$, then $f(x) > 0$ and $f'(x) < 0$.

3.2.2 $f(x)$ refers to the value of the function at x, while $f'(x)$ refers to the slope of the graph. If the function is decreasing and positive, such as $f(x) = -x^3$ for $x = -2$, then $f'(x) < 0$ and $f(x) > 0$. But if the function is decreasing and negative, such as $f(x) = -x^3$ for $x = 2$, then $f'(x) < 0$ and $f(x) < 0$ as well.

3.2.3 Yes, differentiable functions are continuous by Theorem 3.1.

3.2.4 No, there are continuous functions which are not differentiable. For example $f(x) = |x|$ is continuous everywhere but the graph of f has a corner at 0, and thus f is not differentiable at 0.

3.2.5

The function f is not differentiable at $x = -2, 0, 2$, so f' is not defined at those points. Elsewhere, the slope is constant.

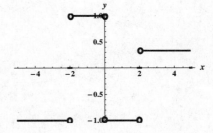

3.2.6

The function f is not differentiable at $x = 1$ so f' is not defined there. Elsewhere, the slope is constant.

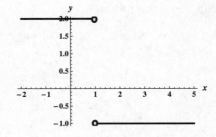

3.2.7 (c) is the only line with negative slope, so it corresponds to derivative (A). Since (d) contains the points $(2,0)$ and $(0,1)$, it has slope $\frac{1}{2}$, so it corresponds to derivative (B). Finally, lines (a) and (b) are parallel; since (b) contains the points $(0,1)$ and $(-1,0)$, it has slope 1, so that (a) has slope 1 as well. They both correspond to derivative (C).

3.2.8 Note that (A) and (C) have positive slope, while (B) and (D) have negative slope. Since (a) is the largest positive derivative, it corresponds to (A), which has larger slope than (B). Thus (b), the other positive derivative, corresponds to (C). Since (d) is the negative derivative of largest magnitude, it corresponds to (D), since the slope of (D) has larger magnitude than that of (B). So (c), the other negative derivative, corresponds to (B).

3.2.9

a. The function has non-negative slope everywhere, and as there is a horizontal tangent at $x = 0$, so the derivative has to be zero at zero. The graph of the derivative has to be above the x-axis and touching it at $x = 0$, so (D) is the graph of the derivative.

b. The graph of this function has three horizontal tangent lines, at $x = -1, 0, 1$, and the matching graph of the derivative with three zeros is (C).

c. The function has negative slope on $(-1, 0)$, and positive slope on $(0, 1)$ and has a horizontal tangent at $x = 0$, so the derivative has to be negative on $(-1, 0)$, positive on $(0, 1)$ and zero at $x = 0$; the graph is (B).

d. The function has negative slope everywhere so the graph of the derivative has to be negative everywhere, which is graph (A).

3.2.10

The function has a positive slope for $x < 1$ and a negative slope for $x > 1$, and a horizontal tangent line at $x = 1$.

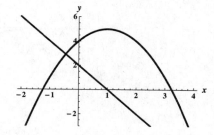

3.2.11

The function always has non-negative slope, so the derivative is never below the x axis.
However, it does have slope zero at about $x = 2$.

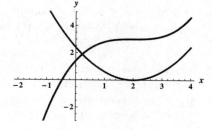

3.2.12

The slope increases until the function crosses the
y axis at $x = 0$, and then the slope is still positive,
but decreases.

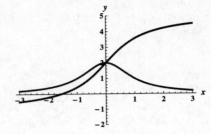

3.2.13 Note that f is undefined at $x = -2$ and $x = 1$, but is differentiable elsewhere. It is decreasing, and increasingly rapidly, as x increases towards $x = -2$. It decreases, but increasingly slowly, and towards a zero slope, as x increases from 1. Finally, between $x = -2$ and $x = 1$, the function increases, but increasingly slowly, until $x = 0$ and then decreases, but increasingly rapidly, as x approaches 1. A graph of the derivative is

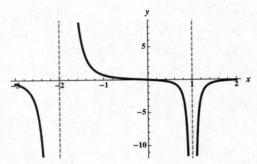

3.2.14 Note that f is undefined at $x = -1$ and $x = 0$, but is differentiable elsewhere. It is decreasing everywhere it is defined. On $(-\infty, -1)$, it decreases increasingly rapidly as $x \to -1$, while on $(-1, 0)$ it decreases more and more slowly from a very large negative slope just to the right of -1 until it is almost flat near $x = 0$. Finally, on $(0, \infty)$ it decreases more and more slowly from a very large negative slope and approaches a zero slope as $x \to \infty$. A graph of the derivative is

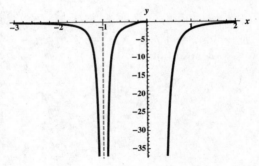

3.2.15

a. The function f is not continuous at $x = 1$,
   because the graph has a jump there.

b. The function f is not differentiable at $x = 1$
   because it is not continuous at that point
   (Theorem 3.1 Alternate Version), and it is
   also not differentiable at $x = 2$ because the
   graph has a corner there.

c.

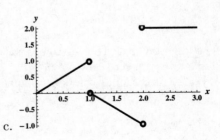

3.2.16

a. The function g is not defined at $x = 1$, because the graph has a hole there.

b. The function g is not differentiable at $x = 1$ because it is not defined at that point, and it is also not differentiable at $x = 2$ because the graph has a cusp there.

c.

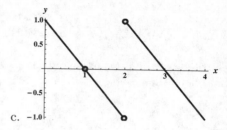

3.2.17

a. True. Differentiability implies continuity, by Theorem 3.1.

b. True. Because the absolute value function is continuous, and $y = x + 1$ is continuous, and the composition of continuous functions is continuous, we know that this function is continuous. Note that it is not differentiable at $x = -1$ because the absolute value function is not differentiable at $x = 0$.

c. False. In order for f to be differentiable on $[a, b]$, f would need to be defined at a and at b. Because the domain of f doesn't include these endpoints, this situation is not possible.

3.2.18 The graph of $f'(x) = 2$ is a horizontal line. The possible graphs of f are all lines with slope 2 (and are thus parallel).

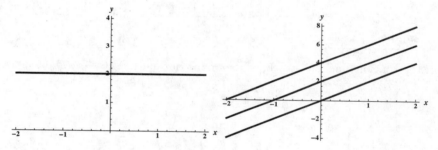

3.2.19

Because $f'(x) = x$ is negative for $x < 0$ and positive for $x > 0$, we have that the graph of f has to have negative slope on $(-\infty, 0)$ and positive slope on $(0, \infty)$ and has to have a horizontal tangent at $x = 0$. Because f' only gives us the slope of the tangent line and not the actual value of f, there are infinitely many graphs possible, they all have the same shape, but are shifted along the y–axis.

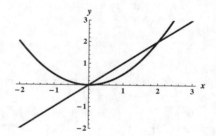

3.2.20

Because the derivative is constant on $(-\infty, 0)$, $(0, 1)$ and $(1, \infty)$, the graph of f has to consist of pieces of straight lines on these intervals. There are infinitely many possible functions f that have f' for its derivative. Because f is assumed to be continuous, each possible f is a shift, up or down, of another possible f.

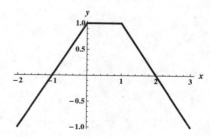

3.2.21 With $f(x) = 3x - 4$, we have

$$f'(x) = \lim_{h \to 0} \frac{f(x+h) - f(x)}{h} = \lim_{h \to 0} \frac{3(x+h) - 4 - (3x - 4)}{h} = \lim_{h \to 0} \frac{3h}{h} = \lim_{h \to 0} 3 = 3.$$

The slope of the tangent line at $(1, -1)$ is 3, so the slope of the normal line is $-\frac{1}{3}$. The equation of the normal line is thus $y - (-1) = -\frac{1}{3}(x - 1)$, or $y = -\frac{1}{3}x - \frac{2}{3}$.

3.2.22 With $f(x) = \sqrt{x}$, we have $f'(x) = \lim_{h \to 0} \frac{f(x+h) - f(x)}{h} = \lim_{h \to 0} \frac{\sqrt{x+h} - \sqrt{x}}{h} =$

$\lim_{h \to 0} \frac{(\sqrt{x+h} - \sqrt{x})(\sqrt{x+h} + \sqrt{x})}{h(\sqrt{x+h} + \sqrt{x})} = \lim_{h \to 0} \frac{x + h - x}{h(\sqrt{x+h} + \sqrt{x})} = \lim_{h \to 0} \frac{1}{\sqrt{x+h} + \sqrt{x}} = \frac{1}{2\sqrt{x}}$. Thus, the slope of the tangent line at $(4, 2)$ is $\frac{1}{4}$, so the slope of the normal line is -4. The equation of the normal line is $y - 2 = -4(x - 4)$, or $y = -4x + 18$.

3.2.23 With $f(x) = \frac{2}{x}$, we have $f'(x) = \lim_{h \to 0} \frac{f(x+h) - f(x)}{h} = \lim_{h \to 0} \frac{\frac{2}{x+h} - \frac{2}{x}}{h} = \lim_{h \to 0} \frac{\frac{2x - (2(x+h))}{x(x+h)}}{h} =$

$\lim_{h \to 0} \frac{-2h}{hx(x+h)} = \lim_{h \to 0} \frac{-2}{x(x+h)} = -\frac{2}{x^2}$. At the point $(1, 2)$ the slope of the tangent line is -2, so the slope of the normal line is $\frac{1}{2}$. The equation of the normal line is $y - 2 = \frac{1}{2}(x - 1)$ or $y = \frac{x}{2} + \frac{3}{2}$.

3.2.24 With $f(x) = x^2 - 3x$, we have $f'(x) = \lim_{h \to 0} \frac{f(x+h) - f(x)}{h} = \lim_{h \to 0} \frac{(x+h)^2 - 3(x+h) - (x^2 - 3x)}{h} =$

$\lim_{h \to 0} \frac{x^2 + 2hx + h^2 - 3x - 3h - x^2 + 3x}{h} = \lim_{h \to 0} \frac{2hx + h^2 - 3h}{h} = \lim_{h \to 0} \frac{h(2x + h - 3)}{h} == 2x - 3$. At the point $(3, 0)$ the slope of the tangent line is 3, so the slope of the normal line is $-\frac{1}{3}$. The equation of the normal line is $y - 0 = -\frac{1}{3}(x - 3)$ or $y = -\frac{x}{3} + 1$.

3.2.25 With $f(x) = x^2 + 1$, we have $f'(x) = \lim_{h \to 0} \frac{f(x+h) - f(x)}{h} = \lim_{h \to 0} \frac{(x+h)^2 + 1 - (x^2 + 1)}{h} =$

$\lim_{h \to 0} \frac{x^2 + 2hx + h^2 + 1 - x^2 - 1}{h} = \lim_{h \to 0} \frac{2hx + h^2}{h} = \lim_{h \to 0} \frac{h(2x + h)}{h} = 2x$. We are looking for points $(x, x^2 + 1)$ where the slope of the line between this point and $Q(3, 6)$ is equal to $2x$. So we seek solutions to the equation

$$\frac{6 - (x^2 + 1)}{3 - x} = 2x,$$

which can be written as $5 - x^2 = 2x(3 - x)$, or $x^2 - 6x + 5 = 0$. Factoring, we obtain $(x - 5)(x - 1) = 0$, so the solutions are $x = 5$ and $x = 1$. Note that at the point $(5, 26)$ on the curve the tangent line is $y - 26 = 10(x - 5)$ which does contain the point $Q(3, 6)$ and at the point $(1, 2)$ the equation of the tangent line is $y - 2 = 2(x - 1)$, which also contains the point $Q(3, 6)$.

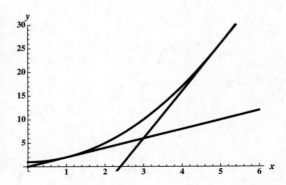

3.2.26 With $f(x) = -x^2 + 4x - 3$, we have

$$\begin{aligned}
f'(x) &= \lim_{h \to 0} \frac{f(x+h) - f(x)}{h} = \lim_{h \to 0} \frac{-(x+h)^2 + 4(x+h) - 3 - (-x^2 + 4x - 3)}{h} \\
&= \lim_{h \to 0} \frac{-x^2 - 2hx - h^2 + 4x + 4h - 3 + x^2 - 4x + 3}{h} \\
&= \lim_{h \to 0} \frac{-2hx - h^2 + 4h}{h} = \lim_{h \to 0} \frac{h(-2x - h + 4)}{h} \\
&= \lim_{h \to 0} (-2x - h + 4) = -2x + 4.
\end{aligned}$$

We are looking for points $(x, -x^2 + 4x - 3)$ where the slope of the line between this point and $Q(0, 6)$ is equal to $-2x + 4$. So we seek solutions to the equation

$$\frac{-x^2 + 4x - 3 - 6}{x - 0} = -2x + 4,$$

which can be written as $-x^2 + 4x - 9 = -2x^2 + 4x$, or $x^2 - 9 = 0$. This factors as $(x - 3)(x + 3) = 0$, so the solutions are $x = \pm 3$. Note that at the point $(3, 0)$ the equation of the tangent line is $y = -2(x-3)$ which does contain the point $Q(0, 6)$, and at the point $(-3, -24)$ the equation of the tangent line is $y + 24 = 10(x + 3)$, which also contains the point $Q(0, 6)$.

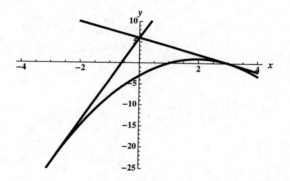

3.2.27 With $f(x) = \frac{1}{x}$, we have

$$\begin{aligned}
f'(x) &= \lim_{h \to 0} \frac{f(x+h) - f(x)}{h} = \lim_{h \to 0} \frac{\frac{1}{x+h} - \frac{1}{x}}{h} = \lim_{h \to 0} \frac{\frac{x - (x+h)}{x(x+h)}}{h} \\
&= \lim_{h \to 0} \frac{-h}{hx(x+h)} = \lim_{h \to 0} \frac{-1}{x(x+h)} = -\frac{1}{x^2}.
\end{aligned}$$

We are looking for points $(x, 1/x)$ where the slope of the line between this point and $Q(-2, 4)$ is equal to $\frac{-1}{x^2}$. So we seek solutions to the equation

$$\frac{1/x - 4}{x + 2} = -\frac{1}{x^2},$$

which can be written as $x - 4x^2 = -x - 2$, or $4x^2 - 2x - 2 = 0$, or $2x^2 - x - 1 = 0$. This factors as $(2x + 1)(x - 1) = 0$, so the solutions are $x = 1$ and $x = -1/2$. Note that at $x = 1$ the equation of the tangent line is $y - 1 = -1(x - 1)$ which does contain the point $Q(-2, 4)$, and at $x = -1/2$ the equation of the tangent line is $y + 2 = -4\left(x + \frac{1}{2}\right)$ or $y = -4x - 4$ which also contains the point $Q(-2, 4)$.

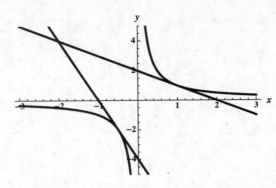

3.2.28 Using a computer algebra system, we see that for $f(x) = e^{-x}$, we have $f'(x) = -e^{-x}$. We are looking for points (x, e^{-x}) where the slope of the line between this point and $Q(1, -4)$ is equal to $-e^{-x}$. So we seek solutions to the equation

$$\frac{e^{-x} + 4}{x - 1} = -e^{-x}.$$

Again using a computer algebra system, we find an approximate solution of $x = -1.2$. At that value of x, the corresponding value of e^{-x} is approximately 3.32. The equation of the tangent line at that point is approximately $y - 3.32 = -3.32(x + 1.2)$, or $y = -3.32x - .664$. Note that this approximation does approximately contain the point $Q(1, -4)$ because $-3.32 - .664 \approx -4$.

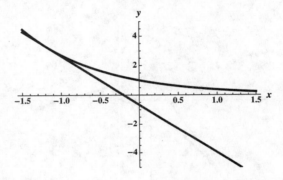

3.2.29

a. The tangent line for Q looks to be the steepest at $t = 0$.

b. All tangent lines for Q have positive slope, so Q' is positive for $t \geq 0$.

c. The tangent lines appear to be getting less steep as t increases, so Q' is decreasing.

d.

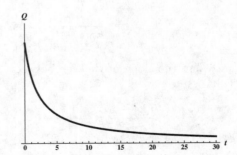

3.2.30

a. The tangent line appears to be the steepest at $t = 10$.

b. The tangent lines to P all have positive slope, so $P' > 0$ for $t \geq 0$.

c. P' appears to increase from $t = 0$ to $t = 10$, and then decrease after that.

d.

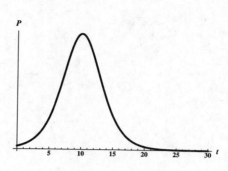

3.2.31

a.
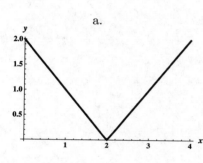

b. $f'_+(2) = \lim\limits_{h \to 0^+} \dfrac{|2 + h - 2| - 0}{h} = \lim\limits_{h \to 0^+} \dfrac{h}{h} = 1$, because for $h > 0$, we have $|h| = h$. Similarly, $f'_-(2) = \lim\limits_{h \to 0^-} \dfrac{|2 + h - 2| - 0}{h} = \lim\limits_{h \to 0^-} -\dfrac{h}{h} = -1$, because for $h < 0$, we have $|h| = -h$.

c. Because f is defined at $a = 2$ and the graph of f does not jump, f is continuous at $a = 2$. Because the left-hand and right-hand derivatives are not equal, f is not differentiable at $a = 2$.

3.2.32

a.
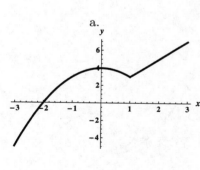

b. Assuming the point $a = 1$, we get $f'_+(1) = \lim\limits_{h \to 0^+} \dfrac{2(1 + h) + 1 - 3}{h} = \lim\limits_{h \to 0^+} \dfrac{2h}{h} = 2$, because for $h > 0$, we have $1 + h > 1$. Similarly, $f'_-(1) = \lim\limits_{h \to 0^-} \dfrac{4 - (1 + h)^2 - 3}{h} = \lim\limits_{h \to 0^-} \dfrac{-2h - h^2}{h} = -2$, because for $h < 0$, we have $1 + h < 1$.

c. Because f is defined at $a = 1$ and the graph of f does not jump, f is continuous at $a = 1$. Because the left-hand and right-hand derivatives are not equal, f is not differentiable at $a = 1$.

3.2.33

a. The graph has a vertical tangent at $x = 2$.

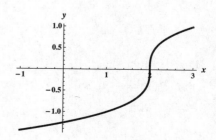

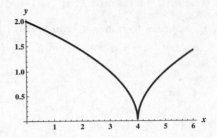

b. The graph has a vertical tangent at $x = 4$.

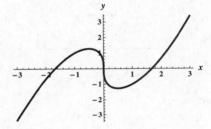

c. The graph has a vertical tangent at $x = -1$.

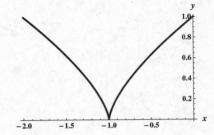

d. The graph has a vertical tangent at $x = 0$.

3.2.34

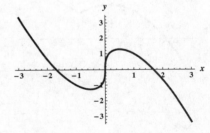

a. This graph has $\displaystyle\lim_{x \to a^-} f'(x) = \lim_{x \to a^+} f'(x) = +\infty$, where $a = 0$.

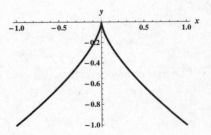

b. This graph has $\displaystyle\lim_{x \to a^-} f'(x) = +\infty$ and $\displaystyle\lim_{x \to a^+} f'(x) = -\infty$, where $a = 0$.

c. This graph has $\lim\limits_{x \to a^-} f'(x) = -\infty$ and $\lim\limits_{x \to a^+} f'(x) = +\infty$, where $a = 0$.

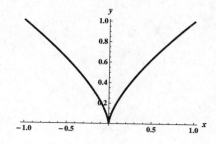

d. This graph has $\lim\limits_{x \to a^-} f'(x) = -\infty$ and $\lim\limits_{x \to a^+} f'(x) = -\infty$, where $a = 0$.

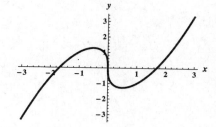

3.2.35 $f'(0) = \lim\limits_{h \to 0} \dfrac{h^{1/3}}{h} = \lim\limits_{h \to 0} \dfrac{1}{h^{2/3}} = +\infty$. Thus the graph of f has a vertical tangent at $x = 0$.

3.2.36

a. This circle has vertical tangents at $x = 3$ and $x = -3$.

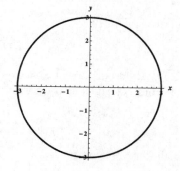

b. This circle has vertical tangents at $x = -2$ and $x = 0$.

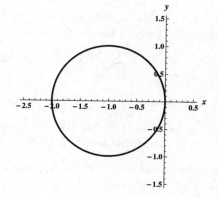

3.2.37

a.

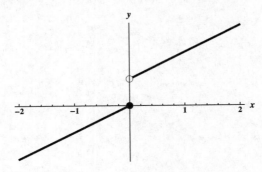

b. For $x < 0$, we have $f'(x) = \lim\limits_{h \to 0} \dfrac{x + h - x}{h} = \lim\limits_{h \to 0} \dfrac{h}{h} = \lim\limits_{h \to 0} 1 = 1.$

c. For $x > 0$, we have $f'(x) = \lim\limits_{h \to 0} \dfrac{x + h + 1 - (x + 1)}{h} = \lim\limits_{h \to 0} \dfrac{h}{h} = \lim\limits_{h \to 0} 1 = 1.$

d.

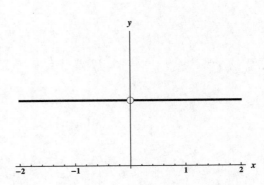

e. f is not differentiable at $x = 0$ as it is not continuous there. Also, if we were to compute the derivative of f from the right at 0 we would have

$$\lim_{h \to 0^+} \frac{f(0 + h) - f(0)}{h} = \lim_{h \to 0^+} \frac{h + 1 - 0}{h} = \lim_{h \to 0^+} \frac{h + 1}{h},$$

which does not exist.

3.3   Rules of Differentiation

3.3.1 Often the limit definition of f' is difficult to compute, especially for functions which are reasonably complicated. The rules for differentiation allow us to easily compute the derivatives of complex functions.

3.3.2 It is shown to be valid for all positive integers n. In future sections we will see that it holds for all real numbers.

3.3.3 The function $f(x) = e^x$ is an example of a function with this property.

3.3.4 The sum rule tells us that the derivative of $f + g$ is $f' + g'$. That is, the derivative of the sum of two functions is the sum of the derivatives of those functions.

3.3.5 By the constant multiple rule, the derivative of the function cf where c is a constant and f is a function is cf'. That is, the derivative of a constant times a function is that same constant times the derivative of the function.

3.3.6 The 5th derivative of a function is found by differentiating the 4th derivative of the function. The 4th derivative is found by differentiating the 3rd derivative of the function, and so on. Thus, one would need to compute f' and then four more derivatives to arrive at the 5th derivative of f.

3.3.7 By the power rule, $y' = 5x^{5-1} = 5x^4$.

3.3.8 By the power rule, $f'(t) = 11t^{11-1} = 11t^{10}$.

3.3.9 By the constant rule, $f'(x) = 0$.

3.3.10 By the constant rule, $g'(x) = 0$. (Note that e^3 is a constant, its value does not depend on x.)

3.3.11 By the power rule $h'(t) = 1t^{1-1} = t^0 = 1$.

3.3.12 By the power rule, $f'(v) = 100v^{100-1} = 100v^{99}$.

3.3.13 By the constant multiple rule and the power rule, $f'(x) = 5 \cdot \frac{d}{dx}x^3 = 5 \cdot 3x^2 = 15x^2$.

3.3.14 By the constant multiple and power rules, $g'(w) = \frac{5}{6} \cdot \frac{d}{dw}w^{12} = \frac{5}{6} \cdot 12w^{11} = 10w^{11}$.

3.3.15 By the constant multiple and power rules, $p'(x) = 8 \cdot \frac{d}{dx}x = 8 \cdot 1 = 8$.

3.3.16 By the constant multiple rule and by the result of example 4 in section 3.1, $g'(t) = 6 \cdot \frac{d}{dt}\sqrt{t} = 6 \cdot \frac{1}{2\sqrt{t}} = \frac{3}{\sqrt{t}}$.

3.3.17 By the constant multiple and power rules, $g'(t) = 100\frac{d}{dt}t^2 = 100 \cdot 2t = 200t$.

3.3.18 By the constant multiple rule and by the result of example 5 in section 3.1, $f'(s) = \frac{1}{4} \cdot \frac{d}{ds}\sqrt{s} = \frac{1}{4} \cdot \frac{1}{2\sqrt{s}} = \frac{1}{8\sqrt{s}}$.

3.3.19 $f'(x) = \frac{d}{dx}(3x^4 + 7x) = \frac{d}{dx}(3x^4) + \frac{d}{dx}(7x) = 12x^3 + 7$.

3.3.20 $g'(x) = \frac{d}{dx}(6x^5 - x) = \frac{d}{dx}(6x^5) - \frac{d}{dx}(x) = 30x^4 - 1$.

3.3.21 $f'(x) = \frac{d}{dx}(10x^4 - 32x + e^2) = \frac{d}{dx}(10x^4) - \frac{d}{dx}(32x) + \frac{d}{dx}(e^2) = 40x^3 - 32 - 0 = 40x^3 - 32$.

3.3.22 $f'(t) = \frac{d}{dt}(6\sqrt{t} - 4t^3 + 9) = \frac{d}{dt}(6\sqrt{t}) - \frac{d}{dt}(4t^3) + \frac{d}{dt}(9) = \frac{6}{2\sqrt{t}} - 12t^2 + 0 = \frac{3}{\sqrt{t}} - 12t^2$.

3.3.23 $g'(w) = \frac{d}{dw}(2w^3 + 3w^2 + 10w) = 2\frac{d}{dw}(w^3) + 3\frac{d}{dw}(w^2) + 10\frac{d}{dw}(w) = 2(3w^2) + 3(2w) + 10(1) = 6w^2 + 6w + 10$.

3.3.24 $s'(t) = \frac{d}{dt}(4\sqrt{t} - \frac{1}{4}t^4 + t + 1) = \frac{d}{dt}(4\sqrt{t}) - \frac{d}{dt}\left(\frac{1}{4}t^4\right) + \frac{d}{dt}(t) + \frac{d}{dt}(1) = \frac{4}{2\sqrt{t}} - t^3 + 1 + 0 = \frac{2}{\sqrt{t}} - t^3 + 1$.

3.3.25 Expanding the product yields $f(x) = 6x^3 + 3x^2 + 4x + 2$. So

$$f'(x) = \frac{d}{dx}(6x^3 + 3x^2 + 4x + 2) = \frac{d}{dx}(6x^3) + \frac{d}{dx}(3x^2) + \frac{d}{dx}(4x) + \frac{d}{dx}(2)$$
$$= 18x^2 + 6x + 4.$$

3.3.26 Expanding the product yields $g(r) = 5r^5 + 18r^3 + r^2 + 9r + 3$. So

$$g'(r) = \frac{d}{dr}(5r^5 + 18r^3 + r^2 + 9r + 3) = \frac{d}{dr}(5r^5) + \frac{d}{dr}(18r^3) + \frac{d}{dr}(r^2) + \frac{d}{dr}(9r) + \frac{d}{dr}(3)$$
$$= 25r^4 + 54r^2 + 2r + 9.$$

3.3.27 Expanding the product yields $h(x) = x^4 + 2x^2 + 1$. So

$$h'(x) = \frac{d}{dx}(x^4 + 2x^2 + 1) = \frac{d}{dx}(x^4) + \frac{d}{dx}(2x^2) + \frac{d}{dx}(1)$$
$$= 4x^3 + 4x.$$

3.3.28 Expanding the product yields $h(x) = x - \sqrt{x}$. So

$$h'(x) = \frac{d}{dx}(x - \sqrt{x}) = \frac{d}{dx}(x) - \frac{d}{dx}(\sqrt{x}) = 1 - \frac{1}{2\sqrt{x}}.$$

3.3.29 f simplifies as $f(w) = w^2 - 1$, so $f'(w) = 2w$ for $w \neq 0$.

3.3.30 y simplifies as $y = \frac{(4s)(3s^2 - 2s + 3)}{4s} = 3s^2 - 2s + 3$. Thus $y' = 6s - 2$, for $s \neq 0$.

3.3.31 g simplifies as $g(x) = \frac{(x-1)(x+1)}{x-1} = x + 1$. Thus $g'(x) = 1$ for $x \neq 1$.

3.3.32 h simplifies as $h(x) = \frac{(x)(x-2)(x-4)}{(x)(x-2)} = x - 4$. Thus, $h'(x) = 1$ for $x \neq 0, 2$.

3.3.33 y simplifies as $y = \frac{(\sqrt{x} - \sqrt{a})(\sqrt{x} + \sqrt{a})}{\sqrt{x} - \sqrt{a}} = \sqrt{x} + \sqrt{a}$. Thus $\frac{dy}{dx} = \frac{1}{2\sqrt{x}}$ for $x \neq a$.

3.3.34 y simplifies as $y = \frac{(x-a)^2}{x-a} = x - a$. Thus $\frac{dy}{dx} = 1$ for $x \neq a$.

3.3.35

a. $y' = -6x$, so the slope of the tangent line at $a = 1$ is -6. Thus, the tangent line at the point $(1, -1)$ is $y + 1 = -6(x - 1)$, or $y = -6x + 5$.

b.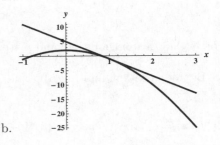

3.3.36

a. $y' = 3x^2 - 8x + 2$, so the slope of the tangent line at $a = 2$ is -2. Thus, the tangent line at the point $(2, -5)$ is $y + 5 = -2(x - 2)$, or $y = -2x - 1$.

b.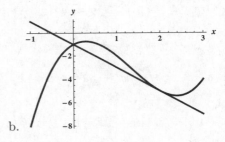

3.3.37

a. $y' = e^x$, so the slope of the tangent line at $a = \ln 3$ is 3. Thus, the tangent line at the point $(\ln 3, 3)$ is $y - 3 = 3(x - \ln 3)$, or $y = 3x + 3 - 3\ln 3$.

b.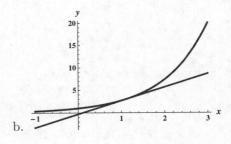

3.3.38

a. $y' = \frac{e^x}{4} - 1$, so the slope of the tangent line at $a = 0$ is $-\frac{3}{4}$. Thus, the tangent line at the point $(0, 1/4)$ is $y - 1/4 = -\frac{3}{4} \cdot (x - 0)$, or $y = -\frac{3x}{4} + \frac{1}{4}$.

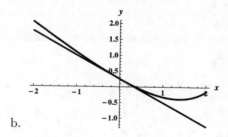

b.

3.3.39

a. $f'(x) = 2x - 6$, so the slope is zero when $2x - 6 = 0$, which is at $x = 3$.

b. The slope is 2 when $2x - 6 = 2$ which is at $x = 4$.

3.3.40

a. $f'(t) = 3t^2 - 27$, so the slope of the tangent line is zero when $3t^2 - 27 = 0$, which is at $t = 3$ and $t = -3$.

b. The slope is 21 where $f'(t) = 3t^2 - 27 = 21$, or when $t^2 = 16$, so at $t = 4$ and $t = -4$.

3.3.41

a. The slope of the tangent line is given by $f'(x) = 6x^2 - 6x - 12$, and this quantity is zero when $x^2 - x - 2 = 0$, or $(x - 2)(x + 1) = 0$. The two solutions are thus $x = -1$ and $x = 2$, so the points on the graph are $(-1, 11)$ and $(2, -16)$.

b. The slope of the tangent line is 60 when $6x^2 - 6x - 12 = 60$, which is when $6x^2 - 6x - 72 = 0$. Simplifying this quadratic expression yields the equation $x^2 - x - 12 = 0$, which has solutions $x = -3$ and $x = 4$, so the points on the graph are $(-3, -41)$, and $(4, 36)$.

3.3.42

a. The slope of the tangent line is given by $f'(x) = 2e^x - 6$. This is equal to zero when $2e^x = 6$, which occurs for $x = \ln 3$. The point on the graph is therefore $(\ln 3, 6 - 6 \ln 3)$.

b. The slope of the tangent line is 12 when $2e^x - 6 = 12$, or $e^x = 9$. This occurs for $x = \ln 9$. The point on the graph is therefore $(\ln 9, 18 - 6 \ln 9)$.

3.3.43

a. The slope of the tangent line is given by $\frac{2}{\sqrt{x}} - 1$. This is equal to zero when $\sqrt{x} = 2$, or $x = 4$. The point on the graph is $(4, 4)$.

b. The slope of the tangent line is $-\frac{1}{2}$ when $\frac{2}{\sqrt{x}} - 1 = -\frac{1}{2}$. Solving for x gives $x = 16$. The point on the graph is $(16, 0)$.

3.3.44 $f'(x) = 9x^2 + 10x + 6$, $f''(x) = 18x + 10$, and $f^{(3)}(x) = 18$.

3.3.45 $f'(x) = 20x^3 + 30x^2 + 3$, $f''(x) = 60x^2 + 60x$, and $f^{(3)}(x) = 120x + 60$.

3.3.46 $f'(x) = 6x + 5e^x$, $f''(x) = 6 + 5e^x$, and $f^{(3)}(x) = 5e^x$.

3.3.47 f simplifies as $f(x) = \frac{(x-8)(x+1)}{x+1} = x - 8$. So for $x \neq -1$, $f'(x) = 1$, $f''(x) = 0$, and $f^{(3)}(x) = 0$.

3.3.48 $f'(x) = f''(x) = f^{(3)}(x) = 10e^x$.

3.3.49

a. False. 10^5 is a constant, so the constant rule assures us that $\frac{d}{dx}(10^5) = 0$.

b. True. This follows because the slope is given by $f'(x) = e^x > 0$ for all x.

c. False. $\frac{d}{dx}(e^3) = 0$.

d. False. $\frac{d}{dx}(e^x) = e^x$, not xe^{x-1}.

e. False. We have $\frac{d}{dx}(5x^3 + 2x + 5) = 15x^2 + 2$. Thus we have $\frac{d^2}{dx^2}(5x^3 + 2x + 5) = 30x$, and $\frac{d^3}{dx^3}(5x^3 + 2x + 5) = 30$. It is true that $\frac{d^n}{dx^n}(5x^3 + 2x + 5) = 0$ for $n \geq 4$.

3.3.50

a. The slope of the tangent line to g at x is given by $g'(x) = 2x + f'(x)$, so $g'(3) = 6 + f'(3) = 10$. The point on the curve $y = g(x)$ at $x = 3$ is $(3, 9 + f(3)) = (3, 9 + 1) = (3, 10)$. Thus the equation of the tangent line at this point is $y - 10 = 10(x - 3)$, or $y = 10x - 20$.

b. The slope of the tangent line to h at x is given by $h'(x) = 3f'(x)$, so $h'(3) = 3f'(3) = 3 \cdot 4 = 12$. The point on the curve $y = h(x)$ at $x = 3$ is $(3, 3 \cdot f(3)) = (3, 3)$. Thus the equation of the tangent line at this point is $y - 3 = 12(x - 3)$, or $y = 12x - 33$.

3.3.51 First note that because the slope of $4x + 1$ is 4, it must be the case that $f'(2) = 4$. Also, at $x = 2$, we have $y = 4 \cdot 2 + 1 = 9$, so $f(2) = 9$. Because the line tangent to the graph of g at 2 has slope 3, we know that $g'(2) = 3$. The tangent line to g at $x = 2$ must be $y - (-2) = 3(x - 0)$, so the value of the tangent line at 2 (which must also be the value of $g(2)$) is 4. So $g(2) = 4$.

a. $y'(2) = f'(2) + g'(2) = 4 + 3 = 7$. The line contains the point $(2, f(2) + g(2)) = (2, 13)$. Thus, the equation of the tangent line is $y - 13 = 7(x - 2)$, or $y = 7x - 1$.

b. $y'(2) = f'(2) - 2g'(2) = 4 - 2 \cdot 3 = -2$. The line contains the point $(2, f(2) - 2g(2)) = (2, 1)$. Thus, the equation of the tangent line is $y - 1 = -2(x - 2)$, or $y = -2x + 5$.

c. $y'(2) = 4f'(2) = 4 \cdot 4 = 16$. The line contains the point $(2, 4f(2)) = (2, 36)$. Thus, the equation of the tangent line is $y - 36 = 16(x - 2)$, or $y = 16x + 4$.

3.3.52 For $y = x + \sqrt{x}$ we have $y' = 1 + \frac{1}{2}\left(x^{-1/2}\right) = 1 + \frac{1}{2\sqrt{x}}$. Setting this equal to 2 yields $1 + \frac{1}{2\sqrt{x}} = 2$, or $\sqrt{x} = \frac{1}{2}$. Thus the tangent line has slope 2 for $x = 1/4$.

3.3.53 For $f(x) = x^2 + bx + c$ we have $f'(x) = 2x + b$, so $f'(1) = 2 + b$. Because the slope of $4x + 2$ is 4, we require $2 + b = 4$, so $b = 2$. Also, because the value of $4x + 2$ at $x = 1$ is 6, we must have $f(1) = 1 + 2 + c = 6$, so $c = 3$. Thus the curve $f(x) = x^2 + 2x + 3$ has $y = 4x + 2$ as its tangent line at $x = 1$.

3.3.54 $F'(2) = f'(2) + g'(2) = -3 + 1 = -2$.

3.3.55 $G'(2) = 3f'(2) - g'(2) = 3(-3) - 1 = -10$.

3.3.56 $F'(5) = f'(5) + g'(5) = 1 - 1 = 0$.

3.3.57 $G'(5) = 3f'(5) - g'(5) = 3 \cdot 1 - (-1) = 4$.

3.3.58 $\frac{d}{dx}[f(x) + g(x)]_{x=1} = f'(1) + g'(1) = 3 + 2 = 5$.

3.3.59 $\frac{d}{dx}[1.5f(x)]_{x=2} = 1.5f'(2) = 1.5 \cdot 5 = 7.5$.

3.3.60 $\frac{d}{dx}[2x - 3g(x)]_{x=4} = 2 - 3g'(4) = 2 - 3 \cdot 1 = -1$.

3.3.61

a. Let $f(x) = \sqrt{x}$ and $a = 9$. Then $\displaystyle\lim_{h \to 0} \frac{f(a+h) - f(a)}{h} = \lim_{h \to 0} \frac{\sqrt{9+h} - \sqrt{9}}{h} = f'(9)$.

b. Because $f'(x) = \frac{1}{2\sqrt{x}}$, we have $f'(9) = \frac{1}{6}$, so this is the value of the original limit.

3.3.62

a. Let $f(x) = x^8 + x^3$, and $a = 1$. Then $\lim\limits_{h \to 0} \dfrac{f(a+h) - f(a)}{h} = \lim\limits_{h \to 0} \dfrac{(1+h)^8 + (1+h)^3 - 2}{h} = f'(1)$.

b. Because $f'(x) = 8x^7 + 3x^2$, we have $f'(1) = 8 + 3 = 11$, so this is the value of the original limit.

3.3.63

a. Let $f(x) = x^{100}$ and $a = 1$. Then $\lim\limits_{x \to 1} \dfrac{f(x) - f(1)}{x - 1} = f'(1)$.

b. Because $f'(x) = 100x^{99}$, we have $f'(1) = 100$, so this is the value of the original limit.

3.3.64

h	$\frac{2^h - 1}{h}$	$\frac{3^h - 1}{h}$
-1.0	0.5	0.666667
-0.1	$.66967$	1.040415
-0.01	$.69075$	1.0926
-0.001	$.692907$	1.098009
-0.0001	$.693123$	1.098552
$-.00001$	$.693145$	1.098606

It appears that $\lim\limits_{h \to 0^-} \dfrac{2^h - 1}{h} \approx .6931$ and $\lim\limits_{h \to 0^-} \dfrac{3^h - 1}{h} \approx 1.0986$.

3.3.65 $\lim\limits_{x \to 0} \dfrac{e^{3x} - 1}{x} = 3$.

3.3.66 $\lim\limits_{n \to \infty} \left(1 + \dfrac{1}{n}\right)^n \approx 2.7183$.

3.3.67 $\lim\limits_{x \to 0^+} x^x = 1$.

3.3.68 $\lim\limits_{x \to 0^+} \left(\dfrac{1}{x}\right)^x = 1$.

3.3.69 Let $f(x) = e^x$ and $a = 0$. Then we have $f'(a) = \lim\limits_{x \to a} \dfrac{f(x) - f(a)}{x - a} = \lim\limits_{x \to 0} \dfrac{e^x - 1}{x}$. Because $f'(0) = e^0 = 1$, this must be the value of $\lim\limits_{x \to 0} \dfrac{e^x - 1}{x}$.

3.3.70

a. The instantaneous velocity is given by $v(t) = \frac{d}{dt} s(t) = -10t + 40$, $0 \le t \le 10$.

b. $v(t) = 0$ when $-10t + 40 = 0$, which occurs at $t = 4$.

c. The magnitude of the velocity is $|v(t)|$. Note that $v(t) \ge 0$ for $0 \le t \le 4$, and $v(t) < 0$ for $4 < t \le 10$. Thus

$$|v(t)| = \begin{cases} -10t + 40 & \text{for } 0 \le t \le 4, \\ 10t - 40 & \text{for } 4 < t \le 10. \end{cases}$$

Note that $|v(0)| = 40$ and $|v(10)| = 60$. The greatest magnitude over this time interval is 60 meters per second.

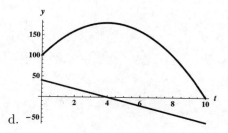

d.

3.3.71

a. $d'(t) = 32t$ is the velocity of the stone after t seconds, measured in feet per second.

b. The stone travels $d(6) = 16 \cdot 6^2 = 576$ feet and strikes the ground with a velocity of $32 \cdot 6 = 192$ feet per second. Converting to miles per hour, we have $192 \cdot \frac{3600}{5280} \approx 130.9$ miles per hour.

3.3.72

a. Because $p(t) = 1200e^t$, we get $p'(t) = 1200 \cdot e^t$ cells per hour.

b. Because $p'(t)$ is also exponential, it is smallest when $t = 0$, and largest when $t = 4$.

3.3.73

a. $A'(t) = -\frac{1}{25}t + 2$ square miles per year.

b. First we must find when $A(t) = 38$. This occurs when $-\frac{t^2}{50} + 2t + 28 = 38$, which can be written as $t^2 - 100t + 900 = 0$. This factors as $(t - 90)(t - 10) = 0$, so the only solution on the given domain is $t = 10$. At this time, we have $A'(10) = -0.4 + 2 = 1.6$ square miles per year.

c. Note that $A'(20) = -0.8 + 2 = 1.2$ square miles per year. In order to maintain a density of 1000 people per square mile, we must multiply the density of people per square mile times the number of square miles per year in order to obtain the rate of people per year required to maintain that density. Thus the population growth rate must be $1000 \cdot 1.2 = 1200$ people per year.

3.3.74 $f'(x) = \lim_{h \to 0} \dfrac{f(x + h) - f(x)}{h} = \lim_{h \to 0} \dfrac{c - c}{h} = \lim_{h \to 0} \dfrac{0}{h} = \lim_{h \to 0} 0 = 0.$

3.3.75

$$\frac{d}{dx}x^n = \lim_{h \to 0} \frac{(x + h)^n - x^n}{h} = \lim_{h \to 0} \left(\frac{x^n + nx^{n-1}h + \frac{n(n-1)}{2}x^{n-2}h^2 + \cdots + nxh^{n-1} + h^n - x^n}{h} \right)$$

$$= \lim_{h \to 0} \left(nx^{n-1} + \frac{n(n-1)}{2}x^{n-2}h + \cdots + nxh^{n-2} + h^{n-1} \right) = nx^{n-1} + 0 + 0 + \cdots + 0 = nx^{n-1}$$

3.3.76

a. Let $m = -n$ so that $m > 0$.

$$f'(a) = \lim_{x \to a} \frac{x^n - a^n}{x - a} = \lim_{x \to a} \frac{x^{-m} - a^{-m}}{x - a} = \lim_{x \to a} \frac{1}{a^m x^m} \cdot \frac{a^m - x^m}{x - a}$$

$$= \left(-\lim_{x \to a} \frac{1}{a^m x^m} \right) \left(\lim_{x \to a} \frac{x^m - a^m}{x - a} \right)$$

$$= -\frac{1}{a^{2m}} \cdot ma^{m-1} = -ma^{-m-1} = na^{n-1}.$$

b. $\frac{d}{dx}(x^{-7}) = -7x^{-8}$. Also, $\frac{d}{dx}(x^{-10}) = -10x^{-11} = -\frac{10}{x^{11}}$.

3.3.77

a. $\frac{d}{dx}(\sqrt{x}) = \frac{d}{dx}x^{1/2} = \frac{1}{2} \cdot x^{-1/2} = \frac{1}{2\sqrt{x}}$.

b.

$$\frac{d}{dx}x^{3/2} = \lim_{h \to 0} \frac{(x + h)^{3/2} - x^{3/2}}{h} = \lim_{h \to 0} \frac{((x + h)^{3/2} - x^{3/2})((x + h)^{3/2} + x^{3/2})}{h((x + h)^{3/2} + x^{3/2})}$$

$$= \lim_{h \to 0} \frac{(x + h)^3 - x^3}{h((x + h)^{3/2} + x^{3/2})} = \lim_{h \to 0} \frac{x^3 + 3x^2h + 3xh^2 + h^3 - x^3}{h((x + h)^{3/2} + x^{3/2})}$$

$$= \lim_{h \to 0} \frac{3x^2 + 3xh + h^2}{((x + h)^{3/2} + x^{3/2})} = \frac{3x^2 + 0 + 0}{x^{3/2} + x^{3/2}} = \frac{3x^2}{2x^{3/2}} = \frac{3}{2}x^{1/2}.$$

c.

$$\frac{d}{dx}x^{5/2} = \lim_{h \to 0} \frac{(x+h)^{5/2} - x^{5/2}}{h} = \lim_{h \to 0} \frac{((x+h)^{5/2} - x^{5/2})((x+h)^{5/2} + x^{5/2})}{h((x+h)^{5/2} + x^{5/2})}$$

$$= \lim_{h \to 0} \frac{(x+h)^5 - x^5}{h((x+h)^{5/2} + x^{5/2})} = \lim_{h \to 0} \frac{x^5 + 5x^4h + 10x^3h^2 + 10x^2h^3 + 5xh^4 + h^5 - x^5}{h((x+h)^{5/2} + x^{5/2})}$$

$$= \lim_{h \to 0} \frac{5x^4 + 10x^3h + 10x^2h^2 + 5xh^3 + h^4}{((x+h)^{5/2} + x^{5/2})}$$

$$= \frac{5x^4 + 0 + 0 + 0 + 0}{x^{5/2} + x^{5/2}} = \frac{5x^4}{2x^{5/2}} = \frac{5}{2}x^{3/2}.$$

d. It appears that $\frac{d}{dx}x^{n/2} = \frac{n}{2} \cdot x^{(n/2)-1}$.

3.3.78

a. $\frac{d}{dx}(e^{-x}) = \lim_{h \to 0} \frac{e^{-(x+h)} - e^{-x}}{h} = \lim_{h \to 0} \frac{e^{-x}(e^{-h} - 1)}{h} = e^{-x} \lim_{h \to 0} \frac{e^{-h} - 1}{h}.$

b. Let $w = -h$. Then $\lim_{h \to 0} \frac{e^{-h} - 1}{h} = \lim_{w \to 0} \frac{e^w - 1}{-w} = -\lim_{w \to 0} \frac{e^w - 1}{w} = -1.$

c. $\frac{d}{dx}(e^{-x}) = e^{-x} \lim_{h \to 0} \frac{e^{-h} - 1}{h} = -e^{-x}.$

3.3.79

a. $\frac{d}{dx}(e^{2x}) = \lim_{h \to 0} \frac{e^{2(x+h)} - e^{2x}}{h} = \lim_{h \to 0} \frac{e^{2x}(e^{2h} - 1)}{h} = e^{2x} \lim_{h \to 0} \frac{e^{2h} - 1}{h}.$

b. Let $z = 2h$. Then $\lim_{h \to 0} \frac{e^{2h} - 1}{h} = \lim_{z \to 0} \frac{e^z - 1}{z/2} = 2 \lim_{z \to 0} \frac{e^z - 1}{z} = 2.$

c. $\frac{d}{dx}(e^{2x}) = e^{2x} \lim_{h \to 0} \frac{e^{2h} - 1}{h} = 2e^{2x}.$

3.3.80

a.

$$\frac{d}{dx}(x^2e^x) = \lim_{h \to 0} \frac{(x+h)^2 e^{x+h} - x^2 e^x}{h}$$

$$= \lim_{h \to 0} e^x \cdot \frac{(x^2 + 2xh + h^2)e^h - x^2}{h} = e^x \cdot \lim_{h \to 0} \frac{(x^2 + 2xh + h^2)e^h - x^2}{h}.$$

b.

$$e^x \cdot \lim_{h \to 0} \frac{(x^2 + 2xh + h^2)e^h - x^2}{h} = e^x \left(\lim_{h \to 0} \frac{x^2 e^h + 2xhe^h + h^2 e^h - x^2}{h} \right)$$

$$= e^x \left(\lim_{h \to 0} \frac{x^2(e^h - 1) + 2xhe^h + h^2 e^h}{h} \right) = e^x \left(x^2 \lim_{h \to 0} \frac{e^h - 1}{h} + 2x \lim_{h \to 0} e^h + \lim_{h \to 0} he^h \right)$$

$$= e^x \left(x^2 + 2x \right).$$

3.4   The Product and Quotient Rules

3.4.1 The derivative of the product fg with respect to x is given by $f'(x)g(x) + f(x)g'(x)$.

3.4.2 The derivative of the quotient $\frac{f}{g}$ with respect to x is given by $\frac{g(x)f'(x) - f(x)g'(x)}{(g(x))^2}$.

3.4.3 $\frac{d}{dx}(x^n) = nx^{n-1}$ for all integers n.

3.4.4 By the extended power rule, $\frac{d}{dx}\frac{1}{x^{10}} = \frac{d}{dx}x^{-10} = -10x^{-11} = -\frac{10}{x^{11}}$.

By the quotient rule, $\frac{d}{dx}\frac{1}{x^{10}} = \frac{x^{10} \cdot 0 - 1 \cdot 10x^9}{(x^{10})^2} = -\frac{10x^9}{x^{20}} = -\frac{10}{x^{11}}$.

3.4.5 $\frac{d}{dx}e^{kx} = ke^{kx}$ for all real numbers k.

3.4.6 Expanding first, we have $f(x) = x^3 - 3x^2 + 4x - 12$, so $f'(x) = 3x^2 - 6x + 4$.
Using the product rule:

$$f'(x) = \frac{d}{dx}(x - 3) \cdot (x^2 + 4) + (x - 3)\frac{d}{dx}(x^2 + 4)$$
$$= x^2 + 4 + (x - 3)(2x) = x^2 + 4 + 2x^2 - 6x = 3x^2 - 6x + 4.$$

3.4.7 $f'(x) = 12x^3(2x^2 - 1) + 3x^4 \cdot 4x = 24x^5 - 12x^3 + 12x^5 = 36x^5 - 12x^3$.

3.4.8 $g'(x) = 6 - (2e^x + 2xe^x)$.

3.4.9 $f'(t) = 5t^4e^t + t^5e^t = t^4e^t(t + 5)$.

3.4.10 $g'(w) = (10w + 3)e^w + (5w^2 + 3w + 1)e^w = e^w(5w^2 + 13w + 4)$.

3.4.11 $h'(x) = (1)(x^3 + x^2 + x + 1) + (x - 1)(3x^2 + 2x + 1) = x^3 + x^2 + x + 1 + 3x^3 + 2x^2 + x - 3x^2 - 2x - 1 = 4x^3$.

3.4.12 $f'(x) = -\frac{2}{x^3} \cdot (x^2 + 1) + \left(1 + \frac{1}{x^2}\right)(2x) = -\frac{2}{x} - \frac{2}{x^3} + 2x + \frac{2}{x} = 2x - \frac{2}{x^3}$.

3.4.13 $g'(w) = e^w(w^3 - 1) + e^w \cdot 3w^2 = e^w(w^3 + 3w^2 - 1)$.

3.4.14 $s'(t) = 4e^t\sqrt{t} + 4e^t \cdot \frac{1}{2\sqrt{t}} = e^t\left(4\sqrt{t} + \frac{2}{\sqrt{t}}\right)$.

3.4.15

    a. $f'(x) = 1(3x + 4) + (x - 1) \cdot 3 = 6x + 1$.

    b. $f'(x) = \frac{d}{dx}(3x^2 + x - 4) = 6x + 1$.

3.4.16

    a. $y' = (2t + 7)(3t - 4) + (t^2 + 7t) \cdot 3 = 9t^2 + 34t - 28$.

    b. $y' = \frac{d}{dt}(3t^3 + 17t^2 - 28t) = 9t^2 + 34t - 28$.

3.4.17

    a. $g'(y) = (12y^3 - 2y)(y^2 - 4) + (3y^4 - y^2) \cdot 2y = 18y^5 - 52y^3 + 8y$.

    b. $g'(y) = \frac{d}{dy}(3y^6 - 13y^4 + 4y^2) = 18y^5 - 52y^3 + 8y$.

3.4.18

    a. $h'(z) = (3z^2 + 8z + 1)(z - 1) + (z^3 + 4z^2 + z) \cdot 1 = 4z^3 + 9z^2 - 6z - 1$.

b. $h'(z) = \frac{d}{dz}(z^4 + 3z^3 - 3z^2 - z) = 4z^3 + 9z^2 - 6z - 1.$

3.4.19 $f'(x) = \frac{(x+1)\cdot 1 - x\cdot 1}{(x+1)^2} = \frac{1}{(x+1)^2}.$

3.4.20 $f'(x) = \frac{(x-2)(3x^2-8x+1)-(x^3-4x^2+x)(1)}{(x-2)^2} = \frac{2x^3-10x^2+16x-2}{(x-2)^2}.$

3.4.21 $f'(x) = \frac{(e^x+1)e^x - e^x(e^x)}{(e^x+1)^2} = \frac{e^x}{(e^x+1)^2}.$

3.4.22 $f'(x) = \frac{(2e^x+1)(2e^x)-(2e^x-1)2e^x}{(2e^x+1)^2} = \frac{2e^x(2e^x+1-(2e^x-1))}{(2e^x+1)^2} = \frac{4e^x}{(2e^x+1)^2}.$

3.4.23 $f'(x) = (1)e^{-x} + x(-e^{-x}) = e^{-x}(1-x).$

3.4.24 $f'(x) = \frac{1}{2}x^{-1/2}e^{-x} + \sqrt{x}(-e^{-x}) = e^{-x}\left(\frac{1}{2\sqrt{x}} - \sqrt{x}\right) = \frac{1-2x}{e^x(2\sqrt{x})}.$

3.4.25 $y' = \frac{d}{dt}\left(\frac{3t-1}{2t-2}\right) = \frac{(2t-2)\cdot 3 - (3t-1)\cdot 2}{(2t-2)^2} = -\frac{4}{(2t-2)^2} = -\frac{1}{(t-1)^2}.$

3.4.26 $h'(w) = \frac{(w^2+1)(2w)-(w^2-1)(2w)}{(w^2+1)^2} = \frac{2w^3+2w-2w^3+2w}{(w^2+1)^2} = \frac{4w}{(w^2+1)^2}.$

3.4.27 $g'(x) = \frac{(x^2-1)\cdot e^x - e^x\cdot 2x}{(x^2-1)^2} = \frac{e^x(x^2-2x-1)}{(x^2-1)^2}.$

3.4.28 $y' = \frac{d}{dx}\left(\frac{2\sqrt{x}-1}{4x+1}\right) = \frac{(4x+1)\left(\frac{1}{\sqrt{x}}\right) - (2\sqrt{x}-1)4}{(4x+1)^2} = \frac{4\sqrt{x}+\frac{1}{\sqrt{x}}-8\sqrt{x}+4}{(4x+1)^2} \cdot \frac{\sqrt{x}}{\sqrt{x}} = \frac{-4x+1+4\sqrt{x}}{\sqrt{x}(4x+1)^2}.$

3.4.29

   a. $f'(w) = \frac{w(3w^2-1)-(w^3-w)\cdot 1}{w^2} = \frac{2w^3}{w^2} = 2w$ for $w \neq 0.$

   b. For $w \neq 0$ this simplifies as $w^2 - 1.$ $f'(w) = \frac{d}{dw}(w^2 - 1) = 2w.$

3.4.30

   a. $y' = \frac{4s(12s^2-16s+4)-(4s^3-8s^2+4s)\cdot 4}{(4s)^2} = \frac{48s^3-64s^2+16s-16s^3+32s^2-16s}{16s^2} = \frac{32s^3-32s^2}{16s^2} = 2s-2$ for $s \neq 0.$

   b. For $s \neq 0$, the function simplifies to $y = s^2 - 2s + 1.$ Then $y' = \frac{d}{ds}(s^2 - 2s + 1) = 2s - 2.$

3.4.31

   a. $y' = \frac{(x-a)(2x)-(x^2-a^2)}{(x-a)^2} = \frac{2x^2-2ax-x^2+a^2}{(x-a)^2} = \frac{x^2-2ax+a^2}{(x-a)^2} = \frac{(x-a)^2}{(x-a)^2} = 1$ for $x \neq a.$

   b. For $x \neq a$, this simplifies as $y = \frac{(x+a)(x-a)}{x-a} = x + a.$ $y' = \frac{d}{dx}(x+a) = 1.$

3.4.32

   a. $y' = \frac{(x-a)(2x-2a)-(x^2-2ax+a^2)\cdot 1}{(x-a)^2} = \frac{x^2-2ax+a^2}{(x-a)^2} = \frac{(x-a)^2}{(x-a)^2} = 1$ for $x \neq a.$

   b. For $x \neq a$, this simplifies as $y = \frac{(x-a)^2}{(x-a)} = x - a.$ $y' = \frac{d}{dx}(x-a) = 1.$

3.4.33

   a. $y' = \frac{(x-1)-(x+5)}{(x-1)^2} = -\frac{6}{(x-1)^2}.$
     At $a = 3$ we have $y' = -\frac{6}{4} = -\frac{3}{2}$ and $y = 4$, so the equation of the tangent line is $y - 4 = -\frac{3}{2}\cdot(x-3)$, or $y = -\frac{3}{2}x + \frac{17}{2}.$

   b.

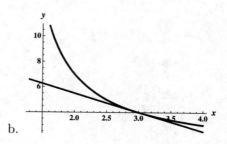

3.4.34

a. $y' = \frac{(3x-1)4x - (2x^2)3}{(3x-1)^2} = \frac{6x^2 - 4x}{(3x-1)^2}$.

At $a = 1$ we have $y' = \frac{1}{2}$ and $y = 1$, so the equation of the tangent line is $y - 1 = \frac{1}{2} \cdot (x - 1)$, or $y = \frac{1}{2}x + \frac{1}{2}$.

b.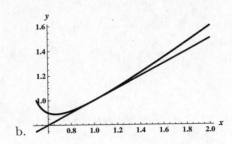

3.4.35

a. $y' = 2 + (1)e^x + xe^x$.

At $a = 0$ we have $y' = 2 + 1 + 0 = 3$ and $y = 1$. So the equation of the tangent line is $y - 1 = 3(x - 0)$, or $y = 3x + 1$.

b.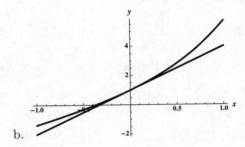

3.4.36

a. $y' = \frac{xe^x - e^x}{x^2}$.

At $a = 1$ we have $y' = \frac{e - e}{1} = 0$, and $y = e$. Thus, the equation of the tangent line is $y - e = 0$, or $y = e$.

b.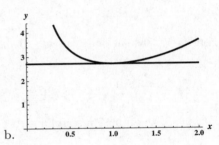

3.4.37 $f'(x) = (-9) \cdot 3 \cdot x^{-9-1} = -27x^{-10}$.

3.4.38 $y' = \frac{d}{dp}(4p^{-3}) = -12p^{-4}$.

3.4.39 $g'(t) = \frac{d}{dt}(3t^2 + 6t^{-7}) = 6t - 42t^{-8}$.

3.4.40 $y' = \frac{d}{dw}(w^2 + 5 + w^{-1}) = 2w - w^{-2}$.

3.4.41 $g'(t) = \frac{d}{dt}(1 + 3t^{-1} + t^{-2}) = -3t^{-2} - 2t^{-3}$.

3.4.42 $p'(x) = \frac{d}{dx}(2x^{-2} + \frac{3}{2}x^{-4} + \frac{1}{2}x^{-5}) = -4x^{-3} - 6x^{-5} - \frac{5}{2}x^{-6}$.

3.4.43 $f'(x) = (1)e^{7x} + x(7e^{7x}) = e^{7x}(7x + 1)$.

3.4.44 $g'(t) = 2e^{t/2} + (2t)e^{t/2}(1/2) = e^{t/2}(t + 2)$.

3.4.45 $f'(x) = 3 \cdot 15 \cdot e^{3x} = 45e^{3x}$.

3.4.46 $y' = 6x - 2 - 2e^{-2x}$.

3.4.47 $g'(x) = \frac{d}{dx}(xe^{-3x}) = e^{-3x} - xe^{-3x}(3) = e^{-3x}(1 - 3x)$.

3.4.48 $f'(x) = (-2)e^{-x} + (1 - 2x)(-e^{-x}) = -3e^{-x} + 2xe^{-x} = e^{-x}(2x - 3)$.

3.4.49 $y'(x) = \frac{d}{dx}\left(\frac{2}{3}e^x + e^{-x}\right) = \frac{2}{3}e^x - e^{-x}$.

3.4.50 $\frac{dA}{dt} = (0.075) \cdot 2500e^{0.075t} = 187.5e^{0.075t}$.

3.4.51

    a. $p'(t) = \frac{(t+2)200 - 200t}{(t+2)^2} = \frac{400}{(t+2)^2}$.

    b. $p'(5) = \frac{400}{49} \approx 8.16$.

    c. The value of p' is as large as possible when its denominator is as small as possible, which is when $t = 0$. The value of $p'(0)$ is 100.

    d. $\lim\limits_{t\to\infty} p'(t) = \lim\limits_{t\to\infty} \frac{400}{(t+2)^2} = 0$. This means that the population eventually has a growth rate of 0, which means that the population approaches a steady state.

    e.

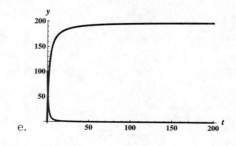

3.4.52

    a. $p'(t) = \frac{-(800 \cdot (-1.4e^{-0.2t}))}{(1 + 7e^{-0.2t})^2} = \frac{1120e^{-0.2t}}{(1 + 7e^{-0.2t})^2}$.

    b. $p'(5) \approx 32.24$.

    c. From the graph we see that the growth rate is maximal at about $t = 9.8$.

    d. $\lim\limits_{t\to\infty} p'(t) = \lim\limits_{t\to\infty} \frac{1120e^{-0.2t}}{(1 + 7e^{-0.2t})^2} = \frac{\lim_{t\to\infty} 1120e^{-0.2t}}{(1 + 7\lim_{t\to\infty} e^{-0.2t})^2} = \frac{0}{1} = 0$. This means that the population eventually has a growth rate of 0, which means that the population approaches a steady state.

    e.

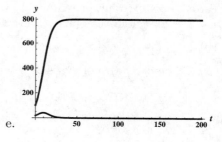

3.4.53

    a. The instantaneous rate of change is $Q'(t) = -1.386e^{-0.0693t}$ mg/hr.

    b. At $t = 0$ hours, we have $Q'(0) = -1.386$, so the amount of antibiotic is decreasing at a rate of 1.386 mg/hr. At $t = 2$ hours, we have $Q'(2) = -1.386e^{-0.1386} \approx -1.207$, so the amount of antibiotic is decreasing at a rate of about 1.207 mg/hr.

    c. $\lim\limits_{t\to\infty} Q(t) = 20 \lim\limits_{t\to\infty} e^{-0.0693t} = 0$. In the long run, the antibiotic is all used up. $\lim\limits_{t\to\infty} Q'(t) = -1.386 \lim\limits_{t\to\infty} e^{-0.0693t} = 0$. The rate of change of the amount of antibiotic in the bloodstream also goes to zero as $t \to \infty$.

3.4.54

    a. After 10 years we will have $A(10) = 200e^{0.398} \approx \$297.77$.

    b. The growth rate is $A'(t) = 200 \cdot (0.0398e^{0.0398t}) = 7.96e^{0.0398t}$. After 10 years, the growth rate is $A'(10) = 7.96e^{0.398} \approx 11.85$ dollars/year.

    c. The tangent line is given by $y - 297.77 = 11.85(t - 10)$, or $y = 11.85t + 179.27$.

3.4.55

    a. The slope is $f'(x) = e^{2x} + 2xe^{2x}$. This is zero when $e^{2x}(1 + 2x) = 0$, which occurs when $x = -\frac{1}{2}$.

    b. The graph of f has a horizontal tangent line at $x = -1/2$.

3.4.56

    a. The slope is $f'(t) = -5e^{-0.05t}$ and equals -5 when $t = 0$.

    b. Because $e^{-0.05t} > 0$ for all t, we have $f'(t) = -5e^{-0.05t} < 0$ for all t. The graph of f therefore has no horizontal tangent line.

3.4.57 $g'(x) = \frac{(x-2)((x+1)e^x + e^x) - (x+1)e^x}{(x-2)^2} = \frac{e^x}{(x-2)^2} \cdot \frac{(x-2)(x+2) - (x+1)}{1} = \frac{e^x}{(x-2)^2} \cdot (x^2 - x - 5)$.

3.4.58 First note that $x^3 - 1 = (x - 1)(x^2 + x + 1)$. So we can simplify $h(x)$ as $h(x) = \frac{2x^2 - 1}{x^2 + x + 1}$. Thus

$$h'(x) = \frac{(x^2 + x + 1)(4x) - (2x^2 - 1)(2x + 1)}{(x^2 + x + 1)^2} = \frac{(4x^3 + 4x^2 + 4x) - (4x^3 + 2x^2 - 2x - 1)}{(x^2 + x + 1)^2} = \frac{2x^2 + 6x + 1}{(x^2 + x + 1)^2}.$$

3.4.59 $h'(x) = \frac{(x+1)e^4 - xe^4}{(x+1)^2} = \frac{e^4}{(x+1)^2}$.

3.4.60 $h'(x) = \frac{(x+1)(e^x + e^x \cdot x) - xe^x}{(x+1)^2} = \frac{e^x((x+1)^2 - x)}{(x+1)^2} = \frac{e^x(x^2 + x + 1)}{(x+1)^2}$.

3.4.61

    a. False. In fact, because e^5 is a constant, its derivative is zero.

    b. False. It is certainly a reasonable way to proceed, but one could also write the given quantity as $x + 3 + 2x^{-1}$, and then proceed using the sum rule and the power rule and the extended power rule.

    c. False. $\frac{d}{dx}\left(\frac{1}{x^5}\right) = \frac{d}{dx}\left(x^{-5}\right) = -5x^{-6} = -\frac{5}{x^6}$.

    d. True. The derivative of e^{3x} is $3e^{3x}$, and each succeeding derivative results in an extra factor of 3.

3.4.62 $f'(x) = -x^{-2} = -\frac{1}{x^2}$. $f''(x) = 2x^{-3} = \frac{2}{x^3}$. $f'''(x) = -6x^{-4} = -\frac{6}{x^4}$.

3.4.63

    $f'(x) = x^2(3e^{3x}) + e^{3x}(2x) = e^{3x}(3x^2 + 2x)$.
    $f''(x) = e^{3x}(6x + 2) + (3x^2 + 2x)3e^{3x} = e^{3x}(9x^2 + 12x + 2)$.
    $f'''(x) = e^{3x}(18x + 12) + (9x^2 + 12x + 2)(3e^{3x}) = e^{3x}(27x^2 + 54x + 18) = 9e^{3x}(3x^2 + 6x + 2)$.

3.4.64

$$f'(x) = \frac{d}{dx}\left(\frac{x}{x+2}\right) = \frac{(x+2) - x}{(x+2)^2} = \frac{2}{(x+2)^2} = \frac{2}{x^2 + 4x + 4}.$$

$$f''(x) = \frac{d}{dx}\left(\frac{2}{x^2 + 4x + 4}\right) = \frac{(x^2 + 4x + 4) \cdot 0 - 2(2x + 4)}{(x+2)^4}$$

$$= \frac{-4(x+2)}{(x+2)^4} = -\frac{4}{(x+2)^3} = -\frac{4}{x^3 + 6x^2 + 12x + 8}.$$

3.4.65

$$f'(x) = \frac{d}{dx}\left(\frac{x^2 - 7x}{x+1}\right) = \frac{(x+1)(2x-7) - (x^2 - 7x) \cdot 1}{(x+1)^2} = \frac{x^2 + 2x - 7}{x^2 + 2x + 1} = \frac{x^2 + 2x - 7}{(x+1)^2}.$$

$$f''(x) = \frac{d}{dx}\left(\frac{x^2 + 2x - 7}{x^2 + 2x + 1}\right) = \frac{(x^2 + 2x + 1)(2x + 2) - (x^2 + 2x - 7)(2x + 2)}{(x+1)^4}$$

$$= \frac{(2x^2 + 4x + 2) - (2x^2 + 4x - 14)}{(x+1)^3} = \frac{16}{(x+1)^3}.$$

3.4.66 $f'(x) = \frac{d}{dx}\left(\frac{(2-x)(2+x)}{x-2}\right) = \frac{d}{dx}(-(2+x)) = \frac{d}{dx}(-2-x) = -1.$

3.4.67 $f'(x) = \frac{d}{dx}\left(4x^2 - \frac{2x}{5x+1}\right) = 8x - \frac{(5x+1)2-(2x)(5)}{(5x+1)^2} = 8x - \frac{2}{(5x+1)^2}.$

3.4.68 $f'(z) = 2z(e^{3z}+4) + z^2 \cdot 3e^{3z} - \frac{(z^2+1)2-(2z)(2z)}{(z^2+1)^2} = 8z + e^{3z}(3z^2+2z) + \frac{2z^2-2}{(z^2+1)^2}.$

3.4.69

$$h'(r) = \frac{(r+1)(-1-\frac{1}{2\sqrt{r}}) - (2-r-\sqrt{r})\cdot 1}{(r+1)^2} = \frac{-r - \frac{\sqrt{r}}{2} - 1 - \frac{1}{2\sqrt{r}} - 2 + r + \sqrt{r}}{(r+1)^2}$$

$$= \frac{\frac{\sqrt{r}}{2} - \frac{1}{2\sqrt{r}} - 3}{(r+1)^2} \cdot \frac{2\sqrt{r}}{2\sqrt{r}} = \frac{r-1-6\sqrt{r}}{2\sqrt{r}(r+1)^2}.$$

3.4.70

$$y' = \frac{(\sqrt{x}-\sqrt{a})\cdot 1 - (x-a)\frac{1}{2\sqrt{x}}}{(\sqrt{x}-\sqrt{a})^2} = \left(\frac{(\sqrt{x}-\sqrt{a})\cdot 1 - (x-a)\frac{1}{2\sqrt{x}}}{(\sqrt{x}-\sqrt{a})^2}\right)\cdot\frac{2\sqrt{x}}{2\sqrt{x}}$$

$$= \frac{2x-2\sqrt{ax}-x+a}{2\sqrt{x}(\sqrt{x}-\sqrt{a})^2} = \frac{x-2\sqrt{ax}+a}{2\sqrt{x}(\sqrt{x}-\sqrt{a})^2} = \frac{(\sqrt{x}-\sqrt{a})^2}{2\sqrt{x}(\sqrt{x}-\sqrt{a})^2} = \frac{1}{2\sqrt{x}}.$$

3.4.71 $h'(x) = (35x^6+5)(6x^3+3x^2+3) + (5x^7+5x)(18x^2+6x) = 15((7x^6+1)(2x^3+x^2+1) + (x^7+x)(6x^2+2x)) = 300x^9 + 135x^8 + 105x^6 + 120x^3 + 45x^2 + 15.$

3.4.72

a. $g'(x) = 2xf(x) + x^2f'(x)$, so $g'(2) = 2\cdot 2\cdot f(2) + 4\cdot f'(2) = 8 + 12 = 20.$ Thus, the tangent line is given by $y - 8 = 20(x-2)$, or $y = 20x - 32.$

b. $h'(x) = \frac{(x-3)f'(x)-f(x)}{(x-3)^2}$, so $h'(2) = \frac{(-1)\cdot 3-2}{(-1)^2} = -5.$ Also, $h(2) = -2.$ Thus, the tangent line is given by $y + 2 = (-5)(x-2)$, or $y = -5x + 8.$

3.4.73

$y' = -\frac{54x}{(x^2+9)^2}.$ At $x = 2$, $y' = -\frac{108}{169}$ and $y = \frac{27}{13}.$ Thus the tangent line is given by

a.
$$y - \frac{27}{13} = -\frac{108}{169}(x-2),$$

or $y = -\frac{108}{169}x + \frac{567}{169}.$

b.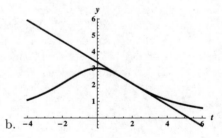

3.4.74 $\frac{d}{dx}\left[f(x)g(x)\right]\big|_{x=1} = f'(1)g(1) + f(1)g'(1) = 3\cdot 4 + 5\cdot 2 = 22.$

3.4.75 $\frac{d}{dx}\left[\frac{f(x)}{g(x)}\right]\bigg|_{x=2} = \frac{g(2)f'(2)-f(2)g'(2)}{(g(2))^2} = \frac{2\cdot 5-4\cdot 4}{4} = -\frac{3}{2}.$

3.4.76 $\frac{d}{dx}\left[xf(x)\right]\big|_{x=3} = f(3) + 3\cdot f'(3) = 3 + 3\cdot 2 = 9.$

3.4.77 $\frac{d}{dx}\left[\frac{f(x)}{x+2}\right]\bigg|_{x=4} = \frac{(4+2)f'(4)-f(4)}{36} = \frac{6-2}{36} = \frac{1}{9}.$

3.4.78 $\frac{d}{dx}\left[\frac{xf(x)}{g(x)}\right]\bigg|_{x=4} = \frac{g(4)(f(4)+4f'(4))-4f(4)g'(4)}{(g(4))^2} = \frac{3(2+4\cdot 1)-4\cdot 2\cdot 1}{9} = \frac{10}{9}.$

3.4.79 $\frac{d}{dx}\left[\frac{f(x)g(x)}{x}\right]\Big|_{x=4} = \frac{4(f'(4)g(4)+f(4)g'(4))-f(4)g(4)}{16} = \frac{4(1\cdot3+2\cdot1)-(2\cdot3)}{16} = \frac{14}{16} = \frac{7}{8}$.

3.4.80

a. Because the slope of f at 2 is $f'(2) = 4$ and the slope of g at 2 is $g'(2) = 3$ and $f(2) = 4\cdot 2 + 1 = 9$, $g(2) = 3\cdot 2 - 2 = 4$ we have $y'(2) = f'(2)g(2) + f(2)g'(2) = 4\cdot 4 + 9\cdot 3 = 43$. Thus, the tangent line at this point is $y - 36 = 43(x - 2)$, or $y = 43x - 50$.

b. $y'(2) = \frac{g(2)f'(2)-f(2)g'(2)}{(g(2))^2} = \frac{4\cdot4-9\cdot3}{16} = -\frac{11}{16}$. So the equation of the tangent line at this point is $y - \frac{9}{4} = -\frac{11}{16}(x - 2)$, or $y = -\frac{11}{16}x + \frac{29}{8}$.

3.4.81

a. The instantaneous rate of change is $\frac{d}{dx}F(x) = -\frac{2kQq}{x^3}$ N/m $= -\frac{1.8\times10^{10}Qq}{x^3}$ N/m.

b. $\left[\frac{d}{dx}F(x)\right]\Big|_{x=0.001} = -\frac{2(9\times10^9)}{(0.001)^3} = -\frac{18\times10^9}{10^{-9}} = -18\times10^{18} = -1.8\times10^{19}$ Newtons per meter.

c. Because the distance x appears in the denominator of $F'(x)$, the absolute value of the instantaneous rate of change decreases with the separation.

3.4.82

a. The instantaneous rate of change if $\frac{d}{dx}F(x) = \frac{2GMm}{x^3}$ Newtons per meter.

b. $\left[\frac{d}{dx}F(x)\right]\Big|_{x=0.01} = \frac{13.4\times10^{-11}\cdot(0.1)^2}{(0.01)^3} = 1.34\times10^{-6}$ Newtons per meter.

c. Because the distance x appears in the denominator of $F'(x)$, the instantaneous rate of change decreases with the separation.

3.4.83 We attempt a solution with functions of the form $f(x) = e^{ax}$ and $g(x) = e^{bx}$, because these functions are multiples of their own derivatives. The derivative of fg is $(a + b)e^{(a+b)x}$, while the product of the derivatives is $abe^{(a+b)x}$. These would be equal if we could have $a + b = ab$, which occurs, for example, when $a = b = 2$. Thus the functions $f(x) = g(x) = e^{2x}$ have the desired property. In general we need $b = \frac{a}{a-1}$, $a \neq 1$.

3.4.84 We attempt a solution with functions of the form $f(x) = e^{ax}$ and $g(x) = e^{bx}$, because these functions are multiples of their own derivatives. The derivative of f/g is $(a - b)e^{(a-b)x}$, while the quotient of the derivatives is $\frac{a}{b}\cdot e^{(a-b)x}$. These would be equal if we could have $a - b = \frac{a}{b}$, which occurs, for example, when $a = 4$ and $b = 2$. Thus the functions $f(x) = e^{4x}$ and $g(x) = e^{2x}$ have the desired property.

3.4.85

a. The tangent line at $x = a$ is $y - a^2 = 2a(x - a)$ and at $x = b$ is $y - b^2 = 2b(x - b)$.

These intersect when $a^2 + 2ax - 2a^2 = b^2 + 2bx - 2b^2$, or $(2a - 2b)x = a^2 - b^2$, which is met when $x = \frac{a+b}{2}$. So $c = \frac{a+b}{2}$.

b. The tangent line at $x = a$ is $y - \sqrt{a} = \frac{1}{2\sqrt{a}}(x - a)$ and at $x = b$ is $y - \sqrt{b} = \frac{1}{2\sqrt{b}}(x - b)$.

These intersect when $\sqrt{a} + \frac{1}{2\sqrt{a}}(x - a) = \sqrt{b} + \frac{1}{2\sqrt{b}}(x - b)$, or $\left(\frac{1}{2\sqrt{a}} - \frac{1}{2\sqrt{b}}\right)x = \frac{\sqrt{b}-\sqrt{a}}{2}$, which is met when $x = \sqrt{ab}$. So $c = \sqrt{ab}$.

c. The tangent line at $x = a$ is $y - \frac{1}{a} = -\frac{1}{a^2}(x - a)$ and at $x = b$ is $y - \frac{1}{b} = -\frac{1}{b^2}(x - b)$.

These intersect when $\frac{1}{a} + -\frac{1}{a^2}(x - a) = \frac{1}{b} - \frac{1}{b^2}(x - b)$, or $\left(\frac{2}{a} - \frac{x}{a^2}\right) = \left(\frac{2}{b} - \frac{x}{b^2}\right)$, which is met when $x\left(\frac{1}{b^2} - \frac{1}{a^2}\right) = \frac{2}{b} - \frac{2}{a}$, or $x\cdot\left(\frac{a^2-b^2}{a^2b^2}\right) = \frac{2(a-b)}{ab}$. Thus we arrive at $x = \frac{2ab}{a+b}$. So $c = \frac{2ab}{a+b}$.

d. The tangent line at $x = a$ is $y - f(a) = f'(a)(x - a)$ and at $x = b$ is $y - f(b) = f'(b)(x - b)$.

These intersect when $f(a) + f'(a)(x - a) = f(b) + f'(b)(x - b)$, or $(f'(a) - f'(b))x = f(b) - f(a) - f'(b)b + f'(a)a$. Solving for x yields $x = \frac{f(b) - f(a) - f'(b)b + f'(a)a}{f'(a) - f'(b)}$ provided $f'(a) \neq f'(b)$ (which occurs when the tangent lines are parallel and don't intersect.)

3.4.86

a.

$$\frac{d}{dx}\left(\frac{f(x)}{g(x)}\right) = \lim_{h \to 0} \frac{\frac{f(x+h)}{g(x+h)} - \frac{f(x)}{g(x)}}{h} = \lim_{h \to 0} \frac{f(x+h)g(x) - f(x)g(x+h)}{h \cdot g(x+h)g(x)}.$$

b.

$$\lim_{h \to 0} \frac{f(x+h)g(x) - f(x)g(x) + f(x)g(x) - f(x)g(x+h)}{h \cdot g(x+h)g(x)}$$

$$= \lim_{h \to 0} \frac{g(x)\left(\frac{f(x+h) - f(x)}{h}\right) - f(x)\left(\frac{g(x+h) - g(x)}{h}\right)}{g(x+h)g(x)} = \frac{g(x)f'(x) - f(x)g'(x)}{(g(x))^2}.$$

c. F' exists provided that f and g are differentiable, and $g(x) \neq 0$. Note that we used the fact that $\lim_{h \to 0} g(x+h) = g(x)$, which is true because g is continuous (because it is differentiable.)

3.4.87

$$\frac{d^2}{dx^2}(f(x)g(x)) = \frac{d}{dx}(f'(x)g(x) + f(x)g'(x)) = f''(x)g(x) + f'(x)g'(x) + f'(x)g'(x) + f(x)g''(x)$$

$$= f''(x)g(x) + 2f'(x)g'(x) + f(x)g''(x).$$

3.4.88

a. $\dfrac{d}{dx}e^{kx} = \lim_{h \to 0} \dfrac{e^{k(x+h)} - e^{kx}}{h} = \lim_{h \to 0} e^{kx} \cdot \dfrac{e^{kh} - 1}{h} = e^{kx} \lim_{h \to 0} k \cdot \dfrac{e^{kh} - 1}{kh} = ke^{kx}.$

b. $\dfrac{d}{dx}e^{(n+1)x} = \dfrac{d}{dx}(e^{nx} \cdot e^x) = \left(\dfrac{d}{dx}e^{nx}\right)e^x + e^{nx}\left(\dfrac{d}{dx}e^x\right) = ne^{nx}e^x + e^{nx}e^x = ne^{(n+1)x} + e^{(n+1)x} = (n+1)e^{(n+1)x}.$

3.4.89 Let $k = -m$, where m is a positive integer. Then $\frac{d}{dx}(e^{kx}) = \frac{d}{dx}\left(\frac{1}{e^{mx}}\right) = \frac{0 - 1 \cdot me^{mx}}{(e^{mx})^2} = -me^{-mx} = ke^{kx}.$

3.4.90

$$\frac{d^2}{dx^2}\left[\frac{f(x)}{g(x)}\right] = \frac{d}{dx}\left[\frac{g(x)f'(x) - f(x)g'(x)}{(g(x))^2}\right]$$

$$= \frac{(g(x))^2\left([g'(x)f'(x) + g(x)f''(x)] - [f(x)g''(x) + g'(x)f'(x)]\right) - [g(x)f'(x) - f(x)g'(x)] \cdot (g(x)g'(x) + g(x)g'(x))}{(g(x))^4}$$

$$= \frac{g(x)f'(x)g'(x) + g^2(x)f''(x) - g(x)f(x)g''(x) - g(x)g'(x)f'(x) - 2g(x)g'(x)f'(x) + 2f(x)(g'(x))^2}{(g(x))^3}$$

$$= \frac{g^2(x)f''(x) - g(x)f(x)g''(x) - 2g(x)g'(x)f'(x) + 2f(x)(g'(x))^2}{(g(x))^3}.$$

3.4.91

a.

$$\frac{d}{dx}[(f(x)g(x))h(x)] = \frac{d}{dx}[f(x)g(x)] \cdot h(x) + f(x)g(x) \cdot \frac{d}{dx}h(x)$$

$$= [f'(x)g(x) + f(x)g'(x)]h(x) + f(x)g(x)h'(x)$$

$$= f'(x)g(x)h(x) + f(x)g'(x)h(x) + f(x)g(x)h'(x).$$

b. $\frac{d}{dx}[e^{2x}(x-1)(x+3)] = 2e^{2x}(x-1)(x+3) + e^{2x}(x+3) + e^{2x}(x-1) = e^{2x}(2x^2+4x-6+x+3+x-1) = e^{2x}(2x^2 + 6x - 4) = 2e^{2x}(x^2 + 3x - 2)$.

3.4.92

a. $(fg)^{(2)} = (f'g + fg')' = f''g + f'g' + f'g' + fg'' = f''g + 2f'g' + fg''$.

b. We proceed by induction. For $n = 1$, we have that

$$(fg)' = \sum_{k=0}^{1} f^{(k)}g^{(1-k)} = f'g + fg'.$$

Now suppose that the rule holds for $n = m$. We will show that the rule holds for $n = m + 1$.

$$(fg)^{(m+1)} = \left((fg)^{(m)}\right)' = \sum_{k=0}^{n}\binom{n}{k}(f^{(k)}g^{(n-k)})' = \sum_{k=0}^{n}\binom{n}{k}\left(f^{(k+1)}g^{(n-k)} + f^{(k)}g^{(n+1-k)}\right)$$

$$= \sum_{k=0}^{n}\binom{n}{k}\left(f^{(k+1)}g^{(n+1-(k+1))} + f^{(k)}g^{(n+1-k)}\right)$$

$$= \sum_{k=1}^{n+1}\binom{n}{k-1}f^{(k)}g^{(n+1-k)} + \sum_{k=0}^{n}\binom{n}{k}f^{(k)}g^{(n+1-k)} = \sum_{k=0}^{n+1}\binom{n+1}{k}f^{(k)}g^{(n+1-k)},$$

because $\binom{n}{0} = \binom{n}{n+1} = 1$ and $\binom{n}{k-1} + \binom{n}{k} = \binom{n+1}{k}$.

c. $(a + b)^n = \sum_{k=0}^{n}\binom{n}{k}a^k b^{n-k}$ follows a similar pattern.

3.5   Derivatives of Trigonometric Functions

3.5.1 A direct substitution would yield the quotient of zero with itself, which isn't defined

3.5.2 It is an important ingredient in the derivation of the formula $\frac{d}{dx}\sin x = \cos x$.

3.5.3 Because $\tan x = \frac{\sin x}{\cos x}$, and $\cot x = \frac{\cos x}{\sin x}$, we can use the quotient rule to compute these derivatives, because we know the derivatives of $\sin x$ and of $\cos x$.

3.5.4 Remember the rule that the derivative of a "co" function can be obtained from the derivative of a function by changing all of the functions in the formula to their cofunctions, and introducing a factor of negative one. Thus, for example, because $\frac{d}{dx}\tan x = \sec^2 x$, we would have $\frac{d}{dx}\cot x = -\csc^2 x$.

3.5.5 $f'(x) = \cos x$ and $f'(\pi) = \cos \pi = -1$.

3.5.6 Because $\frac{d}{dx}\sin x = \cos x$, the graph of $\sin x$ will have a horizontal tangent line where the cosine function crosses the x axis. This happens at all real numbers of the form $x = \frac{2n+1}{2} \cdot \pi$ where n is an integer.

3.5.7 $\lim_{x \to 0}\frac{\sin 3x}{x} = \lim_{x \to 0}\frac{3\sin 3x}{3x} = 3\lim_{x \to 0}\frac{\sin 3x}{3x} = 3 \cdot 1 = 3$.

3.5.8 $\lim\limits_{x\to 0}\dfrac{\sin 5x}{3x}=\dfrac{1}{3}\lim\limits_{x\to 0}\dfrac{5\sin 5x}{5x}=\dfrac{5}{3}\lim\limits_{x\to 0}\dfrac{\sin 5x}{5x}=\dfrac{5}{3}\cdot 1=\dfrac{5}{3}.$

3.5.9 $\lim\limits_{x\to 0}\dfrac{\sin 7x}{\sin 3x}=\lim\limits_{x\to 0}\dfrac{\frac{7\sin 7x}{7x}}{\frac{3\sin 3x}{3x}}=\dfrac{7}{3}\cdot\lim\limits_{x\to 0}\dfrac{\frac{\sin 7x}{7x}}{\frac{\sin 3x}{3x}}=\dfrac{7}{3}\cdot\dfrac{1}{1}=\dfrac{7}{3}.$

3.5.10 $\lim\limits_{x\to 0}\dfrac{\sin 3x}{\tan 4x}=\lim\limits_{x\to 0}\dfrac{\sin 3x\cos 4x}{\sin 4x}=\lim\limits_{x\to 0}\dfrac{\frac{3\sin 3x}{3x}\cdot\cos 4x}{\frac{4\sin 4x}{4x}}=\dfrac{3\cdot 1\cdot 1}{4\cdot 1}=\dfrac{3}{4}.$

3.5.11 $\lim\limits_{x\to 0}\dfrac{\tan 5x}{x}=\lim\limits_{x\to 0}\dfrac{5\sin 5x}{5x\cos 5x}=5\lim\limits_{x\to 0}\dfrac{\sin 5x}{5x}\cdot\lim\limits_{x\to 0}\dfrac{1}{\cos 5x}=5\cdot 1\cdot 1=5.$

3.5.12 $\lim\limits_{\theta\to 0}\dfrac{\cos^2\theta-1}{\theta}=\left(\lim\limits_{\theta\to 0}(\cos\theta+1)\right)\cdot\left(\lim\limits_{\theta\to 0}\dfrac{\cos\theta-1}{\theta}\right)=2\cdot 0=0.$

3.5.13 $\lim\limits_{x\to 0}\dfrac{\tan 7x}{\sin x}=\lim\limits_{x\to 0}\dfrac{\sin 7x}{\cos 7x\cdot\sin x}=\lim\limits_{x\to 0}\left(\dfrac{1}{\cos 7x}\cdot\dfrac{x}{\sin x}\cdot\dfrac{7\sin 7x}{7x}\right)=$

$7\cdot\lim\limits_{x\to 0}\dfrac{1}{\cos 7x}\cdot\lim\limits_{x\to 0}\dfrac{x}{\sin x}\cdot\lim\limits_{x\to 0}\dfrac{\sin 7x}{7x}=7\cdot 1\cdot 1\cdot 1=7.$

3.5.14 $\lim\limits_{\theta\to 0}\dfrac{\sec\theta-1}{\theta}=\lim\limits_{\theta\to 0}\dfrac{\frac{1}{\cos\theta}-1}{\theta}=\lim\limits_{\theta\to 0}\dfrac{1-\cos\theta}{\theta\cos\theta}=\lim\limits_{\theta\to 0}\dfrac{1}{\cos\theta}\cdot\lim\limits_{\theta\to 0}\dfrac{1-\cos\theta}{\theta}=1\cdot 0=0.$

3.5.15 $\lim\limits_{x\to 2}\dfrac{\sin(x-2)}{x^2-4}=\lim\limits_{x\to 2}\left(\dfrac{1}{x+2}\cdot\dfrac{\sin(x-2)}{x-2}\right)=\lim\limits_{x\to 2}\dfrac{1}{x+2}\cdot\lim\limits_{x\to 2}\dfrac{\sin(x-2)}{x-2}=\dfrac{1}{4}\cdot 1=\dfrac{1}{4}.$

3.5.16 $\lim\limits_{x\to -3}\dfrac{\sin(x+3)}{x^2+8x+15}=\lim\limits_{x\to -3}\dfrac{\sin(x+3)}{(x+5)(x+3)}=\lim\limits_{x\to -3}\dfrac{1}{x+5}\cdot\lim\limits_{x\to -3}\dfrac{\sin(x+3)}{(x+3)}=\dfrac{1}{2}\cdot 1=\dfrac{1}{2}.$

3.5.17 $y'=\cos x-\sin x.$

3.5.18 $y'=10x-\sin x.$

3.5.19 $y=-e^{-x}\sin x+e^{-x}\cos x=e^{-x}(\cos x-\sin x).$

3.5.20 $y'=\cos x+2e^{0.5x}.$

3.5.21 $y'=\sin x+x\cos x.$

3.5.22 $y'=6e^{6x}\sin x+e^{6x}\cos x=e^{6x}(6\sin x+\cos x).$

3.5.23 $y'=\dfrac{(\sin x+1)(-\sin x)-(\cos x)(\cos x)}{(1+\sin x)^2}=\dfrac{-1(\sin^2 x+\cos^2 x)-\sin x}{(1+\sin x)^2}=\dfrac{-1(1+\sin x)}{(1+\sin x)^2}=-\dfrac{1}{1+\sin x}.$

3.5.24 $y'=\dfrac{(1+\sin x)(-\cos x)-(1-\sin x)(\cos x)}{(1+\sin x)^2}=\dfrac{-2\cos x}{(1+\sin x)^2}.$

3.5.25 $y'=\cos x\cos x+\sin x\cdot(-\sin x)=\cos^2 x-\sin^2 x=\cos(2x).$

3.5.26

$$y'=\dfrac{(\sin x+1)(2x\sin x+(x^2-1)\cos x)-\cos x(x^2-1)\sin x}{(\sin x+1)^2}$$

$$=\dfrac{2x\sin^2 x+2x\sin x+x^2\cos x-\cos x}{(\sin x+1)^2}.$$

3.5.27 $y'=-\sin x\cos x+\cos x(-\sin x)=-2\sin x\cos x=-\sin(2x).$

3.5.28

$$y' = \frac{(1 + \cos x)(\sin x + x \cos x) - x \sin x(-\sin x)}{(1 + \cos x)^2} = \frac{\sin x + x \cos x + \sin x \cos x + x \cos^2 x + x \sin^2 x}{(1 + \cos x)^2}$$

$$= \frac{\sin x + x \cos x + \sin x \cos x + x}{(1 + \cos x)^2} = \frac{\sin x(1 + \cos x) + x(1 + \cos x)}{(1 + \cos x)^2} = \frac{\sin x + x}{1 + \cos x}.$$

3.5.29 $\dfrac{d}{dx}(\cot x) = \dfrac{d}{dx}\left(\dfrac{\cos x}{\sin x}\right) = \dfrac{\sin x(-\sin x) - \cos x(\cos x)}{\sin^2 x} = \dfrac{-(\sin^2 x + \cos^2 x)}{\sin^2 x} = -\dfrac{1}{\sin^2 x} = -\csc^2 x.$

3.5.30 $\dfrac{d}{dx}(\sec x) = \dfrac{d}{dx}\left(\dfrac{1}{\cos x}\right) = \dfrac{0 - (-\sin x)}{\cos^2 x} = \dfrac{1}{\cos x} \cdot \dfrac{\sin x}{\cos x} = \sec x \tan x.$

3.5.31 $\dfrac{d}{dx}(\csc x) = \dfrac{d}{dx}\left(\dfrac{1}{\sin x}\right) = \dfrac{0 - \cos x}{\sin^2 x} = -\dfrac{1}{\sin x} \cdot \dfrac{\cos x}{\sin x} = -\csc x \cot x.$

3.5.32 $y' = \sec^2 x - \csc^2 x.$

3.5.33 $y' = \sec x \tan x - \csc x \cot x.$

3.5.34 $y' = \sec x \tan x \tan x + \sec x \sec^2 x = \sec x(\tan^2 x + \sec^2 x).$

3.5.35 $y' = 5e^{5x} \csc x + e^{5x}(-\csc x \cot x) = e^{5x} \csc x(5 - \cot x).$

3.5.36 $y' = \dfrac{(1 + \tan w)\sec^2 w - \tan w \sec^2 w}{(1 + \tan w)^2} = \dfrac{\sec^2 w}{(1 + \tan w)^2}.$

3.5.37

$$y' = \frac{(1 + \csc x)(-\csc^2 x) - \cot x(-\csc x \cot x)}{(1 + \csc x)^2} = \frac{-\csc^2 x - \csc^3 x + \csc x(\csc^2 x - 1)}{(1 + \csc x)^2}$$

$$= \frac{-\csc x(1 + \csc x)}{(1 + \csc x)^2} = -\frac{\csc x}{1 + \csc x}$$

3.5.38

$$y' = \frac{(1 + \sec t)\sec^2 t - \tan t(\sec t \tan t)}{(1 + \sec t)^2} = \frac{\sec^2 t + \sec^3 t - \sec t(\sec^2 t - 1)}{(1 + \sec t)^2}$$

$$= \frac{\sec t(1 + \sec t)}{(1 + \sec t)^2} = \frac{\sec t}{1 + \sec t}.$$

3.5.39

$$y' = \frac{0 - (\sec z \tan z \csc z - \sec z \csc z \cot z)}{\sec^2 z \csc^2 z} = \frac{\sec z \csc z(\cot z - \tan z)}{\sec^2 z \csc^2 z}$$

$$= \frac{\cot z - \tan z}{\sec z \csc z} = \cos^2 z - \sin^2 z = \cos(2z).$$

3.5.40 Because $\csc^2 \theta - 1 = \cot^2 \theta$, we have $y' = \dfrac{d}{d\theta} \cot^2 \theta = -\csc^2 \theta \cot \theta + \cot \theta(-\csc^2 \theta) = -2 \csc^2 \theta \cot \theta.$

3.5.41 $y' = \sin x + x \cos x$, so $y'' = \cos x + \cos x + -x \sin x = 2 \cos x - x \sin x.$

3.5.42 $y' = -\sin x$, so $y'' = -\cos x.$

3.5.43 $y' = e^x \sin x + e^x \cos x$, so $y'' = e^x \sin x + e^x \cos x + e^x \cos x + e^x(-\sin x) = 2e^x \cos x.$

3.5.44 $y' = \frac{1}{2}e^x \cos x + \frac{1}{2}e^x(-\sin x)$, so $y'' = \frac{1}{2}e^x \cos x + \frac{1}{2}e^x(-\sin x) + \frac{1}{2}e^x(-\sin x) + \frac{1}{2}e^x(-\cos x) = -e^x \sin x.$

3.5.45 $y' = -\csc^2 x$ and $y'' = -((-\csc x \cot x)\csc x + \csc x(-\csc x \cot x)) = 2\cot x \csc^2 x$.

3.5.46 $y' = \sec^2 x$ and $y'' = \sec x \tan x(\sec x) + \sec x(\sec x \tan x) = 2\tan x \sec^2 x$.

3.5.47

$$y' = \sec x \tan x \csc x - \sec x \csc x \cot x = \sec x \csc x(\tan x - \cot x) = \sec^2 x - \csc^2 x.$$

$$y'' = \sec x(\sec x \tan x) + (\sec x \tan x)\sec x - ((-\csc x \cot x)\csc x + \csc x(-\csc x \cot x))$$
$$= 2\sec^2 x \tan x + 2\csc^2 x \cot x.$$

3.5.48 $y' = (-\sin x)\sin x + \cos x \cos x = \cos^2 x - \sin^2 x = \cos(2x)$.
$y'' = 2\cos x(-\sin x) - 2\sin x \cos x = -2(2\sin x \cos x) = -2\sin(2x)$.

3.5.49

a. False. $\frac{d}{dx}\sin^2 x = \sin x \cos x + \cos x \sin x = 2\sin x \cos x \neq \cos^2 x$.

b. False. $\frac{d^2}{dx^2}\sin x = \frac{d}{dx}\cos x = -\sin x \neq \sin x$.

c. True. $\frac{d^4}{dx^4}\cos x = \frac{d^3}{dx^3}(-\sin x) = \frac{d^2}{dx^2}(-\cos x) = \frac{d}{dx}\sin x = \cos x$.

d. True. In fact, $\pi/2$ isn't even in the domain of $\sec x$.

3.5.50 $\lim_{x \to 0} \dfrac{\sin ax}{bx} = \dfrac{a}{b}\lim_{x \to 0}\dfrac{\sin ax}{ax} = \dfrac{a}{b} \cdot 1 = \dfrac{a}{b}$.

3.5.51 $\lim_{x \to 0} \dfrac{\sin ax}{\sin bx} = \lim_{x \to 0} \dfrac{a\sin ax}{ax} \cdot \dfrac{bx}{b\sin bx} = \dfrac{a}{b}\lim_{x \to 0}\dfrac{\sin ax}{ax} \cdot \lim_{x \to 0}\dfrac{bx}{\sin bx} = \dfrac{a}{b} \cdot 1 \cdot 1 = \dfrac{a}{b}$.

3.5.52 Let $x = t + \pi/2$. Then as $t \to 0$, $x \to \pi/2$.
$$\lim_{x \to \pi/2} \frac{\cos x}{x - \pi/2} = \lim_{t \to 0} \frac{\cos(t + \pi/2)}{t} = \lim_{t \to 0} -\frac{\sin t}{t} = -1.$$

3.5.53 $\lim_{x \to 0} \dfrac{3\sec^5 x}{x^2 + 4} = \dfrac{3\sec^5(0)}{4} = \dfrac{3}{4}$.

3.5.54 $\lim_{x \to \infty} \dfrac{\cos x}{x} = 0$, because $-\frac{1}{x} \leq \frac{\cos x}{x} \leq \frac{1}{x}$, and $\lim_{x \to -\infty} \dfrac{1}{x} = 0$, so we can apply the squeeze theorem.

3.5.55 $\lim_{x \to \pi/4} 3\csc(2x)\cot(2x) = \lim_{x \to \pi/4} 3\dfrac{1}{\sin 2x}\dfrac{\cos 2x}{\sin 2x} = 3\dfrac{\cos \pi/2}{(\sin \pi/2)^2} = 3 \cdot \dfrac{0}{1} = 0$.

3.5.56 $\dfrac{dy}{dx} = \dfrac{(1 + \cos x)\cos x - \sin x(-\sin x)}{(1 + \cos x)^2} = \dfrac{1 + \cos x}{(1 + \cos x)^2} = \dfrac{1}{1 + \cos x}$.

3.5.57 $\frac{dy}{dx} = \cos x \sin x + x(-\sin x)\sin x + x\cos x \cos x = \sin x \cos x - x\sin^2 x + x\cos^2 x = \frac{1}{2}\sin 2x + x\cos 2x$.

3.5.58 $\dfrac{dy}{dx} = \dfrac{0 - 1 \cdot \cos x}{(2 + \sin x)^2} = -\dfrac{\cos x}{(2 + \sin x)^2}$.

3.5.59 $\dfrac{dy}{dx} = \dfrac{(\sin x - \cos x)\cos x - \sin x(\cos x + \sin x)}{(\sin x - \cos x)^2} = \dfrac{-(\sin^2 x + \cos^2 x)}{(\sin x - \cos x)^2} =$

$\dfrac{-1}{\sin^2 x - 2\sin x \cos x + \cos^2 x} = \dfrac{-1}{1 - \sin 2x} = \dfrac{1}{\sin(2x) - 1} = \dfrac{1}{2\sin x \cos x - 1}$.

3.5.60 $\dfrac{dy}{dx} = \dfrac{(1+x^3)(\cos x - x\sin x) - x(\cos x)(3x^2)}{(1+x^3)^2} = \dfrac{\cos x - x\sin x - x^4\sin x - 2x^3\cos x}{(1+x^3)^2}.$

3.5.61 $\dfrac{dy}{dx} = \dfrac{(1+\cos x)\sin x - (1-\cos x)(-\sin x)}{(1+\cos x)^2} = \dfrac{2\sin x}{(1+\cos x)^2}.$

3.5.62

a. $y' = 4\cos^2 x - 4\sin^2 x$, so $y'(\pi/3) = 4\left(\frac{1}{4} - \frac{3}{4}\right) = -2$. $y(\pi/3) = 4\cdot(\sqrt{3}/2)\cdot(1/2) = \sqrt{3}$. The tangent line is thus given by $y - \sqrt{3} = -2(x - \pi/3)$, or $y = -2x + \sqrt{3} + \frac{2\pi}{3}$.

b.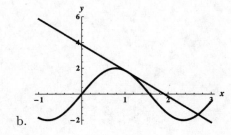

3.5.63

a. $y' = 2\cos x$, so $y'(\pi/6) = \sqrt{3}$. $y(\pi/6) = 2$. The tangent line is thus given by $y - 2 = \sqrt{3}(x - \pi/6)$, or $y = \sqrt{3}x + 2 - \frac{\pi\sqrt{3}}{6}$.

b.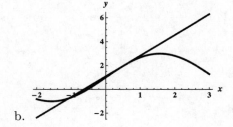

3.5.64

a. $y' = -\csc x \cot x$, so $y'(\pi/4) = -\sqrt{2}$. $y(\pi/4) = \sqrt{2}$. The tangent line is thus given by $y - \sqrt{2} = -\sqrt{2}(x - \pi/4)$, or $y = -\sqrt{2}x + \sqrt{2} + \frac{\sqrt{2}\pi}{4}$.

b.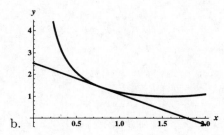

3.5.65

a. $y' = \dfrac{(1-\cos x)(-\sin x) - \cos x \sin x}{(1-\cos x)^2} = -\dfrac{\sin x}{(1-\cos x)^2}$, so $y'(\pi/3) = -2\sqrt{3}$. $y(\pi/3) = 1$. The tangent line is thus given by $y - 1 = -2\sqrt{3}(x - \pi/3)$, or $y = -2\sqrt{3}x + \frac{2\sqrt{3}\pi}{3} + 1$.

b.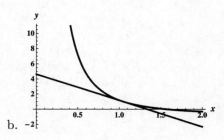

3.5.66

a. A horizontal tangent line occurs when $g'(x) = 1 - \cos x = 0$, which is when $\cos x = 1$. This occurs when $x = 2n\pi$, where n is any integer.

b. A slope of 1 occurs when $g'(x) = 1 - \cos x = 1$, which is when $\cos x = 0$. This occurs when $x = \frac{2n+1}{2} \cdot \pi$, where n is any integer.

3.5.67 For a horizontal tangent line we need $f'(x) = 1 + 2\sin x = 0$, or $\sin x = -\frac{1}{2}$. This occurs for $x = \frac{7\pi}{6} + 2n\pi$ where n is any integer, or for $x = \frac{11\pi}{6} + 2n\pi$ where n is any integer.

3.5.68

a. The derivative of graph (a) is graph (D), because graph (a) has a positive slope everywhere, its derivative must be positive everywhere, and graph (D) is the only one with this property.

b. The derivative of graph (b) is graph (B), because graph (b) has negative slope everywhere, its derivative must be negative everywhere, and graph (B) is the only one with this property.

c. The derivative of graph (c) is graph (A), because graph (c) has horizontal tangents at 0 and $\pm\pi$, its derivative needs to be 0 at these points, and only graph (A) has this property.

d. The derivative of graph (d) is graph (C), because graph (d) has horizontal tangents at $\pm\pi/2$ and $\pm3\pi/2$, its derivative needs to be 0 at these points, and only graph (C) has this property.

3.5.69

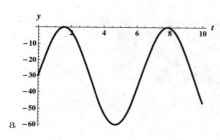

b. $v(t) = y'(t) = 30\cos t$ cm per second.

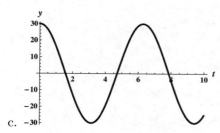

d. $v(t) = 30\cos t = 0$ when $t = \frac{2n+1}{2} \cdot \pi$ where n is a non-negative integer. At those times, the position is given by $\begin{cases} 0 & \text{if } n \text{ is even} \\ -60 & \text{if } n \text{ is odd.} \end{cases}$

e. The maximum velocity is 30 cm per second because $|\cos t| \le 1$ for all t. We have $\cos t = 1$ for $t = 2n\pi$ for a positive integer n. At those times, $y(2n\pi) = -30$.

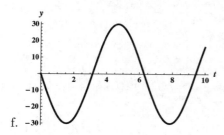

$a(t) = v'(t) = -30\sin t.$

3.5.70

a.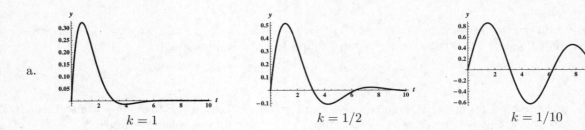
$$k = 1 \qquad\qquad k = 1/2 \qquad\qquad k = 1/10$$

The graph of $f(t) = e^{-kt}\sin t$ oscillates between $-e^{-kt}$ and e^{-kt} because $-1 \le \sin t \le 1$. Because e^{-kt} decreases as k increases, the oscillations have a smaller and smaller amplitude as k increases.

b. For $k = 1$, we have $f'(t) = -e^{-t}\sin t + e^{-t}\cos t$, which is zero when $\cos t - \sin t = 0$, which occurs for $t = \frac{\pi}{4} + n\pi$ where n is any integer.

c. Because $-1 \le \sin t \le 1$ and $e^{-t} > 0$ for all t, we have $-e^{-t} \le e^{-t}\sin t \le e^{-t}$. And because $\lim\limits_{t\to\infty} e^{-t} = 0$, we have that $\lim\limits_{t\to\infty} e^{-t}\sin t = 0$ by the squeeze theorem. This means that the vibrations approach zero in the long run.

3.5.71

a. $y'(t) = A\cos t$, $y''(t) = -A\sin t$, so $y''(t) + y(t) = -A\sin t + A\sin t = 0$ for all A and all t.

b. $y'(t) = -B\sin t$, $y''(t) = -B\cos t$, so $y''(t) + y(t) = -B\cos t + B\cos t = 0$ for all B and all t.

c. $y' = A\cos t - B\sin t$, $y'' = -A\sin t - B\cos t$, so $y''(t) + y(t) = -A\sin t - B\cos t + A\sin t + B\cos t = 0$ for all A, B, t.

3.5.72 $\frac{d}{dx}(\sin 2x) = \frac{d}{dx}(2\sin x\cos x) = (2\cos x)\cos x + (2\sin x)(-\sin x) = 2(\cos^2 x - \sin^2 x) = 2\cos 2x.$

3.5.73

$$\lim_{x\to0}\frac{\cos x - 1}{x} = \lim_{x\to0}\frac{(\cos x - 1)(\cos x + 1)}{x(\cos x + 1)} = \lim_{x\to0}\frac{\cos^2 x - 1}{x(\cos x + 1)} = \lim_{x\to0} -\frac{\sin^2 x}{x(\cos x + 1)}$$

$$= \lim_{x\to0}\frac{\sin x}{x} \cdot \lim_{x\to0} -\frac{\sin x}{(\cos x + 1)} = 1 \cdot \frac{0}{2} = 0.$$

3.5.74 We will use this version of the half-angle formula: $\frac{1-\cos x}{2} = \sin^2(x/2)$.

We have $\lim\limits_{x\to0}\dfrac{\cos x - 1}{x} = \lim\limits_{x\to0} -\dfrac{1 - \cos x}{2x/2} = \lim\limits_{x\to0} -\dfrac{\sin^2(x/2)}{x/2} = -\lim\limits_{x\to0}\sin(x/2)\cdot\lim\limits_{x\to0}\dfrac{\sin x/2}{x/2} = -1\cdot0\cdot1 = 0.$

3.5.75

$$\frac{d}{dx}\cos x = \lim_{h\to0}\frac{\cos(x+h) - \cos x}{h} = \lim_{h\to0}\frac{\cos x\cos h - \sin x\sin h - \cos x}{h}$$

$$= \cos x\left(\lim_{h\to0}\frac{\cos h - 1}{h}\right) - \sin x\left(\lim_{h\to0}\frac{\sin h}{h}\right) = \cos x\cdot0 - \sin x\cdot1 = -\sin x.$$

3.5.76 f is continuous at 0 if and only if $\lim\limits_{x\to0} f(x) = f(0)$. Because $\lim\limits_{x\to0} f(x) = \lim\limits_{x\to0}\dfrac{3\sin x}{x} = 3$, we require $a = 3$ in order for f to be continuous.

3.5.77 g is continuous at 0 if and only if $\lim\limits_{x\to0} g(x) = g(0)$. Because $\lim\limits_{x\to0} g(x) = \lim\limits_{x\to0}\dfrac{1 - \cos x}{2x} = \dfrac{1}{2}\cdot0 = 0$, we require $a = 0$ in order for g to be continuous.

3.5.78

a. The unit circle consists of 360 degrees and 2π radians, so each degree corresponds to $\frac{2\pi}{360} = \frac{\pi}{180}$ radians.

b. $\lim\limits_{x \to 0} \dfrac{s(x)}{x} = \lim\limits_{x \to 0} \dfrac{\sin(\pi x/180)}{x} = \dfrac{\pi}{180} \lim\limits_{x \to 0} \dfrac{\sin(\pi x/180)}{\pi x/180} = \dfrac{\pi}{180} \cdot 1 = \dfrac{\pi}{180}$.

3.5.79

a. $\dfrac{d}{dx} \sin^2 x = \sin x \cos x + \cos x \sin x = 2 \sin x \cos x$.

b. $\dfrac{d}{dx} \sin^3 x = \dfrac{d}{dx}(\sin^2 x)(\sin x) = (2 \sin x \cos x) \sin x + \sin^2 x \cdot \cos x = 3 \sin^2 x \cos x$.

c. $\dfrac{d}{dx} \sin^4 x = \dfrac{d}{dx}(\sin^3 x)(\sin x) = (3 \sin^2 x \cos x)(\sin x) + (\sin^3 x)(\cos x) = 4 \sin^3 x \cos x$.

d. We guess that $\dfrac{d}{dx} \sin^n x = n \sin^{n-1} x \cos x$.

We have already seen that the claim is valid for $n = 2$. Suppose our guess is valid for a given positive integer n. Then

$$\frac{d}{dx} \sin^{n+1} x = \frac{d}{dx}(\sin^n x)(\sin x) = (n \sin^{n-1} x \cos x)(\sin x) + \sin^n x \cos x = (n+1) \sin^n x \cos x.$$

Thus by induction, the result holds for all n.

3.5.80 Consider the statement $\frac{d^{2n}}{dx^{2n}}(\sin x) = (-1)^n \sin x$. This statement is valid for $n = 1$ because

$$\frac{d^2}{dx^2} \sin x = \frac{d}{dx} \cos x = -\sin x.$$

Now suppose the statement is valid for some positive integer n. Then

$$\frac{d^{2n+2}}{dx^{2n+2}} \sin x = \frac{d^2}{dx^2}\left(\frac{d^{2n}}{dx^{2n}} \sin x\right) = \frac{d^2}{dx^2}\left((-1)^n \sin x\right) = (-1)^n \cdot (-1) \sin x = (-1)^{n+1} \sin x,$$

which completes the proof.

Similarly, consider the statement $\frac{d^{2n}}{dx^{2n}}(\cos x) = (-1)^n \cos x$ This statement is valid for $n = 1$ because

$$\frac{d^2}{dx^2} \cos x = \frac{d}{dx}(-\sin x) = -\cos x.$$

Now suppose the statement is valid for some positive integer n. Then

$$\frac{d^{2n+2}}{dx^{2n+2}} \cos x = \frac{d^2}{dx^2}\left(\frac{d^{2n}}{dx^{2n}} \cos x\right) = \frac{d^2}{dx^2}\left((-1)^n \cos x\right) = (-1)^n \cdot (-1) \cos x = (-1)^{n+1} \cos x,$$

which completes the proof.

3.5.81

a. $f(x) = \sin x$, $a = \pi/6$.

b. $\lim\limits_{h \to 0} \dfrac{\sin(\pi/6 + h) - (1/2)}{h} = f'(\pi/6) = \cos(\pi/6) = \sqrt{3}/2$.

3.5.82

a. $f(x) = \cos x$, $a = \pi/6$.

b. $\displaystyle\lim_{h\to 0}\frac{\cos(\pi/6 + h) - (\sqrt{3}/2)}{h} = f'(\pi/6) = -\sin(\pi/6) = -1/2.$

3.5.83

a. $f(x) = \cot x$, $a = \pi/4$.

b. $\displaystyle\lim_{x\to\pi/4}\frac{\cot(x) - 1}{x - \pi/4} = f'(\pi/4) = -\csc^2(\pi/4) = -2.$

3.5.84

a. $f(x) = \tan x$, $a = 5\pi/6$.

b. $\displaystyle\lim_{h\to 0}\frac{\tan(5\pi/6 + h) + (1/\sqrt{3})}{h} = f'(5\pi/6) = \sec^2(5\pi/6) = 4/3.$

3.5.85 Because D is a difference quotient, and because $h = 0.01$ is small, D is a good approximation to f'. Therefore, the graph of D is nearly indistinguishable from the graph of $f'(x) = \cos x$.

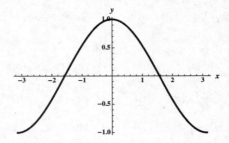

3.5.86 Because D is a difference quotient, and because $h = 0.01$ is small, D is a good approximation to f'. Therefore, the graph of D is nearly indistinguishable from the graph of $f'(x) = x^2$.

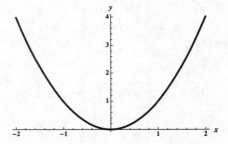

3.6 Derivatives as Rates of Change

3.6.1

The average rate of change over the interval $[a, a + \Delta x]$ is the slope of the line through $(a, f(a))$ and $(a + \Delta x, f(a + \Delta x))$, given by $m_{\text{avg}} = \frac{f(a+\Delta x)-f(a)}{\Delta x}$. The instantaneous rate of change is the limit of this expression as $\Delta x \to 0$, which is the slope of the tangent line at $(a, f(a))$.

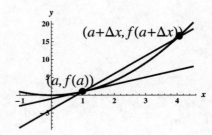

3.6.2 If $\frac{dy}{dx}$ is large, then small changes in x will result in relatively large changes in the value of y.

3.6.3 If $\frac{dy}{dx}$ is small, then small changes in x will result in relatively small changes in the value of y.

3.6.4 The speed of an object is the absolute value of its velocity. Thus, velocity encompasses the direction that the object is moving, while speed does not (it is always positive).

3.6.5 Acceleration is the instantaneous rate of change of the velocity; that is, if $s(t)$ is the position of an object at time t, then $s''(t) = \frac{d}{dt}(v(t)) = a(t)$ is the acceleration of the object at time t.

3.6.6 If the object is moving in the positive direction, the velocity will decrease. If it is moving in the negative direction, the velocity will increase.

3.6.7 Each of the first 200 stoves cost on average \$70 to produce, while the 201st stove costs \$65 to produce.

3.6.8 If $D(p)$ is decreasing, then $\frac{dD}{dp}$ is negative. Both p and D are positive, so $E(p) = \frac{dD}{dp}\frac{p}{D}$ is negative.

3.6.9

a. $v_{\text{avg}} = \dfrac{f(0.75) - f(0)}{0.75} = \dfrac{30 - 0}{0.75} = 40$ mph.

b. $v_{\text{avg}} = \dfrac{f(0.75) - f(0.25)}{0.75 - 0.25} = \dfrac{30 - 10}{0.5} = 40$ mph.

This is a pretty good estimate, since the graph is nearly linear over that time interval.

c. $v_{\text{avg}} = \dfrac{f(2.25) - f(1.75)}{2.25 - 1.75} = \dfrac{-14 - 16}{0.5} = -60$ mph.

At 11 a.m. the velocity is $v(2) \approx -60$ mph. The car is moving south with a speed of approximately 60 mph.

d. From 9 a.m. until about 10:08 a.m., the car moves north, away from the station. Then it moves south, passing the station at approximately 11:02 a.m., and continues south until about 11:40 a.m. Then the car drives north until 12:00 noon stopping south of the station.

3.6.10

a. $v_{\text{avg}} = \dfrac{s(1.5) - s(0)}{1.5 - 0} = \dfrac{600 - 0}{1.5} = 400$ mph.

b. $v_{\text{avg}} = \dfrac{s(8.5) - s(7.5)}{8.5 - 7.5} = \dfrac{0 - 300}{1} = -300$ mph.

c. The velocity is zero from about 9 a.m. until 11:10 a.m. when the plane is at the gate in Minneapolis.

d. $v(6) \approx \frac{800 - 1400}{1} = -600$ mph. The velocity is negative as the plane returns to Seattle.

3.6.11

a.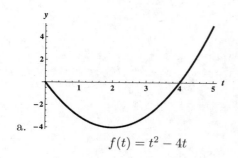

$$f(t) = t^2 - 4t$$

b.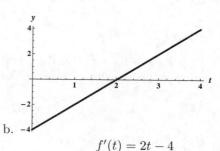

$$f'(t) = 2t - 4$$

b. $f'(t) = 0$ when $t = 2$ – that is when the object is stationary. For $0 \le t < 2$ we have $f'(t) < 0$ so the object is moving to the left. For $2 < t \le 5$ we have $f'(t) > 0$ so the object is moving to the right.

c. $f'(1) = -2$ ft/sec and $f''(t) = 2$ ft/sec^2, so in particular, $f''(1) = 2$ ft/sec^2.

d. $f'(t) = 0$ when $t = 2$ and $f''(2) = 2$ ft/sec^2.

e. On the interval $(2, 5]$ the velocity and acceleration are both positive, so the object's speed is increasing.

3.6.12

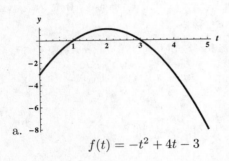

a. $f(t) = -t^2 + 4t - 3$

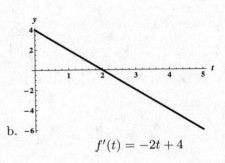

b. $f'(t) = -2t + 4$

b. $f'(t) = 0$ when $t = 2$ – that is when the object is stationary. For $0 \le t < 2$ we have $f'(t) > 0$ so the object is moving to the right. For $2 < t \le 5$ we have $f'(t) < 0$ so the object is moving to the left.

c. $f'(1) = 2$ ft/sec and $f''(t) = -2$ ft/sec^2, so in particular, $f''(1) = -2$ ft/sec^2.

d. $f'(t) = 0$ when $t = 2$ and $f''(2) = -2$ ft/sec^2.

e. On the interval $(2, 5]$ the velocity and the acceleration are both negative, so the object's speed is increasing.

3.6.13

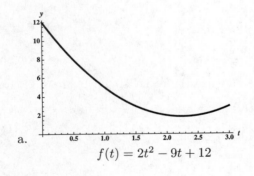

a. $f(t) = 2t^2 - 9t + 12$

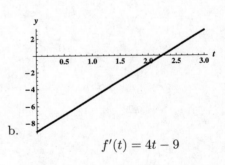

b.

$f'(t) = 4t - 9$

b. $f'(t) = 0$ when $t = 9/4$ – that is when the object is stationary. For $0 \le t < 9/4$ we have $f'(t) < 0$ so the object is moving to the left. For $9/4 < t \le 3$ we have $f'(t) > 0$ so the object is moving to the right.

c. $f'(1) = -5$ ft/sec and $f''(t) = 4$ ft/sec^2, so in particular, $f''(1) = 4$ ft/sec^2.

d. $f'(t) = 0$ when $t = 9/4$ and $f''(9/4) = 4$ ft/sec^2.

e. On the interval $(9/4, 3]$ both the velocity and acceleration are positive, so the object's speed is increasing.

3.6.14

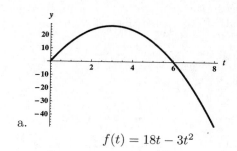

a.

$$f(t) = 18t - 3t^2$$

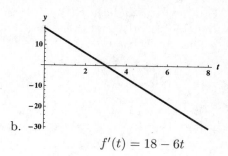

b.

$$f'(t) = 18 - 6t$$

b. $f'(t) = 0$ when $t = 3$ – that is when the object is stationary. For $0 \le t < 3$ we have $f'(t) > 0$ so the object is moving to the right. For $3 < t \le 8$ we have $f'(t) < 0$ so the object is moving to the left.

c. $f'(1) = 12$ ft/sec and $f''(t) = -6$ ft/sec², so in particular, $f''(1) = -6$ ft/sec².

d. $f'(t) = 0$ when $t = 3$ and $f''(3) = -6$ ft/sec².

e. On the interval $(3, 8]$ both the velocity and acceleration are negative, so the object's speed is increasing on that interval.

3.6.15

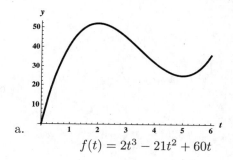

a.

$$f(t) = 2t^3 - 21t^2 + 60t$$

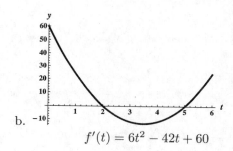

b.

$$f'(t) = 6t^2 - 42t + 60$$

b. $f'(t) = 0$ when $6(t - 2)(t - 5) = 0$, which is at $t = 2$ and $t = 5$ – that is when the object is stationary. For $0 \le t < 2$ we have $f'(t) > 0$ so the object is moving to the right. For $2 < t < 5$ we have $f'(t) < 0$ so the object is moving to the left. For $5 < t \le 8$ we have $f'(t) > 0$, so the object is moving to the right again.

c. $f'(1) = 24$ ft/sec and $f''(t) = 12t - 42$, so $f''(1) = -30$ ft/sec².

d. $f'(t) = 0$ when $t = 2$ and $t = 5$. We have $f''(2) = -18$ ft/sec² and $f''(5) = 18$ ft/sec².

e. $f''(t) = 12t - 42$ is positive for $t > \frac{42}{12} = \frac{7}{2}$ and negative for $t < \frac{7}{2}$. So f' and f'' are both positive on $(5, 6]$ and are both negative on $(2, 3.5)$, so that is where the object is speeding up.

3.6.16

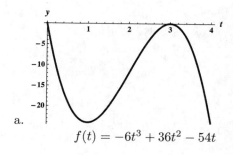

a.

$$f(t) = -6t^3 + 36t^2 - 54t$$

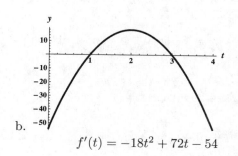

b.

$$f'(t) = -18t^2 + 72t - 54$$

b. $f'(t) = 0$ when $-18(t-3)(t-1) = 0$, which is at $t = 1$ and $t = 3$ – that is when the object is stationary. For $0 \leq t < 1$ we have $f'(t) < 0$ so the object is moving to the left. For $1 < t < 3$ we have $f'(t) > 0$ so the object is moving to the right. For $3 < t \leq 4$ we have $f'(t) < 0$, so the object is moving to the left again.

c. $f'(1) = 0$ ft/sec and $f''(t) = -36t + 72$, so $f''(1) = 36$ ft/sec^2.

d. $f'(t) = 0$ when $t = 1$ and $t = 3$. We have $f''(1) = 36$ ft/sec^2 and $f''(3) = -36$ ft/sec^2.

e. $f''(t) = -36t + 72$ is positive on $[0, 2)$, so the object's velocity and acceleration are both negative on $(1, 2)$ and they are both negative on $(3, 4]$, so that is where the object is speeding up.

3.6.17

a. $v(t) = s'(t) = -32t + 64$ ft/sec.

b. The highest point is reached at the instant when the stone changes from moving upward (where $v > 0$) to moving downward (where $v < 0$), so it must occur when $v = 0$, which is at $t = 2$.

c. The height of the stone at its highest point is $s(2) = -16 \cdot 4 + 64 \cdot 2 + 32 = 96$ feet.

d. The stone strikes the ground when $s(t) = 0$ for $t > 0$. Using the quadratic formula we see that this occurs when $t = 2 + \sqrt{6} \approx 4.45$ seconds.

e. The velocity when the stone hits the ground is $v(2 + \sqrt{6}) = -32(2 + \sqrt{6}) + 64 = -32\sqrt{6} \approx -78.38$ feet per second.s

f. The acceleration due to gravity is always negative, so the object is speeding up when its velocity is negative; that is, on its downward journey during the interval $(2, 2 + \sqrt{6})$.

3.6.18

a. $v(t) = s'(t) = -12t + 64$ ft/sec.

b. The highest point is reached at the instant when the stone changes from moving upward (where $v > 0$) to moving downward (where $v < 0$), so it must occur when $v = 0$, which is at $t = 16/3$.

c. The height of the stone at its highest point is $s(16/3) = 1088/3 \approx 362.67$ feet.

d. The stone strikes the ground when $s(t) = 0$ for $t > 0$. Using the quadratic formula we see that this occurs when $t = 16/3 + (4/3)\sqrt{34} \approx 13.11$ seconds.

e. The velocity when the stone hits the ground is $v(16/3 + (4/3)\sqrt{34}) \approx -93.3$ feet per second.

3.6.19

a. The average growth rate from 1995 to 2005 is
$$\frac{p(10) - p(0)}{10 - 0} = \frac{8038 - 7055}{10} = 98.3 \text{ thousand}$$
people/year.

b The instantaneous growth rate is $p'(t) = -0.54t + 101$. In 1997 we have $p'(2) = 99.92$ thousand people per year and in 2005 we have $p'(10) = 95.6$ thousand people per year.

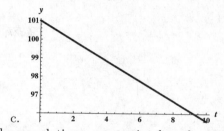

c.

The population was growing but the rate was slowing over this time interval.

3.6.20

a. The average growth rate from 1995 to 2000 is
$$\frac{c(5) - c(0)}{5 - 0} \approx \frac{171.96 - 151}{5} \approx 4.19.$$
Between 2005 and 2010 it is $\frac{c(10) - c(5)}{10 - 5} \approx$
$\frac{195.84 - 171.96}{5} \approx 4.78$, so the average growth
rate is larger between 2005 and 2010.

b The instantaneous growth rate is $c'(t) = 3.926e^{0.026t}$. We have $c'(5) \approx 4.47$ and $c'(10) \approx 5.09$. Again, the growth rate is greater at the later date.

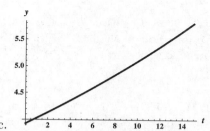

c.

The rate of change of the CPI is increasing.

3.6.21

a. The average cost function is given by $\overline{C}(x) = \frac{C(x)}{x} = \frac{1000}{x} + .1$. The marginal cost function is given by $M(x) = C'(x) = .1$.

b. At $a = 2000$ we have $\overline{C}(2000) = \frac{1000}{2000} + .1 = .6$, and $M(2000) = .1$.

c. The average cost per item when producing 2000 items is \$0.60. The cost of producing the next item is \$0.10.

3.6.22

a. The average cost function is given by $\overline{C}(x) = \frac{C(x)}{x} = \frac{500}{x} + .02$. The marginal cost function is given by $M(x) = C'(x) = .02$.

b. At $a = 1000$ we have $\overline{C}(1000) = \frac{500}{1000} + .02 = .52$, and $M(1000) = .02$.

c. The average cost per item when producing 1000 items is \$0.52. The cost of producing the next item is \$0.02.

3.6.23

a. The average cost function is given by $\overline{C}(x) = \frac{C(x)}{x} = \frac{100}{x} + 40 - 0.01x$. The marginal cost function is given by $M(x) = C'(x) = 40 - 0.02x$.

b. At $a = 1000$ we have $\overline{C}(1000) = \frac{100}{1000} + 40 - (.01)(1000) = 30.1$, and $M(1000) = 20$.

c. The average cost per item when producing 1000 items is \$30.10. The cost of producing the next item is \$20.00.

3.6.24

a. The average cost function is given by $\overline{C}(x) = \frac{C(x)}{x} = \frac{800}{x} + 100 - 0.04x$. The marginal cost function is given by $M(x) = C'(x) = 100 - 0.08x$.

b. At $a = 500$ we have $\overline{C}(500) = \frac{800}{500} + 100 - (.04)(500) = 81.6$, and $M(500) = 60$.

c. The average cost per item when producing 500 items is \$81.60. The cost of producing the next item is \$60.00.

3.6.25

a. $D(10) = 40 - 20 = 20$ DVDs per day.

b. Demand is zero when $D(p) = 40 - 2p = 0$, which occurs for $p = 20$ dollars.

c. The elasticity is $E(p) = \frac{dD}{dp} \frac{p}{D} = -2 \left(\frac{p}{40-2p} \right) = \frac{p}{p-20}$.

d. This quantity satisfies $-1 < E(p) < 0$ when $-1 < \frac{p}{p-20} < 0$ which occurs when $p < 20 - p$, or $p < 10$. So for prices in the interval $(0, 10)$ the demand is inelastic, while for prices in the interval $(10, 20)$ the demand is elastic.

e. If the price goes up from 10 to 10.25, that is a $\frac{.25}{10} = .025 = 2.5\%$ increase in price.

f. If the price goes up from 10 to 10.25, the demand goes from $D(10) = 40 - 20 = 20$ to $D(10.25) = 40 - 20.5 = 19.5$, which is a $\frac{.5}{20} = 2.5\%$ decrease.

3.6.26

a. The domain of the demand function is $(40, \infty)$.

b. $D(60) = \frac{1800}{60-40} = \frac{1800}{20} = 90$.

c. $E(p) = \frac{dD}{dp} \frac{p}{D} = \frac{-1800}{(p-40)^2} \cdot \frac{p(p-40)}{1800} = \frac{p}{40-p}$.

d. Note that $E(p) = \frac{p}{40-p}$ is always less than -1 on the interval $(40, \infty)$. (Note that the equation $\frac{p}{40-p} = -1$ has no solutions). So the demand is always elastic.

e. $E(60) = \frac{60}{40-60} = \frac{60}{-20} = -3$. So a $\frac{2}{60} = 3.\overline{33}\%$ change in price will decrease the demand by about $3 \cdot 3.\overline{33}\% = 10\%$.

3.6.27 $E(p) = \frac{dD}{dp} \frac{p}{D} = -abe^{-bp} \left(\frac{p}{ae^{-bp}} \right) = -bp$. Note that $-bp = -1$ for $p = \frac{1}{b}$. So the demand is elastic for $p > \frac{1}{b}$ and inelastic for $0 < p < \frac{1}{b}$.

3.6.28 $E(p) = \frac{dD}{dp} \frac{p}{D} = -abp^{-b-1} \left(\frac{p}{ap^{-b}} \right) = -b \left(\frac{p^{-b-1}}{p^{-b-1}} \right) = -b$.

3.6.29

a. False. For example, when a ball is thrown up in the air near the surface of the earth, its acceleration is constant (due to gravity) but its velocity changes during its trip.

b. True. If the rate of change of velocity is zero, then velocity must be constant.

c. False. If the velocity is constant over an interval, then the average velocity is equal to the instantaneous velocity over the interval.

d. True. For example, a ball dropped from a tower has negative acceleration and increasing speed as it falls toward the earth.

3.6.30 The velocity is $v(t) = s'(t) = -1.6t$. The feather strikes the surface of the moon when $s(t) = 40 - 0.8t^2 = 0$. This occurs when $t = \sqrt{50} \approx 7.07$ seconds. The velocity at this time is $v(\sqrt{50}) = -1.6\sqrt{50} \approx -11.31$ meters per second, and $a(\sqrt{50}) = -1.6$ meters per second^2.

3.6.31 In each case, the stone reaches its maximum height when its velocity is zero.

On Mars, this occurs when $v(t) = s'(t) = 96 - 12t = 0$, or when $t = 8$ seconds. So the maximum height on Mars is $s(8) = 384$ feet.

On Earth, this occurs when $v(t) = s'(t) = 96 - 32t = 0$, or when $t = 3$ seconds. So the maximum height on Earth is $s(3) = 144$ feet.

The stone will travel $384 - 144 = 240$ feet higher on Mars.

3.6.32

a. Both stones reach their highest points when the derivative of their position functions are 0. Note, however that $f'(t) = -32t + 48 = g'(t)$. Thus both stones reach their maximum height at $t = \frac{48}{32} = \frac{3}{2}$.

b. The height of the stone thrown from the bridge at $t = 1.5$ seconds is $f(1.5) = 68$ feet, while the other stone reaches $g(1.5) = 36$ feet, so the one thrown from the bridge goes 32 feet higher.

c. The stone from ground level hits the ground when $g(t) = 0$, which occurs when $t = 3$. The velocity at this time is $g'(3) = -48$ feet per second. The stone thrown from the bridge hits the ground when
$f(t) = 0$, which occurs when $-16t^2 + 48t + 32 = 0$, or $t^2 - 3t - 2 = 0$, or $t = \frac{3 + \sqrt{9 - (4)(-2)}}{2} = \frac{3 + \sqrt{17}}{2} \approx 3.56$.
At that time, the velocity is approximately -65.97 feet per second.

3.6.33 The first stone reaches its maximum height when $f'(t) = -32t + 32 = 0$, so after 1 second, and its maximum height is therefore $f(1) = -16 + 32 + 48 = 64$ feet.

The second stone reaches its maximum height when $g'(t) = -32t + v_0 = 0$, so when $t = \frac{v_0}{32}$. Its height at that time is $g(v_0/32) = -16(v_0/32)^2 + (v_0^2/32) = \frac{v_0^2}{64}$. This is equal to 64 when $v_0 = 64$ feet per second.

3.6.34

a. The slope of the curve (which is the velocity) increases until about 5:30 p.m., so the car is speeding up over that time interval. From 5:30 p.m. until about 6:20 p.m. the velocity is decreasing. After that it is speeding up until 7:00 p.m.

b. The slope is the largest at about 5:30 p.m. and smallest at about 6:20 p.m.

c. The maximum velocity is approximately 40 mph and the minimum is about 5 mph. These are estimates based on visually computing slopes of tangent lines. Your mileage may vary.

3.6.35

a. The velocity is zero at $t = 1, 2,$ and 3.

b. The object is moving in the positive direction when the slope of s is positive, so from $t = 0$ to $t = 1$, and from $t = 2$ to $t = 3$. It is moving in the negative direction from $t = 1$ to $t = 2$, and for $t > 3$.

c.

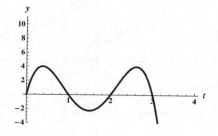

d. The speed is increasing on $(0, 1/2)$ as the velocity is positive and the acceleration is positive there. On $(1/2, 1)$ the speed is decreasing as the velocity is positive but the acceleration is negative. On $(1, 3/2)$ the speed is increasing as the velocity is negative and the acceleration is negative, but on $(3/2, 2)$ the speed is decreasing as the velocity is negative but the acceleration is positive. On approximately $(2, 2.6)$ the speed is increasing as the velocity is positive and the acceleration is positive, but on about $(2.6, 3)$ the velocity is positive but the acceleration is negative, so the speed is decreasing. On $(3, \infty)$ both the velocity and the acceleration are negative, so the object is speeding up.

3.6.36

a. $\frac{dL}{dt}$ represents the rate of change of the length of the species. The derivative is decreasing over time.

b. Over time, the species is getting bigger, but the rate of change is approaching zero.

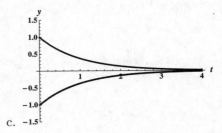

c.

3.6.37

a. $P(x) = xp(x) - C(x) = 100x + 0.02x^2 - 50x - 100 = 0.02x^2 + 50x - 100$.

b. The average profit is $\overline{P}(x) = \frac{P(x)}{x} = 0.02x + 50 - \frac{100}{x}$. The marginal profit is $P'(x) = .04x + 50$.

c. $\overline{P}(500) = 59.8$. $P'(500) = 70$.

d. The average profit for the first 500 items sold is $59.80, while the profit on the 501st item is $70.00.

3.6.38

a. $P(x) = xp(x) - C(x) = 100x - .1x^2 - (-.02x^2 + 50x + 100) = 50x - .08x^2 - 100$.

b. The average profit is $\overline{P}(x) = \frac{P(x)}{x} = -.08x + 50 - \frac{100}{x}$. The marginal profit is $P'(x) = -.16x + 50$.

c. $\overline{P}(500) = 9.8$. $P'(500) = -30$.

d. The average profit for the first 500 items sold is $9.80, while the profit on the 501st item is $-$30.00.

3.6.39

a. $P(x) = xp(x) - C(x) = 100x + 0.04x^2 - 800$.

b. The average profit is $\overline{P}(x) = \frac{P(x)}{x} = .04x + 100 - \frac{800}{x}$. The marginal profit is $P'(x) = .08x + 100$.

c. $\overline{P}(1000) = 139.2$. $P'(1000) = 180$.

d. The average profit for the first 1000 items sold is $139.20, while the profit on the 1001st item is $180.00.

3.6.40

a. $P(x) = xp(x) - C(x) = 100x - 0.06x^2 - 800$.

b. The average profit is $\overline{P}(x) = \frac{P(x)}{x} = -0.06x + 100 - \frac{800}{x}$. The marginal profit is $P'(x) = -0.12x + 100$.

c. $\overline{P}(1000) = 39.2$. $P'(1000) = -20$.

d. The average profit for the first 1000 items sold is $39.20, while the profit on the 1001st item is $-$20.00.

3.6.41

  a. Because the graph represents the growth rate, the slowest rate (of about 1.1 million people per year) occurs at about $t = 30$, which corresponds to the year 1930.

  b. The largest growth rate occurs at $t = 60$, so the year 1960 at the largest growth rate of about 2.9 million per year.

  c. Because $p'(t) > 0$ for all t shown on the graph, $p(t)$ is never decreasing.

  d. The population growth rate $p'(t)$ is increasing from about 1905 to 1915, from 1930 to 1960, and from 1980 to 1990.

3.6.42

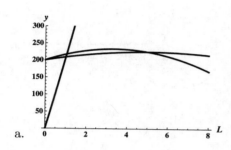

a.

  b. The peak of $A(L) = \frac{P(L)}{L} = -L^2 + 10L + 200$ occurs when the slope is zero. Note that $P'(L) = -3L^2 + 20L + 200$.

We seek L_0 so that $\frac{dA}{dL}(L_0) = 0$, which occurs when $\dfrac{L_0 \cdot P'(L_0) - P(L_0)}{L_0^2} = 0$, or when $P'(L_0) = \frac{P(L_0)}{L_0} = A(L_0)$. Thus if the peak of A occurs at L_0, we have $M(L_0) = A(L_0)$.

3.6.43

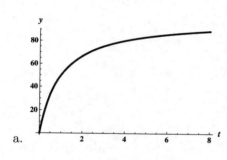

a.

  b. $v(t) = s'(t) = \frac{(t+1)100 - 100t \cdot 1}{(t+1)^2} = \frac{100}{(t+1)^2}$.

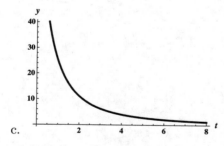

c.

The velocity of the marble is decreasing.

  d. $s(t) = 80$ when $\frac{100t}{t+1} = 80$, or $100t = 80t + 80$, which occurs when $t = 4$ seconds.

  e. $v(t) = 50$ when $\frac{100}{(t+1)^2} = 50$, or $(t+1)^2 = 2$. This occurs for $t = \sqrt{2} - 1 \approx 0.414$ seconds.

3.6.44

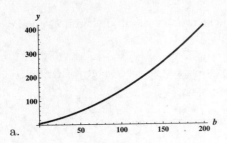

a.

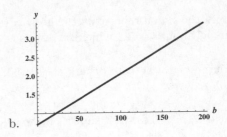

b.

The function $\frac{dh}{db}$ shows the rate of increase in height (in meters) per cm increase in the base diameter of the tree.

3.6.45

a. The average cost function is $\overline{C}(x) = \frac{C(x)}{25000} = 50 + \frac{5000}{x} + 0.00006x$. The marginal cost function is $C'(x) = -\frac{125000000}{x^2} + 1.5$.
The average cost decreases to about 50 per unit as the batch size increases, while the marginal cost is negative but increases.

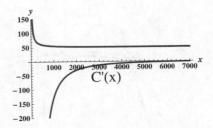

b. $\overline{C}(5000) = 51.3$, $C'(5000) = -3.5$.

c. If the batch size is 5000, then the average cost of producing 25000 items is \$51.30 per item. If the batch size is increased from 5000 to 5001, then the cost of producing 25000 items would decrease by about \$3.50.

3.6.46

All these functions are increasing, so the cost per item increases as more items are produced. And we will have less revenue unless we charge more.

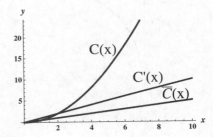

3.6.47

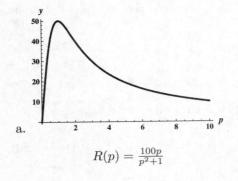

a.

$$R(p) = \frac{100p}{p^2 + 1}$$

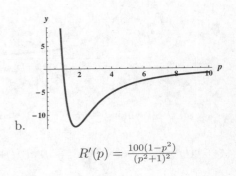

b.

$$R'(p) = \frac{100(1 - p^2)}{(p^2 + 1)^2}$$

    c. $R'(p)$ is zero at $p = 1$, and the maximum of $R(p)$ occurs at this same value of p, so that is the price to charge in order to maximize revenue. The revenue at this price is $50.00.

3.6.48

a. The number of miles increases with the number of gallons of gasoline.

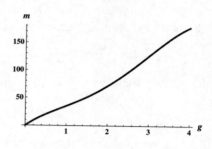

b. The gas mileage is $m(g)/g$. The number of miles per gallon decreases during the first 1.5 gallons or so, then increases until it peaks again just short of 4 gallons.

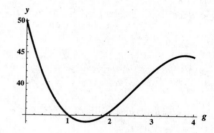

c. $\frac{dm}{dg}$ represents the instantaneous rate of change of the number of miles driven per unit of gasoline consumed.

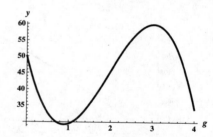

3.6.49

a. The mass oscillates about the equilibrium point.

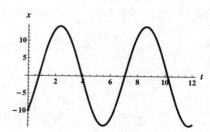

b. $\frac{dx}{dt} = 10\cos t + 10\sin t$ is the velocity of the mass at time t.

c. $\frac{dx}{dt} = 0$ when $\sin t = -\cos t$, which occurs when $t = \frac{4n+3}{4} \cdot \pi$ where n is any positive integer.

d. The model is unrealistic as it ignores the effects of friction and gravity. In reality, the amplitude would decrease as the mass oscillates.

3.6.50

a. $p(10) = 1000e^{-1} \approx 368$ mb, so the pressure on Mt. Everest is about 632 mb less than at sea level.

b. The average pressure change is $\frac{p(5)-p(0)}{5} = \frac{1000(e^{-0.5}-1)}{5} \approx -78.7$ mb per km.

c. The rate of change in pressure is $p'(5) = -100e^{-5/10} \approx -60.7$ mb per km.

d. Because $p'(z) = -100e^{-z/10}$, it increases as z increases.

e. $\lim_{z \to \infty} p(z) = 0$ means that if we go high enough, there is essentially no atmospheric pressure.

3.6.51

a. Juan starts out faster, but slows toward the end, while Jean starts slower but increases her speed toward the end.

b. Because both start and finish at the same time, they finish with the same average angular velocity.

c. It is a tie.

d. Jean's velocity is given by $\theta'(t) = \frac{\pi t}{4}$. At $t = 2$, $\theta'(2) = \frac{\pi}{2}$ radians per minute. Her velocity is greatest at $t = 4$.

e. Juan's velocity is given by $\phi'(t) = \pi - \frac{\pi t}{4}$. At $t = 2$, $\phi'(2) = \frac{\pi}{2}$ radians per minute as well. His velocity is greatest at $t = 0$.

3.6.52

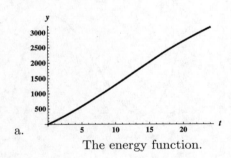

a. The energy function.

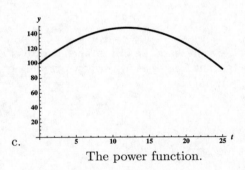

c. The power function.

b. The power increases from midnight to noon, then decreases again until midnight. The units are kilowatts.

3.6.53

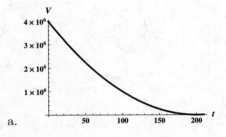

a.

At the beginning the volume is 4,000,000 cubic meters.

b. The tank is empty when $V(t) = 100(200 - t)^2 = 0$, which occurs when $t = 200$.

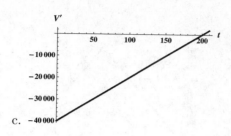

Because $V(t)$ can be written as $V(t) = 4,000,000 - 40,000t + 100t^2$, the flow rate is $V'(t) = -40,000 + 200t$ cubic meters per minute.

c.

d. The flow rate is largest (in absolute value) when $t = 0$ and smallest when $t = 200$.

3.6.54

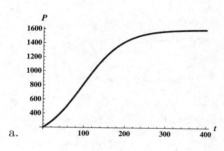

a.

b. The average growth rate for the first ten days is
$$\frac{P(10) - P(0)}{10} \approx \frac{237.7 - 200}{10} = 3.77 \text{ cells per day.}$$

c. The maximum growth rate is where the curve $P(t)$ is the steepest, which appears to be at just shy of 100 days.

d. $P'(t) = \frac{0 - 1600 \cdot (-.14 e^{-.02t})}{(1 + 7e^{-.02t})^2} = \frac{224 e^{-.02t}}{(1 + 7e^{-.02t})^2}.$

e. At 100 days the populations is a little larger than 800. By doing a little bit of zooming, we can see that the maximum occurs at about $t = 97.3$ days with a population of 800.

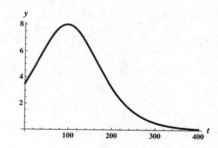

3.6.55

a. $v(t) = y'(t) = -15e^{-t} \cos t - 15e^{-t} \sin t$, so $v(1) \approx -7.625$ meters per second, and $v(3) \approx .63$ meters per second.

b. She is moving down for approximately 2.4 seconds, and then up until about 5.5 seconds, and then down again until about 8.6 seconds, and then up again.

c. The maximum velocity going up appears to be about about 0.65 meters per second.

3.6.56

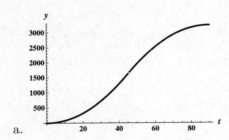

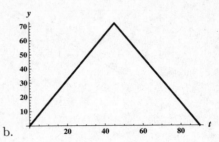

a.   b.

$$V'(t) = \begin{cases} \frac{8}{5}t & \text{for } 0 \leq t \leq 45, \\ -\frac{8}{5}t + 144 & \text{for } 45 \leq t \leq 90. \end{cases} \quad \text{This is in cubic feet per day.}$$

c. The flow increases for the first 45 days, then decreases. The flow rate is at a maximum at 45 days.

3.6.57

a. $T'(t) = 160 - 80x$, so $T'(1) = 80$, so the heat flux at 1 is -80. At $x = 3$ we have $T'(3) = -80$, so the heat flux at 3 is 80.

b. The heat flux $-T'(x)$ is negative for $0 \leq x < 2$ and positive for $2 < x \leq 4$.

c. At any point other than the midpoint of the rod, heat flows toward the closest end of the rod, and "out the end."

3.7 The Chain Rule

3.7.1 If $y = f(x)$ and $u = g(x)$ then $\frac{dy}{dx} = \frac{dy}{du} \cdot \frac{du}{dx}$. Alternatively, we have $\frac{d}{dx}(f(g(x))) = f'(g(x))g'(x)$.

3.7.2 We would need to know $f'(3)$. This is because $h'(1) = f'(g(1))g'(1) = f'(3) \cdot 5$, but we can't finish this calculation unless we know $f'(3)$.

3.7.3 The derivative of $f(g(x))$ equals f' evaluated at $g(x)$ multiplied by g' evaluated at x.

3.7.4 The inner function is $\cos x$ and the outer function is u^4, so with $y = f(u)$ and $u = g(x)$, we have $f(u) = u^4$ and $g(x) = \cos x$. Then $y = (\cos x)^4 = \cos^4 x$.

3.7.5 The inner function is $x^2 + 10$ and the outer function is u^{-5}, so with $y = f(u)$ and $u = g(x)$, we have $f(u) = u^{-5}$ and $g(x) = x^2 + 10$. Then $y = (x^2 + 10)^{-5}$.

3.7.6 Let $h(x) = x^2 + 1$, $g(u) = \cos u$, and $f(v) = v^4$. Then $f(g(h(x))) = f(g(x^2 + 1)) = f(\cos(x^2 + 1)) = (\cos(x^2 + 1))^4 = Q(x)$.

3.7.7 With $u = 3x + 7$ and $y = u^{10}$ we have $\frac{dy}{dx} = \frac{dy}{dx} \cdot \frac{du}{dx} = 10u^9 \cdot 3 = 30(3x + 7)^9$.

3.7.8 With $u = 5x^2 + 11x$ and $y = u^{20}$ we have $\frac{dy}{dx} = \frac{dy}{du} \cdot \frac{du}{dx} = 20u^{19} \cdot (10x + 11) = 20(5x^2 + 11x)^{19} \cdot (10x + 11)$.

3.7.9 With $u = \sin x$ and $y = u^5$ we have $\frac{dy}{dx} = \frac{dy}{du} \cdot \frac{du}{dx} = 5u^4 \cdot \cos x = 5\sin^4 x \cos x$.

3.7.10 With $u = x^5$ and $y = \cos u$, we have $\frac{dy}{dx} = \frac{dy}{du} \cdot \frac{du}{dx} = -\sin u \cdot 5x^4 = -5x^4 \sin x^5$.

3.7.11 With $u = 5x - 7$ and $y = e^u$, we have $\frac{dy}{dx} = \frac{dy}{du}\frac{du}{dx} = e^u(5) = 5e^{5x-7}$.

3.7.12 With $u = 7x - 1$ and $y = \sqrt{u}$ we have $\frac{dy}{dx} = \frac{dy}{du}\frac{du}{dx} = \frac{1}{2\sqrt{u}} \cdot 7 = \frac{7}{2\sqrt{7x-1}}$.

3.7.13 With $u = x^2 + 1$ and $y = \sqrt{u}$ we have $\frac{dy}{dx} = \frac{dy}{du} \cdot \frac{du}{dx} = \frac{1}{2\sqrt{u}} \cdot (2x) = \frac{x}{\sqrt{x^2+1}}$.

3.7.14 With $u = \sqrt{x}$ and $y = e^u$ we have $\frac{dy}{dx} = \frac{dy}{du} \cdot \frac{du}{dx} = e^u \cdot \frac{1}{2\sqrt{x}} = \frac{e^{\sqrt{x}}}{2\sqrt{x}}$.

3.7.15 With $u = 5x^2$ and $y = \tan u$ we have $\frac{dy}{dx} = \frac{dy}{du} \cdot \frac{du}{dx} = \sec^2 u \cdot (10x) = 10x \sec^2 5x^2$.

3.7.16 With $u = x/4$ and $y = \sin u$ we have $\frac{dy}{dx} = \frac{dy}{du} \cdot \frac{du}{dx} = \cos u \cdot (1/4) = \frac{1}{4} \cdot \cos(x/4)$.

3.7.17 With $u = e^x$ and $y = \sec u$ we have $\frac{dy}{dx} = \frac{dy}{du} \cdot \frac{du}{dx} = (\sec u \cdot \tan u) \cdot (e^x) = e^x \cdot \sec e^x \cdot \tan e^x$.

3.7.18 With $u = -x^2$ and $y = e^u$ we have $\frac{dy}{dx} = \frac{dy}{du} \cdot \frac{du}{dx} = e^u \cdot (-2x) = -2xe^u = -2xe^{-x^2}$.

3.7.19 With $g(x) = 3x^2 + 7x$ and $f(u) = u^{10}$ we have $\frac{d}{dx}[f(g(x))] = f'(g(x))g'(x) = 10(3x^2 + 7x)^9(6x + 7)$.

3.7.20 With $g(x) = x^2 + 2x + 7$ and $f(u) = u^8$, we have $\frac{d}{dx}[f(g(x))] = f'(g(x))g'(x) = 8(x^2 + 2x + 7)^7(2x+2) = 16(x^2 + 2x + 7)^7(x + 1)$.

3.7.21 With $g(x) = 10x + 1$ and $f(u) = \sqrt{u}$, we have $\frac{d}{dx}[f(g(x))] = f'(g(x))g'(x) = \frac{1}{2\sqrt{10x+1}} \cdot 10 = \frac{5}{\sqrt{10x+1}}$.

3.7.22 With $g(x) = x^2 + 9$ and $f(u) = \sqrt{u}$ we have $\frac{d}{dx}[f(g(x))] = f'(g(x))g'(x) = \frac{1}{2\sqrt{u}} \cdot (2x) = \frac{x}{\sqrt{x^2+9}}$.

3.7.23 With $g(x) = 7x^3 + 1$ and $f(u) = 5u^{-3}$ we have $\frac{d}{dx}[f(g(x))] = f'(g(x))g'(x) = -15(7x^3+1)^{-4}(21x^2) = -315(7x^3 + 1)^{-4} \cdot x^2$.

3.7.24 With $g(t) = 5t$ and $f(u) = \cos u$ we have $\frac{d}{dt}[f(g(t))] = f'(g(t))g'(t) = -\sin 5t \cdot 5 = -5 \sin 5t$.

3.7.25 With $g(x) = 3x + 1$ and $f(u) = \sec u$, we have $\frac{d}{dx}[f(g(x))] = f'(g(x))g'(x) = \sec(3x + 1)\tan(3x + 1) \cdot 3 = 3\sec(3x + 1)\tan(3x + 1)$.

3.7.26 With $g(x) = e^x$ and $f(u) = \csc u$, we have $\frac{d}{dx}[f(g(x))] = f'(g(x))g'(x) = -(\csc e^x \cot e^x)e^x = -e^x \csc e^x \cot e^x$.

3.7.27 With $g(x) = e^x$ and $f(u) = \tan u$ we have $\frac{d}{dx}[f(g(x))] = f'(g(x))g'(x) = \sec^2 u \cdot e^x = e^x \sec^2 e^x$.

3.7.28 With $g(t) = \tan t$ and $f(u) = e^u$ we have $\frac{d}{dt}[f(g(t))] = f'(g(t))g'(t) = e^{\tan t} \cdot \sec^2 t$.

3.7.29 With $g(x) = 4x^3 + 3x + 1$ and $f(u) = \sin u$ we have $\frac{d}{dx}[f(g(x))] = f'(g(x))g'(x) = \cos u \cdot (12x^2 + 3) = (12x^2 + 3) \cdot \cos(4x^3 + 3x + 1)$.

3.7.30 With $g(t) = t^2 + t$ and $f(u) = \csc u$ we have $\frac{d}{dt}[f(g(t))] = f'(g(t))g'(t) = -(\csc u)(\cot u) \cdot (2t + 1) = -(2t + 1)\csc(t^2 + t)\cot(t^2 + t)$.

3.7.31 With $g(x) = 2\sqrt{x}$ and $f(u) = \sin u$, we have $\frac{d}{dx}[f(g(x))] = f'(g(x))g'(x) = \cos(2\sqrt{x}) \cdot \frac{1}{\sqrt{x}} = \frac{\cos(2\sqrt{x})}{\sqrt{x}}$.

3.7.32 First note that $\frac{dy}{d\theta} = \frac{d}{d\theta}\left(\cos^4 \theta\right) + \frac{d}{d\theta}\left(\sin^4 \theta\right)$. To compute the first term, let $g_1(\theta) = \cos \theta$ and $f(u) = u^4$. Then $\frac{d}{d\theta}\cos^4 \theta = 4\cos^3(\theta)(-\sin \theta) = -4\sin \theta \cos^3 \theta$.

Similarly, to compute the second term, let $g_2(\theta) = \sin \theta$ and $f(u) = u^4$. Then $\frac{d}{d\theta}\sin^4 \theta = 4\sin^3 \theta \cos \theta = 4\cos \theta \sin^3 \theta$. Thus, $\frac{dy}{d\theta} = -4\sin \theta \cos^3 \theta + 4\cos \theta \sin^3 \theta$. This can be further simplified to $4\cos \theta \sin \theta(\sin^2 \theta - \cos^2 \theta) = 2\sin 2\theta(-\cos 2\theta) = -\sin 4\theta$.

3.7.33 With $g(x) = \sec x + \tan x$ and $f(u) = u^5$ we have $\frac{d}{dx}[f(g(x))] = f'(g(x))g'(x) = 5u^4 \cdot (\sec x \tan x + \sec^2 x) = 5(\sec x + \tan x)^4(\sec x \tan x + \sec^2 x) = 5\sec x(\sec x + \tan x)^5$.

3.7.34 With $g(z) = 4\cos z$ and $f(u) = \sin u$ we have $\frac{dy}{dz} = f'(g(z))g'(z) = \cos(4\cos z) \cdot (-4\sin z) = -4\sin z \cos(4\cos z)$.

3.7.35

a. $u = g(x) = \cos x$, $y = f(u) = u^3$. So $\frac{dy}{dx} = \frac{dy}{du} \cdot \frac{du}{dx} = 3\cos^2 x \cdot (-\sin x) = -3\cos^2 x \sin x$.

b. $u = g(x) = x^3$, $y = f(u) = \cos u$. So $\frac{dy}{dx} = \frac{dy}{du} \cdot \frac{du}{dx} = -\sin x^3 \cdot 3x^2 = -3x^2 \sin x^3$.

3.7.36

a. $u = g(x) = e^x$, $y = f(u) = u^3$. So $\frac{dy}{dx} = \frac{dy}{du} \cdot \frac{du}{dx} = 3(e^x)^2 \cdot e^x = 3e^{3x}$.

b. $u = g(x) = x^3$, $y = f(u) = e^u$. So $\frac{dy}{dx} = \frac{dy}{du} \cdot \frac{du}{dx} = e^{x^3} \cdot 3x^2$.

3.7.37

a. $h'(3) = f'(g(3))g'(3) = f'(1) \cdot 20 = 5 \cdot 20 = 100$.

b. $h'(2) = f'(g(2))g'(2) = f'(5) \cdot 10 = -10 \cdot 10 = -100$.

c. $p'(4) = g'(f(4))f'(4) = g'(1) \cdot (-8) = 2 \cdot (-8) = -16$.

d. $p'(2) = g'(f(2))f'(2) = g'(3) \cdot 2 = 20 \cdot 2 = 40$.

e. $h'(5) = f'(g(5))g'(5) = f'(2) \cdot 20 = 2 \cdot 20 = 40$.

3.7.38

a. $h'(1) = f'(g(1))g'(1) = f'(4) \cdot 9 = 7 \cdot 9 = 63$.

b. $h'(2) = f'(g(2))g'(2) = f'(1) \cdot 7 = (-6) \cdot 7 = -42$.

c. $h'(3) = f'(g(3))g'(3) = f'(5) \cdot 3 = 2 \cdot 3 = 6$.

d. $k'(3) = g'(g(3))g'(3) = g'(5) \cdot 3 = (-5) \cdot 3 = -15$.

e. $k'(1) = g'(g(1))g'(1) = g'(4) \cdot 9 = (-1) \cdot 9 = -9$.

f. $k'(5) = g'(g(5))g'(5) = g'(3) \cdot (-5) = 3 \cdot (-5) = -15$.

3.7.39 Note that $a(70) = 13330$. $\frac{d}{dt} p(a(t))|_{t=70} = p'(a(70))a'(70) \approx \frac{738-765}{14330-13330} \cdot \frac{13440-13330}{80-70} = -.297$ hPa per minute.

3.7.40

a. $\frac{dT}{dt} = \frac{dT}{dA}\frac{dA}{dt} \approx 6.5 \cdot \frac{2.5-2.1}{2-1.5} = 6.5 \cdot .8 = 5.2$ degrees per hour. The temperature is dropping at about 5.2 degrees per hour.

b. An increase in lapse rate would increase the answer to part (a).

c. No. The calculation depends on the lapse rate and on the rate at which the balloon is ascending, but not on the actual temperature.

3.7.41 Take $g(x) = 2x^6 - 3x^3 + 3$, and $n = 25$. Then $y' = n(g(x))^{n-1}g'(x) = 25(2x^6 - 3x^3 + 3)^{24}(12x^5 - 9x^2)$.

3.7.42 Take $g(x) = \cos x + 2\sin x$, and $n = 8$. Then $y' = n(g(x))^{n-1}g'(x) = 8(\cos x + 2\sin x)^7(2\cos x - \sin x)$.

3.7.43 Take $g(x) = 1 + 2\tan x$, and $n = 15$. Then $y' = n(g(x))^{n-1}g'(x) = 15(1 + 2\tan x)^{14}(2\sec^2 x) = 30(1 + 2\tan x)^{14}\sec^2 x$.

3.7.44 Take $g(x) = 1 - e^x$, and $n = 4$. Then $y' = n(g(x))^{n-1}g'(x) = 4(1 - e^x)^3(-e^x) = -4e^x(1 - e^x)^3$.

3.7.45

$$\frac{d}{dx}\sqrt{1+\cot^2 x} = \frac{1}{2\sqrt{1+\cot^2 x}} \cdot \frac{d}{dx}(1+\cot^2 x) = \frac{1}{2\sqrt{1+\cot^2 x}} \cdot 2\cot x \cdot \frac{d}{dx}\cot x$$

$$= \frac{1}{2\sqrt{1+\cot^2 x}} \cdot 2\cot x \cdot (-\csc^2 x) = -\frac{\cot x \csc^2 x}{\sqrt{1+\cot^2 x}}.$$

3.7.46

$$\frac{d}{dx}\sqrt{(3x-4)^2+3x} = \frac{1}{2\sqrt{(3x-4)^2+3x}} \cdot \frac{d}{dx}((3x-4)^2+3x)$$

$$= \frac{1}{2\sqrt{(3x-4)^2+3x}} \cdot \left(2(3x-4)\cdot\frac{d}{dx}(3x-4)+3\right)$$

$$= \frac{1}{2\sqrt{(3x-4)^2+3x}} \cdot (2(3x-4)\cdot 3+3)$$

$$= \frac{18x-21}{2\sqrt{(3x-4)^2+3x}}.$$

3.7.47

$$\frac{d}{dx}\sin(\sin(e^x)) = \cos(\sin(e^x))\frac{d}{dx}\sin(e^x)$$

$$= \cos(\sin(e^x))\cdot\cos(e^x)\cdot e^x$$

3.7.48

$$\frac{d}{dx}\sin^2(e^{3x+1}) = 2\sin(e^{3x+1})\frac{d}{dx}\sin(e^{3x+1})$$

$$= 2\sin(e^{3x+1})\cos(e^{3x+1})\frac{d}{dx}e^{3x+1}$$

$$= 2\sin(e^{3x+1})\cos(e^{3x+1})e^{3x+1}\cdot 3$$

$$= 3e^{3x+1}\sin(2e^{3x+1})$$

3.7.49

$$\frac{d}{dx}\sin^5(\cos 3x) = 5\sin^4(\cos 3x)\cdot\frac{d}{dx}(\sin(\cos 3x))$$

$$= 5\sin^4(\cos 3x)\cdot\cos(\cos 3x)\cdot\frac{d}{dx}\cos 3x$$

$$= 5\sin^4(\cos 3x)\cdot\cos(\cos 3x)\cdot(-\sin 3x)\cdot 3$$

$$= -15\sin^4(\cos 3x)\cos(\cos 3x)\sin 3x.$$

3.7.50

$$\frac{d}{dx}\cos^4(7x^3) = 4\cos^3(7x^3)\cdot\frac{d}{dx}\cos(7x^3) = 4\cos^3(7x^3)(-\sin(7x^3))\cdot\frac{d}{dx}(7x^3)$$

$$= 4\cos^3(7x^3)(-\sin(7x^3))\cdot 21x^2 = -84x^2\sin(7x^3)\cos^3(7x^3).$$

3.7.51

$$\frac{d}{dx}\tan(e^{\sqrt{3x}}) = \sec^2(e^{\sqrt{3x}})\cdot\frac{d}{dx}e^{\sqrt{3x}} = \sec^2(e^{\sqrt{3x}})\cdot e^{\sqrt{3x}}\cdot\frac{d}{dx}\sqrt{3x}$$

$$= \sec^2(e^{\sqrt{3x}})\cdot e^{\sqrt{3x}}\cdot\frac{3}{2\sqrt{3x}}.$$

3.7.52

$$\frac{d}{dx}(1 - e^{-0.05x})^{-1} = -\frac{1}{(1 - e^{-0.05x})^2} \cdot \frac{d}{dx}(1 - e^{-0.05x})$$

$$= -\frac{1}{(1 - e^{-0.05x})^2} \cdot (0.05e^{-0.05x}) = -\frac{0.05e^{-0.05x}}{(1 - e^{-0.05x})^2}.$$

3.7.53 $\frac{d}{dx}\sqrt{x + \sqrt{x}} = \frac{1}{2\sqrt{x+\sqrt{x}}} \cdot \frac{d}{dx}(x + \sqrt{x}) = \frac{1}{2\sqrt{x+\sqrt{x}}} \cdot \left(1 + \frac{1}{2\sqrt{x}}\right).$

3.7.54

$$\frac{d}{dx}\sqrt{x + \sqrt{x + \sqrt{x}}} = \frac{1}{2\sqrt{x + \sqrt{x + \sqrt{x}}}} \cdot \frac{d}{dx}(x + \sqrt{x + \sqrt{x}})$$

$$= \frac{1}{2\sqrt{x + \sqrt{x + \sqrt{x}}}} \cdot \left(1 + \frac{1}{2\sqrt{x + \sqrt{x}}} \cdot \left(1 + \frac{1}{2\sqrt{x}}\right)\right).$$

Note that on the last step, we used the result of the previous problem.

3.7.55 $\frac{d}{dx}f(g(x^2)) = f'(g(x^2)) \cdot \frac{d}{dx}(g(x^2)) = f'(g(x^2)) \cdot g'(x^2) \cdot 2x.$

3.7.56 $\frac{d}{dx}[f(g(x^m))]^n = n[f(g(x^m))]^{n-1}f'(g(x^m))g'(x^m)(mx^{m-1}).$

3.7.57 $y' = 5\left(\frac{x}{x+1}\right)^4 \cdot \frac{(x+1)(1) - x(1)}{(x+1)^2} = \frac{5x^4}{(x+1)^6}.$

3.7.58 $y' = 8\left(\frac{e^x}{x+1}\right)^7 \cdot \frac{(x+1)e^x - e^x}{(x+1)^2} = \frac{8xe^{8x}}{(x+1)^9}.$

3.7.59 $y' = e^{x^2+1}(2x)\sin x^3 + e^{x^2+1}(\cos x^3)3x^2 = xe^{x^2+1}(2\sin x^3 + 3x\cos x^3).$

3.7.60 $y' = \sec^2(xe^x)((1)e^x + xe^x) = e^x(1+x)\sec^2(xe^x).$

3.7.61 $\frac{dy}{d\theta} = 2\theta\sec 5\theta + \theta^2(5\sec 5\theta\tan 5\theta) = \theta\sec 5\theta(2 + 5\theta\tan 5\theta).$

3.7.62 $5\left(\frac{3x}{4x+2}\right)^4 \cdot \frac{(4x+2)3 - (3x)4}{(4x+2)^2} = 5\left(\frac{3x}{4x+2}\right)^4 \cdot \frac{6}{(4x+2)^2} = \frac{5(3x)^4}{(4x+2)^4} \cdot \frac{6}{(4x+2)^2} = \frac{2430x^4}{(4x+2)^6}.$

3.7.63 $y' = 4((x+2)(x^2+1))^3 \cdot ((1)(x^2+1) + (x+2)(2x)) = 4((x+2)(x^2+1))^3(3x^2+4x+1) = 4(x+2)^2(x^2+1)^3(3x+1)(x+1).$

3.7.64 $y' = 2e^{2x}(2x-7)^5 + e^{2x}(5(2x-7)^42) = e^{2x}(2x-7)^4(2(2x-7) + 10) = e^{2x}(2x-7)^4(4x-4) = 4e^{2x}(2x-7)^4(x-1).$

3.7.65 $y' = \frac{1}{2}(x^4 + \cos 2x)^{-1/2}(4x^3 - 2\sin 2x) = \frac{2x^3 - \sin 2x}{\sqrt{x^4 + \cos 2x}}.$

3.7.66 $y' = \frac{(t+1)(1 \cdot e^t + te^t) - te^t \cdot 1}{(t+1)^2} = \frac{te^t + t^2e^t + e^t + te^t - te^t}{(t+1)^2} = \frac{e^t(t^2+t+1)}{(t+1)^2}.$

3.7.67 $y' = 2(p+\pi)^1 \sin p^2 + (p+\pi)^2(\cos p^2)(2p) = (p+\pi)(2\sin p^2 + 2p^2\cos p^2 + 2p\pi\cos p^2) = 2(p+\pi)(\sin p^2 + p^2\cos p^2 + p\pi\cos p^2).$

3.7.68 $y' = 3(z+4)^2 \tan z + (z+4)^3 \sec^2 z = (z+4)^2(3\tan z + (z+4)\sec^2 z).$

3.7.69

   a. True. The product rule alone will suffice.

   b. True. This function is the composition of e^x with $\sqrt{x+1}$.

   c. True. The derivative of the composition $f(g(x))$ is the product of $f'(g(x))$ with $g'(x)$, so it is the product of two derivatives.

   d. False. In fact, $\frac{d}{dx}P(Q(x)) = P'(Q(x))Q'(x)$.

3.7.70 $\frac{d^2}{dx^2}(x\cos(x^2)) = \frac{d}{dx}(\cos(x^2) - 2x^2\sin(x^2)) = -2x\sin(x^2) - 4x\sin(x^2) - 4x^3\cos(x^2) = -6x\sin(x^2) - 4x^3\cos(x^2)$.

3.7.71

$$\frac{d^2}{dx^2}\sin x^2 = \frac{d}{dx}(2x\cos x^2) = 2(\cos x^2 - 2x^2\sin x^2)$$
$$= 2\cos x^2 - 4x^2\sin x^2.$$

Note that in the middle of this calculation we used a result from the middle of the previous problem – namely the derivative of $x\cos x^2$.

3.7.72

$$\frac{d^2}{dx^2}\sqrt{x^2+2} = \frac{d}{dx}\left(\frac{1}{2}(x^2+2)^{-1/2}2x\right)$$
$$= \frac{d}{dx}\left(\frac{x}{\sqrt{x^2+2}}\right)$$
$$= \frac{\sqrt{x^2+2} - x\cdot\left(\frac{x}{\sqrt{x^2+2}}\right)}{x^2+2}$$
$$= \frac{\frac{x^2+2-x^2}{\sqrt{x^2+2}}}{x^2+2}$$
$$= \frac{2}{(x^2+2)^{3/2}}.$$

3.7.73 $\frac{d^2}{dx^2}e^{-2x^2} = \frac{d}{dx}\left(-4xe^{-2x^2}\right) = -4e^{-2x^2} + 16x^2e^{-2x^2} = 4e^{-2x^2}(4x^2 - 1)$.

3.7.74

   a. $\frac{d}{dx}(x^2+x)^2 = 2(x^2+x)\cdot\frac{d}{dx}(x^2+x) = 2(x^2+x)(2x+1) = 4x^3 + 6x^2 + 2x$.

   b. $\frac{d}{dx}(x^2+x)^2 = \frac{d}{dx}(x^4 + 2x^3 + x^2) = 4x^3 + 6x^2 + 2x$.

3.7.75 $\frac{d}{dx}\sqrt{f(x)} = \frac{1}{2\sqrt{f(x)}}\cdot f'(x)$.

3.7.76 $\frac{d}{dx}\sqrt{f(x)g(x)} = \frac{1}{2\sqrt{f(x)g(x)}}\cdot\frac{d}{dx}(f(x)g(x)) = \frac{f'(x)g(x)+f(x)g'(x)}{2\sqrt{f(x)g(x)}}$.

3.7.77

$y' = \frac{(x^3-6x-1)(2)(x^2-1)(2x)-(x^2-1)^2(3x^2-6)}{(x^3-6x-1)^2}$,
so $y'(3) = \frac{(27-18-1)(2)(8)(6)-(64)(21)}{64} = \frac{768-1344}{64} = -\frac{576}{64} = -9$. The equation of the tangent line is thus $y - 8 = -9(x - 3)$, or $y = -9x + 35$.

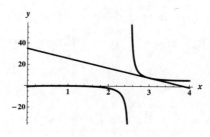

3.7.78

$y' = \sqrt{5 - x^2} - \frac{x^2}{\sqrt{5-x^2}}$. Thus we have $y'(1) = 2 - (1/2) = 3/2$, and $y'(-2) = 1 - (4/1) = -3$. The tangents line we are seeking are $y - 2 = (3/2)(x-1)$ and $y + 2 = -3(x + 2)$, or $y = \frac{3}{2}x + \frac{1}{2}$.

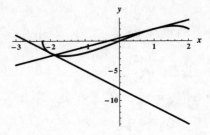

3.7.79

a. $g'(4) = 3$, $g(4) = 3 \cdot 4 - 5 = 7$. $f'(7) = -2$, $f(7) = -2 \cdot 7 + 23 = 9$. Thus, $h(4) = f(g(4)) = f(7) = 9$, and $h'(4) = f'(g(4))g'(4) = f'(7) \cdot 3 = -2 \cdot 3 = -6$.

b. The tangent line to h at $(4, 9)$ is given by $y - 9 = -6(x - 4)$, or $y = -6x + 33$.

3.7.80

a. $g(1) = f(1^2) = f(1) = 4$.

b. $g'(x) = f'(x^2) \cdot 2x$.

c. Using the previous result, $g'(1) = f'(1) \cdot 2 = 3 \cdot 2 = 6$.

d. The tangent line is given by $y - 4 = 6(x - 1)$, or $y = 6x - 2$.

3.7.81

$y'(x) = 2e^{2x}$, so $y'\left(\frac{\ln 3}{2}\right) = 2e^{\ln 3} = 6$. Also, $y\left(\frac{\ln 3}{2}\right) = e^{\ln 3} = 3$. The tangent line is therefore given by $y - 3 = 6\left(x - \frac{\ln 3}{2}\right)$, or $y = 6x + 3 - 3\ln 3$.

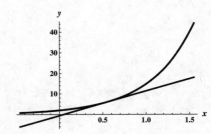

3.7.82 First, note that $g'(x) = f'(\sin x) \cdot \cos x$.

a. $g'(0) = f'(0) \cdot \cos 0 = 3 \cdot 1 = 3$.

b. $g'(\pi/2) = f'(1) \cdot \cos(\pi/2) = 5 \cdot 0 = 0$.

c. $g'(\pi) = f'(0) \cdot \cos \pi = 3 \cdot (-1) = -3$.

3.7.83 First, note that $g'(x) = \cos(\pi f(x)) \cdot \pi f'(x)$.

a. $g'(0) = \cos(\pi \cdot f(0)) \cdot \pi f'(0) = \cos(-3\pi) \cdot 3\pi = -3\pi$.

b. $g'(1) = \cos(\pi \cdot f(1)) \cdot \pi f'(1) = \cos(3\pi) \cdot 5\pi = -5\pi$.

3.7.84

a. $\frac{dy}{dt} = -y_0 \sqrt{\frac{k}{m}} \sin\left(t\sqrt{\frac{k}{m}}\right)$.

b. The amplitude of the velocity (which is $y_0\sqrt{\frac{k}{m}}$) would decrease by a factor of 2, and the period would increase by a factor of 2.

c. The amplitude of the velocity would increase by a factor of 2, and the period would decrease by a factor of 2.

d. The units for $-y_0\sqrt{\frac{k}{m}}$ would be meters $\cdot\sqrt{\frac{kg/sec^2}{kg}}=\frac{meters}{sec}$. Inside the sine function the units for $t\cdot\sqrt{\frac{k}{m}}$ are sec $\cdot\frac{1}{sec}=1$, so the factor involving the sine function is unit-less (as it should be).

3.7.85

a. $\frac{d^2y}{dt^2}=\frac{d}{dt}\left(-y_0\sqrt{\frac{k}{m}}\sin\left(t\sqrt{\frac{k}{m}}\right)\right)=-y_0\cdot\frac{k}{m}\cdot\cos\left(t\sqrt{\frac{k}{m}}\right)$.

b. $-\frac{k}{m}y=-\frac{k}{m}\left(y_0\cos\left(t\sqrt{\frac{k}{m}}\right)\right)=\frac{d^2y}{dt^2}$.

3.7.86

a. The period of $\cos x$ is 2π. The period of a function of the form $y=a\cos bx$ is $\frac{2\pi}{b}$. Thus, the period of y is $\frac{2\pi}{\sqrt{\frac{k}{m}}}=2\pi\sqrt{\frac{m}{k}}$.

b. $\frac{dT}{dm}=\frac{d}{dm}\left(2\pi\sqrt{\frac{m}{k}}\right)=\frac{2\pi}{\sqrt{k}}\cdot\frac{1}{2\sqrt{m}}=\frac{\pi}{\sqrt{mk}}$.

c. Because k and m are greater than 0, and π is greater than 0, this quotient is greater than 0. Physically this means that the period is increasing as mass increases: the oscillations get slower.

3.7.87

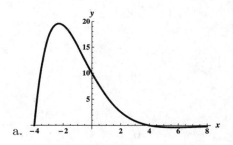

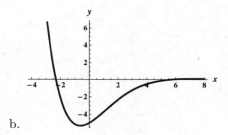

$$\frac{dy}{dt}=-5e^{-t/2}\cos\left(\frac{\pi t}{8}\right)-\frac{5\pi}{4}e^{-t/2}\sin\left(\frac{\pi t}{8}\right).$$

c. The velocity is zero at about -2.3 and at about 5.7, and the displacement has a maximum and a minimum at these points.

3.7.88 $\frac{dy}{dt}=-e^{-t}(\sin 2t-2\cos 2t)+e^{-t}(2\cos 2t+4\sin 2t)=e^{-t}(3\sin 3t+4\cos 2t)$.

$\frac{d^2y}{dt^2}=-e^{-t}(3\sin 2t+4\cos 2t)+e^{-t}(6\cos 2t-8\sin 2t)=e^{-t}(-11\sin 2t+2\cos 2t)$.

Then $y''(t)+2y'(t)+5y(t)=e^{-t}(-11\sin 2t+2\cos 2t)+e^{-t}(6\sin 2t+8\cos 2t)+e^{-t}(5\sin 2t-10\cos 2t)=$
$e^{-t}((-11+6+5)\sin 2t+(2+8-10)\cos 2t)=e^{-t}(0+0)=0$, as desired.

3.7.89

a. Assuming a non leap year, March 1st corresponds to $t=59$. We have $D(59)=12-3\cos\left(\frac{2\pi(69)}{365}\right)\approx$ 10.88 hours.

b. $\frac{d}{dt}D(t)=3\cdot\frac{2\pi}{365}\sin\left(\frac{2\pi(t+10)}{365}\right)$ hours per day.

c. $D'(59) \approx 0.048$ hours per day ≈ 2 minutes and 52 seconds per day. This means that on March 1st, the days are getting longer by just shy of 3 minutes per day.

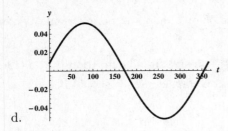

e. The largest increase in the length of the days appears to be at about $t = 81$, and the largest decrease at about $t = 265$. These correspond to March 22nd and to September 22nd. The least rapid changes occur at about $t = 172$ and $t = 355$. These correspond to June 21st and December 21st.

d.

3.7.90

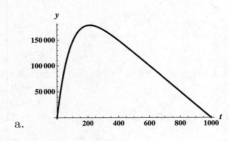

a.

$M(0) = 250(1000)(1 - (10)^{-30} \cdot 10^{30}) = 250,000 \cdot (1 - 1) = 0$ grams.

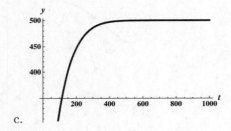

b.

$V(1000) = 500 - (.5)(1000) = 500 - 500 = 0$.

c.

$C(0) = \frac{M(0)}{V(0)} = \frac{0}{500} = 0$. $C(1000)$ isn't defined because $V(1000) = 0$, but it appears that $\lim_{t \to 1000} C(t) = 500$. The concentration of the salt in the tank increases with time, although it levels off as it nears 500 grams per liter.

d. $M'(t) = 250(1000 - t)(10^{-30}(10(1000 - t)^9)) - 250(1 - 10^{-30}(1000 - t)^{10}) = \frac{250(1-t)^{10}}{10^{29}} - 250\left(1 - \frac{(1000-t)^{10}}{10^{30}}\right)$.

e. It is convenient to rewrite $C(t)$ first. We can rewrite $C(t) = \frac{M(t)}{V(t)} = \frac{250(1000-t)}{\frac{1000-t}{2}} \cdot \left(1 - \frac{(1000-t)^{10}}{1000^{10}}\right) = 500 \cdot \left(1 - \left(1 - \frac{t}{1000}\right)^{10}\right)$.

Then $C'(t) = 500 \cdot \left(0 - 10\left(1 - \frac{t}{1000}\right)^9 \cdot -\frac{1}{1000}\right) = 5\left(1 - \frac{t}{1000}\right)^9$.

f. The derivative is positive for $0 \le t \le 1000$, so the concentration is increasing on this interval.

3.7.91

a. $E'(t) = 400 + 200 \cos\left(\frac{\pi t}{12}\right)$ MW.

b. Because the maximum value of $\cos\theta$ is 1, the maximum value of $E'(t)$ will be 600 MW, where $\cos\left(\frac{\pi t}{12}\right) = 1$, which is where $t = 0$, which corresponds to noon.

c. Because the minimum value of $\cos\theta$ is -1, the minimum value of $E'(t)$ will be 200 MW, where $\cos\left(\frac{\pi t}{12}\right) = -1$, which is where $\frac{\pi t}{12} = \pi$, or $t = 12$, which corresponds to midnight.

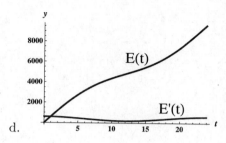

d.

3.7.92

a. $\frac{d}{dt}\cos 2t = -2\sin 2t$, and $\frac{d}{dt}(\cos^2 t - \sin^2 t) = -2\sin t \cos t - 2\sin t \cos t = -4\sin t \cos t$. Thus, $-2\sin 2t = -4\sin t \cos t$, so $\sin 2t = 2\sin t \cos t$.

b. $\frac{d}{dt}(2\cos^2 t - 1) = -4\cos t \sin t$, so again, $\sin 2t = 2\sin t \cos t$.

c. $\frac{d}{dt}(\sin 2t) = 2\cos 2t$, and $\frac{d}{dt}(2\sin t \cos t) = 2\cos t \cos t + 2\sin t(-\sin t) = 2\cos^2 t - 2\sin^2 t$, so $\cos 2t = \cos^2 t - \sin^2 t$.

3.7.93

a. $f'(x) = \frac{d}{dx}(\cos^2 x + \sin^2 x) = 2(\cos x)(-\sin x) + 2\sin x \cos x = 0$.

b. If $f(x)$ is a constant, then the output value must be the same at any input value, so we choose to evaluate f at a nice value like $x = 0$. We see that $f(0) = \cos^2 0 + \sin^2 0 = 1^2 + 0^2 = 1$, so we must have $\cos^2 x + \sin^2 x = 1$ for all x.

3.7.94

a. $g(x) = kx$ and $f(u) = e^u$. Then $f(g(x)) = f(kx) = e^{kx}$.

b. $\frac{d}{dx}f(g(x)) = f'(g(x))g'(x) = e^{kx} \cdot k = ke^{kx}$.

3.7.95 $\frac{d}{dx}\left(f(x)(g(x))^{-1}\right) = f'(x)(g(x))^{-1} + f(x)(-(g(x))^{-2}g'(x)) = \frac{f'(x)}{g(x)} - \frac{f(x)g'(x)}{(g(x))^2} = \frac{g(x)f'(x) - f(x)g'(x)}{(g(x))^2}$.

3.7.96

a.

$$\frac{d^2}{dx^2}[f(g(x))] = \frac{d}{dx}[f'(g(x))g'(x)]$$
$$= f''(g(x))g'(x)g'(x) + f'(g(x))g''(x)$$
$$= f''(g(x))(g'(x))^2 + f'(g(x))g''(x).$$

b. Let $g(x) = 3x^4 + 5x^2 + 2$. Then $g'(x) = 12x^3 + 10x$ and $g''(x) = 36x^2 + 10$. Let $f(u) = \sin u$. Then $f'(u) = \cos u$ and $f''(u) = -\sin u$.

We have $\frac{d^2}{dx^2}\sin(3x^4 + 5x^2 + 2) = -\sin(3x^4 + 5x^2 + 2) \cdot (12x^3 + 10x)^2 + \cos(3x^4 + 5x^2 + 2) \cdot (36x^2 + 10)$.

3.7.97

a. $h(x) = (x^2 - 3)^5$, $a = 2$.

b. $h'(x) = 5(x^2 - 3)^4(2x) = 10x(x^2 - 3)^4$, so the value of this limit is $h'(2) = 20$.

3.7.98

  a. $h(x) = \sqrt{4 + \sin x}$, $a = 0$.

  b. $h'(x) = \frac{1}{2} \cdot (4 + \sin x)^{-1/2} \cdot \cos x = \frac{\cos x}{2\sqrt{4 + \sin x}}$, so the value of this limit is $h'(0) = \frac{1}{4}$.

3.7.99

  a. $h(x) = \sin x^2$, $a = \frac{\pi}{2}$.

  b. $h'(x) = (\cos x^2)(2x)$, so the value of this limit is $h'\left(\frac{\pi}{2}\right) = \pi \cdot \cos\left(\frac{\pi^2}{4}\right) \approx -2.45$.

3.7.100

  a. $h(x) = \frac{1}{3(x^5 + 7)^{10}}$, $a = 1$.

  b. $h'(x) = -\frac{50x^4}{3(x^5 + 7)^{11}}$, so the value of this limit is $h'(1) = -\frac{50}{3 \cdot 8^{11}} \approx -1.94 \times 10^{-9}$.

3.7.101 $\lim\limits_{x \to 5} \dfrac{f(x^2) - f(25)}{x - 5} = \dfrac{d}{dx}\left[f(x^2)\right]_{x=5} = 2 \cdot 5 \cdot f'(25) = 10f'(25)$.

3.7.102

  a. First note that $\frac{d}{dx} f(-x) = -f'(-x)$.

  If f is even then $f(-x) = f(x)$. Because the derivatives of both sides of this equation must be equal, we have $-f'(-x) = f'(x)$ or $f'(-x) = -f'(x)$, so f' must be an odd function.

  b. If f is odd then $f(-x) = -f(x)$. Because the derivatives of both sides of this equation must be equal, we have $-f'(-x) = -f'(x)$ or $f'(-x) = f'(x)$, so f' must be an even function.

3.7.103

  a. $\lim\limits_{v \to u} H(v) = \lim\limits_{v \to u} \left(\dfrac{f(v) - f(u)}{v - u} - f'(u)\right) = \lim\limits_{v \to u}\left(\dfrac{f(v) - f(u)}{v - u}\right) - f'(u) = f'(u) - f'(u) = 0$.

  b. Suppose $u = v$. Then clearly both sides of the given expression are 0, so they are equal. Suppose $u \neq v$. Then $H(v) = \frac{f(v) - f(u)}{v - u} - f'(u)$, so $H(v) + f'(u) = \frac{f(v) - f(u)}{v - u}$, so the result holds by multiplying both sides of this equation by $v - u$.

  c.

$$h'(a) = \lim_{x \to a} \frac{f(g(x)) - f(g(a))}{x - a} = \lim_{x \to a} \frac{H(g(x)) + f'(g(a))}{x - a} \cdot (g(x) - g(a))$$
$$= \lim_{x \to a}\left[(H(g(x)) + f'(g(a))) \cdot \frac{g(x) - g(a)}{x - a}\right].$$

  d. $h'(a) = \lim\limits_{x \to a}\left[(H(g(x)) + f'(g(a))) \cdot \dfrac{g(x) - g(a)}{x - a}\right] = (0 + f'(g(a))) \cdot g'(a) = f'(g(a))g'(a)$.

3.8   Implicit Differentiation

3.8.1 Implicit differentiation gives a single unified derivative, whereas solving for y explicitly yields two different functions.

3.8.2 In implicit differentiation, the independent and dependent variables may both appear on the same side of an equation, so one must keep track of which is which.

3.8.3 The result of implicit differentiation is often an expression involving both the dependent and independent variables, so one would need to know both in order to calculate the value of the derivative.

3.8.4 Previously we had seen that this result held for all integers. In this section, we extended the result to all rational numbers.

3.8.5

a. $4x^3 + 4y^3 \frac{dy}{dx} = 0$. Thus $4y^3 \frac{dy}{dx} = -4x^3$, so $\frac{dy}{dx} = -\frac{x^3}{y^3}$.

b. When $x = 1$ and $y = -1$, we have $\frac{dy}{dx} = \frac{-1}{-1} = 1$.

3.8.6

a. $1 = e^y \frac{dy}{dx}$, so $\frac{dy}{dx} = \frac{1}{e^y} = \frac{1}{x}$.

b. When $x = 2$, $\frac{dy}{dx} = \frac{1}{x} = \frac{1}{2}$.

3.8.7

a. $2y \frac{dy}{dx} = 4$, so $\frac{dy}{dx} = \frac{2}{y}$.

b. $\left. \frac{dy}{dx} \right|_{(1,2)} = \frac{2}{2} = 1$.

3.8.8

a. $2y \frac{dy}{dx} + 3 = 0$, so $\frac{dy}{dx} = -\frac{3}{2y}$.

b. $\left. \frac{dy}{dx} \right|_{(1,\sqrt{5})} = -\frac{3}{2\sqrt{5}} = -\frac{3\sqrt{5}}{10}$.

3.8.9

a. $\frac{dy}{dx} \cos y = 20x^3$, so $\frac{dy}{dx} = \frac{20x^3}{\cos y}$.

b. $\left. \frac{dy}{dx} \right|_{(1,\pi)} = \frac{20}{\cos \pi} = -20$.

3.8.10

a. $\frac{1}{2\sqrt{x}} - \frac{1}{\sqrt{y}} \frac{dy}{dx} = 0$, so $\frac{dy}{dx} = \frac{\sqrt{y}}{2\sqrt{x}}$.

b. When $x = 4$ and $y = 1$ we have $\frac{dy}{dx} = \frac{\sqrt{1}}{2\sqrt{4}} = \frac{1}{4}$.

3.8.11

a. $-\frac{dy}{dx} \sin y = 1$, so $\frac{dy}{dx} = -\frac{1}{\sin y} = -\csc y$.

b. $\left. \frac{dy}{dx} \right|_{(0,\pi/2)} = -\csc(\pi/2) = -1$.

3.8.12

a. $(y + x \frac{dy}{dx}) \sec^2(xy) = 1 + \frac{dy}{dx}$, so $x \frac{dy}{dx} \sec^2(xy) - \frac{dy}{dx} = 1 - y \sec^2(xy)$. Factoring out $\frac{dy}{dx}$ on the left-hand side gives

$\frac{dy}{dx}(x \sec^2(xy) - 1) = 1 - y \sec^2(xy)$, so $\frac{dy}{dx} = \frac{1 - y \sec^2(xy)}{x \sec^2(xy) - 1}$.

b. $\left. \frac{dy}{dx} \right|_{(0,0)} = \frac{1-0}{0-1} = -1$.

3.8.13 $(y + x \frac{dy}{dx}) \cos(xy) = 1 + \frac{dy}{dx}$, so $y \cos(xy) + x \frac{dy}{dx} \cos(xy) = 1 + \frac{dy}{dx}$. If we rearrange terms in order to have the terms with a factor of $\frac{dy}{dx}$ all on the same side, we obtain $y \cos(xy) - 1 = \frac{dy}{dx} - x \frac{dy}{dx} \cos(xy)$. Factoring out the $\frac{dy}{dx}$ factor gives $y \cos(xy) - 1 = \frac{dy}{dx}(1 - x \cos(xy))$, so $\frac{dy}{dx} = \frac{y \cos(xy) - 1}{1 - x \cos(xy)}$.

3.8.14 $(y + x \frac{dy}{dx}) e^{xy} = 2 \frac{dy}{dx}$, so $y e^{xy} + x \frac{dy}{dx} e^{xy} = 2 \frac{dy}{dx}$. We can write this as $y e^{xy} = 2 \frac{dy}{dx} - x \frac{dy}{dx} e^{xy}$, and factoring out the factor of $\frac{dy}{dx}$ on the right yields $y e^{xy} = \frac{dy}{dx}(2 - x e^{xy})$. Finally, we can divide to obtain $\frac{dy}{dx} = \frac{y e^{xy}}{2 - x e^{xy}}$.

3.8.15 $1 + \frac{dy}{dx} = -\sin y \cdot \frac{dy}{dx}$, so $\frac{dy}{dx} + (\sin y) \frac{dy}{dx} = -1$, and $\frac{dy}{dx} = -\frac{1}{1 + \sin y}$.

3.8.16 $1 + 2 \frac{dy}{dx} = \frac{1}{2\sqrt{y}} \frac{dy}{dx}$, so $1 = \frac{1}{2\sqrt{y}} \frac{dy}{dx} - 2 \frac{dy}{dx}$, and thus $1 = \frac{dy}{dx} \left(\frac{1}{2\sqrt{y}} - 2 \right)$. Because the right-hand side of this equation can be written as $\frac{dy}{dx} \left(\frac{1 - 4\sqrt{y}}{2\sqrt{y}} \right)$, we have $\frac{dy}{dx} = \frac{2\sqrt{y}}{1 - 4\sqrt{y}}$.

3.8.17 $-2y\frac{dy}{dx}\sin y^2 + 1 = \frac{dy}{dx}e^y$, which we can write as $1 = \frac{dy}{dx}e^y + 2y\frac{dy}{dx}\sin y^2$, or $1 = \frac{dy}{dx}(e^y + 2y\sin y^2)$. Thus, $\frac{dy}{dx} = \frac{1}{e^y + 2y\sin y^2}$.

3.8.18 $\frac{dy}{dx} = \frac{(y-1)-(x+1)\frac{dy}{dx}}{(y-1)^2}$, which we can write as $(y-1)^2 \cdot \frac{dy}{dx} = y - 1 - (x+1)\frac{dy}{dx}$. If we rearrange terms in order to have terms with a factor of $\frac{dy}{dx}$ on the same side, we obtain $\frac{dy}{dx}(y-1)^2 + \frac{dy}{dx}(x+1) = y - 1$. Factoring out the common factor of $\frac{dy}{dx}$ yields $\frac{dy}{dx}((y-1)^2 + (x+1)) = y - 1$, so $\frac{dy}{dx} = \frac{y-1}{(y-1)^2 + x + 1}$.

3.8.19

$$3x^2 = \frac{(x-y)(1+\frac{dy}{dx}) - (x+y)(1-\frac{dy}{dx})}{(x-y)^2}$$

$$3x^2(x-y)^2 = x + x\frac{dy}{dx} - y - y\frac{dy}{dx} - x + x\frac{dy}{dx} - y + y\frac{dy}{dx}$$

$$3x^2(x-y)^2 + 2y = 2x\frac{dy}{dx}$$

$$\frac{dy}{dx} = \frac{3x^2(x-y)^2 + 2y}{2x}$$

3.8.20

$$3(y + x\frac{dy}{dx})(xy+1)^2 = 1 - 2y\frac{dy}{dx}$$

$$3x\frac{dy}{dx}(xy+1)^2 + 2y\frac{dy}{dx} = 1 - 3y(xy+1)^2$$

$$\frac{dy}{dx}(3x(xy+1)^2 + 2y) = 1 - 3y(xy+1)^2$$

$$\frac{dy}{dx} = \frac{1 - 3y(xy+1)^2}{3x(xy+1)^2 + 2y}.$$

3.8.21

$$18x^2 + 21\frac{dy}{dx}y^2 = 13(y + x\frac{dy}{dx})$$

$$21\frac{dy}{dx}y^2 - 13x\frac{dy}{dx} = 13y - 18x^2$$

$$\frac{dy}{dx} = \frac{13y - 18x^2}{21y^2 - 13x}.$$

3.8.22

$$\cos x \cos y + \sin x(-\sin y)\frac{dy}{dx} = \cos x + (-\sin y)\frac{dy}{dx}$$

$$\cos x \cos y - \cos x = \sin x \sin y \frac{dy}{dx} - \sin y \frac{dy}{dx}$$

$$\cos x \cos y - \cos x = (\sin x \sin y - \sin y)\frac{dy}{dx}$$

$$\frac{dy}{dx} = \frac{\cos x \cos y - \cos x}{\sin x \sin y - \sin y}.$$

3.8.23

$$\frac{4x^3 + 2y\frac{dy}{dx}}{2\sqrt{x^4+y^2}} = 5 + 6y^2\frac{dy}{dx}$$

$$y\frac{dy}{dx} - 6\frac{dy}{dx}y^2\sqrt{x^4+y^2} = 5\sqrt{x^4+y^2} - 2x^3$$

$$\frac{dy}{dx} = \frac{5\sqrt{x^4+y^2} - 2x^3}{y - 6y^2\sqrt{x^4+y^2}}.$$

3.8.24

$$\frac{1}{2}(x+y^2)^{-1/2}\left(1+2y\frac{dy}{dx}\right) = (\cos y)\frac{dy}{dx}$$

$$\frac{1}{2\sqrt{x+y^2}} = \cos y\frac{dy}{dx} - \frac{y \cdot dy/dx}{\sqrt{x+y^2}}$$

$$\frac{1}{2\sqrt{x+y^2}} = \left(\cos y - \frac{y}{\sqrt{x+y^2}}\right)\frac{dy}{dx}$$

$$\frac{1}{2\sqrt{x+y^2}} = \left(\frac{\cos y\sqrt{x+y^2}-y}{\sqrt{x+y^2}}\right)\frac{dy}{dx}$$

$$\frac{dy}{dx} = \frac{1}{2(\cos y\sqrt{x+y^2}-y)}$$

3.8.25

a. $2^2 + 2\cdot 1 + 1^2 = 7$, so the point $(2,1)$ does lie on the curve.

b. $2x+y+xy'+2yy' = 0$, which can be written $(x+2y)y' = -2x-y$. Solving for y' yields $y' = \frac{-2x-y}{x+2y}$. Thus, at the point $(2,1)$ we have $y' = -\frac{5}{4}$. The equation of the tangent line is therefore $y-1 = -\frac{5}{4}(x-2)$, or $y = -\frac{5}{4}x + \frac{7}{2}$.

3.8.26

a. $(-1)^4 - (-1)^2\cdot 1 + 1^4 = 1$, so the point $(-1,1)$ does lie on the curve.

b. $4x^3 - 2xy - x^2y' + 4y^3y' = 0$, which can be written $y'(4y^3-x^2) = 2xy - 4x^3$. Thus, $y' = \frac{2xy-4x^3}{4y^3-x^2}$. Thus, at the point $(-1,1)$ we have $y' = \frac{2}{3}$. The equation of the tangent line is therefore $y-1 = \frac{2}{3}(x+1)$, or $y = \frac{2}{3}x + \frac{5}{3}$.

3.8.27

a. $\sin\pi + 5\frac{\pi^2}{5} = \pi^2$, so the point $(\pi^2/5, \pi)$ does lie on the curve.

b. $y'\cos y + 5 = 2yy'$, so $5 = y'(2y-\cos y)$, so $y' = \frac{5}{2y-\cos y}$. At the given point we have $y' = \frac{5}{2\pi+1}$. The equation of the tangent line is therefore $y - \pi = \frac{5}{1+2\pi}\left(x-\pi^2/5\right)$, or $y = \frac{5}{1+2\pi}x + \frac{\pi(1+\pi)}{1+2\pi}$.

3.8.28

a. $1^3 + 1^3 = 2\cdot 1\cdot 1$, so the point $(1,1)$ does lie on the curve.

b. $3x^2 + 3y^2y' = 2(y+xy')$, which can be written $(3y^2-2x)y' = 2y-3x^2$, so $y' = \frac{2y-3x^2}{3y^2-2x}$. At the given point we have $y' = \frac{2-3}{3-2} = -1$. The equation of the tangent line is therefore $y-1 = -1(x-1)$, or $y = -x+2$.

3.8.29

a. $\cos(\pi/2 - \pi/4) + \sin(\pi/4) = (\sqrt{2}/2) + (\sqrt{2}/2) = \sqrt{2}$, so the point $(\pi/2, \pi/4)$ does lie on the curve.

b. $(1-y')(-\sin(x-y)) + y'\cos y = 0$, which can be written as $y'(\cos y + \sin(x-y)) = \sin(x-y)$, so $y' = \frac{\sin(x-y)}{\cos y+\sin(x-y)}$. At the given point we have $y' = 1/2$. The equation of the tangent line is therefore $y - (\pi/4) = (1/2)(x-\pi/2)$, or $y = \frac{1}{2}x$.

3.8.30

a. $(1 + 2^2)^2 = 25 = \frac{25}{4} \cdot 1 \cdot 2^2$, so the point $(1, 2)$ does lie on the curve.

b. $2(x^2 + y^2)(2x + 2yy') = \frac{25}{4} \cdot (y^2 + 2xyy')$, which can be written as $y'[4y(x^2 + y^2) - (25/2)xy] = (25/4)y^2 - 4x(x^2 + y^2)$, so $y' = \frac{25y^2/4 - 4x(x^2+y^2)}{4y(x^2+y^2) - (25xy/2)}$. At the given point we have $y' = \frac{25-20}{40-25} = \frac{1}{3}$. The equation of the tangent line is therefore $y - 2 = \frac{1}{3}(x - 1)$, or $y = \frac{1}{3}x + \frac{5}{3}$.

3.8.31 $1 + 2yy' = 0$, so $y' = -\frac{1}{2y}$. Differentiating again, we obtain

$$y'' = -\frac{1}{2} \cdot \frac{-y'}{y^2} = \frac{y'}{2y^2} = \left(-\frac{1}{2y}\right) \cdot \frac{1}{2y^2} = -\frac{1}{4y^3}.$$

3.8.32 $4x + 2yy' = 0$, so $y' = -\frac{2x}{y}$. Differentiating again, we obtain

$$y'' = \frac{-2y + 2xy'}{y^2} = \frac{-2y + \frac{-4x^2}{y}}{y^2} = \frac{-2y^2 - 4x^2}{y^3}.$$

3.8.33 $1 + \frac{dy}{dx} = (\cos y)\frac{dy}{dx}$, so $1 = \frac{dy}{dx}(\cos y - 1)$, and thus $\frac{dy}{dx} = \frac{1}{\cos y - 1}$. Thus

$$\frac{d^2y}{dx^2} = -\frac{1}{(\cos y - 1)^2} \cdot \left(-\sin y \frac{dy}{dx}\right) = \frac{\sin y}{(\cos y - 1)^2} \cdot \frac{1}{(\cos y - 1)} = \frac{\sin y}{(\cos y - 1)^3}.$$

3.8.34 $4x^3 + 4y'y^3 = 0$, so $y' = -\frac{x^3}{y^3}$. Differentiating again, we obtain

$$y'' = -\frac{3x^2y^3 - x^3 \cdot 3y^2y'}{y^6} = \frac{3x^3y' - 3x^2y}{y^4} = \frac{3x^3 \cdot \left(-\frac{x^3}{y^3}\right) - 3x^2y}{y^4} = \frac{-3x^6 - 3x^2y^4}{y^7}.$$

3.8.35 $2y'e^{2y} + 1 = y'$, so $y' = \frac{1}{1 - 2e^{2y}}$. Differentiating again, we obtain

$$y'' = -\left(1 - 2e^{2y}\right)^{-2}\left(-4e^{2y}y'\right) = \frac{4e^{2y}}{(1 - 2e^{2y})^3}.$$

3.8.36 $\cos x + 2xy + x^2y' = 0$, so $y' = -\frac{2xy + \cos x}{x^2}$. Differentiating again, we obtain

$$y'' = -\frac{x^2(2y + 2xy' - \sin x) - 2x(2xy + \cos x)}{x^4} = \frac{x^2\sin x + 2x\cos x + 2x^2y - 2x^3y'}{x^4}$$

$$= \frac{x\sin x + 2\cos x + 2xy + 2(2xy + \cos x)}{x^3} = \frac{x\sin x + 4\cos x + 6xy}{x^3}.$$

3.8.37 $\frac{dy}{dx} = \frac{5}{4}x^{\frac{5}{4}-1} = \frac{5}{4}x^{\frac{1}{4}}.$

3.8.38 $\frac{dy}{dx} = \frac{2x - 1}{3(x^2 - x + 1)^{2/3}}.$

3.8.39 $\frac{dy}{dx} = 5 \cdot \frac{2}{3}(5x + 1)^{-\frac{1}{3}} = \frac{10}{3(5x + 1)^{\frac{1}{3}}}.$

3.8.40 $\frac{dy}{dx} = e^x\sqrt{x^3} + \frac{3}{2}e^x\sqrt{x}.$

3.8.41 $\frac{dy}{dx} = \frac{1}{4}\left(\frac{2x}{4x-3}\right)^{-\frac{3}{4}} \cdot \frac{2(4x-3) - 2x \cdot 4}{(4x-3)^2} = -\frac{3}{2}\left(\frac{4x-3}{2x}\right)^{\frac{3}{4}} \cdot \frac{1}{(4x-3)^2} = -\frac{3}{2^{7/4}x^{3/4}(4x-3)^{5/4}}.$

3.8.42 $y' = 1 \cdot (x+1)^{1/3} + x \cdot (1/3)(x+1)^{-2/3} = \frac{3(x+1)}{3(x+1)^{2/3}} + \frac{x}{3(x+1)^{2/3}} = \frac{4x+3}{3(x+1)^{2/3}}.$

3.8.43 Note that $y = (1 + x^{1/3})^{2/3}$, so $y' = (2/3)(1 + x^{1/3})^{-1/3} \cdot (1/3)x^{-2/3} = \frac{2}{9x^{2/3}(1+x^{1/3})^{1/3}}$.

3.8.44 $\dfrac{dy}{dx} = \dfrac{(x^{\frac{1}{5}} + x) - x(\frac{1}{5}x^{-\frac{4}{5}} + 1)}{(x^{\frac{1}{5}} + x)^2} = \dfrac{4}{5}\dfrac{x^{\frac{1}{5}}}{(x^{\frac{1}{5}} + x)^2}$.

3.8.45 $\dfrac{1}{3}x^{-\frac{2}{3}} + \dfrac{4}{3}y^{\frac{1}{3}}y' = 0$, so at the given point we have $\frac{1}{3} + \frac{4}{3}y' = 0$, so $y' = -\frac{1}{4}$.

3.8.46 $\dfrac{2}{3}x^{-\frac{1}{3}} + \dfrac{2}{3}y^{-\frac{1}{3}}y' = 0$, so at the given point we have $\frac{2}{3} + \frac{2}{3}y' = 0$, so $y' = -1$.

3.8.47 $y^{\frac{1}{3}} + \dfrac{1}{3}xy^{-\frac{2}{3}}y' + y' = 0$, so at the given point we have $2 + \frac{1}{3} \cdot 1 \cdot \frac{1}{4}y' + y' = 0$, so $\frac{13}{12}y' = -2$, so $y' = -\frac{24}{13}$.

3.8.48 $\dfrac{2}{3}(x + y)^{-\frac{1}{3}}(1 + y') = y'$, so at the given point we have $\frac{2}{3} \cdot \frac{1}{2} \cdot (1 + y') = y'$, so $\frac{1}{3} = \frac{2}{3}y'$, so $y' = \frac{1}{2}$.

3.8.49 $y + xy' + \dfrac{3}{2}x^{\frac{1}{2}}y^{-\frac{1}{2}} - \dfrac{1}{2}x^{\frac{3}{2}}y^{-\frac{3}{2}}y' = 0$, so at the given point we have $1 + y' + \frac{3}{2} - \frac{1}{2}y' = 0$, so $\frac{1}{2}y' = -\frac{5}{2}$, so $y' = -5$.

3.8.50 $y^{\frac{5}{2}} + \dfrac{5}{2}xy^{\frac{3}{2}}y' + \dfrac{3}{2}x^{\frac{1}{2}}y + x^{\frac{3}{2}}y' = 0$, so at the given point we have $1 + 10y' + 3 + 8y' = 0$, so $y' = -\frac{2}{9}$.

3.8.51

a. False. For example, the equation $y\cos(xy) = x$, cannot be solved explicitly for y in terms of x.

b. True. We have $2x + 2yy' = 0$, and the result follows by solving for y'.

c. False. The equation $x = 1$ doesn't represent any sort of function – it is either just a number, or perhaps a vertical line, but it doesn't represent a differentiable function.

d. False. $y + xy' = 0$, so $y' = -\frac{y}{x}$, $x \neq 0$.

3.8.52

a. There are three points on the curve associated with $x = 1$. When $x = 1$, we have $1 + y^3 - y = 1$, so $y(y^2 - 1) = 0$. The three points are thus $(1, 0)$, $(1, 1)$ and $(1, -1)$. Differentiating yields $1 + 3y^2y' - y' = 0$, so $y' = \frac{1}{1 - 3y^2}$.
At $(1, 0)$, we have $y' = 1$, so the tangent line is given by $y = x - 1$.
At $(1, 1)$, we have $y' = -\frac{1}{2}$, so the tangent line is given by $y - 1 = -\frac{1}{2}(x - 1)$, or $y = -\frac{1}{2}x + \frac{3}{2}$.
At $(1, -1)$, we have $y' = -\frac{1}{2}$, so the tangent line is given by $y + 1 = -\frac{1}{2}(x - 1)$, or $y = -\frac{1}{2}x - \frac{1}{2}$.

b.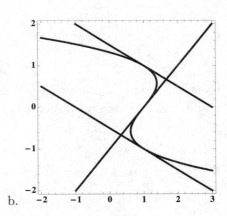

3.8.53

a. There are two points on the curve associated with $x = 1$. When $x = 1$, we have $1 + y^2 - y = 1$, so $y(y-1) = 0$. The two points are thus $(1,0)$ and $(1,1)$. Differentiating yields $1 + 2yy' - y' = 0$, so $y' = \frac{1}{1-2y}$.

At $(1,0)$, we have $y' = 1$, so the tangent line is given by $y = x - 1$.

At $(1,1)$, we have $y' = -1$, so the tangent line is given by $y - 1 = -1(x-1)$, or $y = -x + 2$.

b.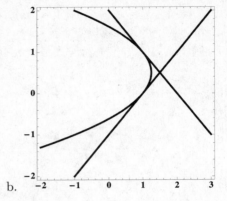

3.8.54

a. There are two points on the curve associated with $x = 2$. When $x = 2$, we have $32 = 2y^2$, so $y^2 = 16$, so $y = \pm 4$. The two points are thus $(2,4)$ and $(2,-4)$. Differentiating yields $12x^2 = 2yy'(4 - x) + -y^2$.

At $(2,-4)$, we have $48 = -8y'(2) - 16$, so $y' = -4$. Thus the tangent line is given by $y + 4 = -4(x-2)$, or $y = -4x + 4$.

At $(2,4)$, we have $y' = 4$, so the tangent line is given by $y - 4 = 4(x - 2)$, or $y = 4x - 4$.

b.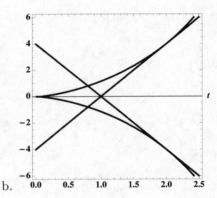

3.8.55

a. $y(2x) + (x^2 + 4)y' = 0$, so $y' = -\frac{2xy}{x^2+4}$.

b. At $y = 1$ we have $x^2 + 4 = 8$, so $x = \pm 2$. At the point $(2,1)$ we have $y' = -\frac{4}{8} = -\frac{1}{2}$. At the point $(-2,1)$ we have $y' = \frac{4}{8} = \frac{1}{2}$. Thus, the equations of the tangent lines are given by $y - 1 = -\frac{1}{2}(x-2)$ and $y - 1 = \frac{1}{2}(x+2)$, or $y = -\frac{1}{2}x + 2$ and $y = \frac{1}{2}x + 2$.

c. $y = \frac{8}{x^2+4}$, so $y' = \frac{0 - 8 \cdot 2x}{(x^2+4)^2} = -\frac{16x}{(x^2+4)^2}$.

d. $y' = -\frac{16x}{(x^2+4)^2} = -\frac{2x}{x^2+4} \cdot \frac{8}{x^2+4} = -\frac{2x}{x^2+4} \cdot y = -\frac{2xy}{x^2+4}$.

3.8.56

a. From number 52, we have that $y' = \frac{1}{1-3y^2}$. A vertical tangent would occur at a point whose y value would make $1 - 3y^2$ equal to zero. So we are looking for where $3y^2 = 1$ or $y = \pm\frac{1}{\sqrt{3}}$.

If $y = \frac{1}{\sqrt{3}}$, then $x + \left(\frac{1}{\sqrt{3}}\right)^3 - \frac{1}{\sqrt{3}} = 1$, so $x = 1 + \frac{2\sqrt{3}}{9}$, and there is a vertical tangent at $\left(\frac{1}{\sqrt{3}}, 1 + \frac{2\sqrt{3}}{9}\right)$.

If $y = -\frac{1}{\sqrt{3}}$, then $x + \left(-\frac{1}{\sqrt{3}}\right)^3 - -\frac{1}{\sqrt{3}} = 1$, so $x = 1 - \frac{2\sqrt{3}}{9}$, and there is a vertical tangent at $\left(-\frac{1}{\sqrt{3}}, 1 - \frac{2\sqrt{3}}{9}\right)$.

b. Because y' is never zero, there are no horizontal tangent lines.

3.8.57

   a. From number 53, we have that $y' = \frac{1}{1-2y}$. A vertical tangent would occur at a point whose y value would make $1 - 2y$ equal to zero. So we are looking for where $2y = 1$ or $y = \frac{1}{2}$.

      If $y = \frac{1}{2}$, then $x + \frac{1}{4} - \frac{1}{2} = 1$, so $x = \frac{5}{4}$, and there is a vertical tangent at $\left(\frac{5}{4}, \frac{1}{2}\right)$.

   b. Because y' is never zero, there are no horizontal tangent lines.

3.8.58 Differentiating with respect to x gives $2x + 8y\frac{dy}{dx} + 2x\frac{dy}{dx} + 2y = 0$, so

$$8y\frac{dy}{dx} + 2x\frac{dy}{dx} = -2x - 2y$$

$$\frac{dy}{dx}(8y + 2x) = -2x - 2y$$

$$\frac{dy}{dx} = \frac{-x - y}{4y + x}.$$

This quantity is zero when $y = -x$ (and not $x = y = 0$). Using the original equation, this means that $x^2 + 4x^2 - 2x^2 = 12$, or $3x^2 = 12$, so $x^2 = 4$ and we have $x = \pm 2$. Thus the points on the curve where the tangent line is horizontal are $(2, -2)$ and $(-2, 2)$.

   The curve has vertical tangent lines where $x = -4y$ (and not $x = y = 0$). Using the original equation, this means that $16y^2 + 4y^2 - 8y^2 = 12$, or $12y^2 = 12$, so $y = \pm 1$. Thus the points on the curve where the tangent line is vertical are $(-4, 1)$ and $(4, -1)$.

3.8.59 Differentiating with respect to x gives $18x + 2y\frac{dy}{dx} - 36 + 6\frac{dy}{dx} = 0$, so

$$2y\frac{dy}{dx} + 6\frac{dy}{dx} = -18x + 36$$

$$(2y + 6)\frac{dy}{dx} = -18x + 36$$

$$\frac{dy}{dx} = \frac{-9x + 18}{y + 3}.$$

This is zero when $x = 2$. Using the original equation, we have $36 + y^2 - 72 + 6y + 36 = 0$, or $y^2 + 6y = 0$, or $y = 0$ and $y = -6$. Thus there are horizontal tangent lines at $(2, 0)$ and $(2, -6)$. So $y = 0$ and $y = -6$ are horizontal tangent lines.

   This curve has vertical tangent lines when $y = -3$. Using the original equation, we have $9x^2 + 9 - 36x - 18 + 36 = 0$ or $9x^2 - 36x + 27 = 0$, or $x^2 - 4x + 3 = 0$. This factors as $(x - 3)(x - 1) = 0$, so the corresponding values of x are 3 and 1. Thus the vertical tangent lines occur at $(3, -3)$ and $(1, -3)$.

3.8.60

   a. $3y^2 y' = 2ax$, so $y' = \frac{2ax}{3y^2}$.

   b. $y = \sqrt[3]{ax^2}$.

   c.

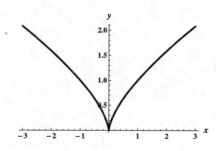

3.8.61

a. If we write $y^3 - 1 = xy - x$, we have $(y-1)(y^2 + y + 1) = x(y-1)$, so $y^2 + y + 1 = x$. Differentiating gives $2y\frac{dy}{dx} + \frac{dy}{dx} = 1$, so $\frac{dy}{dx} = \frac{1}{1+2y}$. Note also that $y = 1$ satisfies the equation; $y' = 0$ on this branch.

b.

$$y^3 - 1 = x(y-1)$$
$$(y-1)(y^2 + y + 1) = x(y-1)$$
$$y^2 + y + 1 = x$$
$$y^2 + y + (1 - x) = 0,$$

so by the quadratic formula we have $y = \frac{-1 \pm \sqrt{4x-3}}{2}$. Note that this means that $\pm\sqrt{4x-3} = 2y + 1$.

c.

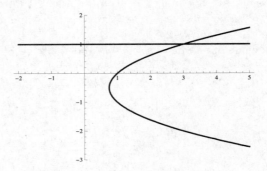

3.8.62

a. $2yy' = \dfrac{(2x(4-x) - x^2)(4+x) - x^2(4-x)}{(4+x)^2}$, so $2yy' = \dfrac{(8x - 3x^2)(4+x) - 4x^2 + x^3}{(4+x)^2}$, and $2yy' = \dfrac{32x - 8x^2 - 2x^3}{(4+x)^2}$. Thus $y' = \dfrac{16x - 4x^2 - x^3}{y(4+x)^2}$.

b. $y = \pm\sqrt{\dfrac{x^2(4-x)}{4+x}}$.

c.

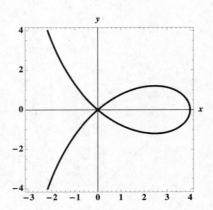

3.8.63

a. $4x^3 = 4x - 4yy'$, so $y' = \frac{x - x^3}{y}$.

b. $y = \pm\sqrt{x^2 - \dfrac{x^4}{2}}$.

c.

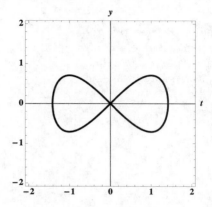

3.8.64

a. $2yy'(x+2) + y^2 = 12x - 3x^2$. So $y' = \frac{12x - 3x^2 - y^2}{2y(x+2)}$.

b. $y^2 = \dfrac{x^2(6-x)}{x+2}$, so $y = \pm\sqrt{\dfrac{x^2(6-x)}{x+2}}$.

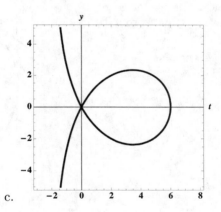

c.

3.8.65

The slope of the normal line is the negative reciprocal of the slope of the tangent line. From 25: $y' = -\frac{5}{4}$, so the slope of the normal line is $\frac{4}{5}$. At the point $(2, 1)$ we have the line $y - 1 = \frac{4}{5}(x - 2)$, or $y = \frac{4}{5}x - \frac{3}{5}$.

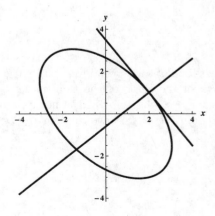

3.8.66

The slope of the normal line is the negative reciprocal of the slope of the tangent line. From 26: $y' = \frac{2}{3}$, so the slope of the normal line is $-\frac{3}{2}$. At the point $(-1, 1)$ we have the line $y - 1 = -\frac{3}{2}(x + 1)$, or $y = -\frac{3}{2}x - \frac{1}{2}$.

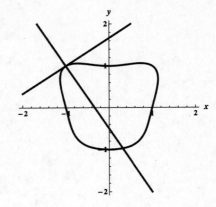

3.8.67

The slope of the normal line is the negative reciprocal of the slope of the tangent line. From 27: $y' = \frac{5}{2\pi+1}$, so the slope of the normal line is $\frac{-2\pi-1}{5}$. At the point $(\frac{\pi^2}{5}, \pi)$ we have the line $y - \pi = \frac{-2\pi-1}{5}(x - \frac{\pi^2}{5})$, or $y = \frac{-2\pi-1}{5}x + \frac{2\pi^3+\pi^2+25\pi}{25}$.

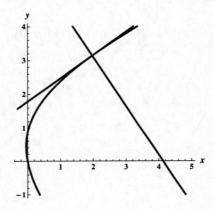

3.8.68

The slope of the normal line is the negative reciprocal of the slope of the tangent line. From 28: $y' = -1$, so the slope of the normal line is 1. At the point $(1, 1)$ we have the line $y - 1 = x - 1$, or $y = x$.

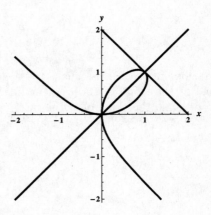

3.8.69

The slope of the normal line is the negative reciprocal of the slope of the tangent line. From 29: $y' = \frac{1}{2}$, so the slope of the normal line is -2. At the point $\left(\frac{\pi}{2}, \frac{\pi}{4}\right)$ we have the line $y - \frac{\pi}{4} = -2\left(x - \frac{\pi}{2}\right)$, or $y = -2x + \frac{5\pi}{4}$.

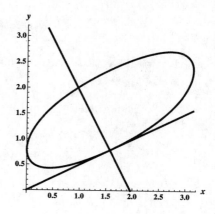

3.8.70

The slope of the normal line is the negative reciprocal of the slope of the tangent line. From 30: $y' = \frac{1}{3}$, so the slope of the normal line is -3. At the point $(1, 2)$ we have the line $y - 2 = -3(x - 1)$, or $y = -3x + 5$.

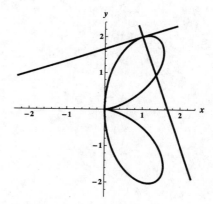

3.8.71

We have $9x^2 + 21y^2y' = 10y'$, so at the point $(1, 1)$ we have $9 + 21y' = 10y'$, so $y' = -\frac{9}{11}$.

Thus, the tangent line is given by $y - 1 = -\frac{9}{11}(x - 1)$, or $y = \frac{-9}{11}x + \frac{20}{11}$. The normal line is given by $y - 1 = \frac{11}{9}(x - 1)$, or $y = \frac{11}{9}x - \frac{2}{9}$.

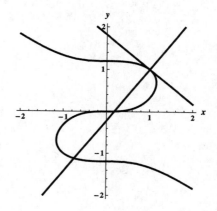

3.8.72

We have $4x^3 = 4x + 4yy'$, so at the point $(2, 2)$ we have $32 = 8 + 8y'$, so $y' = 3$.
Thus, the tangent line is given by $y - 2 = 3(x - 2)$, or $y = 3x - 4$. The normal line is given by $y - 2 = -\frac{1}{3}(x - 2)$, or $y = \frac{-1}{3}x + \frac{8}{3}$.

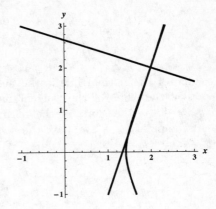

3.8.73

We have $2(x^2 + y^2 - 2x)(2x + 2yy' - 2) = 4x + 4yy'$, so at the point $(2, 2)$ we have $2(4 + 4 - 4)(4 + 4y' - 2) = 8 + 8y'$, so $16 + 32y' = 8 + 8y'$, so $y' = -\frac{1}{3}$.
Thus, the tangent line is given by $y - 2 = -\frac{1}{3}(x - 2)$, or $y = \frac{-1}{3}x + \frac{8}{3}$. The normal line is given by $y - 2 = 3(x - 2)$, or $y = 3x - 4$.

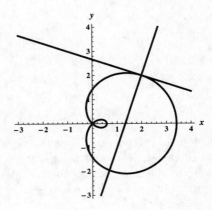

3.8.74

We have $2(x^2 + y^2)(2x + 2yy') = \frac{25}{3}(2x - 2yy')$, so at the point $(2, -1)$ we have $2 \cdot 5 \cdot (4 - 2y') = \frac{25}{3}(4 + 2y')$, so $40 - 20y' = \frac{100}{3} + \frac{50}{3}y'$, so $120 - 60y' = 100 + 50y'$, and thus $y' = \frac{2}{11}$.
Thus, the tangent line is given by $y + 1 = \frac{2}{11}(x - 2)$, or $y = \frac{2}{11}x - \frac{15}{11}$. The normal line is given by $y + 1 = -\frac{11}{2}(x - 2)$, or $y = \frac{-11}{2}x + 10$.

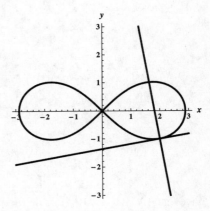

3.8.75

a. $1280 = 40L^{1/3}K^{2/3}$, so $0 = \frac{40}{3}L^{-2/3}K^{2/3} + \frac{80}{3}L^{1/3}K^{-1/3} \cdot \frac{dK}{dL}$. Multiplying both sides by $\frac{3}{40}L^{2/3}K^{1/3}$ yields

$0 = K + 2L\frac{dK}{dL}$, so $\frac{dK}{dL} = -\frac{1}{2}\frac{K}{L}$.

b. With $L = 8$ and $K = 64$, $\frac{dK}{dL} = -\frac{64}{16} = -4$.

3.8.76 $A = \pi r \sqrt{r^2 + h^2} = 1500\pi$. So $\pi r' \sqrt{r^2 + h^2} + \pi r \frac{rr' + h}{\sqrt{r^2 + h^2}} = 0$. So $r'(r^2 + h^2) + r^2 r' + rh = 0$, so $r' = -\frac{rh}{2r^2 + h^2}$. At $r = 30$ and $h = 40$, we have $r' = -\frac{1200}{1800 + 1600} = -\frac{6}{17}$.

3.8.77 $V = \frac{\pi h^2 (3r - h)}{3} = \frac{5\pi}{3}$. So

$$\frac{1}{3}[2\pi h(3r - h) + \pi h^2 (3r' - 1)] = 0,$$

$$6rh - 2h^2 + 3h^2 r' - h^2 = 0,$$

so $r' = 1 - \frac{2r}{h}$.

At $r = 2$ and $h = 1$, we have $r' = 1 - 4 = -3$.

3.8.78 $V = \frac{\pi^2 (b+a)(b-a)^2}{4} = 64\pi^2$. So

$$(b' + 1)(b - a)^2 + (b + a) \cdot 2 \cdot (b - a)(b' - 1) = 0,$$

$$b'(b - a)^2 + 2(b^2 - a^2)b' = 2(b^2 - a^2) - (b - a)^2,$$

$$b'(b - a)(b - a + 2b + 2a) = (b - a)(2b + 2a - (b - a)),$$

$$\frac{db}{da} = \frac{(b - a)(b + 3a)}{(b - a)(3b + a)} = \frac{b + 3a}{3b + a}.$$

At $a = 6$ and $b = 10$ we have $\frac{db}{da} = \frac{28}{36} = \frac{7}{9}$.

3.8.79 Note for $y = mx$, $\frac{dy}{dx} = m = \frac{y}{x}$, and for $x^2 + y^2 = a^2$, $\frac{dy}{dx} = -\frac{x}{y}$. So for any point (x, y), we have $\frac{y}{x}$ and $-\frac{x}{y}$ are negative reciprocals.

3.8.80 For $y = cx^2$ we have $y' = 2cx$ and for $x^2 + 2y^2 = k$, we have $y' = -\frac{x}{2y}$. Let (a, b) be a point on both curves. Then $b = ca^2$, so the point has the form (a, ca^2). A normal line to the ellipse $x^2 + 2y^2 = k$ would have slope $\frac{2y}{x} = \frac{2ca^2}{a} = 2ca$, which is the slope of the tangent line to the parabola $y = cx^2$ at the point in question. Thus the two curves are orthogonal at any points of intersection.

3.8.81 For $xy = a$ we have $xy' + y = 0$, so $y' = -\frac{y}{x}$. For $x^2 - y^2 = b$, we have $2x - 2yy' = 0$, so $y' = \frac{x}{y}$. Let (c, d) be a point on both curves. Then the slope of the normal line to the first curve is $\frac{c}{d}$, but that is the slope of the tangent line to the second curve. Thus the two curves are orthogonal at any points of intersection.

3.8.82

$$\frac{5}{2\sqrt{x}} - \frac{5y'}{\sqrt{y}} = \cos x, \text{ so } \frac{5y'}{\sqrt{y}} = \frac{5}{2\sqrt{x}} - \cos x, \text{ and thus } y' = \frac{\sqrt{y}}{5} \cdot \left(\frac{5}{2\sqrt{x}} - \cos x\right) = \frac{\sqrt{y}}{5} \cdot \left(\frac{5 - 2\sqrt{x}\cos x}{2\sqrt{x}}\right)$$

At the point $(4\pi, \pi)$ we have $y'(4\pi, \pi) = \frac{\sqrt{\pi}}{5} \cdot \left(\frac{5 - 2\sqrt{4\pi}(1)}{2\sqrt{4\pi}}\right) = \frac{5 - 4\sqrt{\pi}}{20}$.

3.8.83

$$(2x + 2yy')(x^2 + y^2 + x) + (x^2 + y^2)(2x + 2yy' + 1) = 8y^2 + 16xyy'$$

$$2yy'(x^2 + y^2 + x) + (x^2 + y^2)2yy' - 16xyy' = 8y^2 - 2x(x^2 + y^2 + x) - (x^2 + y^2)(2x + 1)$$

$$y' = \frac{8y^2 - 2x(x^2 + y^2 + x) - (x^2 + y^2)(2x + 1)}{2y(x^2 + y^2 + x) + 2y(x^2 + y^2) - 16xy}$$

$$= \frac{8y^2 - 2x^3 - 2xy^2 - 2x^2 - 2x^3 - x^2 - 2xy^2 - y^2}{2y(x^2 + y^2 + x + x^2 + y^2 - 8x)}$$

$$= \frac{7y^2 - 3x^2 - 4xy^2 - 4x^3}{2y(2x^2 + 2y^2 - 7x)}.$$

3.8.84

$$\frac{21x^6 + 2yy'}{2\sqrt{3x^7 + y^2}} = 2y' \sin y \cos y + 100(y + xy')$$

$$21x^6 + 2yy' = 4y' \sin y \cos y \sqrt{3x^7 + y^2} + 200y\sqrt{3x^7 + y^2} + 200xy' \sqrt{3x^7 + y^2}$$

$$200y\sqrt{3x^7 + y^2} - 21x^6 = 2yy' - 4y' \sin y \cos y \sqrt{3x^7 + y^2} - 200xy'\sqrt{3x^7 + y^2}$$

$$y' = \frac{200y\sqrt{3x^7 + y^2} - 21x^6}{2y - 4\sin y \cos y \sqrt{3x^7 + y^2} - 200x\sqrt{3x^7 + y^2}}.$$

3.8.85 $\dfrac{y'}{2\sqrt{y}} + y + xy' = 0$, so $y' + 2x\sqrt{y}y' = -2y\sqrt{y}$, so $y' = \dfrac{-2y\sqrt{y}}{2x\sqrt{y}+1} = -\dfrac{2y^{3/2}}{2x\sqrt{y}+1}$.
Differentiating again we obtain

$$y'' = -\frac{(2x\sqrt{y}+1)(3\sqrt{y}y') - 2y^{3/2}\left(2\sqrt{y} + \frac{xy'}{\sqrt{y}}\right)}{(2x\sqrt{y}+1)^2} = \frac{-(2x\sqrt{y}+1)(3\sqrt{y}y') + 4y^2 + 2xyy'}{(2x\sqrt{y}+1)^2}$$

$$= \left(\frac{-(2x\sqrt{y}+1)(3\sqrt{y})\left(\frac{-2y\sqrt{y}}{2x\sqrt{y}+1}\right) + 4y^2 + 2xy\left(\frac{-2y\sqrt{y}}{1+2x\sqrt{y}}\right)}{(2x\sqrt{y}+1)^2}\right) \cdot \frac{2x\sqrt{y}+1}{2x\sqrt{y}+1}$$

$$= \frac{(2x\sqrt{y}+1)(6y^2) + 4y^2(1 + 2x\sqrt{y}) - 4xy^{5/2}}{(2x\sqrt{y}+1)^3} = \frac{10y^2 + 16xy^2\sqrt{y}}{(2x\sqrt{y}+1)^3}.$$

3.8.86 Differentiating with respect to x yields $2yy' - 3y - 3xy' = 0$; simplifying gives $y' = \frac{3y}{2y-3x}$. There could be a horizontal tangent line when $y = 0$, but using the original equation we see that there are no points on the curve where this occurs. (Letting $y = 0$ in the original equation gives the untrue equation $0 = 2$).

Considering where the tangent line might be vertical we consider points where $2y = 3x$. Using the original equation and replacing $3x$ by $2y$, we obtain $y^2 - 2y^2 = 2$, or $-y^2 = 2$, which is again impossible. So the tangent is never vertical nor horizontal.

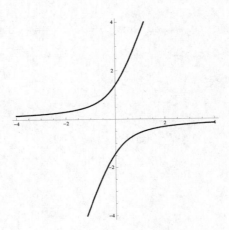

3.8.87 Differentiating with respect to x yields $2x(3y^2 - 2y^3) + x^2(6y - 6y^2)\frac{dy}{dx} = 0$. Solving for $\frac{dy}{dx}$ yields $\frac{dy}{dx} = \frac{-2x(3y^2 - 2y^3)}{6x^2(y - y^2)} = \frac{3y^2 - 2y^3}{3x(y^2 - y)} = \frac{3y - 2y^2}{3x(y - 1)}$. The numerator is zero when $y = 0$ or when $y = \frac{3}{2}$. Using the original equation, there are no points where $y = 0$, and there are also no points where $y = \frac{3}{2}$ because we obtain the equation $x^2(\frac{27}{4} - \frac{27}{4}) = 4$, which has no solutions. So there are no horizontal tangent lines.

There could be vertical tangent lines where $x = 0$ or $y = 1$; in fact, when $y = 1$ the original equation becomes $x^2(3 - 2) = 4$, so $x = \pm 2$. There are vertical tangents at $(2, 1)$ and $(-2, 1)$. Letting $x = 0$ doesn't yield any points in the original equation.

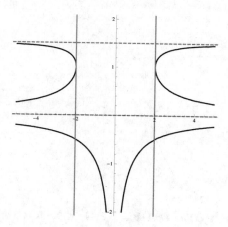

3.8.88 Differentiating with respect to x yields $2x(y - 2) + x^2 y' - e^y y' = 0$, and solving for y' yields $y' = \frac{2x(2 - y)}{x^2 - e^y}$. This quantity is zero for $x = 0$ or $y = 2$. Using the original equation we find no solutions for $x = 0$ or $y = 2$, so there are no horizontal tangent lines. There could be vertical tangent lines where $x^2 = e^y$. Using the original equation (and disallowing $x^2 = 0$) we have $x^2(y - 2) - x^2 = 0$, so $x^2(y - 2 - 1) = 0$, so $y = 3$. Using the original equation with $y = 3$ we have $x^2 - e^3 = 0$, so $x = \pm\sqrt{e^3}$. There are vertical tangent lines at $(\sqrt{e^3}, 3)$ and $-\sqrt{e^3}, 3)$.

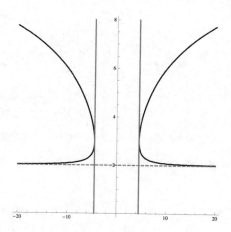

3.8.89 Differentiating with respect to x yields $(1 - y^2) + x(-2yy') + 3y^2y' = 0$. Solving for y' yields $y' = \frac{y^2-1}{3y^2-2xy} = \frac{y^2-1}{y(3y-2x)}$. There could be a horizontal tangent line where $y = \pm 1$, but the original equation with $y = \pm 1$ yields $\pm 1 = 0$, so there are no horizontal tangent lines.

There could be a vertical tangent line for $y = 0$ or for $y = \frac{2}{3}x$. Using the original equation, letting $y = 0$ yields $x = 0$, and letting $y = \frac{2}{3}x$ yields $x\left(1 - \frac{4x^2}{9}\right) + \frac{8x^3}{27} = 0$. For $x \neq 0$, this yields $27 - 12x^2 + 8x^2 = 0$, or $x^2 = \frac{27}{4}$, so $x = \pm\frac{\sqrt{27}}{2} = \pm\frac{3\sqrt{3}}{2}$. The corresponding y values are $y = \pm\frac{2}{3}x = \pm\sqrt{3}$. So there are vertical tangent lines at $(0,0)$ and at $(3\sqrt{3}/2, \sqrt{3})$ and $(-3\sqrt{3}/2, -\sqrt{3})$.

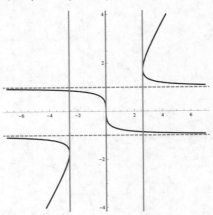

3.9 Derivatives of Logarithmic and Exponential Functions

3.9.1 $y = \ln x$ if and only if $x = e^y$. Differentiating implicitly yields $1 = e^y \cdot y'$, so $y' = \frac{1}{e^y} = \frac{1}{e^{\ln x}} = \frac{1}{x}$ for $x > 0$.

3.9.2

We have already established that if $y = \ln x$ for $x > 0$ then $y' = \frac{1}{x}$. By the symmetry about the y-axis, we know that for $x < 0$, the derivative of $y = \ln |x|$ should have the same absolute value but the opposite sign of the derivative for the corresponding positive x value. But this is the property that $\frac{1}{x}$ has for $x < 0$ – it is negative and has the right absolute value. So we see that for both $x > 0$ and $x < 0$, $\frac{d}{dx} \ln |x| = \frac{1}{x}$.

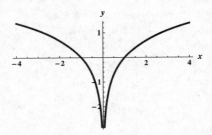

3.9.3 $\frac{d}{dx} \ln(kx) = \frac{1}{kx} \cdot k = \frac{1}{x}$. This is valid for $x > 0$ if $k > 0$ and $x < 0$ if $k < 0$. Also, we can write $\ln(kx) = \ln(k) + \ln(x)$, so its derivative is $0 + \frac{1}{x} = \frac{1}{x}$.

3.9.4 $\frac{d}{dx} b^x = b^x \ln b$, for $b > 0$ and all x. In the case $b = e$, the rule states that $\frac{d}{dx} e^x = e^x \ln e = e^x$ because $\ln e = 1$.

3.9.5 $\frac{d}{dx} \log_b x = \frac{1}{x \ln b}$ for $b > 0$, $b \neq 1$ and $x > 0$. If $b = e$, we have $\frac{d}{dx} \log_e x = \frac{1}{x \ln e} = \frac{1}{x}$.

3.9.6 We use inverse property 3 from the text: $b^x = (e^{\ln b})^x = e^{(\ln b) \cdot x} = e^{x \ln b}$.

3.9.7 $f(x) = e^{\ln(g(x)^{h(x)})} = e^{h(x) \cdot \ln(g(x))}$.

3.9.8 To apply the procedure of logarithmic differentiation to an equation of the form $y = f(x)$ (where f is likely a complicated expression): Take the logarithm to both sides of the equation, then use the properties of logarithms to simplify the expression $\ln(f(x))$. Then differentiate both sides, obtaining $\frac{1}{y}y'$ on the left and some other expression on the right. Then solve for y', replacing y by $f(x)$ if desired.

3.9.9 $\frac{d}{dx}\ln(7x) = \frac{1}{7x} \cdot 7 = \frac{1}{x}$.

3.9.10 $\frac{d}{dx}(x^2 \ln x) = 2x \ln x + x^2 \cdot \frac{1}{x} = 2x \ln x + x = x(2 \ln x + 1)$.

3.9.11 $\frac{d}{dx}\ln(x^2) = \frac{1}{x^2} \cdot (2x) = \frac{2}{x}$.

3.9.12 $\frac{d}{dx}\ln(2x^8) = \frac{1}{2x^8} \cdot (16x^7) = \frac{8}{x}$.

3.9.13 $\frac{d}{dx}(\ln|\sin x|) = \frac{1}{\sin x} \cdot (\cos x) = \cot x$.

3.9.14 $\frac{d}{dx}\frac{\ln x^2}{x} = \frac{x(2/x) - \ln x^2}{x^2} = \frac{2 - 2\ln x}{x^2}$.

3.9.15 $\frac{d}{dx}\left[\ln\left(\frac{x+1}{x-1}\right)\right] = \frac{x-1}{x+1}\left(\frac{(x-1)-(x+1)}{(x-1)^2}\right) = -\frac{2}{(x+1)(x-1)} = \frac{2}{1-x^2}$.

3.9.16 $\frac{d}{dx}e^x \ln x = e^x \ln x + \frac{e^x}{x}$.

3.9.17 $\frac{d}{dx}((x^2+1)\ln x) = 2x \ln x + \frac{x^2+1}{x}$.

3.9.18 $\frac{d}{dx}\ln|x^2-1| = \frac{1}{x^2-1} \cdot 2x = \frac{2x}{x^2-1}$.

3.9.19 $\frac{d}{dx}(\ln \ln x) = \frac{1}{\ln x} \cdot \frac{1}{x}$.

3.9.20 $\frac{d}{dx}(\ln(\cos^2 x)) = \frac{1}{\cos^2 x} \cdot (-2 \sin x \cos x) = -2 \tan x$.

3.9.21 $\frac{d}{dx}\left(\frac{\ln x}{\ln x + 1}\right) = \frac{(\ln x + 1)(1/x) - (\ln x)(1/x)}{(\ln x + 1)^2} = \frac{1}{x(\ln x + 1)^2}$.

3.9.22 $\frac{d}{dx}(\ln(e^x + e^{-x})) = \frac{1}{e^x + e^{-x}}(e^x - e^{-x}) = \frac{e^x - e^{-x}}{e^x + e^{-x}}$.

3.9.23 $\frac{dy}{dx} = 8^x \ln 8$.

3.9.24 $y' = 5^{3t} \cdot \ln 5 \cdot 3 = 3(\ln 5)(5^{3t})$.

3.9.25 $y' = 5 \cdot \frac{d}{dx}4^x = 5 \cdot \ln 4 \cdot 4^x$.

3.9.26 $y' = -\ln 4 \cdot 4^{-x} \cdot \sin x + 4^{-x} \cos x$.

3.9.27 $y' = 3x^2 3^x + x^3 3^x \ln 3 = 3^x x^2(3 + x \ln 3)$.

3.9.28 $\frac{dP}{dt} = \frac{0 - 40(-\ln 2 \cdot 2^{-t})}{(1 + 2^{-t})^2} = \frac{40 \ln 2 \cdot 2^{-t}}{(1 + 2^{-t})^2}$.

3.9.29 $\frac{dA}{dt} = 250(1.045)^{4t} \cdot \ln(1.045) \cdot 4 = 1000 \cdot \ln 1.045 \cdot (1.045^{4t})$.

3.9.30 $\frac{d}{dx}\ln 10^x = \frac{d}{dx}x \cdot \ln 10 = \ln 10$.

3.9.31

a. $T = 10 \cdot 2^{-0.274 \cdot 16}$ minutes ≈ 28.7 seconds.

b. $\frac{\Delta T}{\Delta a} = \frac{10 \cdot 2^{-0.274 \cdot 8} - 10 \cdot 2^{-0.274 \cdot 2}}{8 - 2} \approx -0.78$ minutes per 1000 feet, which is about -46.512 seconds per 1000 feet.

c. $\frac{dT}{da} = -2.74 \cdot 2^{-0.274 \cdot a} \cdot \ln 2$. At $a = 8$ we have $\frac{dT}{da} = -2.74 \cdot 2^{-0.274 \cdot 8} \cdot \ln 2 \approx -0.42$ minutes per 1000 feet. Every 1000 feet the airplane climbs, leaves about .42 minutes less time of consciousness, which corresponds to about 24.94 seconds.

3.9.32

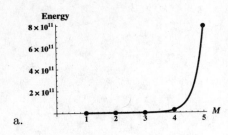

b. $\frac{dE}{dM} = 25000 \cdot 1.5 \cdot \ln 10 \cdot 10^{1.5M}$. At $M = 3$ we have $\frac{dE}{dM} = 25000 \cdot 1.5 \cdot \ln 10 \cdot 10^{9/2} \approx 2,730,530,025$ Joules per unit change in M. As the magnitude goes from 3 to 4, the energy goes up by this amount.

a.

3.9.33

a. At $Q = 10\mu$Ci we have $10 = 350 \cdot \left(\frac{1}{2}\right)^{t/13.1}$, so $\ln(1/35) = \frac{t}{13.1} \ln(1/2)$, so $t = 13.1 \cdot \frac{\ln 35}{\ln 2} \approx 67.19$ hours.

b. $\frac{dQ}{dt} = \frac{350}{13.1} \cdot \ln\left(\frac{1}{2}\right) \cdot \left(\frac{1}{2}\right)^{t/13.1}$. We have $Q'(12) \approx -9.81453$, $Q'(24) \approx -5.20136$, and $Q'(48) \approx -1.46087$. The rate at which the iodine decreases is decreasing in absolute value as time increases.

3.9.34 $f'(x) = ex^{e-1}$.

3.9.35 $f'(x) = 2^x(\ln 2)$.

3.9.36 $f'(x) = 2\sqrt{2}x^{\sqrt{2}-1}$.

3.9.37 $g'(y) = e^y y^e + e^{y+1} y^{e-1}$.

3.9.38 $s'(t) = -\sin(2^t) \cdot 2^t \ln 2$.

3.9.39 $r'(\theta) = e^{2\theta} \cdot 2 = 2e^{2\theta}$.

3.9.40 $\frac{dy}{dx} = \frac{d}{dx}(\pi \cdot \ln(x^3 + 1)) = \pi \cdot \frac{3x^2}{x^3+1}$.

3.9.41 $f'(x) = 2x^{3/2} + \frac{3}{2}(2x - 3)x^{1/2} = 5x^{3/2} - \frac{9}{2}x^{1/2}$.

3.9.42 $\frac{dy}{dx} = 0.74x^{-0.26}\sec^2(x^{0.74})$.

3.9.43 $f'(x) = \frac{(2^x+1)2^x \ln 2 - 2^x(2^x \ln 2)}{(2^x+1)^2} = \frac{2^x \ln 2}{(2^x+1)^2}$.

3.9.44 $f'(x) = \pi(2^x + 1)^{\pi-1}(2^x \ln 2)$.

3.9.45 Let $y = x^{\cos x}$. Then $\ln y = \cos x \ln x$. Differentiating both sides gives

$$\frac{1}{y}y' = (-\sin x)\ln x + \cos x \cdot \frac{1}{x}.$$

Therefore,

$$y' = x^{\cos x}\left(\frac{\cos x}{x} - \sin x \ln x\right).$$

At $\pi/2$ we have $y'(\pi/2) = (\pi/2)^0(0/(\pi/2) - \ln(\pi/2)) = -\ln(\pi/2)$.

3.9.46 Let $y = x^{\ln x}$. Then $\ln y = \ln x \ln x = (\ln x)^2$. Differentiating both sides gives

$$\frac{1}{y}y' = 2\ln x \cdot \frac{1}{x}.$$

Therefore,

$$y' = x^{\ln x - 1} \cdot 2\ln x.$$

At e we have $y'(e) = e^{1-1} \cdot 2\ln e = 2$.

3.9.47 Let $y = x^{\sqrt{x}}$. Then $\ln y = \sqrt{x} \cdot \ln x$. Differentiating both sides gives

$$\frac{1}{y}y' = \frac{1}{2\sqrt{x}}\ln x + \frac{\sqrt{x}}{x}.$$

Therefore,

$$y' = x^{\sqrt{x}}\left(\frac{\ln x + 2}{2\sqrt{x}}\right).$$

At 4 we have $y'(4) = 4^2\left(\frac{\ln 4 + 2}{4}\right) = 4\ln 4 + 8$.

3.9.48 Because $f(x) = (x^2 + 1)^x$, we have $\ln f(x) = x\ln(x^2 + 1)$. Thus,

$$\frac{1}{f(x)}f'(x) = (1)\ln(x^2 + 1) + x \cdot \frac{1}{x^2 + 1} \cdot 2x.$$

Therefore,

$$f'(x) = (x^2 + 1)^x\left(\ln(x^2 + 1) + \frac{2x^2}{x^2 + 1}\right).$$

We have $f'(1) = (1 + 1)^1(\ln(1 + 1) + \frac{2}{1+1}) = 2(\ln 2 + 1) = 2\ln 2 + 2$.

3.9.49 Because $f(x) = (\sin x)^{\ln x}$, we have $\ln f(x) = \ln x \ln \sin x$. Differentiating both sides gives

$$\frac{1}{f(x)}f'(x) = \frac{1}{x} \cdot \ln\sin x + \ln x \cdot \frac{1}{\sin x}\cos x.$$

Therefore,

$$f'(x) = (\sin x)^{\ln x}\left(\frac{\ln\sin x + x\ln x\cot x}{x}\right).$$

We have $f'(\pi/2) = 0$ because $\cot \pi/2 = 0$ and $\ln\sin(\pi/2) = \ln 1 = 0$.

3.9.50 Because $f(x) = \tan^{x-1} x$, we have $\ln f(x) = (x - 1)\ln\tan x$. Differentiating both sides gives

$$\frac{1}{f(x)}f'(x) = (1)\ln\tan x + (x - 1)\frac{1}{\tan x}\sec^2 x.$$

Therefore,

$$f'(x) = (\tan^{x-1} x)(\ln\tan x + (x - 1)\csc x\sec x).$$

We have $f'(\pi/4) = (1)^{\pi/4-1}(\ln 1 + (\pi/4 - 1)(\sqrt{2})(\sqrt{2})) = \pi/2 - 2$.

3.9.51 Let $y = x^{\sin x}$. Then $\ln y = \sin x\ln x$, so $\frac{1}{y}y' = \cos x\ln x + \frac{\sin x}{x}$. At the point $(1, 1)$ we have $y' = \sin 1$, so the tangent line is given by $y - 1 = (\sin 1)(x - 1)$, or $y = (\sin 1)x + 1 - \sin 1$.

3.9.52 Let $y = x^{\sqrt{x}}$. Then we have $\ln y = \sqrt{x} \cdot \ln x$, so $\frac{1}{y}y' = \frac{\ln x}{2\sqrt{x}} + \frac{\sqrt{x}}{x}$, so $y' = x^{\sqrt{x}}\left(\frac{\ln x}{2\sqrt{x}} + \frac{\sqrt{x}}{x}\right) = x^{\sqrt{x}}\left(\frac{\sqrt{x}\ln x + 2\sqrt{x}}{2x}\right)$. This expression is zero only when $\ln x + 2 = 0$, or $x = e^{-2}$.

3.9.53 Let $y = (x^2)^x = x^{2x}$. Then $\ln y = x\ln x^2$ and $\frac{1}{y}y' = \ln x^2 + 2$, so $y' = x^{2x}(\ln x^2 + 2)$. This quantity is zero when $\ln x^2 = -2$, or $x^2 = e^{-2}$. Thus there are horizontal tangents at $|x| = e^{-1}$, so for $x = \pm\frac{1}{e}$. The two tangent lines are given by $y = \frac{1}{e^{2/e}}$ (at $\left(\frac{1}{e}, \frac{1}{e^{2/e}}\right)$) and $y = e^{2/e}$ (at $\left(-\frac{1}{e}, e^{2/e}\right)$.)

3.9.54 Let $y = x^{\ln x}$. Then $\ln y = (\ln x)^2$. Thus $\frac{1}{y}y' = 2\ln x \cdot \frac{1}{x}$, so $y' = x^{\ln x}\left(\frac{2\ln x}{x}\right)$. This quantity is zero when $\ln x = 0$, which is at $x = 1$. The equation of the tangent line at $(1, 1)$ is therefore $y = 1$.

3.9.55 $y' = 4 \cdot \frac{2x}{(x^2-1)\cdot\ln 3} = \frac{8x}{(x^2-1)\cdot\ln 3}$.

3.9.56 $y' = \frac{1}{x \ln 10}$.

3.9.57 $y' = -\sin x (\ln(\cos^2 x)) + \cos x \cdot \left(\frac{2\cos x(-\sin x)}{\cos^2 x} \right) = (-\sin x)(\ln(\cos^2 x) + 2)$.

3.9.58 $y' = \frac{1}{\ln 8 \tan x} \cdot \sec^2 x$.

3.9.59 $y' = \frac{d}{dx} (\log_4 x)^{-1} = - (\log_4 x)^{-2} \cdot \frac{1}{x \ln 4} = -\frac{1}{x(\ln 4)(\log_4 x)^2} = -\frac{\ln 4}{x \ln^2 x}$.

3.9.60 $y' = \frac{1}{(\ln 2)(\log_2 x)} \cdot \frac{1}{x \ln 2} = \frac{1}{(\ln 2)^2 \cdot x \cdot \log_2 x} = \frac{1}{x(\ln 2) \ln x}$.

3.9.61 Let $y = \frac{(x+1)^{10}}{(2x-4)^8}$, so $\ln y = \ln \left(\frac{(x+1)^{10}}{(2x-4)^8} \right) = 10 \ln(x+1) - 8 \ln(2x - 4)$. Then

$$\frac{1}{y} y' = \frac{10}{x+1} - \frac{8}{2x-4} \cdot 2,$$

$$y' = \frac{(x+1)^{10}}{(2x-4)^8} \cdot \left(\frac{10}{x+1} - \frac{8}{x-2} \right).$$

3.9.62 Let $y = x^2 \cos x$. Then $\ln y = \ln(x^2 \cos x) = 2 \ln x + \ln(\cos x)$. So $\frac{1}{y} y' = \frac{2}{x} + \frac{1}{\cos x} \cdot (-\sin x)$, so

$$y' = x^2 \cos x \cdot \left(\frac{2}{x} + \frac{1}{\cos x} \cdot (-\sin x) \right) = 2x \cos x - x^2 \sin x.$$

3.9.63 Let $y = x^{\ln x}$. Then $\ln y = (\ln x)^2$. Thus $\frac{1}{y} y' = 2 \ln x \cdot \frac{1}{x}$, so $y' = x^{\ln x} \left(\frac{2 \ln x}{x} \right)$.

3.9.64 Let $y = \frac{\tan^{10} x}{(5x+3)^6}$. Then $\ln y = \ln \left(\frac{\tan^{10} x}{(5x+3)^6} \right) = 10 \ln(\tan x) - 6 \ln(5x + 3)$. Then

$$\frac{1}{y} y' = \frac{10}{\tan x} \sec^2 x - \frac{6}{5x+3} \cdot 5,$$

$$y' = \frac{\tan^{10} x}{(5x+3)^6} \left(\frac{10 \sec^2 x}{\tan x} - \frac{30}{5x+3} \right).$$

3.9.65 Let $y = \frac{(x+1)^{3/2}(x-4)^{5/2}}{(5x+3)^{2/3}}$. Then $\ln y = \ln \left(\frac{(x+1)^{3/2}(x-4)^{5/2}}{(5x+3)^{2/3}} \right) = \frac{3}{2} \ln(x+1) + \frac{5}{2} \ln(x-4) - \frac{2}{3} \ln(5x+3)$. Then

$$\frac{1}{y} y' = \frac{3}{2(x+1)} + \frac{5}{2(x-4)} - \frac{10}{3(5x+3)},$$

$$y' = \frac{(x+1)^{3/2}(x-4)^{5/2}}{(5x+3)^{2/3}} \cdot \left(\frac{3}{2(x+1)} + \frac{5}{2(x-4)} - \frac{10}{3(5x+3)} \right).$$

3.9.66 Let $y = \frac{x^8 \cos^3 x}{\sqrt{x-1}}$. Then $\ln y = \ln \left(\frac{x^8 \cos^3 x}{\sqrt{x-1}} \right) = 8 \ln x + 3 \ln \cos x - \frac{1}{2} \ln(x-1)$. Then

$$\frac{1}{y} y' = \frac{8}{x} - \frac{3 \sin x}{\cos x} - \frac{1}{2x-2},$$

$$y' = \frac{x^8 \cos^3 x}{\sqrt{x-1}} \left(\frac{8}{x} - 3 \tan x - \frac{1}{2x-2} \right).$$

3.9.67 Let $y = (\sin x)^{\tan x}$, and assume $0 < x < \pi$, $x \neq \frac{\pi}{2}$. Then $\ln y = (\tan x) \ln(\sin x)$. Then

$$\frac{1}{y} y' = (\sec^2 x) \ln(\sin x) + \frac{\tan x \cos x}{\sin x},$$

$$y' = (\sin x)^{\tan x} \left((\sec^2 x) \ln(\sin x) + 1 \right).$$

3.9.68 Let $y = \left(1 + \frac{1}{x}\right)^{2x}$. Then $\ln y = 2x \ln\left(1 + \frac{1}{x}\right)$. Then

$$\frac{1}{y}y' = 2\ln\left(1 + \frac{1}{x}\right) + 2x\left(\frac{1}{1 + \frac{1}{x}}\right)\cdot\left(-\frac{1}{x^2}\right),$$

$$y' = \left(1 + \frac{1}{x}\right)^{2x}\cdot\left(2\ln\left(1 + \frac{1}{x}\right) - \frac{2}{x+1}\right).$$

3.9.69

a. False. $\log_2 9$ is a constant, so its derivative is 0.

b. False. If $x < -1$, then the right-hand side is defined while the left-hand side isn't.

c. False. The correct way to write that function would be $e^{(x+1)\ln 2}$.

d. False. $\frac{d}{dx}(\sqrt{2})^x = (\sqrt{2})^x \ln(\sqrt{2})$.

e. True. This follows from the generalized power rule.

3.9.70 $\frac{d^3}{dx^3}(x^{4.2}) = \frac{d^2}{dx^2}(4.2x^{3.2}) = \frac{d}{dx}(4.2)(3.2)x^{2.2} = (4.2)(3.2)(2.2)x^{1.2}$. So $\frac{d^3}{dx^3}\Big|_{x=1} = (4.2)(3.2)(2.2) = 29.568$.

3.9.71 $\frac{d^2}{dx^2}(\log x) = \frac{d}{dx}\left(\frac{1}{x\ln 10}\right) = -\frac{1}{x^2\ln 10}$.

3.9.72 $\frac{d}{dx}(2^x) = (2^x)\ln 2$. $\frac{d^2}{dx^2}(2^x) = \frac{d}{dx}(2^x)\ln 2 = (2^x)(\ln 2)^2$. Clearly, each new derivative is the same as the old multiplied by a factor of $\ln 2$. So after n derivatives, the result is $\frac{d^n}{dx^n}(2^x) = (2^x)\cdot(\ln 2)^n$.

3.9.73 $\frac{d^3}{dx^3}(x^2\ln x) = \frac{d^2}{dx^2}(2x\ln x + x) = \frac{d}{dx}(2\ln x + 2 + 1) = \frac{2}{x}$.

3.9.74

a. $y' = \frac{d}{dx}e^{x\ln(x^2+1)} = e^{x\ln(x^2+1)}\left(\ln(x^2+1) + \frac{2x^2}{x^2+1}\right) = (x^2+1)^x\left(\ln(x^2+1) + \frac{2x^2}{x^2+1}\right)$.

b. Let $y = (x^2+1)^x$. Then $\ln y = x\ln(x^2+1)$, so $\frac{1}{y}y' = \ln(x^2+1) + \frac{2x^2}{x^2+1}$, and thus $y' = (x^2+1)^x\left(\ln(x^2+1) + \frac{2x^2}{x^2+1}\right)$.

3.9.75

a. $y' = \frac{d}{dx}\left(e^{x\ln 3}\right) = (e^{x\ln 3})\cdot\ln 3 = 3^x\ln 3$.

b. Let $y = 3^x$. Then $\ln y = x\ln 3$. So $\frac{1}{y}y' = \ln 3$, and $y' = 3^x\ln 3$.

3.9.76

a. $y' = \frac{d}{dx}e^{h(x)\ln(g(x))} = e^{h(x)\ln(g(x))}\cdot\left(h'(x)\ln(g(x)) + \frac{h(x)g'(x)}{g(x)}\right) = g(x)^{h(x)}\cdot\left(h'(x)\ln(g(x)) + \frac{h(x)g'(x)}{g(x)}\right)$.

b. Let $y = g(x)^{h(x)}$. Then $\ln y = h(x)\ln g(x)$. So $\frac{1}{y}y' = \left(h'(x)\ln(g(x)) + \frac{h(x)g'(x)}{g(x)}\right)$, and thus
$y' = g(x)^{h(x)}\left(h'(x)\ln(g(x)) + \frac{h(x)g'(x)}{g(x)}\right)$.

3.9.77 $f'(x) = \frac{d}{dx}(4\ln(3x+1)) = \frac{4}{3x+1}\cdot 3 = \frac{12}{3x+1}$.

3.9.78 $f'(x) = \frac{d}{dx}(\ln 2x - 3\ln(x^2+1)) = \frac{1}{x} - \frac{6x}{x^2+1}$.

3.9.79 $f'(x) = \frac{d}{dx}\left(\frac{1}{2}\ln 10x\right) = \frac{d}{dx}\frac{1}{2}[\ln 10 + \ln x] = \frac{1}{2x}$.

3.9.80 $f'(x) = \frac{d}{dx}\left(\log_2 2^3 - \frac{1}{2}\log_2(x+1)\right) = 0 - \frac{1}{2}\cdot\frac{1}{(x+1)\ln 2} = -\frac{1}{(\ln 4)(x+1)}$.

3.9.81 $f'(x) = \frac{d}{dx}(\ln(2x-1) + 3\ln(x+2) - 2\ln(1-4x)) = \frac{2}{2x-1} + \frac{3}{x+2} + \frac{8}{1-4x}.$

3.9.82 $f'(x) = \frac{d}{dx}(4\ln(\sec x) + 2\ln(\tan x)) = \frac{4\sec x \tan x}{\sec x} + \frac{2\sec^2 x}{\tan x} = 4\tan x + 2\sec x \csc x.$

3.9.83

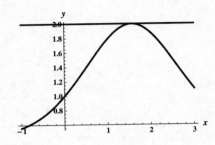

$y' = \frac{d}{dx}e^{\sin x \ln 2} = (\cos x)(\ln 2)2^{\sin x}.$ At $x = \pi/2$ we have $y' = 0$, so the tangent line is given by $y = 2$.

3.9.84 We have

$$y' = -\sin x(\ln(\cos^2 x)) + \cos x\left(\frac{2(\cos x)(-\sin x)}{\cos^2 x}\right) = -\sin x(2 + \ln(\cos^2 x)).$$

This quantity is zero when $\sin x = 0$ or $2 + \ln(\cos^2 x) = 0$, and the latter occurs when $\cos^2 x = e^{-2}$, or $\cos x = \pm e^{-1}$.

$\sin x = 0$ for $x = 0, \pi, 2\pi$. $\cos x = e^{-1}$ for $x \approx 1.194$ and $x \approx 5.089$. Finally, $\cos x = -e^{-1}$ for $x \approx 1.948$ and $x \approx 4.336$. These seven numbers represent the locations of the horizontal tangent lines on $[0, 2\pi]$.

3.9.85 Let $y = x^{10x}$. Then $\ln y = 10x \ln x$, so $\frac{1}{y}y' = 10\ln x + 10$, and $y' = x^{10x}(10)(\ln x + 1)$.

3.9.86 Let $y = (2x)^{2x}$. Then $\ln y = 2x \ln(2x)$, and $\frac{1}{y}y' = 2\ln(2x) + 2$, so $y' = (2x)^{2x}(2)(\ln(2x) + 1)$.

3.9.87 Let $y = x^{\cos x}$. Then we have $\ln y = \cos x \ln x$, and $\frac{1}{y}y' = -\sin x \ln x + \frac{\cos x}{x}$. Thus, $y' = x^{\cos x}\left(\frac{\cos x}{x} - \sin x \ln x\right)$.

3.9.88 $\frac{d}{dx}(x^\pi + \pi^x) = \pi x^{\pi-1} + \pi^x \ln \pi.$

3.9.89 Let $y = \left(1 + \frac{1}{x}\right)^x$. Then $\ln y = x\ln\left(1 + \frac{1}{x}\right)$, so $\frac{1}{y}y' = \ln\left(1 + \frac{1}{x}\right) + x\left(\frac{-1/x^2}{1+1/x}\right) = \ln\left(1 + \frac{1}{x}\right) - \frac{1}{x+1}.$ Therefore, $y' = \left(1 + \frac{1}{x}\right)^x\left(\ln\left(1 + \frac{1}{x}\right) - \frac{1}{x+1}\right).$

3.9.90 Let $y = (1+x^2)^{\sin x}$. Then $\ln y = \sin x \cdot \ln(1+x^2)$, so $\frac{1}{y}y' = \cos x \cdot \ln(1+x^2) + \sin x \cdot \frac{2x}{1+x^2}$. Therefore we have $y' = (1+x^2)^{\sin x}\left(\cos x \cdot \ln(1+x^2) + \frac{2x\sin x}{1+x^2}\right).$

3.9.91 Let $y = x^{x^{10}}$. Then $\ln y = x^{10}\ln x$, so $\frac{1}{y}y' = 10x^9 \ln x + \frac{x^{10}}{x} = x^9(10\ln x + 1)$. Thus $y' = x^{x^{10}} \cdot x^9(10\ln x + 1)$.

3.9.92 Let $y = (\ln x)^{x^2}$. Then $\ln y = x^2 \cdot \ln(\ln(x))$. So $\frac{1}{y}y' = 2x \cdot \ln(\ln(x)) + \frac{x^2}{x \ln x}$. Therefore, $y' = (\ln x)^{x^2}(x)\left(2 \cdot \ln(\ln(x)) + \frac{1}{\ln x}\right).$

3.9.93

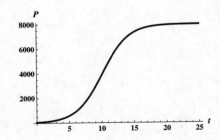

a.   We used a graphing rectangle of $[0, 25] \times [0, 8000]$.

b. To find when $P(t)$ hits 5000, we solve $5000 = \frac{400000}{50+7950e^{-0.5t}}$, or $50 + 7950e^{-0.5t} = 80$. This leads to $7950e^{-0.5t} = 30$, or $-0.5t = \ln\left(\frac{30}{7950}\right)$. So we have $t = 2\ln(265) \approx 11.16$ years.

The carrying capacity is $\lim_{t\to\infty} P(t) = \frac{400,000}{50} = 8000$. Ninety percent of 8000 is 7200, so we seek the time when $P(t) = 7200$. We have $7200 = \frac{400000}{50+7950e^{-0.5t}}$, or $50 + 7950e^{-0.5t} = \frac{500}{9}$. This leads to $7950e^{-0.5t} = \frac{50}{9}$, or $-0.5t = \ln\left(\frac{50}{71550}\right)$. So we have $t = 2\ln\left(\frac{71550}{50}\right) \approx 14.53$ years.

c. $\frac{dP}{dt} = -\frac{400000}{(50+7950e^{-0.5t})^2} \cdot (7950)(-0.5)e^{-0.5t}$.

At $t = 0$ we have $P'(0) = \frac{400,000 \cdot 7950 \cdot .5}{8000^2} = \frac{1,590,000,000}{8000^2} \approx 25$ fish per year.

At $t = 5$ we have $P'(5) = \frac{1,590,000,000e^{-5/2}}{(50+7950e^{-5/2})^2} \approx 264$ fish per year.

d. The maximum is at about $t = 10$ years.

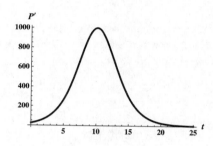

3.9.94

a. $P(t) = \frac{6\times10^9 \cdot 15\times10^9}{6\times10^9 + 9\times10^9 \cdot e^{-0.025t}} = \frac{3\times10^{10}}{2+3\cdot e^{-0.025t}}$.

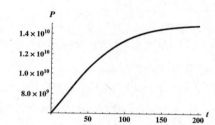

b. $P(21) = \frac{3\times10^{10}}{2+3\cdot e^{-0.525}} \approx 7.95 \times 10^9$.

$P(t) = 12,000,000,000$ when $2 + 3e^{-0.025t} = \frac{5}{2}$, which is when $e^{-0.025t} = \frac{1}{6}$. This occurs for $t = 40\ln 6 \approx 71.67$ years.

3.9.95

a. $\ln(P(t)) = \ln(3\cdot10^{10}) - \ln(2+3e^{-0.025t})$. $\frac{d}{dt}\ln(P(t)) = \frac{P'(t)}{P(t)} = r(t) = \frac{0.075\cdot e^{-0.025t}}{2+3e^{-0.025t}}$. $r(0) = \frac{0.075}{5} = 0.015$, so the population is growing at 1.5% per year in 1999.

b. $r(11) = \frac{0.075e^{-0.275}}{2+3e^{-0.275}} \approx 0.0133$.

$r(21) = \frac{0.075e^{-0.525}}{2+3e^{-0.525}} \approx 0.0118$.

The relative growth rate decreases over time.

c. $\lim_{t\to\infty} r(t) = \lim_{t\to\infty} \frac{0.075}{3 + 2e^{0.025t}} = 0$, because the denominator increases without bound. The relative growth rate becomes smaller and smaller as the population nears the carrying capacity.

3.9.96

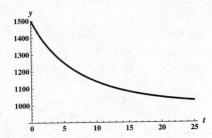

a. $P(t) = \frac{1500 \cdot 1000}{1500 - 500e^{-0.1t}}$. As $t \to \infty$, the population decreases and gets closer to the carrying capacity of 1000.

b. $P'(t) = -\frac{7.5 \times 10^7 e^{-0.1t}}{(1500 - 500e^{-0.1t})^2}$. $P'(0) = -\frac{7.5 \times 10^7}{(1000)^2} = -75$ deer per year.

c. The population reaches 1200 deer when $1200 = \frac{1500 \cdot 1000}{1500 - 500e^{-0.1t}}$. This occurs when $-500e^{-0.1t} = \frac{1.5 \times 10^6}{1200} - 1500$, or when $-0.1t = \ln(0.5)$, or when $t = -10\ln(0.5) \approx 6.93$ years. It will take almost 7 years until the deer population reaches 1200.

3.9.97

a.

t	$A(t)$
5	\$17,442.50
15	\$72,704.68
25	\$173,248.49
35	\$356,177.57

Average growth on $[5, 15]$ is $\frac{A(15) - A(5)}{10} \approx \$5526$ per year. Average growth on $[15, 25]$ is $\frac{A(25) - A(15)}{10} \approx \$10,054$ per year. Average growth on $[25, 35]$ is $\frac{A(35) - A(25)}{10} \approx \$18,293$ per year.

b. $A(40) \approx \$497,872.68$.

c. $A'(t) = 50,000 \cdot 12 \cdot (1.005)^{12t} \cdot \ln(1.005) \approx 2993 \cdot (1.005)^{12t}$. The rate of growth of the investment increases over time, so the earlier you start saving, the higher the rate of increase will be when you retire.

3.9.98 We search for a solution to $x^p = e^x$. If the two curves will have only one point of intersection, then they should be tangent at the point of intersection. So we need $px^{p-1} = e^x$, so we require $px^{p-1} = x^p$, so $x = p$. So $p^p = e^p$, and therefore we must have $p = e$. So we have $x^e = e^x$ intersecting at the point (e, e^e), and that is the only point of intersection.

3.9.99 We search for a solution to $x = p^x$. If the two curves will have only one point of intersection, then they should be tangent at the point of intersection. So we need $1 = p^x \ln p$, or $\frac{1}{\ln p} = p^x = x$. So $\ln p = \frac{1}{x}$ and $p = e^{1/x}$. Then we have $x = p^x = (e^{1/x})^x = e$. So the point of intersection is (e, e) and the value of p is $e^{1/e} \approx 1.44467$.

3.9.100 By inspection, we see that the point $(3, 27)$ is on all three curves

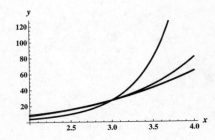

3.9.101 Let $f(x) = \ln x$ and $a = e$. Then $f'(e) = \lim_{x \to e} \dfrac{\ln x - 1}{x - e} = \dfrac{1}{e}$.

3.9.102 Let $f(x) = \ln x$ and $a = e^8$. Then $f'(e^8) = \lim_{h \to 0} \dfrac{\ln(e^8 + h) - 8}{h} = \dfrac{1}{e^8}$.

3.9.103 Let $f(x) = x^x$ and $a = 3$. Then $f'(3) = \lim_{h \to 0} \dfrac{(3 + h)^{3+h} - 27}{h} = 3^3 \cdot (\ln 3 + 1) = 27(1 + \ln 3)$.

3.9.104 Let $f(x) = 5^x$ and $a = 2$. Then $f'(2) = \lim_{x \to 2} \dfrac{5^x - 25}{x - 2} = 25 \ln 5$.

3.9.105 Let $y = u(x)^{v(x)}$. Then $\ln y = v(x) \ln u(x)$, so $\frac{1}{y} y' = v'(x) \ln u(x) + v(x) \cdot \frac{u'(x)}{u(x)}$. Thus we have
$y' = u(x)^{v(x)} \cdot \left(v'(x) \ln u(x) + v(x) \cdot \frac{u'(x)}{u(x)} \right) = u(x)^{v(x)} \cdot \left(\frac{v(x)}{u(x)} \frac{du}{dx} + \ln u(x) \frac{dv}{dx} \right)$.

3.9.106 The slope of the tangent line to $y = b^x$ is $y' = b^x \ln b$. We are seeking the y-coordinate of the point (x, b^x) where $b^x \ln b = \frac{b^x}{x}$. we must have $x = \frac{1}{\ln b}$, in which case the y-coordinate is $b^{\frac{1}{\ln b}} = e$. To see that $b^{\frac{1}{\ln b}} = e$, let $z = b^{\frac{1}{\ln b}}$. Then $\ln z = \ln b^{\frac{1}{\ln b}} = \frac{\ln b}{\ln b} = 1$, so $z = e$.

3.10 Derivatives of Inverse Trigonometric Functions

3.10.1 $\frac{d}{dx} \sin^{-1} x = \frac{1}{\sqrt{1-x^2}}$, $-1 < x < 1$.
$\frac{d}{dx} \tan^{-1} x = \frac{1}{1+x^2}$, $-\infty < x < \infty$.
$\frac{d}{dx} \sec^{-1} x = \frac{1}{|x|\sqrt{x^2-1}}$, $|x| > 1$.

3.10.2 $y' = \frac{1}{\sqrt{1-x^2}}$. At $x = 0$ we have $y'(0) = 1$.

3.10.3 $y' = \frac{1}{1+x^2}$. At $x = -2$ we have $y'(-2) = \frac{1}{1+4} = \frac{1}{5}$.

3.10.4 $\frac{d}{dx} \sin^{-1} x = \frac{1}{\sqrt{1-x^2}} = -- \frac{1}{\sqrt{1-x^2}} = -\frac{d}{dx} \cos^{-1} x$.

3.10.5 $(f^{-1})'(8) = \frac{1}{f'(2)} = \frac{1}{4}$.

3.10.6 $(f^{-1})'(y_0) = \frac{1}{f'(x_0)}$ where $f(x_0) = y_0$.

3.10.7 $\frac{d}{dx} \sin^{-1}(2x) = \frac{2}{\sqrt{1-4x^2}}$.

3.10.8 $\frac{d}{dx}(x \sin^{-1} x) = \sin^{-1} x + \frac{x}{\sqrt{1-x^2}}$.

3.10.9 $\frac{d}{dw} \cos(\sin^{-1}(2w)) = (-\sin(\sin^{-1}(2w))) \cdot \frac{d}{dw} \left(\sin^{-1}(2w) \right) = -2w \cdot \frac{2}{\sqrt{1-4w^2}} = -\frac{4w}{\sqrt{1-4w^2}}$.

3.10.10 $\frac{d}{dx} \sin^{-1}(\ln x) = \frac{1}{\sqrt{1-(\ln x)^2}} \cdot \frac{d}{dx} \ln x = \frac{1}{x\sqrt{1-(\ln x)^2}}$.

3.10.11 $\frac{d}{dx} \sin^{-1}(e^{-2x}) = \frac{1}{\sqrt{1-e^{-4x}}} \cdot \frac{d}{dx} e^{-2x} = -\frac{2e^{-2x}}{\sqrt{1-e^{-4x}}}$.

3.10.12 $\frac{d}{dx} \sin^{-1}(e^{\sin x}) = \frac{1}{\sqrt{1-e^{2\sin x}}} \cdot \frac{d}{dx} e^{\sin x} = \frac{(\cos x) \cdot (e^{\sin x})}{\sqrt{1-e^{2\sin x}}}$.

3.10.13 $f'(x) = \frac{1}{1+100x^2} \cdot 10 = \frac{10}{100x^2+1}$.

3.10.14 $f'(x) = 1 \cdot \cot^{-1}(x/3) + x \cdot -\frac{1}{1+(x^2/9)} \cdot \frac{1}{3} = \cot^{-1}(x/3) - \frac{3x}{x^2+9}$.

3.10.15 $\frac{d}{dy} \tan^{-1}(2y^2 - 4) = \frac{1}{1+(2y^2-4)^2} \cdot \frac{d}{dy}(2y^2 - 4) = \frac{4y}{1+(2y^2-4)^2}$.

3.10.16 $\frac{d}{dz}\tan^{-1}(1/z) = \frac{1}{1+(1/z)^2}\cdot\frac{d}{dz}\frac{1}{z} = -\frac{1}{z^2(1+(1/z)^2)} = -\frac{1}{z^2+1}$.

3.10.17 $\frac{d}{dz}\cot^{-1}\sqrt{z} = -\frac{1}{1+\sqrt{z}^2}\cdot\frac{d}{dz}\sqrt{z} = -\frac{1}{1+z}\cdot\frac{1}{2\sqrt{z}} = -\frac{1}{2\sqrt{z}(1+z)}$.

3.10.18 $\frac{d}{dx}\sec^{-1}\sqrt{x} = \frac{1}{\sqrt{x}\sqrt{x-1}}\cdot\frac{d}{dx}\sqrt{x} = \frac{1}{2x\sqrt{x-1}}$ for $x>1$.

3.10.19 $\frac{d}{dx}\cos^{-1}\frac{1}{x} = -\frac{1}{\sqrt{1-\frac{1}{x^2}}}\cdot\left(-\frac{1}{x^2}\right) = \frac{1}{x^2\sqrt{\frac{x^2-1}{x^2}}} = \frac{|x|}{x^2\sqrt{x^2-1}} = \frac{1}{|x|\sqrt{x^2-1}}$, for $|x|>1$.

3.10.20 $\frac{d}{dt}(\cos^{-1}t)^2 = 2\cos^{-1}t\cdot\left(-\frac{1}{\sqrt{1-t^2}}\right) = -\frac{2\cos^{-1}t}{\sqrt{1-t^2}}$.

3.10.21 $\frac{d}{du}\csc^{-1}(2u+1) = -\frac{1}{|2u+1|\sqrt{(2u+1)^2-1}}\cdot 2 = -\frac{2}{|2u+1|\sqrt{(2u+1)^2-1}} = -\frac{1}{|2u+1|\sqrt{u^2+u}}$.

3.10.22 $\frac{d}{dt}\ln(\tan^{-1}t) = \frac{1}{\tan^{-1}t}\cdot\frac{1}{1+t^2}$.

3.10.23 $\frac{d}{dy}\cot^{-1}\left(\frac{1}{1+y^2}\right) = \left(-\frac{1}{1+\left(\frac{1}{1+y^2}\right)^2}\right)\cdot\left(-\frac{2y}{(1+y^2)^2}\right) = \frac{2y}{(1+y^2)^2+1}$.

3.10.24 $\frac{d}{dw}\sin[\sec^{-1}2w] = \cos[\sec^{-1}2w]\cdot\frac{2}{|2w|\sqrt{4w^2-1}} = \frac{1/w}{2|w|\sqrt{4w^2-1}} = \frac{1}{2w|w|\sqrt{4w^2-1}}$.

3.10.25 $\frac{d}{dx}\sec^{-1}(\ln x) = \frac{1}{|\ln x|\sqrt{(\ln x)^2-1}}\cdot\frac{1}{x} = \frac{1}{x|\ln x|\sqrt{(\ln x)^2-1}}$.

3.10.26 $\frac{d}{dx}\tan^{-1}(e^{4x}) = \frac{1}{1+e^{8x}}\cdot 4e^{4x} = \frac{4e^{4x}}{1+e^{8x}}$.

3.10.27 $\frac{d}{dx}\csc^{-1}(\tan e^x) = -\frac{1}{|\tan e^x|\sqrt{(\tan e^x)^2-1}}\cdot(\sec^2 e^x)\cdot e^x$.

3.10.28 $\frac{d}{dx}\sin(\tan^{-1}(\ln x)) = \cos(\tan^{-1}(\ln x))\cdot\frac{1}{1+(\ln x)^2}\cdot\frac{1}{x} = \frac{\cos(\tan^{-1}(\ln x))}{x(1+(\ln x)^2)}$.

3.10.29 $\frac{d}{ds}\cot^{-1}(e^s) = -\frac{1}{1+e^{2s}}\cdot e^s = -\frac{e^s}{1+e^{2s}}$.

3.10.30

$$\frac{d}{dx}\frac{1}{\tan^{-1}(x^2+4)} = \frac{d}{dx}\left(\tan^{-1}(x^2+4)\right)^{-1} = -\left(\tan^{-1}(x^2+4)\right)^{-2}\cdot\frac{1}{1+(x^2+4)^2}\cdot 2x$$
$$= -\frac{2x}{(1+(x^2+4)^2)\cdot(\tan^{-1}(x^2+4))^2}.$$

3.10.31 $f'(x) = \frac{1}{1+4x^2}\cdot 2$, so $f'(1/2) = \frac{1}{1+1}\cdot 2 = 1$. Thus the equation of the tangent line is $y-\pi/4 = 1(x-1/2)$, or $y = x+\frac{\pi}{4}-\frac{1}{2}$.

3.10.32 $f'(x) = \frac{1}{\sqrt{1-x^2/16}}\cdot\frac{1}{4} = \frac{1}{\sqrt{16-x^2}}$, so $f'(2) = \frac{1}{\sqrt{12}}$. Thus the equation of the tangent line is $y-\pi/6 = \frac{1}{\sqrt{12}}(x-2)$, or $y = \frac{1}{2\sqrt{3}}x+\frac{\pi}{6}-\frac{1}{\sqrt{3}}$.

3.10.33 $f'(x) = -\frac{1}{\sqrt{1-x^4}}\cdot 2x = -\frac{2x}{\sqrt{1-x^4}}$, so $f'(1/\sqrt{2}) = -\frac{\sqrt{2}}{\sqrt{1-(1/4)}} = -\frac{2\sqrt{2}}{\sqrt{3}}$. Thus the equation of the tangent line is $y-\pi/3 = -\frac{2\sqrt{2}}{\sqrt{3}}(x-1/\sqrt{2})$, or $y = -\frac{2\sqrt{2}}{\sqrt{3}}x+\frac{\pi}{3}+\frac{2}{\sqrt{3}}$.

3.10.34 $f'(x) = \frac{1}{e^x\sqrt{e^{2x}-1}}\cdot e^x$, so $f'(\ln 2) = \frac{2}{2\sqrt{4-1}} = \frac{1}{\sqrt{3}}$. Thus the equation of the tangent line is $y-\pi/3 = \frac{1}{\sqrt{3}}(x-\ln 2)$, or $y = \frac{1}{\sqrt{3}}x+\frac{\pi}{3}-\frac{\ln 2}{\sqrt{3}}$.

3.10.35

    a. $\frac{x}{150} = \cot\theta$, so $\theta = \cot^{-1}\left(\frac{x}{150}\right)$. Then $\frac{d\theta}{dx} = -\frac{1}{1+\left(\frac{x}{150}\right)^2} \cdot \frac{1}{150} = -\frac{150}{(150)^2+x^2}$. When $x = 500$, we have $\frac{d\theta}{dx} = -\frac{150}{150^2+500^2} \approx -0.00055$ radians per meter.

    b. The most rapid change is at $x = 0$ where $\frac{d\theta}{dx} = -\frac{1}{150} \approx -0.0067$ radians per meter.

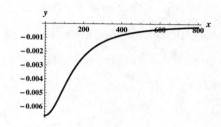

3.10.36

    a. $\frac{x}{400} = \cot\theta$, so $\theta = \cot^{-1}\left(\frac{x}{400}\right)$. Then $\frac{d\theta}{dx} = -\frac{1}{1+\left(\frac{x}{400}\right)^2} \cdot \frac{1}{400} = -\frac{400}{(400)^2+x^2}$. When $x = 500$, we have $\frac{d\theta}{dx} = -\frac{400}{400^2+500^2} \approx -0.000976$ radians per meter.

    b. The most rapid change is at $x = 0$, where the plane is directly over head.

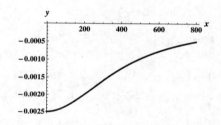

3.10.37 $f(4) = 16$ so $(f^{-1})'(16) = \frac{1}{f'(4)} = \frac{1}{3}$.

3.10.38 $f(4) = 10$ so $(f^{-1})'(10) = \frac{1}{f'(4)} = \frac{1}{1/2} = 2$.

3.10.39 $f(1) = -1$ so $(f^{-1})'(-1) = \frac{1}{f'(1)} = \frac{1}{-5} = -\frac{1}{5}$.

3.10.40 $f(2) = 5$ so $(f^{-1})'(5) = \frac{1}{f'(2)} = \frac{1}{4}$.

3.10.41 $f\left(\frac{\pi}{4}\right) = 1$ so $(f^{-1})'(1) = \frac{1}{f'\left(\frac{\pi}{4}\right)} = \frac{1}{\sec^2\left(\frac{\pi}{4}\right)} = \frac{1}{2}$.

3.10.42 $f(-3) = 12$ so $(f^{-1})'(12) = \frac{1}{f'(-3)} = \frac{1}{-8} = -\frac{1}{8}$.

3.10.43 $f(4) = 2$ so $(f^{-1})'(2) = \frac{1}{f'(4)} = \frac{1}{(1/2\sqrt{4})} = 4$.

3.10.44 $f(2) = 8$ and $(f^{-1})'(8) = \frac{1}{f'(2)} = \frac{1}{3 \cdot 2^2} = \frac{1}{12}$.

3.10.45 $f(4) = 36$ and $(f^{-1})'(36) = \frac{1}{f'(4)} = \frac{1}{2(4+2)} = \frac{1}{12}$.

3.10.46 $f(1) = 7$ and $(f^{-1})'(7) = \frac{1}{f'(1)} = \frac{1}{-2 \cdot 1} = -\frac{1}{2}$.

3.10.47 Note that $f(1) = 3$. So $(f^{-1})'(3) = \frac{1}{f'(1)} = \frac{1}{4}$.

3.10.48 $(f^{-1})'(4) = \frac{1}{f'(7)} = \frac{1}{2/3} = \frac{3}{2}$.

3.10.49 $(f^{-1})'(4) = \frac{1}{f'(7)} = \frac{4}{5}$, so $f'(7) = \frac{5}{4}$.

3.10.50 $(f^{-1})'(7) = \frac{1}{f'(4)} = \frac{1}{1/5} = 5.$

3.10.51

   a. Note that $f(0) = 4$, so $f^{-1}(4) = 0$. $(f^{-1})'(4) = \frac{1}{f'(0)} = \frac{1}{2}$.

   b. Note that $f(1) = 6$, so $f^{-1}(6) = 1$. $(f^{-1})'(6) = \frac{1}{f'(1)} = \frac{1}{3/2} = \frac{2}{3}$.

   c. Note that there is no given x so that $f(x) = 1$, so the desired derivative cannot be determined.

   d. From the table directly, $f'(1) = \frac{3}{2}$.

3.10.52

   a. $f'(f(0)) = f'(2) = 2$.

   b. Note that $f(-4) = 0$, so $f^{-1}(0) = -4$. $(f^{-1})'(0) = \frac{1}{f'(-4)} = \frac{1}{5}$.

   c. Note that $f(-2) = 1$, so $f^{-1}(1) = -2$. $(f^{-1})'(1) = \frac{1}{f'(-2)} = \frac{1}{4}$.

   d. $(f^{-1})'(f(4)) = \frac{1}{f'(4)} = \frac{1}{1} = 1$.

3.10.53

   a. True, because $\frac{d}{dx}\sin^{-1}x = -\frac{d}{dx}\cos^{-1}x$.

   b. False. $\frac{d}{dx}\tan^{-1}x = \frac{1}{1+x^2}$ for all x, and this doesn't equal $\sec^2 x$ anywhere except at the origin (one curve is always less than or equal to one, and the other is always greater than or equal to one).

   c. True. $\frac{d}{dx}\sin^{-1}x = \frac{1}{\sqrt{1-x^2}}$, and this is minimal when its denominator is as big as possible, which occurs when $x = 0$. So the smallest possible slope of a tangent line for this function on $(-1, 1)$ is $\frac{1}{\sqrt{1-0^2}} = 1$.

   d. True. $\frac{d}{dx}\sin x = \cos x$ and $\cos x = 1$ for $x = 0$ and $-1 \leq \cos x \leq 1$ for all x. Thus 1 is the largest possible slope for a tangent line to the sine function.

   e. True. This follows because the function $\frac{1}{x}$ is its own inverse. (Note that $f(f(x)) = \frac{1}{f(x)} = \frac{1}{1/x} = x$.) Thus, the derivative of the inverse of f is the derivative of f, which is $-\frac{1}{x^2}$.

3.10.54

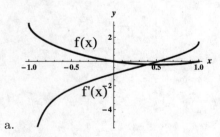

   a.

   b. $f'(x) = \sin^{-1}(x) + \frac{x-1}{\sqrt{1-x^2}}$.

   c. Note that f' is zero and f has a horizontal tangent line at about $x = 0.53$.

3.10.55

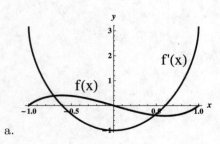

   a.

   b. $f'(x) = 2x\sin^{-1}(x) + \frac{x^2-1}{\sqrt{1-x^2}}$.

   c. Note that f' is zero and f has a horizontal tangent line at about $x = -0.61$ and at about $x = 0.61$.

3.10.56

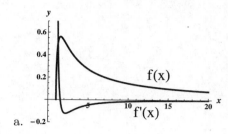

a.

b. $f'(x) = \dfrac{x \cdot \frac{1}{|x|\sqrt{x^2-1}} - \sec^{-1}x}{x^2} = \dfrac{1}{x|x|\sqrt{x^2-1}} - \dfrac{\sec^{-1}x}{x^2}$.

c. Note that f' is zero and f has a horizontal tangent line at about $x = 1.53$.

3.10.57

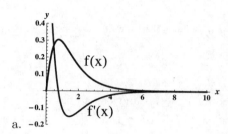

a.

b. $f'(x) = -e^{-x}\tan^{-1}x + e^{-x}\dfrac{1}{1+x^2}$.

c. Note that f' is zero and f has a horizontal tangent line at about $x = .75$.

3.10.58

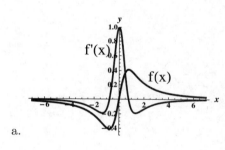

a.

b. $f'(x) = \dfrac{(x^2+1)\frac{1}{x^2+1} - \tan^{-1}(x)(2x)}{(x^2+1)^2} = \dfrac{1-2x\tan^{-1}(x)}{(x^2+1)^2}$.

c. Note that f' is zero and f has a horizontal tangent line at about $x = .765$ and at about $x = -.765$.

3.10.59 Let $f(y) = 3y - 4$. Then $f'(y) = 3$ for all y in the domain of f. Let $y = f^{-1}(x)$. $(f^{-1})'(x) = \frac{1}{f'(y)} = \frac{1}{3}$.

3.10.60 Let $f(y) = |y+2|$ for $y \le -2$. Then $f(y) = -(y+2)$, and $f'(y) = -1$. Thus $(f^{-1})'(x) = \frac{1}{f'(y)} = \frac{1}{-1} = -1$.

3.10.61 Let $x = f(y) = y^2 - 4$ for $y > 0$. Note that this means that $y = \sqrt{x+4}$. Then $f'(y) = 2y$. So $(f^{-1})'(x) = \frac{1}{f'(y)} = \frac{1}{2y} = \frac{1}{2\sqrt{x+4}}$.

3.10.62 Let $x = \frac{y}{y+5}$. Then $x(y+5) = y$, so $y - xy = 5x$. Thus, $y = f^{-1}(x) = \frac{5x}{1-x}$. Therefore $(f^{-1})'(x) = \frac{(1-x)5 - 5x(-1)}{(1-x)^2} = \frac{5}{(1-x)^2}$.

3.10.63 For $y \ge -2$, let $x = \sqrt{y+2}$. Note that it then follows that $x \ge 0$. Then $1 = \frac{y'}{2\sqrt{y+2}}$, and $x^2 = y+2$, so $y = x^2 - 2$. Thus we have $(f^{-1})'(x) = y' = 2\sqrt{x^2 - 2 + 2} = 2|x| = 2x$, because $x \ge 0$.

3.10.64 For $y > 0$, let $x = y^{2/3}$. Then $1 = \frac{2}{3}y^{-1/3}y'$. So $y' = \frac{3}{2}y^{1/3} = \frac{3}{2}(x^{3/2})^{1/3} = \frac{3}{2}x^{1/2}$ where $x > 0$.

3.10.65 For $y > 0$, let $x = y^{-1/2}$. Then $1 = -\frac{1}{2}y^{-3/2}y'$, so $y' = -2y^{3/2} = -2(x^{-2})^{3/2} = -2x^{-3}$ where $x > 0$.

3.10.66 Let $x = y^3 + 3$. Then $1 = 3y^2 y'$, so $y' = \frac{1}{3y^2} = \frac{1}{3(x-3)^{2/3}}$, where $x \neq 3$.

3.10.67

a. Because $\frac{l}{10} = \csc(\theta)$, $\theta = \csc^{-1}\left(\frac{l}{10}\right)$, and $\frac{d\theta}{dl} = -\frac{1}{(l/10)\sqrt{(l/10)^2 - 1}} \cdot \frac{1}{10} = -\frac{10}{l\sqrt{l^2 - 100}}$.

b. $\frac{d\theta}{dl}\Big|_{l=50} = -\frac{10}{50\sqrt{2500 - 100}} \approx -0.0041$ radians per foot.

   $\frac{d\theta}{dl}\Big|_{l=20} = -\frac{10}{20\sqrt{400 - 100}} \approx -0.029$ radians per foot.

   $\frac{d\theta}{dl}\Big|_{l=11} = -\frac{10}{11\sqrt{121 - 100}} \approx -0.198$ radians per foot.

c. $\lim_{l \to 10^+} -\frac{10}{l\sqrt{l^2 - 100}} = -\infty$. The angle changes very quickly as we approach the dock.

d. $\frac{d\theta}{dl}$ is negative because this measures the change in θ as l increases – but when the boat is approaching the dock, l is decreasing.

3.10.68

a. Because the triangle from the top of the cliff to the falcon is isosceles and has a base of $80 - h$, we get that the falcon is also $80 - h$ feet from the cliff. So $\tan \theta = \frac{h}{80 - h}$, or $\theta = \tan^{-1}\left(\frac{h}{80 - h}\right)$.

b. $\frac{d\theta}{dh} = \frac{d}{dh} \tan^{-1}\left(\frac{h}{80 - h}\right) = \frac{1}{1 + \left(\frac{h}{80-h}\right)^2} \cdot \frac{80 - h + h}{(80 - h)^2} = \frac{80}{(80 - h)^2 + h^2}$.

   $\frac{d\theta}{dh}\Big|_{h=60} = \frac{80}{20^2 + 60^2} = \frac{1}{50}$ radians per foot.

3.10.69

a. $\sin \theta = \frac{c}{D}$, so $\theta = \sin^{-1}\left(\frac{c}{D}\right)$. Thus $\dfrac{d\theta}{dc} = \dfrac{1/D}{\sqrt{1 - \left(\frac{c}{D}\right)^2}} = \dfrac{1}{\sqrt{D^2 - c^2}}$.

b. $\dfrac{d\theta}{dc}\Big|_{c=0} = \dfrac{1}{\sqrt{D^2}} = \dfrac{1}{D}$.

3.10.70

a. $\cos \theta = \frac{c}{D}$, so $\theta = \cos^{-1}\left(\frac{c}{D}\right)$. Thus $\dfrac{d\theta}{dc} = -\dfrac{1/D}{\sqrt{1 - \left(\frac{c}{D}\right)^2}} = -\dfrac{1}{\sqrt{D^2 - c^2}}$.

b. $\dfrac{d\theta}{dc}\Big|_{c=0} = -\frac{1}{D}$. This is the opposite result of number 69, as θ now increases with decreasing c.

3.10.71 $(f^{-1})'(y_0) = \frac{1}{f'(x_0)}$ where $y_0 = f(x_0)$.

$\frac{d}{dx} \sin^{-1} x = \frac{1}{\cos(\sin^{-1} x)} = \frac{1}{\sqrt{1 - \sin^2(\sin^{-1} x)}} = \frac{1}{\sqrt{1 - x^2}}$.

3.10.72

a. $\frac{d}{dx} \cos^{-1} x = \frac{1}{-\sin(\cos^{-1} x)} = -\frac{1}{\sqrt{1 - \cos^2(\cos^{-1} x)}} = -\frac{1}{\sqrt{1 - x^2}}$.

b. $\frac{d}{dx}(\sin^{-1} x + \cos^{-1} x) = \frac{d}{dx}\frac{\pi}{2} = 0$, so $\frac{d}{dx} \sin^{-1} x = -\frac{d}{dx} \cos^{-1} x$. But $\frac{d}{dx} \sin^{-1} x = \frac{1}{\sqrt{1 - x^2}}$, so $\frac{d}{dx} \cos^{-1} x = -\frac{1}{\sqrt{1 - x^2}}$.

3.10.73 Using the identity $\cot^{-1} x + \tan^{-1} x = \frac{\pi}{2}$, we have the $\frac{d}{dx} \cot^{-1} x + \frac{d}{dx} \tan^{-1} x = 0$, so $\frac{d}{dx} \cot^{-1} x = -\frac{d}{dx} \tan^{-1} x$. Likewise, because $\csc^{-1} x + \sec^{-1} x = \frac{\pi}{2}$, we have $\frac{d}{dx} \csc^{-1} x + \frac{d}{dx} \sec^{-1} x = 0$, so $\frac{d}{dx} \csc^{-1} x = -\frac{d}{dx} \sec^{-1} x$.

3.10.74

a. $y_0 = f(x_0)$, so $y_0 = ax_0 + b$ and $b = y_0 - ax_0$.

b. $x_0 = f^{-1}(y_0)$, so $x_0 = cy_0 + d$ and $c = \frac{x_0 - d}{y_0}$. Also, because $(f^{-1})'(y_0) = \frac{1}{f'(x_0)}$ and $f'(x_0) = a$, $(f^{-1})'(y_0) = c$, we have that $c = \frac{1}{a}$.

c. We show that $L(M(x)) = x$.

$L(M(x)) = a(cx+d) + b = acx + ad + b = x + ad + b = x + a(x_0 - cy_0) + (y_0 - ax_0) = x + ax_0 - acy_0 + y_0 - ax_0 = x - y_0 + y_0 = x$.

3.10.75 $\cos(\sin^{-1}(x)) = \sqrt{1 - \sin^2(\sin^{-1}(x))} = \sqrt{1 - x^2}$ for $-1 \le x \le 1$.

3.10.76 $\cos(2\sin^{-1}(x)) = \cos^2(\sin^{-1}(x)) - \sin^2(\sin^{-1}(x)) = 1 - \sin^2(\sin^{-1}(x)) - \sin^2(\sin^{-1}(x)) = 1 - 2x^2$ for $-1 \le x \le 1$.

3.10.77 $\tan(2\tan^{-1}(x)) = \frac{2\tan(\tan^{-1}(x))}{1 - \tan^2(\tan^{-1}(x))} = \frac{2x}{1-x^2}$ for $-1 < x < 1$.

3.10.78 $\sin(2\sin^{-1}(x)) = 2\sin(\sin^{-1}(x))\cos(\sin^{-1}(x)) = 2x\sqrt{1-x^2}$ for $-1 \le x \le 1$.

3.10.79

a.

$$\frac{d}{dx}\tan^{-1}(2/x^2) = \frac{1}{1 + 4/x^4} \cdot -\frac{4}{x^3} = \frac{1}{1+4/x^4} \cdot -\frac{4}{x^3} \cdot \frac{x}{x} = -\frac{4x}{x^4 + 4}.$$

$$\frac{d}{dx}\left(\tan^{-1}(x+1) - \tan^{-1}(x-1)\right) = \frac{1}{1 + (x+1)^2} - \frac{1}{1 + (x-1)^2}$$
$$= \frac{x^2 - 2x + 2 - (x^2 + 2x + 2)}{1 + (x+1)^2 + (x-1)^2 + (x^2-1)^2}$$
$$= -\frac{4x}{1 + x^2 + 2x + 1 + x^2 - 2x + 1 + x^4 - 2x^2 + 1}$$
$$= -\frac{4x}{x^4 + 4}.$$

Because these two functions have the same derivative, they differ by a constant. So for any n, $\tan^{-1}(2/n^2) - \left(\tan^{-1}(n+1) - \tan^{-1}(n-1)\right)$ is a constant.

b. Because the two function in part (a) differ by a constant, we can compute the constant by evaluating for a specific number n. Choosing $n = 1$, we have $\tan^{-1}2 - \left(\tan^{-1}2 - \tan^{-1}0\right) = 0$, so the constant is 0, and we have

$$\tan^{-1}(2/n^2) = \left(\tan^{-1}(n+1) - \tan^{-1}(n-1)\right).$$

3.11 Related Rates

3.11.1 The area of a circle of radius r is $A(r) = \pi r^2$. If the radius $r = r(t)$ changes with time, then the area of the circle is a function of r and r is a function of t, so ultimately A is a function of t. If the radius changes at rate $\frac{dr}{dt}$, then the area changes at rate $2\pi r\frac{dr}{dt}$.

3.11.2 Using implicit differentiation, we can find the rate of change of a function which implicitly depends on a variable without needing the explicit dependence.

3.11.3 Because area is width times height, if one increases, the other must decrease in order for the area to remain constant.

3.11.4 In this section, we typically have related quantities which change with time, and by differentiating, we obtain relationships between the rates of change of these quantities.

3.11.5

$A(x) = x^2$, $\frac{dx}{dt} = 2$ meters per second.

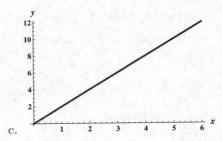

a. $\frac{dA}{dt} = 2x\frac{dx}{dt}$, so at $x = 10$ meters we have $\frac{dA}{dt} = 2 \cdot 10\text{m} \cdot 2\text{m/s} = 40\text{m}^2/\text{s}$.

b. At $x = 20$m we have $\frac{dA}{dt} = 2 \cdot 20\text{m} \cdot 2\text{m/s} = 80\text{m}^2/\text{s}$.

c.

3.11.6

a. Let x be the length of a side of the square. Then $\frac{dx}{dt} = -1$ meters per second. Because $A = x^2$, we have $\frac{dA}{dt} = \frac{dA}{dx}\frac{dx}{dt} = 2x \cdot (-1) = -2x$ square meters per second. Thus $A'(5) = -10$, and so the area of the square is decreasing at 10 square meters per second when $x = 5$.

b. If l is the length of a diagonal of a square with side length x, then $x^2 + x^2 = l^2$ by the Pythagorean Theorem, so $l(x) = \sqrt{2}x$. Thus $\frac{dl}{dt} = \frac{dl}{dx}\frac{dx}{dt} = \sqrt{2} \cdot (-1) = -\sqrt{2}$. The diagonals are decreasing at a rate of $\sqrt{2}$ meters per second.

3.11.7

a. Let x be the length of a leg of an isosceles right triangle. Then $\frac{dx}{dt} = 2$ meters per second. The area is given by $A(x) = \frac{1}{2}x^2$. Thus, $\frac{dA}{dt} = \frac{dA}{dx}\frac{dx}{dt} = x \cdot 2 = 2x$ square meters per second. When $x = 2$, we have $\frac{dA}{dx} = 4$, so the area is increasing at 4 square meters per second.

b. When the hypotenuse is 1 meter long, the legs are $1/\sqrt{2}$ meters long. So $A'(1/\sqrt{2}) = 2 \cdot \frac{1}{\sqrt{2}} = \sqrt{2}$, so the area is increasing at $\sqrt{2}$ square meters per second.

c. If h is the length of the hypotenuse, then $x^2 + x^2 = h^2$, so $h = \sqrt{2}x$. So $\frac{dh}{dt} = \frac{dh}{dx}\frac{dx}{dt} = \sqrt{2}\frac{dx}{dt} = \sqrt{2} \cdot 2 = 2\sqrt{2}$ meters per second.

3.11.8

a. Let x be the length of a leg, and h the length of the hypotenuse. Then $x^2 + x^2 = h^2$, so $h = \sqrt{2}x$. Thus $\frac{dh}{dt} = \sqrt{2}\frac{dx}{dt}$, and because we are given that $\frac{dh}{dt} = -4$, we must have $\frac{dx}{dt} = -\frac{4}{\sqrt{2}} = -2\sqrt{2}$ meters per second.

Therefore, $\frac{dA}{dt} = \frac{dA}{dx}\frac{dx}{dt} = 2x \cdot -2\sqrt{2} = -4\sqrt{2}x$. When $x = 5$, we have $\frac{dA}{dt} = -20\sqrt{2}$ square meters per second. The area is decreasing at a rate of $20\sqrt{2}$ square meters per second.

b. As mentioned above, $\frac{dx}{dt} = -2\sqrt{2}$, so the legs are decreasing at a rate of $2\sqrt{2}$ meters per second.

c. When the triangle has area 4 square meters, the legs have length $x = 2\sqrt{2}$ meters. At that time, $\frac{dA}{dt} = \frac{dA}{dx}\frac{dx}{dt} = 2x(-2\sqrt{2}) = -4\sqrt{2}x = -4\sqrt{2}(2\sqrt{2}) = -16$. The area is decreasing at 16 square meters per second.

3.11.9

a. Let r be the radius of the circle and A the area, and note that we are given $\frac{dA}{dt} = 1$ square cm per second. Because $A = \pi r^2$, we have $\frac{dA}{dt} = \frac{dA}{dr}\frac{dr}{dt}$, so

$$1 = 2\pi r \frac{dr}{dt},$$

and thus

$$\frac{dr}{dt} = \frac{1}{2\pi r}.$$

When $r = 2$, we have $\frac{dr}{dt} = \frac{1}{4\pi}$ cm per second.

b. When $c = 2\pi r = 2$, we have $r = 1/\pi$. At this time, $\frac{dr}{dt} = \frac{1}{2\pi r} = \frac{1}{2\pi(1/\pi)} = \frac{1}{2}$ cm per second.

3.11.10 $V(x) = x^3$, so $\frac{dV}{dt} = 3x^2\frac{dx}{dt}$. At $x = 50$ cm and $\frac{dx}{dt} = 2$ cm/s we have $\frac{dV}{dt} = 3 \cdot (50)^2 \cdot 2 = 15000$ cm^3/s.

3.11.11 $A(x) = \pi x^2$, so $\frac{dA}{dt} = 2\pi x\frac{dx}{dt}$. At $x = 10$ ft and $\frac{dx}{dt} = -2$ ft/min we have $\frac{dA}{dt} = 2\pi \cdot 10 \cdot (-2) = -40\pi$ ft^2/min.

3.11.12 $V(x) = x^3$, so $\frac{dV}{dt} = 3x^2\frac{dx}{dt} = -0.5$ ft^3/min. When $x = 12$ ft we have $3(144)$ft$^2\frac{dx}{dt} = -0.5$ ft^3/min, so $\frac{dx}{dt} = -\frac{1}{864}$ ft/min ≈ -0.0012 ft/min.

3.11.13 $V(r) = \frac{4}{3}\pi r^3$, so $\frac{dV}{dt} = 4\pi r^2\frac{dr}{dt} = 15$ in^3/min. At $r = 10$ inches we have $4\pi(10 \text{ in})^2\frac{dr}{dt} = 15$ in^3/min. Thus, $\frac{dr}{dt} = \frac{3}{80\pi}$ in/min ≈ 0.012 in/min.

3.11.14 Let x be the distance from the bottom of the cylinder to the position of the piston. Let $V(x)$ be the volume of the cylinder when the piston is at position x. $V(x) = 25\pi x$, so $\frac{dV}{dt} = 25\pi\frac{dx}{dt}$. Because $\frac{dx}{dt} = -3$ cm/s we have $\frac{dV}{dt} = 25\pi(-3)$ cm^3/s $= -75\pi$ cm^3/s.

3.11.15 $V(r) = \frac{4}{3}\pi r^3$, and $S(r) = 4\pi r^2$. $\frac{dV}{dt} = 4\pi r^2\frac{dr}{dt} = k \cdot 4\pi r^2$, so $\frac{dr}{dt} = k$, the constant of proportionality.

3.11.16 Let z be the distance from the origin to the bug's position $P(x, x^2)$ on the parabola. Then $z = \sqrt{x^2 + x^4} = x\sqrt{1 + x^2}$. We have

$$1 = \frac{dz}{dt} = \frac{dz}{dx}\frac{dx}{dt} = \left(1 \cdot \sqrt{1 + x^2} + x \cdot \frac{1}{2\sqrt{1 + x^2}} \cdot 2x\right)\frac{dx}{dt} = \left(\frac{1 + 2x^2}{\sqrt{1 + x^2}}\right)\frac{dx}{dt}.$$

Therefore, $\frac{dx}{dt} = \frac{\sqrt{1 + x^2}}{1 + 2x^2}$. When $x = 2$, we have $\frac{dx}{dt} = \frac{\sqrt{5}}{9}$ cm per minute.

Also, $\frac{dy}{dt} = \frac{dy}{dx}\frac{dx}{dt} = 2x\frac{dx}{dt}$. So at the given point, $\frac{dy}{dt} = \frac{4\sqrt{5}}{9}$ cm per minute.

3.11.17 Using the results of the previous exercise, we are seeking the value of x where $\frac{dx}{dt} = \frac{dy}{dt} = 2x\frac{dx}{dt}$. This occurs for $x = 1/2$, so the desired points is $(1/2, 1/4)$.

3.11.18 Let x be the excess of the short side of the rectangle over the original 2 cm, so that the at time t the rectangle has dimensions $2 + x$ by $4 + x$. Then the area $A(x)$ is given by $A(x) = (2 + x)(4 + x) = 8 + 6x + x^2$. So $\frac{dA}{dt} = (6 + 2x)\frac{dx}{dt}$. With $\frac{dx}{dt} = 1$ cm/s, and at $t = 20$ s we have $x = 20$ cm, so $\frac{dA}{dt} = (6 + 2 \cdot 20)$ cm $\cdot 1$ cm/s $= 46$ cm^2/s.

3.11.19

By similar triangles, $\frac{2}{50} = \frac{h}{b}$, so $b = 25h$. Also, $A = \frac{1}{2}bh = 12.5h^2$, so the volume for $0 \le h \le 2$ is $V(h) = 12.5 \cdot h^2 \cdot 20 = 250h^2$. For $2 < h \le 3$, $V(h) = 250 \cdot 2^2 + 50 \cdot 20 \cdot (h - 2) = 1000h - 1000$. When $t = 250$ minutes, then $V = 250$ min $\cdot 1$ m^3/min $= 250$ m^3. So $V(h) = 250h^2 = 250$, so $h = 1$ m. At that time $\frac{dV}{dt} = 500h\frac{dh}{dt} = 500 \cdot 1 \cdot \frac{dh}{dt} = 1$ m^3/min. So $\frac{dh}{dt} = \frac{1}{500}$ m/min $= 0.002$ m/min $= 2$ mm/min.

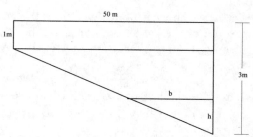

Fill time: The volume of the entire swimming pool is 2000 cubic meters, so at 1 cubic meter per minute, it will take 2000 minutes.

3.11.20

Let x be the distance the shadow has traveled, h the altitude of the jet, and z the line of flight of the jet. We have that $\frac{dz}{dt} = 550\,\text{mi/hr}$ and $h = z \cdot \sin(10°) \approx 0.174z$, so $\frac{dh}{dt} = 0.174\frac{dz}{dt} = 95.51\,\text{mi/hr}$. Also, $x = z \cdot \cos(10°) \approx 0.985z$, so $\frac{dx}{dt} = 0.985\frac{dz}{dt} = 541.64\,\text{mi/hr}$. So the shadow is moving at about 541.64 miles per hour.

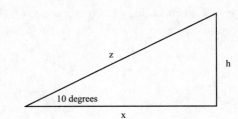

3.11.21

Let x be the distance the surface ship has traveled and D the depth of the submarine. We have $\frac{dx}{dt} = 10\,\text{km/hr}$. Note that $\frac{D}{x} = \tan 20°$, so $D = x \cdot \tan 20° \approx 0.364x$. We have $\frac{dD}{dt} = 0.364\frac{dx}{dt} = 3.64\,\text{km/hr}$. The depth of the submarine is increasing at a rate of 3.64 km/hr.

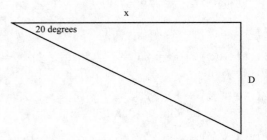

3.11.22 Let $x(t)$ be the distance that the westbound boat has traveled at time t and $y(t)$ the distance the southbound boat has traveled at time t. Note that the distance z between them is given by $z = \sqrt{x^2 + y^2}$. Also note that we are given that $\frac{dx}{dt} = 20$ and $\frac{dy}{dt} = 15$. We have

$$\frac{dz}{dt} = \frac{1}{2\sqrt{x^2 + y^2}} \cdot \left(2x\frac{dx}{dt} + 2y\frac{dy}{dt}\right) = \frac{20x + 15y}{\sqrt{x^2 + y^2}}.$$

After 30 minutes (which is 1/2 hour), we have $x = 10$ and $y = 7.5$, and so $\sqrt{x^2 + y^2} = \sqrt{10^2 + (7.5)^2} = 12.5$. So $\frac{dz}{dt} = \frac{200 + 112.5}{12.5} = 25$ miles per hour.

3.11.23

Let h be the vertical distance from the ground to the top of the ladder, and let x be the horizontal distance from the wall to the bottom of the ladder. By the Pythagorean Theorem, we have that $x^2 + h^2 = 169$. Thus, $2x\frac{dx}{dt} + 2h\frac{dh}{dt} = 0$, so $\frac{dh}{dt} = -\frac{x}{h}\frac{dx}{dt}$, and we are given that $\frac{dx}{dt} = 0.5$ feet per second. At $x = 5$ we have $h = \sqrt{169 - 25} = 12$ feet. Thus, $\frac{dh}{dt} = -\frac{5}{12} \cdot \frac{1}{2} = -\frac{5}{24}$ feet per second. So the top of the ladder slides down the wall at $\frac{5}{24}$ feet per second.

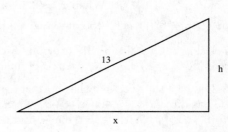

3.11.24

Let h be the vertical distance from the ground to the top of the ladder, and let x be the horizontal distance from the wall to the bottom of the ladder. By the Pythagorean Theorem, we have that $x^2 + h^2 = 144$. Thus, $2x\frac{dx}{dt} + 2h\frac{dh}{dt} = 0$. We are given that $\frac{dx}{dt} = 0.2$ feet per second. We are seeking the configuration when $\frac{dh}{dt} = -0.2$ feet per second. This occurs when $0.2x - 0.2h = 0$, or $x = h$. At this point in time, the triangle is forming a 45-45-90 triangle with $x = h = 6\sqrt{2}$.

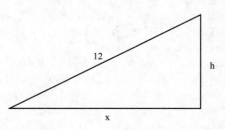

3.11.25

By similar triangles, $\frac{x+y}{20} = \frac{y}{5}$, so $x + y = 4y$, so $x = 3y$, and $\frac{dx}{dt} = 3\frac{dy}{dt}$. Because we are given that $\frac{dx}{dt} = -8$, we have $\frac{dy}{dt} = -\frac{8}{3}$ feet per second. The tip of her shadow is therefore moving at $-8 - \frac{8}{3} = -\frac{32}{3}$ feet per second.

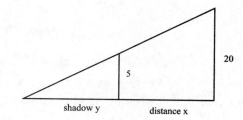

3.11.26

Let D, x and y be as pictured. By the Pythagorean theorem, we know that $D^2 = (90 - x)^2 + y^2$. We are given that $\frac{dx}{dt} = 18$ feet per second, and $\frac{dy}{dt} = 20$ feet per second. Differentiating, we obtain $2D\frac{dD}{dt} = -2(90 - x)\frac{dx}{dt} + 2y\frac{dy}{dt}$. After 1 second, we have that $x = 18$ and $y = 20$, and $D = 4\sqrt{349}$ feet. So $\frac{dD}{dt} = \frac{1}{4\sqrt{349}}(-72 \cdot 18 + 20 \cdot 20) \approx -11.99$ feet per second. So the distance between the runners is decreasing at a rate of about 11.99 feet per second.

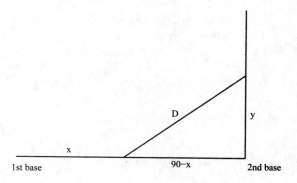

3.11.27 $V = \frac{1}{3}\pi r^2 h$ where $r = 3h$, so $V = 3\pi h^3$. We have that $\frac{dV}{dt} = 9\pi h^2 \frac{dh}{dt}$, and we given that $\frac{dh}{dt} = 2$ at the moment when $h = 12$, so at that time, $\frac{dV}{dt} = 9\pi \cdot 144\,\text{cm}^2 \cdot 2\,\text{cm/sec} = 2592\pi\,\text{cm}^3/\text{s}$. This is the rate at which the volume of the sandpile is increasing, so it must also be the rate at which the sand is leaving the bin, because there is no other sand involved.

3.11.28 Let $h(t)$ be the height of the water in the tank at time t. Then the volume of the water in the tank at time t is given by $V = \pi r^2 h = \pi h$. We are seeking $\frac{dV}{dt}$ when $\frac{dh}{dt} = -1/2$ foot per minute. Because $\frac{dV}{dt} = \frac{dV}{dh}\frac{dh}{dt} = -\frac{1}{2}\pi$, the volume of the water in the tank is decreasing at $\pi/2$ cubic feet per minute, so the water is draining out at $\pi/2$ cubic feet per minute.

3.11.29 Let h be the depth of the water in the tank at time t, and let r be the radius of the cone-shaped water at time t. By similar triangles, we have that $\frac{h}{r} = \frac{12}{6}$, so $h = 2r$. The volume of the water in the tank is given by $V = \frac{1}{3}\pi r^2 h = \frac{1}{3}\pi \frac{h^2}{4} \cdot h = \frac{\pi h^3}{12}$. Thus, $\frac{dV}{dt} = \frac{\pi h^2}{4}\frac{dh}{dt}$, and so when $h = 3$ we have $-2\,\text{ft}^3/\text{s} = \frac{9\pi\,\text{ft}^2}{4}\frac{dh}{dt}$, so $\frac{dh}{dt} = -\frac{8}{9\pi}\,\text{ft/s}$. So the depth of the water is decreasing at a rate of $8/(9\pi)$ feet per second.

3.11.30 We have that $V = \pi r^2 h$, and r is a constant 2 inches, so $V = 4\pi h$, and $\frac{dV}{dt} = 4\pi\frac{dh}{dt}$. Because we are given that $\frac{dh}{dt} = -0.25$ inches per second, we have that $\frac{dV}{dt} = 4\pi(-0.25) = -\pi\,\text{in}^3/\text{s}$. Thus, the soda is being sucked out at a rate of π cubic inches per second.

3.11.31 Let h be the depth of the water in the tank at time t, and let r be the radius of the cone-shaped water at time t. By similar triangles, we have that $\frac{h}{r} = \frac{12}{6}$, so $h = 2r$. The volume of the water in the tank is given by $V = \frac{1}{3}\pi r^2 h = \frac{1}{3}\pi \frac{h^2}{4} \cdot h = \frac{\pi h^3}{12}$. Thus, $\frac{dV}{dt} = \frac{\pi h^2}{4}\frac{dh}{dt}$. When $\frac{dh}{dt} = -1$, we have $\frac{dV}{dt} = -\frac{\pi h^2}{4}$. when $h = 6$, we have $\frac{dV}{dt} = -9\pi$, so the water is draining from the tank at 9π cubic feet per minute.

3.11.32 The volume of a segment of water of height h within a hemisphere of radius 10 is given by $V = \frac{1}{3}\pi h^2(30 - h) = 10\pi h^2 - \frac{1}{3}\pi h^3$. We have that $\frac{dV}{dt} = 20\pi h\frac{dh}{dt} - \pi h^2\frac{dh}{dt}$. We are given that $\frac{dV}{dt} = 3\,\text{m}^3/\text{min}$, so when $h = 5$ we have $3 = (100\pi - 25\pi)\frac{dh}{dt}$, so $\frac{dh}{dt} = \frac{3}{75\pi} = \frac{1}{25\pi}$ meters per minute.

3.11.33 Let r be the radius of the exposed surface of the water of height h at time t. Consider the right triangle with legs of length r and $10 - h$ (from the center of the sphere measured down to where the water level is). The hypotenuse is given by the radius of the sphere, which is 10. By the Pythagorean theorem, we have

$$r^2 + (10 - h)^2 = 10^2,$$

which can be written as $r^2 + 100 - 20h + h^2 = 100$, so $r^2 + h^2 = 20h$. So $20\frac{dh}{dt} = 2h\frac{dh}{dt} + 2r\frac{dr}{dt}$. When $h = 5$, we have $10 \cdot \frac{1}{25\pi} = 5 \cdot \frac{1}{25\pi} + 5\sqrt{3}\frac{dr}{dt}$, so $\frac{dr}{dt} = \frac{\sqrt{3}}{75\pi}$. The surface area is given by $S = \pi r^2$, so $\frac{dS}{dt} = 2\pi r\frac{dr}{dt}$, so at this moment it is given by $\frac{dS}{dt} = 2\pi \cdot 5\sqrt{3} \cdot \frac{\sqrt{3}}{75\pi} = \frac{2}{5}$ square meters per minute.

3.11.34

Let h be the height of the balloon at time t. We have $\tan\theta = \frac{h}{300}$, so $\theta = \tan^{-1}\left(\frac{h}{300}\right)$. Thus, $\frac{d\theta}{dt} = \frac{1}{300\left(1+\left(\frac{h}{300}\right)^2\right)}\frac{dh}{dt}$. At the moment when $h = 400$, we have $\frac{d\theta}{dt} = \frac{1}{300+\frac{160000}{300}} \cdot 20 = .024$ radians per second.

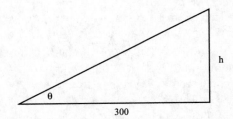

3.11.35 Let x be the distance the motorcycle has traveled since the instant it went under the balloon, and let y be the height of the balloon above the ground t seconds after the motorcycle went under it. We have $x^2 + y^2 = D^2$ where D is the distance between the motorcycle and the balloon. Thus, $2x\frac{dx}{dt} + 2y\frac{dy}{dt} = 2D\frac{dD}{dt}$, and we are given that $\frac{dy}{dt} = 10$ feet per second, and $\frac{dx}{dt} = 40\,\text{mph} = \frac{176}{3}\,\text{ft/s}$. After 10 seconds have passed, we have that $y = 150 + 100 = 250\,\text{ft}$, $x = \frac{1760}{3}\,\text{ft}$ and $D = \sqrt{250^2 + \left(\frac{1760}{3}\right)^2} \approx 638\,\text{ft}$. Thus, $\frac{dD}{dt} \approx \frac{1}{638}\left(\frac{1760}{3} \cdot \frac{176}{3} + 2500\right) \approx 57.86$ feet per second.

3.11.36 We have that the radius of the reel is 2 inches, so if L is the length and R is the number of revolutions, that $L = 4\pi R$. So $\frac{dL}{dt} = 4\pi\frac{dR}{dt}$, so $\frac{dL}{dt} = 4\pi \cdot 1.5 = 6\pi$ inches per second.

3.11.37

Let x be the distance between the fish and the fisherman's feet, and let D be the distance between the fish and the tip of the pole. Then $D^2 = x^2 + 144$, so $2D(dD/dt) = 2x(dx/dt)$. Note that $dD/dt = -1/3\,\text{ft/sec}$, so when $x = 20\,\text{ft}$, we have $dx/dt = \sqrt{400 + 144}/20 \cdot (-1/3) \approx -0.3887\,\text{ft/sec} \approx -4.66\,\text{in/sec}$. The fish is moving toward the fisherman at about 4.66 in/sec.

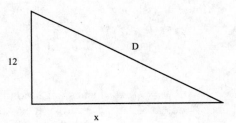

3.11.38

Let x be the horizontal distance of the kite, and let D be the length of the string. Then $D^2 = x^2 + 2500$, so $2D\frac{dD}{dt} = 2x\frac{dx}{dt}$, so $\frac{dD}{dt} = \frac{x}{D}\frac{dx}{dt}$. When $D = 120$ feet, then $x = \sqrt{11900} \approx 109$ feet. Therefore, $\frac{dD}{dt} \approx \frac{109}{120} \cdot 5 \approx 4.55$ feet per second.

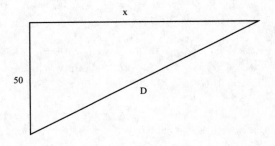

3.11.39

Let D be the length of the rope from the boat to the capstan, and let x be the horizontal distance from the boat to the dock. By the Pythagorean Theorem, $x^2 + 25 = D^2$, so $2x\frac{dx}{dt} = 2D\frac{dD}{dt}$, so $\frac{dx}{dt} = \frac{D}{x}\frac{dD}{dt}$. We are given that $\frac{dD}{dt} = -3$ feet per second, so when $x = 10$, we have $\frac{dx}{dt} = \frac{\sqrt{125}}{10} \cdot (-3) = -\frac{3\sqrt{5}}{2}$ feet per second. The boat is approaching the dock at $\frac{3\sqrt{5}}{2}$ feet per second.

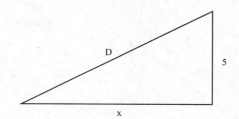

3.11.40 $y = 50x - x^2$, so $\frac{dy}{dt} = 50\frac{dx}{dt} - 2x\frac{dx}{dt}$. We are given that $\frac{dx}{dt} = 30$ feet per second. For $x = 10$, we have $\frac{dy}{dt} = 1500 - 600 = 900$ feet per second. For $x = 40$, $\frac{dy}{dt} = 1500 - 2400 = -900$ feet per second.

3.11.41 Let x be the distance the westbound airliner has traveled between noon and t hours after 1:00, and let y be the distance the northbound airliner has traveled t hours after 1:00, and let D be the distance between the planes. We have $D^2 = x^2 + y^2$, so $2D\frac{dD}{dt} = 2x\frac{dx}{dt} + 2y\frac{dy}{dt}$. We are given that $\frac{dx}{dt} = 500$ mph and $\frac{dy}{dt} = 550$ mph. At 2:30, we have that $x = 500 + 500 \cdot 1.5 = 1250$, and $y = 550 \cdot 1.5 = 825$ miles. $D = \sqrt{2243125} \approx 1497.7$ miles. Thus $\frac{dD}{dt} \approx \frac{1250 \cdot 500 + 825 \cdot 550}{1497.7} \approx 720.27$ miles per hour.

3.11.42 Let l be the length of a side of triangle, and let x be the line segment from a vertex to the midpoint of the opposite side. Then $\sin(\pi/3) = \frac{x}{l}$, so $l = \frac{2}{\sqrt{3}}x$. Now $A = \frac{xl}{2} = \frac{x^2}{\sqrt{3}}$. Thus $\frac{dA}{dt} = \frac{2x}{\sqrt{3}}\frac{dx}{dt}$, and when $x = 0$, this quantity is zero.

3.11.43 Let θ be the angle between the hands of the clock, and D the distance between the tips of the hands. By the law of cosines, $D^2 = 2.5^2 + 3^2 - 15\cos\theta$. So $2D\frac{dD}{dt} = 15\sin\theta\frac{d\theta}{dt}$. At 9:00 AM, we have $D^2 = 6.25 + 9$, so $D = \sqrt{15.25}$. Also, $\theta = \pi/2$ so $\sin\theta = 1$. Thus, $\frac{dD}{dt} = \frac{15}{2\sqrt{15.25}}\frac{d\theta}{dt}$. Now $\frac{d\theta}{dt} = \frac{d\theta_1}{dt} - \frac{d\theta_2}{dt}$ where $\frac{d\theta_1}{dt}$ is the angular change of the minute hand and $\frac{d\theta_2}{dt}$ is the angular change of the hour hand. We have $\frac{d\theta_1}{dt} = \frac{\pi}{30}$ radians per minute and $\frac{d\theta_2}{dt} = \frac{\pi}{360}$ radians per minute, so $\frac{d\theta}{dt} = \frac{11\pi}{360}$ radians per minute. Thus $\frac{dD}{dt} = \frac{15}{2\sqrt{15.25}} \cdot \frac{11\pi}{360} \approx .18436$ meters per minute, or about 11.06 meters per hour.

3.11.44 For the small pool, $V_s = 25\pi h_s$, so $\frac{dV_s}{dt} = 25\pi\frac{dh_s}{dt}$, and we are given that $\frac{dh_s}{dt} = .5$ meters per minutes, so $\frac{dV_s}{dt} = 12.5\pi$ m^3/min. Because the pools are being filled at the same rate, this number is also $\frac{dV_L}{dt}$ for the large pool. We have $V_L = 64\pi h_L$, so $\frac{dV_L}{dt} = 12.5\pi = 64\pi\frac{dh_L}{dt}$, so $\frac{dh_L}{dt} = \frac{25}{128}$ meters per minute.

3.11.45

a. Let A be the point where the dragster started, let B be the point where camera 1 is located and let $C = y(t)$ be the position of the car at time t. Let θ be angle ABC. Note that $\tan\theta = \frac{y}{50}$, so $\sec^2\theta \cdot \frac{d\theta}{dt} = \frac{1}{50}\frac{dy}{dt}$. At time $t = 2$, we have that $\tan^2\theta = 4$, so $\sec^2\theta = \tan^2\theta + 1 = 5$. So $\frac{dy}{dt} = 5 \cdot 50 \cdot .75 = 187.5$ feet per second.

b. Let D be the point where camera 2 is located, and let ϕ be angle ADC. The $\phi = \tan^{-1}\left(\frac{y}{100}\right)$, so $\frac{d\phi}{dt} = \frac{1}{100\left(1 + \left(\frac{y}{100}\right)^2\right)} \cdot \frac{dy}{dt}$. After 2 seconds, we know that $y = 100$ and $\frac{dy}{dt} = 187.5$. Thus $\frac{d\phi}{dt} = \frac{100}{20,000} \cdot 187.5 = .9375$ radians per second.

3.11.46 The volume of the upper tank is $V_u = \frac{1}{3}\pi r^2 h$ with $\frac{h}{r} = \frac{5}{4}$, so $V_u = \frac{\pi}{3}\frac{16}{25}h^3$. We have $\frac{dV_u}{dt} = \frac{16\pi}{25}h^2\frac{dh}{dt}$, and we are given that $\frac{dh}{dt} = -0.5$ meters per minute. If $h = 3$, we have $\frac{dV_u}{dt} = -\frac{144\pi}{50}$ meters per minute.

The volume of the lower tank is given by $V_l = 16\pi h_l$, so $\frac{dV_l}{dt} = 16\pi\frac{dh_l}{dt} = \frac{144\pi}{50}$, so $\frac{dh_l}{dt} = \frac{9}{50}$ meters per minute.

Now suppose that $h = 1$. Then $\frac{dV_u}{dt} = \frac{16\pi}{50}$ meters per minute. Then $\frac{dV_l}{dt} = 16\pi\frac{dh_l}{dt} = \frac{16\pi}{50}$, so $\frac{dh_l}{dt} = \frac{1}{50}$ meters per minute.

3.11.47 By the Law of Sines, $\frac{\sin\theta}{s} = \frac{\sin\left(\frac{3\pi}{4}-\theta\right)}{2}$, so $2\sin\theta = s\sin\left(\frac{3\pi}{4}-\theta\right) = s\left(\sin\left(\frac{3\pi}{4}\right)\cos\theta - \cos\left(\frac{3\pi}{4}\right)\sin\theta\right)$.
We have

$$2\sin\theta = \frac{\sqrt{2}}{2}s(\sin\theta + \cos\theta)$$

$$2\tan\theta = \frac{\sqrt{2}}{2}s(\tan\theta + 1)$$

$$\tan\theta = \frac{(\sqrt{2}/2)\cdot s}{2-(\sqrt{2}/2)s} = \frac{\sqrt{2}s}{4-\sqrt{2}s}$$

$$\theta = \tan^{-1}\left(\frac{\sqrt{2}s}{4-\sqrt{2}s}\right).$$

Thus, $\frac{d\theta}{dt} = \frac{\sqrt{2}\cdot\frac{ds}{dt}}{4-2\sqrt{2}s+s^2}$. When $\frac{ds}{dt} = 15$ and $s = 7.5$ we arrive at $\frac{d\theta}{dt} = 0.54$ radians per hour.

3.11.48 Let s be the distance the ship has traveled. By the Law of Sines, $\frac{\sin\theta}{s} = \frac{\sin\left(\frac{3\pi}{4}-\theta\right)}{1.5}$, so $1.5\sin\theta = s\cdot\left(\sin\left(\frac{3\pi}{4}\right)\cos\theta - \cos\left(\frac{3\pi}{4}\right)\sin\theta\right)$. We have

$$\sin\theta = \frac{\sqrt{2}}{3}s(\sin\theta + \cos\theta)$$

$$\tan\theta = \frac{\sqrt{2}}{3}s(\tan\theta + 1)$$

$$\tan\theta = \frac{(\sqrt{2}/3)\cdot s}{1-(\sqrt{2}/3)s} = \frac{\sqrt{2}s}{3-\sqrt{2}s}$$

$$\theta = \tan^{-1}\left(\frac{\sqrt{2}s}{3-\sqrt{2}s}\right).$$

Thus, $\frac{d\theta}{dt} = \frac{3\sqrt{2}\cdot\frac{ds}{dt}}{9-6\sqrt{2}s+4s^2}$. At noon, $2s^2 = 1.5^2$, so $s = \frac{3}{\sqrt{8}}$. At 1:30 pm $s = 18 + \frac{3}{\sqrt{8}} \approx 19.06$ mi, and $\frac{ds}{dt} = 12$ mi/hr, so $\frac{d\theta}{dt} \approx 0.04$ radians per hour.

3.11.49

Let h be the vertical distance between the point on the elevator shaft positioned directly opposite the observer and the point on the elevator shaft that the observer is observing. So $h > 0$ corresponds to $\theta > 0$ and $h < 0$ corresponds to $\theta < 0$. We have $\frac{h}{20} = \tan\theta$, so $\frac{1}{20}\frac{dh}{dt} = \sec^2\theta\frac{d\theta}{dt}$. We are given that $\frac{dh}{dt} = 5$ m/s. At $h = -10$, we have $\tan\theta = -.5$, so $\sec^2\theta = 1 + \tan^2\theta = 1 + (.5)^2 = 1.25$. So $\frac{d\theta}{dt} = \frac{1}{20\cdot1.25}\cdot 5 = \frac{1}{5}$ radian per second.
When $h = 20$, we have that $\tan\theta = 1$, so $\sec^2\theta = 1 + 1^2 = 2$, and thus $\frac{d\theta}{dt} = \frac{1}{20\cdot2}\cdot 5 = \frac{1}{8}$ radian per second.

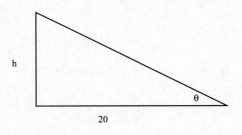

3.11.50 Let θ be the angle RLP where L represents the lighthouse and R represents the point on the land where the light is currently hitting. Let s be the distance from the point P to the point R. We are given that $\frac{d\theta}{dt} = \frac{2\pi}{15}$ radians per second. Note that $\tan\theta = \frac{s}{500}$, so $\sec^2\theta \cdot \frac{d\theta}{dt} = \frac{1}{500}\frac{ds}{dt}$. When the light is at point Q, $\tan\theta = \frac{2}{5}$, so $\sec^2\theta = 1 + \frac{4}{25} = \frac{29}{25}$. Then

$$\frac{ds}{dt} = 500 \cdot \frac{2\pi}{15} \cdot \frac{29}{25} = \frac{232\pi}{3}\text{ m/s}.$$

The beam moves more slowly when R is near P, and more quickly when it is further away from P.

3.11.51 Let x be the distance the eastbound boat has traveled at time t and let s be the distance the northeastbound boat has traveled. Note the diagram shown. By the Law of Sines, $\frac{\sin\left(\frac{\pi}{2}-\theta\right)}{s} = \frac{\sin\left(\frac{\pi}{4}+\theta\right)}{x}$. Thus,

$$x\left(\sin\left(\frac{\pi}{2}\right)\cos\theta - \cos\left(\frac{\pi}{2}\right)\sin\theta\right) =$$
$$s\left(\sin\left(\frac{\pi}{4}\right)\cos\theta + \cos\left(\frac{\pi}{4}\right)\sin\theta\right)$$

So

$$x\cos\theta = \frac{\sqrt{2}}{2}\cdot s\cdot\cos\theta + \frac{\sqrt{2}}{2}\cdot s\cdot\sin\theta,$$

$$x = \frac{\sqrt{2}}{2}\cdot s + \frac{\sqrt{2}}{2}\cdot s\cdot\tan\theta,$$

and thus $\tan\theta = \frac{x - \frac{\sqrt{2}}{2}s}{\frac{\sqrt{2}}{2}s} = \frac{\sqrt{2}x - s}{s}$, and therefore $\theta = \tan^{-1}\left(\frac{\sqrt{2}x - s}{s}\right)$.

We have

$$\frac{d\theta}{dt} = \frac{1}{1 + \left(\frac{\sqrt{2}x-s}{s}\right)^2}\cdot\frac{\left(\sqrt{2}\left(\frac{dx}{dt}\right) - \left(\frac{ds}{dt}\right)\right)\cdot s - \left(\sqrt{2}x - s\right)\cdot\frac{ds}{dt}}{s^2} = \frac{\sqrt{2}\left(s\frac{dx}{dt} - x\frac{ds}{dt}\right)}{s^2 + (\sqrt{2}x - s)^2}.$$

At time t, we have $s(t) = 15t$ and $x(t) = 12t$. Note that

$$s\frac{dx}{dt} - x\frac{ds}{dt} = 15t\cdot 12 - 12t\cdot 15 = 0.$$

Thus $\theta' = 0$ for every value of t, so that the angle is constant.

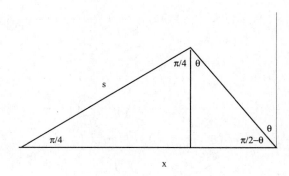

3.11.52

Let D be the distance from the bottom center of the Ferris wheel to the cart. Note that $\tan\theta = \frac{D}{20}$, so $\theta = \tan^{-1}\left(\frac{D}{20}\right)$, and

$$\frac{d\theta}{dt} = \frac{20\cdot\frac{dD}{dt}}{400 + D^2} = \frac{20}{400 + D^2}\cdot\frac{dD}{dt}.$$

Let α be the angle pictured. By the Law of Cosines,

$$D^2 = 5^2 + 5^2 - 2 \cdot 5 \cdot 5 \cdot \cos\alpha = 50 - 50\cos\alpha.$$

So $2D\frac{dD}{dt} = 50\frac{d\alpha}{dt} \cdot \sin\alpha$, and solving for $\frac{dD}{dt}$ gives

$$\frac{dD}{dt} = \frac{25\sin\alpha}{D} \cdot \frac{d\alpha}{dt}.$$

At $t = 40$ seconds (which is $\frac{2}{3}$ minutes), we have $\alpha = \frac{2\pi}{3}$, so that $D^2 = 50 - 50\cos(2\pi/3) = 75$, and thus $D = 5\sqrt{3}$. Also $\sin\alpha = \frac{\sqrt{3}}{2}$. Finally, we are given that $\frac{d\alpha}{dt} = \pi$ radians per minute. Then we have

$$\frac{dD}{dt} = \frac{25 \cdot \frac{\sqrt{3}}{2}}{5\sqrt{3}} \cdot \pi = \frac{5}{2}\pi.$$

Finally, we have

$$\frac{d\theta}{dt} = \frac{20}{400 + 75} \cdot \frac{5}{2}\pi = \frac{2\pi}{19} \approx 0.331 \text{ radians per second.}$$

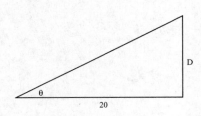
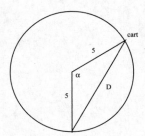

3.11.53 Let α be the angle between the line of sight to the bottom of the screen and the line of sight to the point 3 feet below where the floor and the wall meet. Note that $\cot\alpha = \frac{x}{3}$ and $\cot(\alpha + \theta) = \frac{x}{10}$, so $\alpha = \cot^{-1}(\frac{x}{3})$ and $\alpha + \theta = \cot^{-1}(\frac{x}{10})$. Thus, $\theta = \cot^{-1}(\frac{x}{10}) - \cot^{-1}(\frac{x}{3})$. So

$$\frac{d\theta}{dt} = -\frac{10x'}{100 + x^2} + \frac{3x'}{9 + x^2},$$

and at $x = 30$ feet, and with $\frac{dx}{dt} = 3$ feet per second, we have $\frac{d\theta}{dt} = -\frac{30}{1000} + \frac{9}{909} \approx -0.0201$ radians per second.

3.11.54 Let r be the distance from the point on the highway perpendicular to the searchlight to the right-hand edge of the beam, and let l be the distance from that point to the left-hand edge of the beam. Then $w = l - r$. We have that

$$r = 100\tan\left(\theta - \frac{\pi}{32}\right) \quad \text{and} \quad l = 100\tan\left(\theta + \frac{\pi}{32}\right).$$

Thus

$$\frac{dw}{dt} = \frac{dl}{dt} - \frac{dr}{dt}$$

$$= 100\left(\sec^2\left(\theta + \frac{\pi}{32}\right) - \sec^2\left(\theta - \frac{\pi}{32}\right)\right) \cdot \frac{d\theta}{dt}$$

$$= 100\left(\tan^2\left(\theta + \frac{\pi}{32}\right) - 1 - \left(\tan^2\left(\theta - \frac{\pi}{32}\right) - 1\right)\right) \cdot \frac{d\theta}{dt}$$

$$= 100\left(\tan^2\left(\theta + \frac{\pi}{32}\right) - \tan^2\left(\theta - \frac{\pi}{32}\right)\right) \cdot \frac{d\theta}{dt}.$$

With $\theta' = \frac{\pi}{6}$ radians per second and $\theta = \frac{\pi}{3}$, we have

$$\frac{dw}{dt} = 100\left(\tan^2\left(\frac{35\pi}{96}\right) - \tan^2\left(\frac{29\pi}{96}\right)\right) \cdot \frac{\pi}{6} \approx 153.081 \text{ meters per second.}$$

3.11.55

a. The volume of the water in the tank (as a function of h – the depth of the water in the tank) is given by 5 times the area of the segment of water in a cross-sectional circle. For a tank of radius 1, the formula for such a segment is $\cos^{-1}(1-h) - (1-h)\sqrt{2h-h^2}$. Thus the volume of the water in the tank is given by $V = 5(\cos^{-1}(1-h) - (1-h)\sqrt{2h-h^2})$. We have

$$\frac{dV}{dt} = 5 \cdot \left(-\frac{1}{\sqrt{1-(1-h)^2}} \cdot \left(-\frac{dh}{dt} \right) + \frac{dh}{dt}\sqrt{2h-h^2} - \frac{(1-h)^2}{\sqrt{2h-h^2}}\frac{dh}{dt} \right)$$

$$= 5\left(\sqrt{2h-h^2} + \frac{1-(1-h)^2}{\sqrt{2h-h^2}} \right)\frac{dh}{dt}$$

$$= 5\left(\frac{2h-h^2+1-1+2h-h^2}{\sqrt{2h-h^2}} \right)\frac{dh}{dt}$$

$$= 5\left(\frac{2(2h-h^2)}{\sqrt{2h-h^2}} \right)\frac{dh}{dt}$$

$$= 10\sqrt{2h-h^2} \cdot \frac{dh}{dt}$$

When $h = .5$, we have $-\frac{3}{2} = \frac{dV}{dt} = 5\sqrt{3}\frac{dh}{dt}$, so $\frac{dh}{dt} = -\frac{\sqrt{3}}{10}$ meters per hr.

b. The surface area of the water is given by $S = 5 \cdot 2\sqrt{2h-h^2}$. So $\frac{dS}{dt} = 10 \cdot \frac{2-2h}{2\sqrt{2h-h^2}} \cdot \frac{dh}{dt}$, so at $h = .5$, we have $\frac{5}{\sqrt{3/4}} \cdot -\frac{\sqrt{3}}{10} = -1$ square meter per hr.

3.11.56 At time t, the boat traveling west has gone $20t$ miles while the boat traveling southwest has gone $15t$ miles. Let D be the distance between the boats; the line between the boats forms the third side of a triangle. Then by the law of cosines,

$$D^2 = (20t)^2 + (15t)^2 - 2 \cdot 20t \cdot 15t\cos(\pi/4) = 625t^2 - 600t^2 \cdot \frac{\sqrt{2}}{2} = (625 - 300\sqrt{2})t^2.$$

Thus,

$$D = \left(625 - 30\sqrt{2} \right)^{1/2}t,$$

so that

$$\frac{dD}{dt} = \left(625 - 30\sqrt{2} \right)^{1/2} \approx 14.168\,\text{mph}.$$

Chapter Three Review

1

a. False. This function is not differentiable at $x = -\frac{1}{2}$. It is possible for a function to be continuous at a point and not differentiable at that point.

b. False. For example, $f(x) = x^2 + 3$ and $g(x) = x^2 + 100$ have the same derivative, but aren't the same function.

c. False. For example, $\frac{d}{dx}|e^{-x}| = \frac{d}{dx}e^{-x} = -e^{-x} \neq |-e^{-x}|$.

d. False. For example, the function $f(x) = |x|$ has no derivative at 0, but there is no vertical tangent there.

e. True. For example, a ball dropping from a high tower has acceleration due to gravity which is negative, but it is speeding up as it falls because the velocity (which is negative also) is in the same direction as the acceleration.

2

a. $f'(2) = \lim\limits_{h \to 0} \dfrac{4(2+h)^2 - 7(2+h) + 5 - 7}{h}$

$= \lim\limits_{h \to 0} \dfrac{16 + 16h + 4h^2 - 14 - 7h - 16 + 14}{h}$

$= \lim\limits_{h \to 0} \dfrac{4h^2 + 9h}{h} = \lim\limits_{h \to 0}(4h + 9) = 9.$

b. The tangent line at $(2, 7)$ is given by $y - 7 = 9(x - 2)$, or $y = 9x - 11$.

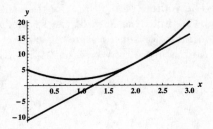

3

a. $f'(1) = \lim\limits_{h \to 0} \dfrac{5(1+h)^3 + (1+h) - 6}{h}$. Expanding

yields $\lim\limits_{h \to 0} \dfrac{5(1 + 3h^2 + 3h + h^3) + 1 + h - 6}{h} =$

$\lim\limits_{h \to 0} \dfrac{5 - 15h^2 + 15h + 5h^3 + h - 5}{h}$. This can be

written as $\lim\limits_{h \to 0} \dfrac{5h^3 - 15h^2 + 16h}{h} = \lim\limits_{h \to 0}(5h^2 - 15h + 16) = 16.$

b. The tangent line at $(1, 6)$ is given by $y - 6 = 16(x - 1)$, or $y = 16x - 10$.

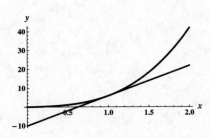

4

a. $y'(0) = \lim\limits_{h \to 0} \dfrac{\frac{h+3}{2h+1} - 3}{h} = \lim\limits_{h \to 0} \dfrac{h + 3 - 6h - 3}{(2h+1)h}$

$= \lim\limits_{h \to 0} -\dfrac{5h}{(2h+1)h} = \lim\limits_{h \to 0} -\dfrac{5}{2h+1} = -5.$

b. The tangent line at $(0, 3)$ is given by $y - 3 = -5x$, or $y = -5x + 3$.

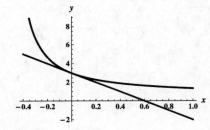

5

a. $f'(0) = \lim\limits_{h \to 0} \dfrac{\frac{1}{2\sqrt{3h+1}} - \frac{1}{2}}{h}$

$= \lim\limits_{h \to 0} \dfrac{1 - \sqrt{3h+1}}{2\sqrt{3h+1} \cdot h} =$

$\lim\limits_{h \to 0} \dfrac{(1 - \sqrt{3h+1})(1 + \sqrt{3h+1})}{2\sqrt{3h+1} \cdot h(1 + \sqrt{3h+1})} =$

$\lim\limits_{h \to 0} \dfrac{1 - (3h+1)}{2\sqrt{3h+1} \cdot h(1 + \sqrt{3h+1})}$. Simplifying

yields $\lim\limits_{h \to 0} -\dfrac{3}{2\sqrt{3h+1}(1 + \sqrt{3h+1})}$, and this

last limit can be seen to be $-\frac{3}{4}$.

b. The tangent line at $\left(0, \frac{1}{2}\right)$ is given by $y - \frac{1}{2} = -\frac{3}{4}x$, or $y = -\frac{3}{4}x + \frac{1}{2}$.

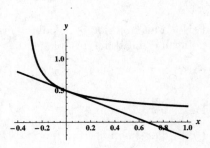

6

h	$\frac{f(1+h)-f(1)}{h}$
0.01	15.151
0.001	15.1951
0.0001	15.1995
0.00001	15.2
0.000001	15.2

a.   Let $f(t) = -4.9t^2 + 25t + 1$.

b. $f'(1) = \lim_{h \to 0} \dfrac{f(1+h) - f(1)}{h} \approx 15.2$ meters per second.

c. $f'(1) = \lim_{h \to 0} \dfrac{-4.9(1+h)^2 + 25(1+h) + 1 + 4.9 - 25 - 1}{h} = \lim_{h \to 0} \dfrac{-4.9 - 9.8h - 4.9h^2 + 25h + 4.9}{h}$
$= \lim_{h \to 0} (-4.9h + 15.2) = 15.2.$

7

a. Average growth is $\frac{p(60)-p(50)}{10} = 2.7$ million people per year.

b. The curve is pretty straight between $t = 50$ and $t = 60$, so the secant line between these two points is approximately as steep as the tangent line at a point in between.

c. A reasonable estimate to the instantaneous grow rate at 1985 would be the slope of the secant line between $t = 80$ and $t = 90$. This is $\frac{p(90)-p(80)}{10} = 2.217$ million people per year.

8

a. The graph has the steepest slope at about $t = 18$. At this point the rate is about $\frac{N(20)-N(16)}{4} = \frac{3500-1900}{4} = 400$ bacteria per hour.

b. It is smallest at $t = 0$ or $t = 36$, where it is about $\frac{N(36)-N(32)}{4} \approx \frac{4900-4800}{4} = 25$ bacteria per hour.

c. The average growth rate over $[0, 36]$ is $\frac{N(36)-N(0)}{36} \approx \frac{4900-400}{36} = \frac{4500}{36} = 125$ bacteria per hour.

9

a. $v(15) \approx \frac{400-200}{5} = 40$ meters per second.

b. Because the graph is a straight line for $t \geq 30$, $v(70) = \frac{D(90)-D(60)}{30} = \frac{1600-1400}{30} = \frac{20}{3}$ meters per second. The points at 60 and 90 were chosen because it is easier to detect the function values at those points using the given grid.

c. The average velocity is $\frac{D(90)-D(20)}{70} \approx \frac{1600-550}{70} = 15$ meters per second.

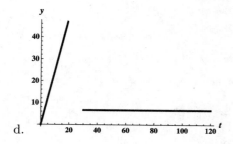

d.

e. The parachute was deployed.

10

$$f'(x) = \lim_{h \to 0} \frac{2(x+h)^2 - 3(x+h) + 1 - (2x^2 - 3x + 1)}{h}$$

$$= \lim_{h \to 0} \frac{2x^2 + 4xh + 2h^2 - 3x - 3h + 1 - 2x^2 + 3x - 1}{h}$$

$$= \lim_{h \to 0} \frac{(4x - 3)h + 2h^2}{h} = \lim_{h \to 0}(4x - 3 + 2h) = 4x - 3.$$

11

$$g'(x) = \lim_{h \to 0} \frac{\sqrt{2(x+h) - 3} - \sqrt{2x - 3}}{h} = \lim_{h \to 0} \frac{\sqrt{2(x+h) - 3} - \sqrt{2x - 3}}{h} \cdot \frac{\sqrt{2(x+h) - 3} + \sqrt{2x - 3}}{\sqrt{2(x+h) - 3} + \sqrt{2x - 3}}$$

$$= \lim_{h \to 0} \frac{2(x+h) - 3 - (2x - 3)}{h(\sqrt{2(x+h) - 3} + \sqrt{2x - 3})} = \lim_{h \to 0} \frac{2}{\sqrt{2(x+h) - 3} + \sqrt{2x - 3}} = \frac{2}{2\sqrt{2x - 3}} = \frac{1}{\sqrt{2x - 3}}.$$

12   **13**

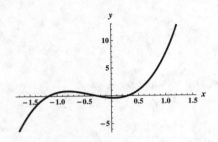   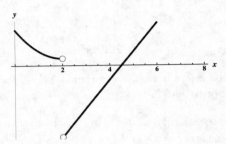

14

a. This has (D) as its derivative. Note that it consists of two pieces each of which are linear with the same slope. So its derivative is constant – but at $x = 2$ the derivative doesn't exist. We can easily know that this is true because the function isn't continuous at $x = 2$, so it can't be differentiable there.

b. This has (C) as its derivative. The slope of the tangent line is positive for $x < 2$ and negative for $x > 2$ and doesn't exist at $x = 2$. Also, near $x = 2$ the slope is near zero.

c. This has (B) as its derivative. Note that the slope of the tangent line is always positive, and gets infinitely steep at $x = 2$.

d. This has (A) as its derivative. Note that the slope of the tangent line is positive for $x < 2$, negative for $x > 2$, and is infinitely steep at $x = 2$ where the cusp occurs.

15 $f'(x) = 2x^2 + 2\pi x + 7$.

16 $f'(x) = 2\sqrt{x^2 - 2x + 2} + 2x \cdot \frac{1}{2\sqrt{x^2 - 2x + 2}}(2x - 2) = 2\left(\sqrt{x^2 - 2x + 2} + \frac{x^2 - x}{\sqrt{x^2 - 2x + 2}}\right) = \frac{4x^2 - 6x + 4}{\sqrt{x^2 - 2x + 2}}$.

17 $f'(t) = 10t \sin t + 5t^2 \cos t$.

18 $f'(x) = 5 + 3\sin^2 x \cos x + 3x^2 \cos x^3$.

19 $f'(\theta) = (4\sec^2(\theta^2 + 3\theta + 2)) \cdot (2\theta + 3) = (8\theta + 12)\sec^2(\theta^2 + 3\theta + 2)$.

20 $f'(x) = 5\csc^4 3x \cdot (-\csc 3x \cot 3x) \cdot 3 = -15\csc^5 3x \cot 3x$.

21 $f'(u) = \frac{(8u+1)(8u+1) - (4u^2+u)(8)}{(8u+1)^2} = \frac{64u^2 + 16u + 1 - 32u^2 - 8u}{(8u+1)^2} = \frac{32u^2 + 8u + 1}{(8u+1)^2}$.

22 $f'(t) = -3\left(\frac{3t^2-1}{3t^2+1}\right)^{-4} \cdot \frac{(3t^2+1)(6t) - (3t^2-1)(6t)}{(3t^2+1)^2} = -36 \cdot \frac{(3t^2+1)^2 \cdot t}{(3t^2-1)^4}$.

23 $f'(\theta) = \sec^2(\sin\theta) \cdot \cos\theta$.

24 $f'(v) = \frac{1}{3}\left(\frac{v}{3v^2+2v+1}\right)^{-2/3}\frac{3v^2+2v+1-v(6v+2)}{(3v^2+2v+1)^2} = \frac{1}{3}\left(\frac{(3v^2+2v+1)^{3/2}}{v^{3/2}}\right)\left(\frac{1-3v^2}{(3v^2+2v+1)^2}\right) = \frac{1-3v^2}{3\cdot v^{3/2}\cdot\sqrt{3v^2+2v+1}}$.

25 $f'(x) = 2(\sin x)\sqrt{3x-1} + 2x(\cos x)\sqrt{3x-1} + \frac{3x\sin x}{\sqrt{3x-1}}$.

26 $f'(x) = e^{-10x} + x(-10e^{-10x}) = e^{-10x}(1-10x)$.

27 $f'(x) = \ln^2 x + x \cdot 2\ln x \cdot \left(\frac{1}{x}\right) = \ln x \cdot (\ln x + 2)$.

28 $f'(w) = -e^{-w}\ln w + e^{-w}\frac{1}{w} = e^{-w}\left(\frac{1-w\ln w}{w}\right)$.

29 $f'(x) = 2^{x^2-x} \cdot \ln 2 \cdot (2x-1)$.

30 $f'(x) = \frac{1}{(x+8)\ln 3}$.

31 $f'(x) = \frac{1}{\sqrt{1-\left(\frac{1}{x}\right)^2}} \cdot -\frac{1}{x^2} = -\frac{1}{|x|\sqrt{x^2-1}}$.

32 $\frac{d}{dx}x^{\sin x} = \frac{d}{dx}e^{\sin x \ln x} = e^{\sin x \ln x}\left(\cos x \ln x + \frac{\sin x}{x}\right) = x^{\sin x}\left(\cos x \ln x + \frac{\sin x}{x}\right)$.

33 $\frac{d}{dx}x^{1/x} = \frac{d}{dx}e^{\frac{\ln x}{x}} = e^{\frac{\ln x}{x}} \cdot \left(\frac{1-\ln x}{x^2}\right) = x^{1/x}\left(\frac{1-\ln x}{x^2}\right)$. So $\frac{d}{dx}x^{1/x}\big|_{x=1} = 1 \cdot \frac{1-0}{1^2} = 1$.

34 $f'(x) = \frac{1}{1+(4x^2)^2} \cdot 8x = \frac{8x}{1+16x^4}$. So $f'(1) = \frac{8}{17}$.

35 $f'(x) = \sec^{-1}x + \frac{1}{\sqrt{x^2-1}}$. So $f'(2/\sqrt{3}) = \frac{\pi}{6} + \sqrt{3}$.

36 $f'(x) = \frac{1}{1+e^{-2x}} \cdot (-e^{-x}) = -\frac{1}{e^{-x}+e^x}$. So $f'(0) = -\frac{1}{2}$.

37 Because

$$y' = \frac{(1+\sin x)y'e^y - e^y\cos x}{(1+\sin x)^2},$$

collecting terms gives

$$y'\left(1 - \frac{e^y}{1+\sin x}\right) = -\frac{\cos x e^y}{(1+\sin x)^2},$$

so

$$y'(1-y) = -\frac{\cos x}{1+\sin x} \cdot y.$$

Thus $y' = -\frac{y\cos x}{(1-y)(1+\sin x)}$. This can also be written as $y' = \frac{y\cos x}{e^y - 1 - \sin x}$.

38 $\cos x \cos(y-1) - (\sin x)y'\sin(y-1) = 0$, so $y' = \cot x \cot(y-1)$.

39 $y'\sqrt{x^2+y^2} + y \cdot \frac{x+yy'}{\sqrt{x^2+y^2}} = 0$, and thus $y'\left(\sqrt{x^2+y^2} + \frac{y^2}{\sqrt{x^2+y^2}}\right) = -\frac{xy}{\sqrt{x^2+y^2}}$. This can be written as $y'\left(\frac{x^2+2y^2}{\sqrt{x^2+y^2}}\right) = -\frac{xy}{\sqrt{x^2+y^2}}$, so $y' = -\frac{xy}{x^2+2y^2}$.

40

a. $f'(a) = \lim_{x\to a}\frac{x^2-a^2}{x-a} = \lim_{x\to a}\frac{(x-a)(x+a)}{x-a} = \lim_{x\to a}(x+a) = 2a$.

b. $f'(a) = \lim_{h\to 0}\frac{b(a+h)^2 + c(a+h) + d - ba^2 - ca - d}{h} = \lim_{h\to 0}\frac{2bah + bh^2 + ch}{h} = \lim_{h\to 0}(2ba + bh + c) = 2ab + c$.

41 $y' = 9x^2 + \cos x$. At $x = 0$, $y' = 1$. So the tangent line is given by $y - 0 = 1(x-0)$, or $y = x$.

42 $y' = \frac{4(x^2+3)-8x^2}{(x^2+3)^2}$, so $y'(3) = -\frac{1}{6}$. The tangent line is given by $y - 1 = -\frac{1}{6}(x-3)$, or $y = -\frac{1}{6}x + \frac{3}{2}$.

43 $y' + \frac{y+xy'}{2\sqrt{xy}} = 0$. At the point $(1,4)$, we have $y' + \frac{4+y'}{4} = 0$, so $y' = -\frac{4}{5}$. The tangent line is given by $y - 4 = -\frac{4}{5}(x-1)$, or $y = -\frac{4}{5}x + \frac{24}{5}$.

44 $2xy + x^2y' + 3y^2y' = 0$. At the point $(4,3)$ we have $24 + 16y' + 27y' = 0$, so $y' = -\frac{24}{43}$. The tangent line is given by $y - 3 = -\frac{24}{43}(x-4)$, or $y = -\frac{24}{43}x + \frac{225}{43}$.

45 We are looking for values of x so that $y'(x) = 0$. We have $y' = \sqrt{6-x} - \frac{x}{2\sqrt{6-x}}$, and this quantity is zero when $2(6-x) - x = 0$, or $12 - 3x = 0$, so when $x = 4$. So at the point $(4, 4\sqrt{2})$ there is a horizontal tangent line. There is a vertical tangent line at $x = 6$, because $\lim\limits_{x \to 6^-} y'(x) = -\infty$.

46

a. Note that $f'(x) = 2x$, so $f'\left(\frac{x+y}{2}\right) = 2 \cdot \frac{x+y}{2} = x + y$. The quantity $\frac{f(x)-f(y)}{x-y}$ can be written as $\frac{x^2-y^2}{x-y} = \frac{(x-y)(x+y)}{x-y} = x + y$, so these quantities are equal for $x \neq y$.

b. Yes. Note that $f'(x) = 2ax$, so $f'\left(\frac{x+y}{2}\right) = 2a \cdot \frac{x+y}{2} = a(x+y)$. The quantity $\frac{f(x)-f(y)}{x-y}$ can be written as $\frac{ax^2-ay^2}{x-y} = a \cdot \frac{(x-y)(x+y)}{x-y} = a(x+y)$, so these quantities are equal for $x \neq y$.

c. The line through $(x, f(x))$ and $(y, f(y))$ is parallel to the tangent line at the midpoint between x and y.

d. No. For example, consider $a = 1$, $x = 0$, and $y = 1$. Note that $f'(x) = 3x^2$. Then $f'\left(\frac{x+y}{2}\right) = f'(1/2) = 3/4$. On the other hand, $\frac{f(x)-f(y)}{x-y} = \frac{1-0}{1-0} = 1$.

47
$y' = \frac{1}{2}x^{-1/2}\cos\sqrt{x}$.
$y'' = -\frac{1}{4}x^{-3/2}\cos\sqrt{x} + -\frac{1}{4}x^{-1}\sin\sqrt{x}$.
$y''' = \frac{3}{8}x^{-5/2}\cos\sqrt{x} + \frac{1}{8}x^{-2}\sin\sqrt{x} + \frac{1}{4}x^{-2}\sin\sqrt{x} - \frac{1}{8}x^{-3/2}\cos\sqrt{x} = \frac{3}{8}x^{-5/2}\cos\sqrt{x} + \frac{3}{8}x^{-2}\sin\sqrt{x} - \frac{1}{8}x^{-3/2}\cos\sqrt{x}$.

48 $y' = \frac{1}{2}\frac{x-3}{\sqrt{x+2}} + \sqrt{x+2}$.
$y'' = \frac{1}{2}\frac{1}{\sqrt{x+2}} - \frac{x-3}{4(x+2)^{3/2}} + \frac{1}{2\sqrt{x+2}} = \frac{1}{\sqrt{x+2}} - \frac{x-3}{4(x+2)^{3/2}}$.
$y''' = -\frac{1}{2(x+2)^{3/2}} - \frac{1}{4}\left(\frac{1}{(x+2)^{3/2}} - \frac{3}{2}\frac{x-3}{(x+2)^{5/2}}\right) = -\frac{3}{4(x+2)^{3/2}} + \frac{3}{8}\frac{x-3}{(x+2)^{5/2}}$.

49 $\frac{d}{dx}[x^2 f(x)] = 2xf(x) + x^2 f'(x)$.

50 $\frac{d}{dx}\sqrt{\frac{f(x)}{g(x)}} = \frac{1}{2\sqrt{\frac{f(x)}{g(x)}}} \cdot \frac{g(x)f'(x) - f(x)g'(x)}{g(x)^2}$.

51 $\frac{d}{dx}\left(\frac{xf(x)}{g(x)}\right) = \frac{(f(x)+xf'(x))g(x) - xf(x)g'(x)}{g(x)^2}$.

52 $\frac{d}{dx}f\left(\sqrt{g(x)}\right) = f'\left(\sqrt{g(x)}\right) \cdot \frac{1}{2\sqrt{g(x)}} \cdot g'(x)$.

53

a. $\frac{d}{dx}[f(x) + 2g(x)]_{x=3} = f'(3) + 2g'(3) = 9 + 2 \cdot 9 = 27$.

b. $\frac{d}{dx}\left[\frac{xf(x)}{g(x)}\right]_{x=1} = \frac{g(1)(1\cdot f'(1)+f(1))-1\cdot f(1)\cdot g'(1)}{(g(1))^2} = \frac{9\cdot[7+3]-15}{81} = \frac{25}{27}$.

c. $\frac{d}{dx} f(g(x^2))\big|_{x=3} = f'(g(9)) \cdot g'(9) \cdot 2 \cdot 3 = f'(1) \cdot 7 \cdot 6 = 7 \cdot 42 = 294.$

d. $\frac{d}{dx} (f(x))^3\big|_{x=5} = 3f(5)^2 f'(5) = 3(9)^2 \cdot 5 = 1215.$

e. $(g^{-1})'(7) = \frac{1}{g'(3)} = \frac{1}{9}.$

54 With $a = \frac{\pi}{4}$, $f(x) = \sin^2(x)$ we have

$$f'\left(\frac{\pi}{4}\right) = \lim_{h \to 0} \frac{f(\pi/4 + h) - f(\pi/4)}{h} = \lim_{h \to 0} \frac{\sin^2(\pi/4 + h) - (1/2)}{h}$$
$$= 2\sin(\pi/4)\cos(\pi/4) = 2(\sqrt{2}/2)(\sqrt{2}/2) = 1.$$

Note that we used the fact that $\frac{d}{dx} \sin^2(x) = 2\sin x \cos x$ in the middle of this derivation.

55 Let $a = 5$ and $f(x) = \tan(\pi\sqrt{3x - 11})$. Note that $f'(5) = \dfrac{3\pi}{2} \dfrac{\sec^2(2\pi)}{2} = \dfrac{3\pi}{4}.$

So $\displaystyle\lim_{x \to 5} \frac{f(x) - f(5)}{x - 5} = \lim_{x \to 5} \frac{\tan(\pi\sqrt{3x - 11}) - 0}{x - 5} = f'(5) = \frac{3\pi}{4}.$

56 $\left(f^{-1}(x)\right)'\big|_{x=f(0)} = \dfrac{1}{f'(0)} = -\dfrac{1}{(0 + 1)^2} = -1.$

57 Note that for $x = 2$, we have $y = \sqrt{8 + 2 - 1} = 3$. $\left(f^{-1}(x)\right)'\big|_{x=f(2)} = \dfrac{1}{f'(2)} = \dfrac{1}{\frac{3(2^2)+1}{2\sqrt{2^3+2-1}}} = \dfrac{6}{13}.$

58 $\left(f^{-1}(x)\right)' = \dfrac{1}{f'(f^{-1}(x))} = \dfrac{1}{12}.$

59 If $f(x) = x^{-1/3}$, then $f^{-1}(x) = x^{-3}$. So $\left(f^{-1}\right)'(x) = -3x^{-4}$ for $x \neq 0$.

60

a.

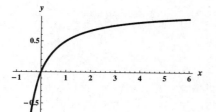

b.

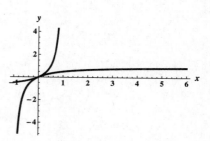

If $y = \frac{x}{x+1}$, then $yx + y = x$, so $y = x - yx$, and $y = x(1 - y)$, so $x = \frac{y}{1-y}$. The inverse function is given by $f^{-1}(x) = \frac{x}{1-x}.$

c. $\left(f^{-1}(x)\right)' = \dfrac{1-x+x}{(1-x)^2} = \dfrac{1}{(1-x)^2}.$ So $\left(f^{-1}\right)\left(\frac{1}{2}\right) = 4.$

d.

61

a. $\left(f^{-1}\right)'\left(\frac{1}{\sqrt{2}}\right) = \frac{1}{f'\left(\frac{\pi}{4}\right)} = \frac{1}{\cos\left(\frac{\pi}{4}\right)} = \sqrt{2}.$

b. $\frac{d}{dx}\sin^{-1}(x)\big|_{x=1/\sqrt{2}} = \frac{1}{\sqrt{1-(1/2)}} = \frac{1}{\sqrt{1/2}} = \sqrt{2}.$

62

a. $\frac{d}{dx}(xf(x))\big|_{x=2} = (f(x) + xf'(x))\big|_{x=2} = f(2) + 2f'(2) = 5 + 2 \cdot 3 = 11.$

b. $\frac{d}{dx}\left(f(x^2)\right)\big|_{x=1} = \left(2xf'(x^2)\right)\big|_{x=1} = 2f'(1) = 2.$

c. $\frac{d}{dx}(f(f(x)))\big|_{x=1} = f'(f(1)) \cdot f'(1) = f'(3) \cdot 1 = 4.$

63

a. Because $f^{-1}(7) = 3$, we have $\left(f^{-1}\right)'(7) = \frac{1}{f'(3)} = \frac{1}{4}.$

b. Because $f^{-1}(3) = 1$, we have $\left(f^{-1}\right)'(3) = \frac{1}{f'(1)} = 1.$

c. $\left(f^{-1}\right)'(f(2)) = \frac{1}{f'(2)} = \frac{1}{3}.$

64

a. The probe climbs quickly, and achieves a maximum height of about 84.1 at about $t = .91$.

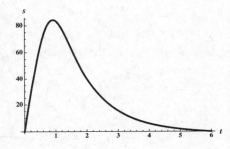

b.

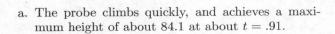

$$v(t) = s'(t) = \frac{(t^3 + 2)(300 - 100t) - (300t - 50t^2)(3t^2)}{(t^3 + 2)^2}$$

$$= \frac{300t^3 - 100t^4 + 600 - 200t - 900t^3 + 150t^4}{(t^3 + 2)^2}$$

$$= \frac{50t^4 - 600t^3 - 200t + 600}{(t^3 + 2)^2}.$$

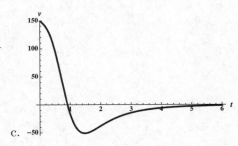

c.

The maximum velocity is attained at $t = 0$.

65

a. The average cost is $\frac{C(3000)}{3000} = \frac{1025000}{3000} \approx \$341.67$. The marginal cost is $C'(3000) = -0.04(3000) + 400 = \$280$.

b. The average cost of producing 3000 lawnmowers is \$341.67 per mower. The cost of producing the 3001st lawnmower is approximately \$280.

66

   a. The marginal cost is given by $C'(x) = -0.0003x^2 + 0.1x + 60$, so $C'(400) = \$52$. The average cost of producing 400 fly rods is $\frac{C(400)}{400} = \$66$.

   b. The average cost of producing 400 fly rods is \$66 per fly rod. The cost of producing the 401st fly rod is approximately \$52.

67

   a. The average growth rate is $\frac{p(50)-p(0)}{50} = \frac{407500-80000}{50} = 6550$ people per year.

   b. The growth rate in 1990 is $p'(40) = -5.1(40^2) + 144 \cdot 40 + 7200 = 4800$ people per year.

68

   a. $v(t) = \pi \cdot 4^2 \cdot \frac{8t}{t+1} = \frac{128\pi t}{t+1}$ cubic cm.

   b. $v'(t) = 128\pi \cdot \frac{(t+1)-t}{(t+1)2} = \frac{128\pi}{(t+1)^2}$.

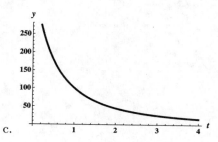

   c.

Because the rate of change of volume is strictly positive, the volume function must be increasing for $t > 0$.

69

Let x be the distance the eastbound boat has traveled, and y the distance the southbound boat has traveled. By the Pythagorean Theorem, $D^2 = x^2 + y^2$, so $2D\frac{dD}{dt} = 2x\frac{dx}{dt} + 2y\frac{dy}{dt}$, so $\frac{dD}{dt} = \frac{x \cdot x' + y \cdot y'}{D}$. We are given that $x' = 40$, $y' = 30$, and at $t = .5$ hours, we have $x = 20$, $y = 15$, and $D = 25$. Thus, $\frac{dD}{dt} = \frac{20 \cdot 40 + 30 \cdot 15}{25} = 50$ mph.

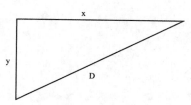

70 $V = \frac{4}{3}\pi r^3 = \frac{\pi d^3}{6}$, so $V' = \frac{\pi d^2 d'}{2}$. With $V' = 10\,\text{cm}^3/\text{min}$ and $d = 5$ cm, we have $d' = \frac{20}{25\pi} = \frac{4}{5\pi}$ cm/min.

71 Let h be the elevation of the balloon, and s the length of the rope. We have $h = s\sin(65°)$, so $h' = s'\sin(65°) = -5 \cdot \sin(65°) \approx -4.53$ feet per second.

72 $\frac{r}{h} = \frac{2}{3}$, so $r = \frac{2}{3}h$. $V = \frac{1}{3}\pi r^2 h = \frac{4}{27}\pi h^3$. So $\frac{dV}{dt} = \frac{4}{9}\pi h^2 \frac{dh}{dt}$. When $h = 2$, $\frac{dV}{dt} = 2$, so $\frac{dh}{dt} = \frac{2}{\frac{4}{9}\pi \cdot 4} = \frac{9}{8\pi}$ feet per minute.

73

Let x be the distance the jet has flown since it went over the spectator. Let θ be the angle of elevation between the ground and the line from the spectator to the jet. Note that θ is also the angle pictured, and that $\cot\theta = \frac{x}{500}$. Thus, $\theta = \cot^{-1}\left(\frac{x}{500}\right)$. We are given that $x' = 450\,\text{mph} = 660\,\text{ft/sec}$.

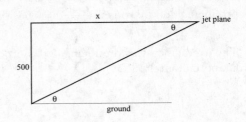

$\theta' = -\dfrac{x'}{500\cdot\left(1+\left(\frac{x}{500}\right)^2\right)} = -\dfrac{500x'}{250,000+x^2}$. After 2 seconds, $x = 1320$ feet, so at this time $\theta' = -\dfrac{500\cdot 660}{250,000+(1320)^2} \approx -0.166$ radians per second.

74 Let D be the distance the man is from the billboard, and let α be the angle between his eye level and the line of sight to the bottom of the billboard, and let θ be the angle between his line of sight to the bottom of the billboard and his line of sight to the top of the billboard. We have that $\cot\alpha = \frac{D}{4}$, so $\alpha = \cot^{-1}\left(\frac{D}{4}\right)$. Also, $\cot(\alpha+\theta) = \frac{D}{19}$, so $\theta = \cot^{-1}\left(\frac{D}{19}\right) - \alpha = \cot^{-1}\left(\frac{D}{19}\right) - \cot^{-1}\left(\frac{D}{4}\right)$.

So $\theta' = -\dfrac{19D'}{361+D^2} + \dfrac{4D'}{16+D^2}$. We are given that $D' = -2$ feet per second, so at $D = 30$ we have $\theta' \approx 0.03 - 0.009 = 0.021$ radians per second.

Chapter 4

Applications of the Derivative

4.1 Maxima and Minima

4.1.1 A number $M = f(c)$ where $c \in [a, b]$ with the property that $f(x) \le M$ for all $x \in [a, b]$ is an absolute maximum for f on $[a, b]$, and a number $m = f(d)$ where $d \in [a, b]$ with the property that $f(x) \ge m$ for all $x \in [a, b]$ is an absolute minimum for f on $[a, b]$.

4.1.2 A number $M = f(c)$ is a local maximum for f if there is an interval (r, s) containing c so that $f(x) \le M$ for all $x \in (r, s)$. A number $m = f(d)$ is a local minimum for f if there is an interval (r, s) containing d so that $f(x) \ge m$ for all $x \in (r, s)$.

4.1.3 The function must be a continuous function defined on a closed interval.

4.1.4 The tangent function on the interval $(-\pi/2, \pi/2)$ is continuous but has no maximum or minimum.

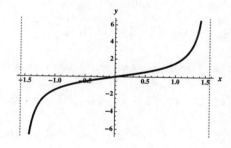

4.1.5 The function shown has no absolute minimum on $[0, 3]$ because $\lim\limits_{x \to 0^+} f(x) = -\infty$. It has an absolute maximum near $x = 1$ and a local minimum near $x = 2.5$.

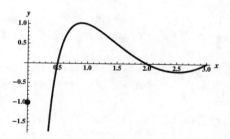

4.1.6 An interior point c of the domain of f at which $f'(c) = 0$ or $f'(c)$ doesn't exist is a critical point of f.

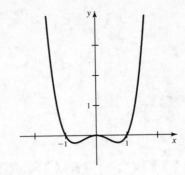

4.1.7 Note the existence of a horizontal tangent line at $x = 0$ where the maximum occurs.

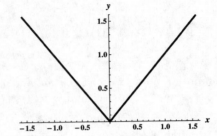

4.1.8 Note the minimum at $x = 0$ where $f'(x)$ does not exist. Note that $\lim\limits_{h \to 0} \dfrac{f(0 + h) - f(0)}{h}$ is different for $h \to 0^-$ and $h \to 0^+$.

4.1.9 First find all the critical points by seeking all points x in the domain of f so that $f'(x) = 0$ or $f'(x)$ doesn't exist. Now compare the y-values of all of these points, together with the y-values of the endpoints. The largest y-value from among these is the maximum, and the smallest is the minimum.

4.1.10 If a is an endpoint of the given interval, and $f(a) \leq f(x)$ for all x in the interval, then $f(a)$ is the absolute minimum. This happens, for example, for a line of positive slope defined on an interval $[a, b]$ – the y-value at the left endpoint is the smallest y-value over the interval.

4.1.11 $y = h(x)$ has an absolute maximum at $x = b$ and an absolute minimum at $x = c_2$.

4.1.12 $y = f(x)$ has an absolute maximum at $x = c$ and no absolute minimum.

4.1.13 $y = g(x)$ has no absolute maximum, but has an absolute minimum at $x = a$.

4.1.14 $y = g(x)$ has an absolute maximum at $x = a$ and an absolute minimum at $x = c$.

4.1.15 $y = f(x)$ has an absolute maximum at $x = b$ and an absolute minimum at $x = a$. It has local maxima at $x = p$ and $x = r$, and local minima at $x = q$ and $x = s$.

4.1.16 $y = f(x)$ has an absolute maximum at $x = p$, and an absolute minimum at $x = a$. It has local minima at $x = q$ and $x = s$, and local maxima at $x = r$ and $x = p$.

4.1.17 $y = g(x)$ has an absolute minimum at $x = b$ and an absolute maximum at $x = p$. It has local maxima at $x = p$ and $x = r$. It has a local minimum at $x = q$.

4.1.18 $y = h(x)$ has an absolute maximum at $x = p$ and an absolute minimum at $x = u$. It has local maxima at $x = p$, $x = r$ and $x = t$. It has local minima at $x = q$, $x = s$, and $x = u$.

4.1.19 Note the horizontal tangent lines at 1 and 2, and the minimum at 0 and the maximum at 4.

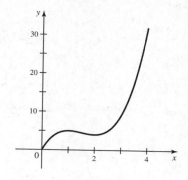

4.1.20 Note the minimum at $x = 1$, the maximum at $x = 3$, and the horizontal tangent lines at 1, 2, and 3.

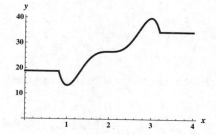

4.1.21 Note the horizontal tangent line at $x = 2$, and the "corners" at $x = 1$ and $x = 3$. Also note the absolute maximum at $x = 3$ and the absolute minimum at $x = 4$.

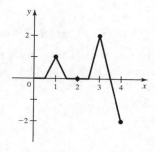

4.1.22 Note the maximum at 2, and the minimum at 3. Note also the horizontal tangent lines at $x = 1$ and $x = 3$, and the sharp "corner" at $x = 2$.

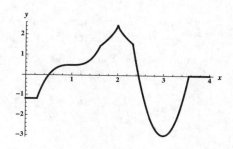

4.1.23

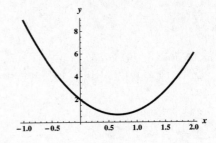

   a. $f'(x) = 6x - 4$, which is zero when $x = 2/3$.

   b. At $x = 2/3$ there is a local minimum.

4.1.24

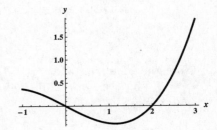

   a. $f'(x) = \frac{3}{8}x^2 - \frac{1}{2}$, which is zero when $3x^2 - 4 = 0$, which occurs for $x = \pm\frac{2}{\sqrt{3}}$. The only critical point on the given interval occurs for $x = \frac{2}{\sqrt{3}}$.

   b. There is a local minimum at $x = \frac{2}{\sqrt{3}}$.

4.1.25

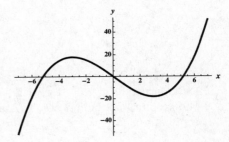

   a. $f'(x) = x^2 - 9$, which is zero for $x = \pm 3$.

   b. There is a local maximum at $x = -3$ and a local minimum at $x = 3$.

4.1.26

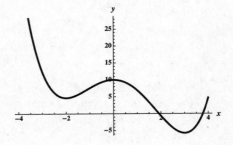

   a. $f'(x) = x^3 - x^2 - 6x = x(x^2 - x - 6) = x(x - 3)(x + 2)$, which is zero for $x = 0, 3$, and -2.

   b. There is a local maximum at $x = 0$ and local minima at $x = -2$ and $x = 3$.

4.1.27

a. $f'(x) = 9x^2 + 3x - 2 = (3x + 2)(3x - 1)$, which is zero for $x = -2/3$ and $x = 1/3$.

b. There is a local maximum at $x = -2/3$ and a local minimum at $x = 1/3$.

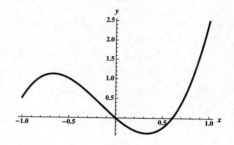

4.1.28

a. $f'(x) = 4x^4 - 9x^2 = x^2(4x^2 - 9) = x^2(2x + 3)(2x - 3)$, which is zero for $x = 0$ and $x = \pm 3/2$.

b. There is a local maximum at $x = -3/2$ and a local minimum at $x = 3/2$, and neither is occurring at $x = 0$.

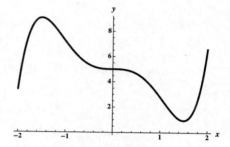

4.1.29

a. $f'(x) = \frac{(x^2+1)(1) - x(2x)}{(x^2+1)^2} = \frac{1 - x^2}{(x^2+1)^2}$. This quantity is zero exactly when $1 - x^2 = 0$, so at $x = 1$ and $x = -1$.

b. At $x = 1$ there is a local maximum (which is also an absolute maximum) and at $x = -1$ there is a local minimum (which is also an absolute minimum.)

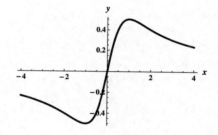

4.1.30

a. $f'(x) = 60x^4 - 60x^2 = 60x^2(x^2 - 1)$, which is zero on the given interval when $x = \pm 1$ and when $x = 0$.

b. There is a local minimum at $x = 1$ and a local maximum at $x = -1$. At $x = 0$ there is neither a maximum nor a minimum.

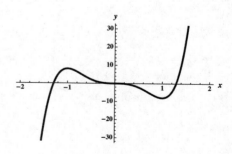

4.1.31

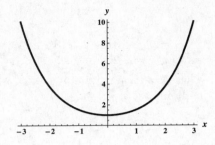

   a. $f'(x) = \frac{e^x - e^{-x}}{2}$, which is zero when $e^x = e^{-x}$ or $x = -x$, so only for $x = 0$.

   b. There is a local (and absolute) minimum at $x = 0$.

4.1.32

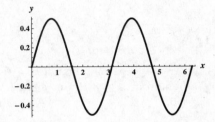

   a. $f'(x) = \cos x \cos x - \sin x \sin x$, which is zero when $\sin^2 x = \cos^2 x$, so when $\sin x = \cos x$ or $\sin x = -\cos x$. This occurs when $x = \frac{\pi}{4} + k\frac{\pi}{2}$ where k is an integer. On $[0, 2\pi]$ this gives us $x = \frac{\pi}{4},\ \frac{3\pi}{4},\ \frac{5\pi}{4}$, and $\frac{7\pi}{4}$.

   b. There are local maxima at $x = \frac{\pi}{4}$ and $\frac{5\pi}{4}$, and local minima at $x = \frac{3\pi}{4}$ and at $x = \frac{7\pi}{4}$.

4.1.33

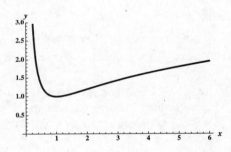

   a. $f'(x) = -\frac{1}{x^2} + \frac{1}{x} = \frac{x-1}{x^2}$. There is a critical point at $x = 1$.

   b. The critical point at $x = 1$ is a local minimum.

4.1.34

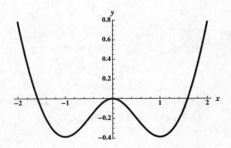

   a. $f'(x) = 2x - \frac{4x}{x^2+1} = \frac{2x^3 - 2x}{x^2+1} = \frac{2x(x+1)(x-1)}{x^2+1}$. This is zero for $x = 0, \pm 1$.

   b. There are absolute minima at $x = \pm 1$ and a local maximum at $x = 0$.

4.1.35

a. $f'(x) = 2x\sqrt{x+1} + x^2 \cdot \frac{1}{2\sqrt{x+1}} = \frac{4x(x+1)}{2\sqrt{x+1}} + \frac{x^2}{2\sqrt{x+1}} = \frac{5x^2+4x}{2\sqrt{x+1}}$. This is zero when $5x^2 + 4x = x(5x+4)$ is zero, which occurs for $x = 0$ and $x = -4/5$. The critical points are $(0,0)$ and $(-4/5, 16/(25\sqrt{5}))$.

b. There is a local maximum at $x = -4/5$ and a local minimum at $x = 0$.

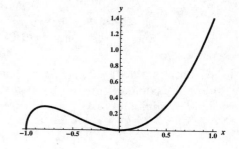

4.1.36

a. $f'(x) = \frac{1}{\sqrt{1-x^2}}\cos^{-1}(x) + \sin^{-1}(x) \cdot -\frac{1}{\sqrt{1-x^2}} = \frac{\cos^{-1}(x) - \sin^{-1}(x)}{\sqrt{1-x^2}}$. This is zero when $\sin^{-1}(x) = \cos^{-1}(x)$, which occurs on the given interval for $x = \frac{\sqrt{2}}{2}$.

b. There is a local maximum at $x = \frac{\sqrt{2}}{2}$.

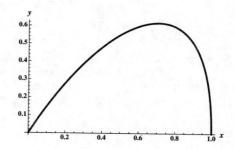

4.1.37

a. $f'(x) = 2x$, which is zero for $x = 0$.

b. We have that $f(-2) = -6$, $f(0) = -10$, and $f(3) = -1$, so the maximum value of f on this interval is -1 and the minimum is -10.

c.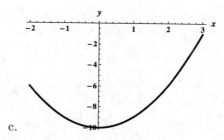

4.1.38

a. $f'(x) = \frac{4}{3}(x+1)^{1/3}$, which is zero for $x = -1$. So $(-1, 0)$ is the only critical point.

b. We have that $f(-9) = (-8)^{4/3} = 16$, $f(-1) = 0$, and $f(7) = 8^{4/3} = 16$, so the maximum value of f on this interval is 16 and the minimum is 0.

c.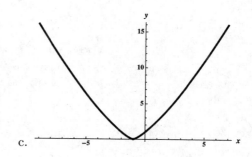

4.1.39

a. $f'(x) = -2\cos x \sin x$, which is zero for $x = 0$, $x = \pi/2$, and $x = \pi$. Because there are endpoints at $x = 0$ and $x = \pi$, only $(\pi/2, 0)$ is a critical point.

b. We have that $f(0) = 1$, $f(\pi/2) = 0$, and $f(\pi) = 1$, so the maximum value of f on this interval is 1 and the minimum is 0.

c.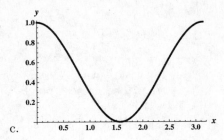

4.1.40

a. $f'(x) = \frac{(x^2+3)^2 - x \cdot 2(x^2+3) \cdot 2x}{(x^2+3)^4} = \frac{(x^2+3) - 4x^2}{(x^2+3)^3} = \frac{3 - 3x^2}{(x^2+3)^3}$, which is zero for $x = \pm 1$.

b. We have that $f(-2) = -\frac{2}{49} \approx -0.041$, $f(2) = \frac{2}{49} \approx 0.041$, $f(\pm 1) = \frac{\pm 1}{16} = \pm 0.0625$. The absolute maximum of f on the given interval is 0.0625 at $x = 1$ and the absolute minimum is -0.0625 at $x = -1$.

c.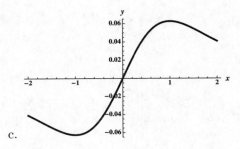

4.1.41

a. $f'(x) = 3\cos 3x$, which is zero when

$$3x = \ldots, -\pi/2, \ \pi/2, \ 3\pi/2, \ldots,$$

so when $x = \ldots, -\pi/6, \ \pi/6, \ \pi/2, \ldots$. The only such values on the given interval are $x = -\pi/6$ and $x = \pi/6$.

b. We have

$$f(-\pi/4) = -\sqrt{2}/2 \approx -0.707,$$

$f(-\pi/6) = -1$, $f(\pi/6) = 1$, and $f(\pi/3) = 0$, so the absolute maximum of f is 1 and the absolute minimum is -1.

c.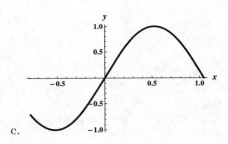

4.1.42

a. $f'(x) = \frac{2}{3}x^{-1/3} = \frac{2}{3\sqrt[3]{x}}$, which is never zero. However, there is a point in the domain (namely $(0,0)$) where the derivative doesn't exist. So this is the only critical point.

b. We have $f(-8) = 4 = f(8)$, and $f(0) = 0$. So the absolute maximum of f on this interval is 4 and the absolute minimum is 0.

c.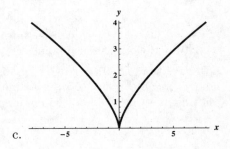

4.1.43

a. Let $y = (2x)^x$, so that $\ln y = x \ln(2x)$. Then $\frac{1}{y} y' = \ln(2x) + \frac{x}{2x} \cdot 2 = 1 + \ln(2x)$. Thus $y' = (2x)^x (1 + \ln(2x))$. This quantity is zero when $1 + \ln(2x) = 0$, which occurs when $\ln(2x) = -1$, or $x = \frac{1}{2e} \approx .184$.

b. We have $f(.1) \approx .851$, $f\left(\frac{1}{2e}\right) = e^{-(1/2e)} \approx .832$, and $f(1) = 2$. So the absolute minimum is $e^{-(1/2e)}$ and the absolute maximum is 2.

c.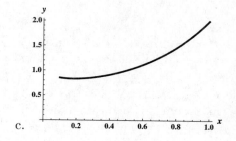

4.1.44

a. $f'(x) = e^{1-x/2} + xe^{1-x/2} \cdot -\frac{1}{2} = e^{1-x/2}\left(\frac{2-x}{2}\right)$. Because the exponential function is never zero, this expression is zero only when $x = 2$. So $(2, 2)$ is the only critical point.

b. We have $f(0) = 0$ and $f(2) = 2$, and $f(5) \approx 1.12$. So the absolute maximum of f on this interval is 2 and the absolute minimum is 0.

c.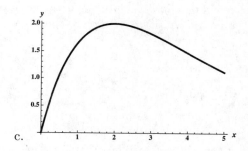

4.1.45

a. $f'(x) = 2x - \frac{1}{\sqrt{1-x^2}} = \frac{2x\sqrt{1-x^2}-1}{\sqrt{1-x^2}}$. This is zero on $(-1, 1)$ when the numerator is zero, which is when $2x\sqrt{1-x^2} = 1$, so when $(4x^2)(1-x^2) = 1$, or $4x^4 - 4x^2 + 1 = 0$. This factors as $(2x^2 - 1)(2x^2 - 1) = 0$, so we have solutions for $x = \pm\sqrt{1/2}$.

b. $f(-1) = 1 + \pi$, $f(-1/\sqrt{2}) = \frac{1}{2} + \frac{3\pi}{4}$, $f(1/\sqrt{2}) = \frac{1}{2} + \frac{\pi}{4}$, and $f(1) = 1$. So the maximum for f is $1 + \pi$ and the minimum is 1.

c.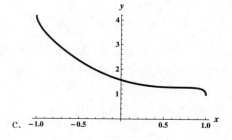

4.1.46

a. $f'(x) = \sqrt{2 - x^2} + x \cdot -\frac{2x}{2\sqrt{2-x^2}} = \frac{2-2x^2}{\sqrt{2-x^2}}$. This is zero on $(-\sqrt{2}, \sqrt{2})$ when $2 - 2x^2 = 0$, which occurs for $x = \pm 1$.

b. $f(-\sqrt{2}) = 0 = f(\sqrt{2})$, $f(-1) = -1$, and $f(1) = 1$, so the absolute maximum of f is 1 and the absolute minimum is -1.

c.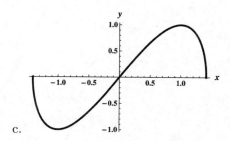

4.1.47

a. $f'(x) = 6x^2 - 30x + 24 = 6(x^2 - 5x + 4) = 6(x - 4)(x - 1)$. This is zero at $x = 4$ and $x = 1$.

b. $f(1) = 11$ and $f(4) = -16$. At the endpoints we have $f(0) = 0$ and $f(5) = -5$. The absolute maximum is 11 and the absolute minimum is -16.

c.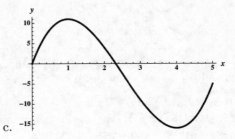

4.1.48

a. f will be non differentiable at the zeros of $2x - x^2$, i.e., at $x = 0$ and $x = 2$, because the absolute value function will have a "corner" there. Writing f as a piecewise function gives

$$f(x) = \begin{cases} x^2 - 2x, & x \le 0, \\ 2x - x^2, & 0 < x \le 2, \\ x^2 - 2x, & x > 2. \end{cases}$$

Thus where f is differentiable we have

$$f'(x) = \begin{cases} 2x - 2, & x < 0, \\ 2 - 2x, & 0 < x < 2, \\ 2x - 2, & x > 2. \end{cases}$$

So $f'(x) = 0$ at $x = 1$, and thus the critical points are $x = 1$ together with $x = 0$ and $x = 2$ where f is not differentiable.

b. Because $f(-2) = 8$, $f(0) = 0$, $f(1) = 1$, $f(2) = 0$, and $f(3) = 3$, we note that f has a maximum of 8 at $x = -2$ and a minimum of 0 at both $x = 0$ and $x = 2$.

c.

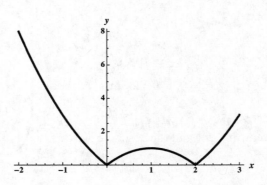

4.1.49

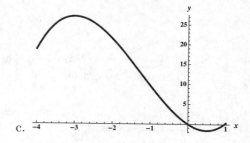

a. $f'(x) = 4x^2 + 10x - 6 = 2(2x^2 + 5x - 3) = 2(x + 3)(2x - 1)$. This is zero when $x = -3$ and when $x = 1/2$.

b. $f(-3) = 27$ and $f(1/2) = -19/12$. At the endpoints we have $f(-4) = 56/3 \approx 18.7$, and $f(1) = 1/3$. The absolute maximum is 27 and the absolute minimum is $-19/12$.

c.

4.1.50

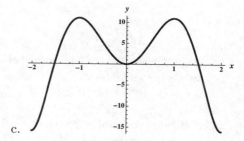

a. $f'(x) = 12x^5 - 60x^3 + 48x = 12x(x^4 - 5x^2 + 4) = 12x(x^2 - 4)(x^2 - 1) = 12x(x+2)(x-2)(x+1)(x-1)$. This is zero for $x = 0$, $x = \pm 2$, and $x = \pm 1$. The critical points occur at 0 and ± 1, since the endpoints are ± 2.

b. $f(\pm 2) = -16$, $f(\pm 1) = 11$, and $f(0) = 0$. The absolute maximum is 11 and the absolute minimum is -16.

c.

4.1.51 The stone will reach its maximum height when its velocity is zero, which occurs at the only critical point for this inverted parabola. We have that $v(t) = s'(t) = -32t + 64$, which is zero when $t = 2$. The height at this time is $s(2) = 256$, the maximum height.

4.1.52

a. $R'(x) = -120x + 300$, which is zero when $x = 2.5$. This is the only critical number.

b. The maximum must occur at either an endpoint or a critical point. Note that $R(0) = 0$, $R(2.5) = 375$, and $R(5) = 0$, so the maximum revenue is \$375, which occurs when the price is \$2.50.

4.1.53

a. Note that $P(n) = 50n - .5n^2 - 100$, so $P'(n) = 50 - n$, which is zero when $n = 50$. It is clear that this is a maximum, since the graph of P is an inverted parabola.

b. Given a domain of $[0, 45]$, since the only critical point is not in the domain, the maximum must occur at an endpoint. Because $P(0) = -100$, and $P(45) = \$1137.50$, he should take 45 people on the tour.

4.1.54 $P(x) = 2x + \frac{128}{x}$, $x > 0$, so $P'(x) = 2 - \frac{128}{x^2}$, which is zero when $x^2 = 64$, or when $x = 8$. So $(8, 32)$ is the only critical point. This does turn out to be a minimum, so the dimensions of the rectangle with minimal perimeter are 8×8.

4.1.55

a. False. The derivative $f'(x) = \frac{1}{2\sqrt{x}}$ is never zero, and the function has no critical points.

b. False. For example, the function $f(x) = \begin{cases} \sin x & \text{if } -5 \le x \le 0, \\ -8 & \text{if } 0 < x \le 5 \end{cases}$ is not continuous on $[-5, 5]$, but has an absolute maximum of 1.

c. False. For example, the function $f(x) = (x-2)^3$ satisfies $f'(2) = 0$, but it has neither a maximum nor a minimum at $x = 2$.

d. True. This follows from the theorems in this section.

4.1.56

a. $f'(x) = \frac{1}{2\sqrt{x-2}}$ which is never zero and exists for $x > 2$. There are no critical points for f on the given interval.

b. $f(2) = 0$ and $f(6) = 2$, so the absolute maximum of this function on the given interval is 2 and the absolute minimum is 0.

c.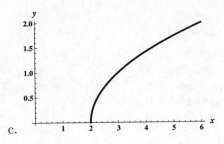

4.1.57

a. $f'(x) = 2^x \cdot \ln 2 \cdot \sin x + 2^x \cos x = 2^x((\ln 2) \cdot \sin x + \cos x)$. Because 2^x is never zero, this expression is zero only when $(\ln 2) \cdot \sin x + \cos x = 0$, or $(\ln 2) \cdot \tan x = -1$, or $\tan x = \left(-\frac{1}{\ln 2}\right)$. So one solution is $x = \tan^{-1}\left(-\frac{1}{\ln 2}\right) \approx -.9647$. And since the tangent function is periodic with period π, we also have solutions at approximately $-.9647 + \pi \approx 2.1769$, and $-.9647 + 2\pi \approx 5.3185$. These are the only solutions on the given interval.

b. $f(-2) \approx -0.2273$, $f(-.9647) \approx -0.4211$, $f(2.1769) \approx 3.7164$, $f(5.3185) \approx -32.7968$, and $f(6) \approx -17.8826$. Thus the absolute maximum is about 3.7164 and the absolute minimum is about -32.7968.

c.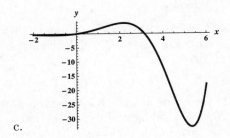

4.1.58

a. $f'(x) = \frac{1}{2\sqrt{x}} \cdot (x^2/5 - 4) + \sqrt{x}\left(\frac{2x}{5}\right) = \frac{x^2-20}{10\sqrt{x}} + \frac{4x^2}{10\sqrt{x}} = \frac{x^2-4}{2\sqrt{x}}$. On the given domain, this expression is zero only for $x = 2$.

b. $f(0) = 0$, $f(2) = -\frac{16\sqrt{2}}{5} \approx -4.5255$, and $f(4) = -\frac{8}{5}$. So the absolute maximum is 0 and the absolute minimum is $-\frac{16\sqrt{2}}{5} \approx -4.5255$.

c.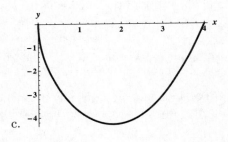

4.1.59

a. $f'(x) = \sec x \tan x$ which is zero when $\tan x = 0$ (since $\sec x$ is never zero.) So we are looking for where $\frac{\sin x}{\cos x} = 0$, which is when $\sin x = 0$, which is at $x = 0$

b. $f(-\pi/4) = \sqrt{2} = f(\pi/4)$ and $f(0) = 1$. So the absolute maximum for f is $\sqrt{2}$ and the absolute minimum is 1.

c.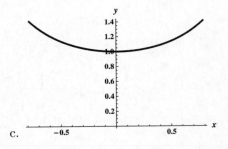

4.1.60

a. $f'(x) = \frac{1}{3} \cdot x^{-2/3} \cdot (x+4) + x^{1/3} = \frac{x+4}{3x^{2/3}} + \frac{3x}{3x^{2/3}} = \frac{4x+4}{3x^{2/3}}$. This expression is zero when $x = -1$, and is undefined when $x = 0$ (although 0 is in the domain of f.) So $(0, 0)$ and $(-1, -3)$ are the critical points.

b. $f(-27) = 69$, $f(-1) = -3$, $f(0) = 0$, and $f(27) = 93$. So the absolute maximum is 93 and the absolute minimum is -3.

c.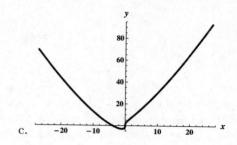

4.1.61

a. $f'(x) = 3x^2 e^{-x} + x^3 \cdot (-e^{-x}) = e^{-x} \cdot (3x^2 - x^3) = e^{-x} \cdot x^2 \cdot (3 - x)$. This expression is zero when $x = 0$ and when $x = 3$, so $(0, 0)$ and $(3, (27/e^3))$ are the critical points.

b. $f(-1) = -e$, $f(0) = 0$, $f(3) = \frac{27}{e^3} \approx 1.344$, and $f(5) \approx .8422$. So the absolute maximum of f on the given interval is about 1.344, and the absolute minimum is $-e \approx -2.718$.

c.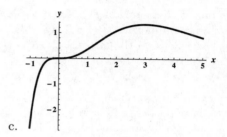

4.1.62

a. $f'(x) = \ln(x/5) + x \cdot \frac{5}{x} \cdot \frac{1}{5} = \ln(x/5) + 1$. This expression is zero when $\ln(x/5) = -1$, or $x = 5e^{-1} = \frac{5}{e} \approx 1.8394$.

b. $f(.1) \approx -.391$, $f\left(\frac{5}{e}\right) = -\frac{5}{e} \approx -1.8394$, and $f(5) = 0$. So the absolute maximum of f is 0, and the absolute minimum is $-\frac{5}{e} \approx -1.8394$.

c.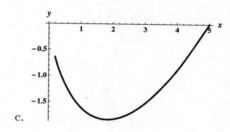

4.1.63

a. $f'(x) = \frac{\sqrt{x-4} \cdot 1 - x \cdot \frac{1}{2\sqrt{x-4}} \cdot 1}{x-4} = \frac{\sqrt{x-4} \cdot 1 - x \cdot \frac{1}{2\sqrt{x-4}} \cdot 1}{x-4} \cdot \frac{2\sqrt{x-4}}{2\sqrt{x-4}} = \frac{2x-8-x}{2(x-4)^{3/2}} = \frac{x-8}{2(x-4)^{3/2}}$. This expression is 0 when $x = 8$. So $(8, 4)$ is the only critical point.

b. $f(6) = 3\sqrt{2} = f(12)$, and $f(8) = 4$. Note that $3\sqrt{2} \approx 4.24 > 4$. So the absolute maximum of f on this interval is $3\sqrt{2}$, and the absolute minimum is 4.

c.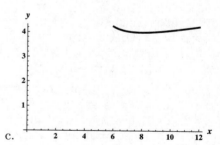

4.1.64 $f'(x) = \frac{\sqrt{x-a} - \frac{x}{2\sqrt{x-a}}}{x-a} = \frac{\sqrt{x-a} - \frac{x}{2\sqrt{x-a}}}{x-a} \cdot \frac{2\sqrt{x-a}}{2\sqrt{x-a}} = \frac{2x-2a-x}{2(x-a)^{3/2}} = \frac{x-2a}{2(x-a)^{3/2}}$. This is zero when $x = 2a$, so there is a critical point at $x = 2a$ for $a > 0$.

4.1.65 $f'(x) = \sqrt{x-a} + \frac{x}{2\sqrt{x-a}} = \frac{2x-2a+x}{2\sqrt{x-a}} = \frac{3x-2a}{2\sqrt{x-a}}$. This expression is zero when $x = \frac{2a}{3}$; however, that number is not in the domain of f if $a > 0$. However, if $a < 0$, then $\frac{2a}{3}$ is in the domain, and thus gives a critical point.

4.1.66 $f'(x) = 3x^2 - 6ax + 3a^2 = 3(x-a)^2$. So the point $x = a$ is a critical point.

4.1.67 $f'(x) = x^4 - a^4$, which is zero when $x^4 = a^4$, or $|x| = a$. So there are critical points at $x = a$ and at $x = -a$.

4.1.68

a. $f'(x) = 24x^3 - 48x^2 - 90x + 54 = 6(4x^3 - 8x^2 - 15x + 9)$, which can be written as $6(2x + 3)(2x - 1)(x - 3)$. Note: to get this factorization, we used the rational root theorem to establish candidates for roots, then used trial-and-error to find that $x = 3$ was one of the roots, which means that $(x - 3)$ is one of the factors of f'. Then we used long division to determine that $f'(x) = 6(x - 3)(4x^2 + 4x - 3)$, then factored the quadratic. After factoring, it is clear that the roots of f' are 3, $-\frac{3}{2}$, and $\frac{1}{2}$, so these are the locations of the critical points.

b. From the graph, it appears that there is a local minimum at $x = -\frac{3}{2}$, a local maximum at $x = \frac{1}{2}$, and a local minimum at $x = 3$.

c. The local minimum at $x = 3$ is also an absolute minimum. The value of the absolute minimum is -166 and the value of the absolute maximum (which occurs at the left endpoint $x = -5$) is 4378.

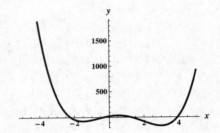

4.1.69

a. $f'(\theta) = 2\cos\theta - \sin\theta$, which is zero when $\tan\theta = 2$. So one critical point occurs at $\theta = \tan^{-1}(2) \approx 1.107$. And since the tangent function is periodic with period π, there are will also be solutions at this number plus or minus integer multiples of π. On the given interval, these are located at approximately $1.107 - 2\pi \approx -5.176$, at $1.107 - \pi \approx -2.034$, and at $1.107 + \pi \approx 4.249$.

b. From the graph, it appears that there is a local minimum at about $\theta = -2.034$ and at $\theta = 4.249$, and there is a local maximum at about $\theta = -5.176$, and at about $\theta = 1.107$.

c. From the graph, it appears that the local minimum at about $\theta = -2.034$ is also an absolute minimum, as is the one at $\theta = 4.249$. The local maximum at about $\theta = -5.176$, and at about $\theta = 1.107$ are also absolute maxima. The value of the absolute maximum appears to be about 2.24 and the value of the absolute minimum appears to be about -2.24.

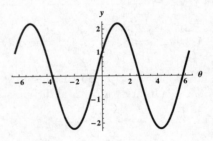

4.1.70

a. $f'(x) = x^{2/3}(-2x) + (4-x^2) \cdot \frac{2}{3\sqrt[3]{x}} = \frac{-6x^2+8-2x^2}{3\sqrt[3]{x}} = \frac{8-8x^2}{3\sqrt[3]{x}}$. This quantity is zero when $x = \pm 1$ and it doesn't exist at $x = 0$. So there are critical points at $(0,0)$, $(-1,3)$, and $(1,3)$.

b. From the graph, it appears that there is a local minimum at $x = 0$, and there is a local maximum of 3 at $x = \pm 1$.

c. The absolute minimum occurs at the right endpoint $x = 4$ where $f(4) \approx -30.24$, and the absolute maximum is 3 (at $x = \pm 1$).

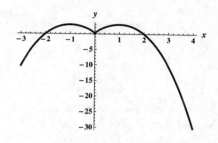

4.1.71

a. $f'(x) = (x-3)^{5/3} + (x+2) \cdot \frac{5}{3}(x-3)^{2/3} = \frac{(x-3)^{2/3}}{3}(3x-9+5x+10) = \frac{(x-3)^{2/3}}{3}(8x+1)$. This is zero when $x = 3$ and when $x = -\frac{1}{8}$. There are critical points at $x = -\frac{1}{8}$ and at $x = 3$.

b. From the graph, it appears that there is a local minimum of about -12.52 at $x = -\frac{1}{8}$.

c. The local minimum mentioned above is also an absolute minimum. The absolute maximum occurs at the left endpoint $x = -4$, where the value of f is about 51.23.

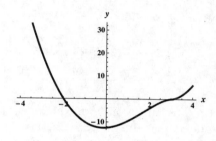

4.1.72

a. $f'(t) = \frac{(t^2+1)\cdot 3 - 3t(2t)}{(t^2+1)^2} = \frac{3-3t^2}{(t^2+1)^2}$. This quantity is zero when $t = \pm 1$. So there are critical points at $(-1, -3/2)$ and $(1, 3/2)$.

b. From the graph, it appears that there is a local minimum at $t = -1$, and a local maximum at $t = 1$.

c. The local minimum at $t = -1$ gives rise to an absolute minimum value of -1.5, and the local maximum at $t = 1$ gives rise to an absolute maximum value of 1.5.

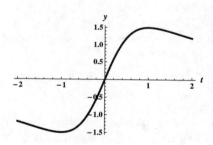

4.1.73

a. $h'(x) = \frac{(x^2+2x-3)(-1)-(5-x)(2x+2)}{(x^2+2x-3)^2} = \frac{x^2-10x-7}{(x^2+2x-3)^2}$. By the quadratic formula, the numerator is zero (making the quotient zero) when $x = \frac{10\pm\sqrt{100-4(-7)}}{2} = 5 \pm \frac{1}{2}\sqrt{128} = 5 \pm 4\sqrt{2}$. Note that $5 + 4\sqrt{2}$ isn't in the domain, so the only critical point is at $x = 5 - 4\sqrt{2}$.

b. From the graph, it appears that the one critical point mentioned above yields a local maximum.

c. The function has no absolute maximum and no absolute minimum on the given interval.

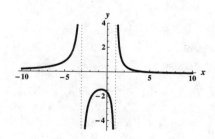

4.1.74

Note that

$$f(x) = \begin{cases} 3 - x - x - 2 = 1 - 2x & \text{if } -4 \le x \le -2, \\ 3 - x + x + 2 = 5 & \text{if } -2 \le x \le 3, \\ x - 3 + x + 2 = 2x - 1 & \text{if } 3 \le x \le 4. \end{cases}$$

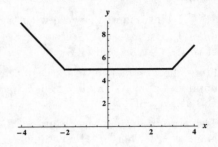

There is an absolute maximum of 9 and an absolute minimum of 5. The absolute maximum occurs at $x = -4$, and the absolute minimum occurs at all of the values of x between -2 and 3.

4.1.75

Note that

$$g(x) = \begin{cases} 3 - x + 2x + 2 = x + 5 & \text{if } -2 \le x \le -1, \\ 3 - x - 2x - 2 = 1 - 3x & \text{if } -1 \le x \le 3. \end{cases}$$

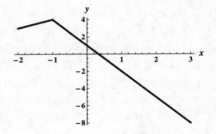

There is an absolute maximum of 4 and an absolute minimum of -8. The absolute maximum occurs at $x = -1$, and the absolute minimum occurs at a $x = 3$.

4.1.76 $S'(x) = 4x - \frac{200}{x^2} = \frac{4x^3 - 200}{x^2}$, which is zero when $x^3 = 50$, so for $x = \sqrt[3]{50} \approx 3.684$. This critical point does indeed yield a minimum (which can be determined via a graphing calculator, or by techniques in an upcoming section). So the minimum surface area is given by $S(\sqrt[3]{50}) \approx 81.433$, when the box has dimensions $\sqrt[3]{50} \times \sqrt[3]{50} \times \sqrt[3]{50}$.

4.1.77

a. Because distance is rate times time, the time will be distance over rate. The swim distance is given by $\sqrt{2500 + x^2}$ meters, so the time for swimming is $\frac{\sqrt{2500+x^2}}{2}$. For running, the distance is $50 - x$, so the time is $\frac{50-x}{4}$. Thus we have $T(x) = \frac{\sqrt{2500+x^2}}{2} + \frac{50-x}{4}$.

b. $T'(x) = \frac{1}{2} \cdot \frac{1}{2} \left(x^2 + 2500 \right)^{-1/2} \cdot 2x - \frac{1}{4} = \frac{x}{2\sqrt{x^2+2500}} - \frac{1}{4}$. This expression is zero when $\frac{x^2}{x^2+2500} = \frac{1}{4}$, so when $4x^2 = x^2 + 2500$, which occurs when $x^2 = \frac{2500}{3}$. So $x = \sqrt{\frac{2500}{3}} \approx 28.868$.

c. $T(0) = 37.5$, $T(28.868) \approx 34.151$, and $T(50) = 25\sqrt{2} \approx 35.355$. The absolute minimum occurs at the only critical point. The minimal crossing time is approximately 34.151 seconds.

d.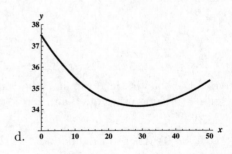

4.1.78

a. $f'(x) = 2x$, so $f'(a) = 2a$ is the slope at $x = a$. The slope of the line perpendicular is $-\frac{1}{2a}$.

b. We are looking for a line through (a, a^2) with slope $-\frac{1}{2a}$, so the equation is given by $y = -\frac{1}{2a}(x - a) + a^2$.

c. To find B's position, we find where the parabola and the line from the last part of this problem intersect. So we seek the solution to $x^2 = -\frac{1}{2a}x + \frac{1}{2} + a^2$, or $x^2 + \frac{1}{2a}x + (-a^2 - \frac{1}{2}) = 0$. By the quadratic formula, we find that $x = \frac{-2a^2 - 1}{2a}$ is the desired point. The other root is $x = a$ which coresponds to point A.

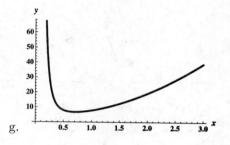

d. $F(a) = \left(a - \left(\frac{-2a^2 - 1}{2a}\right)\right)^2 + \left(a^2 - \frac{(2a^2+1)^2}{4a^2}\right)^2$

$= \frac{(4a^2+1)^2}{4a^2} + \left(\frac{4a^4 - 4a^4 - 4a^2 - 1}{4a^2}\right)^2 =$

$\frac{64a^6 + 48a^4 + 12a^2 + 1}{16a^4} = \frac{(4a^2+1)^3}{16a^4}$.

e. $F'(a) = \frac{16a^4 \cdot 3(4a^2+1)^2 \cdot 8a - (4a^2+1)^3 \cdot 64a^3}{256a^8} =$

$\frac{64a^3 \cdot (4a^2+1)^2 \left(6a^2 - (4a^2+1)\right)}{256a^8} = \frac{(4a^2+1)^2 \cdot (2a^2 - 1)}{4a^5}$.

The critical point of F for $a > 0$ occurs at $a = \sqrt{.5}$.

g.

f. The value of F at the critical point is $F(\sqrt{.5}) = \frac{27}{4}$. The points are at $A = (\sqrt{.5}, .5)$ and $B = (-\sqrt{2}, 2)$.

4.1.79

a. Note that since there is a local extreme value at 2 for f and since f is differentiable everywhere, we must have $f'(2) = 0$.

$g(2) = 2f(2) + 1 = 1$.

$h(2) = 2f(2) + 2 + 1 = 3$.

$g'(2) = 2 \cdot f'(2) + f(2) = 0$.

$h'(2) = 2f'(2) + f(2) + 1 = 1$.

b. h doesn't, since its derivative isn't zero at $x = 2$. However g might: for example, if $f(x) = (x - 2)^2$ then $g(x) = x(x - 2)^2 + 1$ has a local minimum at $x = 2$.

4.1.80 Because a parabola either opens up and has a minimum at its vertex, or open down and has a maximum at its vertex, it will always have exactly one extreme value. We have $f'(x) = 2ax + b$, which is zero when $x = -\frac{b}{2a}$, so that one critical point is the location of the vertex which gives the extreme point.

4.1.81

a. Because of the symmetry about the y-axis for an even function, a minimum at $x = c$ will correspond to a minimum at $x = -c$ as well.

b. Because of the symmetry about the origin, a minimum at $x = c$ will correspond to a maximum at $x = -c$. It is helpful to think about the symmetry about the origin as being the result of flipping about the y-axis and then flipping about the x-axis.

4.1.82

a. $f(-x) = -\frac{x}{((-x)^2 + 1)^n} = -\frac{x}{(x^2 + 1)^n} = -\frac{x}{(x^2 + 1)^n} = -f(x)$.

b. $f'(x) = \frac{(x^2+1)^n - x \cdot n(x^2+1)^{n-1} \cdot 2x}{(x^2+1)^{2n}} = \frac{(x^2+1)^{n-1}[x^2+1-2x^2n]}{(x^2+1)^{2n}} = \frac{1-(2n-1)x^2}{(x^2+1)^{n+1}}$. This quantity is zero when $x^2 = \frac{1}{2n-1}$, so $x = \pm\sqrt{\frac{1}{2n-1}}$ is a critical point.

c. The maximum value occurs at the positive critical number. The value of the maximum is given by $\frac{\sqrt{\frac{1}{2n-1}}}{\left(\left(\sqrt{\frac{1}{2n-1}}\right)^2+1\right)^n} = \frac{1}{\sqrt{2n-1}} \cdot \left(1 - \frac{1}{2n}\right)^n$. As $n \to \infty$, this quantity has limit 0.

d. Here are the graphs for $n = 1$, $n = 2$, and $n = 3$.

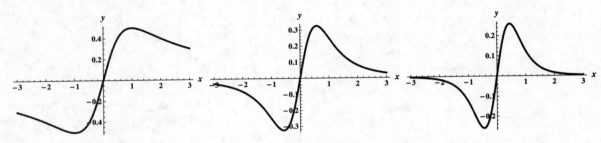

4.1.83

a. If $f(c)$ is a local maximum, then when x is near c but not equal to c, $f(c) \geq f(x)$, so $f(x) - f(c) \leq 0$.

b. When x is near to c but a little bigger than c, $x - c > 0$. So in this case, $\frac{f(x)-f(c)}{x-c} \leq 0$, since the numerator is negative (or 0) and the denominator is positive.

   Thus, $\lim\limits_{x \to c^+} \frac{f(x) - f(c)}{x - c} = f'(c) \leq 0$

c. When x is near to c but a little smaller than c, $x - c < 0$. So in this case, $\frac{f(x)-f(c)}{x-c} \geq 0$, since the numerator is negative (or 0) and the denominator is negative, making the quotient positive (or 0).

   Thus, $\lim\limits_{x \to c^-} \frac{f(x) - f(c)}{x - c} = f'(c) \geq 0$.

d. From the above, we have that $f'(c) \leq 0$ and $f'(c) \geq 0$, so $f'(c) = 0$.

4.2   What Derivatives Tell Us

4.2.1 If f' is positive on an interval, f is increasing on that interval. If f' is negative on an interval, f is decreasing on that interval.

4.2.2 The First Derivative Test can be used to tell whether or not a critical point is a local maximum or minimum, as follows: If $(c, f(c))$ is a critical point, we investigate the sign of f' for points that are just to the left and just to the right of c. If the sign of f' changes from positive to negative, then f is changing from increasing to decreasing at c, so there is a local maximum at c. If the signs of f' are changing from negative to positive, then f is changing from decreasing to increasing at c, so there is a local minimum at c. If the signs of f' are the same on either side of c, then there is neither kind of local extremum at $x = c$.

Note that if we find *all* of the critical points of f, and if the domain of f is an interval or union of intervals, then the critical points naturally divide up the domain into intervals on which we can check the sign of f' and look for places where the sign changes.

4.2.3

One such example is $f(x) = x^3$ at $x = 0$.

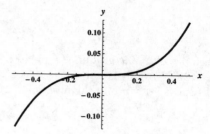

4.2.4 Suppose that c is the kind of critical point where $f'(c) = 0$. We can sometimes tell whether or not there is a local extremum at $x = c$ by simply looking at the sign of $f''(c)$. If $f''(c) > 0$, we know that $f(c)$ is a local minimum, and if $f''(c) < 0$, we know that $f(c)$ is a local maximum. One useful way to remember this is to also think about concavity, and imagine a nice parabola. If the second derivative is positive at a critical number, then the graph is concave up there, corresponding to a minimum. If the second derivative is negative, then the graph is concave down, corresponding to a maximum.

Note that if $f''(c) = 0$, it does not necessarily follow that there isn't a local extremum at $x = c$. The test doesn't tell us anything for sure in this case.

4.2.5 Under these circumstances the tangent lines lie below the graph of f.

4.2.6

The second derivative is positive to the left of the inflection point, and negative to the right.

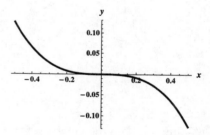

4.2.7 An inflection point is a point on the graph of a function where the concavity changes. Thus, if $(c, f(c))$ is an inflection point, either $f''(x) < 0$ for x a little less than c and $f''(x) > 0$ for x a little bigger than c, or vice versa.

4.2.8

$f(x) = x^4$ has this property at 0. Note that $f''(x) = 12x^2$, which is 0 at $x = 0$, but the function doesn't have an inflection point there.

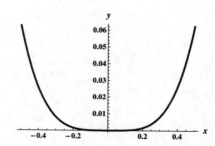

4.2.9

Yes, for example, consider $f(x) = 100 - x^2$ on the interval $(-8, 0)$. It is above the x axis, increasing, and concave down on that interval.

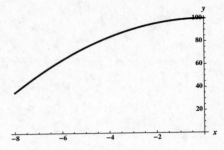

4.2.10 Because the Second Derivative Test is inconclusive, the First Derivative Test should be used in this case.

4.2.11

Such a function would be decreasing until $x = 2$, then increasing until $x = 5$, and then decreasing again after that.

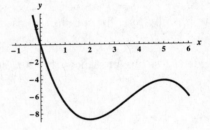

4.2.12

Such a function would be increasing on $(-\infty, -1)$, and decreasing on $(-1, \infty)$. It should have a point of non-differentiability at $x = -1$.

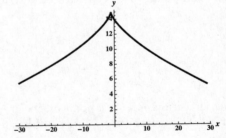

4.2.13

Such a function has extrema (minima) at 0 and 4, where the y value is zero. The function should never go below the x axis.

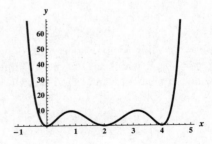

4.2.14

Such a function is never decreasing, but is flat at -2, 2, and 4.

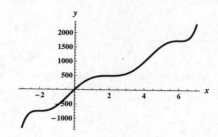

4.2.15

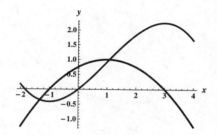

4.2.16

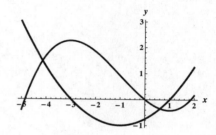

4.2.17

$f'(x) = -2x$, which is zero exactly when $x = 0$. On $(-\infty, 0)$ we note that $f' > 0$, so that f is increasing on this interval. On $(0, \infty)$, we note that $f' < 0$, so f is decreasing on this interval.

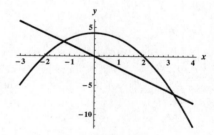

4.2.18

$f'(x) = 2x$, which is zero exactly when $x = 0$. On $(-\infty, 0)$ we note that $f' < 0$, so that f is decreasing on this interval. On $(0, \infty)$, we note that $f' > 0$, so f is increasing on this interval.

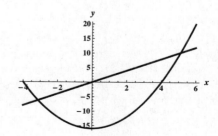

4.2.19

$f'(x) = 2(x-1)$, which is zero exactly when $x = 1$. On $(-\infty, 1)$ we note that $f' < 0$, so that f is decreasing on this interval. On $(1, \infty)$, we note that $f' > 0$, so f is increasing on this interval.

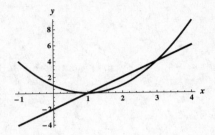

4.2.20

$f'(x) = 3x^2 + 4$, which is always positive, because it is always 4 or greater. So f is increasing on $(-\infty, \infty)$.

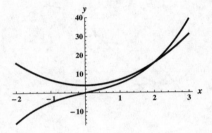

4.2.21

$f'(x) = 1 - 2x$, which is 0 when $x = 1/2$. On $(-\infty, 1/2)$ $f' > 0$ so f is increasing on this interval, while on $(1/2, \infty)$ $f' < 0$, so f is decreasing on this interval.

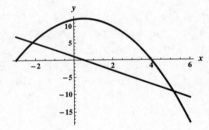

4.2.22

$f'(x) = 4x^3 - 12x^2 + 8x = 4x(x^2 - 3x + 2) = 4x(x-2)(x-1)$, which is 0 when x is 0, 1, or 2. On $(-\infty, 0)$ $f' < 0$ so f is decreasing. On $(0,1)$, $f' > 0$ so f is increasing, on $(1,2)$ $f' < 0$ so f is decreasing, and on $(2, \infty)$ $f' > 0$ so f is increasing.

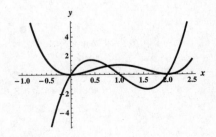

4.2.23

$f'(x) = -x^3 + 3x^2 - 2x = -x(x^2 - 3x + 2) = -x(x-1)(x-2)$. This is zero when $x = 0$, $x = 1$, and $x = 2$. Note that $f'(-1) > 0$, and $f'(1.5) > 0$, while $f'(.5) < 0$, and $f'(3) < 0$. So f is increasing on $(-\infty, 0)$ and on $(1, 2)$, while it is decreasing on $(0, 1)$ and on $(2, \infty)$.

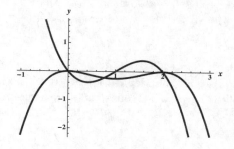

4.2.24

$f'(x) = 10x^4 - 15x^3 + 5x^2 = 5x^2(2x^2 - 3x + 1) = 5x^2(x-1)(2x-1)$. This is zero when $x = 0$, $x = 1$ and $x = 1/2$. Note that $f'(-1) > 0$, and $f'(1/4) > 0$. Because the given function is continuous, we can combine the intervals and conclude that f is increasing on $(-\infty, 1/2)$. Also, $f'(3/4) < 0$, so f is decreasing on $(1/2, 1)$, and $f'(2) > 0$, so f is increasing on $(1, \infty)$.

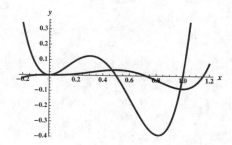

4.2.25

$f'(x) = 2x \ln x^2 + x^2 \cdot \frac{1}{x^2} \cdot 2x = 2x(\ln x^2 + 1)$. This is undefined for $x = 0$, and when $\ln x^2 + 1 = 0$. For $x > 0$, this occurs when $2 \ln x + 1 = 0$, which occurs when $\ln x = -1/2$, or $x = \frac{1}{\sqrt{e}}$. By symmetry, we also have that $f'(x)$ is zero for $x = -\frac{1}{\sqrt{e}}$. Note that $\frac{1}{\sqrt{e}} \approx .6$, and that $f'(-1) < 0$, $f'(-1/2) > 0$, $f'(1/2) < 0$, and $f'(1) > 0$. Thus, f is decreasing on $(-\infty, -1/\sqrt{e})$ and on $(0, 1/\sqrt{e})$, and is increasing on $(-1/\sqrt{e}, 0)$ and on $(1/\sqrt{e}, \infty)$.

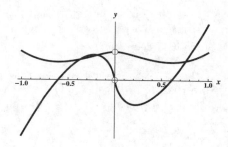

4.2.26

$f'(x) = \frac{(e^{2x}+1)e^x - e^x(2e^{2x})}{(e^{2x}+1)^2} = \frac{e^x(1-e^{2x})}{(e^{2x}+1)^2}$. This is zero when $e^{2x} = 1$, which occurs when $x = 0$. Note that $f'(-1) > 0$ and $f'(1) < 0$, so f is increasing on $(-\infty, 0)$ and decreasing on $(0, \infty)$.

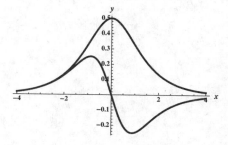

4.2.27 $f'(x) = -9\sin 3x$, which is 0 for $3x = -3\pi, -2\pi, -\pi, 0, \pi, 2\pi$, and 3π, which corresponds to $x = -\pi, -2\pi/3, -\pi/3, 0, \pi/3, 2\pi/3$ and π. Note that $f'(-5\pi/6) = 9 > 0$, $f'(-\pi/2) = -9 < 0$, $f'(-\pi/6) = 9 > 0$, $f'(\pi/6) = -9 < 0$, $f'(\pi/2) = 9 > 0$, and $f'(5\pi/6) = -9 < 0$. Thus f is increasing on $(-\pi, -2\pi/3)$, on $(-\pi/3, 0)$, and on $(\pi/3, 2\pi/3)$, while f is decreasing on $(-2\pi/3, -\pi/3)$, on $(0, \pi/3)$, and on $(2\pi/3, \pi)$.

4.2.28 $f'(x) = 2(\cos x)(-\sin x) = -\sin 2x$. This is 0 for $2x = -2\pi, -\pi, 0, \pi$, and 2π, which corresponds to $x = -\pi, -\pi/2, 0, \pi/2$, and π. Note that $f'(-3\pi/4) = -1 < 0$, $f'(-\pi/4) = 1 > 0$, $f'(\pi/4) = -1 < 0$, and $f'(3\pi/4) = 1 > 0$. So f is decreasing on $(-\pi, -\pi/2)$ and on $(0, \pi/2)$, and is increasing on $(-\pi/2, 0)$ and on $(\pi/2, \pi)$.

4.2.29 $f'(x) = (2/3)x^{-1/3}(x^2 - 4) + x^{2/3} \cdot 2x = \frac{2(x^2-4)}{3x^{1/3}} + \frac{2x^{5/3}}{1} \cdot \frac{3x^{1/3}}{3x^{1/3}} = \frac{8x^2-8}{3x^{1/3}} = \frac{8(x+1)(x-1)}{3x^{1/3}}$. This is zero for $x = \pm 1$ and is undefined for $x = 0$. Note that $f'(-8) = -84 < 0$, $f'(-1/8) = \frac{21}{4} > 0$, $f'(1/8) = \frac{-21}{4} < 0$, and $f''(8) = 84 > 0$. Thus f is decreasing on $(-\infty, -1)$ and on $(0, 1)$, while f is increasing on $(-1, 0)$ and on $(1, \infty)$.

4.2.30 $f'(x) = 2x\sqrt{9 - x^2} + x^2 \cdot \frac{1}{2\sqrt{9-x^2}} \cdot (-2x) = \frac{2x(9-x^2)}{\sqrt{9-x^2}} + -\frac{x^3}{\sqrt{9-x^2}} = \frac{18x-3x^3}{\sqrt{9-x^2}} = \frac{3x(6-x^2)}{\sqrt{9-x^2}}$. This is zero when $x = 0$, and when $x = \pm\sqrt{6}$. Note that $\sqrt{6} \approx 2.4$. Also note that $f'(-2.7) > 0$, $f'(-1) < 0$, $f'(1) > 0$ and $f'(2.7) < 0$. Thus, f is increasing on $(-3, -\sqrt{6})$ and on $(0, \sqrt{6})$, and is decreasing on $(-\sqrt{6}, 0)$ and on $(\sqrt{6}, 3)$.

4.2.31 $f'(x) = \frac{1}{x^2+1}$, which is always positive, so f is increasing on $(-\infty, \infty)$.

4.2.32 $f'(x) = \frac{1}{x}$, which is positive on the interval $(0, \infty)$ and which is negative on $(-\infty, 0)$. Thus, f is increasing on $(0, \infty)$ and decreasing on $(-\infty, 0)$.

4.2.33 $f'(x) = -60x^4 + 300x^3 - 240x^2 = -60x^2(x^2 - 5x + 4) = -60x^2(x-4)(x-1)$. This is 0 for $x = 0$, $x = 1$, and $x = 4$. Note that $f'(-1) = -600 < 0$, $f'(1/2) = -26.25 < 0$, $f'(2) = 480 > 0$, and $f'(5) = -6000 < 0$. Thus f is increasing on $(1, 4)$ and is decreasing on $(-\infty, 1)$ and on $(4, \infty)$.

4.2.34 $f'(x) = 2x - \frac{2}{x} = \frac{2(x^2-1)}{x}$ which is 0 for $x = 1$. Note that the domain of f is $(0, \infty)$ and that $f'(1/2) = -3 < 0$ and $f'(2) = 3 > 0$, so f is decreasing on $(0, 1)$ and increasing on $(1, \infty)$.

4.2.35 $f'(x) = -8x^3 + 2x = -2x(4x^2 - 1) = -2x(2x + 1)(2x - 1)$. This is zero for $x = 0$ and $x = \pm 1/2$. Note that $f'(-1) > 0$, $f'(-1/4) < 0$, $f'(1/4) > 0$, and $f'(1) < 0$, so f is increasing on $(-\infty, -1/2)$ and on $(0, 1/2)$, while it is decreasing on $(-1/2, 0)$ and on $(1/2, \infty)$.

4.2.36 $f'(x) = x^3 - 8x^2 + 15x = x(x^2 - 8x + 15) = x(x - 5)(x - 3)$. This is zero when $x = 0$, $x = 3$, and $x = 5$. Note that $f'(-1) < 0$, $f'(1) > 0$, $f'(4) < 0$, and $f'(6) > 0$. Thus f is increasing on $(0, 3)$ and on $(5, \infty)$, while it is decreasing on $(-\infty, 0)$ and on $(3, 5)$.

4.2.37 We have $f'(x) = e^{-x^2/2} + xe^{-x^2/2} \cdot (-x) = (1 - x^2)e^{-x^2/2}$. This is zero only when $x = \pm 1$. Note that $f'(-2) = -3e^{-2} < 0$, $f'(0) = 1 > 0$, and $f'(2) = -3e^{-2} < 0$. Thus f is decreasing on $(-\infty, -1)$ and on $(1, \infty)$, and is increasing on $(-1, 1)$.

4.2.38 $f'(x) = \frac{1}{1+\left(\frac{x}{x^2+2}\right)^2} \cdot \frac{(x^2+2)-x(2x)}{(x^2+2)^2} = \frac{1}{1+\left(\frac{x}{x^2+2}\right)^2} \cdot \frac{2-x^2}{(x^2+2)^2}$. Note that the first factor is always positive, so the expression is zero exactly when $2 - x^2 = 0$, so only at $\pm\sqrt{2}$. Note that $f'(0) > 0$ while $f'(\pm 2) < 0$, so f is increasing on $(-\sqrt{2}, \sqrt{2})$ and decreasing on $(-\infty, -\sqrt{2})$ and on $(\sqrt{2}, \infty)$.

4.2.39

    a. $f'(x) = 2x$, so $x = 0$ is the only critical point.

    b. Note that $f' < 0$ for $x < 0$ and $f' > 0$ for $x > 0$, so f has a local minimum of $f(0) = 3$ at $x = 0$.

    c. Note that $f(-3) = 12$, $f(0) = 3$ and $f(2) = 7$, so the absolute maximum is 12 and the absolute minimum is 3.

4.2.40

    a. $f'(x) = -2x - 1$, which exists everywhere and is zero only for $x = -1/2$, so that is the only critical point.

b. Note that $f'(-2) = 3 > 0$ and $f'(0) = -1 < 0$, so f has a local maximum of $f(-1/2) = 9/4$ at $x = -1/2$.

c. Note that $f(-4) = -10$ and $f(4) = -18$, so the absolute maximum is 9/4 at $x = -1/2$ and the absolute minimum is -18 at $x = 4$.

4.2.41

a. $f'(x) = x \cdot \frac{1}{2}(4 - x^2)^{-1/2} \cdot (-2x) + \sqrt{4 - x^2} \cdot 1 = \frac{4 - 2x^2}{\sqrt{4 - x^2}}$, which exists everywhere on $(-2, 2)$ and is zero only for $x = \pm\sqrt{2}$, so those are the only critical points.

b. Note that $f'(-1.5) < 0$, $f'(0) > 0$ and $f'(1.5) < 0$, so f has a local minimum of $f(-\sqrt{2}) = -2$ and a local maximum of $f(\sqrt{2}) = 2$.

c. Note that $f(-2) = 0 = f(2)$. So the absolute maximum is 2 at $x = \sqrt{2}$ and the absolute minimum is -2 at $x = -\sqrt{2}$.

4.2.42

a. $f'(x) = 6x^2 + 6x - 12 = 6(x + 2)(x - 1)$, which exists everywhere and is 0 at $x = -2$ (an endpoint of the given domain) and $x = 1$.

b. Note that $f'(-1.5) < 0$ and $f'(2) > 0$, so f has a local minimum at $x = 1$ of $f(1) = -6$.

c. Note that $f(-2) = 21$ and $f[4] = 129$, so the absolute maximum of f on $[-2, 4]$ is 129 and the absolute minimum is -6.

4.2.43

a. $f'(x) = -3x^2 + 9$, which is zero when $9 = 3x^2$, or $x^2 = 3$. So the critical points are at $x = \pm\sqrt{3}$.

b. Note that $f'(-2) < 0$, $f'(0) > 0$, and $f'(2) < 0$, so there is a local minimum of $f(-\sqrt{3}) = -6\sqrt{3}$ and a local maximum of $f(\sqrt{3}) = 6\sqrt{3}$.

c. There is an absolute maximum of 28 at $x = -4$ and an absolute minimum of $-6\sqrt{3}$ at $x = -\sqrt{3}$.

4.2.44

a. $f'(x) = 10x^4 - 20x^3 - 30x^2 = 10x^2(x^2 - 2x - 3) = 10x^2(x + 1)(x - 3)$. This is zero for $x = 0$, $x = -1$, and $x = 3$.

b. Note that $f'(-2) > 0$, $f'(-.5) < 0$, $f'(1) < 0$, and $f'(4) > 0$. So there is a local maximum of $f(-1) = 7$ and a local minimum of $f(3) = -185$. There isn't any sort of extremum at $x = 0$.

c. The local minimum value of -185 is an absolute minimum, and the absolute maximum is $f(4) = 132$.

4.2.45

a. $f'(x) = x^{2/3} + (x - 5) \cdot \frac{2}{3}x^{-1/3} = \frac{5x - 10}{3x^{1/3}}$, which is undefined at $x = 0$ and is 0 at $x = 2$. So these are the two critical points.

b. Note that $f'(-1) > 0$ and $f'(1) < 0$, and $f'(3) > 0$ so f has a local maximum at $x = 0$ of $f(0) = 0$ and a local minimum at $x = 2$ of $-3\sqrt[3]{4} \approx -4.762$.

c. Note that $f(-5) = -10\sqrt[3]{25} \approx -29.24$, $f(0) = 0$, and $f(5) = 0$, so the absolute maximum of f on $[-5, 5]$ is 0 and the absolute minimum is $-10\sqrt[3]{25}$.

4.2.46 First note that even though the interval given is $[-4, 4]$, the function isn't defined at $x = \pm 1$, so we will assume that the given domain is $[-4, -1) \cup (-1, 1) \cup (1, 4]$.

a. $f'(x) = \frac{(x^2-1)\cdot 2x - (x^2)(2x)}{(x^2-1)^2} = -\frac{2x}{(x^2-1)^2}$, which is 0 only at $x = 0$.

b. Note that $f'(-2) > 0$ and $f'(-1/2) > 0$, and $f'(1/2) < 0$ and $f'(2) < 0$, so f is increasing on $(-4, -1)$ and on $(-1, 0)$, while it is decreasing on $(0, 1)$ and on $(1, 4)$. There is a local maximum of 0 at $x = 0$.

c. Because f becomes arbitrarily large as x approaches 1 from the left, and arbitrarily large in the negative sense as x approaches 1 from the right, it has no absolute extrema.

4.2.47

a. $f'(x) = \frac{\sqrt{x}}{x} + \frac{\ln x}{2\sqrt{x}} = \frac{2 + \ln x}{2\sqrt{x}}$. This is defined everywhere on $(0, \infty)$ and is 0 only at $x = e^{-2}$.

b. Note that $f' < 0$ on $(0, \frac{1}{e^2})$ and $f' > 0$ on $(\frac{1}{e^2}, \infty)$, so there is a local minimum at $x = \frac{1}{e^2}$.

c. Because there is only one critical point, the local minimum at $x = \frac{1}{e^2}$ yields an absolute minimum of $f(1/e^2) = -\frac{2}{e} \approx -.736$. There is no absolute maximum because f increases without bound as $x \to \infty$.

4.2.48

a. $f'(x) = \frac{1}{x^2+1} - 3x^2 = \frac{-3x^4 - 3x^2 + 1}{x^2+1}$. This is 0 when $-3x^4 - 3x^2 + 1 = 0$. Letting $u = x^2$, we seek roots of $-3u^2 - 3u + 1$. Using the quadratic formula and solving for u, and then writing in terms of x, we have the roots $x = \pm\sqrt{\frac{1}{6}\left(\sqrt{21} - 3\right)} \approx \pm 0.514$. Let $r_1 = -\sqrt{\frac{1}{6}\left(\sqrt{21} - 3\right)}$ and $r_2 = \sqrt{\frac{1}{6}\left(\sqrt{21} - 3\right)}$.

b. Note that $f' < 0$ on $(-1, r_1)$ and $f' > 0$ on (r_1, r_2), and $f' < 0$ on $(r_2, 1)$. Thus there is a local minimum at r_1 and a local maximum at r_2.

c. Note that $f(-1) = -\pi/4 + 1 \approx .215$ and $f(1) = \pi/4 - 1 \approx -.215$, and $f(r_1) \approx -.339$ and $f(r_2) \approx .339$. The absolute maximum is $f(r_2) \approx .339$ and the absolute minimum is $f(r_1) \approx -.339$.

4.2.49 $f'(x) = -xe^{-x} + e^{-x} = e^{-x}(1 - x)$, which is 0 only for $x = 1$. Note that f is continuous on $(-\infty, \infty)$ and contains only one critical point.

Note that $f' > 0$ for $x < 1$ and $f' < 0$ for $x > 1$. So there is a local maximum of $f(1) = 1/e$ at $x = 1$. The local maximum of $1/e$ at $x = 1$ is an absolute maximum. There is no absolute minimum, because the function is unbounded in the negative direction as $x \to -\infty$.

4.2.50 Note that f is continuous on $(0, \infty)$.

$f'(x) = 4 - \frac{1}{2x^{3/2}} = \frac{8x^{3/2} - 1}{2x^{3/2}}$, which exists for $x > 0$. This quantity is 0 for $x = \frac{1}{4}$. So f has only one critical point on $(0, \infty)$.

Note that $f' < 0$ on $(0, 1/4)$ and $f' > 0$ on $(1/4, \infty)$. So there is a local minimum of $f(1/4) = 3$ at $x = 1/4$.

The local minimum of 3 at $x = 1/4$ is an absolute minimum. There is no absolute maximum, because the function is unbounded as $x \to \infty$.

4.2.51 Note that A is continuous on $(0, \infty)$.

$A'(r) = -\frac{24}{r^2} + 4\pi r = \frac{4\pi r^3 - 24}{r^2}$, which is 0 for $r = \sqrt[3]{6/\pi}$, so there is only one critical point on the stated interval.

Note that $A' < 0$ on $(0, \sqrt[3]{6/\pi})$ and $A' > 0$ on $(\sqrt[3]{6/\pi}, \infty)$, so there is a local minimum of $A(\sqrt[3]{6/\pi}) = 36\sqrt[3]{\pi/6}$.

The local minimum mentioned above is an absolute minimum. There is no absolute maximum, because A is unbounded as $r \to \infty$.

4.2.52 Note that f is continuous on $(-\infty, 3)$. $f'(x) = -\frac{x}{2\sqrt{3-x}} + \sqrt{3-x} = \frac{-3x+6}{2\sqrt{3-x}}$, which is 0 only for $x = 2$, so there is only one critical point on the stated interval. Note that $f' > 0$ for $x < 2$ and $f' < 0$ on $(2, 3)$. Thus there is a local maximum of $f(2) = 2$ which is also an absolute maximum. There is no absolute minimum, because the function is unbounded in the negative direction as $x \to -\infty$.

4.2.53

The function sketched should be increasing and concave up everywhere.

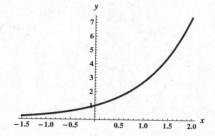

4.2.54

The function sketched should be concave up everywhere, decreasing for $x < 0$ and increasing for $x > 0$.

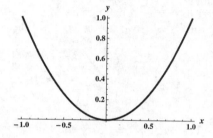

4.2.55

The function sketched should be decreasing everywhere, concave down for $x < 0$, and concave up for $x > 0$.

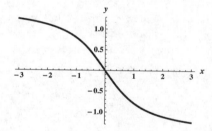

4.2.56

The function sketched should be decreasing everywhere, concave up for $x < 0$, and concave down for $x > 0$.

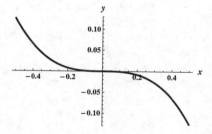

4.2.57 $f'(x) = 4x^3 - 6x^2$, so $f''(x) = 12x^2 - 12x = 12x(x - 1)$. Note that f'' is zero when $x = 0$ and $x = 1$, so these are potential inflection points. Also note that $f''(-1) > 0$, $f''(.5) < 0$, and $f''(2) > 0$, so f is concave up on $(-\infty, 0)$ and on $(1, \infty)$, and is concave down on $(0, 1)$. There are inflection points at $(0, 1)$ and $(1, 0)$.

4.2.58 $f'(x) = -4x^3 - 6x^2 + 24x$, so $f''(x) = -12x^2 - 12x + 24 = -12(x^2 + x - 2) = -12(x + 2)(x - 1)$. Note the f'' is zero for $x = -2$ and $x = 1$, so these are potential inflection points. Now note that $f''(-3) < 0$, $f''(0) > 0$, and $f''(2) < 0$. Thus f is concave up on $(-2, 1)$ and is concave down on $(-\infty, -2)$ and on $(1, \infty)$. There are inflection points at $(-2, 48)$ and $(1, 9)$.

4.2.59 $f'(x) = 20x^3 - 60x^2$, and $f''(x) = 60x^2 - 120x = 60x(x-2)$. This is 0 for $x = 0$ and for $x = 2$. Note that $f''(-1) > 0$, $f''(1) < 0$, and $f''(3) > 0$. So f is concave up on $(-\infty, 0)$, concave down on $(0, 2)$, and concave up on $(2, \infty)$. There are inflection points at $x = 0$ and $x = 2$.

4.2.60 $f'(x) = -1(1 + x^2)^{-2} \cdot 2x = -\frac{2x}{(1+x^2)^2}$. $f''(x) = \frac{(-2)(1+x^2)^2 - (-2x) \cdot 2 \cdot (1+x^2) \cdot 2x}{(1+x^2)^4} = \frac{6x^2 - 2}{(1+x^2)^3}$. Note that f'' is 0 for $x = \pm\sqrt{1/3}$. Also, $f''(-1) > 0$, $f''(0) < 0$, and $f''(1) > 0$, so f is concave up on $(-\infty, \sqrt{1/3})$, concave down on $(-\sqrt{1/3}, \sqrt{1/3})$, and concave up on $(\sqrt{1/3}, \infty)$. There are inflection points at $x = \pm\sqrt{1/3}$.

4.2.61 $f'(x) = e^x(x-3) + e^x = e^x(x-3+1) = e^x(x-2)$. $f''(x) = e^x(x-2) + e^x = e^x(x-2+1) = e^x(x-1)$. Note that f'' is zero only at $x = 1$. Also note that $f''(0) < 0$ and $f''(2) > 0$, so f is concave down on $(-\infty, 1)$ and is concave up on $(1, \infty)$. The point $(1, -2e)$ is an inflection point.

4.2.62 $f'(x) = 4x \ln x + 2x^2 \cdot \frac{1}{x} - 10x = 4x \ln x - 8x$. $f''(x) = 4 \ln x + 4x \cdot \frac{1}{x} - 8 = 4 \ln x - 4$. Note that f'' is zero when $\ln x = 1$, which occurs for $x = e$. Also note that $f''(1) < 0$ and $f''(4) > 0$, so f is concave down on $(0, e)$ and is concave up on (e, ∞). There is an inflection point at $(e, -3e^2)$.

4.2.63 $g'(t) = \frac{6t}{3t^2+1}$, and $g''(t) = \frac{(3t^2+1) \cdot 6 - 6t(6t)}{(3t^2+1)^2} = \frac{6-18t^2}{(3t^2+1)^2}$. Note that g'' is 0 for $t = \pm\sqrt{1/3}$. Also, $g''(-1) < 0$, $g''(0) > 0$, and $g''(1) < 0$, so g is concave down on $(-\infty, -\sqrt{1/3})$ and on $(\sqrt{1/3}, \infty)$, and is concave up on $(-\sqrt{1/3}, \sqrt{1/3})$. There are inflection points at $t = \pm\sqrt{1/3}$.

4.2.64 $g'(x) = \frac{1}{3\sqrt[3]{(x-4)^2}}$, and $g''(x) = -\frac{2}{9\sqrt[3]{(x-4)^5}}$. Note that g'' is never zero, but is undefined at $x = 4$. On $(-\infty, 4)$ we have $g'' > 0$ so g is concave up, and on $(4, \infty)$ we have $g'' < 0$, so g is concave down. There is an inflection point at $(4, 0)$.

4.2.65 $f'(x) = -xe^{-x^2/2}$, and $f''(x) = (-x)(-xe^{-x^2/2}) + e^{-x^2/2} \cdot -1 = e^{-x^2/2}(x^2 - 1)$. Note that $f''(x)$ is 0 for $x = \pm 1$. Also note that $f'' > 0$ on $(-\infty, -1)$ and on $(1, \infty)$, so f is concave up there, while on $(-1, 1)$ f is concave down because $f'' < 0$ on that interval. The inflection points are at $(\pm 1, e^{-1/2})$.

4.2.66 $f'(x) = \frac{1}{x^2+1}$ and $f''(x) = -\frac{2x}{(1+x^2)^2}$. Note that f'' is 0 only at $x = 0$. On $(-\infty, 0)$ we note that $f''(x) > 0$ so f is concave up, and on $(0, \infty)$ we note that $f''(x) < 0$ so f is concave down. There is an inflection point at $(0, 0)$.

4.2.67 $f'(x) = \sqrt{x}/x + (\ln x)\left(\frac{1}{2\sqrt{x}}\right) = \frac{2 + \ln x}{2\sqrt{x}}$. $f''(x) = \frac{2\sqrt{x}/x - (2 + \ln x)/\sqrt{x}}{(2\sqrt{x})^2} = -\frac{\ln x}{4\sqrt{x^3}}$. Note that f'' is 0 only at $x = 1$. On $(0, 1)$ we note that $f'' > 0$ so f is concave up, and on $(1, \infty)$ we note that $f'' < 0$ so f is concave down. There is an inflection point at $(1, 0)$.

4.2.68 $h'(t) = -2\sin 2t$ and $h''(t) = -4\cos 2t$, which on the stated domain is 0 when $2t = -3\pi/2, -\pi/2, \pi/2$, and $3\pi/2$, which means for $t = -3\pi/4, -\pi/4, \pi/4$, and $3\pi/4$. $h'' < 0$ on $(-\pi, -3\pi/4)$, and on $(-\pi/4, \pi/4)$, and on $(3\pi/4, \pi)$, so h is concave down those intervals, while $h'' > 0$ on $(-3\pi/4, -\pi/4)$ and on $(\pi/4, 3\pi/4)$, so h is concave up on those intervals. There are inflection points at $t = -3\pi/4$, $t = -\pi/4$, $t = \pi/4$, and $t = 3\pi/4$.

4.2.69 $g'(t) = 15t^4 - 120t^3 + 240t^2$, and $g''(t) = 60t^3 - 360t^2 + 480t = 60t(t-2)(t-4)$. Note that g'' is 0 for $t = 0, 2$, and 4. Note also that $g'' < 0$ on $(-\infty, 0)$ and on $(2, 4)$, so g is concave down on those intervals, while $g'' > 0$ on $(0, 2)$ and on $(4, \infty)$, so g is concave up there. There are inflection points at $t = 0, 2$, and 4.

4.2.70 $f'(x) = 8x^3 + 24x^2 + 24x - 1$, and $f''(x) = 24x^2 + 48x + 24 = 24(x+1)^2$. Note that this quantity is always greater than 0 for $x \neq -1$, and is 0 only at $x = -1$. Thus f is concave up on $(-\infty, -1)$ and on $(-1, \infty)$, and because f and f' are continuous at -1, we can say that f is concave up on $(-\infty, \infty)$.

4.2.71 $f'(x) = 3x^2 - 6x = 3x(x-2)$. This is zero when $x = 0$ and when $x = 2$, and these are the critical points. $f''(x) = 6x - 6$. Note that $f''(0) < 0$ and $f''(2) > 0$. Thus by the Second Derivative Test, there is a local maximum at $x = 0$ and a local minimum at $x = 2$.

4.2.72 $f'(x) = 12x - 3x^2 = 3x(4 - x)$. This is zero when $x = 0$ and when $x = 4$, and these are the critical points. $f''(x) = 12 - 6x$. Note that $f''(0) > 0$ and $f''(4) < 0$, so there is a local minimum at 0 and a local maximum at 4.

4.2.73 $f'(x) = -2x$, so $x = 0$ is a critical point. $f''(x) = -2$, so $f''(0) = -2$ and the critical point yields a local maximum.

4.2.74 $g'(x) = 3x^2$, so $x = 0$ is a critical point. $g''(x) = 6x$ so $g''(0) = 0$ and the test is inconclusvive.

4.2.75 $f'(x) = e^x(x - 7) + e^x = e^x(x - 6)$. This is zero when $x = 6$, and this is a critical point. $f''(x) = e^x(x - 6) + e^x = e^x(x - 5)$. Note that $f''(6) > 0$, so there is a local minimum at $x = 6$.

4.2.76 $f'(x) = e^x(x^2 - 7x - 12) + e^x(2x - 7) = e^x(x^2 - 5x - 19)$. This is zero for $x = \frac{5 \pm \sqrt{25 - 4 \cdot 1 \cdot (-19)}}{2} = \frac{5 \pm \sqrt{101}}{2}$, so these are critical points. Note that these values are approximately -2.52 and 7.52. We have $f''(x) = e^x(x^2 - 5x - 19) + e^x(2x - 5) = e^x(x^2 - 3x - 24)$. Evaluating f'' at these points gives $f''\left(\frac{5 - \sqrt{101}}{2}\right) < 0$ and $f''\left(\frac{5 + \sqrt{101}}{2}\right) > 0$, so there is a local maximum at $\frac{5 - \sqrt{101}}{2}$ and a local minimum at $\frac{5 + \sqrt{101}}{2}$.

4.2.77 $f'(x) = 6x^2 - 6x = 6x(x - 1)$, so $x = 0$ and $x = 1$ are critical points. $f''(x) = 12x - 6$, so $f''(1) = 6 > 0$, so the critical point at $x = 1$ yields a local minimum. Also, $f''(0) = -6 < 0$, so the critical point at 0 yields a local maximum.

4.2.78 $f'(x) = 4x^3 e^{-x} + x^4 e^{-x} \cdot (-1) = (4x^3 - x^4)e^{-x}$, so $x = 0$ and $x = 4$ are critical points. We have

$$f''(x) = (12x^2 - 4x^3)e^{-x} + (4x^3 - x^4)e^{-x} \cdot (-1) = (12x^2 - 8x^3 + x^4)e^{-x},$$

and then $f''(4) = (12 \cdot 16 - 8 \cdot 64 + 256)e^{-4} = -64e^{-4} < 0$, so $x = 4$ corresponds to a local maximum. However, $f''(0) = 0$, so the Second Derivative Test is inconclusive about the point $x = 0$. But because $f'(x) < 0$ for $x < 0$ but close to zero, and $f'(x) > 0$ for $x > 0$ but close to zero, the First Derivative Test assures us that there is a local minimum at $x = 0$.

4.2.79 $f'(x) = x^2 \cdot (-e^{-x}) + e^{-x} \cdot 2x = e^{-x}(2x - x^2)$, which is zero for $x = 0$ and $x = 2$, so these are the critical points. $f''(x) = e^{-x}(2 - 2x) + (2x - x^2)(-e^{-x}) = e^{-x}(2 - 4x + x^2)$. Note that $f''(0) = 2 > 0$, so there is a local minimum at $x = 0$. Also, $f''(2) = -2e^{-2} < 0$, so there is a local maximum at $x = 2$.

4.2.80

$$g'(x) = \frac{(2 - 12x^2)(4x^3) - x^4(-24x)}{(2 - 12x^2)^2} = \frac{-24x^5 + 8x^3}{(2 - 12x^2)^2} = 2\left(\frac{-3x^5 + x^3}{(1 - 6x^2)^2}\right).$$

g' is zero at 0 and at $\pm\frac{1}{\sqrt{3}}$. We have

$$g''(x) = 2\left(\frac{(1 - 6x^2)^2(-15x^4 + 3x^2) - (-3x^5 + x^3)(2(1 - 6x^2) \cdot (-12x))}{(1 - 6x^2)^4}\right)$$

$$= 2\left(\frac{(1 - 6x^2)((1 - 6x^2)(-15x^4 + 3x^2) - (72x^6 - 24x^4))}{(1 - 6x^2)^4}\right)$$

$$= 2\left(\frac{-15x^4 + 3x^2 + 90x^6 - 18x^4 - 72x^6 + 24x^4}{(1 - 6x^2)^3}\right)$$

$$= 2\left(\frac{3x^2 - 9x^4 + 18x^6}{(1 - 6x^2)^3}\right)$$

$$= 6\left(\frac{x^2 - 3x^4 + 6x^6}{(1 - 6x^2)^3}\right).$$

Then $g''\left(\pm\frac{1}{\sqrt{3}}\right) = -\frac{4}{3}$, so these critical points give local maxima by the Second Derivative Test. However, $g''(0) = 0$, so the Second Derivative Test is inconclusive at $x = 0$. Using the First Derivative Test, note that $0.5 < \frac{1}{\sqrt{3}}$, and $g'(0.5) = 0.25 > 0$, and using the fact that g' is an odd function, $g'(-0.5) = -0.25 < 0$, so there is a local minimum for g at $x = 0$.

4.2.81 $f'(x) = 4x \ln x + 2x^2 \cdot \frac{1}{x} - 22x = 4x \ln x - 20x = 4x(\ln x - 5)$. This is zero for $x = e^5$, so that is the critical point. $f''(x) = 4\ln x + 4x \cdot \frac{1}{x} - 20 = 4\ln x - 16$. Note that $f''(e^5) > 0$, so there is a local minimum at e^5.

4.2.82 Note that $f(x)$ can be written as $f(x) = \frac{12}{7}x^{7/2} - 4x^{5/2}$. Thus $f'(x) = 6x^{5/2} - 10x^{3/2} = 2x^{3/2}(3x - 5)$. This is zero on the given interval only at $x = 5/3$, so that is the critical point. $f''(x) = 15x^{3/2} - 15x^{1/2}$, and $f''(5/3) > 0$, so there is a local minimum at $x = 5/3$.

4.2.83

a. True. $f'(x) > 0$ implies that f is increasing, and $f''(x) < 0$ implies that f' is decreasing. So f is increasing, but at a decreasing rate.

b. False. In fact, if $f'(c)$ exists and isn't zero, then there isn't any kind of local extrema at $x = c$.

c. True. In fact, if two functions differ by a constant, then all of their derivatives are the same.

d. False. For example, consider $f(x) = x$ and $g(x) = x - 10$. Both are increasing, but $f(x)g(x) = x^2 - 10x$ is decreasing on $(-\infty, 5)$.

e. False. A continuous function with two local maxima must have a local minimum in between.

4.2.84

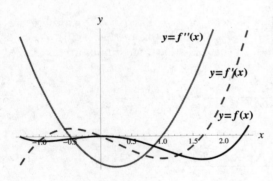

4.2.85

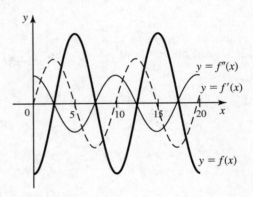

4.2.86

a. Not Possible. The closest thing would be a function like $f(x) = x^{2/3}$ which is positive and is concave down on $(-\infty, 0)$ and on $(0, \infty)$.

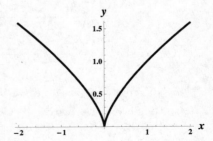

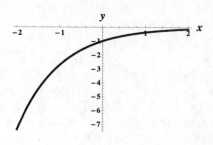

b. This is possible, for example $y = -e^{-x}$ has this property.

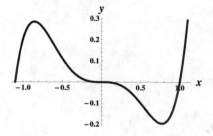

c. This is possible. See graphic pictured.

d. This is not possible. Between every pair of zeros, there must be a maximum or a minimum, so a continuous function with four zeros must have at least three local extrema.

4.2.87 The graphs match as follows: (a) – (f) – (g);   (b) – (e) –(i);   (c) – (d) –(h). Note that (a) is always increasing, so its derivative must be always positive, and (f) switches from decreasing to increasing at 0, so its derivative must be negative for $x < 0$ and positive for $x > 0$.

Note that (b) has three extrema where there are horizontal tangent lines, so its derivative must cross the x-axis three times, and (e) has two extrema, so its derivative must cross the x-axis two times.

4.2.88 Note that C is increasing where B is positive, and is decreasing where B is negative, so it seems reasonable to assert that B is the derivative of C. Also, B is increasing where A is positive and decreasing where A is negative, so it is reasonable to assert that A is the derivative of B. So it appears that $C = f(x)$, $B = f'(x)$, and $A = f''(x)$.

4.2.89

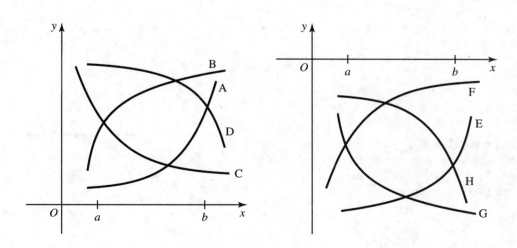

4.2.90

The graph sketched must be concave up on $(-\infty, -2)$ and on $(4, \infty)$, and must have a flat tangent line at $x = -1$, $x = 1$, and $x = 3$. A convenient way to ensure that $f''(-2) = f''(2) = 0$ is to have inflection points occur there. The example to the right is only one possible such graph.

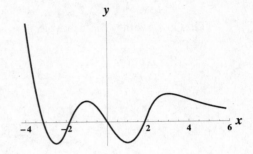

4.2.91

The graph sketched must have a flat tangent line at $x = -3/2$, $x = 0$, and $x = 1$, and must contain the points $(-2, 0)$, $(0, 0)$, and $(1, 0)$. The example to the right is only one possible such graph.

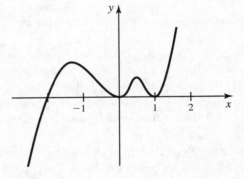

4.2.92

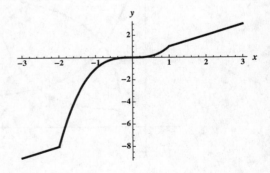

The graph sketched must be increasing everywhere and differentiable everywhere except at $x = -2$ and $x = 1$. We also have $f''(0) = 0$. The example to the right is only one possible such graph.

4.2.93

The graph sketched must be concave up on $(-\infty, -2)$ and on $(1, 3)$, and concave down on $(-2, 1)$ and on $(3, \infty)$. The example to the right is only one possible such graph.

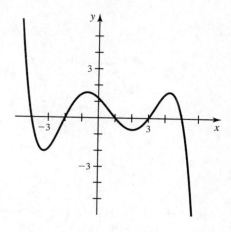

4.2.94

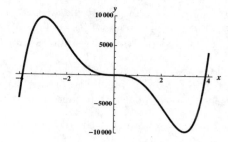

It appears that there are 2 extreme values near $x = \pm 3$ and perhaps a flat tangent line corresponding to an inflection point at $(0, 0)$. However, note that $f'(x) = 300x^4 - 2703x^2 + 27 = 3(100x^4 - 901x^2 + 9) = 3(x^2 - 9)(100x^2 - 1) = 3(x - 3)(x + 3)(10x - 1)(10x + 1)$. It turns out that there are 4 critical points at $x = \pm 3$ and $x = \pm \frac{1}{10}$ (and there isn't one at $x = 0$). Below is a graph on the range $[-.2, .2]$, which clearly shows a maximum at $x = 0.1$ and a minimum at $x = -0.1$.

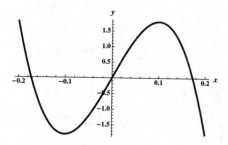

4.2.95

a. f is increasing on $(-2, 2)$. It is decreasing on $(-3, -2)$.

b. There are critical points of f at $x = -2$ and at $x = 0$. There is a local minimum at $x = -2$ and no extremum at $x = 0$.

c. There are inflection points of f at $x = -1$ and at $x = 0$.

d. f is concave up on $(-3, -1)$ and on $(0, 2)$, while it is concave down on $(-1, 0)$.

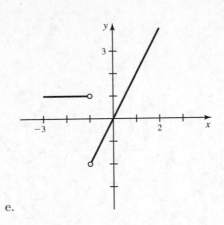

e.

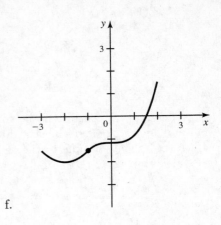

f.

4.2.96 $p'(t) = 6t^2 + 6t - 36 = 6(t+3)(t-2)$, which is 0 at $t = -3$ and $t = 2$. Note that $p''(t) = 12t + 6$, so $p''(-3) = -30 < 0$ and $p''(2) = 30 > 0$, so there is a local maximum at $t = -3$ and a local minimum at $t = 2$.

4.2.97 $f'(x) = x^3 - 5x^2 - 8x + 48 = (x-4)^2(x+3)$. (This can be obtained by using trial-and-error to determine that $x = 4$ is a root, and then using long division of polynomials to see that $f'(x) = (x-4)(x^2 - x - 12)$.) Note that $f''(x) = 3x^2 - 10x - 8$, so $f''(-3) = 49 > 0$ and $f''(4) = 0$. So there is a local minimum at $x = -3$, but the test is inconclusive for $x = 4$. The first derivative test shows that there is neither a maximum nor a minimum at $x = 4$.

4.2.98 $f'(x) = 4(x+a)^3$, which is 0 for $x = -a$. Note that $f''(x) = 12(x+a)^2$, which is 0 at $x = -a$, so the test is inconclusive. The first derivative test shows that there is a local minimum at $x = -a$.

4.2.99 $f'(x) = 3x^2 + 4x + 4$, which is never 0. (Note that the discriminant $4^2 - 4 \cdot 3 \cdot 4 < 0$, so this quadratic has no real roots.) So there are no critical points.

4.2.100 $f'(x) = 2ax + b$, and $f''(x) = 2a$. Note that $f''(x)$ is positive for $a > 0$ and negative for $a < 0$. So f is concave up for $a > 0$ and concave down for $a < 0$.

4.2.101

a. $E = \frac{dD}{dp} \cdot \frac{p}{D} = -10 \frac{p}{500 - 10p} = \frac{p}{p - 50}$.

b. $E = \frac{12}{12 - 50} \cdot .045 = -1.42\%$.

c. If $D(p) = a - bp$, then $E(p) = -b \cdot \frac{p}{a - bp} = \frac{bp}{bp - a}$. So $E'(p) = \frac{(bp-a)b - bpb)}{(bp-a)^2} = -\frac{ab}{(bp-a)^2}$, which is less than 0 for $a, b > 0$ and $p \neq a/b$.

d. If $D(p) = \frac{a}{p^b}$, then $E(p) = -\frac{ab}{p^{b+1}} \cdot \frac{p}{a/p^b} = -b$.

4.2.102 The growth rate is given by the slope of the tangent line to the curve. Up to the inflection point, the curve is concave up, meaning that the slopes are increasing. After the inflection point, the curve is concave down, meaning that the slopes are decreasing. So the maximum slope occurs at the inflection point.

4.2.103

a. $\lim\limits_{t \to \infty} \frac{300t^2}{t^2 + 30} \cdot \frac{1/t^2}{1/t^2} = \lim\limits_{t \to \infty} \frac{300}{1 + (30/t^2)} = 300$.

b. Note that $P'(t) = \frac{(t^2+30)(600t) - 300t^2(2t)}{(t^2+30)^2} = \frac{18000t}{(t^2+30)^2}$. We want to maximize this, so we compute its derivative $P''(t) = \frac{(t^2+30)^2 \cdot 18000 - 18000t \cdot 2(t^2+30) \cdot 2t}{(t^2+30)^4} = \frac{54000(10 - t^2)}{(t^2+30)^3}$. This is 0 for $t = \sqrt{10}$, and an analysis of $P''(t)$ reveals that $P''(t) > 0$ for $t < \sqrt{10}$ and $P''(t) < 0$ for $t > \sqrt{10}$ so there is a local maximum for $P'(t)$ at $t = \sqrt{10}$.

c. Following the outline from the previous problem, we see that $P'(t) = \frac{2bKt}{(t^2+b)^2}$, and $P''(t) = \frac{2bK(b-3t^2)}{(t^2+b)^3}$. $P''(t)$ is 0 for $t = \sqrt{b/3}$, and the first derivative test reveals that this is a local maximum.

4.2.104 If f is concave up at $x = c$, then $f''(c) > 0$. This means that f' is increasing in a neighborhood near c. So for $x < c$, the slope of the function is less than the slope of the tangent line at c, and for $x > c$ it is greater than the slope of the tangent line. This means that the curve is "bending upward," away from its tangent line, so the tangent line is below the curve in a neighborhood near c.

4.2.105

a. $f'(x) = 3x^2 + 2ax + b$, and $f''(x) = 6x + 2a$, which is 0 only for $x = -\frac{a}{3}$. Note that the sign of $f''(x)$ is different for $x < -a/3$ and $x > -a/3$, so this does represent an inflection point.

b.

$$f(x^*) - f(x^* + x)$$
$$= f(-a/3) - f(-a/3 + x) = (-a/3)^3 + a(-a/3)^2 + b(-a/3) + c$$
$$- ((-a/3 + x)^3 + a(-a/3 + x)^2 + b(-a/3 + x) + c)$$
$$= (-a/3)^3 + a(-a/3)^2 + b(-a/3) + c$$
$$- (-a/3)^3 - 3(-a/3)^2 x - 3(-a/3)x^2 - x^3 - a(-a/3)^2 - 2a(-a/3)x - ax^2 - b(-a/3) - bx - c$$
$$= -x^3 + \left(\frac{a^2}{3} - b\right) x.$$

Also,

$$f(x^* - x) - f(x^*) = f(-a/3 - x) - f(-a/3)$$
$$= (-a/3)^3 + 3(-a/3)^2(-x) + 3(-a/3)(-x)^2 + (-x)^3$$
$$+ a(-a/3)^2 + 2a(-a/3)(-x) + a(-x)^2$$
$$+ b(-a/3) + b(-x) + c - (-a/3)^3 - a(-a/3)^2 - b(-a/3) - c$$
$$= -x^3 + \left(\frac{a^2}{3} - b\right) x.$$

Thus the two expressions are the same for all x.

4.2.106

a. $f'(x) = 3x^2 + 2ax + b$, which is 0 when $x = \frac{-2a \pm \sqrt{4a^2 - 12b}}{6} = \frac{-a \pm \sqrt{a^2 - 3b}}{3}$. These solutions represent distinct real numbers when $a^2 > 3b$. Let the two distinct roots be $r_1 < r_2$. Note that f' is negative on the interval (r_1, r_2) and positive on $(-\infty, r_1)$ and on (r_2, ∞) so there is a maximum at r_1 and a minimum at r_2.

b. If $a^2 < 3b$, then there are no real critical points, so there are no extreme values.

4.2.107

a. $f(-x) = \frac{1}{((-x)^2)^n + 1} = \frac{1}{x^{2n} + 1} = f(x)$, so f is even.

b. Note that $f(\pm 1) = \frac{1}{((-1)^2)^n + 1} = \frac{1}{2}$, for all n.

c. $f'(x) = -(x^{2n} + 1)^{-2}(2nx^{2n-1}) = -2nx^{2n-1}(x^{2n} + 1)^{-2}$. So $f''(x) = -2nx^{2n-1} \cdot (-2(x^{2n} + 1)^{-3}) \cdot 2nx^{2n-1} + (x^{2n} + 1)^{-2} \cdot (-2n(2n-1)x^{2n-2}) = \frac{-2nx^{2n-2}((-2n-1)x^{2n} + 2n-1)}{(x^{2n}+1)^3}$. This is 0 when $x = 0$ for $n \geq 2$, and when $x = \pm \sqrt[2n]{\frac{2n-1}{2n+1}}$ for all positive n. An analysis of the sign of f'' shows that there is no sign change at $x = 0$, and f has inflection points at $x = \pm \sqrt[2n]{\frac{2n-1}{2n+1}}$.

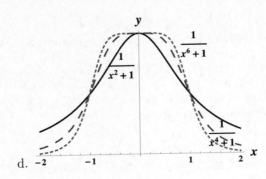

e. As n increases, the inflection points move further away from the y-axis, and closer to the point $(1, 1/2)$, although this movement is slight. The graphs become steeper and more "box-like."

4.2.108

a. $f(-x) = (-x)^4 + b(-x)^2 + d = x^4 + bx^2 + d = f(x)$, so f is symmetric about the y axis.

b. $f'(x) = 4x^3 + 2bx = 2x(2x^2 + b)$, which is 0 for $x = 0$ and for no other values of x when $b \geq 0$, because if $b > 0$ then $2x^2 + b = 0$ has no real solutions, and for $b = 0$, only $x = 0$ is a solution. So $x = 0$ is the only critical point.

$f''(x) = 12x^2 + 2b$, which has only the solution $x = 0$ for the case $b = 0$, and in this case $x = 0$ isn't an inflection point because there is no sign change for f'' at 0.

c. For the case $b < 0$, the three critcal points are $x = 0$ and $x = \pm\sqrt{-b/2}$. Note that a continuous cubic function with three roots always has sign changes between the roots, so in this case each critical point yields either a local maximum or a local minimum. Note that $f''(x) = 12x^2 + 2b$ has roots at $x = \pm\sqrt{-b/6}$, both of which yield inflection points.

d. Let $u = x^2$, so that $f(u) = u^2 + bu + d$. The roots of this quadratic are $u = \frac{-b \pm \sqrt{b^2 - 4d}}{2}$, so the roots of f in terms of x are $\pm\sqrt{\frac{-b \pm \sqrt{b^2 - 4d}}{2}}$. In the regions above the parabola, $4d > b^2$, so these do not represent any real solutions. Below the parabola but for $d > 0$ and $b > 0$, note that $\sqrt{b^2 - 4d} < b$. So $-b < -\sqrt{b^2 - 4d}$, so $-b + \sqrt{b^2 - 4d} < 0$ (and certainly $-b - \sqrt{b^2 - 4d} < 0$.) Thus, there are no real roots in this area either. However, below the parabola but when $d > 0$ but $b < 0$, note that $-b \pm \sqrt{b^2 - 4d} > 0$, so all 4 potential roots mentioned above are actual real roots.

When $d < 0$, note that $b^2 < b^2 - 4d$, so $|b| < \sqrt{b^2 - 4d}$, so $-\sqrt{b^2 - 4d} < -b < \sqrt{b^2 - 4d}$. So $-b + \sqrt{b^2 - 4d} > 0$ but $-b - \sqrt{b^2 - 4d} < 0$. So in both regions below the b-axis, the two roots are $\pm\sqrt{\frac{-b + \sqrt{b^2 - 4d}}{2}}$.

e. When $b = 0$, we have $f(x) = x^4 + d$, which has no roots for $d > 0$, only the root $x = 0$ when $d = 0$, and the two roots $x = \pm\sqrt[4]{-d}$ when $d < 0$. For the case $d = 0$, we have $f(x) = x^4 + bx^2 = x^2(x^2 + b)$, which has the root $x = 0$ for all b, has no other roots for the case $b > 0$, and has the two additional roots $x = \pm\sqrt{-b}$ for the case $b < 0$. In the case $d = b^2/4$, then there are no roots for $b > 0$, but there are the two roots $\pm\sqrt{-b/2}$ for the case $b < 0$.

4.2.109 $f'(x) = 4x^3 + 3ax^2 + 2bx + c$, and $f''(x) = 12x^2 + 6ax + 2b = 2(6x^2 + 3ax + b)$. Note that $f''(x) = 0$ exactly when $x = \frac{-3a \pm \sqrt{9a^2 - 24b}}{12}$. This represents no real solutions when $9a^2 - 24b < 0$, which occurs when $b > 3a^2/8$. When $b = 3a^2/8$, there is one root, but in this case the sign of f'' doesn't change at the double root $x = -a/4$, so there are no inflection points for f. In the case $b < 3a^2/8$, there are two roots of f'', both of which yield inflection points of f, as can be seen by the change in sign of f'' at its two roots.

4.2.110 One possible such function is $f(x) = \begin{cases} (x-1)^3 + 1 & \text{if } x \leq 1 \\ 1 & \text{if } x > 1. \end{cases}$

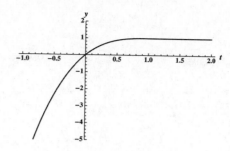

Note that the derivative of f to the left of 1 is positive, and to the right it is 0 (so it is neither positive nor negative). This example highlights the fact that the statement of the First Derivative Test does not include all possible cases for what might be happening on either side of the critical point. The missing cases include:

- f' changes from negative to 0 as x increases through c (in which case f has a local minimum at c).

- f' changes from positive to 0 as x increases through c (in which case f has a local maximum at c).

- f' changes from 0 to positive as x increases through c (in which case f has a local maximum at c).

- f' changes from 0 to negative as x increases through c (in which case f has a local minimum at c).

- f' remains 0 as x increases through c (in which case f has both a local minimum and local maximum at c – f is constant near c.

4.3 Graphing Functions

4.3.1 Because the intervals of increase and decrease and the intervals of concavity must be subsets of the domain, it is helpful to know what the domain is at the outset.

4.3.2 If a function is symmetric, then only one half the function needs to be graphed, and the information about the other half will follow immediately. Also, knowledge about symmetry can help catch mistakes.

4.3.3 No. Polynomials are continuous everywhere, so they have no vertical asymptotes. Also, polynomials in x always tend to $\pm\infty$ as $x \to \pm\infty$.

4.3.4 If a rational function is in simplified form (with no common factors in the numerator and denominator), then there is a vertical asymptote wherever the denominator is zero.

4.3.5 The maximum and minimum must occur at either an endpoint or a critical point. So to find the absolute maximum and minimum, it suffices to find all the critical points, and then compare the values of the function at those points and at the endpoints. The largest such value is the maximum and the smallest is the minimum.

4.3.6 For every polynomial $p(x)$, $\lim\limits_{x\to\pm\infty} p(x) = \pm\infty$.

4.3.7

The function sketched should be decreasing and concave down for $x < 3$ and decreasing and concave up for $x > 3$.

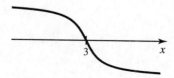

4.3.8

The function sketched should be decreasing on $(-\infty, 2)$ and increasing on $(2, \infty)$. It should be concave down on $(-\infty, -1)$ and on $(8, 10)$. It should be concave up on $(-1, 8)$ and on $(10, \infty)$.

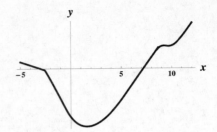

4.3.9 The domain of f is $(-\infty, \infty)$, and there is no symmetry. The y intercept is $f(0) = 0$, and the x-intercepts are 0 and 3 because $f(x) = x(x-3)^2$. $f'(x) = 3x^2 - 12x + 9 = 3(x^2 - 4x + 3) = 3(x-3)(x-1)$. This is zero when $x = 1$ and $x = 3$. Note that $f'(0) > 0$, $f'(2) < 0$ and $f'(4) > 0$, so f is increasing on $(-\infty, 1)$ and on $(3, \infty)$. It is decreasing on $(1, 3)$. Note that $f''(x) = 6x - 12$ which is zero at $x = 2$. Because $f''(1) < 0$ and $f''(3) > 0$, we conclude that f is concave down on $(-\infty, 2)$ and concave up on $(2, \infty)$. There is an inflection point at $(2, 2)$, a local maximum at $(1, 4)$ and a local minimum at $(3, 0)$.

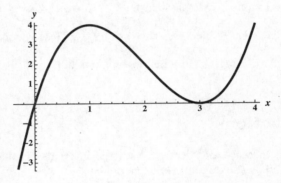

4.3.10 The domain of f is $(-\infty, \infty)$, and there is odd symmetry, because $f(-x) = 3(-x) - (-x)^3 = -(3x - x^3) = -f(x)$. The y intercept is $f(0) = 0$, and the x-intercepts are 0 and $\pm\sqrt{3}$ because $f(x) = x(3 - x^2)$. $f'(x) = 3 - 3x^2 = 3(1 - x^2)$, which is zero for $x = \pm 1$. Note that $f'(-2) < 0$, $f'(0) > 0$, and $f'(2) < 0$, so f is decreasing on $(-\infty, -1)$ and on $(1, \infty)$, and is increasing on $(-1, 1)$. There is a local minimum at $(-1, -2)$ and a local maximum at $(1, 2)$.

$f''(x) = -6x$, which is zero at $x = 0$. Note that $f''(x) > 0$ for $x < 0$ and $f''(x) < 0$ for $x > 0$, so f is concave up on $(-\infty, 0)$ and is concave down on $(0, \infty)$. There is an inflection point at $(0, 0)$.

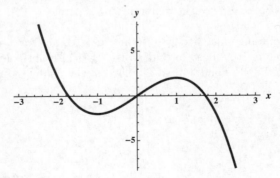

4.3.11

The domain of f is $(-\infty, \infty)$, and there is even symmetry, because $f(-x) = f(x)$. $f'(x) = 4x^3 - 12x = 4x(x^2 - 3)$. This is 0 when $x = \pm\sqrt{3}$ and when $x = 0$. $f''(x) = 12x^2 - 12 = 12(x^2 - 1)$, which is 0 when $x = \pm 1$. Note that $f'(-2) < 0$, $f'(-1) > 0$, $f'(1) < 0$, and $f'(2) > 0$. So f is decreasing on $(-\infty, -\sqrt{3})$ and on $(0, \sqrt{3})$. It is increasing on $(-\sqrt{3}, 0)$ and on $(\sqrt{3}, \infty)$. There is a local maximum of 0 at $x = 0$ and local minima of -9 at $x = \pm\sqrt{3}$. Note also that $f''(x) > 0$ for $x < -1$ and for $x > 1$ and $f''(x) < 0$ for $-1 < x < 1$, so there are inflection points at $x = \pm 1$. Also, f is concave down on $(-1, 1)$ and concave up on $(-\infty, -1)$ and on $(1, \infty)$. There is a y-intercept at $f(0) = 0$ and x-intercepts where $f(x) = x^4 - 6x^2 = x^2(x^2 - 6) = 0$, which is at $x = \pm\sqrt{6}$ and $x = 0$.

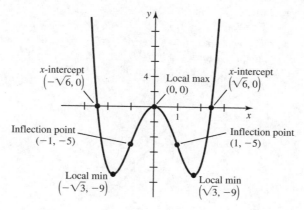

4.3.12

The domain of f is $(-\infty, \infty)$, and there is even symmetry, because $f(-x) = f(x)$. $f'(x) = 12x^5 - 12x^3 = 12x^3(x^2 - 1)$. This is 0 when $x = \pm 1$ and $x = 0$. $f''(x) = 60x^4 - 36x^2 = 12x^2(5x^2 - 3)$, which is 0 when $x = \pm\sqrt{3/5}$ and $x = 0$. Note that $f'(-2) < 0$, $f'(-.5) > 0$, $f'(.5) < 0$, and $f'(2) > 0$. Thus f is decreasing on $(-\infty, -1)$ and on $(0, 1)$, while it is increasing on $(-1, 0)$ and on $(1, \infty)$.

There is a local maximum of 0 at $x = 0$ and local minima of -1 at $x = \pm 1$. Note also that $f''(x) > 0$ for $x < -\sqrt{3/5}$ and for $x > \sqrt{3/5}$, and $f''(x) < 0$ for $-\sqrt{\frac{3}{5}} < x < \sqrt{\frac{3}{5}}$, so there are inflection points at $x = \pm\sqrt{3/5}$, and f is concave up on $(-\infty, -\sqrt{3/5})$ and on $(\sqrt{3/5}, \infty)$, and is concave down on $(-\sqrt{3/5}, \sqrt{3/5})$.

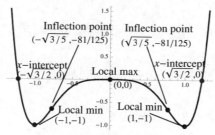

4.3.13 The domain of f is $(-\infty, \infty)$, and there is no symmetry. The y- intercept is $f(0) = -216$. The x-intercepts are 6 and -6.

$f'(x) = (x + 6)^2 + (x - 6)2(x + 6) = (x + 6)(x + 6 + 2x - 12) = (x + 6)(3x - 6) = 3(x + 6)(x - 2)$. The critical numbers are -6 and 2. Note that $f'(-7) > 0$, $f'(-2) < 0$, and $f'(3) > 0$, so f is increasing on $(-\infty, -6)$ and on $(2, \infty)$. It is decreasing on $(-6, 2)$. There is a local maximum of 0 at -6 and a local minimum of -256 at $x = 2$.

$f''(x) = 3(x - 2) + 3(x + 6) = 3(x - 2 + x + 6) = 3(2x + 4) = 6(x + 2)$, which is zero for $x = -2$. Note that $f''(x) < 0$ for $x < -2$ and $f''(x) > 0$ for $x > -2$, so f is concave down on $(-\infty, -2)$ and concave up on $(-2, \infty)$. The point $(-2, -128)$ is an inflection point.

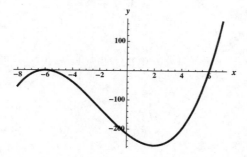

4.3.14 The domain of f is $(-\infty, \infty)$ and there is no symmetry. The y- intercept is $f(0) = 216$ and the x-intercepts are ± 2.

$f'(x) = 27 \cdot 2(x-2)(x+2) + 27(x-2)^2 = 27(x-2)(2x+4+x-2) = 27(x-2)(3x+2)$. This is zero for $x = 2$ and $x = -2/3$. Note that $f'(-1) > 0$, $f'(0) < 0$, and $f'(3) > 0$. Thus f is increasing on $(-\infty, -2/3)$ and on $(2, \infty)$, and is decreasing on $(-2/3, 2)$. There is a local maximum of 256 at $x = -2/3$ and a local minimum of 0 at $x = 2$.

$f''(x) = 27(3x+2) + 27(x-2) \cdot 3 = 27(3x+2+3x-6) = 27(6x-4) = 54(3x-2)$. This is zero when $x = 2/3$. Note that $f''(x) < 0$ for $x < 2/3$ and $f''(x) > 0$ for $x > 2/3$, so f is concave down on $(-\infty, 2/3)$ and concave up on $(2/3, \infty)$. There is an inflection point at $(2/3, 128)$.

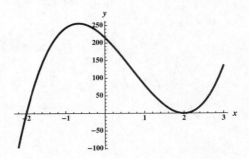

4.3.15

The domain of f is $(-\infty, 2) \cup (2, \infty)$, and there is no symmetry. Note that $\lim\limits_{x \to 2^+} f(x) = \infty$ and $\lim\limits_{x \to 2^-} f(x) = -\infty$, so there is a vertical asymptote at $x = 2$. There isn't a horizontal asymptote, because $\lim\limits_{x \to \pm\infty} f(x) = \pm\infty$.

$f'(x) = \frac{(x-2) \cdot 2x - x^2}{(x-2)^2} = \frac{x(x-4)}{(x-2)^2}$. This is 0 when $x = 4$ and when $x = 0$.

$f''(x) = \frac{(x-2)^2(2x-4) - (x^2-4x) \cdot 2 \cdot (x-2)}{(x-2)^4} = \frac{8}{(x-2)^3}$. This is never 0.

Note that $f'(-1) > 0$, $f'(1) < 0$, $f'(3) < 0$ and $f'(5) > 0$. So f is decreasing on $(0, 2)$ and on $(2, 4)$. It is increasing on $(-\infty, 0)$ and on $(4, \infty)$. There is a local maximum of 0 at $x = 0$ and a local minimum of 8 at $x = 4$.

Note that $f''(x) > 0$ for $x > 2$ and $f''(x) < 0$ for $x < 2$, So f is concave up on $(2, \infty)$ and concave down on $(-\infty, 4)$. There are no inflection points, because the only change in concavity occurs at a vertical asymptote. The only intercept is $(0, 0)$.

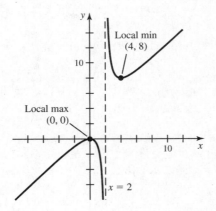

4.3.16

The domain of f is $(-\infty, -2) \cup (-2, 2) \cup (2, \infty)$, and there is even symmetry because $f(-x) = \frac{(-x)^2}{(-x)^2 - 4} = \frac{x^2}{x^2-4} = f(x)$.

Because $\lim\limits_{x \to \pm\infty} \frac{x^2}{x^2-4} \cdot \frac{1/x^2}{1/x^2} = \lim\limits_{x \to \pm\infty} \frac{1}{1 - (4/x^2)} = 1$, there is a horizontal asymptote at $y = 1$. Also, because $\lim_{x \to -2^-} f(x) = \infty$, $\lim_{x \to -2^+} f(x) = -\infty$, $\lim_{x \to 2^-} f(x) = -\infty$ and $\lim_{x \to 2^+} f(x) = \infty$, there are vertical asymptotes at $x = -2$ and $x = 2$.

$f'(x) = \frac{(x^2-4)\cdot 2x - x^2 \cdot 2x}{(x^2-4)^2} = -\frac{8x}{(x^2-4)^2}$. This is 0 when $x = 0$. $f''(x) = \frac{(x^2-4)^2(-8)-(-8x)\cdot 2\cdot(x^2-4)\cdot 2x}{(x^2-4)^4} = \frac{8(3x^2+4)}{(x^2-4)^3}$, which is never 0.

Note that $f'(x) > 0$ on $(-\infty, -2)$ and on $(-2, 0)$, while $f'(x) < 0$ on $(0, 2)$ and on $(2, \infty)$. So f is increasing on $(-\infty, -2)$ and on $(0, 2)$, and is decreasing on $(0, 2)$ and on $(2, \infty)$. There is a local maximum of 0 at $x = 0$.

Note also that $f''(x) > 0$ for $x < -2$, and $f''(x) > 0$ for $x > 2$, while $f''(x) < 0$ for $-2 < x < 2$. So f is concave up on $(-\infty, -2)$ and on $(2, \infty)$, while it is concave down on $(-2, 2)$. There are no inflection points because the only changes in concavity occur at asymptotes.

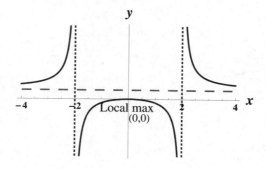

4.3.17

The domain of f is $(-\infty, -1) \cup (-1, 1) \cup (1, \infty)$, and there is odd symmetry, because $f(-x) = \frac{3(-x)}{(-x)^2-1} = -\frac{3x}{x^2-1} = -f(x)$. The only intercept is $(0, 0)$ which is both the y- and x-intercept.

Note that $\lim\limits_{x \to -1^+} f(x) = \infty$ and $\lim\limits_{x \to -1^-} f(x) = -\infty$, so there is a vertical asymptote at $x = -1$. Also, $\lim\limits_{x \to 1^+} f(x) = \infty$ and $\lim\limits_{x \to 1^-} f(x) = -\infty$, so there is a vertical asymptote at $x = 1$

Note that $\lim\limits_{x \to \pm\infty} \frac{3x}{x^2-1} \cdot \frac{1/x^2}{1/x^2} = \lim\limits_{x \to \pm\infty} \frac{3/x}{1-(1/x^2)} = 0$, so $y = 0$ is a horizontal asymptote.

$f'(x) = \frac{(x^2-1)\cdot 3 - 3x\cdot 2x}{(x^2-1)^2} = \frac{-3x^2-3}{(x^2-1)^2} = -\frac{3(x^2+1)}{(x^2-1)^2}$. This is never 0, and is in fact negative wherever it is defined. Thus, f is decreasing on $(-\infty, -1)$, on $(-1, 1)$, and on $(1, \infty)$. There are no extrema.

$f''(x) = \frac{(x^2-1)^2(-6x)+3(x^2+1)\cdot 2\cdot(x^2-1)\cdot 2x}{(x^2-1)^4} = \frac{-6x^3+6x+12x^3+12x}{(x^2-1)^3} = \frac{6x(x^2+3)}{(x^2-1)^3}$. This is 0 for $x = 0$. The point $(0, 0)$ is an point of inflection, because it is an interior point on the domain, and the second derivative changes from positive to negative there. The other concavity changes take place at the asymptotes. Note that f is concave down on $(-\infty, -1)$ and on $(0, 1)$, and concave up on $(-1, 0)$ and on $(1, \infty)$.

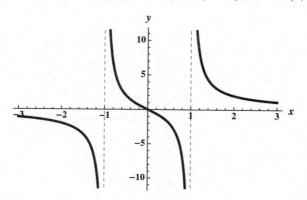

4.3.18

The domain of f is $(-\infty, 4) \cup (4, \infty)$, and there is no symmetry.

Because $\lim\limits_{x \to \pm\infty} \frac{2x-3}{2x-8} \cdot \frac{1/x}{1/x} = \lim\limits_{x \to \pm\infty} \frac{2-(3/x)}{2-(8/x)} = \frac{2}{2} = 1$, there is a horizontal asymptote of $y = 1$.

Also, because $\lim_{x \to 4^-} f(x) = -\infty$ and $\lim_{x \to 4^+} f(x) = \infty$, there is a vertical asymptote at $x = 4$. $f'(x) = \frac{(2x-8)\cdot 2 - (2x-3)\cdot 2}{(2x-8)^2} = -\frac{10}{(2x-8)^2}$. This is never 0. $f''(x) = \frac{40}{(2x-8)^3}$ which is also never 0.

Note that $f'(x) < 0$ on $(-\infty, 4)$ and on $(4, \infty)$. So f is decreasing on $(-\infty, 4)$ and on $(4, \infty)$. There are no extrema.

Note also that $f''(x) < 0$ for $x < 4$, and $f''(x) > 0$ for $x > 4$, so f is concave down on $(-\infty, 4)$ and is concave up on $(4, \infty)$. There are no inflection points because the only change in concavity occurs at the vertical asymptote. The x-intercept is $x = 3/2$ and the y-intercept is $f(0) = 3/8$.

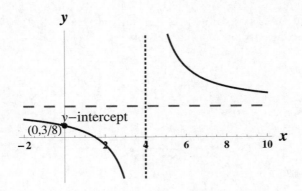

4.3.19

The domain of f is $(-\infty, -1/2) \cup (-1/2, \infty)$, and there is no symmetry.

Because $\lim\limits_{x \to \pm\infty} \dfrac{x^2 + 12}{2x + 1} \cdot \dfrac{1/x}{1/x} = \lim\limits_{x \to \pm\infty} \dfrac{x + (12/x)}{2 + (1/x)} = \pm\infty$, there is no horizontal asymptote. However, there is an oblique asymptote of $y = \frac{x}{2} - \frac{1}{4}$, because we can write f as $f(x) = \frac{x}{2} - \frac{1}{4} + \frac{49/4}{2x+1}$ by long division.

Also, because $\lim_{x \to (-1/2)^-} f(x) = -\infty$ and $\lim_{x \to (-1/2)^+} f(x) = \infty$, there is a vertical asymptote at $x = -1/2$.

$f'(x) = \frac{(2x+1) \cdot 2x - (x^2+12) \cdot 2}{(2x+1)^2} = \frac{2x^2 + 2x - 24}{(2x+1)^2} = \frac{2(x+4)(x-3)}{(2x+1)^2}$. This is 0 for $x = -4$ and $x = 3$. $f''(x) = \frac{(2x+1)^2(4x+2) - (2x^2+2x-24) \cdot 2(2x+1) \cdot 2}{(2x+1)^4} = \frac{98}{(2x+1)^3}$, which is never 0.

Note that $f'(x) > 0$ on $(-\infty, -4)$ and on $(3, \infty)$. So f is increasing on $(-\infty, -4)$ and on $(3, \infty)$. Also, $f'(x) < 0$ on $(-4, -1/2)$ and on $(-1/2, 3)$. So f is decreasing on those intervals. There is a local maximum of -4 at $x = -4$ and a local minimum of 3 at $x = 3$.

Note also that $f''(x) < 0$ for $x < -1/2$, and $f''(x) > 0$ for $x > -1/2$, so f is concave down on $(-\infty, -1/2)$ and is concave up on $(-1/2, \infty)$. There are no inflection points because the only change in concavity occurs at the vertical asymptote. There are no x-intercepts because $x^2 + 12 > 0$ for all x, and the y-intercept is $f(0) = 12$.

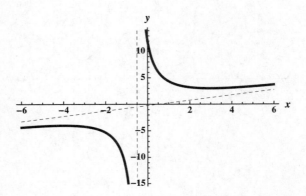

4.3.20

The domain of f is $(-\infty, \infty)$, there is no symmetry, and f has no vertical asymptotes. Note that $\lim\limits_{x \to \pm\infty} \dfrac{4x + 4}{x^2 + 3} \cdot \dfrac{1/x^2}{1/x^2} = \lim\limits_{x \to \pm\infty} \dfrac{(4/x) + (4/x^2)}{1 + (3/x^2)} = 0$, so there is a horizontal asymptote of $y = 0$. $f'(x) = $

$\frac{(x^2+3)\cdot4-(4x+4)\cdot2x}{(x^2+3)^2} = \frac{-4(x^2+2x-3)}{(x^2+3)^2} = \frac{(-4)(x+3)(x-1)}{(x^2+3)^2}$. This is 0 for $x = -3$ and $x = 1$.

$$f''(x) = \frac{(x^2+3)^2(-8-8x) - (12-8x-4x^2)\cdot2(x^2+3)\cdot2x}{(x^2+3)^4} = \frac{8(x^3+3x^2-9x-3)}{(x^3+3)^3}.$$

The numerator of this last expression has three roots, which we will call r_1, r_2, and r_3. Note that $r_1 \approx -4.76$, $r_2 \approx -0.31$, and $r_3 \approx 2.06$.

Note that $f'(x) < 0$ on $(-\infty, -3)$ and on $(1, \infty)$. So f is decreasing on those intervals, while $f'(x) > 0$ on $(-3, 1)$, so f is increasing there. f has a local maximum of 2 at $x = 1$ and a local minimum of $-2/3$ at $x = -3$.

Note also that $f''(x) < 0$ for $x < r_1$, and for $r_2 < x < r_3$, so f is concave down on $(-\infty, r_2)$ and on (r_2, r_3). However, $f''(x) > 0$ for $r_1 < x < r_2$ and for $x > r_3$, so f is concave up on (r_1, r_2) and on (r_3, ∞). There are inflection points at each of r_1, r_2, and r_3. The x-intercept is $x = -1$ and the y-intercept is $f(0) = 4/3$.

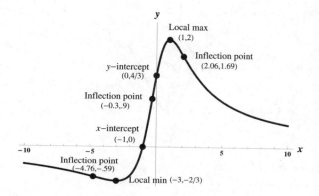

4.3.21

The domain of f is $(-\infty, \infty)$, and f is symmetric about the y-axis, because $f(-x) = \tan^{-1}((-x)^2) = \tan^{-1}(x^2) = f(x)$. The only intercept is $(0,0)$. Note that $\lim_{x\to\pm\infty} \tan^{-1}(x^2) = \frac{\pi}{2}$, so $y = \pi/2$ is a horizontal asymptote in both directions.

$f'(x) = \frac{2x}{1+x^4}$, which is zero for $x = 0$. Note that f' is negative when x is negative and positive when x is positive, so f is decreasing on $(-\infty, 0)$ and increasing on $(0, \infty)$, and there is a local (in fact, absolute) minimum at $(0,0)$.

$f''(x) = \frac{(1+x^4)\cdot2 - 2x\cdot4x^3}{(1+x^4)^2} = \frac{2-6x^4}{(1+x^4)^2} = \frac{2(1-3x^4)}{(1+x^4)^2}$. This is zero for $x = \pm\sqrt[4]{1/3}$. Also note that $f''(-2) < 0$, $f''(0) > 0$, and $f''(2) < 0$, so f is concave down on $(-\infty, -\sqrt[4]{1/3})$ and on $(\sqrt[4]{1/3}, \infty)$, and is concave up on $(-\sqrt[4]{1/3}, \sqrt[4]{1/3})$. There are inflection points at $(-\sqrt[4]{1/3}, \pi/6)$ and $(\sqrt[4]{1/3}, \pi/6)$.

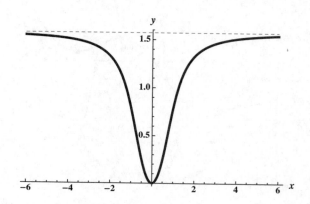

4.3.22

The domain of f is $(-\infty, \infty)$, and f is symmetric about the y-axis, because $f(-x) = \ln((-x)^2 + 1) = f(x)$. The only intercept is $(0,0)$. Note that $\lim_{x \to \pm\infty} \ln(x^2 + 1) = \infty$, so there are no horizontal asymptotes.

We have $f'(x) = \frac{2x}{1+x^2}$, which is zero for $x = 0$. Note that f' is negative when x is negative and positive when x is positive, so f is decreasing on $(-\infty, 0)$ and increasing on $(0, \infty)$, and there is a local (in fact, absolute) minimum at $(0,0)$.

$f''(x) = \frac{(1+x^2) \cdot 2 - 2x \cdot 2x}{(1+x^2)^2} = \frac{2(1-x^2)}{(1+x^2)^2}$. This is zero for $x = \pm 1$. Also note that $f''(-2) < 0$, $f''(0) > 0$, and $f''(2) < 0$, so f is concave down on $(-\infty, -1)$ and on $(1, \infty)$, and is concave up on $(-1, 1)$. There are inflection points at $(-1, \ln 2)$ and $(1, \ln 2)$.

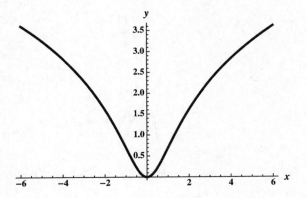

4.3.23

The domain of f is given to be $[-2\pi, 2\pi]$, and there is no symmetry, and no vertical asymptotes. There are no horizontal asymptotes to consider on this restricted domain.

$f'(x) = 1 - 2\sin x$. This is 0 when $\sin x = 1/2$, which occurs on the given interval for $x = -11\pi/6$, $-7\pi/6$, $\pi/6$, and $5\pi/6$. $f''(x) = -2\cos x$, which is 0 for $x = -3\pi/2, -\pi/2, \pi/2$, and $3\pi/2$.

Note that $f'(x) > 0$ on $(-2\pi, -11\pi/6)$, and on $(-7\pi/6, \pi/6)$, and on $(5\pi/6, 2\pi)$. So f is increasing on those intervals, while $f'(x) < 0$ on $(-11\pi/6, -7\pi/6))$ and on $(\pi/6, 5\pi/6)$, so f is decreasing there. f has local maxima at $x = -11\pi/6$ and at $x = \pi/6$ and local minima at $x = -7\pi/6$ and at $x = 5\pi/6$. Note also that $f''(x) < 0$ on $(-2\pi, -3\pi/2)$ and on $(-\pi/2, \pi/2)$ and on $(3\pi/2, 2\pi)$, so f is concave down on those intervals, while $f''(x) > 0$ on $(-3\pi/2, -\pi/2)$ and on $(\pi/2, 3\pi/2)$, so f is concave up there and there are inflection points at $x = \pm 3\pi/2$ and $x = \pm\pi/2$. The y-intercept is $f(0) = 2$ and the x-intercept is at approximately -1.030.

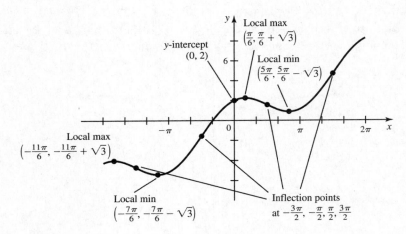

4.3.24

The domain of f is $(-\infty, \infty)$. There are no asymptotes. There are x-intercepts at $(0,0)$ and $(27, 0)$.

$f'(x) = 1 - \frac{2}{\sqrt[3]{x}} = \frac{\sqrt[3]{x}-2}{\sqrt[3]{x}}$. This is undefined at $x = 0$, and is equal to zero at $x = 8$. Note that $f'(-1) > 0$, $f'(1) < 0$, and $f'(27) > 0$, so f is increasing on $(-\infty, 0)$, decreasing on $(0, 8)$, and increasing on $(8, \infty)$. There is a local maximum at $(0, 0)$ and a local minimum at $(8, -4)$.

$f''(x) = \frac{2}{3\sqrt[3]{x^4}}$, which is never zero, but is undefined at $x = 0$. Because this is always positive, f is concave up on $(-\infty, 0)$ and on $(0, \infty)$. There are no inflection points.

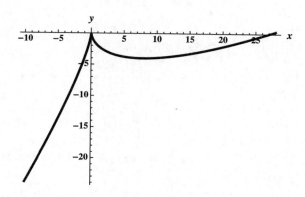

4.3.25

The domain of f is $(-\infty, \infty)$. There are no asymptotes. There are x-intercepts at $(0, 0)$ and $(\pm 3\sqrt{3}, 0)$. f does have odd symmetry, because $f(-x) = -x - 3((-x)^{1/3}) = -(x - 3x^{1/3}) = -f(x)$.

$f'(x) = 1 - \frac{1}{\sqrt[3]{x^2}} = \frac{\sqrt[3]{x^2}-1}{\sqrt[3]{x^2}}$. This is undefined at $x = 0$, and is equal to zero at ± 1. Note that $f'(-2) > 0$, $f'(-1/2) < 0$, $f'(1/2) < 0$, $f'(2) > 0$. Thus, f is increasing on $(-\infty, -1)$ and on $(1, \infty)$. Because f is continuous at 0 (even though f' doesn't exist there), we can combine the intervals $(-1, 0)$ and $(0, 1)$ and state that f is decreasing on $(-1, 1)$. There is a local maximum at $(-1, 2)$ and a local minimum at $(1, -2)$.

$f''(x) = \frac{2}{3\sqrt[3]{x^5}}$, which is never zero, but is undefined at $x = 0$. Note that $f''(x) < 0$ for $x < 0$ and $f''(x) > 0$ for $x > 0$, so f is concave down on $(-\infty, 0)$ and is concave up on $(0, \infty)$. There is an inflection point at $(0, 0)$.

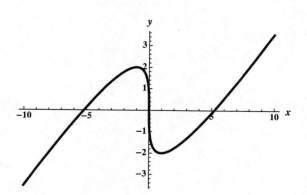

4.3.26

The domain of f is $(-\infty, \infty)$. There are no asymptotes, nor x-intercepts. f does have even symmetry, because $f(-x) = 2 - (-x)^{2/3} + (-x)^{4/3} = 2 - x^{2/3} + x^{4/3} = f(x)$.

$f'(x) = -\frac{2}{3x^{1/3}} + \frac{4}{3}x^{1/3} = \frac{4x^{2/3}-2}{3x^{1/3}}$. This is undefined at $x = 0$, and is equal to zero when $x^{2/3} = \frac{1}{2}$, which is when $x = \pm\frac{1}{2\sqrt{2}} \approx \pm.354$. Note that $f'(-1) < 0$, $f'(-.1) > 0$, $f'(.1) < 0$, and $f'(1) > 0$, so f is decreasing on $(-\infty, -\frac{1}{2\sqrt{2}})$ and on $(0, \frac{1}{2\sqrt{2}})$, and is increasing on $(-\frac{1}{2\sqrt{2}}, 0)$ and on $(\frac{1}{2\sqrt{2}}, \infty)$. There are local minima at $(\pm\frac{1}{2\sqrt{2}}, 1.75)$ and a local maximum at $(0, 2)$.

$f''(x) = \frac{2}{9x^{4/3}} + \frac{4}{9x^{2/3}} = \frac{4x^{2/3}+2}{9x^{4/3}}$. This is undefined at $x = 0$, but otherwise, is always positive. So f is concave up on $(-\infty, 0)$ and on $(0, \infty)$. There are no inflection points.

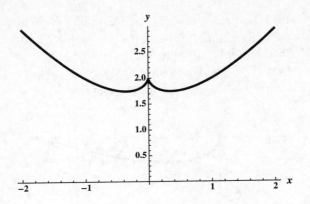

4.3.27

The domain of f is given to be $[0, 2\pi]$, so questions about symmetry and horizontal asymptotes aren't relevant. There are no vertical asymptotes.

$f'(x) = \cos x - 1$. This is never 0 on $(0, 2\pi)$. $f''(x) = -\sin x$, which is 0 on the given interval only for $x = \pi$. Note that $f'(x) < 0$ on $(0, 2\pi)$, so f is decreasing on the given interval and there are no relative extrema. Note also that $f''(x) < 0$ on $(0, \pi)$ and $f''(x) > 0$ on $(\pi, 2\pi)$, so f is concave down on $(0, \pi)$ and is concave up on $(\pi, 2\pi)$, and there is an inflection point at $x = \pi$. The only intercept is the origin $(0, 0)$.

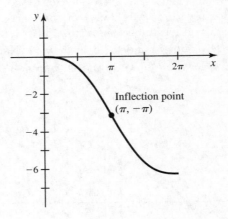

4.3.28

The domain of f is $(-3, \infty)$, and there is no symmetry, and there are no vertical asymptotes. Note that $\lim\limits_{x \to \infty} f(x) = \infty$, so there are no horizontal asymptotes.

$f'(x) = x \cdot (1/2) \cdot (x + 3)^{-1/2} + (x + 3)^{1/2} = \frac{3x+6}{2\sqrt{x+3}}$. This is 0 for $x = -2$.

$f''(x) = \frac{2(x+3)^{1/2} \cdot 3 - (3x+6)(x+3)^{-1/2}}{4(x+3)} = \frac{3x+12}{4(x+3)^{3/2}}$. The numerator is zero for $x = -4$, but that number isn't in the domain of f.

Note that $f'(x) < 0$ on $(-3, -2)$ and $f'(x) > 0$ on $(-2, \infty)$, so f is decreasing on $(-3, -2)$ and increasing on $(-2, \infty)$, and there is a local (and absolute) minimum of -2 at $x = -2$.

Note also that $f''(x) > 0$ for all x in the domain of f, so f is concave up on its domain, and there are no inflection points. The function is equal to zero at the x-intercepts $(-3, 0)$ and $(0, 0)$, and the latter is also the y-intercept.

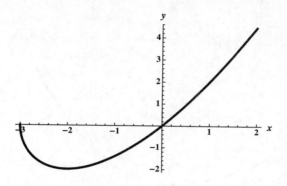

4.3.29

The domain of g is given to be $[-\pi, \pi]$, and there is no symmetry and no vertical asymptotes. Because the domain is finite, questions about horizontal asymptotes are not relevant.

$g'(t) = e^{-t}\cos t + \sin t \cdot (-e^{-t}) = e^{-t}(\cos t - \sin t)$. This is 0 on the given interval for $t = -3\pi/4$ and $t = \pi/4$. $g''(t) = e^{-t}(-\sin t - \cos t) + (\cos t - \sin t)(-e^{-t}) = -2e^{-t}\cos t$, which is 0 for $t = -\pi/2$ and $t = \pi/2$.

Note that $g'(t) < 0$ on $(-\pi, -3\pi/4)$ and on $(\pi/4, \pi)$, so g is decreasing on those intervals. On $(-3\pi/4, \pi/4)$ we have $g'(t) > 0$ and so g is increasing. There is a local minimum of about -7.460 at $t = -3\pi/4$ and a local maximum of about 0.322 at $t = \pi/4$.

Note also that $g''(t) > 0$ on $(-\pi, -\pi/2)$ and on $(\pi/2, \pi)$, while $g''(t) < 0$ on $(-\pi/2, \pi/2i)$, so g is concave down on $(-\pi/2, \pi/2)$ and is concave up on $(\pi/2, \pi)$ and on $(-\pi, -\pi/2)$. There are inflection points at $t = \pm\pi/2$. The origin is both the y-intercept and an x-intercept. The endpoints are x-intercepts as well.

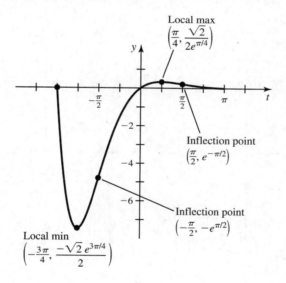

4.3.30

The domain of g is $(0, \infty)$, and there is no symmetry, and there are no vertical asymptotes. Note that $\lim\limits_{x\to\infty} g(x) = \infty$, so there are no horizontal asymptotes.

$g'(x) = x^2 \cdot \frac{1}{x} + \ln x \cdot 2x = x(1 + 2\ln x)$. This is 0 for $x = e^{-1/2}$.

$g''(x) = x(2/x) + (1 + 2\ln x) = 3 + 2\ln x$. This is 0 for $x = e^{-3/2}$.

Note that $g'(x) < 0$ on $(0, e^{-1/2})$ and $g'(x) > 0$ on $(e^{-1/2}, \infty)$, so g is decreasing on $(0, e^{-1/2})$ and increasing on $(e^{-1/2}, \infty)$, and there is a local (and absolute) minimum at $x = e^{-1/2}$.

Note also that $g''(x) < 0$ for $0 < x < e^{-3/2}$ and $g''(x) > 0$ for $x > e^{-3/2}$, so g is concave down on $(0, e^{-3/2})$ and concave up on $(e^{-3/2}, \infty)$ and there is an inflection point at $x = e^{-3/2}$. The only x-intercept is $(1, 0)$.

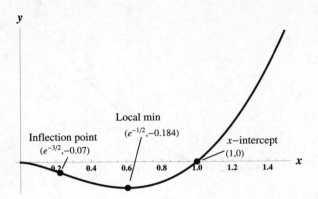

4.3.31

The domain of f is given to be $(-3\pi/2, 3\pi/2)$, but note that the function is not defined at $x = \pm\pi/2$, so the domain is actually $(-3\pi/2, -\pi/2) \cup (-\pi/2, \pi/2) \cup (\pi/2, 3\pi/2)$. Note that $f(-x) = -x + \tan(-x) = -x - \tan x = -(x + \tan x) = -f(x)$, so f has odd symmetry. f has vertical asymptotes at $x = \pm - 3\pi/2$ and at $x = \pm\pi/2$, because the tangent function increases or decreases without bound as x approaches these values.

$f'(x) = 1 + \sec^2 x$ which is always greater than 0. Thus f is increasing on each interval on which it is defined, and it has no extrema. $f''(x) = 2\sec x \cdot \sec x \tan x = 2\sec^2 x \tan x$. This is 0 at $x = \pm\pi$ and $x = 0$.

Note that $f''(x)$ is positive on $(-\pi, -\pi/2)$ and on $(0, \pi/2)$ and on $(\pi, 3\pi/2)$, so f is concave up on these intervals. Also, $f''(x)$ is negative on $(-3\pi/2, -\pi)$ and on $(-\pi/2, 0)$, and on $(\pi/2, \pi)$, so f is concave down on these intervals. There are points of inflection at $x = \pm\pi$ and at $x = 0$. The other changes in concavity occur at the vertical asymptotes.

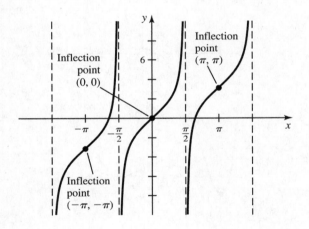

4.3.32

The domain of f is $(0, \infty)$. Note that $\lim_{x \to 0^+} \dfrac{\ln x}{x^2} = -\infty$, so $x = 0$ is a vertical asymptote. Questions about symmetry aren't relevant. Later in this chapter we will show that $\lim_{x \to \infty} \dfrac{\ln x}{x^2} = 0$, so $y = 0$ is a horizontal asymptote.

$f'(x) = \dfrac{x^2 \cdot (1/x) - \ln x \cdot 2x}{x^4} = \dfrac{1 - 2\ln x}{x^3}$, which is 0 for $x = e^{1/2}$. Note that $f'(x) > 0$ for $0 < x < e^{1/2}$ and $f'(x) < 0$ for $x > e^{1/2}$, so f is increasing on $(0, e^{1/2})$ and decreasing on $(e^{1/2}, \infty)$, and there is a local maximum (which is actually an absolute maximum) at $x = e^{1/2}$ of about .184.

$f''(x) = \dfrac{x^3(-2/x) - (1 - 2\ln x) \cdot 3x^2}{x^6} = \dfrac{6\ln x - 5}{x^4}$, which is 0 for $x = e^{5/6}$. Note that $f''(x) < 0$ for $0 < x < e^{5/6}$ and $f''(x) > 0$ for $x > e^{5/6}$, so there is a point of inflection at $e^{5/6}$ where the concavity changes from down (to the left) to up (to the right).

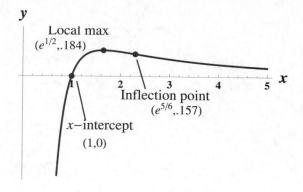

4.3.33

The domain of f is $(0, \infty)$, so questions about symmetry aren't relevant. There are no asymptotes.

$f'(x) = x \cdot 1/x + \ln x = 1 + \ln x$. This is 0 for $x = 1/e$. Note that $f'(x) < 0$ for $0 < x < 1/e$ and $f'(x) > 0$ for $x > 1/e$, so f is decreasing on $(0, 1/e)$ and increasing on $(1/e, \infty)$ and there is a local minimum (which is also an absolute minimum) at $x = 1/e$.

$f''(x) = 1/x$, which is always positive on the domain, so f is concave up on its domain and there are no inflection points.

There is an x-intercept at $x = 1$.

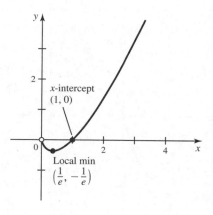

4.3.34

The domain of g is $(-\infty, \infty)$. Note that $g(-x) = e^{-(-x)^2/2} = e^{-x^2/2} = g(x)$, so g has even symmetry. There are no vertical asymptotes, but $\lim_{x \to \pm\infty} \frac{1}{e^{x^2}} = 0$, so the x-axis is a horizontal asymptote.

$g'(x) = -xe^{-x^2/2}$, which is 0 only for $x = 0$, and is positive on $(-\infty, 0)$ and is negative on $(0, \infty)$, so g is increasing on $(-\infty, 0)$ and is decreasing on $(0, \infty)$, so there is a local maximum which is actually an absolute maximum of $g(0) = 1$ at $x = 0$.

$g''(x) = -x \cdot (-xe^{-x^2/2}) + e^{-x^2/2}(-1) = e^{-x^2/2}(x^2 - 1)$ which is 0 only for $x = \pm 1$. Note that $g''(x) < 0$ on $(-1, 1)$ (so g is concave down there) and $g''(x) > 0$ on $(-\infty, -1)$ and on $(1, \infty)$, where g is concave up. There are inflection points at $x = \pm 1$, and there are no x-intercepts. There is a y-intercept at $(0, 1)$.

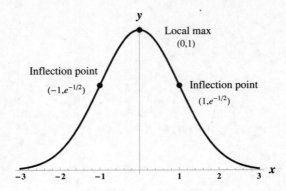

4.3.35

The domain of p is $(-\infty, \infty)$. There are no vertical asymptotes. Note that $p(-x) = -xe^{-(-x)^2} = -(xe^{-x^2}) = -p(x)$, so p has odd symmetry. Later in this chapter we will show that $\lim\limits_{x \to \pm\infty} p(x) = 0$, so $y = 0$ is a horizontal asymptote.

$p'(x) = x \cdot (-2xe^{-x^2} + e^{-x^2} \cdot 1 = e^{-x^2}(1 - 2x^2)$. This is 0 for $x = \pm\sqrt{2}/2$. Note that $p'(x) < 0$ on $(-\infty, -\sqrt{2}/2)$ and on $(\sqrt{2}/2, \infty)$, so p is decreasing on those intervals, and $p'(x) > 0$ on $(-\sqrt{2}/2, \sqrt{2}/2)$, so p is increasing on that interval. There is a local maximum at $x = \sqrt{2}/2$ and a local minimum at $x = -\sqrt{2}/2$.

$p''(x) = e^{-x^2}(-4x) + (1 - 2x^2) \cdot (-2x)e^{-x^2} = 2x(2x^2 - 3)e^{-x^2}$, which is 0 at $x = 0$ and at $x = \pm\sqrt{3/2}$. Note that $p''(x) > 0$ on $(-\sqrt{3/2}, 0)$ and on $(\sqrt{3/2}, \infty)$, so p is concave up on those intervals, while $p''(x) < 0$ on $(-\infty, -\sqrt{3/2})$ and on $(0, \sqrt{3/2})$, so p is concave down on those intervals. There are inflection points at each of $x = \pm\sqrt{3/2}$ and at $x = 0$.

There is an x-intercept at $(0,0)$, which is also the y-intercept.

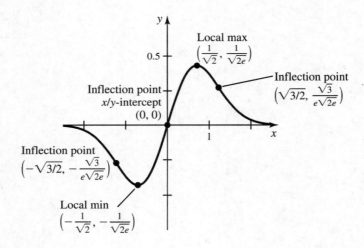

4.3.36

The domain of g is $(-\infty, 0) \cup (0, \infty)$, and g has no symmetry. Note that $\lim\limits_{x \to \infty} \dfrac{1}{e^{-x} - 1} = \dfrac{1}{0 - 1} = -1$, so $y = -1$ is a horizontal asymptote as $x \to \infty$. Also, $\lim\limits_{x \to -\infty} \dfrac{1}{e^{-x} - 1} = 0$, so $y = 0$ is a horizontal asymptote as $x \to -\infty$.

$g'(x) = -(e^{-x} - 1)^{-2}(-e^{-x}) = \dfrac{e^{-x}}{(e^{-x}-1)^2}$, which is never 0, and is positive on $(-\infty, 0)$ and on $(0, \infty)$, so g is increasing on $(-\infty, 0)$ and is increasing on $(0, \infty)$. Thus g has no extrema.

$g''(x) = \dfrac{(e^{-x}-1)^2(-e^{-x}) - e^{-x} \cdot 2 \cdot (e^{-x}-1)(-e^{-x})}{(e^{-x}-1)^4} = \dfrac{e^{-x}(e^{-x}+1)}{(e^{-x}-1)^3}$, which is never 0. It is positive on $(-\infty, 0)$ and negative on $(0, \infty)$, so there are no inflection points as the only change in concavity occurs at the vertical asymptote, where the concavity changes from concave up (for $x < 0$) to concave down (for $x > 0$).

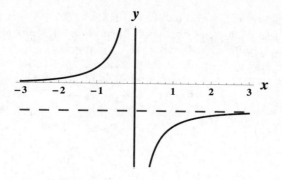

4.3.37

The domain of f is $(-\infty, \infty)$, and there is no symmetry. $f'(x) = x^2 - 4x - 5 = (x-5)(x+1)$. This is 0 when $x = -1, 5$. $f''(x) = 2x - 4$, which is 0 when $x = 2$. Note that $f'(-2) > 0$, $f'(0) < 0$, and $f'(6) > 0$. So f is increasing on $(-\infty, -1)$ and on $(5, \infty)$. It is decreasing on $(-1, 5)$. There is a local maximum of $14/3$ at $x = -1$ and a local minimum of $-94/3$ at $x = 5$. Note also that $f''(x) < 0$ for $x < 2$ and $f''(x) > 0$ for $x > 2$, so there is an inflection point at $(2, -40/3)$, and f is concave down on $(-\infty, 2)$ and concave up on $(2, \infty)$. The y intercept is $f(0) = 2$.

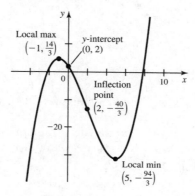

4.3.38

The domain of f is $(-\infty, \infty)$, and there is no symmetry. $f'(x) = \frac{1}{5}x^2 - 1$. This is 0 when $x = \pm\sqrt{5}$. $f''(x) = \frac{2}{5}x$, which is 0 when $x = 0$. Note that $f'(-3) > 0$, $f'(0) < 0$, and $f'(3) > 0$. So f is increasing on $(-\infty, -\sqrt{5})$ and on $(\sqrt{5}, \infty)$. It is decreasing on $(-\sqrt{5}, \sqrt{5})$. There is a local maximum of $\frac{3+2\sqrt{5}}{3}$ at $x = -\sqrt{5}$ and a local minimum of $\frac{3-2\sqrt{5}}{3}$ at $x = \sqrt{5}$. Note also that $f''(x) < 0$ for $x < 0$ and $f''(x) > 0$ for $x > 0$, so there is an inflection point at the y-intercept $(0, 1)$, and f is concave down on $(-\infty, 0)$ and concave up on $(0, \infty)$.

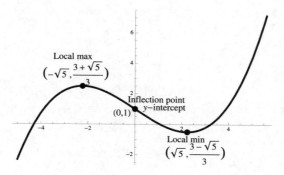

4.3.39

The domain of f is $(-\infty, \infty)$, and there is no symmetry. $f'(x) = 12x^3 + 12x^2 - 24x = 12x(x+2)(x-1)$. This is 0 when $x = -2$, when $x = 1$, and when $x = 0$. $f''(x) = 36x^2 + 24x - 24 = 12(3x^2 + 2x - 2)$, which is 0 when $x = \frac{-1\pm\sqrt{7}}{3}$. These values are at approximately -1.215 and 0.549. Note that $f'(-3) < 0$, $f'(-1) > 0$, $f'(.5) < 0$, and $f'(2) > 0$. So f is decreasing on $(-\infty, -2)$ and on $(0, 1)$. It is increasing on $(-2, 0)$ and on $(1, \infty)$. There is a local maximum of 0 at $x = 0$ and a local minimum of -32 at $x = -2$ and a local minimum of -5 at $x = 1$. Let $r_1 < r_2$ be the two roots of $f''(x)$ mentioned above. Note that $f''(x) > 0$ for $x < r_1$ and for $x > r_2$ and $f''(x) < 0$ for $r_1 < x < r_2$, so there are inflection points at $x = r_1$ and at $x = r_2$. Also, f is concave down on (r_1, r_2) and concave up on $(-\infty, r_1)$ and on (r_2, ∞). There is a y-intercept at $f(0) = 0$ and x-intercepts where $f(x) = 3x^4 + 4x^3 - 12x^2 = x^2(3x^2 + 4x - 12) = 0$, which is at $x = \frac{-2\pm2\sqrt{10}}{3}$ and $x = 0$.

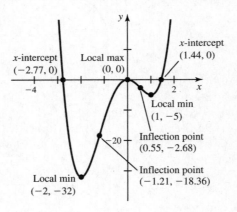

4.3.40

The domain of f is $(-\infty, \infty)$, and there is no symmetry. $f'(x) = 3x^2 - 66x + 216 = 3(x - 4)(x - 18)$. This is 0 when $x = 4$ and when $x = 18$. $f''(x) = 6x - 66 = 6(x - 11)$, which is 0 when $x = 11$. Note that $f'(0) > 0$, $f'(10) < 0$, and $f'(20) > 0$. Thus f is decreasing on $(4, 18)$, while it is increasing on $(-\infty, 4)$ and on $(18, \infty)$.

There is a local maximum of 398 at $x = 4$ and a local minimum of -974 at $x = 18$. Note also that $f''(x) < 0$ for $x < 11$, and $f''(x) > 0$ for $x > 11$, so there is an inflection point at $x = 11$, and f is concave up on $(11, \infty)$ and is concave down on $(-\infty, 11)$.

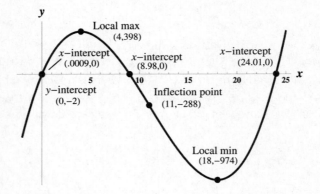

4.3.41

The domain of f is $(-\infty, -1) \cup (-1, 1) \cup (1, \infty)$, and there is no symmetry. Note that $\lim_{x \to -1^+} f(x) = \infty$ and $\lim_{x \to -1^-} f(x) = -\infty$, so there is a vertical asymptote at $x = -1$. Also, $\lim_{x \to 1^+} f(x) = -\infty$ and $\lim_{x \to 1^-} f(x) = \infty$, so there is a vertical asymptote at $x = 1$

Note that $\lim_{x \to \pm\infty} \frac{3x - 5}{x^2 - 1} \cdot \frac{1/x^2}{1/x^2} = \lim_{x \to \pm\infty} \frac{3/x}{1 - (1/x^2)} = 0$, so $y = 0$ is a horizontal asymptote.

$f'(x) = \frac{(x^2-1)\cdot 3 - (3x-5)\cdot 2x}{(x^2-1)^2} = \frac{-3x^2+10x-3}{(x^2-1)^2} = \frac{(-3x+1)(x-3)}{(x^2-1)^2}$. This is 0 when $x = 3$ and when $x = 1/3$.

$f''(x) = \frac{(x^2-1)^2(-6x+10)-(-3x^2+10x-3)(2)(x^2-1)\cdot 2x}{(x^2-1)^4} = \frac{2(3x^3-15x^2+9x-5)}{(x^2-1)^3}$. This is 0 for $x \approx 4.405$. Let r be this root of $f''(x)$.

Note that $f'(-2) < 0$, $f'(-1/2) < 0$, $f'(1/2) > 0$, $f'(2) > 0$ and $f'(4) < 0$. So f is decreasing on $(-\infty, -1)$, on $(-1, 1/3)$ and on $(3, \infty)$. It is increasing on $(1/3, 1)$ and on $(1, 3)$. There is a local maximum of $1/2$ at $x = 3$ and a local minimum of $9/2$ at $x = 1/3$.

Note that $f''(x) < 0$ for $x < -1$ and $f''(x) < 0$ for $1 < x < r$, while $f''(x) > 0$ for $-1 < x < 1$, and for $x > r$. Thus f is concave up on $(-1, 1)$ and on (r, ∞) and concave down on $(-\infty, -1)$ and on $(1, r)$. There is an inflection point at r. There is a y-intercept at $f(0) = 5$ and an x-intercept at $(5/3, 0)$.

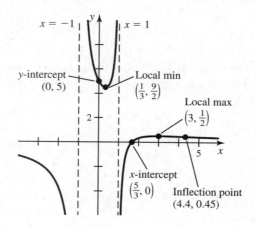

4.3.42

The domain of f is $(-\infty, \infty)$, and there is no symmetry, and no vertical asymptotes. Note that $\lim\limits_{x \to \pm\infty} f(x) = \pm\infty$, so there are no horizontal asymptotes.

$f'(x) = x^{1/3} \cdot 2 \cdot (x - 2) + (x - 2)^2 (1/3) x^{-2/3} = \frac{(x-2)(7x-2)}{3x^{2/3}}$. This is 0 for $x = 2$ and $x = 2/7$, and does not exist for $x = 0$.

$f''(x) = \frac{3x^{2/3}(14x-16)-(7x^2-16x+4)(2x^{-1/3})}{9x^{4/3}} = \frac{4(7x^2-4x-2)}{9x^{5/3}}$. The numerator of this last expression has two roots, which we will call r_1 and r_2. Note that $r_1 \approx -0.320$ and $r_2 \approx 0.892$. Note also that f'' doesn't exist for $x = 0$.

$f'(x) > 0$ on $(-\infty, 0)$ and $(0, 2/7)$ and $(2, \infty)$, so f is increasing on those intervals, while $f'(x) < 0$ on $(2/7, 2)$, so f is decreasing there. f has a local maximum at $x = 2/7$ and a local minimum of 0 at $x = 2$.

Note also that $f''(x) < 0$ for $x < r_1$ and for $0 < x < r_2$, so f is concave down on $(-\infty, r_1)$ and on $(0, r_2)$. However, $f''(x) > 0$ for $r_1 < x < 0$ and for $x > r_2$, so f is concave up on $(r_1, 0)$ and on (r_2, ∞). There are inflection points at each of r_1, r_2, and 0. The inflection point $(0, 0)$ serves also as the x- and y- intercept.

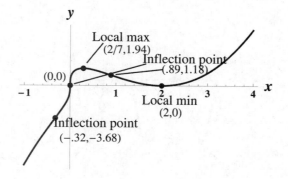

4.3.43

a. False. Maxima and minima can also occur at points where $f'(x)$ doesn't exist. Also, it is possible to have a zero of f' which doesn't correspond to an extreme point.

b. False. Inflection points can also occur at points where $f''(x)$ doesn't exist, and a zero of f'' might not correspond to an inflection point.

c. False. For example, $f(x) = \frac{(x^2-9)(x^2-16)}{(x+3)(x-4)}$ doesn't have a vertical asymptote at $x = -3$ or $x = 4$.

d. True. The limit of a rational function as $x \to \infty$ is a finite number when the degree of the denominator is greater than or equal to that of the numerator. If they both have the same degree, the limit is the ratio of the leading coefficients, and this is also true of the limit as $x \to -\infty$. In the case where the denominator has greater degree than the numerator, the limit is 0 as $x \to -\infty$ and as $x \to \infty$.

4.3.44

$f'(x)$ is 0 at $x = -4$, $x = -2$, and $x = 1$. $f'(x) > 0$ on $(-4, -2)$ and on $(1, \infty)$, so f is increasing there, while $f'(x) < 0$ on $(-\infty, -4)$ and on $(-2, 1)$, so f is decreasing on those intervals. There must be a local maximum at $x = -2$ and local minimums at $x = -4$ and $x = 1$. An example of such a function is sketched.

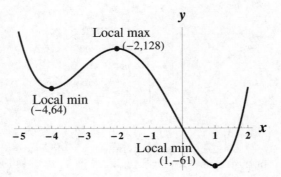

4.3.45

$f'(x)$ is 0 on the interior of the given interval at $x = \pm 3\pi/2$, $x = \pm \pi$, $x = \pm \pi/2$, and at $x = 0$.

$f'(x) > 0$ on $(-2\pi, -3\pi/2)$, $(-\pi, -\pi/2)$, $(0, \pi/2)$, and on $(\pi, 3\pi/2)$, so f is increasing on those intervals. $f'(x) < 0$ on $(-3\pi/2, -\pi)$, $(-\pi/2, 0)$, $(\pi/2, \pi)$, and on $(3\pi/2, 2\pi)$, so f is decreasing on those intervals. There are local maxima at $x = \pm 3\pi/2$ and $x = \pm \pi/2$, and local minima at $x = 0$ and at $x = \pm \pi$. An example of such a function is sketched.

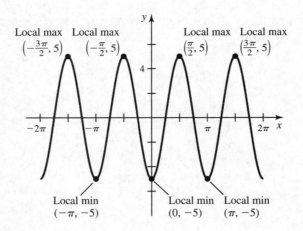

4.3.46

$f'(x)$ is 0 at -1, 2, and 3. On the interval $(-\infty, -1)$, f' is positive (so f is increasing), and likewise on the interval $(3, \infty)$. On the interval $(-1, 2)$ and on $(2, 3)$, f' is negative (so f is decreasing). There is a local maximum at $x = -1$ and a local minimum at $x = 3$.

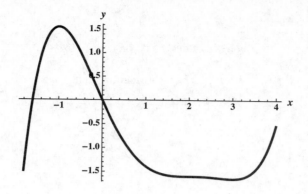

4.3.47

$f'(x)$ is 0 at $x = 0$, $x = -2$, and $x = 1$. $f'(x) > 0$ on $(-\infty, -2)$ and on $(1, \infty)$, so f is increasing on those intervals. $f'(x) < 0$ on $(-2, 0)$ and on $(0, 1)$, so f is decreasing on those intervals. There is a local maximum at $x = -2$ and a local minimum at $x = 1$. There isn't an extremum at $x = 0$.

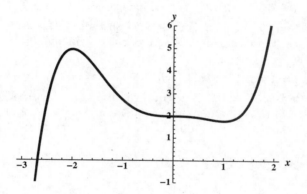

4.3.48

$f'(x) > 0$ on $(-\infty, 1)$ and on $(1, \infty)$, so f should be increasing on both of those intervals. There should be an inflection point at $x = 1$, because the 2nd derivative changes from negative to positive there, so f should change from concave down to concave up at that point.

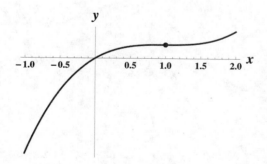

4.3.49

$f'(x)$ is 0 at $x = 1$ and $x = 3$.

$f'(x) > 0$ on $(0, 1)$ and on $(3, 4)$, so f is increasing on those intervals. $f'(x) < 0$ on $(1, 3)$, so f is decreasing on that interval. There is a local maximum at $x = 1$ and a local minimum at $x = 3$.

$f''(x)$ changes sign at $x = 2$ from negative to positive, so $x = 2$ is an inflection point where the concavity of f changes from down to up. An example of such a function is sketched.

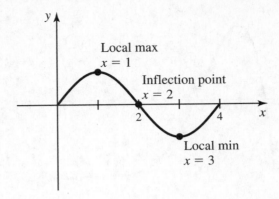

4.3.50

The domain of f is $(-\infty, \infty)$ and there is no symmetry. There are no asymptotes because f is a polynomial.

$f'(x) = 4x^3 + 24x^2 - 540x = 4x(x-9)(x+15)$, which is 0 for $x = 9$, $x = -15$, and $x = 0$.

$f'(x) > 0$ on $(-15, 0)$ and on $(9, \infty)$, so f is increasing on those intervals. $f'(x) < 0$ on $(-\infty, -15)$ and on $(0, 9)$, so f is decreasing on those intervals. There is a local maximum at $x = 0$ and local minima at $x = -15$ and $x = 9$.

$f''(x) = 12x^2 + 48x - 540 = 12(x-5)(x+9)$, which is 0 for $x = 5$ and $x = -9$.

$f''(x) > 0$ on $(-\infty, -9)$ and on $(5, \infty)$, so f is concave up on those intervals. $f''(x) < 0$ on $(-9, 5)$ so f is concave down on that interval. There are points of inflection at $x = -9$ and $x = 5$. The y-intercept is 1 and the x-intercepts are ≈ -20.912 and ≈ 12.911. There are also x-intercepts at approximately ± 0.061.

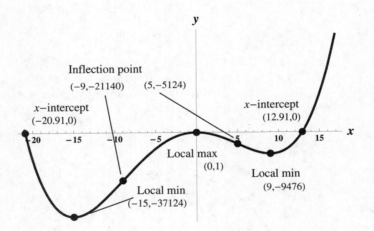

4.3.51

The domain of f is $(-\infty, \infty)$ and there is no symmetry. There are no asymptotes because f is a polynomial.

$f'(x) = 3x^2 - 12x - 135 = 3(x-9)(x+5)$, which is 0 for $x = 9$ and $x = -5$. $f'(x) > 0$ on $(-\infty, -5)$ and on $(9, \infty)$, so f is increasing on those intervals. $f'(x) < 0$ on $(-5, 9)$, so f is decreasing on that interval. There is a local maximum at $x = -5$ and a local minimum at $x = 9$.

$f''(x) = 6x - 12$, which is 0 for $x = 2$. $f''(x) > 0$ on $(2, \infty)$, so f is concave up on that interval. $f''(x) < 0$ on $(-\infty, 2)$, so f is concave down on that interval. There is a point of inflection at $x = 2$. The y-intercept is 0 and the x-intercepts are -9 and 15.

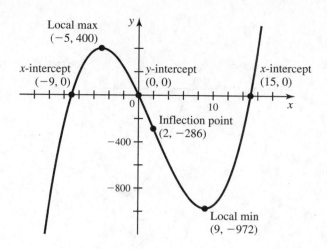

4.3.52

The domain of f is $(-\infty, \infty)$ and there is no symmetry. There are no asymptotes because f is a polynomial. $f'(x) = 3x^2 - 147 = 3(x+7)(x-7)$, which is 0 for $x = 7$ and $x = -7$. $f'(x) > 0$ on $(-\infty, -7)$ and on $(7, \infty)$, so f is increasing on those intervals. $f'(x) < 0$ on $(-7, 7)$, so f is decreasing on that interval. There is a local maximum at $x = -7$ and a local minimum at $x = 7$.

$f''(x) = 6x$, which is 0 for $x = 0$. $f''(x) > 0$ on $(0, \infty)$, so f is concave up on that interval. $f''(x) < 0$ on $(-\infty, 0)$, so f is concave down on that interval. There is a point of inflection at $x = 0$. The y-intercept is 286 and the x-intercepts are at -13, 2, and 11.

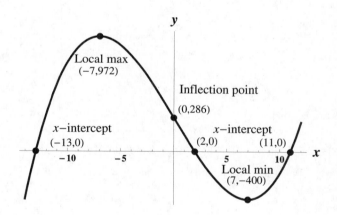

4.3.53

The domain of f is $(-\infty, \infty)$ and there is no symmetry. There are no asymptotes because f is a polynomial.

$f'(x) = 3x^2 - 6x - 144 = 3(x+6)(x-8)$, which is 0 for $x = -6$ and $x = 8$. $f'(x) > 0$ on $(-\infty, -6)$ and on $(8, \infty)$, so f is increasing on those intervals. $f'(x) < 0$ on $(-6, 8)$, so f is decreasing on that interval. There is a local maximum at $x = -6$ and a local minimum at $x = 8$.

$f''(x) = 6x - 6$, which is 0 for $x = 1$. $f''(x) > 0$ on $(1, \infty)$, so f is concave up on that interval. $f''(x) < 0$ on $(-\infty, 1)$, so f is concave down on that interval. There is a point of inflection at $x = 1$. The y-intercept is -140 and the x-intercepts are at -10, -1, and 14.

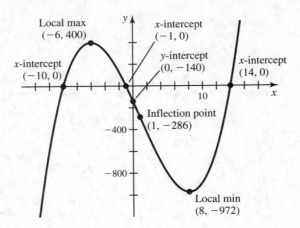

4.3.54

a. $f'(x) = -\sin(\ln x) \cdot \frac{1}{x} = -\frac{\sin(\ln x)}{x}$, which is 0 when $\ln x = k\pi$ for an integer k, which occurs for $x = e^{k\pi}$. On the given interval, this occurs for $x = 1$, $x = e^{-\pi}$, $x = e^{-2\pi}$, ...

b. $f''(x) = \frac{x(-\cos(\ln x) \cdot (1/x)) - (-\sin(\ln x))}{x^2} = \frac{\sin(\ln x) - \cos(\ln x)}{x^2}$. This is 0 when $\ln x = \frac{4k+1}{4}\pi$ where k is an integer. For our domain, this occurs for $x = e^{\pi/4}$, $x = e^{-3\pi/4}$, $x = e^{-7\pi/4}$, ...

c. Using a computer algebra system, the three smallest zeroes on $(.1, \infty)$ are at $\approx .208$, ≈ 4.81, and ≈ 111.318.

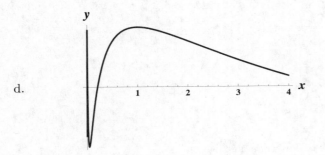

d.

Here it is shown graphed on $(0, 4)$.   Here it is shown graphed on $(0, .06)$.

4.3.55

   f can be written as $f(x) = e^{(\ln x)/x}$. $f'(x) = e^{(\ln x)/x}\left(\frac{1-\ln x}{x^2}\right)$. This is 0 for $x = e$, and is positive on $(0, e)$ and negative on (e, ∞). There is a local maximum at $x = e$ of $e^{1/e}$.

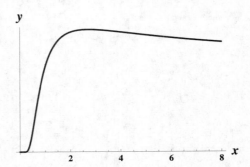

4.3.56

   f can be written as $f(x) = e^{x \ln x}$. $f'(x) = e^{x \ln x}(1 + \ln x)$. This is 0 for $x = 1/e$, and is positive on $(1/e, \infty)$ and negative on $(0, 1/e)$. There is a local minimum at $x = 1/e$ of $1/(e^{1/e})$.

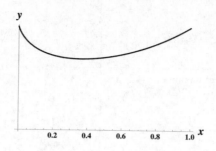

4.3.57

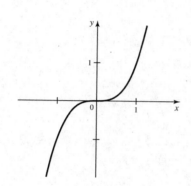

4.3.58

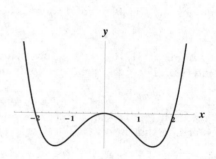

4.3.59

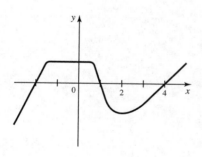

4.3.60

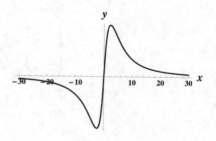

4.3.61

The domain of f is $(-\infty, -2) \cup (2, \infty)$ and there is no symmetry. There is a vertical asymptote at $x = 2$ because $\lim_{x \to 2^+} -\frac{x\sqrt{x^2-4}}{x-2} = -\infty$. There are no horizontal asymptotes.

$f'(x) = \frac{(x-2)(-x^2(x^2-4)^{-1/2}+(x^2-4)^{1/2}(-1))-((-x)(x^2-4)^{1/2})}{(x-2)^2}$. This can be written as $\frac{-x^2+2x+4}{(x-2)\sqrt{x^2-4}}$, and this quantity is 0 on the given domain only for $x = 1 + \sqrt{5} \approx 3.236$.

$f'(x) > 0$ on $(-\infty, -2)$ and on $(2, 1+\sqrt{5})$, so f is increasing on those intervals. $f'(x) < 0$ on $(1+\sqrt{5}, \infty)$, so f is decreasing on that interval. There is a local maximum at $x = 1 + \sqrt{5}$.

$f''(x)$ simplifies to be $-\frac{4(x+4)}{(x-2)^2(x+2)\sqrt{x^2-4}}$, which is 0 at $x = -4$

$f''(x) > 0$ on $(-4, -2)$, so f is concave up on that interval. $f''(x) < 0$ on $(-\infty, -4)$ and on $(1+\sqrt{5}, \infty)$, so f is concave down on those intervals. There is a point of inflection at $x = -4$.

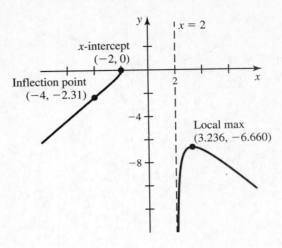

4.3.62

The domain of f is $[0, \infty)$ and there is no symmetry. There are no asymptotes.

$f'(x) = (3/4)x^{-3/4} - (1/2)x^{-1/2} = \frac{3 - 2x^{1/4}}{4x^{3/4}}$, which is 0 for $x = \frac{81}{16}$.

$f'(x) > 0$ on $(0, 81/16)$, so f is increasing on that interval. $f'(x) < 0$ on $(81/16, \infty)$, so f is decreasing on that interval. There is a local maximum at $81/16$ (which also gives an absolute maximum.)

$f''(x) = (-9/6)x^{-7/4} + (1/4)x^{-3/2} = \frac{4x^{1/4} - 9}{16x^{7/4}}$, which is 0 at $x = 6561/256$.

$f''(x) > 0$ on $(6561/256, \infty)$, so f is concave up on that interval. $f''(x) < 0$ on $(0, 6561/256)$, so f is concave down on that interval. There is a point of inflection at $x = 6561/256$.

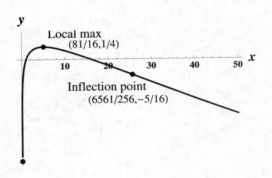

4.3.63

The domain of f is $(-\infty, \infty)$ and there is no symmetry. There are no asymptotes because f is a polynomial.

$f'(x) = 12x^3 - 132x^2 + 120x = 12x(x - 10)(x - 1)$, which is 0 for $x = 0$, $x = 1$, and $x = 10$.

$f'(x) > 0$ on $(0, 1)$ and on $(10, \infty)$, so f is increasing on those intervals. $f'(x) < 0$ on $(-\infty, 0)$ and on $(1, 10)$, so f is decreasing on those intervals. There is a local maximum at $x = 1$, and local minima at $x = 0$ and at $x = 10$.

$f''(x) = 36x^2 - 264x + 120 = 12(3x^2 - 22x + 10)$. This is 0 at approximately $x = .487$ and $x = 6.846$. Let these two roots be r_1 and r_2 with $r_1 < r_2$. $f''(x) > 0$ on $(-\infty, r_1)$ and on (r_2, ∞), so f is concave up on those intervals. $f''(x) < 0$ on (r_1, r_2), so f is concave down on that interval. There are points of inflection at $x = r_1$ and $x = r_2$.

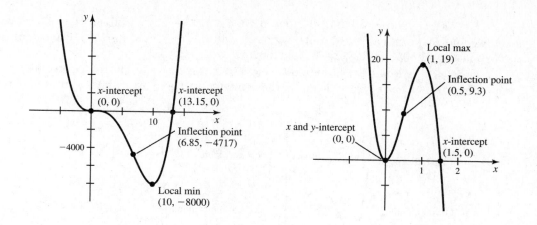

4.3.64

The domain of f is given to be $(1, 3)$ and there is no symmetry. There are vertical asymptotes at $x = 1$ and $x = 3$ because $\lim_{x \to 1^+} \frac{1}{1+\cos(\pi x)} = \infty$ and $\lim_{x \to 3^-} \frac{1}{1+\cos(\pi x)} = \infty$.

$$f'(x) = -(1 + \cos(\pi x))^{-2}(-\sin(\pi x) \cdot \pi) = \frac{\pi \sin \pi x}{(1 + \cos(\pi x))^2},$$

which is 0 on the given interval for $x = 2$.

$f'(x) > 0$ on $(2, 3)$, so f is increasing on that interval. $f'(x) < 0$ on $(1, 2)$, so f is decreasing on that interval. There is a local minimum at $x = 2$.

$$f''(x) = \frac{(1 + \cos \pi x)^2(\pi^2 \cos(\pi x) + 2\pi^2 \sin^2(\pi x)(1 + \cos(\pi x)))}{(1 + \cos(\pi x))^4}.$$

This simplifies to be

$$\frac{\pi^2(\cos(\pi x) + \cos^2(\pi x) + 2\sin^2(\pi x))}{(1 + \cos(\pi x))^3}.$$

This isn't ever 0 on the interval $(1, 3)$, and in fact is always positive, so f is concave up, and there are no points of inflection.

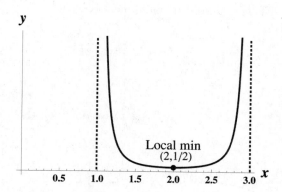

4.3.65

The domain of f is $(-\infty, \infty)$ and there is no symmetry. There are no asymptotes because f is a polynomial.

$f'(x) = 60x^5 - 180x^4 - 300x^3 + 900x^2 + 240x - 720 = 60(x + 2)(x + 1)(x - 1)(x - 2)(x - 3)$, which is 0 for $x = -2$, $x = -1$, $x = 1$, $x = 2$, and $x = 3$.

$f'(x) > 0$ on $(-2, -1)$, $(1, 2)$ and on $(3, \infty)$, so f is increasing on those intervals. $f'(x) < 0$ on $(-\infty, -2)$, $(-1, 2)$ and on $(2, 3)$, so f is decreasing on those intervals. There are local minima at $x = -2$, $x = 1$, and $x = 3$, and local maxima at $x = -1$ and $x = 2$.

$f''(x) = 300x^4 - 720x^3 - 900x^2 + 1800x + 240 = 60(5x^4 - 12x^3 - 15x^2 + 30x + 4)$.   Using a computer algebra system, we find that this has 4 real roots, which we will call $r_1 < r_2 < r_3 < r_4$. They values of these roots are approximately -1.605, -0.125, 1.502, and 2.629.

$f''(x) > 0$ on $(-\infty, r_1)$, and on (r_2, r_3) and on (r_4, ∞), so f is concave up on those intervals. $f''(x) < 0$ on (r_1, r_2) and on (r_3, r_4), so f is concave down on those intervals. There are points of inflection at each r_i for i from 1 to 4.

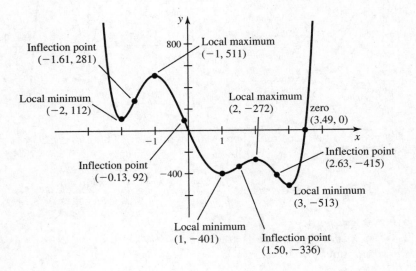

4.3.66

The domain of f is $(0, 3/2) \cup (3/2, 2)$ and there is no symmetry. There is a vertical asymptote at $x = 3/2$, because $\lim_{x \to 3/2} f(x) = -\infty$.

$$f'(x) = \frac{(1 + \sin \pi x)\cos(\pi x) \cdot \pi - \sin(\pi x)\cos(\pi x) \cdot \pi}{(1 + \sin(\pi x))^2} = \frac{\pi \cos \pi x}{(1 + \sin \pi x)^2},$$

which is 0 for $x = 1/2$.

$f'(x) > 0$ on $(0, 1/2)$ and on $(3/2, 2)$, so f is increasing on those intervals. $f'(x) < 0$ on $(1/2, 3/2)$, so f is decreasing on that interval. There is a local maximum at $x = 1/2$.

$$f''(x) = \frac{(1 + \sin \pi x)^2 (-\pi^2)(\sin \pi x) - 2\pi^2 \cos^2 \pi x (1 + \sin \pi x)}{(1 + \sin \pi x)^4} = \frac{-\pi^2 (2 - \sin \pi x)(1 + \sin \pi x)}{(1 + \sin \pi x)^3}.$$

This expression isn't 0 on the given interval.

$f''(x) < 0$ on both $(0, 3/2)$ and on $(3/2, 2)$, so f is concave down on those intervals. There are no points of inflection.

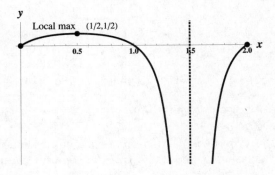

4.3.67

The domain of f is $(-\infty, \infty)$ and there is odd symmetry, because $f(-x) = -f(x)$. There are no vertical asymptotes, but $y = 0$ is a horizontal asymptote, because

$$\lim_{x \to \infty} \frac{x\sqrt{|x^2 - 1|}}{x^4 + 1} \cdot \frac{1/x^4}{1/x^4} = \lim_{x \to \infty} \frac{\sqrt{(1/x^4) - (1/x^6)}}{1 + (1/x^4)} = 0.$$

Note that $f(x) = \begin{cases} \frac{x\sqrt{x^2-1}}{x^4+1} & \text{if } |x| \geq 1; \\ \frac{x\sqrt{1-x^2}}{x^4+1} & \text{if } |x| < 1. \end{cases}$

Differentiating each part of the above and simplifying yields

$$f'(x) = \begin{cases} \dfrac{-2x^6 + 3x^4 + 2x^2 - 1}{(x^4 + 1)^2 \sqrt{x^2 - 1}} & \text{if } |x| > 1; \\ \dfrac{2x^6 - 3x^4 - 2x^2 + 1}{(x^4+1)^2\sqrt{1-x^2}} & \text{if } |x| < 1. \end{cases}$$

The roots of this expression (on the respective domains) are approximately ± 1.374 and ± 0.596. Also, this derivative doesn't exist at $x = \pm 1$. Let the roots of f' be $\pm r_1$ and $\pm r_2$ where $0 < r_1 < r_2$. An analysis of the sign of f' shows that f is increasing on $(-r_2, -1)$ on $(-r_1, r_1)$ and on $(1, r_2)$, while f is decreasing on $(-\infty, -r_2)$, $(-1, -r_1)$, $(r_1, 1)$ and on (r_2, ∞), so there are local maxima at $x = -1$, $x = r_1$, and $x = r_2$, and local minima at $x = -r_1$, $x = -r_2$, and $x = 1$.

An analysis without computer of $f''(x)$ is not for the fainthearted. In the case $|x| > 1$ the second derivative is given by $\dfrac{x\left(6x^{10} - 19x^8 - 12x^6 + 42x^4 - 18x^2 - 3\right)}{(x^2 - 1)^{3/2}(x^4 + 1)^3}$, and for the case $|x| < 1$ we have $\dfrac{x\left(6x^{10} - 19x^8 - 12x^6 + 42x^4 - 18x^2 - 3\right)}{(1 - x^2)^{3/2}(x^4 + 1)^3}$. There is a root of approximately ± 1.790, and 0 is a root as well. Let the non-zero roots be $\pm r_3$ where $r_3 > 0$. An analysis of the sign of f'' reveals that f is concave down on $(-\infty, -r_3)$, $(0, 1)$ and on $(1, r_3)$, while it is concave up on $(-r_3, -1)$, $(-1, 0)$ and on (r_3, ∞). There are inflection points at $\pm r_3$ and at 0. The x-intercepts are ± 1 and 0.

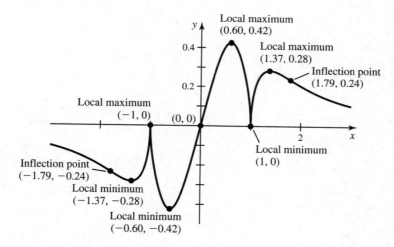

4.3.68

The given domain is $[-\pi/2, \pi/2]$, and because $f(-x) = \sin(3\pi \cos(-x)) = \sin(3\pi \cos x) = f(x)$, the function has even symmetry. There are no asymptotes.

$f'(x) = \cos(3\pi \cos x)(-3\pi \sin x)$, which has 7 roots on the given interval, at 0, at $r_1 \approx .586$, at $r_2 \approx 1.047$, and at $r_3 \approx 1.403$, and also at the opposites of these numbers. These roots can best be found with the aid of a computer. An analysis of the sign of f' reveals that f is increasing on $(-\pi/2, -r_3)$, $(-r_2, -r_1)$, $(0, r_1)$ and on (r_2, r_3), while f is decreasing on the complementary intervals. There are thus local maxima at $\pm r_3$

and $\pm r_1$, and local minima at $\pm r_2$ and 0. All the local maxima have value 1, and the local minima have value -1, except for $x = 0$ where the value is 0.

$f''(x) = -3\pi \sin x(-\sin(3\pi \cos x))(-3\pi \sin x) + \cos(3\pi \cos x)(-3\pi \cos x) = -9\pi^2 \sin^2 x \sin(3\pi \cos x) - 3\pi \cos x \cos(3\pi \cos x)$. This is 0 at $r_4 \approx .372$, $r_5 \approx .858$, and $r_6 \approx 1.235$ and their opposites. An analysis of f'' reveals that there is a concavity change at each of the induced intervals, starting with downward concavity on $(-\pi/2, -r_6)$. Each of $\pm r_4$, $\pm r_5$ and $\pm r_6$ are inflection points. The values of f at the inflection points are $f(\pm r_4) \approx .6$, $f(\pm r_5) \approx -.12$, and $f(\pm r_6) \approx .04$.

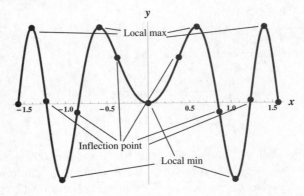

4.3.69

a. f has even symmetry, so we will analyze the function on $(0, 2\pi]$, and use the symmetry to graph the function over $[-2\pi, 0)$.

   $f'(x) = \frac{x^2(-3\cos^2 x(-\sin x)) - (1 - \cos^3 x) \cdot 2x}{x^4} = \frac{3x \sin x \cos^2 x - 2(1 - \cos^3 x)}{x^3}$. This has no roots on $(0, 2\pi)$, and in fact is always negative, so f is decreasing on $(0, 2\pi)$.

   $f''(x)$ when simplified is given by $\frac{3((x^2 - 2)\cos^3(x) - 2x^2 \sin^2(x)\cos(x) - 4x \sin(x)\cos^2(x) + 2)}{x^4}$. The roots of f'' on $(0, 2\pi)$ are $r_1 \approx .89$, $r_2 \approx 2.47$, $r_3 \approx 3.48$, $r_4 \approx 4.76$, and $r_5 \approx 5.5$. An analysis of the sign of f'' reveals that there is a change in concavity at each of these roots, starting with concavity downward on $(-r_1, r_1)$. So each of $\pm r_i$ is an inflection point.

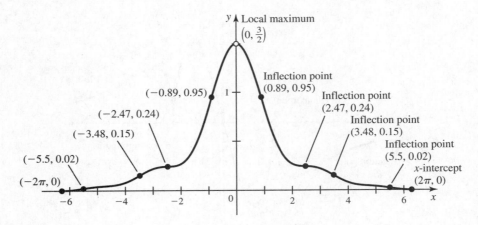

b. f has even symmetry, so we will analyze the function on $(0, 2\pi]$, and use the symmetry to graph the function over $[-2\pi, 0)$.

$$f'(x) = \frac{x^2(-5\cos^4 x(-\sin x)) - (1 - \cos^5 x)(2x)}{x^4} = \frac{5x \cos^4 x \sin x - 2(1 - \cos^5 x)}{x^3}.$$

This has roots on $(0, 2\pi)$ of $r_1 \approx 2.41$ and $r_2 \approx 2.83$. An analysis of the sign of f' shows that f is decreasing on $(0, r_1)$, increasing on (r_1, r_2), decreasing on $(r_2, 2\pi)$, so there is a local minimum at r_1 and a local maximum at r_2.

$f''(x)$ when simplified is given by

$$\frac{\left(5x^2 - 6\right)\cos^5(x) - 20x^2 \sin^2(x)\cos^3(x) - 20x\sin(x)\cos^4(x) + 6}{x^4}.$$

The roots of f'' on $(0, 2\pi)$ are $r_3 \approx .63$, $r_4 \approx 2.62$, $r_5 \approx 3.45$, $r_6 \approx 4.96$, and $r_7 \approx 5.74$. An analysis of the sign of f'' reveals that there is a change in concavity at each of these roots, starting with concavity downward on $(-r_3, r_3)$. So each of $\pm r_i$ is an inflection point for $i = 3, 4, 5, 6$ and 7.

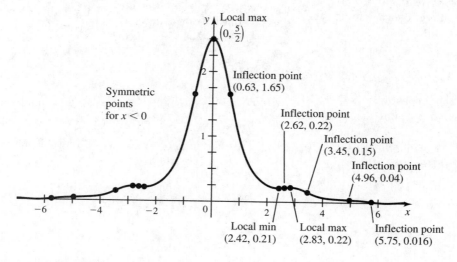

4.3.70 First note that $f'(x) = 3x^2 - 6bx + 3a^2$, which is zero for $x = b \pm \sqrt{b^2 - a^2}$ by the quadratic formula.

a. Suppose $|a| < |b|$. There is a max for f at $x = b - \sqrt{b^2 - a^2}$ and a minimum for f at $b + \sqrt{b^2 - a^2}$.

b. Suppose $|b| < |a|$. Then f' has no roots, and there are no extrema.

c. If $|a| = |b|$, the f' has a double root at $x = b$, but f has no extrema.

4.3.71

(a)

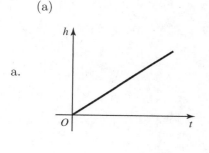

a.

(b)

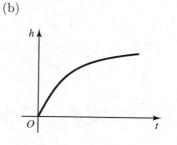

(c)

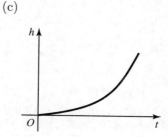

(d)

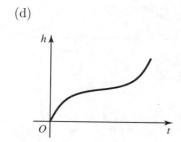

(e)

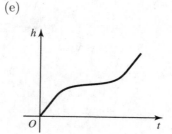

(f)

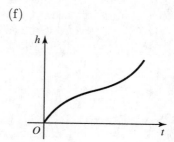

b. The water is being poured in at a constant rate, so the depth is always increasing, so $y = h(t)$ is an increasing function.

c. (a) No concavity

(b) Always concave down.

(c) Always concave up.

(d) Concave down for for the first half and concave up for the second half.

(e) At the beginning, in the middle, and at the end, there is no concavity. In the lower middle it is concave down and in the upper middle it will be concave up.

(f) This is concave down for the first half, and concave up for the second half.

d. (a) $h'(t)$ is constant, so there is no local max/min.

(b) $h'(t)$ is maximal at $t = 0$.

(c) $h'(t)$ is maximal at $t = 10$.

(d) $h'(t)$ is maximal at $t = 0$ and $t = 10$.

(e) $h'(t)$ is maximal on the first and last straight parts of $h(t)$.

(f) $h'(t)$ is maximal at $t = 0$ and $t = 10$.

4.3.72

As s increases, the man reaches the dog faster.

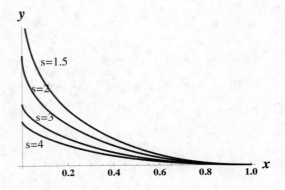

4.3.73

If $f''(x) > 0$ on $(-\infty, 0)$ and on $(0, \infty)$, then $f'(x)$ is increasing on both of those intervals. But if there is a local max at 0, the function f must be switching from increasing to decreasing there. This means that f' must be switching from positive to negative. But if f' is switching from positive to negative, but increasing, there must be a cusp at $x = 0$, so $f'(0)$ does not exist.

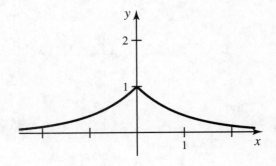

4.3.74 Let $f(x) = \frac{\ln x}{x}$. $f'(x) = \frac{1 - \ln x}{x^2}$, which is 0 at $x = e$. Note that $f'(x) > 0$ on $(0, e)$ and $f'(x) < 0$ on (e, ∞), so $f(x)$ has its maximal value at $x = e$. Thus, $f(\pi) < f(e)$, so $\frac{\ln \pi}{\pi} < \frac{1}{e}$, so $\ln \pi < \pi/e$, so $e \ln \pi < \pi$. Thus $\ln \pi^e < \pi$, and so $\pi^e < e^\pi$.

4.3.75

The equation is valid on only for $|x| \leq 1$ and $|y| \leq 1$. Using implicit differentiation, we have $(2/3)x^{-1/3} + (2/3)y^{-1/3}y' = 0$, so $y' = \frac{-y^{1/3}}{x^{1/3}}$. This is 0 for $y = 0$ (in which case $x = \pm 1$) and doesn't exist for $x = 0$ (in which case $x = \pm 1$.) In the first quadrant the curve is decreasing, in the 2nd it is increasing, in the 3rd it is decreasing, and in the 4th it is increasing. Differentiating y' yields $y'' = \frac{x^{1/3}(-1/3)y^{-2/3}y' + y^{1/3}(1/3)(x^{-2/3})}{x^{2/3}} = \frac{y^{2/3}+x^{2/3}}{3x^{4/3}y^{1/3}}$, which is positive when y is positive and negative when y is negative, so the curve is concave up in the first and 2nd quadrants, and concave down in the 3rd and 4th.

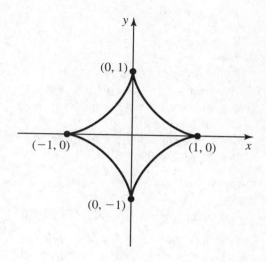

4.3.76

The domain of f is $(-\infty, \infty)$ and f has even symmetry, because $f(-x) = f(x)$. Note that $\lim_{x \to \infty} \frac{8}{x^2+4} = 0$, so $y = 0$ is a horizontal asymptote.

$f'(x) = -\frac{16x}{(x^2+4)^2}$, which is negative for $x > 0$ and positive for $x < 0$, so f is increasing on $(-\infty, 0)$ and decreasing on $(0, \infty)$, and there is a local maximum of 2 at $x = 0$.

$$f''(x) = \frac{(x^2+4)^2(-16) - (-16x)(2)(x^2+4)(2x)}{(x^2+4)^4}$$

$$= -\frac{16(4-3x^2)}{(x^2+4)^3},$$

which is 0 for $x = \pm\sqrt{4/3}$. Note that $f'' < 0$ on $(-2/\sqrt{3}, 2/\sqrt{3})$, and is positive elsewhere, so f is concave up on $(-\infty, -2/\sqrt{3})$ and on $(2/\sqrt{3}, \infty)$, and is concave down on $(-2/\sqrt{3}, 2/\sqrt{3})$. There are inflection points at $x = \pm 2/\sqrt{3}$.

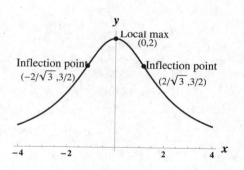

4.3.77

First note that the expression is symmetric when x and y are switched, so the curve should be symmetric about the line $y = x$. Also, if $y = x$, then $2x^3 = 3x^2$, so either $x = 0$ or $x = 3/2$, so this is where the curve intersects the line $y = x$.

Differentiating implicitly yields $3x^2 + 3y^2 y' = 3xy' + 3y$, so $y' = \frac{y-x^2}{y^2-x}$. This is 0 when $y = x^2$, but this occurs on the curve when $x^3 + x^6 = 3x^3$, which yields $x = 0$ (and $y = 0$), or $x^3 = 2$, so $x = \sqrt[3]{2} \approx 1.260$. Note also that the derivative doesn't exist when $x = y^2$, which again yields $(0,0)$ and $y^6 + y^3 = 3y^3$, or $y = \sqrt[3]{2}$. So there should be a flat tangent line at approximately $(1.260, 1.587)$ and a vertical tangent line at about $(1.587, 1.260)$.

Differentiating again and solving for y'' yields $y''(x) = \frac{2xy(x^3 - 3xy + y^3 + 1)}{(x-y^2)^3} = \frac{2xy}{(x-y^2)^3}$. In the first quadrant, when $x > y^2$, the curve is concave up, when $x < y^2$, the curve is concave down. In both the 2nd and 4th quadrants, the curve is concave up.

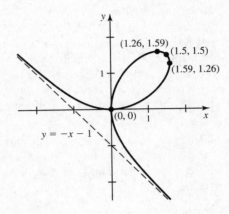

4.3.78

Note that the equation requires $0 \le x < 2$, and that the curve is symmetric about the x axis, because replacing y by $-y$ yields the same curve.

Writing the curve in the form $2y^2 - xy^2 = x^3$ and differentiating implicitly yields $4yy' - 2xyy' - y^2 = 3x^2$, so $y' = \frac{3x^2 + y^2}{2y(2-x)}$. Note that this is 0 only at the origin. Also note that in the first quadrant this is positive, so the curve is increasing, while in the 4th quadrant, this is negative, so the curve is decreasing. Differentiating again and solving for y'' yields $y''(x) = \frac{3(-3x^4 - 2(x-4)xy^2 + y^4)}{4(x-2)^2 y^3}$, which can be written as $y'' = \frac{3(y^4 + 2xy^2 + x^2y^2)}{4(x-2)^2 y^3}$ (by replacing x^4 in the numerator by $x(x^3) = xy^2(2-x)$.)

In the first quadrant, this is positive so the curve is concave up, in the 4th quadrant, this is negative, so the curve is concave down.

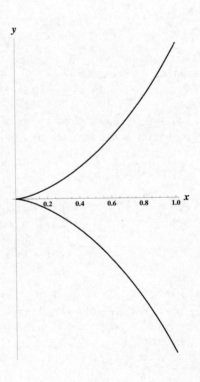

4.3.79

Note that the curve is symmetric about both the x-axis and the y-axis, so we can just consider the first quadrant, and obtain the rest by reflection.

Differentiating implicitly and solving for y' yields $y'(x) = \frac{2x^3 - 5x}{2y(y^2 - 2)}$. The numerator is negative on $(0, \sqrt{5/2})$ and positive on $(\sqrt{5/2}, \infty)$, while the denominator is negative for $0 < y < \sqrt{2}$ and positive for $y > \sqrt{2}$. Thus the relation is increasing in the rectangle $(0, \sqrt{5/2}) \times (0, \sqrt{2})$ and in the region $(\sqrt{5/2}, \infty) \times (\sqrt{2}, \infty)$, while it is decreasing in the other regions in the first quadrant. There are vertical tangent lines when $y = \sqrt{2}$. When $y = 2$ and $x = 0$ there is a horizontal tangent line.

Note that when $x = 0$, we have $y = 0$ or $y = \pm 2$, while if $y = 0$, we have $x = 0$ or $x = \pm\sqrt{5}$. Also, if $y = \sqrt{2}$ then $x = 1$ or $x = 2$. So some sample points to plot are $(0,0)$, $(\pm\sqrt{5}, 0)$, $(0, \pm 2)$, $(\pm 1, \pm\sqrt{2})$, and $(\pm\sqrt{5}, \pm\sqrt{2})$. Also, when $1 < x < 2$, there are no corresponding y values on the curve.

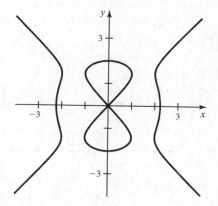

4.3.80

Note that the curve requires $0 \le x < 1$.

Note also that the curve is symmetric about the x-axis, so we can just consider the first quadrant, and obtain the rest by reflection.

Differentiating implicitly and solving for y' yields $y'(x) = \frac{3x^2 - 4x^3}{2y}$. This quantity is positive on the first quadrant for $0 < x < 3/4$ and negative for $3/4 < x < 1$, so f is increasing in the first quadrant for $0 < x < 3/4$ and decreasing for $3/4 < x < 1$. There is a maximum at $x = 3/4$.

Differentiating again and solving for y'' yields

$$y''(x) = \frac{-x\left((3 - 4x)^2 x^3 + 12(2x - 1)y^2\right)}{4y^3}.$$

Rewriting and simplifying yields $y''(x) = \frac{x^4(8x^2 - 12x + 3)}{4y^3}$ which is positive in the first quadrant for $0 < x < r_1$ where $r_1 \approx .317$, and negative for $r_1 < x < 1$. So the function in the first quadrant is concave up for $0 < x < r_1$ and concave down for $r_1 < x < 1$, and there is a point of inflection at r_1.

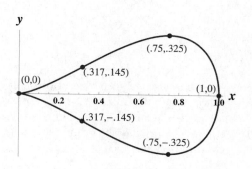

4.3.81

Note that the curve requires $-1 \leq x < 1$.

Note also that the curve is symmetric about both the x-axis and the y-axis, so we can just consider the first quadrant, and obtain the rest by reflection.

Differentiating implicitly yields $4x^3 - 2x + 2yy' = 0$, so $y' = \frac{x - 2x^3}{y}$. This is 0 in the first quadrant for $x = \sqrt{2}/2$. Note also that there is a vertical tangent line at the point $(1, 0)$. The derivative is positive on $(0, \sqrt{2}/2)$ and negative on $(\sqrt{2}/2, 1)$, so in the first quadrant the curve is increasing on that first interval and decreasing on the second.

Differentiating again and solving for y'' (and rewriting) yields $y''(x) = \frac{x^4(2x^2-3)}{y}$, which is negative in the first quadrant for $0 < x < 1$, so this curve is concave down in the first quadrant.

The rest of the curve can be found by reflection.

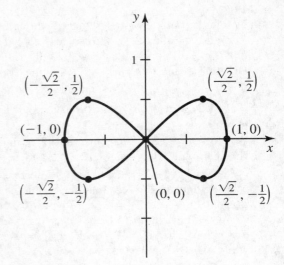

4.3.82

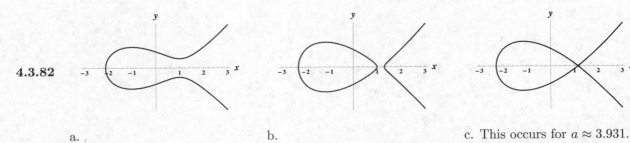

a.

b.

c. This occurs for $a \approx 3.931$.

4.3.83

As n increases, the curves retain their symmetry, but move "outward." That is, the curves enclose a greater area. It appears that the figures approach the 2×2 square centered at the origin with sides parallel to the coordinate axes.

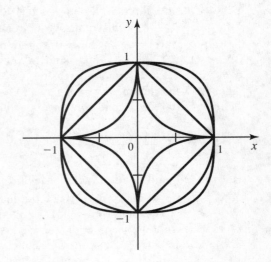

4.3.84

$f'(x) = \frac{(1+x^6 \sin^2 x) - x(x^6(2\sin x \cos x + \sin^2 x(6x^5)))}{(1+x^6 \sin^2 x)^2}$ which can be written as $\frac{1+(x^6 - 6x^5)\sin^2 x - x^7 \sin 2x}{(1+x^6 \sin^2 x)^2}$. A graph of $f'(x)$ with a plot range of $-0.001 < y < .0.001$ is shown. The roots are approximately .8134, 2.3797, 3.1417, 5.1633, 6.2833, 8.1516, and 9.4248. These roots can be found using numerical methods – a computer is helpful. The roots of f' at .8134, 3.1417, 6.2833, and 9.4248 yield local maximums for f.

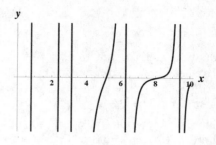

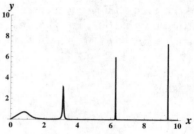

4.3.85

a. The domain is $(-\infty, a]$, because the base must be non-negative.

b. $\lim\limits_{x \to a^-} f(x) = 0$, $\lim\limits_{x \to -\infty} f(x) = 0$.

c. Write $f(x) = e^{x \ln(a-x)}$. Then $f'(x) = e^{x \ln(a-x)} \left(x \cdot -\frac{1}{a-x} + \ln(a-x) \right) = (a-x)^x \left(-\frac{x}{a-x} + \ln(a-x) \right)$.

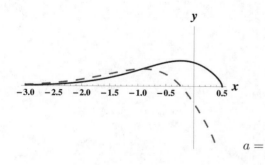

$a = .5$

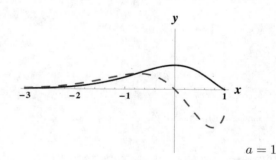

$a = 1$

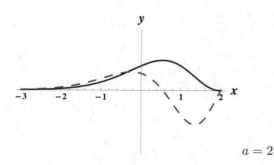

$a = 2$

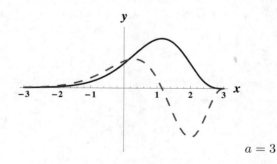

$a = 3$

d. $f'(x) = (a-x)^x \left(-\frac{x}{a-x} + \ln(a-x) \right) = \frac{-(x+(x-a)\ln(a-x))}{(a-x)^{1-x}}$. The numerator is 0 when $x = (a-x)(\ln(a-x))$. If z is a solution to the above, note that z gives a maximum, because f is continuous and positive, and the end behavior of the function is 0 at each end of its domain.

e. As a increases, the value of z increases, and the value of $f(z)$ increases as well, as demonstrated in the above graphs.

4.3.86 Consider the function $w = \frac{\ln z}{z}$. This curve is pictured below. Note that on $(1, \infty)$ the curve is positive, has $\lim_{z \to \infty} (\ln z)/z = 0$, and has range $(0, 1/e]$. Also note that every horizontal line $w = w_0$ for $0 < w_0 < 1/e$ hits the curve once for a value of z between 1 and e and once for $z > e$. Let z_1 and z_2 be these two numbers. Then $\frac{\ln z_1}{z_1} = \frac{\ln z_2}{z_2}$, so $z_2 \ln z_1 = z_1 \ln z_2$, so $z_1^{z_2} = z_2^{z_1}$.

Thus the equation $y^x = x^y$ has solutions along the line $y = x$, but also solutions along a curve which is asymptotic to $x = 1$ and $y = 1$, and goes through the point (e, e), and for every x value with $1 < x < e$ there is a corresponding y value with $e < y$, and vice-versa. The curve and the line $y = x$ where $x^y = y^x$ are shown to the right. The 1st quadrant is thus divided up into regions where either $x^y < y^x$ or $y^x < x^y$. The regions where $x^y < y^x$ are shown shaded gray.

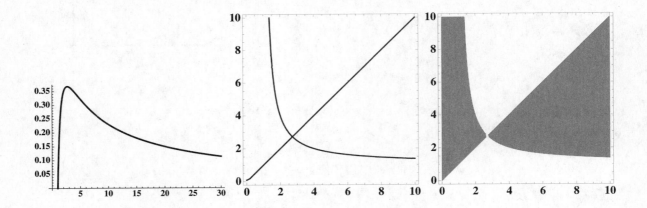

4.3.87

The domain of p is $(-\infty, \infty)$. There are no vertical asymptotes. Note that $f(-x) = \frac{\tan^{-1}(-x)}{(-x)^2 + 1} = -\frac{\tan^{-1}(x)}{x^2 + 1} = -f(x)$, so f has odd symmetry. Because $\lim_{x \to \pm\infty} \tan^{-1}(x) = \pm\pi/2$, $\lim_{x \to \pm\infty} f(x) = 0$, so $y = 0$ is a horizontal asymptote.

$f'(x) = \frac{(x^2+1)(1/(x^2+1)) - \tan^{-1} x \cdot 2x}{(x^2+1)^2} = \frac{1 - 2x \tan^{-1} x}{(x^2+1)^2}$. Using a computer algebra system shows that the numerator has two roots at approximately $\pm.765$. Let the roots be $\pm r_1$ where $r_1 > 0$. Note that $f'(x) < 0$ on $(-\infty, -r_1)$ and on (r_1, ∞), so f is decreasing there, while $f'(x) > 0$ on $(-r_1, r_1)$, so f is increasing on that interval. There is a local minimum at $-r_1$ and a local maximum at r_1.

$$f''(x) = \frac{(x^2+1)^2 \left[(-2x)(1/(x^2+1)) - \tan^{-1} x \cdot 2\right] - (1 - 2x \tan^{-1} x) \cdot 2(x^2+1)(2x)}{(x^2+1)^4}$$

$$= \frac{(6x^2-2)\tan^{-1} x - 6x}{(x^2+1)^3}.$$

Again, using a computer algebra system reveals roots at approximately ± 1.330 in addition to the root at 0. Let the non-zero roots of the numerator be $\pm r_2$ where $r_2 > 0$. We see that $f''(x) < 0$ on $(-\infty, -r_2)$, and on $(0, r_2)$, so f is concave down on those intervals, while $f''(x) > 0$ on $(-r_2, 0)$ and on (r_2, ∞), so f is concave up on those intervals, and there are points of inflection at $-r_2$, 0, and r_2.

There is an x-intercept at $(0, 0)$, which is also the y-intercept.

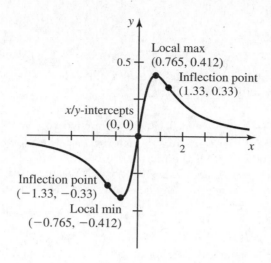

4.3.88

The domain of f is $(-\infty, \infty)$. Note that $f(-x) = \frac{\sqrt{4(-x)^2+1}}{(-x)^2+1} = \frac{\sqrt{4x^2+1}}{x^2+1} = f(x)$, so f has even symmetry.

Note that $\lim\limits_{x \to \infty} \frac{\sqrt{4x^2+1}}{x^2+1} \cdot \frac{\sqrt{(1/x^4)}}{1/x^2} = \lim\limits_{x \to \infty} \frac{\sqrt{(4/x^2)+(1/x^4)}}{1+(1/x^2)} = 0$, so $y = 0$ is a horizontal asymptote as $x \to \infty$, and by symmetry it is a horizontal asymptote as $x \to -\infty$ as well.

$f'(x) = \frac{(x^2+1)(4x)(4x^2+1)^{-1/2} - \sqrt{4x^2+1}(2x)}{(x^2+1)^2} = \frac{4x^3+4x-8x^3-2x}{(x^2+1)^2 \cdot \sqrt{4x^2+1}} = \frac{2x-4x^3}{(x^2+1)^2 \cdot \sqrt{4x^2+1}} = \frac{2x(1-2x^2)}{(x^2+1)^2 \cdot \sqrt{4x^2+1}}$. This expression is 0 for $x = 0$ and $x = \pm\sqrt{1/2}$. Note that $f'(x) > 0$ on the interval $(-\infty, -\sqrt{1/2})$ and on $(0, \sqrt{1/2})$, so f is increasing on those intervals, while $f'(x) < 0$ on $(-\sqrt{1/2}, 0)$ and on $(\sqrt{1/2}, \infty)$, so f is decreasing on those intervals. There is a local minimum at $(0, 1)$ and local maxima at approximately $(\pm\sqrt{1/2}, 1.16)$.

$f''(x)$ has numerator $(4x^2+1)^{1/2}(x^2+1)^2(2-12x^2)$ $-(2x-4x^3)((4x^2+1)^{1/2}(2)(x^2+1)(2x)+(x^2+1)^2(4x)(4x^2+1)^{-1/2}$ and denominator $(4x^2+1)(x^2+1)^4$. When simplified, this yields

$$f''(x) = \frac{2(16x^6-30x^4-9x^2+1)}{(4x^2+1)^{3/2}(x^2+1)^3}.$$

Using a computer algebra system, the roots of the polynomial are determined to be approximately ±1.458 and $\pm.295$. We will refer to these roots as $\pm r_1$ and $\pm r_2$ where $0 < r_1 < r_2$. Note that $f''(x) < 0$ on $(-r_2, -r_1)$ and on (r_1, r_2), so f is concave down there, while $f''(x) > 0$ on $(-\infty, -r_2)$, and on $(-r_1, r_1)$, and on (r_2, ∞), so f is concave up on these intervals, and there are inflection points at each of $\pm r_1$ and $\pm r_2$. The y-intercept is $(0, 1)$.

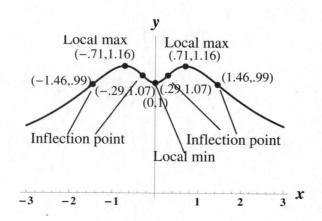

4.3.89

The domain of f is given to be $[-2\pi, 2\pi]$. There are no vertical asymptotes. Note that $f(-x) = \frac{(-x)(\sin(-x))}{((-x)^2+1)} = \frac{x \sin x}{x^2+1} = f(x)$, f has even symmetry. Questions about horizontal asymptotes aren't relevant because the given domain is an interval with finite length.

$f'(x) = \frac{(x^2+1)(x\cos x + \sin x) - x\sin x \cdot (2x)}{(x^2+1)^2}$, which can be simplified to $\frac{x(x^2+1)\cos x + (1-x^2)\sin x}{(x^2+1)^2}$, and with the aid of a computer algebra system, the roots of this expression can be found to be approximately ± 4.514 and ± 1.356, as well as $x = 0$. We will call the non-zero roots $\pm r_1$ and $\pm r_2$ where $0 < r_1 < r_2$. Note that $f'(x) < 0$ on $(-2\pi, -r_2)$ and on $(-r_1, 0)$ and (r_1, r_2), so f is decreasing there, while $f'(x) > 0$ on $(-r_2, -r_1)$, on $(0, r_1)$, and on $(r_2, 2\pi)$, so f is increasing on these intervals. There are local maxima at $x = \pm r_1$ and local minima at $x = 0$ and at $x = \pm r_2$.

$f''(x)$ has numerator $(x^2+1)^2((x^3+x)(-\sin x) + \cos x(3x^2+1) + (1-x^2)(\cos x) + \sin x(-2x)) - ((x^3+x)\cos x + (1-x^2)\sin x)(4x)(x^2+1)$ and denominator $(x^2+1)^4$. This simplifies to

$$f''(x) = \frac{(-x^5 - 7x)\sin x + (-2x^4 + 2)\cos x}{(x^2+1)^3},$$

which is 0 at approximately ± 5.961 and ± 2.561 and ± 0.494. We will call these 6 roots $\pm r_3$, $\pm r_4$ and $\pm r_5$ where $0 < r_3 < r_4 < r_5$. Note that $f''(x) < 0$ on $(-2\pi, -r_5)$ and on $(-r_4, -r_3)$, and on (r_3, r_4), and on $(r_5, 2\pi)$, so f is concave down on these intervals, while $f''(x) > 0$ on $(-r_5, -r_4)$, and on $(-r_3, r_3)$, and on (r_4, r_5), so f is concave up on these intervals. There are points of inflection at each of $\pm r_3$, $\pm r_4$, and $\pm r_5$.

There is an x-intercept at $(0,0)$, which is also the y-intercept, as well as x-intercepts at $\pm 2\pi$.

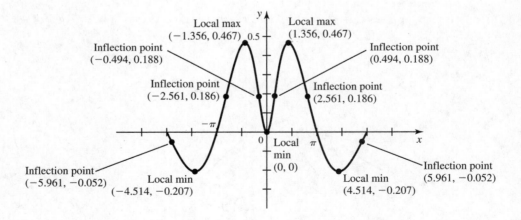

4.3.90

The domain of f is $(0,1) \cup (1,\infty)$. There is no symmetry. There is a vertical asymptote at $x = 1$, because $\lim_{x \to 1^+} f(x) = \infty$ and $\lim_{x \to 1^-} f(x) = -\infty$. There are no horizontal asymptotes, as the function increases without bound as $x \to \infty$.

$f'(x) = \frac{\ln x - 1}{(\ln x)^2}$, which is 0 for $x = e$. Note that $f'(x) < 0$ on $(0,1)$ and on $(1,e)$ (so f is decreasing there), while $f'(x) > 0$ on (e,∞). There is a local minimum at $x = e$.

$f''(x) = \frac{(\ln x)^2(1/x) - (\ln x - 1)(2)(\ln x)(1/x)}{(\ln x)^4} = \frac{2 - \ln x}{x(\ln x)^3}$. This is 0 for $x = e^2$. Note that $f''(x) < 0$ on $(0,1)$ and on (e^2,∞) (so f is concave down there), while $f''(x) > 0$ and thus f is concave up on $(1,e^2)$. The only inflection point is $(e^2, e^2/2)$. There are no intercepts.

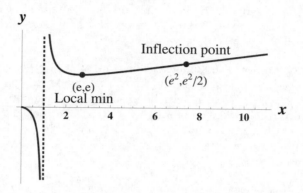

4.4 Optimization Problems

4.4.1 ...objective... constraints ....

4.4.2 The constraints are used to express all but one of the variables in terms of one independent variable.

4.4.3 The constraint is $x + y = 10$, so we can express $y = 10 - x$ or $x = 10 - y$. Therefore the objective function can be expressed $Q = x^2(10 - x)$ or $Q = (10 - y)^2 y$.

4.4.4 The minimum will occur at one of the endpoints of the closed interval.

4.4.5 Let x and y be the dimensions of the rectangle. The perimeter is $2x + 2y$, so the constraint is $2x + 2y = 10$, which gives $y = 5 - x$. The objective function to be maximized is the area of the rectangle, $A = xy$. Thus we have $A = xy = x(5 - x) = 5x - x^2$. We have $x, y \geq 0$, which also implies $x \leq 5$ (otherwise $y < 0$). Therefore we need to maximize $A(x) = 5x - x^2$ for $0 \leq x \leq 5$. The critical points of the objective function satisfy $A'(x) = 5 - 2x = 0$, which has the solution $x = 5/2$. To find the absolute maximum of A, we check the endpoints of $[0,5]$ and the critical point $x = 5/2$. Because $A(0) = A(5) = 0$ and $A(5/2) = 25/4$, the absolute maximum occurs when $x = y = 5/2$, so width = length = $5/2$ m.

4.4.6 Let x and y be the dimensions of the rectangle. The perimeter is $2x + 2y$, so the constraint is $2x + 2y = P$, which gives $y = P/2 - x$. The objective function to be maximized is the area of the rectangle, $A = xy$. Thus we have $A = xy = x(P/2 - x) = (P/2)x - x^2$. We have $x, y \geq 0$, which also implies $x \leq P/2$ (otherwise $y < 0$). Therefore we need to maximize $A(x) = (P/2)x - x^2$ for $0 \leq x \leq P/2$. The critical points of the objective function satisfy $A'(x) = P/2 - 2x = 0$, which has the solution $x = P/4$. To find the absolute maximum of A, we check the endpoints of $[0, P/2]$ and the critical point $x = P/4$. Because $A(0) = A(P/2) = 0$ and $A(P/4) = P^2/8 - P^2/16 = P^2/16$, the absolute maximum occurs when $x = y = P/4$, so width = length = $P/4$.

4.4.7 Let x and y be be the dimensions of the rectangle. The area is $xy = 100$, so the constraint is $y = 100/x$. The objective function to be minimized is the perimeter of the rectangle, $P = 2x + 2y$. Using $y = 100/x$, we have $P = 2x + 2y = 2x + \frac{200}{x}$. Because $xy = 100 > 0$ we must have $x > 0$, so we need to minimize $P(x) = 2x + 200/x$ on the interval $(0,\infty)$. The critical points of the objective function satisfy

$P'(x) = 2 - \frac{200}{x^2} = 0$, which has the solution $x = 10$. By the First (or Second) Derivative Test, this critical point corresponds to a local minimum, and by Theorem 4.5, this solitary local minimum is also the absolute minimum on the interval $(0, \infty)$. Therefore the dimensions of the rectangle with minimum perimeter are $x = 10$ and $y = \frac{100}{10} = 10$, so width = length = 10.

4.4.8 Let x and y be be the dimensions of the rectangle. The area is $xy = A$ and A is fixed, so the constraint is $xy = A$, which gives $y = A/x$. The objective function to be minimized is the perimeter of the rectangle, $P = 2x + 2y$. Using $y = A/x$, we have $P = 2x + 2y = 2x + \frac{2A}{x}$. Because $xy = A > 0$ we must have $x > 0$, so we need to minimize $P(x) = 2x + 2A/x$ on the interval $(0, \infty)$. The critical points of the objective function satisfy $P'(x) = 2 - \frac{2A}{x^2} = 0$, which has the solution $x = \sqrt{A}$. By the First (or Second) Derivative Test, this critical point corresponds to a local minimum, and by Theorem 4.5, this solitary local minimum is also the absolute minimum on the interval $(0, \infty)$. Therefore the dimensions of the rectangle with minimum perimeter are $x = \sqrt{A}$ and $y = A/\sqrt{A} = \sqrt{A}$, so width = length = $\sqrt{A}$.

4.4.9 Let x and y be the two non-negative numbers. The constraint is $x + y = 23$, which gives $y = 23 - x$. The objective function to be maximized is the product of the numbers, $P = xy$. Using $y = 23 - x$, we have $P = xy = x(23 - x) = 23x - x^2$. Now x must be at least 0, and cannot exceed 23 (otherwise $y < 0$). Therefore we need to maximize $P(x) = 23x - x^2$ for $0 \le x \le 23$. The critical points of the objective function satisfy $P'(x) = 23 - 2x = 0$, which has the solution $x = 23/2$. To find the absolute maximum of P, we check the endpoints of $[0, 23]$ and the critical point $x = 23/2$. Because $P(0) = P(23) = 0$ and $P(23/2) = (23/2)^2$, the absolute maximum occurs when $x = y = 23/2$.

4.4.10 Let a and b be the two non-negative numbers. The constraint is $a + b = 23$, which gives $b = 23 - a$. The objective function to be maximized/minimized is the quantity $Q = a^2 + b^2$. Using $b = 23 - a$, we have $Q = a^2 + b^2 = a^2 + (23 - a)^2 = 2a^2 - 46a + 529$. Now a must be at least 0, and cannot exceed 23 (otherwise $b < 0$). Therefore we need to maximize $Q(a) = 2a^2 - 46a + 529$ for $0 \le a \le 23$. The critical points of the objective function satisfy $Q'(a) = 4a - 46 = 0$, which has the solution $a = 23/2$. To find the absolute maximum/minimum of Q, we check the endpoints of $[0, 23]$ and the critical point $a = 23/2$. Observe that $Q(0) = Q(23) = 529$ and $Q(23/2) = 529/2$, so the absolute maximum occurs when $a, b = 0, 23$ or $23, 0$ and the absolute minimum occurs when $a = b = 23/2$.

4.4.11 Let x and y be the two positive numbers. The constraint is $xy = 50$, which gives $y = 50/x$. The objective function to be minimized is the sum of the numbers, $S = x + y$. Using $y = 50/x$, we have $S = x + y = x + \frac{50}{x}$. Now x can be any positive number, so we need to maximize $S(x) = x + 50/x$ on the interval $(0, \infty)$. The critical points of the objective function satisfy $S'(x) = 1 - \frac{50}{x^2} = 0$, which has the solution $x = \sqrt{50} = 5\sqrt{2}$. By the First (or Second) Derivative Test, this critical point corresponds to a local minimum, and by Theorem 4.5, this solitary local minimum is also the absolute minimum on the interval $(0, \infty)$. Therefore the numbers with minimum sum are $x = 5\sqrt{2}$ and $y = \frac{50}{5\sqrt{2}} = \frac{10}{\sqrt{2}} = 5\sqrt{2}$, so $x = y = 5\sqrt{2}$.

4.4.12 We seek to maximize $P = xy$ subject to the constraint $y = 12 - 3x$. Substituting gives $P = x(12 - 3x) = 12x - 3x^2$. Then $P'(x) = 12 - 6x$, which is zero for $x = 2$. Because $P'(x) > 0$ for $0 < x < 2$ and $P'(x) < 0$ for $x > 2$, we have a maximum at $x = 2$. When $x = 2$, we have $y = 12 - 3x = 6$. So the two numbers are 2 and 6.

4.4.13 We seek to minimize $S = 2x + y$ subject to the constraint $y = 12/x$. Substituting gives $S = 2x + 12/x$, so $S'(x) = 2 - 12/x^2$. This is zero when $x^2 = 6$, or $x = \sqrt{6}$. Note that for $0 < x < \sqrt{6}$ we have $S'(x) < 0$, and for $x > \sqrt{6}$ we have $S'(x) > 0$, so we have a minimum at $x = \sqrt{6}$. Note that when $x = \sqrt{6}$, we have $y = 12/x = 12/\sqrt{6} = 2\sqrt{6}$.

4.4.14

    a. Let x and y be the lengths of the sides of the pen, with y the side parallel to the barn. Then the constraint is $2x + y = 200$, which gives $y = 200 - 2x$. The objective function to be maximized is the area of the pen, $A = xy$. Using $y = 200 - 2x$, we have $A = xy = x(200 - 2x) = 200x - 2x^2$. The length x must be at least 0, and cannot exceed 100 (otherwise $y < 0$). Therefore we need to maximize $A(x) = 200x - 2x^2$ for $0 \le x \le 100$. The critical points of the objective function satisfy

$A'(x) = 200 - 4x = 0$, which has the solution $x = 50$. To find the absolute maximum of A, we check the endpoints of $[0, 100]$ and the critical point $x = 50$. Because $A(0) = A(100) = 0$ and $A(50) = 5000$, the absolute maximum occurs when $x = 50$ m and $y = 200 - 2 \cdot 50 = 100$ m.

b. Let x and y be the lengths of the sides of each individual rectangular pen, with y the side parallel to the barn. Then the constraint is $xy = 100$, which gives $y = 100/x$. The objective function to be minimized is the total amount of fencing required, which is $Q = 5x + 4y$. Using the constraint, we have $Q = 5x + 4y = 5x + \frac{400}{x}$. Now x can be any positive number, so so we need to minimize $Q(x) = 5x + 400/x$ on the interval $(0, \infty)$. The critical points of the objective function satisfy $Q'(x) = 5 - \frac{400}{x^2} = 0$, which has the solution $x = \sqrt{80} = 4\sqrt{5}$. By the First (or Second) Derivative Test, this critical point corresponds to a local minimum, and by Theorem 4.5, this solitary local minimum is also the absolute minimum on the interval $(0, \infty)$. Therefore the dimensions which require the least fencing are $x = 4\sqrt{5}$ m and $y = 100/4\sqrt{5} = 5\sqrt{5}$ m.

4.4.15 Let x be the length of the sides of the base of the box and y be the height of the box. The volume is $x \cdot x \cdot y = 100$, so the constraint is $x^2 y = 100$, which gives $y = 100/x^2$. The objective function to be minimized is the surface area S of the box, which consists of $2x^2$ (for the top and base) $+ 4xy$ (for the 4 sides); therefore $S = 2x^2 + 4xy$. Using $y = 100x^2$, we have $S = 2x^2 + 4xy = 2x^2 + 4x \cdot \frac{100}{x^2} = 2x^2 + \frac{400}{x}$. The base side length can be any $x > 0$, so we need to maximize $S(x) = 2x^2 + 400/x$ on the interval $(0, \infty)$. The critical points of the objective function satisfy $S'(x) = 4x - \frac{400}{x^2} = 0$; clearing denominators gives $4x^3 = 400$ so $x = \sqrt[3]{100}$. By the First (or Second) Derivative Test, this critical point corresponds to a local minimum, and by Theorem 4.5, this solitary local minimum is also the absolute minimum on the interval $(0, \infty)$. Therefore the dimensions of the box with minimum surface area are $x = \sqrt[3]{100}$ and $y = 100/\sqrt[3]{100}^2 = \sqrt[3]{100}$, so length = width = height = $\sqrt[3]{100}$ m.

4.4.16 Let x be the length of the sides of the base of the box and y be the height of the box. The constraint is $2x + y = 108$, which gives $y = 108 - 2x$. The objective function to be maximized is the volume V of the box, which is given by $V = x \cdot x \cdot y = x^2 y$. Using $y = 108 - 2x$, we have $V = x^2 y = x^2(108 - 2x) = 108x^2 - 2x^3$. The length x must be at least 0, and cannot exceed $108/2 = 54$ (otherwise $y < 0$). Therefore we need to maximize $V(x) = 108x^2 - 2x^3$ for $0 \le x \le 54$. The critical points of the objective function satisfy $V'(x) = 216x - 6x^2 = 0$, which has solutions $x = 0$ and $x = 216/6 = 36$. To find the absolute maximum of V, we check the endpoints of $[0, 54]$ and the critical point $x = 36$. Because $V(0) = V(54) = 0$ and $V(36) = 36^3$, the absolute maximum occurs when $x = 36$ in and $y = 108 - 2 \cdot 36 = 36$ in.

4.4.17 Let x be the length of the sides of the base of the box and y be the height of the box. The volume of the box is $x \cdot x \cdot y = x^2 y$, so the constraint is $x^2 y = 16$, which gives $y = 16/x^2$. Let c be the cost per square foot of the material used to make the sides. Then the cost to make the base is $2cx^2$, the cost to make the 4 sides is $4cxy$, and the cost to make the top is $\frac{1}{2}cx^2$. The objective function to be minimized is the total cost, which is $C = 2cx^2 + 4cxy + \frac{1}{2}cx^2 = \frac{5}{2}cx^2 + 4cx \cdot \frac{16}{x^2} = c\left(\frac{5x^2}{2} + \frac{64}{x}\right)$. The base side length can be any $x > 0$, so we need to maximize $C(x) = c(5x^2/2 + 64/x)$ on the interval $(0, \infty)$. The critical points of the objective function satisfy $5x - \frac{64}{x^2} = 0$, which gives $x^3 = 64/5$ or $x = 4/\sqrt[3]{5}$. By the First (or Second) Derivative Test, this critical point corresponds to a local minimum, and by Theorem 4.5, this solitary local minimum is also the absolute minimum on the interval $(0, \infty)$. Therefore the box with minimum cost has base $4/\sqrt[3]{5}$ ft by $4/\sqrt[3]{5}$ ft and height $y = 16/(4/\sqrt[3]{5})^2 = 5^{2/3}$ ft.

4.4.18

a. Label the starting point, finishing point and transition point P as in Figure 4.55 in the text. In terms of the angle θ, the swimming distance is $2\sin(\theta/2)$ and the walking distance is $\pi - \theta$, as derived in Example 3. So the time for the swimming leg is $\frac{\text{distance}}{\text{rate}} = \frac{2\sin(\theta/2)}{2} = \sin\frac{\theta}{2}$ and the time for the walking leg is $\frac{\text{distance}}{\text{rate}} = \frac{\pi - \theta}{4}$. The total travel time for the trip is the objective function $T(\theta) = \sin\frac{\theta}{2} + \frac{\pi - \theta}{4}$, $0 \le \theta \le \pi$. The critical points of T satisfy $\frac{dT}{d\theta} = \frac{1}{2}\cos\frac{\theta}{2} - \frac{1}{4} = 0$ or $\cos\frac{\theta}{2} = \frac{1}{2}$. Because $0 \le \theta/2 \le \pi/2$, the only solution is given by $\theta/2 = \pi/3$ or $\theta = 2\pi/3$. Evaluating the objective function at the critical point and the endpoints, we find that $T(2\pi/3) = \sqrt{3}/2 + \pi/12 \approx 1.128$ hr, $T(0) = \pi/4 \approx 0.785$ hr and $T(\pi) = 1$ hr. Therefore the minimum travel time is $T(0) \approx 0.785$ hr when the entire trip is done walking. The maximum travel time, corresponding to $\theta = 120^\circ$, is $T \approx 1.128$ hr.

b. In this case the time for the walking leg is $\frac{\text{distance}}{\text{rate}} = \frac{\pi-\theta}{1.5}$, so the total travel time for the trip is now given by $T(\theta) = \sin\frac{\theta}{2} + \frac{\pi-\theta}{1.5}$, $0 \le \theta \le \pi$. The critical points of T satisfy $\frac{dT}{d\theta} = \frac{1}{2}\cos\frac{\theta}{2} - \frac{1}{1.5} = 0$ or $\cos\frac{\theta}{2} = \frac{4}{3}$. Therefore in this case there are no critical points. Evaluating the objective function at the endpoints, we find that $T(0) = \pi/1.5 \approx 2.09$ hr and $T(\pi) = 1$ hr. Therefore the minimum travel time is $T(\pi) = 1$ hr when the entire trip is done swimming, and the maximum travel time is $T(0) \approx 2.09$ hr when the entire trip is done walking.

c. Denote the walking speed by $v > 0$. Then the time for the walking leg is $\frac{\text{distance}}{\text{rate}} = \frac{\pi-\theta}{v}$, so the total travel time for the trip is now given by $T(\theta) = \sin\frac{\theta}{2} + \frac{\pi-\theta}{v}$, $0 \le \theta \le \pi$. Observe that $\frac{d^2T}{d\theta^2} = -\frac{1}{4}\sin\frac{\theta}{2} < 0$ on the interval $(0,\pi)$. Therefore by the Second Derivative Test, the function T cannot have a local minimum in $(0,\pi)$, and so the minimum travel time must occur either at $\theta = 0$ (all walking) or $\theta = \pi$ (all swimming) in all cases. Evaluating the objective function at the endpoints, we find that $T(0) = \pi/v$ and $T(\pi) = 1$. In the case $v > \pi$ we have $T(0) < 1$ and the minimum corresponds to all walking; when $v < \pi$ we have $T(0) > 1$ and the minimum corresponds to all swimming (and when $v = \pi$ the travel time is 1 hr for both all walking and all swimming). Hence the minimum walking speed for which it is quickest to walk the entire distance is $v = \pi$ m/hr.

4.4.19 The distance between $(x, 3x)$ and $(50, 0)$ is $d(x) = \sqrt{(3x-0)^2 + (x-50)^2}$. Instead of working with the distance, we can instead work with the square of the distance, because these two functions have minima which occur at the same place. So consider

$$(d(x))^2 = D(x) = (3x)^2 + (x-50)^2 = 9x^2 + x^2 - 100x + 2500 = 10(x^2 - 10x + 250).$$

$\frac{dD}{dx} = 10(2x-10)$, which is zero for $x = 5$. Because $\frac{d^2D}{dx^2} = 20 > 0$, we see that the critical point at $x = 5$ is a minimum. So the minimum of D (and d) occurs at $x = 5$. The value of d at the point $(5, 15)$, is $d(5) = \sqrt{15^2 + (-45)^2} = 15\sqrt{10} \approx 47.4$.

4.4.20 The distance between (x, x^2) and $(18, 0)$ is $d(x) = \sqrt{(x^2-0)^2 + (x-18)^2}$. Instead of working with the distance, we can instead work with the square of the distance, because these two functions have minima which occur at the same place. So consider

$$d(x)^2 = D(x) = (x^2)^2 + (x-18)^2 = x^4 + x^2 - 36x + 324$$

$\frac{dD}{dx} = 4x^3 + 2x - 36 = 2(2x^3 + x - 18) = 2(x-2)(2x^2 + 4x + 9)$, which has only one real root at $x = 2$. This critical point gives a minimum, so the closest point is $(2, 4)$. The distance at this point is $d(4) = \sqrt{16 + 256} = \sqrt{272} = 4\sqrt{17}$.

4.4.21

a. Let x be the distance from the point on the shoreline nearest to the boat to the point where the woman lands on shore; then the remaining distance she must travel on shore is $6 - x$. By the Pythagorean theorem, the distance the woman must row is $\sqrt{x^2 + 16}$. So the time for the rowing leg is $\frac{\text{distance}}{\text{rate}} = \frac{\sqrt{x^2+16}}{2}$ and the time for the walking leg is $\frac{\text{distance}}{\text{rate}} = \frac{6-x}{3}$. The total travel time for the trip is the objective function $T(x) = \frac{\sqrt{x^2+16}}{2} + \frac{6-x}{3}$. We wish to minimize this function for $0 \le x \le 6$. The critical points of the objective function satisfy $T'(x) = \frac{x}{2\sqrt{x^2+16}} - \frac{1}{3} = 0$, which when simplified gives $5x^2 = 64$, so $x = 8/\sqrt{5}$ is the only critical point in $(0,6)$. From the First Derivative Test we see that T has a local minimum at this point, so $x = 8/\sqrt{5}$ must give the minimum value of T on $[0,6]$.

b. Let $v > 0$ be the woman's rowing speed. Then the total travel time is now given by $T(x) = \frac{\sqrt{x^2+16}}{v} + \frac{6-x}{3}$. The derivative of the objective function is $T'(x) = \frac{x}{v\sqrt{x^2+16}} - \frac{1}{3}$. If we try to solve the equation $T'(x) = 0$ as in part (a) above, we see that there is at most one solution $x > 0$. Therefore there can be at most one critical point of T in the interval $(0,6)$. Observe also that $T'(0) = -1/3 < 0$ so the absolute minimum of T on $[0,6]$ cannot occur at $x = 0$. So one of two things must happen: there is a unique critical point for T in $(0,6)$ which is the absolute minimum for T on $[0,6]$, and then $T'(6) > 0$; or, T is decreasing on $[0,6]$, and then $T'(6) \le 0$ (the quickest way to the restaurant is to row directly in this case). The condition $T'(6) \le 0$ is equivalent to $\frac{6}{\sqrt{6^2+16}} \le \frac{v}{3}$ which gives $v \ge 9/\sqrt{13}$ mi/hr.

4.4.22 Let L be the ladder length and x be the distance between the foot of the ladder and the fence. The Pythagorean theorem gives the relationship $L^2 = (x+4)^2 + b^2$, where b is the height of the top of the ladder. We see that $b/(x+4) = 10/x$ by similar triangles, which gives $b = 10(x+4)/x$. Substituting in the expression for L^2 above gives $L^2 = (x+4)^2 + 100\frac{(x+4)^2}{x^2} = (x+4)^2\left(1 + \frac{100}{x^2}\right)$. It suffices to minimize L^2 for $x > 0$ because L and L^2 have the same local extrema (L is positive). We have $\frac{d}{dx}L^2 = (x+4)^2\left(-\frac{200}{x^3}\right) + 2(x+4)\left(1 + \frac{100}{x^2}\right) = \frac{2(x+4)(x^3-400)}{x^3}$. Because $x > 0$, the only critical point is $x = \sqrt[3]{400} \approx 7.368$. By the First Derivative Test, this critical point corresponds to a local minimum, and by Theorem 4.5, this solitary local minimum is also the absolute minimum on the interval $(0, \infty)$. Substituting $x \approx 7.368$ in the expression for L^2 we find the length of the shortest ladder $L \approx 19.16$ ft.

4.4.23 Let L be the ladder length and x be the distance between the foot of the ladder and the fence. The Pythagorean theorem gives the relationship $L^2 = (x+5)^2 + b^2$, where b is the height of the top of the ladder. We see that $b/(x+5) = 8/x$ by similar triangles, which gives $b = 8(x+5)/x$. Substituting in the expression for L^2 above gives $L^2 = (x+5)^2 + 64\frac{(x+5)^2}{x^2} = (x+5)^2\left(1 + \frac{64}{x^2}\right)$. It suffices to minimize L^2 instead of L. However in this case x and b must satisfy $x, b \leq 20$. Solving $20 = 8(x+5)/x$ for x gives $x = 10/3$, so the condition $b \leq 20$ corresponds to $x \geq 10/3$, and we see that we must minimize L^2 for $10/3 \leq x \leq 20$. We have $\frac{d}{dx}L^2 = (x+5)^2\left(-\frac{128}{x^3}\right) + 2(x+5)\left(1 + \frac{64}{x^2}\right) = \frac{2(x+5)(x^3-320)}{x^3}$. Because $x > 0$, the only critical point is $x = \sqrt[3]{320} \approx 6.840$. By the First Derivative Test, this critical point corresponds to a local minimum, and by Theorem 4.5, this solitary local minimum is also the absolute minimum on the interval $[10/3, 20]$. Substituting $x \approx 6.840$ in the expression for L^2 we find the length of the shortest ladder $L \approx 18.220$ ft.

4.4.24 Let the coordinates of the base of the rectangle be $(x, 0)$ and $(-x, 0)$ where $0 \leq x \leq 4$. Then the width of the rectangle is $2x$ and the height is $16 - x^2$, so the area A is given by $A(x) = 2x(16 - x^2) = 2(16x - x^3)$. The critical points of this function satisfy $A'(x) = 2(16 - 3x^2) = 0$, which has unique solution $x = 4/\sqrt{3}$ in $(0, 4)$. We have $A(0) = A(4) = 0$, so the rectangle of maximum area has width $2x = 8/\sqrt{3} = 8\sqrt{3}/3$, height $y = 16 - x^2 = 32/3$ and area $A(4/\sqrt{3}) = 256\sqrt{3}/9$.

4.4.25 Let the coordinates of the base of the rectangle be $(x, 0)$ and $(-x, 0)$ where $0 \leq x \leq 5$. Then the width of the rectangle is $2x$ and the height is $\sqrt{25 - x^2}$, so the area A is given by $A(x) = 2x\sqrt{25 - x^2}$. The critical points of this function satisfy $A'(x) = 2\sqrt{25 - x^2} + \frac{2x \cdot (-x)}{\sqrt{25-x^2}} = \frac{2(25-2x^2)}{\sqrt{25-x^2}} = 0$, which has unique solution $x = 5/\sqrt{2}$ in $(0, 5)$. We have $A(0) = A(5) = 0$, so the rectangle of maximum area has width $2x = 10/\sqrt{2}$ cm, height $y = \sqrt{25 - (25/2)} = 5/\sqrt{2}$ cm.

4.4.26 Let x be the length of the piece of wire used to make the circle; then $60 - x$ is the length of the piece used to make the square. Let r be the radius of the circle and s the side length of the square. The circle has circumference $2\pi r$ so we have $x = 2\pi r$ or $r = x/2\pi$; the square has perimeter $4s$ so $60 - x = 4s$ which gives $s = (60 - x)/4$. The objective function to be maximized/minimized is the combined area of the circle and square given by $A = \pi r^2 + s^2 = \pi\left(\frac{x}{2\pi}\right)^2 + \left(\frac{60-x}{4}\right)^2 = \left(\frac{1}{4\pi} + \frac{1}{16}\right)x^2 - \frac{15}{2}x + 225$. The critical points of this function satisfy $A'(x) = \left(\frac{1}{2\pi} + \frac{1}{8}\right)x - \frac{15}{2} = \left(\frac{4+\pi}{8\pi}\right)x - \frac{15}{2} = 0$, which has unique solution $x = 60\pi/(4+\pi) \approx 26.39$. By the First (or Second) Derivative test, this critical point gives a local minimum, which by Theorem 4.5 must be the absolute minimum of A over the interval $[0, 60]$. So the area is minimized by using 26.394 cm of wire for the circle and 33.606 cm of wire for the square. The maximum area must therefore occur at the endpoints, and because $A(0) = 225$, $A(60) \approx 286.479$, the maximum area occurs when all 60 cm of wire is used to make the circle.

4.4.27 If we remove a sector of angle θ from a circle of radius 20, the remaining circumference is $2\pi \cdot 20 - \theta \cdot 20 = 20(2\pi - \theta)$, so the base of the cone formed has radius $r = \frac{20(2\pi - \theta)}{2\pi} = \frac{10(2\pi - \theta)}{\pi}$. As θ varies from 0 to 2π, the radius ranges from 0 to 20, but all possible cones formed have side length 20. The height h of the cone is given by the Pythagorean theorem: $h^2 + r^2 = 20^2$, so $h = \sqrt{400 - r^2}$. The volume of the cone given by $V = \frac{\pi}{3}r^2 h = \frac{\pi}{3}r^2\sqrt{400 - r^2}$.

Thus

$$V'(r) = \frac{2\pi}{3}r\sqrt{400-r^2} + \frac{\pi}{3}r^2(400-r^2)^{-1/2}\cdot\frac{1}{2}\cdot(-2r)$$

$$= \frac{\pi}{3}\cdot\frac{2r(400-r^2)-r^3}{\sqrt{400-r^2}}$$

$$= \frac{\pi}{3}\cdot\frac{800r-3r^3}{\sqrt{400-r^2}}.$$

The only positive critical point occurs where $r = \sqrt{\frac{800}{3}} = 20\sqrt{\frac{2}{3}}$. An application of the First Derivative Test shows that this is a maximum. So

$$h = \sqrt{400 - \left(20\sqrt{\frac{2}{3}}\right)^2} = \sqrt{400 - 400\cdot\frac{2}{3}} = 20\sqrt{\frac{1}{3}}.$$

4.4.28 If we fill the pot with just enough water to cover the marble, the water in the pot will have height $2r$. Because the pot has radius 4, the water and marble together have volume $\pi\cdot 4^2\cdot 2r = 32\pi r$. The marble has volume $4\pi r^3/3$, so the volume of water needed to cover the marble is $V(r) = 32\pi r - \frac{4}{3}\pi r^3$. The critical points of this function satisfy $V'(r) = 32\pi - 4\pi r^2 = 0$, which has unique solution $r = \sqrt{8} = 2\sqrt{2}$ cm. By the First (or Second) Derivative test, this critical point gives a local maximum, which by Theorem 4.5 must be the absolute maximum of A over the interval $[0,4]$.

4.4.29 Let x and y be the dimensions of the flower garden; the area of the flower garden is 30, so we have the constraint $xy = 30$ which gives $y = 30/x$. The dimensions of the garden and borders are $x+4$ and $y+2$, so the objective function to be minimized for $x > 0$ is $A = (x+4)(y+2) = (x+4)\left(\frac{30}{x}+2\right) = 2x+\frac{120}{x}+38$. The critical points of $A(x)$ satisfy $A'(x) = 2 - \frac{120}{x^2} = 0$, which has unique solution $x = \sqrt{60} = 2\sqrt{15}$. By the First (or Second) Derivative test, this critical point gives a local minimum, which by Theorem 4.5 must be the absolute minimum of A over $(0,\infty)$. The corresponding value of y is $30/2\sqrt{15} = \sqrt{15}$, so the dimensions are $\sqrt{15}$ by $2\sqrt{15}$ m.

4.4.30

a. Suppose the side on the x-axis extends to the point $(a,0)$ and the side on the y-axis to $(0,b)$. Then $b = 10-2a$ and the rectangle has area $A = ab = a(10-2a) = 10a-2a^2$. We must have $0 \le a \le 5$ to ensure that both $a,b \ge 0$. The critical points of $A(a)$ satisfy $A'(a) = 10-4a = 0$, which has unique solution $a = 5/2$. Because $A(0) = A(5) = 0$, $a = 5/2$ gives the maximum area. The corresponding b value is 5, and the maximum area is $25/2$.

b. Let $(a,0)$ be the vertex on the x-axis and $(0,b)$ the vertex on the y-axis, and label the two vertices on the line $y = 10-2x$ as P and Q. The line joining $(a,0)$ and $(0,b)$ must be parallel to the line $y = 10-2x$, which has slope -2. This gives the constraint $\frac{0-b}{a-0} = -\frac{b}{a} = -2$, so $b = 2a$. The segment joining $(a,0)$ and $(0,b)$ has length $\sqrt{a^2+b^2} = \sqrt{5}a$. The other side length of the rectangle can be found by observing that the triangle with vertices $(0,0),(a,0),(0,b)$ is similar to the triangle with vertices $P,(5,0),(a,0)$ in that order, so the remaining side of the rectangle has length l satisfying $\frac{l}{5-a} = \frac{2a}{\sqrt{5}a}$; hence $l = \frac{2}{\sqrt{5}}(5-a)$. Therefore the area of the rectangle is given by $A(a) = \sqrt{5}a\frac{2}{\sqrt{5}}(5-a) = 10a-2a^2$, which is the same function as in part (a) above! The maximum again occurs when $a = 5/2$, and the dimensions of the rectangle of maximum area are $5\sqrt{5}/2$ and $\sqrt{5}$.

4.4.31 The radius r and height h of the barrel satisfy the constraint $r^2+h^2 = d^2$, which we can rewrite as $r^2 = d^2-h^2$. The volume of the barrel is given by $V = \pi r^2 h = \pi(d^2-h^2)h = \pi(d^2h-h^3)$. The height h must satisfy $0 \le h \le d$, so we need to maximize $V(h)$ on the interval $[0,d]$. The critical points of V satisfy $V'(h) = \pi(d^2-3h^2) = 0$. The only critical point in $(0,d)$ is $h = d/\sqrt{3}$, which gives the maximum volume because at the endpoints $V(0) = V(d) = 0$. The corresponding r value satisfies $r^2 = d^2-d^2/3 = 2d^2/3$, so $r = \sqrt{2}d/\sqrt{3}$ and we see that the ratio r/h that maximizes the volume is $\sqrt{2}$.

4.4.32

  a. The dimensions of the box are $3-2x, 4-2x$ and x, so the volume is given by $V(x) = x(3-2x)(4-2x) = 4x^3 - 14x^2 + 12x$. The dimensions cannot be negative, so we must have $0 \le x \le 3/2$. The critical points of $V(x)$ satisfy $V'(x) = 12x^2 - 28x + 12 = 4(3x^2 - 7x + 3) = 0$. This quadratic equation has roots $x = (7 - \sqrt{13})/6 \approx 0.57$ and $x = (7 + \sqrt{13})/6 \approx 1.77$, so the only critical point in $(0, 3/2)$ is $x = (7 - \sqrt{13})/6 \approx 0.57$. We have $V(0) = V(3/2) = 0$, so the maximum volume is $V(0.57) \approx 3.03$ ft^3.

  b. In this case the dimensions of the box are $l - 2x$, $l - 2x$ and x, so the volume is given by $V(x) = x(l - 2x)^2 = 4x^3 - 4lx^2 + l^2 x$. The dimensions cannot be negative, so we must have $0 \le x \le l/2$. The critical points of $V(x)$ satisfy $V'(x) = 12x^2 - 8lx + l^2 = (6x - l)(2x - l) = 0$. This quadratic equation has roots $x = l/6$ and $l/2$, so the only critical point in $(0, l/2)$ is $x = l/6$. We have $V(0) = V(l/2) = 0$, so the maximum volume is $V(l/6) = 2l^3/27$.

  c. In this case the dimensions of the box are $l - 2x$, $L - 2x$ and x, so the volume is given by $V(x) = x(l - 2x)(L - 2x) = 4x^3 - 2(l + L)x^2 + lLx$. The dimensions cannot be negative, so we must have $0 \le x \le l/2$ (because we are letting $L \to \infty$, we may assume that $l \le L$). The critical points of $V(x)$ satisfy $V'(x) = 12x^2 - 4(l + L)x + lL = 0$, and this quadratic equation has roots $x = \frac{L+l \pm \sqrt{L^2 - lL + l^2}}{6}$. Now $V(x)$ is a cubic polynomial with roots $x = 0, l/2, L/2$, and so has exactly one critical point between 0 and $l/2$, which gives the maximum of $V(x)$ on the interval $[0, l/2]$. This critical point is given by the smaller root of the quadratic above: $x = \frac{L+l - \sqrt{L^2 - lL + l^2}}{6} = \frac{L+l - \sqrt{L^2 - lL + l^2}}{6} \frac{(L+l+\sqrt{L^2-lL+l^2})}{(L+l+\sqrt{L^2-lL+l^2})} = \frac{(L+l)^2 - (L^2 - lL + l^2)}{6(L+l+\sqrt{L^2-lL+l^2})} = \frac{3lL}{6(L+l+\sqrt{L^2-lL+l^2})} = \frac{l}{2\left(1 + \frac{l}{L} + \sqrt{1 - \frac{l}{L} + \frac{l^2}{L^2}}\right)}$ (for the last step, divide all terms by L).

  As $L \to \infty$ with l fixed, $l/L \to 0$ so the size x of the corner squares that maximizes the volume has limit $l/4$ as $L \to \infty$.

4.4.33 Let h be the height of the cylindrical tower and r the radius of the dome. The cylinder has volume $\pi r^2 h$, and the hemispherical dome has volume $2\pi r^3/3$ (half the volume of a sphere of radius r). The total volume is 750, so we have the constraint $\pi r^2 h + \frac{2\pi r^3}{3} = 750$ which gives $h = \frac{750}{\pi r^2} - \frac{2r}{3}$. We must have $h \ge 0$, which is equivalent to $r \le \sqrt[3]{1125/\pi}$. The objective function to be maximized is the cost of the metal to make the silo, which is proportional to the surface area of the cylinder $(= 2\pi r h)$ plus 1.5 times the surface area of the hemisphere $(= 2\pi r^2)$. So we can take as objective function $C = 2\pi r h + 1.5 \cdot 2\pi r^2 = 2\pi r\left(\frac{750}{\pi r^2} - \frac{2r}{3}\right) + 3\pi r^2 = \frac{1500}{r} + \frac{5}{3}\pi r^2$. The critical points of $C(r)$ satisfy $C'(r) = -\frac{1500}{r^2} + \frac{10}{3}\pi r = 0$, which gives $\pi r^3 = 450$ and hence $r = \sqrt[3]{450/\pi}$. The corresponding value of h is $h = \frac{750}{\pi r^2} - \frac{2r}{3} = \frac{750r}{\pi r^3} - \frac{2r}{3} = \left(\frac{750}{450} - \frac{2}{3}\right)r = r$. By the First (or Second) Derivative Test, this critical point corresponds to a local minimum, and by Theorem 4.5, this solitary local minimum is also the absolute minimum on the interval $[0, \sqrt[3]{1125/\pi}]$. Therefore the dimensions that minimize the cost are $r = h = \sqrt[3]{450/\pi}$ m.

4.4.34 The two cables joined to the ceiling each have length $\sqrt{x^2 + 1}$ by the Pythagorean theorem, and the vertical cable has length $6 - x$. The objective function to be minimized is the total length of the three cables, given by $L(x) = 2\sqrt{x^2 + 1} + 6 - x$. Because the lengths cannot be negative, we must have $0 \le x \le 6$. The critical points of $L(x)$ satisfy $L'(x) = \frac{2x}{\sqrt{x^2+1}} - 1 = 0$, which occurs when $3x^2 = 1$, so $x = 1/\sqrt{3} = \sqrt{3}/3$ is the unique critical point in $(0, 6)$. By the First (or Second) Derivative Test, this critical point corresponds to a local minimum, and by Theorem 4.5, this solitary local minimum is also the absolute minimum on the interval $[0, 6]$. Therefore the cables should be joined at distance $x = \sqrt{3}/3$ m below the ceiling.

4.4.35 Let x be the distance between the point and the weaker light source; then $12 - x$ is the distance to the stronger light source. The intensity is proportional to $I(x) = \frac{1}{x^2} + \frac{2}{(12-x)^2}$, so we can take this as our objective function to be minimized for $0 < x < 12$. The critical points of $I(x)$ satisfy $I'(x) = -\frac{2}{x^3} + \frac{4}{(12-x)^3} = 0$ which gives $\left(\frac{12-x}{x}\right)^3 = 2$, or $\frac{12-x}{x} = \sqrt[3]{2}$, or $x = \frac{12}{\sqrt[3]{2}+1} \approx 5.310$. By the First (or Second) Derivative Test, this critical point corresponds to a local minimum, and by Theorem 4.5, this solitary local minimum is also the absolute minimum on the interval $(0, 12)$. Therefore the intensity is weakest at the point $12/(\sqrt[3]{2}+1) \approx 5.310$ m from the weaker source.

4.4.36 Let x and y be the base and height of the triangle that is folded over, and z the height of point P above the base (see figure in the text). The Pythagorean theorem gives $z^2 = x^2 - (a-x)^2 = 2ax - a^2$, so $z = \sqrt{2ax - a^2}$. The Pythagorean theorem also gives $(y - \sqrt{2ax - a^2})^2 + a^2 = y^2$, which can be simplified to $2y\sqrt{2ax - a^2} = 2ax$, so $y = ax/\sqrt{2ax - a^2}$. The length L of the crease satisfies $L^2 = x^2 + y^2 = x^2 + \frac{a^2 x^2}{2ax - a^2} = x^2\left(1 + \frac{a^2}{2ax - a^2}\right) = \frac{x^3}{x - \frac{a}{2}}$. Because L is positive, it suffices to minimize the function L^2 over $a/2 < x \le a$. We have $\frac{dL^2}{dx} = \frac{3x^2}{x - \frac{a}{2}} - \frac{x^3}{(x - \frac{a}{2})^2} = \frac{x^2}{x - \frac{a}{2}}\left(3 - \frac{x}{x - \frac{a}{2}}\right)$, and we solve $3(x - a/2) = x$ to obtain $x = 3a/4$. By the First (or Second) Derivative Test, this critical point corresponds to a local minimum, and by Theorem 4.5, this solitary local minimum is also the absolute minimum on the interval $(a/2, a]$. Substituting in the equation for L^2 above, we find that the shortest crease has length $L = 3\sqrt{3}a/4$, and the height of the point P is $z = a/\sqrt{2}$. (The corresponding value of $y = 3\sqrt{2}a/4 \approx 1.061a$; so the height b of the rectangle must satisfy $b > 1.061a$ to be able to form the minimal crease.)

4.4.37 Let x be the distance from the point on shore nearest the island to the point where the underwater cable meets the shore, and let y be the be the length of the underwater cable. By the Pythagorean theorem, $y = \sqrt{x^2 + 3.5^2}$. The objective function to be minimized is the cost given by $C(x) = 2400\sqrt{x^2 + 3.5^2} + 1200 \cdot (8 - x) = 2400\sqrt{x^2 + 3.5^2} - 1200x + 9600$. We wish to minimize this function for $0 \le x \le 8$. The critical points of $C(x)$ satisfy $C'(x) = \frac{2400x}{\sqrt{x^2 + 3.5^2}} - 1200 = 1200\left(\frac{2x}{\sqrt{x^2 + 3.5^2}} - 1\right) = 0$, which we solve to obtain $x = 7\sqrt{3}/6$. By the First Derivative Test, this critical point corresponds to a local minimum, and by Theorem 4.5, this solitary local minimum is also the absolute minimum on the interval $[0, 8]$. Therefore the optimal point on shore has distance $x = 7\sqrt{3}/6$ mi from the point on shore nearest the island, in the direction of the power station.

4.4.38 Let x be the distance from the point on shore nearest the island to the point where the underwater cable meets the shore, and let y be the be the length of the underwater cable. In terms of the angle θ in the figure, $\tan\theta = 3.5/x$ so $x = 3.5\cot\theta$, and $\sin\theta = 3.5/y$ so $y = 3.5\csc\theta$. The objective function to be minimized is the cost given by $C(\theta) = 2400 \cdot 3.5\csc\theta + 1200 \cdot (8 - 3.5\cot\theta) = 8400\csc\theta - 4200\cot\theta + 9600$. The angle θ must be between $\tan^{-1}(3.5/8)$ (≈ 0.412) and $\pi/2$. The critical points of $C(\theta)$ satisfy $C'(\theta) = 8400(-\csc\theta\cot\theta) - 4200(-\csc^2\theta) = 4200\csc^2\theta(1 - 2\cos\theta)$, which has unique solution $\theta = \pi/3$ in the interval under consideration. By the First Derivative Test, this critical point corresponds to a local minimum, and by Theorem 4.5, this solitary local minimum is also the absolute minimum on the interval $[\tan^{-1}(3.5/8), \pi/2]$. Therefore the optimal point on shore has distance $x = 3.5\cot(\pi/3) = 7\sqrt{3}/6$ mi from the point on shore nearest the island, in the direction of the power station.

4.4.39

a. Using the Pythagorean theorem, we find that the height of this triangle is 2. Let x be the distance from the point P to the base of the triangle; then the distance from P to the top vertex is $2 - x$ and the distance to each of the base vertices is $\sqrt{x^2 + 4}$, again by the Pythagorean theorem. Therefore the sum of the distances to the three vertices is given by $S(x) = 2\sqrt{x^2 + 4} + 2 - x$. We wish to minimize this function for $0 \le x \le 2$. The critical points of $S(x)$ satisfy $S'(x) = \frac{2x}{\sqrt{x^2 + 4}} - 1 = 0$, which has unique solution $x = 2/\sqrt{3}$ in $(0, 2)$. By the First Derivative Test, this critical point corresponds to a local minimum, and by Theorem 4.5, this solitary local minimum is also the absolute minimum on the interval $[0, 2]$. Therefore the optimal location for P is $2/\sqrt{3}$ units above the base.

b. In this case the objective function to be minimized is $S(x) = 2\sqrt{x^2 + 4} + h - x$ where $0 \le x \le h$. Exactly as above, we find that the only critical point $x > 0$ is $x = 2/\sqrt{3}$. This will give the absolute minimum on $[0, h]$ as long as $h \ge 2/\sqrt{3}$. When $h < 2/\sqrt{3}$, $S(x)$ is decreasing on $[0, h]$ and the minimum occurs at the endpoint $x = h$.

4.4.40 The radius r of a circle inscribed in a triangle is given by the formula $r = 2A/P$, where A is the area and P the perimeter of the triangle. Let x be the length of the base of the isosceles triangle. The height is then $\sqrt{1 - (x/2)^2}$ by the Pythagorean theorem, and therefore the area is given by $A = \frac{1}{2}x\sqrt{1 - \frac{x^2}{4}} = \frac{1}{4}x\sqrt{4 - x^2}$. The perimeter is $x + 2$, so the radius of the inscribed triangle is $r = \frac{2A}{P} = \frac{1}{2} \cdot \frac{x\sqrt{4 - x^2}}{x + 2}$. The possible x values here satisfy $0 \le x \le 2$, so we need to maximize the function $r(x)$ on $[0, 2]$. We have $r'(x) = \frac{1}{2}\left(\frac{\sqrt{4-x^2}}{x+2} + \frac{x}{x+2}\left(\frac{-x}{\sqrt{4-x^2}}\right) - \frac{x\sqrt{4-x^2}}{(x+2)^2}\right)$, which simplifies to $r'(x) = \frac{4-2x-x^2}{2(x+2)\sqrt{4-x^2}}$. Thus the critical points satisfy $x^2 + 2x - 4 = 0$. This equation has roots $-1 \pm \sqrt{5}$, so the only critical point in $(0, 2)$ is $x = \sqrt{5} - 1$. Because $r(0) = r(2) = 0$, the maximum radius must occur at $x = \sqrt{5} - 1$. For this value of x we have $r = \frac{\sqrt{2}}{8}(\sqrt{5}-1)^{5/2} \approx 0.300$, $\quad \pi r^2 = \frac{\pi}{32}(\sqrt{5}-1)^5 \approx 0.283$.

4.4.41 Let r and h be the radius and height of the cone; then we have the constraint $r^2 + h^2 = 3^2 = 9$, which gives $r^2 = 9 - h^2$. The objective function to be maximized is the volume of the cone, given by $V = \frac{\pi}{3}r^2 h = \frac{\pi}{3}(9 - h^2)h = \frac{\pi}{3}(9h - h^3)$. Because $r, h \ge 0$ we must have $0 \le h \le 3$. Therefore we need to maximize $V(h)$ over $[0, 3]$. The critical points of $V(h)$ satisfy $V'(h) = \frac{\pi}{3}(9 - 3h^2) = \pi(3 - h^2) = 0$, so $h = \sqrt{3}$ is the only critical point in $[0, 3]$. Because $V(0) = V(3) = 0$, the cone of maximum volume has height $h = \sqrt{3}$ and radius $r = \sqrt{6}$.

4.4.42 The objective function to be minimized is the average number of tests required, given by $A(x) = N\left(1 - q^x + \frac{1}{x}\right)$ where x is the group size, $N = 10,000$ and $q = 0.95$. We may assume that $1 \le x \le 10,000$. The critical points of this function satisfy $A'(x) = N\left(-(\ln q)q^x - \frac{1}{x^2}\right) = 0$, which is equivalent to the equation $(0.95)^{-x} + \ln(0.95)x^2 = 0$. Using a numerical solver, we find that this equation has one root between 5 and 6, and one between 132 and 133. By the First Derivative Test, we see that the smaller of these roots gives a local minimum and the larger a local maximum. Therefore the minimum value of $A(x)$ for $1 \le x \le 10,000$ occurs either at the smaller root or at the endpoint 10,000. The group size x must be an integer, so the possible optimal choices are $x = 5, 6$ and 10,000; comparing the value of $A(x)$ at these points shows that $x = 5$ is the optimal group size.

4.4.43 The critical points of the function $a(\theta)$ satisfy

$$a'(\theta) = \omega^2 r\left(-\sin\theta - \frac{2r\sin 2\theta}{L}\right) = -\omega^2 r \sin\theta\left(1 + \frac{4r\cos\theta}{L}\right) = 0,$$

using the identity $\sin 2\theta = 2\sin\theta\cos\theta$. There are two cases to consider separately: (a) $0 < L < 4r$ and (b) $L \ge 4r$. In case (a) the critical points in $[0, 2\pi]$ are $\theta = 0, \pi, 2\pi$ and also $\theta = \cos^{-1}(-L/(4r))$ and $2\pi - \cos^{-1}(-L/(4r))$. Comparing the values of $a(\theta)$ at these points shows that the maximum acceleration occurs at $\theta = 0$ and 2π and the minimum occurs at $\theta = \cos^{-1}(-L/(4r))$ and $2\pi - \cos^{-1}(-L/(4r))$. (There is a local maximum at $\theta = \pi$.) In case (b) the only critical points are $\theta = 0, \pi$ and 2π, and comparing the values of $a(\theta)$ at these points shows that the maximum acceleration occurs at $\theta = 0$ and 2π as in case (a), whereas the minimum occurs at $\theta = \pi$ in this case.

4.4.44 The cross-section is a trapezoid with height $3\sin\theta$; the larger of the parallel sides has length $3 + 2 \cdot 3\cos\theta = 3 + 6\cos\theta$ and the smaller parallel side has length 3. The area of this trapezoid is given by

$$A(\theta) = \frac{1}{2}(3 + (3 + 6\cos\theta)) \cdot 3\sin\theta = 9(1 + \cos\theta)\sin\theta = 9\left(\sin\theta + \frac{\sin 2\theta}{2}\right),$$

using the identity $\sin 2\theta = 2\sin\theta\cos\theta$. We wish to maximize this function for $0 \le \theta \le \pi/2$. The critical points of $A(\theta)$ satisfy $\cos\theta + \cos 2\theta = \cos\theta + 2\cos^2\theta - 1 = 0$, using the identity $\cos 2\theta = 2\cos^2\theta - 1$. Therefore $x = \cos\theta$ satisfies the quadratic equation $2x^2 + x - 1 = 0$, which has roots $x = 1/2$ and -1. So the only critical point in $(0, \pi/2)$ is $\theta = \cos^{-1}(1/2) = \pi/3$, which by the First (or Second) Derivative Test and Theorem 4.5 gives the maximum area.

4.4.45

   a. Let r and h be the radius and height of the can. The volume of the can is $V = \pi r^2 h$, which gives the constraint $\pi r^2 h = 354$ or $h = 354/(\pi r^2)$. The objective function to be minimized is the surface area, which consists of $2\pi r^2$ (for the top and bottom of the can) and $2\pi r h$ (for the side of the can). Therefore the objective function to be minimized is $A = 2\pi r^2 + 2\pi r h = 2\pi\left(r^2 + r\left(\frac{354}{\pi r^2}\right)\right) = 2\pi\left(r^2 + \frac{354}{\pi r}\right)$. We need to minimize $A(r)$ for $r > 0$. The critical points of $A(r)$ satisfy $A'(r) = 2\pi\left(2r - \frac{354}{\pi r^2}\right) = 0$, which gives $r = \sqrt[3]{(177/\pi)} \approx 3.834$ cm. The corresponding value of h is $h = \frac{354}{\pi r^2} = \frac{354r}{\pi r^3} = 2r \cdot \frac{177}{\pi r^3} = 2r$, so $h = 2\sqrt[3]{(177/\pi)} \approx 7.667$ cm. By the First (or Second) Derivative Test, this critical point corresponds to a local minimum, and by Theorem 4.5, this solitary local minimum is also the absolute minimum on the interval $(0, \infty)$.

b. We modify the objective function in part (a) above to account for the fact that the top and bottom of the can have double thickness: $A = 4\pi r^2 + 2\pi rh = 2\pi \left(2r^2 + r\left(\frac{354}{\pi r^2}\right)\right) = 4\pi \left(r^2 + \frac{177}{\pi r}\right)$. We need to minimize $A(r)$ for $r > 0$. The critical points of $A(r)$ satisfy $A'(r) = 4\pi \left(2r - \frac{177}{\pi r^2}\right) = 0$, which gives $r = \sqrt[3]{(177/2\pi)} \approx 3.043$ cm. The corresponding value of h is $h = \frac{354}{\pi r^2} = \frac{354r}{\pi r^3} = 4r \cdot \frac{177}{2\pi r^3} = 4r$, so $h = 4\sqrt[3]{(177/2\pi)} \approx 12.171$ cm. These dimensions are closer to those of a real soda can.

4.4.46 Let r and h be the radius and height of both the cylinder and cones. The surface area of each cone is $\pi r \sqrt{r^2 + h^2}$ and the surface area of the cylinder is $2\pi rh$, so we have the constraint $2\pi r\sqrt{r^2 + h^2} + 2\pi rh = A$, which we rewrite as $h + \sqrt{r^2 + h^2} = \frac{A}{2\pi r}$. Square to obtain $h^2 + 2h\sqrt{r^2 + h^2} + r^2 + h^2 = \left(\frac{A}{2\pi r}\right)^2$, and substitute $\sqrt{r^2 + h^2} = A/(2\pi r) - h$ in this equation to obtain $h^2 + 2h\left(\frac{A}{2\pi r} - h\right) + r^2 + h^2 = \left(\frac{A}{2\pi r}\right)^2$. Solving for h yields $h = \frac{\pi r}{A}\left(\frac{A^2}{4\pi^2 r^2} - r^2\right) = \frac{A}{4\pi r} - \frac{\pi r^3}{A}$.

We must have $h \geq 0$, which is equivalent to the condition $r \leq \sqrt{A}/\sqrt{2\pi}$. So the possible r under consideration satisfy $0 \leq r \leq \sqrt{A}/\sqrt{2\pi}$. The objective function to be maximized is the combined volume of the cylinder and cones, which is given by

$$V = \pi r^2 h + 2 \cdot \frac{\pi}{3} r^2 h = \frac{5\pi}{3} r^2 h = \frac{5\pi}{3} r^2 \left(\frac{A}{4\pi r} - \frac{\pi r^3}{A}\right) = \frac{5A}{12} r - \frac{5\pi^2}{3A} r^5.$$

The critical points of $V(r)$ satisfy $V'(r) = \frac{5A}{12} - \frac{25\pi^2}{3A} r^4 = 0$, which has unique positive solution $r = \sqrt{A}/(\sqrt[4]{20}\sqrt{\pi})$. To find the corresponding value of h, observe that $\pi r^3/A = A/(20\pi r)$, so $h = \frac{A}{4\pi r} - \frac{\pi r^3}{A} = \frac{A}{4\pi r} - \frac{A}{20\pi r} = \frac{A}{5\pi r}$ which gives $h = \sqrt{A}\sqrt[4]{20}/(5\sqrt{\pi})$. Note that $V(r) = 0$ at the endpoints of the interval $[0, \sqrt{A}/\sqrt{2\pi}]$, so the maximum volume must occur at the values of r and h given above.

4.4.47 The viewing angle θ is given by $\theta = \cot^{-1}\left(\frac{x}{10}\right) - \cot^{-1}\left(\frac{x}{3}\right)$, and we wish to maximize this function for $x > 0$. The critical points satisfy $\theta'(x) = -\frac{1}{1+\left(\frac{x}{10}\right)^2} \cdot \frac{1}{10} - (-)\frac{1}{1+\left(\frac{x}{3}\right)^2} \cdot \frac{1}{3} = \frac{3}{x^2+3^2} - \frac{10}{x^2+10^2} = 0$ which simplifies to $3(x^2 + 100) = 10(x^2 + 9)$ or $x^2 = 30$. Therefore $x = \sqrt{30} \approx 5.477$ ft is the only critical point in $(0, \infty)$. By the First (or Second) Derivative Test, this critical point corresponds to a local maximum, and by Theorem 4.5, this solitary local maximum must be the absolute maximum on the interval $(0, \infty)$.

4.4.48 We have $x = 100\tan\theta$, so the rate at which the beam sweeps along the highway is

$$\frac{dx}{dt} = 100\sec^2\theta \frac{d\theta}{dt} = 100\sec^2\theta \cdot \frac{\pi}{6} = \frac{50\pi}{3}\sec^2\theta.$$

The beam meets the highway provided that the angle θ satisfies $-\pi/2 < \theta < \pi/2$. The function $\sec^2\theta$ is unbounded on this interval, and so has no maximum. The minimum value occurs at $\theta = 0$, because everywhere else $\sec^2\theta > 1$. Therefore the minimum rate is $50\pi/3 \approx 52.360$ m/s, and there is no maximum rate.

4.4.49 Let the radius of the ferris wheel have length r, and let α be the angle the specific seat on the ferris wheel makes with the center of the wheel (see the figure in the text). This point has coordinates $(r\cos\alpha, r + r\sin\alpha)$ so the distance from the seat to the base of the wheel is

$$d = \sqrt{r^2\cos^2\alpha + r^2(1 + \sin\alpha)^2} = \sqrt{2}r\sqrt{1 + \sin\alpha}.$$

Therefore the observer's angle satisfies $\tan\theta = \frac{r\sqrt{2}}{20}\sqrt{1 + \sin\alpha}$. Think of θ and α as functions of time t and differentiate: $\sec^2\theta\frac{d\theta}{dt} = \frac{r\sqrt{2}}{20} \cdot \frac{\cos\alpha}{2\sqrt{1+\sin\alpha}}\frac{d\alpha}{dt} = \frac{\pi r\sqrt{2}}{40} \cdot \frac{\cos\alpha}{\sqrt{1+\sin\alpha}}$. Therefore

$$\frac{d\theta}{dt} = \frac{\pi r\sqrt{2}}{40}\frac{\cos^2\theta\cos\alpha}{\sqrt{1+\sin\alpha}}.$$

Observe that $\left|\frac{d\theta}{dt}\right| = \frac{\pi r\sqrt{2}}{40} \frac{\cos^2\theta |\cos\alpha|}{\sqrt{1+\sin\alpha}} \frac{\sqrt{1-\sin\alpha}}{\sqrt{1-\sin\alpha}}$, which can be written as $\frac{\pi r\sqrt{2}}{40}\cos^2\theta\sqrt{1-\sin\alpha}$. When the seat on the ferris wheel is at its lowest point we have $\theta = 0$ and $\alpha = -\pi/2$, which gives $\cos^2\theta = 1$ and $\sqrt{1-\sin\alpha} = \sqrt{2}$. At any other point on the wheel we have $\cos^2\theta \leq 1$ and $\sqrt{1-\sin\alpha} < \sqrt{2}$, so θ is changing most rapidly when the seat is at its lowest point.

4.4.50

Let α and β be the angles labeled below (see figure). Then $\left(\frac{\pi}{2} - \alpha\right) + \theta + \left(\frac{\pi}{2} - \beta\right) = \pi$ so $\theta = \alpha + \beta$. We have $\tan\alpha = x/3$ and $\tan\beta = (4-x)/3$, so we can express θ in terms of x as $\theta(x) = \tan^{-1}\left(\frac{x}{3}\right) + \tan^{-1}\left(\frac{4-x}{3}\right)$. We wish to maximize this function for $0 \leq x \leq 4$. The critical points of $\theta(x)$ satisfy

$$\theta'(x) = \frac{1}{1 + \left(\frac{x}{3}\right)^2} \cdot \frac{1}{3} + \frac{1}{1 + \left(\frac{4-x}{3}\right)^2} \cdot \left(-\frac{1}{3}\right)$$

which can be written as $\frac{3}{x^2+9} - \frac{3}{(4-x)^2+9}$. This is equal to zero for $x^2 = (4-x)^2$ and because $x, 4-x \geq 0$ we must have $x = 4-x$, so $x = 2$ is the only critical point. We compare $\theta(x)$ at $x = 2$ and the endpoints $x = 0, 4$: $\theta(2) = 2\tan^{-1}\left(\frac{2}{3}\right) \approx 1.176$, $\theta(0) = \theta(4) = \tan^{-1}\left(\frac{4}{3}\right) \approx 0.937$. Therefore the maximum angle occurs when $x = 2$.

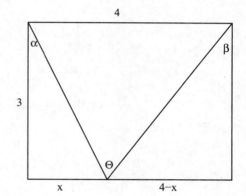

4.4.51 Let r and h be the radius and height of the cylinder. The distance d from the centroid of the cylinder (the midpoint of the cylinder's axis of rotation) to any point on the top or bottom edge satisfies $d^2 = r^2 + \left(\frac{h}{2}\right)^2$ so the constraint is $r^2 + (h/2)^2 = R^2$. The volume of the cylinder is given by $V = \pi r^2 h = \pi\left(R^2 - \left(\frac{h}{2}\right)^2\right)h = \pi\left(R^2 h - \frac{h^3}{4}\right)$. Because $r, h \geq 0$ we must have $0 \leq h \leq 2R$. We wish to maximize $V(h)$ on this interval. The critical points of $V(h)$ satisfy $V'(h) = \pi\left(R^2 - \frac{3h^2}{4}\right) = 0$ which gives $h = 2R/\sqrt{3}$, and from the constraint we obtain $r = \sqrt{2}R/\sqrt{3}$. The volume $V(h) = 0$ at the endpoints $h = 0$ and $h = 2R$, so the maximum volume must occur at this critical point.

4.4.52

a. Let a and b be the side lengths of a particular right triangle with hypotenuse L, and let x and y be the side lengths of an inscribed rectangle (see figure). Then using similar triangles we see that $y/(a-x) = b/a$, so $y = (b/a)(a-x)$. The area to be maximized is $A(x) = \frac{b}{a}x(a-x)$ over $0 \leq x \leq a$. This function has unique critical point $x = a/2$ and is 0 at the endpoints $x = 0$ and $x = a$; hence the maximum occurs when $x = a/2$. The other side of the rectangle has length $y = b/2$, so the maximum area is $A(a/2) = ab/4$. Note: We could also consider inscribing the rectangle so that one side rests on the hypotenuse. The maximum area is also $ab/4$ using this configuration. Now consider all possible right triangles with hypotenuse L. The side lengths a and b must satisfy $a, b \geq 0$ and $a^2 + b^2 = L^2$, which gives $b = \sqrt{L^2 - a^2}$. For each triangle, the largest area of an inscribed rectangle is $A = \frac{ab}{4} = \frac{a}{4}\sqrt{L^2 - a^2}$, which now we must maximize over $0 \leq a \leq L$. This function has unique critical point $a = L/\sqrt{2}$, and is 0 at the endpoints $a = 0$ and $a = L$. The constraint gives $b = a$, so the optimal triangle is an isosceles right triangle, and the largest inscribed rectangle is a square with side length $L/(2\sqrt{2})$ and area $L^2/8$.

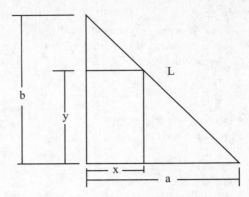

b. Let x and y be the dimensions of a rectangle inscribed in an equilateral triangle with side length L (see figure). Then $\tan\frac{\pi}{3} = \frac{y}{\frac{1}{2}(L-x)} = \sqrt{3}$ so $y = \frac{\sqrt{3}}{2}(L-x)$. The area to be maximized is $A = xy = \frac{\sqrt{3}}{2}x(L-x)$ over $0 \le x \le L$. This function has unique critical point $x = L/2$, and is 0 at the endpoints $x = 0$ and $x = L$; hence the maximum occurs when $x = L/2$. The other side of the rectangle has length $y = L\sqrt{3}/4$, so the maximum area is $A = L^2\sqrt{3}/8$.

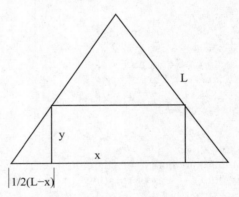

c. Let a and b be the (non-hypotenuse) side lengths of a right triangle; then as shown in part (a) above, the inscribed rectangle of maximum area has side lengths $a/2$ and $b/2$ and area $ab/4 = A/2$.

d. Let b and h be the base and height of the triangle, assume the angles to the base are both less than or equal to $90°$, and let x and y be the side lengths of an inscribed rectangle (see figure). Then by similar triangles $\frac{h-y}{h} = \frac{x}{b}$ so $y = h\left(1 - \frac{x}{b}\right)$. The rectangle has area $xy = (h/b)x(b-x)$, and the maximum value of this function over $0 \le x \le b$ occurs at $x = b/2$, which gives $y = h/2$ and area $= bh/4 = A/2$ if the triangle has area A. (Note that if a rectangle is inscribed in a triangle, then two of the vertices of the rectangle must lie on the same side of the triangle, so the rectangle must rest on one of the sides of the triangle, and therefore the angles to that side must both be less than or equal to $90°$. So the maximum area of an inscribed rectangle is $A/2$ in all cases.)

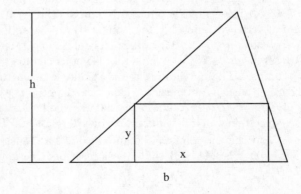

4.4.53

a. Let r and h be the radius and height of the inscribed cylinder. The region that lies above the cylinder inside the cone is a cone with radius r and height $H-h$; by similar triangles we have $\frac{H-h}{r} = \frac{H}{R}$ so $h = \frac{H}{R}(R-r)$. The volume of the cylinder is $V = \pi r^2 h = \frac{\pi H}{R}(Rr^2 - r^3)$, which we must maximize over $0 \le r \le R$. The critical points of $V(r)$ satisfy $V'(r) = \frac{\pi H}{R}(2Rr - 3r^2) = 0$, which has unique solution $r = 2R/3$ in $(0, R)$. Because $V(r) = 0$ at the endpoints $r = 0$ and $r = R$, the cylinder with maximum volume has radius $r = 2R/3$, height $h = H/3$ and volume $V = \pi r^2 h = \frac{4\pi}{27}R^2 H = \frac{4}{9} \cdot \frac{\pi}{3}R^2 H$; i.e. 4/9 the volume of the cone.

b. The lateral surface area of the cylinder is $A = 2\pi rh = 2\pi r \cdot \frac{H}{R}(R-r) = \frac{2\pi H}{R}r(R-r)$. This function takes its maximum over $0 \le r \le R$ at $r = R/2$, so the cylinder with maximum lateral surface area has dimensions $r = R/2$ and $h = H/2$.

4.4.54 Let x be the number of tickets sold. The cost per ticket is $30 - 0.25x$, and the fixed expenses are 200, so the profit is $P(x) = x(30 - 0.25x) - 200 = -0.25x^2 + 30x - 200$. We wish to maximize this function for $20 \le x \le 70$. The critical points of $P(x)$ satisfy $P'(x) = -0.5x + 30 = 0$ so $x = 60$ is the only critical point. By the First (or Second) Derivative Test, this critical point corresponds to a local maximum, and by Theorem 4.5, this solitary local maximum is also the absolute maximum on the interval $[20, 70]$. Therefore the profit is maximized by selling 60 tickets.

4.4.55 Let R and H be the radius and height of the larger cone and let r and h be the radius and height of the smaller inscribed cone. The region that lies above the smaller cone inside the larger cone is a cone with radius r and height $H - h$; by similar triangles we have $\frac{H-h}{r} = \frac{H}{R}$ so $h = \frac{H}{R}(R-r)$. The volume of the smaller cone is $V = \frac{\pi}{3}r^2 h = \frac{\pi H}{3R}(Rr^2 - r^3)$, which we must maximize over $0 \le r \le R$. The critical points of $V(r)$ satisfy $V'(r) = \frac{\pi H}{3R}(2Rr - 3r^2) = 0$ which has unique solution $r = 2R/3$ in $(0, R)$. Because $V(r) = 0$ at the endpoints $r = 0$ and $r = R$, the smaller cone with maximum volume has radius $r = 2R/3$ and height $h = H/3$, so the optimal ratio of the heights is 3:1.

4.4.56

a. Referring to the diagram in the text, note that if we drop a perpendicular from the 150° angle, the trapezoid is divided into a 30–60–90 triangle and an $x \times y$ rectangle. The slanted side has length $y \sec 60° = 2y$, and the base of the trapezoid has length $x + 2y\cos 30° = x + \sqrt{3}y$. The perimeter of the trapezoid is 1000, so we get the constraint $P = 2x + (3 + \sqrt{3})y = 1000$, which gives $x = 500 - (3 + \sqrt{3})y/2$. The objective function to be maximized is the area of the trapezoid, which is $A = \frac{1}{2}\left(x + (x + \sqrt{3}y)\right)y = (x + \frac{\sqrt{3}}{2}y)y = (500 - \frac{3}{2}y)y = 500y - \frac{3}{2}y^2$. Because we need both $x, y \ge 0$, we also must have $y \le 1000/(3 + \sqrt{3}) \approx 211.325$. The maximum value of the quadratic function $A(y)$ occurs at $y = 500/3 \approx 166.667$ ft, which is in the interval under consideration; the corresponding value of x is $250(3 - \sqrt{3}/3) \approx 105.662$ ft.

b. In this case we do not use fencing for the slanted side with length $2y$, so we modify the constraint to be $2x + (1 + \sqrt{3})y = 1000$, which gives $x = 500 - (1 + \sqrt{3})y/2$. The area of the trapezoid is $A = \frac{1}{2}\left(x + (x + \sqrt{3}y)\right)y = (x + \frac{\sqrt{3}}{2}y)y = (500 - \frac{1}{2}y)y = 500y - \frac{1}{2}y^2$. Because we need both $x, y \ge 0$ we also must have $y \le 1000/(1 + \sqrt{3}) \approx 366.025$. But the maximum value of the quadratic function $A(y)$ occurs at $y = 500$, which is outside the interval under consideration. Hence $A(y)$ is increasing over the interval $[0, 1000/(1 + \sqrt{3})]$ and the maximum area occurs when $y = 1000/(1 + \sqrt{3}) \approx 366.025$ ft and $x = 0$.

4.4.57

Following the hint, place two points P and Q above the midpoint of the base of the square, at distances x and y to the sides (see figure), where $0 \leq x, y \leq 1/2$. Then join the bottom vertices of the square to P, the upper vertices to Q and join P to Q. This road system has total length $L = 2\sqrt{x^2 + \frac{1}{4}} + 2\sqrt{y^2 + \frac{1}{4}} + (1 - x - y) = 1 + \left(\sqrt{4x^2 + 1} - x\right) + \left(\sqrt{4y^2 + 1} - y\right)$. We can minimize the contributions from x and y separately; the critical points of the function $f(x) = \sqrt{4x^2 + 1} - x$ satisfy $f'(x) = \frac{4x}{\sqrt{4x^2+1}} - 1 = 0$ which gives $\sqrt{4x^2 + 1} = 4x$, so $12x^2 = 1$ and $x = 1/(2\sqrt{3})$. By the First (or Second) Derivative Test, this critical point corresponds to a local minimum, and by Theorem 4.5, this solitary local minimum is also the absolute minimum on the interval $[0, 1/2]$. The minimum value of $f(x)$ on this interval is $f(1/(2\sqrt{3})) = \sqrt{3}/2$, so the shortest road system has length $L = 1 + 2 \cdot \frac{\sqrt{3}}{2} = 1 + \sqrt{3} \approx 2.732$.

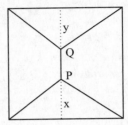

4.4.58 Suppose that the base of the rectangle has dimension x and the side of the rectangle has dimension y. The semicircular pane has radius $x/2$, so the perimeter of the window is $P = 2y + x + \frac{1}{2} \cdot 2\pi \cdot \frac{x}{2} = 2y + \left(1 + \frac{\pi}{2}\right) x$ which gives the constraint $y = \frac{P}{2} - \left(\frac{1}{2} + \frac{\pi}{4}\right) x$. The rectangular pane has area xy and the semicircular pane has area $(1/2)\pi(x/2)^2$, so the amount of light transmitted through the window is proportional to $L = 2xy + \frac{\pi x^2}{8} = 2x\left(\frac{P}{2} - \left(\frac{1}{2} + \frac{\pi}{4}\right)x\right) + \frac{\pi x^2}{8} = Px - \left(1 + \frac{3\pi}{8}\right)x^2$. Because $x, y \geq 0$ we must have $0 \leq x \leq P/(1 + (\pi/2)) \approx 0.389P$. The quadratic function $L(x)$ has maximum at $x = \frac{P}{2 + \frac{3\pi}{4}} = \frac{4P}{8 + 3\pi} \approx 0.230P$, which is in the interval under consideration. The corresponding value of y is $y = \frac{P}{2} - \left(\frac{1}{2} + \frac{\pi}{4}\right) \frac{4P}{8 + 3\pi} = \frac{4 + \pi}{16 + 6\pi} P \approx 0.205P$.

4.4.59 Let x be the distance between the point on the track nearest your initial position to the point where you catch the train. If you just catch the back of the train, then the train will have travelled $x + 1/3$ miles, which will require time $T = \frac{\text{distance}}{\text{rate}} = \frac{x + \frac{1}{3}}{20}$. The distance you must run is $\sqrt{x^2 + 1/(16)}$, so your running speed must be $v = \frac{\text{distance}}{\text{time}} = \frac{20\sqrt{x^2 + \frac{1}{16}}}{x + \frac{1}{3}}$. We wish to minimize this function for $x \geq 0$. The derivative of $v(x)$ can be written $v'(x) = \left(\frac{x}{x^2 + \frac{1}{16}} - \frac{1}{x + \frac{1}{3}}\right) v(x)$, so the critical points of $v(x)$ satisfy $\frac{x}{x^2 + \frac{1}{16}} = \frac{1}{x + \frac{1}{3}}$ so $x\left(x + \frac{1}{3}\right) = x^2 + \frac{1}{16}$ which gives $x = 3/16$ mi. By the First (or Second) Derivative Test, this critical point corresponds to a local minimum, and by Theorem 4.5, this solitary local minimum is also the absolute minimum on the interval $[0, \infty)$. The minimum running speed is $v\left(\frac{3}{16}\right) = \frac{20\sqrt{\left(\frac{3}{16}\right)^2 + \frac{1}{16}}}{\frac{3}{16} + \frac{1}{3}} = \frac{60\sqrt{9 + 16}}{9 + 16} = 12$ mph.

4.4.60

a. Let x be the diameter of the smaller semicircle joining points A and B; then the other smaller semicircle has diameter $1 - x$. The area of a semicircle with diameter d is $\pi d^2/8$, so the area of the arbelos is given by

$$A(x) = \frac{\pi}{8}\left(1 - x^2 - (1 - x)^2\right) = \frac{\pi}{8}\left(2x - 2x^2\right) = \frac{\pi}{4}x(1 - x).$$

The quadratic function $x(1 - x)$ takes its maximum at $x = 1/2$, so the largest area is obtained when we position point B at the center of the larger semicircle.

b. Point B has distance $|x - 1/2|$ to the center of the larger semicircle, so the length l of the segment BD can be found using the Pythagorean theorem: $l^2 = \frac{1}{4} - \left(x - \frac{1}{2}\right)^2 = x(1-x)$, so $l = \sqrt{x(1-x)}$ and a circle with diameter l has area $\pi\left(\frac{l}{2}\right)^2 = \frac{\pi}{4}x(1-x)$, which is the area of the arbelos.

4.4.61

a. A point on the line $y = 3x + 4$ has the form $(x, 3x+4)$, which has distance L to the origin given by $L^2 = x^2 + (3x+4)^2 = 10x^2 + 24x + 16$. Because L is positive, it suffices to minimize L^2. The quadratic function $10x^2 + 24x + 16$ takes its minimum at $x = -24/20 = -6/5$, and the corresponding value of $y = 2/5$. Therefore the point closest to the origin on this line is $(-6/5, 2/5)$.

b. A point on the parabola $y = 1 - x^2$ has the form $(x, 1 - x^2)$, which has distance L to the point $(1,1)$ given by $L^2 = (x-1)^2 + \left(1 - (1 - x^2)\right)^2 = x^4 + x^2 - 2x + 1$. Because L is positive, it suffices to minimize L^2. The critical points of L^2 satisfy $\frac{dL^2}{dx} = 4x^3 + 2x - 2 = 2(2x^3 + x - 1) = 0$ This cubic equation has a unique root $x \approx 0.590$, so the point closest to $(1,1)$ on this parabola is approximately $(0.590, 0.652)$.

c. A point on the curve $y = \sqrt{x}$ has the form $(x, \sqrt{x})$, which has distance L to the point $(p,0)$ given by $L^2 = (x - p)^2 + \sqrt{x}^2 = x^2 + (1 - 2p)x + p^2$. Because L is positive, it suffices to minimize L^2 for $x \geq 0$. This quadratic function takes its minimum at $x = -(1 - 2p)/2 = p - 1/2$, so in case (i) the minimum occurs at the point $(p - 1/2, \sqrt{p - 1/2})$ and in case (ii) there are no critical points for $x > 0$, the function L^2 is increasing on $[0, \infty)$ so the minimum occurs at $(0, 0)$.

4.4.62

a. The length of the longest pole that can be carried around the corner is equal to the shortest length of a segment that joins the outer walls of the corridor while touching the inner corner (see figure). Using similar triangles, we can express this length in terms of the length x in the figure:

$$L(x) = \sqrt{x^2 + 4^2} + \frac{3}{x}\sqrt{x^2 + 4^2} = \left(1 + \frac{3}{x}\right)\sqrt{x^2 + 16}.$$

We wish to minimize this function for $x > 0$. The critical points of $L(x)$ satisfy

$$L'(x) = \left(1 + \frac{3}{x}\right)\frac{x}{\sqrt{x^2 + 16}} - \frac{3}{x^2}\sqrt{x^2 + 16} = 0$$

which simplifies to $(x^2 + 3x)x = 3(x^2 + 16)$ or $x^3 = 48$. This gives a unique critical point $x = \sqrt[3]{48}$ in the interval $(0, \infty)$. By the First (or Second) Derivative Test, this critical point corresponds to a local minimum, and by Theorem 4.5, this solitary local minimum is also the absolute minimum on the interval $(0, \infty)$. The length of the longest pole is therefore $L(\sqrt[3]{48}) \approx 9.866$ ft.

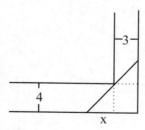

b. For this case we replace 4 with a and 3 with b in the objective function from part (a) above, so we need to minimize the function $L(x) = \left(1 + \frac{b}{x}\right)\sqrt{x^2 + a^2}$ for $x > 0$. The critical points of $L(x)$ satisfy

$$L'(x) = \left(1 + \frac{b}{x}\right)\frac{x}{\sqrt{x^2 + a^2}} - \frac{b}{x^2}\sqrt{x^2 + a^2} = 0$$

which simplifies to $(x^2 + bx)x = b(x^2 + a^2)$ or $x^3 = ba^2$. As above, this gives a unique critical point $x = \sqrt[3]{ba^2}$ in the interval $(0, \infty)$ which minimizes $L(x)$. The length of the longest pole is therefore

$$L(a^{\frac{2}{3}}b^{\frac{1}{3}}) = \left(1 + b^{\frac{2}{3}}a^{-\frac{2}{3}}\right)\sqrt{a^{\frac{4}{3}}b^{\frac{2}{3}} + a^2} = \left(1 + b^{\frac{2}{3}}a^{-\frac{2}{3}}\right)a^{\frac{2}{3}}\sqrt{a^{\frac{2}{3}} + b^{\frac{2}{3}}} = \left(a^{\frac{2}{3}} + b^{\frac{2}{3}}\right)^{\frac{3}{2}}.$$

c. As above, we need to minimize the length $L = y + z$ as shown in the figure for $x > 0$. Note that $c = 5\csc 60° = \frac{10}{\sqrt{3}}$ and by the law of cosines, $y^2 = x^2 + c^2 - 2cx\cos 120° = x^2 + cx + c^2$. By similar triangles $z/y = c/x$, so we have $L(x) = y + z = \left(1 + \frac{c}{x}\right)\sqrt{x^2 + cx + c^2}$. The critical points of $L(x)$ satisfy

$$L'(x) = \left(1 + \frac{c}{x}\right)\frac{2x + c}{2\sqrt{x^2 + cx + c^2}} - \frac{c}{x^2}\sqrt{x^2 + cx + c^2} = 0,$$

which simplifies to $(x^2 + cx)(2x + c) = 2c(x^2 + cx + c^2)$ or $2x^3 + cx^2 - c^2x - 2c^3 = (x - c)(2x^2 + 3cx + 2c^2) = 0$. The quadratic equation $2x^2 + 3cx + 2c^2 = 0$ has discriminant $-7c^2 < 0$, so $x = c$ is the only critical point in $(0, \infty)$. By the First (or Second) Derivative Test, this critical point corresponds to a local minimum, and by Theorem 4.5, this solitary local minimum is also the absolute minimum on the interval $(0, \infty)$. The length of the longest pole is therefore $L(c) = 2\sqrt{3}c = 20$ ft.

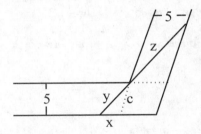

d. Imagine a pole in any position in this corridor, and form a right triangle by dropping a segment perpendicular to the floor from the highest point on the pole down to the height of the lowest point on the pole. The base of this triangle can be no longer than the maximum length for the two-dimensional corridor in part (b), and the height is at most 8, so the maximum length L is given by combining the result from part (b) with the Pythagorean theorem:

$$L = \sqrt{64 + \left(a^{\frac{2}{3}} + b^{\frac{2}{3}}\right)^3}.$$

4.4.63

a. We find $g(0) = 0$, $g(40) = 30$ and $g(60) = 25$ miles per gallon. The value at $v = 0$ is reasonable because when a car first starts moving it needs a lot of power from its engine, so the gas mileage is very low. The decline from 30 to 25 mi/gal as v increases from 40 mi/hr to 60 mi/hr reflects the fact that gas mileage tends to decrease at speeds over 55 mi/hr.

b. The quadratic function $g(v) = (85v - v^2)/60$ takes its maximum value at $v = 85/2 = 42.5$ mi/hr.

c. At speed v the amount of gas needed to drive one mile is $1/g(v)$ and the time it takes is $1/v$. Hence the cost of gas for one mile is $p/g(v)$ and the cost for the driver is w/v, and so the cost for L miles is $C(v) = Lp/g(v) + Lw/v$.

d. We have $C(v) = 400\left(\frac{4}{g(v)} + \frac{20}{v}\right) = 1600\left(\frac{1}{g(v)} + \frac{5}{v}\right)$. The critical points of $C(v)$ satisfy $\frac{g'(v)}{g(v)^2} + \frac{5}{v^2} = 0$, which simplifies to $v^2g'(v) + 5g(v)^2 = 0$. Substituting the formula for $g(v)$ above and using $g'(v) = (85 - 2v)/60$, we can factor out v^2 and reduce to the quadratic equation $v^2 - 194v + 8245 = 0$, which has roots $v \approx 62.883, 131.117$. The First (or Second) Derivative Test shows that $C(v)$ has a local minimum at $v \approx 62.9$, which is the unique critical point for $0 \leq v \leq 131$. Therefore the cost is minimized at this value of v.

e. Because L is a constant factor in the cost function $C(v)$, changing L will not change the critical points of $C(v)$.

f. The critical points of $C(v)$ now satisfy the equation $\frac{4.2g'(v)}{g(v)^2} + \frac{20}{v^2} = 0$, which simplifies to $4.2v^2 g'(v) + 20g(v)^2 = 0$. As above, substituting the formula for $g(v)$ above and using $g'(v) = (85 - 2v)/60$, we can factor out v^2 and reduce to the quadratic equation $v^2 - 195.2v + 8296 = 0$, which has roots $v \approx 62.532, 132.668$. As in part (d), the minimum cost occurs for $v \approx 62.532$, slightly less than the speed in part (d).

g. The critical points of $C(v)$ now satisfy the equation $\frac{4g'(v)}{g(v)^2} + \frac{15}{v^2} = 0$, which simplifies to $4v^2 g'(v) + 15g(v)^2 = 0$. As above, substituting the formula for $g(v)$ above and using $g'(v) = (85 - 2v)/60$, we can factor out v^2 and reduce to the quadratic equation $v^2 - 202v + 8585 = 0$, which has roots $v \approx 60.800, 141.200$. As in part (d), the minimum cost occurs for $v \approx 60.8$, less than the speed in part (d).

4.4.64

a. The dog runs distance $z - y$ and swims distance $\sqrt{x^2 + y^2}$. Using time = distance/speed, we see that the total time it takes the dog to get to the tennis ball is $T(y) = \frac{z-y}{r} + \frac{\sqrt{x^2+y^2}}{s}$.

b. The critical points of $T(y)$ satisfy $T'(y) = -\frac{1}{r} + \frac{y}{s\sqrt{x^2+y^2}} = 0$, which simplifies to $\frac{\sqrt{x^2+y^2}}{y} = \frac{r}{s}$ so $\left(\frac{r^2}{s^2} - 1\right) y^2 = x^2$, so $y = \frac{x}{\sqrt{r/s+1}\sqrt{r/s-1}}$. The First (or Second) Derivative Test shows that a local minimum occurs for this value of y, which by Theorem 4.5 must give the absolute minimum of $T(y)$ for $y > 0$. If $y \le z$ then $T(y)$ is minimized for this value of y; otherwise, the minimum occurs at $y = z$ (all swimming).

c. The ratio is $\frac{y}{x} = \frac{1}{\sqrt{8+1}\sqrt{8-1}} = \frac{1}{\sqrt{63}}$.

d. Elvis's optimal ratio is $\frac{y}{x} \approx \frac{1}{\sqrt{7.033+1}\sqrt{7.033-1}} \approx 0.144$, so Elvis appears to know calculus!

4.4.65

a. Let x, $d - x$ be the distances from the point where the rope meets the ground to the poles of height m, n respectively. Then the rope has length $L(x) = \sqrt{x^2 + m^2} + \sqrt{(d-x)^2 + n^2}$. We wish to minimize this function for $0 \le x \le d$. The critical points of $L(x)$ satisfy $L'(x) = \frac{x}{\sqrt{x^2+m^2}} - \frac{d-x}{\sqrt{(d-x)^2+n^2}} = 0$, which is equivalent to $\frac{x}{\sqrt{x^2+m^2}} = \frac{d-x}{\sqrt{(d-x)^2+n^2}}$, or in terms of the angles θ_1 and θ_2 in the figure, $\sec\theta_1 = \sec\theta_2$ and therefore $\theta_1 = \theta_2$. Observe that $L'(0) < 0$ and $L'(d) > 0$, so the minimum value of $L(x)$ must occur at some $x \in (0, d)$. There must be exactly one critical point, because as x ranges from 0 to d, θ_1 decreases and θ_2 increases, and so $\theta_1 = \theta_2$ can occur for at most one value of x.

b. Because the speed of light is constant, travel time is minimized when distance is minimized, which we saw in part (a) occurs when $\theta_1 = \theta_2$.

4.4.66

Let x, d, m, n be the distances labeled in the figure below. Then using time = distance/speed, we see that the time for light to travel from A to B is $T(x) = \frac{\sqrt{x^2+m^2}}{v_1} + \frac{\sqrt{(d-x)^2+n^2}}{v_2}$. We wish to minimize this function for $0 \le x \le d$. The critical points of $T(x)$ satisfy $T'(x) = \frac{x}{v_1\sqrt{x^2+m^2}} - \frac{d-x}{v_2\sqrt{(d-x)^2+n^2}} = 0$, which is equivalent to $\frac{x}{v_1\sqrt{x^2+m^2}} = \frac{d-x}{v_2\sqrt{(d-x)^2+n^2}}$, or in terms of the angles θ_1 and θ_2 in the figure, $\frac{\sin\theta_1}{v_1} = \frac{\sin\theta_2}{v_2}$ (Snell's Law). Observe that $T'(0) < 0$ and $T'(d) > 0$, so the minimum value of $T(x)$ must occur at some $x \in (0, d)$. There must be exactly one critical point, because as x ranges from 0 to d, $\sin\theta_1$ decreases and $\sin\theta_2$ increases, so Snell's Law can hold for at most one value of x.

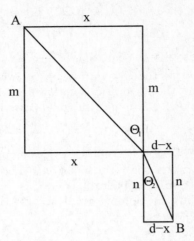

4.4.67 Let the angle of the cuts with the horizontal be ϕ_1 and ϕ_2, where $\phi_1 + \phi_2 = \theta$. The volume of the notch is proportional to $\tan\phi_1 + \tan\phi_2 = \tan\phi_1 + \tan(\theta - \phi_1)$, so it suffices to minimize the objective function $V(\phi_1) = \tan\phi_1 + \tan(\theta - \phi_1)$ for $0 \le \phi_1 \le \theta$. The critical points of $V(\phi_1)$ satisfy $\sec^2\phi_1 - \sec^2(\theta - \phi_1) = 0$, which is equivalent to the condition $\cos\phi_1 = \cos(\theta - \phi_1)$. This is satisfied if $\phi_1 = \theta - \phi_1$ which gives $\phi_1 = \theta/2$. There are no other solutions in $(0, \theta)$, because $\cos\phi_1$ is decreasing and $\cos(\theta - \phi_1)$ is increasing on $(0, \theta)$ and therefore can intersect at most once. So the only critical point occurs when $\phi_1 = \phi_2 = \theta/2$, and the First Derivative Test shows that this critical point is a local minimum; by Theorem 4.5, this must be the absolute minimum on $[0, \theta]$.

4.4.68

a. Gliding is more efficient if $S > 0$; substituting $m = 200$ in the equation for $S(m, \theta)$ gives

$$S > 0 \iff 8.46 \cdot 200^{2/3} - 1.36 \cdot 200 \tan\theta > 0 \iff \tan\theta < 1.064$$

so $\theta < \tan^{-1} 1.064 \approx 46.768°$.

b. We solve $S(m, \theta) = 0$ for θ, which gives $\tan\theta \approx 6.22 m^{-1/3}$, so $\theta = g(m) \approx \tan^{-1}(6.22 m^{-1/3})$. This is a decreasing function of body mass.

c. Because $\theta = g(m)$ is a decreasing function of body mass, larger gliders have a smaller selection of glide angles for which gliding is more efficient than walking.

d.

Gliding is more efficient when $S(m, 25°) > 0$, which is true if and only if $8.46 m^{2/3} > 1.36 m \tan 25°$, which is true if and only if $m^{1/3} < \frac{8.46}{1.36 \tan 25°} \approx 13.34$, which again is true if and only if $m < 2374$ g.

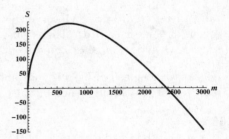

e. We have $\frac{d}{dm} S(m, \theta) = 5.64 m^{-1/3} - 1.36 \tan\theta$, which is 0 for $m^* \approx 71.32 \cot^3\theta$. For $\theta = 25°$ this gives $m^* \approx 703$ g. The First Derivative Test shows that m^* is a local maximum, which by Theorem 4.5 is the absolute maximum for $m \ge 0$.

f. Because $\cot\theta$ is a decreasing function on $0 < \theta < 90°$, we see that m^* decreases with increasing θ.

g. From part (b) we have $g(10^6) \approx \tan^{-1}(6.22 m^{-1/3}) \approx 3.56°$, so any angle $\theta < 3.56°$.

4.4.69 Let x and y be the lengths of the sides of the pen, with y the side parallel to the barn. The diagonal has length $\sqrt{x^2 + y^2}$, by the Pythagorean theorem. Therefore the constraint is $2x + y + \sqrt{x^2 + y^2} = 200$, which we rewrite as $2x + y = 200 - \sqrt{x^2 + y^2}$. Square both sides to obtain $4x^2 + 4xy + y^2 = 40{,}000 - 400\sqrt{x^2 + y^2} + x^2 + y^2$, which simplifies to $3x^2 + 4xy = 40{,}000 - 400\sqrt{x^2 + y^2}$. Now substitute $\sqrt{x^2 + y^2} = 200 - 2x - y$ in this equation and simplify to obtain $(3x - 200)(x - 200) = 4(100 - x)y$ so $y = \frac{(3x-200)(x-200)}{4(100-x)}$. The objective function to be maximized is the area of the pen, $A = xy$. Using the expression above for y in terms of x, we have $A = xy = \frac{x(3x-200)(x-200)}{4(100-x)} = -\frac{1}{4} \cdot \frac{x(3x-200)(x-200)}{(x-100)}$. The length x must be at least 0, and because the diagonal is at least as long as x, we must have $3x \le 200$; so x cannot exceed $200/3$. Therefore we need to maximize the function $A(x)$ defined above for $0 \le x \le 200/3$. We have $A'(x) = -\frac{1}{4} \cdot \left(\frac{(3x-200)(x-200)}{(x-100)} + \frac{x \cdot 3(x-200)}{(x-100)} + \frac{x(3x-200)}{(x-100)} - \frac{x(3x-200)(x-200)}{(x-100)^2} \right) = \left(\frac{1}{x} + \frac{3}{3x-200} + \frac{1}{x-200} - \frac{1}{x-100} \right) A(x)$. Because $A(x) > 0$ for $0 < x < 200/3$, the critical points of the objective function satisfy $\frac{1}{x} + \frac{3}{3x-200} + \frac{1}{x-200} = \frac{1}{x-100}$ which when simplified gives the equation $6x^3 - 1700x^2 + 160{,}000x - 4{,}000{,}000 = 0$. Using a numerical solver, we find that this equation has exactly one solution in the interval $(0, 200/3)$, which is $x \approx 38.81$. To find the absolute maximum of A, we check the endpoints of $[0, 200/3]$ and the critical point $x \approx 38.814$. We have $A(0) = A(200/3) = 0$, so the absolute maximum occurs when $x \approx 38.814$ m; using the formula for y in terms of x above gives $y \approx 55.030$ m.

4.4.70

a. $f'(x) = 2(x - 1) + 2(x - 5) = 4x - 12$. This is zero for $x = 12/4 = 3$. Because $f'(x) < 0$ for $x < 3$ and $f'(x) > 0$ for $x > 3$, we have a minimum at $x = 3$.

b. $f'(x) = 2(x - a) + 2(x - b) = 4x - (2a + 2b)$. This is zero for $x = \frac{2a+2b}{4} = \frac{a+b}{2}$. Because $f'(x) < 0$ for $x < (a+b)/2$ and $f'(x) > 0$ for $x > (a+b)/2$, we have a minimum at $x = (a+b)/2$.

c. $f'(x) = 2\sum_{k=1}^{n}(x - a_k) = 2nx - 2\sum_{k=1}^{n} a_k$. This is zero when $x = \frac{\sum_{k=1}^{n} a_k}{n}$. An application of the First Derivative Test shows that this value of x yields a minimum.

4.5 Linear Approximation and Differentials

4.5.1

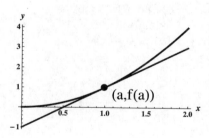

4.5.2 The derivative of a function is 0 at a local maximum, so the linear approximation is a horizontal line.

4.5.3 If f is differentiable at the point, then near that point, f is approximately linear, so the function nearly coincides with the tangent line at that point.

4.5.4 The change in $y = f(x)$ may be approximated by the formula $\Delta y \approx f'(x)\Delta x$.

4.5.5 The relationship is given by $dy = f'(x)dx$, which is the linear approximation of the change Δy in $y = f(x)$ corresponding to a change dx in x.

4.5.6 The differential dy is precisely the change in the linear approximation to f, which is an approximation of the change in f for small changes dx in x.

4.5.7 The approximate average speed is $L(-1) = 60 - (-1) = 61$ miles per hour. The exact speed is $\frac{3600}{59}$ miles per hour which is about 61.02 miles per hour.

4.5.8 The approximate average speed is $L(3) = 60 - (3) = 57$ miles per hour. The exact speed is $\frac{3600}{63}$ miles per hour which is about 57.14 miles per hour.

4.5.9 Let $T(x) = \frac{60D}{60+x}$. Then $T'(x) = -\frac{60D}{(60+x)^2}$, so $T'(0) = -\frac{D}{60}$. The linear approximation is given by $L(x) = T(0) - \frac{D}{60}(x - 0)$, or $L(x) = D\left(1 - \frac{x}{60}\right)$.

4.5.10 With $D = 45$, we have $T(2) \approx L(2) = 45(1 - \frac{2}{60}) = 45 - (3/2) = 43.5$ minutes. The exact time required is $T(2) = \frac{60 \cdot 45}{60+2} \approx 43.55$ minutes.

4.5.11 With $D = 80$, we have $T(-3) \approx L(-3) = 80(1 - \frac{-3}{60}) = 80 + 4 = 84$ minutes. The exact time required is $T(-3) = \frac{60 \cdot 80}{60-3} \approx 84.211$ minutes.

4.5.12 With $D = 93$, we have $T(3) \approx L(3) = 93(1 - \frac{3}{60}) = 93 - \frac{93}{20} = 88.35$ minutes. The exact time required is $T(3) = \frac{60 \cdot 93}{60+3} \approx 88.57$ minutes.

4.5.13

a. Note that $f(a) = f(2) = 8$ and $f'(a) = -2a = -4$, so the linear approximation has equation

$$y = L(x) = f(a) + f'(a)(x-a) = 8 + (-4)(x-2) = -4x + 16.$$

c. We have $f(2.1) \approx L(2.1) = 7.6$.

d. The percentage error is $100 \cdot \frac{|7.6-7.59|}{7.59} \approx 0.13\%$.

b.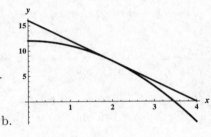

4.5.14

a. Note that $f(\pi/4) = \sin(\pi/4) = \sqrt{2}/2$ and $f'(a) = \cos a = \sqrt{2}/2$, so the linear approximation has equation $y = L(x) = f(a) + f'(a)(x - a) = \sin\frac{\pi}{4} + \frac{\sqrt{2}}{2}(x - \frac{\pi}{4}) = \frac{\sqrt{2}}{2}\left(x + 1 - \frac{\pi}{4}\right)$.

c. We have $f(0.75) \approx L(0.75) \approx 0.68$.

d. The percentage error is $100 \cdot \frac{\left|\frac{\sqrt{2}}{2}(1.75 - \frac{\pi}{4}) - \sin 0.75\right|}{\sin 0.75} \approx 0.064\%$.

b.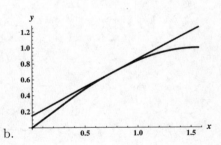

4.5.15

a. Note that $f(a) = f(0) = \ln 1 = 0$ and $f'(a) = 1/(1 + a) = 1$, so the linear approximation has equation

$$y = L(x) = f(a) + f'(a)(x - a) = x.$$

c. We have $f(0.9) \approx L(0.9) = 0.9$.

d. The percentage error is $100 \cdot \frac{|0.9 - \ln 1.9|}{|\ln 1.9|} \approx 40\%$.

b.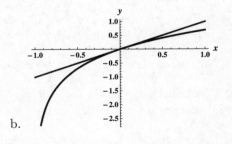

4.5.16

a. Note that $f(a) = a/(a+1) = 1/2$ and $f'(a) = 1/(1+a)^2 = 1/4$, so the linear approximation has equation $y = L(x) = f(a) + f'(a)(x-a) = \frac{1}{2} + \frac{1}{4}(x-1) = \frac{1}{4}(x+1)$.

c. We have $f(1.1) \approx L(1.1) = 0.525$.

d. The percentage error is $100 \cdot \frac{|0.525 - (1.1/2.1)|}{1.1/2.1} \approx 0.23\%$.

b.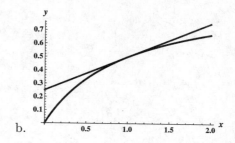

4.5.17

a. Note that $f(a) = f(0) = \cos 0 = 1$ and $f'(a) = -\sin a = 0$, so the linear approximation has equation

$$y = L(x) = f(a) + f'(a)(x-a) = 1.$$

c. We have $f(-0.01) \approx L(-0.01) = 1$.

d. The percentage error is $100 \cdot \frac{|1 - \cos(-0.01)|}{\cos(-0.01)} \approx 0.005\%$.

b.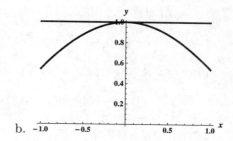

4.5.18

a. Note that $f(a) = e^a = e^0 = 1$ and $f'(a) = e^a = 1$, so the linear approximation has equation

$$y = L(x) = f(a) + f'(a)(x-a) = 1 + x.$$

c. We have $f(0.05) \approx L(0.05) = 1.05$.

d. The percentage error is $100 \cdot \frac{|1.05 - e^{0.05}|}{e^{0.05}} \approx 0.12\%$.

b.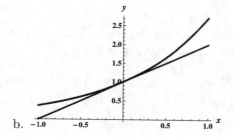

4.5.19

a. Note that $f(a) = 8^{-1/3} = 1/2$ and $f'(a) = (-1/3)(8)^{-4/3} = -1/48$, so the linear approximation has equation

$$y = L(x) = f(a) + f'(a)(x-a) = \frac{1}{2} + \frac{-1}{48}x.$$

c. We have $f(-0.1) \approx L(-0.1) \approx .50208333$

d. The percentage error is $100 \cdot \frac{|7.9^{-1/3} - .50208333|}{(7.9)^{-1/3}} \approx 0.003\%$.

b.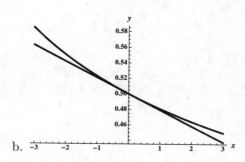

4.5.20

a. Note that $f(a) = \sqrt[4]{81} = 3$ and $f'(a) = \frac{1}{4}(81)^{-3/4} = \frac{1}{108}$, so the linear approximation has equation

$$y = L(x) = f(a) + f'(a)(x-a) = 3 + \frac{1}{108}(x-81).$$

c. We have $f(85) \approx L(85) = 3 + \frac{4}{108} = 3 + \frac{1}{27} \approx 3.04.$

d. The percentage error is $100 \cdot \frac{|3.04 - \sqrt[4]{85}|}{\sqrt[4]{85}} \approx 0.12\%.$

b.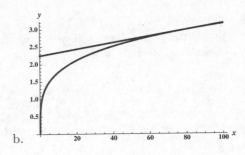

4.5.21 Let $f(x) = 1/x$, $a = 200$. Then $f(a) = 0.005$ and $f'(a) = -1/a^2 = -0.000025$, so the linear approximation to f near $a = 200$ is $L(x) = f(a) + f'(a)(x-a) = 0.005 - 0.000025(x-200)$. Therefore $\frac{1}{203} = f(203) \approx L(203) = .004925.$

4.5.22 Let $f(x) = \tan x$, $a = 0$. Then $f(a) = 0$ and $f'(a) = \sec^2 a = 1$, so the linear approximation to f near $a = 0$ is $L(x) = f(a) + f'(a)(x-a) = x$. Therefore $\tan 3° = \tan \frac{\pi}{60} = f\left(\frac{\pi}{60}\right) \approx L\left(\frac{\pi}{60}\right) \approx 0.0524$. Note that we must convert 3° to radians before applying the linear approximation formula.

4.5.23 Let $f(x) = \sqrt{x}$, $a = 144$. Then $f(a) = 12$ and $f'(a) = 1/(2\sqrt{a}) = 1/24$, so the linear approximation to f near $a = 144$ is $L(x) = f(a) + f'(a)(x-a) = 12 + \frac{1}{24}(x-144)$. Therefore $\sqrt{146} = f(146) \approx L(146) = \frac{145}{12}.$

4.5.24 Let $f(x) = x^{1/3}$, $a = 64$. Then $f(a) = 4$ and $f'(a) = (1/3)a^{-2/3} = 1/48$, so the linear approximation to f near $a = 144$ is $L(x) = f(a) + f'(a)(x-a) = 4 + \frac{1}{48}(x-64)$. Therefore $\sqrt[3]{65} = f(65) \approx L(65) = 4\frac{1}{48}.$

4.5.25 Let $f(x) = \ln x$, $a = 1$. Then $f(a) = 0$ and $f'(a) = 1/a = 1$, so the linear approximation to f near $a = 1$ is $L(x) = f(a) + f'(a)(x-a) = x - 1$. Therefore $\ln(1.05) = f(1.05) \approx L(1.05) = .05.$

4.5.26 Let $f(x) = \sqrt{x}$, $a = 0.16$ (note that $5/29 \approx 0.17$). Then $f(a) = 0.4$ and $f'(a) = 1/(2\sqrt{a}) = 1.25$, so the linear approximation to f near $a = 0.16$ is $L(x) = f(a) + f'(a)(x-a) = 0.4 + 1.25(x-0.16)$. Therefore $\sqrt{5/29} = f(5/29) \approx L(5/29) \approx 0.416.$

4.5.27 Let $f(x) = e^x$, $a = 0$. Then $f(a) = 1$ and $f'(a) = e^a = 1$, so the linear approximation to f near $a = 0$ is $L(x) = f(a) + f'(a)(x-a) = 1 + x$. Therefore $e^{0.06} = f(0.06) \approx L(0.06) \approx 1.060.$

4.5.28 Let $f(x) = 1/\sqrt{x}$, $a = 121$. Then $f(a) = 1/11$ and $f'(a) = -1/(2a^{3/2}) = -1/2662$, so the linear approximation to f near $a = 121$ is $L(x) = f(a) + f'(a)(x-a) = \frac{1}{11} - \frac{1}{2662}(x-121)$. Therefore $\frac{1}{\sqrt{119}} = f(119) \approx L(119) \approx 0.0917.$

4.5.29 Let $f(x) = 1/\sqrt[3]{x}$, $a = 512$. Then $f(a) = 1/8$ and $f'(a) = -1/(3a^{4/3}) = -1/12,288$, so the linear approximation to f near $a = 512$ is $L(x) = f(a) + f'(a)(x-a) = \frac{1}{8} - \frac{1}{12,288}(x-512)$. Therefore $\frac{1}{\sqrt[3]{510}} = f(510) \approx L(510) = \frac{769}{6144} \approx 0.1252.$

4.5.30 Let $f(x) = \cos x$, $a = \pi/6$ ($= 30°$). Then $f(a) = \sqrt{3}/2$ and $f'(a) = -\sin a = -1/2$, so the linear approximation to f near $a = 0$ is $L(x) = f(a) + f'(a)(x-a) = \frac{\sqrt{3}}{2} - \frac{1}{2}\left(x - \frac{\pi}{6}\right)$. Therefore $\cos 31° = \cos \frac{31\pi}{180} = f\left(\frac{31\pi}{180}\right) \approx L\left(\frac{31\pi}{180}\right) \approx 0.857$. Note that we must convert 31° to radians before applying the linear approximation formula.

4.5.31

a. With $f(x) = \frac{2}{x}$ and $a = 1$, we have $f(a) = 2$ and $f'(a) = -\frac{2}{a^2} = -2$. Thus the linear approximation to $f(x)$ at $x = 1$ is $L(x) = f(1) + f'(1)(x-1) = 2 + -2(x-1) = -2x + 4.$

b. A plot of f with L in gray:

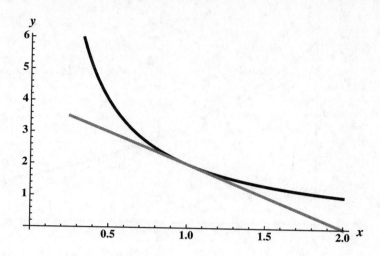

c. The linear approximation in part (b) appears to be an underestimate everywhere, because it lies below the graph of f.

d. Because $f'(x) = -\frac{2}{x^2}$, we have $f''(x) = \frac{4}{x^3}$, so that $f''(1) > 0$, and f is concave up at $x = 1$. This is consistent with L being an underestimate near $x = 1$.

4.5.32

a. With $f(x) = 5 - x^2$ and $a = 2$, we have $f(a) = 1$ and $f'(a) = -2a = -4$. Thus the linear approximation to f at $x = 2$ is $L(x) = f(2) + f'(2)(x-2) = 1 + -4(x-2) = -4x + 9$.

b. A plot of f with L in gray:

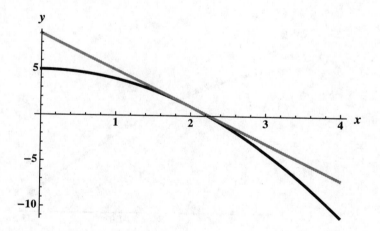

c. The linear approximation in part (b) appears to be an overestimate everywhere, because it lies above the graph of f

d. Because $f'(x) = -2x$, we have $f''(x) = -2$, so that $f''(x) < 0$ for all values of x and f is therefore concave down everywhere. This is consistent with L being an overestimate.

4.5.33

a. With $f(x) = e^{-x}$ and $a = \ln 2$, we have $f(a) = \frac{1}{2}$ and $f'(a) = -e^{-a} = -\frac{1}{2}$. Thus the linear approximation to f at $x = \ln 2$ is $L(x) = f(\ln 2) + f'(\ln 2)(x - \ln 2) = \frac{1}{2} + -\frac{1}{2}(x - \ln 2) = -\frac{1}{2}x + \frac{1}{2}(1 + \ln 2)$.

b. A plot of f with L in gray:

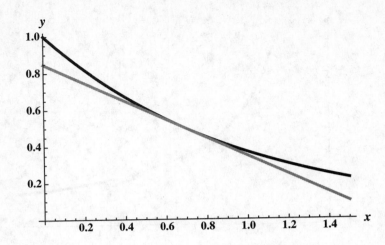

c. The linear approximation in part (b) appears to be an underestimate everywhere, because it lies below the graph of f

d. Because $f'(x) = -e^{-x}$, we have $f''(x) = e^{-x}$, so that $f''(x) > 0$ for all values of x and f is therefore concave up everywhere. This is consistent with L being an underestimate.

4.5.34

a. With $f(x) = \sqrt{2}\cos x$ and $a = \frac{\pi}{4}$, we have $f(a) = \sqrt{2} \cdot \frac{\sqrt{2}}{2} = 1$ and $f'(a) = -\sqrt{2}\sin(\pi/4) = -1$. Thus the linear approximation to f at $x = a$ is $L(x) = f(a) + f'(a)(x - a) = 1 + -1\left(x - \frac{\pi}{4}\right) = -x + 1 + \frac{\pi}{4}$.

b. A plot of f with L in gray:

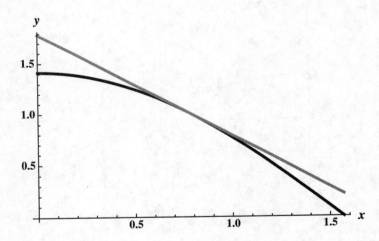

c. The linear approximation in part (b) appears to be an overestimate everywhere, because it lies above the graph of f

d. Because $f'(x) = -\sqrt{2}\sin x$, we have $f''(x) = -\sqrt{2}\cos x$, so that $f''(a) < 0$ for x near $a = \frac{\pi}{4}$ and f is therefore concave down near $x = a$. This is consistent with L being an overestimate.

4.5.35 Note that $V'(r) = 4\pi r^2$, so $\Delta V \approx V'(a)\Delta r = 4\pi a^2 \Delta r$. Substituting $a = 5$ and $\Delta r = 0.1$ gives $\Delta V \approx 4\pi \cdot 25 \cdot 0.1 = 10\pi \approx 31.416$ ft^3.

4.5.36 Note that $P'(z) = -100e^{-z/10}$, so $\Delta P \approx P'(a)\Delta z = -100e^{-a/10}\Delta z$. Substituting $a = 2$ and $\Delta z = 0.01$ gives $\Delta P \approx -100e^{-0.2} \cdot 0.01 = -0.819$.

4.5.37 Note that V is a linear function of h with $V'(h) = \pi r^2 = 400\pi$, so $\Delta V = V'(a)\Delta r = 400\pi\Delta r$. Substituting $\Delta r = -0.1$ gives $\Delta V = -40\pi \approx -125.664$ cm^3.

4.5.38 Note that $V'(r) = 2\pi rh/3 = 8\pi r/3$, so $\Delta V \approx V'(a)\Delta h = \frac{8\pi a}{3}\Delta h$. Substituting $a = 3$ and $\Delta h = 0.05$ gives $\Delta V \approx 8\pi \cdot (0.05) = 0.4\pi \approx 1.257$ cm^3.

4.5.39 Note that $S'(r) = \pi\sqrt{r^2+h^2} + \pi r \cdot \frac{r}{\sqrt{r^2+h^2}} = \pi\frac{2r^2+h^2}{\sqrt{r^2+h^2}}$, so $\Delta S \approx S'(a)\Delta r = \pi\frac{2a^2+h^2}{\sqrt{a^2+h^2}}\Delta r$. Substituting $h = 6$, $a = 10$ and $\Delta r = -0.1$ gives $\Delta S \approx \pi\frac{236}{\sqrt{136}}(-0.1) = \frac{-59\pi}{5\sqrt{34}} \approx -6.358$ m^2.

4.5.40 Note that $F'(r) = -0.02r^{-3}$, so $\Delta F \approx F'(a)\Delta r = -0.02a^{-3}\Delta r$. Substituting $a = 20$ and $\Delta r = 1$ gives $\Delta F \approx -0.02 \cdot 20^{-3} \cdot 1 = -2.5 \cdot 10^{-6}$.

4.5.41 We have $f'(x) = 2$, so $dy = 2\,dx$.

4.5.42 We have $f'(x) = 2\sin x \cos x$, so $dy = 2\sin x \cos x\,dx$.

4.5.43 We have $f'(x) = -3/x^4$, so $dy = -\frac{3}{x^4}\,dx$.

4.5.44 We have $f'(x) = 2e^{2x}$, so $dy = 2e^{2x}\,dx$.

4.5.45 We have $f'(x) = a\sin x$, so $dy = a\sin x\,dx$.

4.5.46 We have $f'(x) = \frac{(4-x)\cdot 1 - (4+x)\cdot(-1)}{(4-x)^2} = \frac{8}{(x-4)^2}$, so $dy = \frac{8}{(x-4)^2}\,dx$.

4.5.47 We have $f'(x) = 9x^2 - 4$, so $dy = (9x^2 - 4)\,dx$.

4.5.48 We have $f'(x) = 1/\sqrt{1-x^2}$, so $dy = \frac{1}{\sqrt{1-x^2}}\,dx$.

4.5.49 We have $f'(x) = \sec^2 x$, so $dy = \sec^2 x\,dx$.

4.5.50 We have $f'(x) = -1/(1-x) = 1/(x-1)$, so $dy = \frac{1}{x-1}\,dx$.

4.5.51

a. True. Note that $f(0) = 0$ and $f'(0) = 0$, so the linear approximation at 0 is in fact $L(x) = 0$.

b. False. The function $f(x) = |x|$ is not differentiable at $x = 0$, so there is no good linear approximation at 0.

c. True. For linear functions, the linear approximation at any point and the function are equal.

d. True. Note that $f'(x) = \frac{1}{x}$, so that $f''(x) = \frac{-1}{x^2}$, and $f''(e) < 0$, so f is concave down near $x = e$. Thus L is an overestimate of f.

4.5.52 We have $L(x) = f(5) + f'(5)(x - 5) = 10 - 2(x - 5)$. So $f(5.1) \approx L(5.1) = 10 - 2(.1) = 9.8$.

4.5.53 We have $L(x) = f(4) + f'(4)(x-4) = 3 + 2(x-4)$. So $f(3.85) \approx L(3.85) = 3 + 2(3.85 - 4) = 3 - .3 = 2.7$.

4.5.54 Note that $f(a) = \tan 0 = 0$ and $f'(a) = \sec^2 0 = 1$, so the linear approximation has equation $y = L(x) = f(a) + f'(a)(x - a) = x$.

b. The linear approximation to $\tan 3°$ is $\tan 3° = \tan\frac{\pi}{60} \approx L\left(\frac{\pi}{60}\right) = \frac{\pi}{60} \approx 0.052$ Note that we must convert $3°$ to radians before applying the linear approximation formula.

c. The percentage error is $100 \cdot \frac{\left|\frac{\pi}{60} - \tan\frac{\pi}{60}\right|}{\frac{\pi}{60}} \approx 0.091\%$.

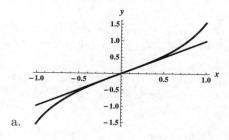

a.

4.5.55 Note that $f(a) = f(0) = 1$ and $f'(a) = -1/(1+a)^2 = -1$, so the linear approximation has equation $y = L(x) = f(a) + f'(a)(x - a) = 1 - x$.

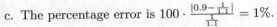

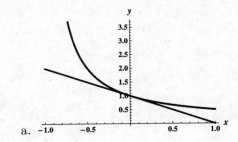

    b. The linear approximation to $1/1.1$ is $\frac{1}{1.1} \approx$ $L(0.1) = 0.9$.

    c. The percentage error is $100 \cdot \frac{|0.9 - \frac{1}{1.1}|}{\frac{1}{1.1}} = 1\%$.

a.

4.5.56 Note that $f(a) = \cos(\pi/4) = \sqrt{2}/2$ and $f'(a) = -\sin(\pi/4) = -\sqrt{2}/2$, so the linear approximation has equation $y = L(x) = f(a) + f'(a)(x - a) = \frac{\sqrt{2}}{2} - \frac{\sqrt{2}}{2}\left(x - \frac{\pi}{4}\right) = \frac{\sqrt{2}}{2}\left(1 + \frac{\pi}{4} - x\right)$.

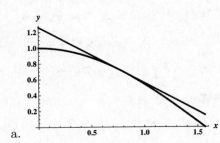

    b. The linear approximation to $\cos(0.8)$ is $\cos(0.8) \approx$ $L(0.8) = \frac{\sqrt{2}}{2}\left(0.2 + \frac{\pi}{4}\right) \approx 0.697$.

    c. The percentage error is $100 \cdot \frac{\left|\frac{\sqrt{2}}{2}\left(0.2 + \frac{\pi}{4}\right) - \cos(0.8)\right|}{\cos(0.8)} \approx$ 0.011%.

a.

4.5.57 Note that $f(a) = f(0) = 1$ and $f'(a) = -e^{-a} = -1$, so the linear approximation has equation $y = L(x) = f(a) + f'(a)(x - a) = 1 - x$.

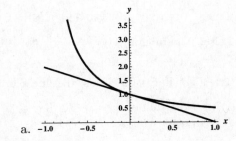

    b. The linear approximation to $e^{-0.03}$ is $e^{-0.03} \approx$ $L(0.03) = 0.97$.

    c. The percentage error is $100 \cdot \frac{|0.97 - e^{-0.03}|}{e^{-0.03}} \approx 0.046\%$.

a.

4.5.58

    a. We have $P = T/V$ with V held constant, which is a linear function of T. Hence $\Delta P = \frac{\Delta T}{V} = \frac{0.05}{V}$. Because this is greater than 0, the pressure increases.

    b. If T is held constant then $dP = -(T/V^2)dV$, and the approximate change in pressure is $\Delta P \approx dP = -0.1\frac{T}{V^2} < 0$, so the pressure decreases.

    c. We have $T = PV$ with P held constant, which is a linear function of V. Hence $\Delta T = P\Delta V = 0.1P > 0$, so the temperature increases.

4.5.59 $E(x) = |L(x) - s(x)| = \left|60 - x - \frac{3600}{60 - x}\right|$. A graph is shown below, for x from -7.26 to 8.26.

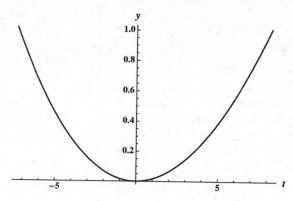

$E(x) \leq 1$ when $-7.26 \leq x \leq 8.26$, which corresponds to driving times for 1 mi from about 53 s to 68 s. Therefore, $L(x)$ gives approximations to $s(x)$ that are within 1 mi/hr of the true value when you drive 1 mile in t seconds, where $53 < t < 68$.

4.5.60 Because $T = \frac{D}{\text{speed}}$, we have $T = \frac{D}{60+x}$ hours which is $\frac{60D}{60+x}$ minutes.

4.5.61 Note that $f(a) = f(8) = 2$ and $f'(a) = (1/3)a^{-2/3} = 1/12$, so the linear approximation has equation $y = L(x) = f(a) + f'(a)(x - a) = 2 + \frac{1}{12}(x - 8) = \frac{x}{12} + \frac{4}{3}$.

x	Linear approx	Exact value	Percent error
8.1	$2.008\overline{3}$	2.00829885	1.717×10^{-3}
8.01	$2.0008\overline{3}$	2.000832986	1.734×10^{-5}
8.001	$2.00008\overline{3}$	2.00008333	1.736×10^{-7}
8.0001	2.0000083	2.00000833	1.736×10^{-9}
7.9999	1.9999916	1.999991667	1.736×10^{-9}
7.999	1.999916	1.999916663	1.736×10^{-7}
7.99	1.99916	1.999166319	1.738×10^{-5}
7.9	1.9916	1.991631701	1.756×10^{-3}

The percentage errors become extremely small as x approaches 8 In fact, each time we decrease Δx by a factor of 10, the percentage error decreases by a factor of 100.

4.5.62 Note that $f(a) = f(0) = 1$ and $f'(a) = -1(1 + a)^2 = -1$, so the linear approximation has equation $y = L(x) = f(a) + f'(a)(x - a) = 1 - x$.

x	Linear approx	Exact value	Percent error
0.1	0.9	$0.\overline{90}$	1
0.01	0.99	$0.\overline{9900}$	1×10^{-2}
0.001	$0.9\overline{99}$	$0.\overline{999000}$	1×10^{-4}
0.0001	0.9999	$0.\overline{99990000}$	1×10^{-6}
-0.0001	1.0001	$1.\overline{0001}$	1×10^{-6}
-0.001	1.001	$1.\overline{001}$	1×10^{-4}
-0.01	1.01	$1.\overline{01}$	1×10^{-2}
$-.1$	1.1	$1.\overline{1}$	1

The percentage errors become extremely small as x approaches 0. In fact, each time we decrease Δx by a factor of 10, the percentage error decreases by a factor of 100.

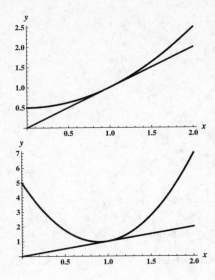

a. The linear approximation near $x = 1$ is more accurate for f because the rate at which f' is changing at 1 is smaller than the rate at which g' is changing at 1. The graph of f bends away from the linear function more slowly than the graph of g.

4.5.63

b. The larger the value of $|f''(a)|$, the greater the deviation of the curve $y = f(x)$ from the tangent line at points near $x = a$.

4.6   Mean Value Theorem

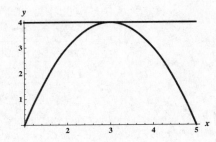

4.6.1 If f is a continuous function on the closed interval $[a, b]$ and is differentiable on (a, b) and the slope of the secant line that joins $(a, f(a))$ and $(b, f(b))$ is zero, then there is at least one value c in (a, b) at which the slope of the line tangent to f at $(c, f(c))$ is also zero.

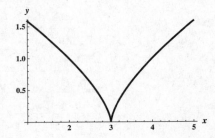

4.6.2 We seek a function over an interval for which it isn't true that there is a horizontal tangent line to the function.

4.6.3 The function $f(x) = |x|$ is not differentiable at 0.

If f is a continuous function on the closed interval $[a, b]$ and is differentiable on (a, b), then there is at **4.6.4** least one value c in (a, b) at which the slope of the line tangent to f at $(c, f(c))$ is equal to the slope of the secant line that joins $(a, f(a))$ and $(b, f(b))$.

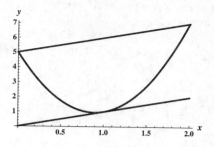

We seek a function over an interval for which it **4.6.5** isn't true that there is a tangent line parallel to the secant line between the endpoints.

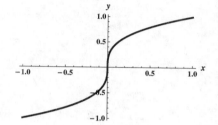

4.6.6 The average rate of change of f on the interval $[-10, 10]$ is $\frac{f(10)-f(-10)}{10-(-10)} = \frac{10^3-(-10)^3}{20} = 100$. We wish to find a point x in $(-10, 10)$ such that $f'(x) = 100$, or equivalently $3x^2 = 100$, which gives $x = \pm 10/\sqrt{3}$.

4.6.7 The function f is differentiable on $[0, 1]$ and $f(0) = f(1) = 0$, so Rolle's theorem applies. We wish to find a point x in $(0, 1)$ such that $f'(x) = 0$; we have $f'(x) = (x-1)^2 + 2x(x-1) = (x-1)(3x-1)$, so $x = 1/3$ satisfies the conclusion of Rolle's theorem.

4.6.8 The function f is differentiable on $[0, \pi/2]$ and $f(0) = f(\pi/2) = 0$, so Rolle's theorem applies. We wish to find a point x in $(0, \pi/2)$ such that $f'(x) = 0$; we have $f'(x) = 2\cos 2x$, so $x = \pi/4$ satisfies the conclusion of Rolle's theorem.

4.6.9 The function f is differentiable on $[\pi/8, 3\pi/8]$ and $f(\pi/8) = f(3\pi/8) = 0$, so Rolle's theorem applies. We wish to find a point x in $(\pi/8, 3\pi/8)$ such that $f'(x) = 0$; we have $f'(x) = -4\sin 4x$, so $x = \pi/4$ satisfies the conclusion of Rolle's theorem.

4.6.10 The function f is not differentiable at $x = 0$, so Rolle's theorem does not apply.

4.6.11 The function f is not differentiable at $x = 0$, so Rolle's theorem does not apply.

4.6.12 The function f is continuous on $[-2, 4]$ and differentiable on $(-2, 4)$, and $f(-2) = f(4) = 0$, so Rolle's theorem does apply. $f'(x) = 3x^2 - 4x - 8$, which is zero at $x = \frac{4\pm\sqrt{16+96}}{6} = \frac{4\pm\sqrt{112}}{6} = 2\left(\frac{1\pm\sqrt{7}}{3}\right)$. Both of these values lie between -2 and 4, so both satisfy the conclusion of Rolle's theorem.

4.6.13 g is continuous on $[-1, 3]$ and differentiable on $(-1, 3)$, and $g(-1) = 0 = g(3)$, so Rolle's theorem does apply. $g'(x) = 3x^2 - 2x - 5 = (x+1)(3x-5)$. This is zero for $x = -1$ (which is not on $(-1, 3)$) and for $x = 5/3$ (which is on $(-1, 3)$.) So $x = 5/3$ satisfies the conclusion of Rolle's theorem.

4.6.14 h is continuous on $[-a, a]$ and differentiable on $(-a, a)$, and $h(-a) = e^{-a^2} = h(a)$, so Rolle's theorem does apply. $h'(x) = -2xe^{-x^2}$, which is zero at $x = 0$. So $x = 0$ satisfies the conclusion of Rolle's theorem.

4.6.15 The average rate of change of the temperature from 3.2 km to 6.1 km is $\frac{-10.3-8.0}{6.1-3.2} \approx -6.3°/\text{km}$. Based on this, we cannot conclude that the lapse rate exceeds the critical value of $7°/$ km.

4.6.16 The average acceleration over the 4.45 seconds is $\frac{330-0}{4.45-0} \approx 74.2 \text{mi/hr/s}$, so at some point during the race, the maximum acceleration of the drag racer is at least 74 mi/hr/s.

4.6.17

  a. The function f is differentiable on $[-1,2]$ so the Mean Value Theorem applies.

  b. The average rate of change of f on $[-1,2]$ is $\frac{f(2)-f(-1)}{2-(-1)} = \frac{3-6}{3} = -1$. We wish to find a point c in $(-1,2)$ such that $f'(c) = -1$, or equivalently $-2c = -1$ which gives $c = 1/2$.

  c.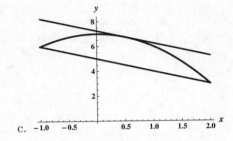

4.6.18

  a. The function f is differentiable on $[0, \pi/4]$ so the Mean Value Theorem applies.

  b. The average rate of change of f on $[0, \pi/4]$ is $\frac{f(\pi/4)-f(0)}{\frac{\pi}{4}-0} = \frac{3\sin\frac{\pi}{2}}{\frac{\pi}{4}} = \frac{12}{\pi}$. We wish to find a point c in $(0, \pi/4)$ such that $f'(c) = 12/\pi$, or equivalently $6\cos 2c = 12/\pi$ which gives $c = (1/2)\cos^{-1}(2/\pi)$.

  c.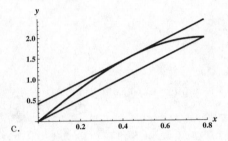

4.6.19

  a. The function f is differentiable on $[0, \ln 4]$ so the Mean Value Theorem applies.

  b. The average rate of change of f on $[0, \ln 4]$ is $\frac{f(\ln 4)-f(0)}{\ln 4-0} = \frac{4-1}{\ln 4} = \frac{3}{\ln 4}$. We wish to find a point c in $(0, \ln 4)$ such that $f'(c) = 3/\ln 4$, or equivalently $e^c = 3/\ln 4$ which gives $c = \ln\left(\frac{3}{\ln 4}\right)$.

  c.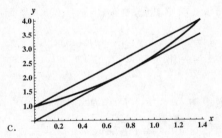

4.6.20

  a. The function f is differentiable on $[1, e]$ so the Mean Value Theorem applies.

  b. The average rate of change of f on $[1, e]$ is $\frac{f(e)-f(1)}{e-1} = \frac{\ln e + \ln 2 - \ln 2}{e-1} = \frac{1}{e-1}$. We wish to find a point c in $(1, e)$ such that $f'(c) = 1/(e-1)$, or equivalently $1/c = 1/(e-1)$ which gives $c = e-1$.

  c.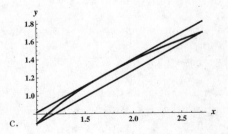

4.6.21

a. The function f is differentiable on $[0, 1/2]$ so the Mean Value Theorem applies.

b. The average rate of change of f on $[0, 1/2]$ is $\frac{f(1/2)-f(0)}{\frac{1}{2}-0} = \frac{\frac{\pi}{6}-0}{\frac{1}{2}} = \frac{\pi}{3}$.

We wish to find a point c in $(0, 1/2)$ such that $f'(c) = \pi/3$, or equivalently $\frac{1}{\sqrt{1-c^2}} = \frac{\pi}{3}$, so $c = \sqrt{1 - \frac{9}{\pi^2}}$.

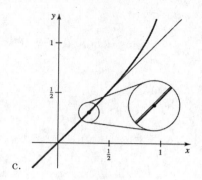

c.

4.6.22

a. The function f is differentiable on $[1, 3]$ so the Mean Value Theorem applies.

b. The average rate of change of f on $[1, 3]$ is $\frac{f(3)-f(1)}{3-1} = \frac{\frac{10}{3}-2}{2} = \frac{2}{3}$. We wish to find a point c in $(1, 3)$ such that $f'(c) = 2/3$, or equivalently $1 - \frac{1}{c^2} = \frac{2}{3}$, so $c = \sqrt{3}$.

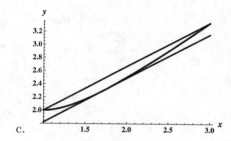

c.

4.6.23

a. The Mean Value Theorem does not apply because the function f is not differentiable at $x = 0$.

b. Even though the Mean Value Theorem doesn't apply, it still happens to be the case that there are numbers c between -8 and 8 where the tangent line has slope $\frac{f(8)-f(-8)}{8-(-8)} = \frac{1}{2}$. This occurs where $\frac{2}{3}c^{-2/3} = 1/2$, which gives $c = \pm\frac{8}{9} \cdot \sqrt{3}$.

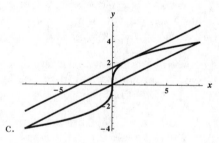

c.

4.6.24

a. The function f is differentiable on $[-1, 2]$ so the Mean Value Theorem applies.

b. The average rate of change of f on $[-1, 2]$ is $\frac{f(2)-f(-1)}{2-(-1)} = \frac{\frac{1}{2}-(-1)}{3} = \frac{1}{2}$. We wish to find a point c in $(-1, 2)$ such that $f'(c) = 1/2$, or equivalently $\frac{2}{(c+2)^2} = \frac{1}{2}$, so $c = 0$.

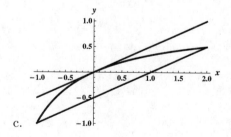

c.

4.6.25

a. False. The function f is not differentiable at $x = 0$.

b. True. If $f(x) - g(x) = c$ is constant, then $f'(x) - g'(x) = 0$.

c. False. If $f'(x) = 0$ then we can conclude that $f(x) = c$ for some constant.

4.6.26 Observe that $\ln 2x = \ln 2 + \ln x$ and $\ln 10x^2 = \ln 10 + \ln x^2$, so the pairs $f(x), g(x)$ and $h(x), p(x)$ have the same derivative.

4.6.27 The functions $h(x)$ and $p(x)$ have the same derivative as $f(x)$ because they differ from $f(x)$ by a constant.

4.6.28 One example of a function f with $f'(x) = x+1$ is $f(x) = \frac{x^2}{2} + x$; therefore the most general function with derivative $x+1$ is $f(x) = \frac{x^2}{2} + x + C$ where C is a constant.

4.6.29 The secant line between the endpoints has slope $\frac{f(4)-f(-4)}{4-(-4)} = \frac{4-1}{8} = \frac{3}{8}$.

   The slope of the tangent line to the graph appears to have this value at approximately -2.5 and at about 2.6. These are eyeballed estimates, so your personal estimate may differ.

4.6.30 Because $f(3) = f(1) \approx 2$, the average rate of change of f on $[1,3]$ is $\frac{f(3)-f(1)}{3-1} = 0$. However, there is no point in $(1,3)$ such that the slope of the tangent to f at that point is zero. This does not contradict the Mean Value Theorem because f is not differentiable everywhere on $(1,3)$; in particular, it is not differentiable at $x = 2$.

4.6.31 Because $f(1) \approx 2$ and $f(3) \approx 2$, the average rate of change of f on $[1,3]$ is $\frac{f(3)-f(1)}{3-1} = 0$. However, the tangent to f between $x = 1$ and $x = 2$ is the graph of f itself, which has slope 2, and the tangent to f between $x = 2$ and $x = 3$ is also the graph of f, which has slope 1. So there is no point in $(1,3)$ where the tangent line has slope 0. This does not contradict the Mean Value Theorem because f is not continuous everywhere on $[1,3]$, nor differentiable everywhere on $(1,3)$ both of these hypotheses fail at x = 2.

4.6.32

   a. The average temperature gradient from $h = 0$ to $h = 1.1$ m is $\frac{2-(-12)}{1.1-0} \approx 12.7°/$m, so by the Mean Value Theorem the temperature gradient must equal $12.7°/$m somewhere in the snowpack, and the formation of a weak layer is likely.

   b. The average temperature gradient from $h = 0$ to $h = 1.4$ m is $\frac{-1-(-12)}{1.4-0} \approx 7.86°/$m. While it is still possible that the temperature gradient exceeds $10°/$m somewhere in the snowpack, one may suspect that the formation of a weak layer is not likely in this case.

   c. If the surface temperature and temperature at the bottom of the snowpack are both roughly constant, then the temperature gradient will be larger in areas where the snowpack is less deep.

   d. If all layers of the snowbank are the same temperature, then the temperature gradient is 0 and a weak layer is not likely to form.

4.6.33 The average speed of the car over the 28 minute period $(= 28/60$ hr$)$ is $\frac{30-0}{28/60} \approx 64.3$mi/hr, so the officer can conclude by the Mean Value Theorem that at some point the car exceeded the speed limit.

4.6.34 The average speed of the car over the 30 minute period $(= 1/2$ hr$)$ is exactly 60 mi/hr. But because the car started from rest, the average speed for the first few seconds of the trip is less than 60 mi/hr, and therefore the average speed for the remainder of the trip must exceed 60 mi/hr, and the officer can conclude that the driver exceeded the speed limit.

4.6.35 The runner's average speed is $6.2/(32/60) \approx 11.6$ mi /hr. By the Mean Value Theorem, the runner's speed was 11.6 mi/hr at least once. By the intermediate value theorem, all speeds between 0 and 11.6 mi/hr were reached. Because the initial and final speed was 0 mi/hr, the speed of 11 mi/hr was reached at least twice.

4.6.36 For linear functions $f(x)$ the average rate of change of f on any interval $[a,b]$ is the same as the slope $f'(c)$ for any point c in (a,b).

4.6.37 Observe that

$$\frac{f(b) - f(a)}{b - a} = \frac{A(b^2 - a^2) + B(b - a)}{b - a} = A(a + b) + B$$

and $f'(c) = 2Ac + B$, so the point c that satisfies the conclusion of the Mean Value Theorem is $c = (a+b)/2$.

4.6.38

a. Observe that $\frac{f(b)-f(a)}{b-a} = \frac{b^2-a^2}{b-a} = (a+b)$ and $f'(c) = 2c$, so the point c that satisfies the conclusion of the Mean Value Theorem is $c = (a + b)/2$.

b. Observe that

$$\frac{f(b) - f(a)}{b - a} = \frac{\frac{1}{b} - \frac{1}{a}}{b - a} = \frac{a - b}{ab(b - a)} = -\frac{1}{ab}$$

and $f'(c) = -1/c^2$, so the point c that satisfies the conclusion of the Mean Value Theorem is $c = \sqrt{ab}$.

4.6.39 Note that $f'(x) = 2\tan x \sec^2 x$ and $g'(x) = 2\sec x \sec x \tan x = 2\tan x \sec^2 x$, so $f'(x) = g'(x)$. This implies that $f - g$ is a constant, which also follows from the trigonometric identity $\sec^2 x = \tan^2 x + 1$.

4.6.40 Note that

$$f'(x) = 2\sin x \cos x \quad \text{and} \quad g'(x) = -2\cos x(-\sin x) = 2\sin x \cos x,$$

so $f'(x) = g'(x)$. This implies that $f - g$ is a constant, which also follows from the trigonometric identity $\sin^2 x + \cos^2 x = 1$.

4.6.41 Bolt's average speed during the race was $\frac{100}{9.58}$ m/s $= \frac{100}{9.58} \cdot \frac{3600}{1000}$ km/hr ≈ 37.58 km/hr, so by the Mean Value Theorem he must have exceeded 37 km/hr during the race.

4.6.42 Observe that f' is positive and decreasing for $x > a$ (because $f'' < 0$ for $x > a$). Fix some $b > a$ and let $a < x < b$. Then by the Mean Value Theorem $\frac{f(x)-f(a)}{x-a} = f'(c)$ for some c in (a, x). We have $f'(c) > f'(b) > 0$, so therefore if $f'(a) = \lim_{x \to a} \frac{f(x)-f(a)}{x-a}$ exists, we must have $f'(a) \geq f'(b) > 0$. On the other hand f' is negative for $x < a$ so the mean values theorem implies $\frac{f(x)-f(a)}{x-a} < 0$ for $x < a$, and so if $f'(a)$ exists we must have $f'(a) \leq 0$. This gives a contradiction, so we conclude that $f'(a)$ does not exist.

More generally, if f' and f'' both change signs at some point a, then one of the functions $f(x)$, $-f(x), f(-x)$ or $-f(-x)$ satisfies the hypotheses above, and so $f'(a)$ does not exist.

4.6.43

a. If $g(x) = x$ then $g'(x) = 1$ and hence $\frac{f(b)-f(a)}{g(b)-g(a)} = \frac{f(b)-f(a)}{b-a} = \frac{f'(c)}{g'(c)} = f'(c)$.

b. We have $\frac{f(b)-f(a)}{g(b)-g(a)} = \frac{0-(-1)}{6-2} = \frac{1}{4}$; $\frac{f'(c)}{g'(c)} = \frac{2c}{4} = \frac{c}{2}$; so $c = 1/2$.

4.7 L'Hôpital's Rule

4.7.1 If $\lim_{x \to a} f(x) = 0$ and $\lim_{x \to a} g(x) = 0$, then we say $\lim_{x \to a} f(x)/g(x)$ is of indeterminate form 0/0.

4.7.2 In general, limits with the form 0/0 or ∞/∞ can have any value, and so cannot be evaluated by direct substitution.

4.7.3 Take the limit of the quotient of the derivatives of the numerator and denominator.

4.7.4 L'Hôpital's rule applies directly to limits of the form 0/0 and ∞/∞.

4.7.5 If $\lim_{x \to a} f(x)g(x)$ has the form $0 \cdot \infty$, then $\lim_{x \to a} \frac{f(x)}{1/g(x)}$ has the indeterminate form 0/0 or ∞/∞.

4.7.6 A simple example is $\lim\limits_{x\to 0}\dfrac{1/x^2}{1/x^2}$.

4.7.7 If $\lim\limits_{x\to a} f(x) = 1$ and $\lim\limits_{x\to a} g(x) = \infty$, then $f(x)^{g(x)} \to 1^{\infty}$ as $x \to a$, which is meaningless; so direct substitution does not work.

4.7.8 First, evaluate $L = \lim\limits_{x\to a} g(x)\ln f(x)$, which can usually be handled by l'Hôpital's rule. Then we have $\lim\limits_{x\to a} f(x)^{g(x)} = e^{L}$.

4.7.9 This means $\lim\limits_{x\to\infty}\dfrac{g(x)}{f(x)} = 0$.

4.7.10 This means $\lim\limits_{x\to\infty}\dfrac{f(x)}{g(x)} = M$ where $0 < M < \infty$.

4.7.11 By Theorem 4.15, we have $\ln x, x^3, 2^x, x^x$ in order of increasing growth rates.

4.7.12 By Theorem 4.15, we have $\ln x^{10}, x^{100}, 10^x, x^x$ in order of increasing growth rates.

4.7.13 L'Hôpital's rule gives $\lim\limits_{x\to 2}\dfrac{x^2 - 2x}{8 - 6x + x^2} = \lim\limits_{x\to 2}\dfrac{2x - 2}{-6 + 2x} = \dfrac{2}{-2} = -1$.

4.7.14 L'Hôpital's rule gives $\lim\limits_{x\to -1}\dfrac{x^4 + x^3 + 2x + 2}{x + 1} = \lim\limits_{x\to -1}\dfrac{4x^3 + 3x^2 + 2}{1} = -4 + 3 + 2 = 1$.

4.7.15 L'Hôpital's rule gives $\lim\limits_{x\to 1}\dfrac{\ln x}{4x - x^2 - 3} = \lim\limits_{x\to 1}\dfrac{1/x}{4 - 2x} = \dfrac{1}{2}$.

4.7.16 L'Hôpital's rule gives $\lim\limits_{x\to 0}\dfrac{e^x - 1}{x^2 + 3x} = \lim\limits_{x\to 0}\dfrac{e^x}{2x + 3} = \dfrac{1}{3}$.

4.7.17 L'Hôpital's rule gives $\lim\limits_{x\to e}\dfrac{\ln x - 1}{x - e} = \lim\limits_{x\to e}\dfrac{1/x}{1} = \dfrac{1}{e}$.

4.7.18 L'Hôpital's rule gives $\lim\limits_{x\to 1}\dfrac{4\tan^{-1} x - \pi}{x - 1} = \lim\limits_{x\to 1}\dfrac{4/(1 + x^2)}{1} = 2$.

4.7.19 L'Hôpital's rule gives $\lim\limits_{x\to 0}\dfrac{3\sin 4x}{5x} = \lim\limits_{x\to 0}\dfrac{12\cos 4x}{5} = \dfrac{12}{5}$.

4.7.20 L'Hôpital's rule gives $\lim\limits_{x\to 2\pi}\dfrac{x\sin x + x^2 - 4\pi^2}{x - 2\pi} = \lim\limits_{x\to 2\pi}\dfrac{x\cos x + \sin x + 2x}{1} = 2\pi + 0 + 4\pi = 6\pi$.

4.7.21 L'Hôpital's rule gives $\lim\limits_{u\to\pi/4}\dfrac{\tan u - \cot u}{u - \pi/4} = \lim\limits_{u\to\pi/4}\dfrac{\sec^2 u + \csc^2 u}{1} = 2 + 2 = 4$.

4.7.22 L'Hôpital's rule gives $\lim\limits_{z\to 0}\dfrac{\tan 4z}{\tan 7z} = \lim\limits_{z\to 0}\dfrac{4\sec^2 4z}{7\sec^2 7z} = \dfrac{4}{7}$.

4.7.23 Apply l'Hôpital's rule twice: $\lim\limits_{x\to 0}\dfrac{1 - \cos 3x}{8x^2} = \lim\limits_{x\to 0}\dfrac{3\sin 3x}{16x} = \lim\limits_{x\to 0}\dfrac{9\cos 3x}{16} = \dfrac{9}{16}$.

4.7.24 Observe that $\lim\limits_{x\to 0}\dfrac{\sin^2 3x}{x^2} = \left(\lim\limits_{x\to 0}\dfrac{\sin 3x}{x}\right)^2$, and apply l'Hôpital's rule to obtain $\lim\limits_{x\to 0}\dfrac{\sin 3x}{x} = \lim\limits_{x\to 0}\dfrac{3\cos 3x}{1} = 3$. Therefore $\lim\limits_{x\to 0}\dfrac{\sin^2 3x}{x^2} = 9$.

4.7.25 Apply l'Hôpital's rule twice:

$$\lim_{x \to \pi} \frac{\cos x + 1}{(x - \pi)^2} = \lim_{x \to \pi} \frac{-\sin x}{2(x - \pi)} = \lim_{x \to \pi} \frac{-\cos x}{2} = \frac{1}{2}.$$

4.7.26 Apply l'Hôpital's rule twice:

$$\lim_{x \to 0} \frac{e^x - x - 1}{5x^2} = \lim_{x \to 0} \frac{e^x - 1}{10x} = \lim_{x \to 0} \frac{e^x}{10} = \frac{1}{10}.$$

4.7.27 Apply l'Hôpital's rule twice:

$$\lim_{x \to 0} \frac{e^x - \sin x - 1}{x^4 + 8x^3 + 12x^2} = \lim_{x \to 0} \frac{e^x - \cos x}{4x^3 + 24x^2 + 24x} = \lim_{x \to 0} \frac{e^x + \sin x}{12x^2 + 48x + 24} = \frac{1}{24}.$$

4.7.28 Apply l'Hôpital's rule three times:

$$\lim_{x \to 0} \frac{\sin x - x}{7x^3} = \lim_{x \to 0} \frac{\cos x - 1}{21x^2} = \lim_{x \to 0} \frac{-\sin x}{42x} = \lim_{x \to 0} \frac{-\cos x}{42} = \frac{-1}{42}.$$

4.7.29 L'Hôpital's rule gives:

$$\lim_{x \to \infty} \frac{e^{1/x} - 1}{1/x} = \lim_{x \to \infty} \frac{e^{1/x}(-1/x^2)}{(-1/x^2)} = \lim_{x \to \infty} e^{1/x} = 1.$$

4.7.30 Apply l'Hôpital's rule twice:

$$\lim_{x \to \infty} \frac{\tan^{-1} x - \pi/2}{1/x} = \lim_{x \to \infty} \frac{1/(1 + x^2)}{(-1/x^2)} = \lim_{x \to \infty} \frac{-x^2}{x^2 + 1} = \lim_{x \to \infty} \frac{-2x}{2x} = -1.$$

4.7.31 Apply l'Hôpital's rule twice:

$$\lim_{x \to -1} \frac{x^3 - x^2 - 5x - 3}{x^4 + 2x^3 - x^2 - 4x - 2} = \lim_{x \to -1} \frac{3x^2 - 2x - 5}{4x^3 + 6x^2 - 2x - 4} = \lim_{x \to -1} \frac{6x - 2}{12x^2 + 12x - 2} = 4.$$

4.7.32 L'Hôpital's rule gives $\displaystyle\lim_{x \to 1} \frac{x^n - 1}{x - 1} = \lim_{x \to 1} \frac{nx^{n-1}}{1} = n.$

4.7.33 L'Hôpital's rule gives $\displaystyle\lim_{v \to 3} \frac{v - 1 - \sqrt{v^2 - 5}}{v - 3} = \lim_{v \to 3} \frac{1 - \dfrac{v}{\sqrt{v^2 - 5}}}{1} = -\frac{1}{2}.$

4.7.34 L'Hôpital's rule gives $\displaystyle\lim_{y \to 2} \frac{y^2 + y - 6}{\sqrt{8 - y^2} - y} = \lim_{y \to 2} \frac{2y + 1}{-\dfrac{y}{\sqrt{8 - y^2}} - 1} = -\frac{5}{2}.$

4.7.35 Apply l'Hôpital's rule twice:

$$\lim_{x \to 2} \frac{x^2 - 4x + 4}{\sin^2 \pi x} = \lim_{x \to 2} \frac{2x - 4}{2\pi(\sin \pi x)(\cos \pi x)} = \lim_{x \to 2} \frac{2x - 4}{\pi \sin 2\pi x} = \lim_{x \to 2} \frac{2}{2\pi^2 \cos 2\pi x} = \frac{2}{2\pi^2} = \frac{1}{\pi^2}.$$

4.7.36 L'Hôpital's rule gives $\displaystyle\lim_{x \to 2} \frac{(3x + 2)^{1/3} - 2}{x - 2} = \lim_{x \to 2} \frac{(3x + 2)^{-2/3}}{1} = 8^{-2/3} = \frac{1}{4}.$ (Notice that this limit is the derivative of $(3x + 2)^{1/3}$ at $x = 2$.)

4.7.37 Apply l'Hôpital's rule three times:

$$\lim_{x \to \infty} \frac{3x^4 - x^2}{6x^4 + 12} = \lim_{x \to \infty} \frac{12x^3 - 2x}{24x^3} = \lim_{x \to \infty} \frac{36x^2 - 2}{72x^2} = \lim_{x \to \infty} \frac{72x}{144x} = \frac{1}{2}.$$

4.7.38 Apply l'Hôpital's rule three times:

$$\lim_{x\to\infty} \frac{4x^3 - 2x^2 + 6}{\pi x^3 + 4} = \lim_{x\to\infty} \frac{12x^2 - 4x}{3\pi x^2} = \lim_{x\to\infty} \frac{24x - 4}{6\pi x} = \lim_{x\to\infty} \frac{24}{6\pi} = \frac{4}{\pi}.$$

4.7.39 Apply l'Hôpital's rule three times:

$$\lim_{x\to\pi/2^-} \frac{\tan x}{3/(2x - \pi)} = \lim_{x\to\pi/2^-} \frac{\sec^2 x}{-6/(2x - \pi)^2} = -(1/6)\lim_{x\to\pi/2^-} \frac{(2x - \pi)^2}{\cos^2 x} = (-1/6)\lim_{x\to\pi/2^-} \frac{4(2x - \pi)}{2\cos x(-\sin x)} =$$

$$(-1/6)\lim_{x\to\pi/2^-} \frac{8x - 4\pi}{-\sin(2x)} = (-1/6)\lim_{x\to\pi/2^-} \frac{8}{-2\cos(2x)} = -\frac{2}{3}.$$

4.7.40 Applying l'Hôpital's rule gives:

$$\lim_{x\to\infty} \frac{e^{3x}}{3e^{3x} + 5} = \lim_{x\to\infty} \frac{3e^{3x}}{9e^{3x}} = \frac{3}{9} = \frac{1}{3}.$$

4.7.41 Applying l'Hôpital's rule twice gives:

$$\lim_{x\to\infty} \frac{\ln(3x + 5)}{\ln(7x + 3) + 1} = \lim_{x\to\infty} \frac{3/(3x + 5)}{7/(7x + 3)} = \frac{3}{7}\lim_{x\to\infty} \frac{7x + 3}{3x + 5} = \frac{3}{7}\lim_{x\to\infty} \frac{7}{3} = 1.$$

4.7.42 Applying l'Hôpital's rule numerous times gives:

$$\lim_{x\to\infty} \frac{\ln(3x + 5e^x)}{\ln(7x + 3e^{2x})} = \lim_{x\to\infty} \frac{(3 + 5e^x)/(3x + 5e^x)}{(7 + 6e^{2x})/(7x + 3e^{2x})} = \lim_{x\to\infty} \frac{3 + 5e^x}{3x + 5e^x} \cdot \lim_{x\to\infty} \frac{7x + 3e^{2x}}{7 + 6e^{2x}} =$$

$$\lim_{x\to\infty} \frac{5e^x}{3 + 5e^x} \cdot \lim_{x\to\infty} \frac{7 + 6e^{2x}}{12e^{2x}} = \lim_{x\to\infty} \frac{5e^x}{5e^x} \cdot \lim_{x\to\infty} \frac{12e^{2x}}{24e^{2x}} = \frac{1}{2}.$$

4.7.43 Applying l'Hôpital's rule twice gives:

$$\lim_{x\to\infty} \frac{x^2 - \ln(2/x)}{3x^2 + 2x} = \lim_{x\to\infty} \frac{2x + (1/x)}{6x + 2} = \lim_{x\to\infty} \frac{2 - 1/x^2}{6} = \frac{2}{6} = \frac{1}{3}.$$

4.7.44 L'Hôpital's rule gives $\displaystyle\lim_{x\to\pi/2} \frac{2\tan x}{\sec^2 x} = \lim_{x\to\pi/2} \frac{2\sec^2 x}{2\sec x \sec x \tan x} = \lim_{x\to\pi/2} \cot x = 0.$

4.7.45 L'Hôpital's rule gives $\displaystyle\lim_{x\to\infty} x\ln\left(1 + \frac{1}{x}\right) = \lim_{x\to\infty} \frac{\ln\left(1 + \frac{1}{x}\right)}{\frac{1}{x}} = \lim_{x\to\infty} \frac{1}{1 + (1/x)} \cdot \frac{\frac{-1}{x^2}}{\frac{-1}{x^2}} = 1.$

4.7.46 Observe that $\displaystyle\lim_{x\to 1^-} (1 - x)\tan\left(\frac{\pi x}{2}\right) = \lim_{x\to 1^-} \frac{1 - x}{\cot\left(\frac{\pi x}{2}\right)} = \lim_{x\to 1^-} \frac{-1}{-\left(\frac{\pi}{2}\right)\csc^2\left(\frac{\pi x}{2}\right)} = \frac{2}{\pi}$

by l'Hôpital's rule.

4.7.47 Observe that the given limit can be written $\displaystyle\lim_{x\to 0} \frac{\sin 7x}{\sin 6x} = \lim_{x\to 0} \frac{7\cos 7x}{6\cos 6x} = \frac{7}{6}.$

4.7.48 Observe that the given limit can be written $\displaystyle\lim_{x\to\infty} \frac{e^{1/x} - 1}{\sin(1/x)} = \lim_{x\to\infty} \frac{e^{1/x} \cdot (-1/x^2)}{\cos(1/x)(-1/x^2)} = \frac{1}{1} = 1.$

4.7.49 Observe that $\displaystyle\lim_{x\to(\pi/2)^-} \left(\frac{\pi}{2} - x\right)\sec x = \lim_{x\to(\pi/2)^-} \frac{\pi/2 - x}{\cos x} = \lim_{x\to(\pi/2)^-} \frac{-1}{-\sin x} = 1$ by l'Hôpital's rule.

4.7.50 Observe that $\displaystyle\lim_{x\to 0^+} \sin x\sqrt{\frac{1 - x}{x}} = \lim_{x\to 0^+} \sin x\sqrt{\frac{x(1 - x)}{x^2}} = \lim_{x\to 0^+} \frac{\sin x}{x} \cdot \lim_{x\to 0^+} \sqrt{x(1 - x)} = 1 \cdot 0 = 0,$
where we use l'Hôpital's rule for $\displaystyle\lim_{x\to 0^+} \sin x/x = 1.$

4.7.51 Observe that $\lim\limits_{x\to 0}\left(\cot x - \dfrac{1}{x}\right) = \lim\limits_{x\to 0}\left(\dfrac{\cos x}{\sin x} - \dfrac{1}{x}\right) = \lim\limits_{x\to 0}\dfrac{x\cos x - \sin x}{x\sin x}$. Apply l'Hôpital's rule twice:

$$\lim_{x\to 0}\frac{x\cos x - \sin x}{x\sin x} = \lim_{x\to 0}\frac{\cos x - x\sin x - \cos x}{\sin x + x\cos x}$$
$$= -\lim_{x\to 0}\frac{x\sin x}{\sin x + x\cos x} = -\lim_{x\to 0}\frac{\sin x + x\cos x}{\cos x + \cos x - x\sin x} = -\frac{0}{2} = 0.$$

4.7.52 Observe that $\lim\limits_{x\to\infty}\left(x - \sqrt{x^2+1}\right) = \lim\limits_{x\to\infty} x\left(1 - \sqrt{1+1/x^2}\right)$. Make the change of variables $t = 1/x$:

$$\lim_{x\to\infty} x\left(1 - \sqrt{1+1/x^2}\right) = \lim_{t\to 0+}\frac{1 - \sqrt{1+t^2}}{t} = \lim_{t\to 0+}\frac{\dfrac{-t}{\sqrt{1+t^2}}}{1} = 0.$$

4.7.53 Observe that $\lim\limits_{\theta\to(\pi/2)^-}(\tan\theta - \sec\theta) = \lim\limits_{\theta\to(\pi/2)^-}\left(\dfrac{\sin\theta}{\cos\theta} - \dfrac{1}{\cos\theta}\right) = \lim\limits_{\theta\to(\pi/2)^-}\dfrac{\sin\theta - 1}{\cos\theta}$. By l'Hôpital's rule $\lim\limits_{\theta\to(\pi/2)^-}\dfrac{\sin\theta - 1}{\cos\theta} = \lim\limits_{\theta\to(\pi/2)^-}\dfrac{\cos\theta}{-\sin\theta} = \dfrac{0}{-1} = 0.$

4.7.54 Observe that $\lim\limits_{x\to\infty}\left(x - \sqrt{x^2+4x}\right) = \lim\limits_{x\to\infty} x\left(1 - \sqrt{1+4/x}\right)$. Make the change of variables $t = 1/x$:

$$\lim_{x\to\infty} x\left(1 - \sqrt{1+4/x}\right) = \lim_{t\to 0+}\frac{1 - \sqrt{1+4t}}{t} = \lim_{t\to 0+}\frac{-\dfrac{4}{2\sqrt{1+4t}}}{1} = -2.$$

4.7.55 Note that $\ln x^{2x} = 2x\ln x$, so we evaluate $L = \lim\limits_{x\to 0+} 2x\ln x = 2\lim\limits_{x\to 0+}\dfrac{\ln x}{1/x} = 2\lim\limits_{x\to 0+}\dfrac{1/x}{-1/x^2} = 2\lim\limits_{x\to 0+}(-x) = 0$ by l'Hôpital's rule. Therefore $\lim\limits_{x\to 0+} x^{2x} = e^L = 1$.

4.7.56 Note that $\ln(1+4x)^{3/x} = \dfrac{3\ln(1+4x)}{x}$, so we evaluate $L = \lim\limits_{x\to 0}\dfrac{3\ln(1+4x)}{x} = 3\lim\limits_{x\to 0}\dfrac{4/(1+4x)}{1} = 12$ by l'Hôpital's rule. Therefore $\lim\limits_{x\to 0}(1+4x)^{3/x} = e^L = e^{12}$.

4.7.57 Note that $\ln(\tan\theta)^{\cos\theta} = \cos\theta\ln\tan\theta$, so we evaluate $L = \lim\limits_{\theta\to\pi/2^-}\cos\theta\ln\tan\theta = \lim\limits_{\theta\to\pi/2^-}\dfrac{\ln\tan\theta}{\sec\theta}$. L'Hôpital's rule gives $\lim\limits_{\theta\to\pi/2^-}\dfrac{\ln\tan\theta}{\sec\theta} = \lim\limits_{\theta\to\pi/2^-}\dfrac{\sec^2\theta/\tan\theta}{\sec\theta\tan\theta} = \lim\limits_{\theta\to\pi/2^-}\dfrac{\sec\theta}{\tan^2\theta} = \lim\limits_{\theta\to\pi/2^-}\dfrac{\cos\theta}{\sin^2\theta} = 0$, so $\lim\limits_{\theta\to\pi/2^-}(\tan\theta)^{\cos\theta} = e^L = 1$.

4.7.58 Note that $\ln(\sin\theta)^{\tan\theta} = \tan\theta\ln\sin\theta$, so we evaluate $L = \lim\limits_{\theta\to 0+}\tan\theta\ln\sin\theta = \lim\limits_{\theta\to 0+}\dfrac{\ln\sin\theta}{\cot\theta}$. L'Hôpital's rule gives $\lim\limits_{\theta\to 0+}\dfrac{\ln\sin\theta}{\cot\theta} = \lim\limits_{\theta\to 0+}\dfrac{\cos\theta/\sin\theta}{-\csc^2\theta} = -\lim\limits_{\theta\to 0+}\cos\theta\sin\theta = 0$, so $\lim\limits_{\theta\to 0+}(\tan\theta)^{\cos\theta} = e^L = 1$.

4.7.59 Note that $\ln(1+x)^{\cot x} = \cot x\ln(1+x)$, so we evaluate $L = \lim\limits_{x\to 0+}\cot x\ln(1+x) = \lim\limits_{x\to 0+}\dfrac{\ln(1+x)}{\tan x} = \lim\limits_{x\to 0+}\dfrac{1/(1+x)}{\sec^2 x} = \lim\limits_{x\to 0+}\dfrac{\cos^2 x}{1+x} = 1$ by l'Hôpital's rule. Therefore $\lim\limits_{x\to 0+}(1+x)^{\cot x} = e^L = e$.

4.7.60 Note that $\ln(1+1/x)^{\ln x} = \ln x\ln(1+1/x)$, so we evaluate

$$L = \lim_{x\to\infty}\ln x\ln(1+1/x) = \lim_{x\to\infty}\frac{\ln(1+1/x)}{1/\ln x} = \lim_{x\to\infty}\frac{\dfrac{1}{1+1/x}\cdot\dfrac{-1}{x^2}}{\dfrac{-1}{(\ln x)^2}\cdot\dfrac{1}{x}} = \lim_{x\to\infty}\frac{(\ln x)^2}{x+1} = 0$$

by l'Hôpital's rule (the last limit is 0 because $x+1$ grows faster than $\ln^2 x$ as $x\to\infty$). Therefore $\lim\limits_{x\to\infty}(1+1/x)^{\ln x} = e^L = 1$.

4.7.61 Note that $\ln(1 + a/x)^x = x\ln(1 + a/x)$, so we evaluate

$$L = \lim_{x \to \infty} x\ln(1 + a/x) = \lim_{x \to \infty} \frac{\ln(1 + a/x)}{1/x} = \lim_{x \to \infty} \frac{\frac{1}{1+a/x} \cdot \frac{-a}{x^2}}{\frac{-1}{x^2}} = \lim_{x \to \infty} \frac{a}{1 + a/x} = a$$

by l'Hôpital's rule. Therefore $\lim_{x \to \infty} (1 + a/x)^x = e^L = e^a$.

4.7.62 Note that $\ln(e^{5x} + x)^{1/x} = \frac{1}{x}\ln(e^{5x} + x)$, so we evaluate

$$L = \lim_{x \to 0} \frac{\ln(e^{5x} + x)}{x} = \lim_{x \to 0} \frac{(5e^{5x} + 1)/(e^{5x} + x)}{1} = \frac{6/1}{1} = 6.$$

Therefore, $\lim_{x \to 0} (e^{5x} + x)^{1/x} = e^6$.

4.7.63 Note that $\ln(e^{ax} + x)^{1/x} = \frac{1}{x}\ln(e^{ax} + x)$, so we evaluate

$$L = \lim_{x \to 0} \frac{\ln(e^{ax} + x)}{x} = \lim_{x \to 0} \frac{(ae^{ax} + 1)/(e^{ax} + x)}{1} = \frac{(a+1)/1}{1} = a + 1.$$

Therefore, $\lim_{x \to 0} (e^{ax} + x)^{1/x} = e^{a+1}$.

4.7.64 Note that $\ln(2^{ax} + x)^{1/x} = \frac{1}{x}\ln(2^{ax} + x)$, so we evaluate

$$L = \lim_{x \to 0} \frac{\ln(2^{ax} + x)}{x} = \lim_{x \to 0} \frac{(a2^{ax}\ln 2 + 1)/(2^{ax} + x)}{1} = \frac{(a\ln 2 + 1)/1}{1} = a\ln 2 + 1.$$

Therefore, $\lim_{x \to 0} (2^{ax} + x)^{1/x} = e^{a\ln 2 + 1} = e^1 \cdot e^{a\ln 2} = e \cdot 2^a$.

4.7.65 Note that $\ln(\tan x)^x = x\ln\tan x$, so we evaluate

$$L = \lim_{x \to 0+} x\ln\tan x = \lim_{x \to 0+} \frac{\ln\tan x}{1/x} = \lim_{x \to 0+} \frac{\sec^2 x/\tan x}{-1/x^2} = -\lim_{x \to 0+} \frac{x^2}{\sin x\cos x}$$

by l'Hôpital's rule. Next, observe that $\lim_{x \to 0+} \frac{x^2}{\sin x\cos x} = \lim_{x \to 0+} \frac{x}{\sin x} \cdot \lim_{x \to 0+} \frac{x}{\cos x} = 1 \cdot 0 = 0$. Therefore $L = 0$ and $\lim_{x \to 0+} (\tan x)^x = e^L = 1$.

4.7.66 Note that $\ln(1 + 10/z^2)^{z^2} = z^2\ln(1 + 10/z^2)$, so we evaluate

$$L = \lim_{z \to \infty} z^2\ln\left(1 + \frac{10}{z^2}\right) = \lim_{z \to \infty} \frac{\ln\left(1 + \frac{10}{z^2}\right)}{\frac{1}{z^2}} = \lim_{z \to \infty} \frac{\frac{1}{1+\frac{10}{z^2}} \cdot \frac{-20}{z^3}}{-\frac{2}{z^3}} = \lim_{z \to \infty} \frac{10z^2}{z^2 + 10} = 10$$

by l'Hôpital's rule. Therefore $\lim_{z \to \infty} \left(1 + \frac{10}{z^2}\right)^{z^2} = e^L = e^{10}$.

4.7.67 Note that $\ln(x + \cos x)^{1/x} = (\ln(x + \cos x))/x$, so we evaluate

$$L = \lim_{x \to 0} \frac{\ln(x + \cos x)}{x} = \lim_{x \to 0} \frac{(x + \cos x)^{-1}(1 - \sin x)}{1} = 1$$

by l'Hôpital's rule. Therefore $\lim_{x \to 0} (x + \cos x)^{1/x} = e^L = e$.

4.7.68 Note that $\ln\left(\frac{1}{3}\cdot 3^x + \frac{2}{3}\cdot 2^x\right)^{1/x} = \frac{\ln\left(\frac{1}{3}\cdot 3^x + \frac{2}{3}\cdot 2^x\right)}{x}$, so we evaluate

$$L = \lim_{x\to 0^+} \frac{\ln\left(\frac{1}{3}\cdot 3^x + \frac{2}{3}\cdot 2^x\right)}{x} = \lim_{x\to 0^+} \frac{\left(\frac{1}{3}\cdot 3^x + \frac{2}{3}\cdot 2^x\right)^{-1}\left(\frac{\ln 3}{3}\cdot 3^x + \frac{2\ln 2}{3}\cdot 2^x\right)}{1} = \frac{\ln 12}{3}$$

by l'Hôpital's rule. Therefore $\displaystyle\lim_{x\to 0+}\left(\frac{1}{3}\cdot 3^x + \frac{2}{3}\cdot 2^x\right)^{1/x} = e^L = \sqrt[3]{12}$.

4.7.69 By Theorem 4.15, $e^{0.01x}$ grows faster than x^{10} as $x\to\infty$.

4.7.70 Observe that $\displaystyle\lim_{x\to\infty}\frac{x^2\ln x}{(\ln x)^2} = \lim_{x\to\infty}\frac{x^2}{\ln x} = \infty$, so $x^2\ln x$ grows faster than $(\ln x)^2$ as $x\to\infty$.

4.7.71 Note that $\ln x^{20} = 20\ln x$, so $\ln x^{20}$ and $\ln x$ have comparable growth rates as $x\to\infty$.

4.7.72 Make the substitution $y = \ln x$; then $y\to\infty$ if $x\to\infty$ and $\displaystyle\lim_{x\to\infty}\frac{\ln(\ln x)}{\ln x} = \lim_{y\to\infty}\frac{\ln y}{y} = 0$. Therefore $\ln x$ grows faster than $\ln(\ln x)$ as $x\to\infty$.

4.7.73 By Theorem 4.15, x^x grows faster than 100^x as $x\to\infty$.

4.7.74 Observe that $\displaystyle\lim_{x\to\infty}\frac{x^2\ln x}{x^3} = \lim_{x\to\infty}\frac{\ln x}{x} = 0$, so x^3 grows faster than $x^2\ln x$ as $x\to\infty$.

4.7.75 By Theorem 4.15, 1.00001^x grows faster than x^{20} as $x\to\infty$.

4.7.76 Observe that $\displaystyle\lim_{x\to\infty}\frac{x^{10}\ln^{10}x}{x^{11}} = \lim_{x\to\infty}\frac{\ln^{10}x}{x} = 0$ by Theorem 4.15, so x^{11} grows faster than $x^{10}\ln^{10}x$ as $x\to\infty$.

4.7.77 Observe that $\displaystyle\lim_{x\to\infty}\frac{(x/2)^x}{x^x} = \lim_{x\to\infty}2^{-x} = 0$, so x^x grows faster than $(x/2)^x$ as $x\to\infty$.

4.7.78 Observe that $\ln\sqrt{x} = (\ln x)/2$ and $\ln x^2 = 2\ln x$, so $\ln\sqrt{x}$ and $\ln x^2$ have comparable growth rates as $x\to\infty$.

4.7.79 Note that $\displaystyle\lim_{x\to\infty}\frac{e^{x^2}}{e^{10x}} = \lim_{x\to\infty}e^{x^2-10x} = \infty$, so e^{x^2} grows faster than e^{10x} as $x\to\infty$.

4.7.80 Observe that $\displaystyle\lim_{x\to\infty}\frac{x^{x/10}}{e^{x^2}} = \lim_{x\to\infty}\left(\frac{x^{1/10}}{e^x}\right)^x = 0$ by Theorem 4.15, so e^{x^2} grows faster than $x^{x/10}$ as $x\to\infty$.

4.7.81

a. False; $\displaystyle\lim_{x\to 2}x^2 - 1 = 3$, so l'Hôpital's rule does not apply. In fact, $\displaystyle\lim_{x\to 2}\frac{x-2}{x^2-1} = \frac{0}{3} = 0$.

b. False; l'Hôpital's rule does not say $\displaystyle\lim_{x\to a}f(x)g(x) = \lim_{x\to a}f'(x)\lim_{x\to a}g'(x)$. In fact, $\displaystyle\lim_{x\to 0}x\sin x = 0\cdot 0 = 0$.

c. False; this limit has the form $0^\infty = 0$.

d. False; this limit has the indeterminate form 1^∞ which is not always 1.

e. True; $\ln x^{100} = 100\ln x$.

f. True; note that $\displaystyle\lim_{x\to\infty}\frac{e^x}{2^x} = \lim_{x\to\infty}\left(\frac{e}{2}\right)^x = \infty$ because $e/2 > 1$.

4.7.82 Observe that $\lim\limits_{x\to\infty} \dfrac{100x^3 - 3}{x^4 - 2} = 0$ because the denominator has larger degree than the numerator (Theorem 2.7). We can also use l'Hôpital's rule: $\lim\limits_{x\to\infty} \dfrac{100x^3 - 3}{x^4 - 2} = \lim\limits_{x\to\infty} \dfrac{300x^2}{4x^3} = \lim\limits_{x\to\infty} \dfrac{75}{x} = 0.$

4.7.83 Observe that $\lim\limits_{x\to\infty} \dfrac{2x^3 - x^2 + 1}{5x^3 + 2x} = \dfrac{2}{5}$ by Theorem 2.7. We can also use l'Hôpital's rule:

$$\lim\limits_{x\to\infty} \dfrac{2x^3 - x^2 + 1}{5x^3 + 2x} = \lim\limits_{x\to\infty} \dfrac{6x^2 - 2x}{15x^2 + 2} = \lim\limits_{x\to\infty} \dfrac{12x - 2}{30x} = \lim\limits_{x\to\infty} \dfrac{12}{30} = \dfrac{2}{5}.$$

4.7.84 By l'Hôpital's rule, $\lim\limits_{x\to a} \dfrac{\sqrt{2a^3x - x^4} - a\sqrt[3]{a^2x}}{a - \sqrt[4]{ax^3}} = \lim\limits_{x\to a} \dfrac{\frac{2a^3 - 4x^3}{2\sqrt{2a^3x - x^4}} - \frac{1}{3}a^{5/3}x^{-2/3}}{-\frac{3}{4}a^{1/4}x^{-1/4}} = \dfrac{-a - \frac{a}{3}}{-\frac{3}{4}} = \dfrac{16}{9}a.$

4.7.85 By l'Hôpital's rule, $\lim\limits_{x\to 6} \dfrac{(5x + 2)^{1/5} - 2}{x^{-1} - 6^{-1}} = \lim\limits_{x\to 6} \dfrac{(5x + 2)^{-4/5}}{-x^{-2}} = -\dfrac{9}{4}.$

4.7.86 We can write the given problem as

$$\lim\limits_{x\to\infty} \dfrac{\ln \cos 1/x}{\frac{1}{x^2}} = \lim\limits_{x\to\infty} \dfrac{1}{\cos 1/x} \cdot \dfrac{-\sin 1/x \cdot \frac{-1}{x^2}}{\frac{-2}{x^3}}$$

by l'Hôpital's rule. Now note that $\lim\limits_{x\to\infty} \dfrac{1}{\cos 1/x} = \dfrac{1}{\cos 0} = 1.$ So what remains is

$$\lim\limits_{x\to\infty} \dfrac{-\sin 1/x \cdot \frac{-1}{x^2}}{\frac{-2}{x^3}} = \lim\limits_{x\to\infty} \dfrac{\sin 1/x}{\frac{-2}{x}} = \dfrac{-1}{2} \lim\limits_{x\to\infty} \dfrac{\sin 1/x}{1/x} = \dfrac{-1}{2} \lim\limits_{x\to\infty} \dfrac{\cos 1/x \cdot \frac{-1}{x^2}}{\frac{-1}{x^2}} = \dfrac{-1}{2} \lim\limits_{x\to\infty} \cos 1/x = -\dfrac{1}{2}.$$

4.7.87 Observe that $(\sqrt{x - 2} - \sqrt{x - 4}) \cdot \dfrac{\sqrt{x-2}+\sqrt{x-4}}{\sqrt{x-2}+\sqrt{x-4}} = \dfrac{x-2-(x-4)}{\sqrt{x-2}+\sqrt{x-4}} = \dfrac{2}{\sqrt{x-2}+\sqrt{x-4}}$, so $\lim\limits_{x\to\infty} \sqrt{x - 2} - \sqrt{x - 4} = \lim\limits_{x\to\infty} \dfrac{2}{\sqrt{x - 2} + \sqrt{x - 4}} = 0.$

4.7.88 Note that $\lim\limits_{x\to\pi/2} (\pi - 2x)\tan x = \lim\limits_{x\to\pi/2} \sin x \left(\dfrac{\pi - 2x}{\cos x}\right)$; we have $\lim\limits_{x\to\pi/2} \sin x = 1$ and $\lim\limits_{x\to\pi/2} \dfrac{\pi - 2x}{\cos x} = \lim\limits_{x\to\pi/2} \dfrac{-2}{-\sin x} = 2$, so $\lim\limits_{x\to\pi/2} (\pi - 2x)\tan x = 2.$

4.7.89 Make the substitution $t = 1/x$; then $\lim\limits_{x\to\infty} x^3 \left(\dfrac{1}{x} - \sin \dfrac{1}{x}\right) = \lim\limits_{t\to 0+} \dfrac{t - \sin t}{t^3} = \lim\limits_{t\to 0+} \dfrac{1 - \cos t}{3t^2} = \lim\limits_{t\to 0+} \dfrac{\sin t}{6t} = \lim\limits_{t\to 0+} \dfrac{\cos t}{6} = \dfrac{1}{6}$, using l'Hôpital's rule.

4.7.90 Make the substitution $t = 1/x$; then $\lim\limits_{x\to\infty} (x^2e^{1/x} - x^2 - x) = \lim\limits_{t\to 0+} \dfrac{e^t - 1 - t}{t^2} = \lim\limits_{t\to 0+} \dfrac{e^t - 1}{2t} = \lim\limits_{t\to 0+} \dfrac{e^t}{2} = \dfrac{1}{2}$, using l'Hôpital's rule.

4.7.91 Observe that $\lim\limits_{x\to 1+} \left(\dfrac{1}{x - 1} - \dfrac{1}{\sqrt{x - 1}}\right) = \lim\limits_{x\to 1+} \dfrac{1 - \sqrt{x - 1}}{x - 1} = \infty.$

4.7.92 Let $y = x^{1/\ln x}$. Then $\ln y = \ln x^{1/\ln x} = 1$, so $\lim\limits_{x\to 0+} \ln y = 1$, so $\lim\limits_{x\to 0+} y = e^1 = e.$

4.7.93 Note that $\log_2 x = \ln x / \ln 2$ and $\log_3 x = \ln x / \ln 3$; therefore $\lim\limits_{x\to\infty} \dfrac{\log_2 x}{\log_3 x} = \dfrac{\ln 3}{\ln 2}.$

4.7.94 Note that $\log_2 x = \ln x / \ln 2$ and $\log_3 x = \ln x / \ln 3$; therefore

$$\lim_{x \to \infty} (\log_2 x - \log_3 x) = \lim_{x \to \infty} \left(\frac{1}{\ln 2} - \frac{1}{\ln 3} \right) \ln x = \infty.$$

4.7.95 Use the identity $1 + 2 + \cdots + n = \frac{n(n+1)}{2}$; then

$$\lim_{n \to \infty} \frac{1 + 2 + \cdots + n}{n^2} = \lim_{n \to \infty} \frac{n(n+1)}{2n^2} = \lim_{n \to \infty} \frac{n+1}{2n} = \frac{1}{2}.$$

4.7.96 Note that

$$\ln \left(\frac{\sin x}{x} \right)^{1/x^2} = \frac{\ln \sin x - \ln x}{x^2},$$

so we evaluate

$$L = \lim_{x \to 0} \frac{\ln \sin x - \ln x}{x^2} = \lim_{x \to 0} \frac{\frac{\cos x}{\sin x} - \frac{1}{x}}{2x} = \lim_{x \to 0} \frac{x \cos x - \sin x}{2x^2 \sin x}$$

by l'Hôpital's rule. Next, observe that

$$\lim_{x \to 0} \frac{x \cos x - \sin x}{2x^2 \sin x} = \lim_{x \to 0} \frac{\cos x - x \sin x - \cos x}{4x \sin x + 2x^2 \cos x} = \lim_{x \to 0} \frac{-\frac{\sin x}{x}}{\frac{4 \sin x}{x} + 2 \cos x} = -\frac{1}{6}$$

using l'Hôpital's rule and $\lim_{x \to 0} \sin x / x = 1$. Therefore $\lim_{x \to 0} \left(\frac{\sin x}{x} \right)^{1/x^2} = e^L = e^{-1/6}$.

4.7.97

$$\lim_{x \to 1} \frac{x \ln x - x + 1}{x \ln^2 x} = \lim_{x \to 1} \frac{\ln x + x \cdot \frac{1}{x} - 1}{\ln^2 x + 2x \ln x \cdot \frac{1}{x}} = \lim_{x \to 1} \frac{\ln x}{\ln^2 x + 2 \ln x} = \lim_{x \to 1} \frac{1}{\ln x + 2} = \frac{1}{2},$$

where the first equality follows from l'Hôpital's rule and the penultimate follows by dividing the numerator and denominator by $\ln x$.

4.7.98

$$\lim_{x \to 1} \frac{x \ln x + \ln x - 2x + 2}{x^2 \ln^3 x} = \lim_{x \to 1} \frac{\ln x + x \cdot \frac{1}{x} + \frac{1}{x} - 2}{2x \ln^3 x + x^2 \cdot 3 \ln^2 x \cdot \frac{1}{x}}$$

$$= \lim_{x \to 1} \frac{\ln x + \frac{1}{x} - 1}{2x \ln^3 x + 3x \ln^2 x}$$

$$= \lim_{x \to 1} \frac{\frac{1}{x} - \frac{1}{x^2}}{2 \ln^3 x + 6x \ln^2 x \cdot \frac{1}{x} + 3 \ln^2 x + 6x \ln x \cdot \frac{1}{x}}$$

$$= \lim_{x \to 1} \frac{\frac{-1}{x^2} + \frac{2}{x^3}}{6 \ln x \cdot \frac{1}{x} + 12 \ln x \cdot \frac{1}{x} + 6 \ln x \cdot \frac{1}{x} + \frac{6}{x}}$$

$$= \frac{1}{6},$$

where each equality except the second follows from l'Hôpital's rule.

4.7.99 Let $z = \ln x^{\frac{1}{1 + \ln x}}$. Then $z = \frac{\ln x}{1 + \ln x}$, and $\lim_{x \to 0^+} z = \lim_{x \to 0^+} \frac{\ln x}{1 + \ln x} = \lim_{x \to 0^+} \frac{1/x}{1/x} = \lim_{x \to 0^+} 1 = 1$. Then $\lim_{x \to 0^+} e^z = \lim_{x \to 0^+} x^{\frac{1}{1 + \ln x}} = e^1 = e$.

4.7.100 Let $z = \frac{1}{n}$. Then as $n \to \infty$ we have $z \to 0^+$. Then

$$\lim_{n\to\infty} \cot(1/n) - n = \lim_{z\to 0^+} \cot z - \frac{1}{z} = \lim_{z\to 0^+} \frac{\cos z}{\sin z} - \frac{1}{z}$$
$$= \lim_{z\to 0^+} \frac{z\cos z - \sin z}{z\sin z}$$
$$= \lim_{z\to 0^+} \frac{\cos z - z\sin z - \cos z}{\sin z + z\cos z}$$
$$= \lim_{z\to 0^+} \frac{-z\sin z}{\sin z + z\cos z}$$
$$= \lim_{z\to 0^+} \frac{-\sin z + -z\cos z}{\cos z + \cos z - z\sin z}$$
$$= \frac{0+0}{1+1-0} = 0,$$

where the fourth and sixth equalities follow from l'Hôpital's rule.

4.7.101 Let $z = \frac{1}{n}$. Then as $n \to \infty$ we have $z \to 0^+$. Then

$$\lim_{n\to\infty} n\cot(1/n) - n^2 = \lim_{z\to 0^+} \frac{\cot z}{z} - \frac{1}{z^2}$$
$$= \lim_{z\to 0^+} \frac{z\cos z - \sin z}{z^2\sin z}$$
$$= \lim_{z\to 0^+} \frac{\cos z - z\sin z - \cos z}{2z\sin z + z^2\cos z}$$
$$= \lim_{z\to 0^+} \frac{-\sin z}{2\sin z + z\cos z}$$
$$= \lim_{z\to 0^+} \frac{-\cos z}{2\cos z + \cos z - z\sin z}$$
$$= -\frac{1}{2+1-0} = -\frac{1}{3},$$

where the third and fifth equalities follow from l'Hôpital's rule.

4.7.102 The given limit can be written as $\displaystyle\lim_{n\to\infty} \frac{\ln(n\sin(1/n))}{\frac{1}{n^2}}$, and by l'Hôpital's rule this is equal to $\displaystyle\lim_{n\to\infty} \frac{1}{n\sin(1/n)} \cdot \frac{\sin(1/n) + n\cos(1/n)\left(\frac{-1}{n^2}\right)}{\frac{-2}{n^3}} = \lim_{n\to\infty}\left(-\frac{n^2}{2} + \frac{n\cot(1/n)}{2}\right)$. This is exactly $\frac{1}{2}$ times the limit in the previous problem, so it is equal to $\frac{1}{2} \cdot -\frac{1}{3} = -\frac{1}{6}$.

4.7.103

a. Approximately 3.43×10^{15}.

b. Approximately 3536.

c. We can explicitly solve for x in this case: $x^{x/100} = e^x \implies x^{1/100} = e \implies x = e^{100}$.

d. Approximately 163.

4.7.104 Note that $\ln(1+ax)^{b/x} = b\ln(1+ax)/x$, so we evaluate

$$L = \lim_{x\to 0} \frac{b\ln(1+ax)}{x} = b\lim_{x\to 0} \frac{\frac{a}{1+ax}}{1} = ab$$

by l'Hôpital's rule. Therefore $\lim_{x\to 0}(1+ax)^{b/x} = e^L = e^{ab}$.

4.7.105 Note that $\ln(a^x - b^x)^x = x \ln(a^x - b^x)$, so we evaluate

$$L = \lim_{x \to 0^+} x \ln(a^x - b^x) = \lim_{x \to 0^+} \frac{\ln(a^x - b^x)}{1/x} = \lim_{x \to 0^+} -x^2 \left(\frac{(\ln a)a^x - (\ln b)b^x}{a^x - b^x} \right)$$

by l'Hôpital's rule. We have $\displaystyle\lim_{x \to 0^+} -x^2 \left(\frac{(\ln a)a^x - (\ln b)b^x}{a^x - b^x} \right) = -\lim_{x \to 0^+} x \left((\ln a)a^x - (\ln b)b^x \right) \frac{x}{a^x - b^x}$ and one more application of l'Hôpital's rule gives $\displaystyle\lim_{x \to 0^+} \frac{x}{a^x - b^x} = \lim_{x \to 0^+} \frac{1}{(\ln a)a^x - (\ln b)b^x} = \frac{1}{\ln a - \ln b}$, so $L = 0$ and therefore $\displaystyle\lim_{x \to 0^+} (a^x - b^x)^x = e^L = 1$.

4.7.106 Note that $\lim_{x \to 0^+} a^x = 1$ and $\lim_{x \to 0^+} b^x = 1$, so we have $\lim_{x \to 0^+} (a^x - b^x) = 1 - 1 = 0$. Also note that $\lim_{x \to 0^+} \frac{1}{x} = \infty$. Thus we do not have an indeterminate form, but rather a 0^∞ form, and this limit is 0 (see the answer to Quick Check 4 for further discussion).

4.7.107 Apply l'Hôpital's rule: $\displaystyle\lim_{x \to 0} \frac{a^x - b^x}{x} = \lim_{x \to 0} \frac{(\ln a)a^x - (\ln b)b^x}{1} = \ln a - \ln b$.

4.7.108 Observe that

$$\lim_{\delta \to 2m\pi} \frac{\sin^2(N\delta/2)}{\sin^2(\delta/2)} = \left(\lim_{\delta \to 2m\pi} \frac{\sin(N\delta/2)}{\sin(\delta/2)} \right)^2,$$

and

$$\lim_{\delta \to 2m\pi} \frac{\sin(N\delta/2)}{\sin(\delta/2)} = \lim_{\delta \to 2m\pi} \frac{(N/2)\cos(N\delta/2)}{(1/2)\cos(\delta/2)} = \pm N,$$

so $\displaystyle\lim_{\delta \to 2m\pi} \frac{\sin^2(N\delta/2)}{\sin^2(\delta/2)} = N^2$.

4.7.109

a. After each year the balance increases by the factor $1 + r$; therefore the balance after t years is $B(t) = P(1 + r)^t$.

b. Observe that

$$\lim_{m \to \infty} (1 + r/m)^m = \lim_{m \to \infty} \left(1 + \frac{1}{m/r} \right)^{(m/r)r} = e^r,$$

because $\displaystyle\lim_{n \to \infty} \left(1 + \frac{1}{n} \right)^n = e$. So with continuous compounding the balance after t years is $B(t) = Pe^{rt}$.

4.7.110 Note that $\sqrt{n} \log_2 n << n \log_2 n << n(\log_2 n)^2 << n^{3/2}$. For the last relation, we note that $n^{3/2}/n(\log_2 n)^2 = n^{1/2}/(\log_2 n)^2 \to \infty$ as $n \to \infty$. Therefore the ranking in order of least to most efficient is A, C, B, D.

4.7.111 L'Hôpital's rule gives $\displaystyle\lim_{x \to \infty} \frac{\sqrt{ax+b}}{\sqrt{cx+d}} = \lim_{x \to \infty} \frac{a}{\sqrt{ax+b}} \cdot \frac{\sqrt{cx+d}}{c} = \frac{a}{c} \lim_{x \to \infty} \frac{\sqrt{cx+d}}{\sqrt{ax+b}}$, which is the same form as the original limit, so l'Hôpital's rule fails in this case. We can evaluate this limit as follows: first observe that $\displaystyle\lim_{x \to \infty} \frac{ax+b}{cx+d} = \frac{a}{c}$ by l'Hôpital's rule; therefore $\displaystyle\lim_{x \to \infty} \frac{\sqrt{ax+b}}{\sqrt{cx+d}} = \lim_{x \to \infty} \sqrt{\frac{ax+b}{cx+d}} = \sqrt{\frac{a}{c}}$.

4.7.112 Observe that $(ax - \sqrt{a^2x^2 - bx}) \cdot \frac{(ax+\sqrt{a^2x^2-bx})}{(ax+\sqrt{a^2x^2-bx})} = \frac{bx}{(ax+\sqrt{a^2x^2-bx})} = \frac{b}{(a+\sqrt{a^2-b/x})}$, so $\displaystyle\lim_{x \to \infty} (ax - \sqrt{a^2x^2 - bx}) = \frac{b}{2a}$.

4.7.113 Let $t = b^x$, as in Example 8; then $x = \ln t / \ln b$ and we have $\displaystyle\lim_{x \to \infty} \frac{x^p}{b^x} = \lim_{t \to \infty} \frac{\ln^p t}{t \ln^p b} = 0$, by Theorem 4.15.

4.7.114 Observe that $\lim\limits_{x \to \infty} \dfrac{a^x}{b^x} = \lim\limits_{x \to \infty} \left(\dfrac{a}{b}\right)^x = \infty$, because $a/b > 1$.

4.7.115 Note that $\log_a x = \ln x / \ln a$, so $\dfrac{\log_a x}{\log_b x} = \dfrac{\ln b}{\ln a}$, and therefore $\log_a x$ and $\log_b x$ grow at a comparable rate as $x \to \infty$.

4.7.116 We have $b^n << n! << n^n$ as $n \to \infty$ for any $b > 1$. To see this, observe that $\lim\limits_{n \to \infty} \dfrac{n!}{b^n} =$
$\lim\limits_{n \to \infty} \dfrac{\sqrt{2\pi n}\, n^n}{(be)^n} = \infty$ and $\lim\limits_{n \to \infty} \dfrac{n!}{n^n} = \lim\limits_{n \to \infty} \dfrac{\sqrt{2\pi n}}{e^n} = 0$, by Theorem 4.15.

4.7.117 The triangle ABP has base $1 - \cos\theta$ and height $\sin\theta$, so its area is $f(\theta) = \frac{1}{2}\sin\theta(1 - \cos\theta)$. The sector OBP has area $\theta/2$, and the triangle OBP has base 1 and height $\sin\theta$; therefore $g(\theta) = \frac{1}{2}(\theta - \sin\theta)$.
We have $\lim\limits_{\theta \to 0} \dfrac{g(\theta)}{f(\theta)} = \lim\limits_{\theta \to 0} \dfrac{\theta - \sin\theta}{\sin\theta(1 - \cos\theta)} = \lim\limits_{\theta \to 0} \dfrac{\theta - \sin\theta}{\sin\theta - (1/2)\sin 2\theta}$. Three applications of l'Hôpital's rule
gives $\lim\limits_{\theta \to 0} \dfrac{g(\theta)}{f(\theta)} = \lim\limits_{\theta \to 0} \dfrac{1 - \cos\theta}{\cos\theta - \cos 2\theta} = \lim\limits_{\theta \to 0} \dfrac{\sin\theta}{2\sin 2\theta - \sin\theta} = \lim\limits_{\theta \to 0} \dfrac{\cos\theta}{4\cos 2\theta - \cos\theta} = \dfrac{1}{3}$.

4.7.118

a.

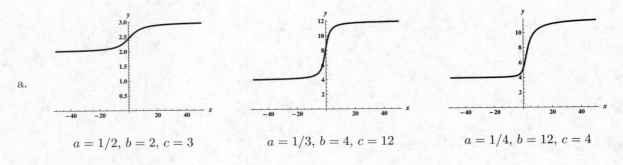

$a = 1/2$, $b = 2$, $c = 3$ $\qquad\qquad$ $a = 1/3$, $b = 4$, $c = 12$ $\qquad\qquad$ $a = 1/4$, $b = 12$, $c = 4$

b. Note that $\ln f(x) = \dfrac{\ln(ab^x + (1-a)c^x)}{x}$; l'Hôpital's rule gives $L = \lim\limits_{x \to 0} \dfrac{\ln(ab^x + (1-a)c^x)}{x}$

$= \lim\limits_{x \to 0} \dfrac{a(\ln b)b^x + (1-a)(\ln c)c^x}{ab^x + (1-a)c^x} = a\ln b + (1-a)\ln c$, and therefore

$$\lim_{x \to 0}(ab^x + (1-a)c^x)^{1/x} = e^L = b^a c^{1-a}.$$

c. Note that $\ln f(x) = \dfrac{\ln(ab^x + (1-a)c^x)}{x}$; l'Hôpital's rule gives $L = \lim\limits_{x \to \infty} \dfrac{\ln(ab^x + (1-a)c^x)}{x}$

$= \lim\limits_{x \to \infty} \dfrac{a(\ln b)b^x + (1-a)(\ln c)c^x}{ab^x + (1-a)c^x}$. Assume $c < b$. Then we have

$$\lim_{x \to \infty} \dfrac{a(\ln b)b^x + (1-a)(\ln c)c^x}{ab^x + (1-a)c^x} \cdot \dfrac{1/b^x}{1/b^x} = \lim_{x \to \infty} \dfrac{a(\ln b) + (1-a)(\ln c)(c/b)^x}{a + (1-a)(c/b)^x} = \ln b.$$

Then $\lim\limits_{x \to \infty} f(x) = b = \max\{c, b\}$. Similarly, if $b < c$, we have

$$\lim_{x \to \infty} \dfrac{a(\ln b)b^x + (1-a)(\ln c)c^x}{ab^x + (1-a)c^x} \cdot \dfrac{1/c^x}{1/c^x} = \lim_{x \to \infty} \dfrac{a(\ln b)(b/c)^x + (1-a)(\ln c)}{a(b/c)^x + (1-a)} = \ln c.$$

Then $\lim\limits_{x \to \infty} f(x) = c = \max\{c, b\}$.

Now consider the case $c > b$ as $x \to -\infty$.

$$\lim_{x \to -\infty} \dfrac{a(\ln b)b^x + (1-a)(\ln c)c^x}{ab^x + (1-a)c^x} \cdot \dfrac{1/b^x}{1/b^x} = \lim_{x \to -\infty} \dfrac{a(\ln b) + (1-a)(\ln c)(c/b)^x}{a + (1-a)(c/b)^x} = \ln b.$$

Then $\lim\limits_{x \to -\infty} f(x) = b = \min\{c, b\}$

Finally if $b > c$, we have

$$\lim_{x \to -\infty} \frac{a(\ln b)b^x + (1-a)(\ln c)c^x}{ab^x + (1-a)c^x} \cdot \frac{1/c^x}{1/c^x} = \lim_{x \to -\infty} \frac{a(\ln b)(b/c)^x + (1-a)(\ln c)}{a(b/c)^x + (1-a)} = \ln c.$$

Then $\lim\limits_{x \to -\infty} f(x) = c = \min\{c, b\}$.

d. The inflection point occurs at $x = 0$ in all cases.

4.7.119 Note that $\ln\left(1 + \frac{a}{x}\right)^x = \frac{\ln(1+a/x)}{1/x}$ so we evaluate $L = \lim\limits_{x \to \infty} \frac{\ln\left(1+a/x\right)}{1/x} = \lim\limits_{x \to \infty} \frac{1}{1+a/x} \cdot -\frac{a}{x^2}$. $\frac{1}{-1/x^2} = \lim\limits_{x \to \infty} \frac{a}{1+a/x} = a$ by l'Hôpital's rule. Therefore $\lim\limits_{x \to \infty} \left(1 + \frac{a}{x}\right)^x = e^L = e^a$.

4.7.120 Because $x \to \infty$, eventually $x > 2b$. Then $\frac{x^x}{b^x} > \frac{(2b)^x}{b^x} = 2^x \to \infty$ as $x \to \infty$, so x^x grows faster than b^x as $x \to \infty$.

4.7.121

a. Observe that $\lim\limits_{x \to \infty} \frac{b^x}{e^x} = \lim\limits_{x \to \infty} \left(\frac{b}{e}\right)^x$. This limit is ∞ exactly when $b > e$.

b. Observe that $\lim\limits_{x \to \infty} \frac{e^{ax}}{e^x} = \lim\limits_{x \to \infty} e^{(a-1)x}$. This limit is ∞ exactly when $a > 1$.

4.8 Newton's Method

4.8.1 Newton's method generates a sequence of x-intercepts of lines tangent to the graph of f to approximate the roots of f.

4.8.2 To get the x_{n+1} iterate from x_n, one puts x_n into the recursive formula and computes x_{n+1}. Thus, starting with x_0, a sequence $x_0, x_1, x_2, x_3, \ldots$ is generated.

4.8.3 Generally, if two successive Newton approximations agree in their first p digits, then those approximations have p digits of accuracy. The method is terminated when the desired accuracy is reached.

4.8.4 Because $f'(x_n) = 2x_n$, we have

$$x_{n+1} = x_n - \frac{x_n^2 - 5}{2x_n} = \frac{2x_n^2 - x_n^2 + 5}{2x_n} = \frac{x_n^2 + 5}{2x_n}.$$

4.8.5 Because $f'(x_n) = 2x_n$, we have

$$x_{n+1} = x_n - \frac{x_n^2 - 6}{2x_n} = \frac{2x_n^2 - x_n^2 + 6}{2x_n} = \frac{x_n^2 + 6}{2x_n}.$$

$x_1 = 2.5$ and $x_2 = 2.45$.

4.8.6 Because $f'(x_n) = 2x_n - 2$, we have

$$x_{n+1} = x_n - \frac{x_n^2 - 2x_n - 3}{2x_n - 2} = \frac{2x_n^2 - 2x_n - (x_n^2 - 2x_n - 3)}{2x_n - 2} = \frac{x_n^2 + 3}{2x_n - 2}.$$

$x_1 = 3.5$ and $x_2 = 3.05$.

4.8.7 Because $f'(x_n) = -e^{-x_n} - 1$, we have

$$x_{n+1} = x_n - \frac{e^{-x_n} - x_n}{-e^{-x_n} - 1} = \frac{(-e^{-x_n} - 1)x_n - (e^{-x_n} - x_n)}{-e^{-x_n} - 1} = \frac{-e^{-x_n}x_n - e^{-x_n}}{-e^{-x_n} - 1} = \frac{x_n + 1}{e^{x_n} + 1}.$$

$x_1 = 0.564382$ and $x_2 = 0.567142$.

4.8.8 Because $f'(x_n) = 3x_n^2$, we have

$$x_{n+1} = x_n - \frac{x_n^3 - 2}{3x_n^2} = \frac{3x_n^3 - (x_n^3 - 2)}{3x_n^2} = \frac{2x_n^3 + 2}{3x_n^2}.$$

$x_1 = 1.5$ and $x_2 = 1.2963$.

n	x_n
0	4.0
1	3.25
2	3.163462
3	3.162278
4	3.162278
5	3.162278
6	3.162278
7	3.162278
8	3.162278
9	3.162278
10	3.162278

4.8.9 Because $f'(x_n) = 2x_n$, we have
$x_{n+1} = x_n - \frac{x_n^2 - 10}{2x_n} = \frac{2x_n^2 - (x_n^2 - 10)}{2x_n} = \frac{x_n^2 + 10}{2x_n}.$

n	x_n
0	-2.0
1	-1.625
2	-1.48579
3	-1.46596
4	-1.46557
5	-1.46557
6	-1.46557
7	-1.46557
8	-1.46557
9	-1.46557
10	-1.46557

4.8.10 Because $f'(x_n) = 3x_n^2 + 2x_n$, we have
$x_{n+1} = x_n - \frac{x_n^3 + x_n^2 + 1}{3x_n^2 + 2x_n} = \frac{x_n(3x_n^2 + 2x_n) - (x_n^3 + x_n^2 + 1)}{3x_n^2 + 2x_n} = \frac{2x_n^3 + x_n^2 - 1}{3x_n^2 + 2x_n}.$

n	x_n
0	1.5
1	0.101436
2	0.501114
3	0.510961
4	0.510973
5	0.510973
6	0.510973
7	0.510973
8	0.510973
9	0.510973
10	0.510973

Because $f'(x_n) = \cos(x_n) + 1$, we have

4.8.11
$$x_{n+1} = x_n - \frac{\sin x_n + x_n - 1}{\cos x_n + 1}.$$

n	x_n
0	2.0
1	1.67668
2	1.61165
3	1.60944
4	1.60944
5	1.60944
6	1.60944
7	1.60944
8	1.60944
9	1.60944
10	1.60944

Because $f'(x_n) = e^{x_n}$, we have

4.8.12
$$x_{n+1} = x_n - \frac{e^{x_n} - 5}{e^{x_n}} = x_n + 5e^{-x_n} - 1.$$

n	x_n
0	1.5
1	1.44389
2	1.36198
3	1.26818
4	1.19618
5	1.16857
6	1.16559
7	1.16556
8	1.16556
9	1.16556
10	1.16556

Because $f'(x_n) = \sec^2(x_n) - 2$, we have

4.8.13
$$x_{n+1} = x_n - \frac{\tan x_n - 2x_n}{\sec^2(x_n) - 2}.$$

n	x_n
0	1.7
1	1.71822
2	1.71828
3	1.71828
4	1.71828
5	1.71828
6	1.71828
7	1.71828
8	1.71828
9	1.71828
10	1.71828

4.8.14 Because $f'(x_n) = \frac{1}{x_n+1}$, we have
$x_{n+1} = x_n - (\ln(x_n + 1) - 1)(x_n + 1) = 1 + 2x_n - (x_n + 1)\ln(x_n + 1)$.

4.8.15 A preliminary sketch of the two curves seems to indicate that they intersect once near $x = 2$.
  Let $f(x) = \sin x - x/2$. Then $f'(x_n) = \cos x_n - 1/2$. The Newton's method formula becomes

$$x_{n+1} = x_n - \frac{\sin x_n - x_n/2}{\cos x_n - 1/2}.$$

If we use an initial estimate of $x_0 = 2$, we obtain $x_1 = 1.901$, $x_2 = 1.89551$, $x_3 = 1.89549$ and $x_4 = 1.89549$, so the point of intersection appears to be at approximately $x = 1.89549$.

4.8.16 A preliminary sketch of the two curves seems to indicate that they intersect once near $x = 2$.
  Let $f(x) = e^x - x^3$. Then $f'(x_n) = e^{x_n} - 3x_n^2$. The Newton's method formula becomes

$$x_{n+1} = x_n - \frac{e^{x_n} - x_n^3}{e^{x_n} - 3x_n^2}.$$

If we use an initial estimate of $x_0 = 2$, we obtain $x_1 = 1.8675$, $x_2 = 1.85725$, $x_3 = 1.85718$, so the point of intersection appears to be at approximately $x = 1.857$.

4.8.17 A preliminary sketch of the two curves seems to indicate that they intersect three times, once between -2.5 and -2, once between 0 and 1/2, and once between 1.5 and 2.
  Let $f(x) = 4 - x^2 - 1/x$. Then $f'(x_n) = -2x_n + (1/x_n^2)$. The Newton's method formula becomes

$$x_{n+1} = x_n - \frac{4 - x_n^2 - (1/x_n)}{-2x_n + (1/x_n^2)}.$$

If we use an initial estimate of $x_0 = -2.25$, we obtain $x_1 = -2.11843$, $x_2 = -2.11491$, $x_3 = -2.11491$, so there appears to be a point of intersection near $x = -2.115$.
  If we use an initial estimate of $x_0 = .25$, we obtain $x_1 = .254032$, $x_2 = .254102$, so there appears to be a point of intersection near $x = .254$.
  If we use an initial estimate of $x_0 = 1.75$, we obtain $x_1 = 1.86535$, $x_2 = 1.86081$, so there appears to be another point of intersection near $x = 1.86$.

4.8.18 A preliminary sketch of the two curves seems to indicate that they intersect once, near $x = 1.5$.
  Let $f(x) = x^3 - (x^2 + 1)$. Then $f'(x_n) = 3x_n^2 - 2x_n$. The Newton's method formula becomes

$$x_{n+1} = x_n - \frac{x_n^3 - x_n^2 - 1}{3x_n^2 - 2x_n}.$$

If we use an initial estimate of $x_0 = 1.5$, we obtain $x_1 = 1.46667$, $x_2 = 1.46557$, $x_3 = 1.46557$, so there appears to be a point of intersection near $x = 1.46557$.

4.8.19 A preliminary sketch of the two curves seems to indicate that they intersect twice, once just to the right of 0, and once between 2 and 2.5.

Let $f(x) = 4\sqrt{x} - (x^2 + 1)$. Then $f'(x_n) = 2/\sqrt{x_n} - 2x_n$. The Newton's method formula becomes

$$x_{n+1} = x_n - \frac{4\sqrt{x_n} - (x_n^2 + 1)}{2/\sqrt{x_n} - 2x_n}.$$

If we use an initial estimate of $x_0 = .1$, we obtain $x_1 = .0583788$, $x_2 = .0629053$, $x_3 = .0629971$, so there appears to be a point of intersection near $x = .06299$.

If we use an initial estimate of $x_0 = 2.25$, we obtain $x_1 = 2.23026$, $x_2 = 2.23012$, $x_3 = 2.23012$, so there appears to be a point of intersection near $x = 2.23012$.

4.8.20 A preliminary sketch of the two curves seems to indicate that they intersect twice, once just to the right of 0, and once between 1 and 1.5

Let $f(x) = \ln x - (x^3 - 2)$. Then $f'(x_n) = 1/x_n - 3x_n^2$. The Newton's method formula becomes

$$x_{n+1} = x_n - \frac{\ln x_n - (x_n^3 - 2)}{1/x_n - 3x_n^2}.$$

If we use an initial estimate of $x_0 = .1$, we obtain $x_1 = .13045$, $x_2 = .13557$, $x_3 = .135674$, so there appears to be a point of intersection near $x = .13567$.

If we use an initial estimate of $x_0 = 1.4$, we obtain $x_1 = 1.32111$, $x_2 = 1.31501$, $x_3 = 1.31498$, so there appears to be a point of intersection near $x = 1.31498$.

4.8.21 $f'(x) = \frac{-x\sin x - \cos x}{x^2}$, which is zero when $x\sin x + \cos x = 0$. Note that $f'(1) < 0$ and $f'(\pi) > 0$, so there must be a local minimum on the interval $(1, \pi)$. Let $g(x) = x\sin x + \cos x$. Then $g'(x_n) = \sin x_n + x_n \cos x_n - \sin x_n = x_n \cos x_n$, and the Newton's method formula becomes

$$x_{n+1} = x_n - \frac{x_n \sin x_n + \cos x_n}{x_n \cos x_n}.$$

If we use an initial estimate of $x_0 = 2.5$, we obtain $x_1 = 2.84702$, $x_2 = 2.79918$, $x_3 = 2.79839$, $x_4 = 2.79839$, so the smallest local minimum of f on $(0, \infty)$ occurs at approximately 2.79839.

4.8.22 $f'(x) = 12x^3 + 24x^2 + 24x + 48 = 12(x^3 + 2x^2 + 2x + 4)$. We are seeking values of x so that $x^3 + 2x^2 + 2x + 4 = 0$. Using Newton's method with an initial estimate of -1.5, we obtain $x_1 = -2.27273$, $x_2 = -2.04023$, $x_3 = -2.00104$, and $x_4 \approx -2$. We realize that $x = -2$ is a root of $f'(x)$. Using long division (by $x + 2$), we see that $f'(x) = 12(x + 2)(x^2 + 2)$, so $f'(x)$ has only the one root of -2.

Note that $f'(-3) < 0$ and $f'(0) > 0$, so there is a local (in fact, absolute) minimum at $x = -2$.

4.8.23 $f'(x) = 9x^4 - 30x^3 + 7x^2 + 60x$ and $f''(x) = 36x^3 - 90x^2 + 14x + 60 = 2(18x^3 - 45x^2 + 7x + 30)$. We are seeking roots of $f''(x)$. If we apply Newton's method to f'' we obtain the recursion

$$x_{n+1} = x_n - \frac{36x_n^3 - 90x_n^2 + 14x_n + 60}{108x_n^2 - 180x_n + 14}.$$

Starting with an initial estimate of $x_0 = 1$, we obtain $x_1 = 1.34483$, $x_2 = 1.45527$, $x_3 = 1.49284$, $x_4 = 1.49974$, and $x_5 \approx 1.5$. We check directly that 1.5 is a root of f'', so $2x - 3$ is a factor of f'', and using long division, we see that $f''(x) = 2(2x - 3)(9x^2 - 9x - 10) = 2(2x - 3)(3x + 2)(3x - 5)$. So the potential inflection points of f are located at $x = -2/3$, $x = 3/2$, and $x = 5/3$. A check of the sign of f'' on the various intervals confirms that these are all the locations of inflection points.

4.8.24 The domain of f is $(-\infty, 0) \cup (0, \infty)$. $f'(x) = \frac{xe^x - e^x}{x^2} = \frac{e^x(x-1)}{x^2}$. This is 0 for $x = 1$. Note that $f'(1/2) < 0$ and $f'(2) > 0$, so there is a local minimum at $x = 1$. The point $(1, e)$ is the only extreme point. However, the questions calls for a solution via Newton's Method, so we attempt to solve the equation $\frac{xe^x - e^x}{x^2} = 0$ for x via Newton's Method. The recursion is given by

$$x_{n+1} = x_n - \frac{(x_n e^{x_n} - e^{x_n})/x_n^2}{e^{x_n}\left(x_n^2 - 2x_n + 2\right)/x_n^3}.$$

. Starting with an initial estimate of $x_0 = 0.5$, we obtain $x_1 = 0.7$, $x_2 = 0.89266$, $x_3 = 0.98739$, $x_4 = 0.999839$, and $x_5 \approx 1$.

4.8.25 The recursion for $f(x)$ is $x_{n+1} = x_n - \frac{(x_n-1)^2}{2x_n-2} = \frac{2x_n^2 - 2x_n - (x_n^2 - 2x_n + 1)}{2x_n - 2} = \frac{x_n^2 - 1}{2(x_n-1)} = \frac{x_n + 1}{2}$.

The recursion for $g(x)$ is $y_{n+1} = y_n - \frac{y_n^2 - 1}{2y_n} = \frac{2y_n^2 - (y_n^2 - 1)}{2y_n} = \frac{y_n^2 + 1}{2y_n}$. The comparison below shows that Newton's method converges much faster for $g(x) = x^2 - 1$. This is because it is steeper near the root $x = 1$ – the value of $g'(1) = 2$, while $f'(1) = 0$. The flatness of f near 1 causes slow convergence.

n	x_n
0	2
1	1.5
2	1.25
3	1.125
4	1.0625
5	1.03125
6	1.01563
7	1.00781
8	1.00391
9	1.00195
10	1.00098

n	y_n
0	2
1	1.25
2	1.025
3	1.0003
4	≈ 1

4.8.26 The Newton's method recursion is given by

$$x_{n+1} = x_n - \frac{x_n^5 + 4x_n^4 + x_n^3 - 10x_n^2 - 4x_n + 8}{5x_n^4 + 16x_n^3 + 3x_n^2 - 20x_n - 4}.$$

We obtain the following, based on the different initial values:

n	x_n
0	-1
1	-1.5
2	-1.69231
3	-1.80333
4	-1.8721
5	-1.91604
6	-1.94457

n	x_n
0	-0.2
1	undefined

n	x_n
0	.2
1	1.08
2	1.0415
3	1.02117
4	1.01069
5	1.00537
6	1.00269

n	x_n
0	2
1	1.63636
2	1.38434
3	1.22014
4	1.12031
5	1.06344
6	1.03268

The initial estimate of -0.2 doesn't work because that number is a root of $f'(x)$. The others converge, with the initial values near $x = 1$ converging faster because the function is steeper near $x = 1$ than it is near $x = -2$.

4.8.27

a. True.

b. False. The quadratic formula gives exact values.

c. False. It sometime fails depending on factors such as the shape of the curve and the closeness of the initial estimate.

4.8.28 Let $g(x) = 5 - x^2 - x$. Fixed points of f are roots of g. Because this is a quadratic, we can find the roots of g directly with the quadratic formula. The roots are $\frac{1 \pm \sqrt{1 - (4)(-1)(5)}}{-2} = \frac{-1}{2} \pm \frac{\sqrt{21}}{2}$. Thus the fixed points of f are approximately -2.79129 and 1.79129.

4.8.29 Let $g(x) = x^3/10 + 1 - x$. Fixed points of f are roots of g. The Newton's method recursion for g is given by

$$x_{n+1} = x_n - \frac{x_n^3/10 + 1 - x_n}{3x_n^2/10 - 1} = x_n - \frac{x_n^3 + 10 - 10x_n}{3x_n^2 - 10} = \frac{2(x_n^3 - 5)}{3x_n^2 - 10}.$$

A preliminary sketch of g indicates that there are three roots, near -3.5, 1, and 2.5.

n	x_n
0	-3.5
1	-3.57944
2	-3.57709
3	-3.57709

n	x_n
0	1
1	1.14286
2	1.1534
3	1.15347
4	1.15347

n	x_n
0	2.5
1	2.42857
2	2.42365
3	2.42362
4	2.42362

The fixed points of f are approximately -3.57709, 1.15347, and 2.42362.

4.8.30 Let $g(x) = \tan(x/2) - x$. Fixed points of f are roots of g. The Newton's method recursion for g is given by

$$x_{n+1} = x_n - \frac{\tan(x_n/2) - x_n}{(1/2)\sec^2(x_n/2) - 1}.$$

A preliminary sketch of g indicates that there are three roots, near $x = 0$ and $x = \pm 2.3$

n	x_n
0	-1.2
1	0.739493
2	-0.0887636
3	0.000116976
4	≈ 0

n	x_n
0	-2.3
1	-2.33281
2	-2.33113
3	-2.33112
4	-2.33112
5	-2.33112

n	x_n
0	2.3
1	2.33281
2	2.33113
3	2.33112
4	2.33112
5	2.33112

The fixed points are 0 and approximately ± 2.33112.

4.8.31 Let $g(x) = 2x\cos x - x$. Fixed points of f are roots of g. Clearly $x = 0$ is a root of g. The Newton's method recursion for g is given by

$$x_{n+1} = x_n - \frac{2x_n \cos x_n - x_n}{2\cos x_n - 2x_n \sin x_n - 1}.$$

A preliminary sketch of g indicates that there is only one nonzero root on $[0, 2]$, near $x = 1$. We have:

n	x_n
0	1
1	1.0503
2	1.04721
3	1.0472
4	1.0472

The fixed points are 0 and approximately 1.0472.

4.8.32 A preliminary sketch of f indicates that there are two roots on $[0, 2\pi]$, near $x = 1.5$. and $x = 5.5$

The Newton's method recursion for f is given by

$$x_{n+1} = x_n - \frac{\cos x_n - (x_n/7)}{-\sin x_n - (1/7)}.$$

We have:

n	x_n
0	5.5
1	5.63692
2	5.65202
3	5.65222
4	5.65222

n	x_n
0	1.5
1	1.37412
2	1.37333
3	1.37333

The roots are approximately 5.65222 and 1.37333.

4.8.33 A preliminary sketch of f indicates that there are two roots, near $x = -0.4$. and $x = 1.3$
The Newton's method recursion for f is given by

$$x_{n+1} = x_n - \frac{\cos(2x_n) - x_n^2 + 2x_n}{-2\sin(2x_n) - 2x_n + 2}.$$

We have:

n	x_n
0	-0.4
1	-0.337825
2	-0.335412
3	-0.335408
4	-0.335408

n	x_n
0	1.3
1	1.33256
2	1.33306
3	1.33306

The roots are approximately -0.335408 and 1.33306.

4.8.34 A preliminary sketch of f indicates that there are two roots on $[0, 8]$, near $x = 6.1$. and $x = 6.9$
The Newton's method recursion for f is given by

$$x_{n+1} = x_n - \frac{x_n/6 - \sec x_n}{1/6 - \sec x_n \tan x_n}.$$

We have:

n	x_n
0	6.1
1	6.10098
2	6.10099
3	6.10099

n	x_n
0	6.9
1	6.79197
2	6.76435
3	6.7627
4	6.7627

The roots are approximately 6.10099 and 6.7627.

4.8.35 A preliminary sketch of f indicates that there is one root, near $x = 0.2$
The Newton's method recursion for f is given by

$$x_{n+1} = x_n - \frac{e^{-x_n} - (x_n + 4)/5}{-e^{-x_n} - 1/5}.$$

We have:

n	x_n
0	0.2
1	0.179122
2	0.179295
3	0.179295

The root is approximately 0.179295.

4.8.36 A preliminary sketch of f indicates that there are three roots, near $x = -1$. $x = -0.7$ and $x = 1.2$. In fact, -1 is a root because $f(-1) = (-1/5) - (-1/4) - (1/20) = 0$.

The Newton's method recursion for f is given by

$$x_{n+1} = x_n - \frac{x_n^5/5 - x_n^3/4 - 1/20}{x_n^4 - 3x_n^2/4}.$$

We have:

n	x_n
0	-0.7
1	-0.683234
2	-0.683551
3	-0.683551

n	x_n
0	1.2
1	1.18424
2	1.18355
3	1.18355

The roots are -1 and approximately -0.683551 and 1.18355.

4.8.37 A preliminary sketch of f indicates that there are two roots, near $x = .5$ and near $x = 3$.

The Newton's method recursion for f is given by

$$x_{n+1} = x_n - \frac{\ln x_n - x_n^2 + 3x_n - 1}{(1/x_n) - 2x_n + 3}.$$

We have:

n	x_n
0	.5
1	.610787
2	.620655
3	.620723
4	.620723

n	x_n
0	3
1	3.03698
2	3.03645
3	3.03645

The roots are approximately $.620723$ and 3.03645.

4.8.38 A preliminary sketch of f indicates that there are three roots; two near $x = 0$ and one near $x = 100$. To avoid division by 0, we use initial estimates of $x_0 = \pm 0.1$ and $x_0 = 100$.

The Newton's method recursion for f is given by

$$x_{n+1} = x_n - \frac{x_n^3 - 100x_n^2 + 1}{3x_n^2 - 200x_n}.$$

We have:

n	x_n
0	-0.1
1	-0.0999501
2	-0.0999501

n	x_n
0	.1
1	.10005
2	.10005

n	x_n
0	100
1	99.9999
2	99.9999

The roots are approximately ± 0.100 and 100.000.

4.8.39 Because the residuals become small quickly, the convergence of x_n is quite slow. This is related to the extreme flatness of the graph of x^{10} between 0 and 1/2.

n	x_n	Error	Residual
0	.5	.5	.000976563
1	.45	.45	.000340506
2	.405	.405	.000118727
3	.3645	.3645	.0000413976
4	.32805	.32805	.0000144345
5	.295245	.295245	5.03298×10^{-6}
6	.265721	.265721	1.75489×10^{-6}
7	.239148	.239148	6.11893×10^{-7}
8	.215234	.215234	2.13354×10^{-7}
9	.19371	.19371	7.43919×10^{-8}
10	.174339	.174339	2.59389×10^{-8}

4.8.40 The graphs of $y = \sin x$ together with $y = \frac{x}{a}$ for $a = 2$, $a = 9$, and a value of a such that there are precisely two points of intersection are shown below:

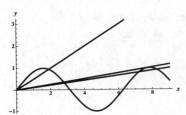

We want to find a point $(b, \sin b)$ on the graph of $y = \sin x$ such that the line joining $(0, 0)$ and $(b, \sin b)$ is tangent to $y = \sin x$ at $(b, \sin b)$. Comparing slopes gives $\frac{\sin b}{b} = \cos b$, or $b - \tan b = 0$. This equation has a root $b \approx 7.725$. The corresponding value of $a = \sec b \approx 7.790$.

4.8.41 The graphs of $y = x$ together ith $y = e^{x/a}$ for $a = 1$, $a = 3$, and a such that there is precisely one point of intersection are shown below:

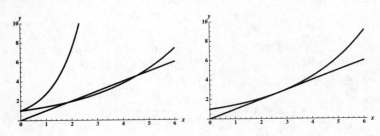

We want to find a point (b, b) on the graph of $y = e^{x/a}$. where the slope is 1. Hence we need $b = e^{b/a}$ and $1 = \frac{1}{a}e^{b/a}$. Dividing these equations gives $b = a$ and thus $a = e^{a/a} = e$.

4.8.42

   a. If r is a root of $x^2 - a$, then $r^2 - a = 0$, so $r^2 = a$, and $|r| = \sqrt{a}$, so either $r = \sqrt{a}$ or $r = -\sqrt{a}$. If we also insist that $r > 0$, then $r = \sqrt{a}$.

b. The Newton's method recursion is

$$x_{n+1} = x_n - \frac{x_n^2 - a}{2x_n} = \frac{2x_n^2 - (x_n^2 - a)}{2x_n} = \frac{x_n^2 + a}{2x_n} = \frac{1}{2}\left(x_n + \frac{a}{x_n}\right).$$

c. Because $3^2 = 9 < 13$ and $4^2 = 16 > 13$, a good starting value for $\sqrt{13}$ would be a number between 3 and 4 (but closer to 4), like 3.6.

Because $8^2 = 64 < 73$ and $9^2 = 81 > 73$, a good starting value for $\sqrt{73}$ would be a number between 8 and 9, like 8.5.

d. The first chart is for $\sqrt{13}$ and the second is for $\sqrt{73}$.

n	x_n
0	3.6
1	3.605555555556
2	3.60555127547
3	3.6055127546
4	3.6055127546
5	3.6055127546
6	3.6055127546
7	3.6055127546
8	3.6055127546
9	3.6055127546
10	3.6055127546

n	x_n
0	8.5
1	8.54411764706
2	8.54400374608
3	8.54400374532
4	8.54400374532
5	8.54400374532
6	8.54400374532
7	8.54400374532
8	8.54400374532
9	8.54400374532
10	8.54400374532

4.8.43

a. The Newton's method formula would be:

$$x_{n+1} = x_n - \frac{1/x_n - a}{-1/x_n^2} = x_n + x_n - ax_n^2 = 2x_n - ax_n^2 = (2 - ax_n)x_n.$$

b. The approximation to $1/7$ is .14285714.

n	x_n
0	.1
1	.13
2	.1417
3	.14284777
4	.14285714
5	.14285714

4.8.44

a. Note that $f(0) = 0$, and $f'(x) = 2e^{2\sin x}\cos x - 2$, so $f'(0) = 2e^0 - 2 = 0$. Also, $f''(x) = 4e^{2\sin(x)}\cos^2(x) - 2e^{2\sin(x)}\sin(x)$, so $f''(0) = 4 \neq 0$. Thus, 0 is a root of multiplicity 2 for f.

b. The first chart is for the traditional Newton's method, and the second is for the modified version. Clearly, x_3 for the modified method is much closer to the actual root.

n	x_n
0	.1
1	.0511487
2	.0258883
3	.0130263

n	x_n
0	.1
1	.00229741
2	.00000131725
3	-3.07429×10^{-11}

c. In example 4, the value of x_3 was .0171665. For the modified version, we obtain:

n	x_n
0	.15
1	-0.010125
2	.00000311391
3	-9.05817×10^{-17}

Clearly the modified version converges much more quickly to the root of multiplicity two at 0.

4.8.45

a. We are seeking the time t when first $y(t) = 2.5e^{-t}\cos 2t$ is zero. This occurs first for $t = \pi/4$.

b. We are seeking the minimum value for y. We have $y'(t) = -2.5e^{-t}\cos 2t + 2.5e^{-t}(-2\sin 2t) = -2.5e^{-t}(\cos 2t + 2\sin 2t)$. This is zero when $\cos 2t = -2\sin 2t$, or $\tan 2t = \frac{-1}{2}$. Let $f(t) = \tan 2t + \frac{1}{2}$. If we apply Newton's method to $f(t)$ with a starting point of $t_0 = 1$, we obtain a root of 1.33897 after five iterations. An application of the First Derivative Test shows that there is a local minimum for y at this number. The displacement at this time is -0.586107. This local minimum is in fact an absolute minimum.

c. The second time that $y(t) = 2.5e^{-t}\cos 2t$ is zero is when $2t = \frac{3\pi}{2}$, or $t = 3\pi/4$.

d. Following our work in part b, we look for a root of $f(t) = \tan 2t + \frac{1}{2}$ that is bigger than 1.33897. From the graph, we are looking near $t = 3$. Applying Newton's method to $f(t)$ with an initial value of $x_0 = 3$ gives a root 2.90977 after three iterations. Applying the First Derivative Test, we see that there is a local maximum of 0.12181 at $x = 2.90977$.

4.8.46

a.
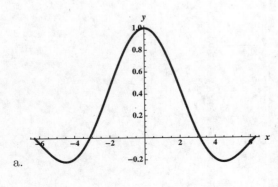

b. $f'(x) = \frac{x\cos x - \sin x}{x^2}$. This is zero when $x\cos x - \sin x = 0$, or $x - \tan x = 0$. Let $g(x) = x - \tan x$. If we apply Newton's method to g with a starting value of $x_0 = 4.5$, we obtain a root at 4.49341 after 2 iterations. The First Derivative Test confirms that there is a local minimum of about -0.217234 at $x = 4.49341$. Applying Newton's method to g with a starting value of 7.8 yields the root 7.72525 after 5 iterations. The First Derivative Test confirms that there is a local maximum of about .128375 at $x = 7.2525$.

4.8.47 Let $f(\lambda) = \tan(\pi\lambda) - \lambda$. We are looking for the first three positive roots of f. A preliminary sketch indicates that they are located near 1.4, 2.4, and 3.4. The Newton's method recursion is given by

$$x_{n+1} = x_n - \frac{\tan(\pi x_n) - x_n}{\pi \sec^2(\pi x_n) - 1}.$$

We obtain the following results:

n	x_n
0	1.4
1	1.34741
2	1.30555
3	1.29121
4	1.29012
5	1.29011
6	1.29011

n	x_n
0	2.4
1	2.37876
2	2.37331
3	2.37305
4	2.37305

n	x_n
0	3.4
1	3.4101
2	3.40919
3	3.40918
4	3.40918

The first three positive eigenvalues are approximately 1.29011, 2.37305, and 3.40918.

4.8.48

a. We are seeking solutions of $f(x) = ax(1-x) = x$. This can be written as $ax^2 + x(1-a) = 0$, or $x(ax + (1-a)) = 0$. The solutions of this equation are $x = 0$ and $x = \frac{a-1}{a}$. If $0 < a < 1$, this does not give a value of x in the range $(0,1)$. If $1 \le a \le 4$, we do get a fixed point $x = \frac{a-1}{a}$.

b. $g(x) = f(f(x)) = f(ax(1-x)) = a(ax(1-x))(1 - ax(1-x)) = (a^2x - a^2x^2)(1 - ax + ax^2) = a^2x - a^2x^2 - a^3x^2 + a^3x^3 + a^3x^3 - a^3x^4 = a^2x - a^2x^2 - a^3x^2 + 2a^3x^3 - a^3x^4$. This is a fourth degree polynomial.

c. From left to right, with $a = 2$, then $a = 3$, then $a = 4$:

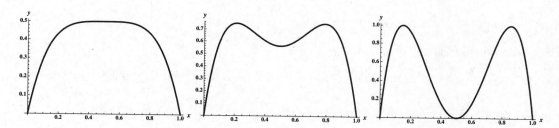

d. The graphs of $y = g(x)$ together with $y = x$ for $a = 2$, then $a = 3$, then $a = 4$.

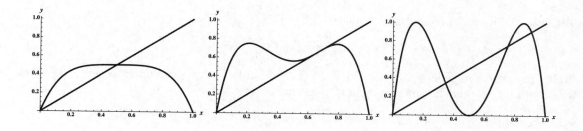

When $a = 2$, we have $g(x) = -8x^4 + 16x^3 - 12x^2 + 4x$, so we are looking for a root of $g(x) - x = -8x^4 + 16x^3 - 12x^2 + 4x - x = -8x^4 + 16x^3 - 12x^2 + 3x = x(-8x^3 + 16x^2 - 12x + 3)$. Clearly $x = 0$

is one root, and the diagram indicates that $g(x) = x$ near $x = .5$. A quick check shows that $x = .5$ is a root of $g(x) - x$, so .5 is a fixed point of g.

When $a = 3$, we have $g(x) = -27x^4 + 54x^3 - 36x^2 + 9x$, so we are looking for a root of $g(x) - x = -27x^4 + 54x^3 - 36x^2 + 9x - x = -27x^4 + 54x^3 - 36x^2 + 8x = x(-27x^3 + 54x^2 - 36x + 8)$. Clearly $x = 0$ is one root, and the diagram indicates that $g(x) = x$ near $x = .6$. Applying Newton's method to $g(x) - x$ with an initial estimate of .6 yields a root of approximately $.\overline{6} = 2/3$. A quick check shows that $2/3$ is a fixed point of g.

When $a = 4$, we have $g(x) = -64x^4 + 128x^3 - 80x^2 + 16x$, so we are looking for a root of $g(x) - x = -64x^4 + 128x^3 - 80x^2 + 16x - x = -64x^4 + 128x^3 - 80x^2 + 15x = x(-64x^3 + 128x^2 - 80x + 15)$. Clearly $x = 0$ is one root, and the diagram indicates that $g(x) = x$ near $x = .3$ and $x = .75$ and $x = .9$. Checking the value of $.75 = 3/4$, we confirm that $g(3/4) = 3/4$. Applying Newton's method to $g(x) - x$ with an initial estimate of .3 yields a root of approximately .345492, and applying it with an initial estimate of .9 yields a root of approximately .904508.

Thus the fixed points of g with $a = 4$ are 0, .345492, .75, and .904508.

4.8.49 This problem can be solved (approximately) by setting up a computer or calculator program to run Newton's method, and then experimenting with different starting values. If this is done, it can be seen that any initial estimate between -4 and the local maximum at approximately -1.53 converges to the root at -2. Initial values between approximately -1.52 and -1.486 converge to the root at 3, while starting values between -1.485 and -1.475 converge to the root at -2. From -1.474 to approximately .841, starting values lead to convergence to the root at -1, while from .842 to .846 they lead to convergence to the root at -2. From about .847 to .862 they lead to convergence to the root at 3, while from .863 to the local minimum at 1.528 they lead to convergence to the root at -2. From about 1.528 to 4, the convergence is to the root at 3. Thus the approximate basis of convergence for -2 is $[-4, -1.53] \cup [-1.485, -1.475] \cup [.842, .846]$. For -1 the approximate basis of convergence is $[-1.474, .841]$, and for 3, it is $[-1.52, -1.486] \cup [.847, .862] \cup [1.53, 4]$.

4.9 Antiderivatives

4.9.1 Derivative, antiderivative.

4.9.2 C, where C is any constant.

4.9.3 $x + C$, where C is any constant.

4.9.4 By Theorem 4.11, if two functions have the same derivative then they differ by a constant.

4.9.5 $\dfrac{x^{p+1}}{p+1} + C$, where C is any real number and $p \neq -1$.

4.9.6 $-e^{-x} + C$, where C is any constant.

4.9.7 $\ln|x| + C$, where C is any constant.

4.9.8 From Table 4.9, $\int \cos ax\, dx = \frac{1}{a} \sin ax + C$, $\int \sin ax\, dx = -\frac{1}{a} \cos ax + C$.

4.9.9 Observe that $F(-1) = 4 + C = 4$, so $C = 0$.

4.9.10 First, find the general solution $F(t)$, which is the family of all antiderivatives of $f(t)$. Then use the initial condition to find the specific value of the constant in the formula for $F(t)$.

4.9.11 The antiderivatives of $5x^4$ are $x^5 + C$. Check: $\frac{d}{dx}(x^5 + C) = 5x^4$.

4.9.12 The antiderivatives of $11x^{10}$ are $x^{11} + C$. Check: $\frac{d}{dx}(x^{11} + C) = 11x^{10}$.

4.9.13 The antiderivatives of $\sin 2x$ are $-(1/2) \cos 2x + C$. Check: $\frac{d}{dx}(-\frac{1}{2} \cos 2x + C) = \sin 2x$.

4.9.14 The antiderivatives of $-4\cos 4x$ are $-\sin 4x + C$. Check: $\frac{d}{dx}(-\sin 4x + C) = -\cos 4x$.

4.9.15 The antiderivatives of $3\sec^2 x$ are $3\tan x + C$. Check: $\frac{d}{dx}(3\tan x + C) = 3\sec^2 x$.

4.9.16 The antiderivatives of $\csc^2 s$ are $-\cot s + C$. Check: $\frac{d}{ds}(-\cot s + C) = \csc^2 s$.

4.9.17 The antiderivatives of $-2/y^3 = -2y^{-3}$ are $y^{-2} + C$. Check: $\frac{d}{dy}(y^{-2} + C) = -2y^{-3}$.

4.9.18 The antiderivatives of $-6z^{-7}$ are $z^{-6} + C$. Check: $\frac{d}{dz}(z^{-6} + C) = -6z^{-7}$.

4.9.19 The antiderivatives of e^x are $e^x + C$. Check: $\frac{d}{dx}(e^x + C) = e^x$.

4.9.20 The antiderivatives of y^{-1} are $\ln|y| + C$. Check: $\frac{d}{dy}(\ln|y| + C) = \frac{1}{y}$.

4.9.21 The antiderivatives of $\frac{1}{s^2+1}$ are $\tan^{-1} s + C$. Check: $\frac{d}{ds}(\tan^{-1}(s) + C) = \frac{1}{s^2+1}$.

4.9.22 The antiderivatives of π are $\pi t + C$. Check: $\frac{d}{dt}(\pi t + C) = \pi$.

4.9.23 $\int(3x^5 - 5x^9)\,dx = 3 \cdot \frac{x^6}{6} - 5 \cdot \frac{x^{10}}{10} + C = \frac{1}{2}x^6 - \frac{1}{2}x^{10} + C$. Check: $\frac{d}{dx}(\frac{1}{2}x^6 - \frac{1}{2}x^{10} + C) = 3x^5 - 5x^9$.

4.9.24 $\int(3u^{-2} - 4u^2 + 1)\,du = 3 \cdot \frac{u^{-1}}{-1} - 4 \cdot \frac{u^3}{3} + u + C = -\frac{4}{3}u^3 + u - \frac{3}{u} + C$. Check: $\frac{d}{du}(-\frac{4}{3}u^3 + u - \frac{3}{u} + C) = -4u^2 + 1 + 3u^{-2}$.

4.9.25 $\int\left(4\sqrt{x} - \frac{4}{\sqrt{x}}\right)dx = \int(4x^{1/2} - 4x^{-1/2})\,dx = 4 \cdot \frac{x^{3/2}}{3/2} - 4 \cdot \frac{x^{1/2}}{1/2} + C = \frac{8}{3}x^{3/2} - 8x^{1/2} + C$. Check: $\frac{d}{dx}(\frac{8}{3}x^{3/2} - 8x^{1/2} + C) = 4\sqrt{x} - \frac{4}{\sqrt{x}}$.

4.9.26 $\int\left(\frac{5}{t^2} + 4t^2\right)dt = 5 \cdot \frac{t^{-1}}{-1} + 4 \cdot \frac{t^3}{3} + C = \frac{4}{3}t^3 - \frac{5}{t} + C$. Check: $\frac{d}{dt}(\frac{4}{3}t^3 - \frac{5}{t} + C) = 4t^2 + \frac{5}{t^2}$.

4.9.27 Note that $\frac{d}{ds}(5s + 3)^3 = 15(5s + 3)^2$; therefore $\int(5s + 3)^2\,ds = \frac{(5s+3)^3}{15} + C$.

4.9.28 $\int 5m(12m^3 - 10m)\,dm = \int(60m^4 - 50m^2)\,dm = 60 \cdot \frac{m^5}{5} - 50 \cdot \frac{m^3}{3} + C = 12m^5 - \frac{50}{3}m^3 + C$. Check: $\frac{d}{dm}(12m^5 - \frac{50}{3}m^3 + C) = 5m(12m^3 - 10m)$.

4.9.29 $\int(3x^{1/3} + 4x^{-1/3} + 6)\,dx = 3 \cdot \frac{3}{4}x^{4/3} + 4 \cdot \frac{3}{2}x^{2/3} + 6x + C = \frac{9}{4}x^{4/3} + 6x^{2/3} + 6x + C$. Check: $\frac{d}{dx}(\frac{9}{4}x^{4/3} + 6x^{2/3} + 6x + C) = 3x^{1/3} + 4x^{-1/3} + 6$.

4.9.30 $\int 6\sqrt[3]{x}\,dx = \int 6x^{1/3}\,dx = 6 \cdot \frac{3}{4}x^{4/3} + C = \frac{9}{2}x^{4/3} + C$. Check $\frac{d}{dx}(\frac{9}{2}x^{4/3} + C) = 6\sqrt[3]{x}$.

4.9.31 $\int(3x + 1)(4 - x)\,dx = \int(12x - 3x^2 + 4 - x)\,dx = \int(-3x^2 + 11x + 4)\,dx = -x^3 + \frac{11}{2}x^2 + 4x + C$. Check: $\frac{d}{dx}\left(\frac{9}{2}x^{4/3} + C\right) = 6\sqrt[3]{x}$.

4.9.32 $\int(4z^{1/3} - z^{-1/3})\,dz = 3z^{4/3} - \frac{3}{2}z^{2/3} + C$. Check: $\frac{d}{dz}\left(3z^{4/3} - \frac{3}{2}z^{2/3} + C\right) = 4z^{1/3} - z^{-1/3}$.

4.9.33 $\int(3x^{-4} + 2 - 3x^{-2})\,dx = -x^{-3} + 2x + 3x^{-1} + C$. Check: $\frac{d}{dx}\left(-x^{-3} + 2x + 3x^{-1} + C\right) = 3x^{-4} + 2 - 3x^{-2}$.

4.9.34 $\int r^{2/5}\,dr = \frac{5}{7}r^{7/5} + C$. Check: $\frac{d}{dr}\left(\frac{5}{7}r^{7/5} + C\right) = r^{2/5}$.

4.9.35 $\int \frac{4x^4 - 6x^2}{x}\,dx = \int\left(\frac{4x^4}{x} - \frac{6x^2}{x}\right)dx = \int(4x^3 - 6x)\,dx = x^4 - 3x^2 + C$. Check: $\frac{d}{dx}\left(x^4 - 3x^2 + C\right) = 4x^3 - 6x$.

4.9.36 $\int \frac{12t^8 - t}{t^3}\,dt = \int\left(\frac{12t^8}{t^3} - \frac{t}{t^3}\right)dt = \int(12t^5 - t^{-2})\,dt = 2t^6 + t^{-1} + C$. Check: $\frac{d}{dt}\left(2t^6 + t^{-1} + C\right) = 12t^5 - t^{-2}$.

4.9.37 Using Table 4.9 (formulas 1 and 2), $\int (\sin 2y + \cos 3y)\, dy = -\frac{1}{2}\cos 2y + \frac{1}{3}\sin 3y + C$.
Check: $\frac{d}{dy}(-\frac{1}{2}\cos 2y + \frac{1}{3}\sin 3y + C) = \sin 2y + \cos 3y$.

4.9.38 Using Table 4.9 (formula 2), $\int \left[\sin 4t - \sin\left(\frac{t}{4}\right)\right] dt = -\frac{1}{4}\cos 4t + 4\cos\left(\frac{t}{4}\right) + C$. Check: $\frac{d}{dt}(-\frac{1}{4}\cos 4t + 4\cos\left(\frac{t}{4}\right) + C) = \sin 4t - \sin\left(\frac{t}{4}\right)$.

4.9.39 Using Table 4.9 (formula 3), $\int (\sec^2 x - 1)\, dx = \tan x - x + C$. Check: $\frac{d}{dx}(\tan x - x + C) = \sec^2 x - 1$.

4.9.40 Using Table 4.9 (formula 3), $\int 2\sec^2 2v\, dv = 2 \cdot \frac{1}{2}\tan 2v + C = \tan 2v + C$. Check: $\frac{d}{dv}(\tan 2v + C) = 2\sec^2 2v$.

4.9.41 Using Table 4.9 (formulas 3 and 5), $\int (\sec^2\theta + \sec\theta\tan\theta)\, d\theta = \tan\theta + \sec\theta + C$. Check: $\frac{d}{d\theta}(\tan\theta + \sec\theta + C) = \sec^2\theta + \sec\theta\tan\theta$.

4.9.42 Using Table 4.9 (formulas 3 and 5), $\int \frac{\sin\theta - 1}{\cos^2\theta}\, d\theta = \int (\sec\theta\tan\theta - \sec^2\theta)\, d\theta = \sec\theta - \tan\theta + C$. Check: $\frac{d}{d\theta}(\sec\theta - \tan\theta + C) = \sec\theta\tan\theta - \sec^2\theta = \frac{\sin\theta - 1}{\cos^2\theta}$.

4.9.43 $\int (3t^2 + \sec^2 2t)\, dt = t^3 + (1/2)\tan 2t + C$.

4.9.44 $\int \csc 3\phi\cot 3\phi\, d\phi = -\frac{1}{3}\csc 3\phi + C$. Check: $\frac{d}{d\phi}(-\frac{1}{3}\csc 3\phi + C) = -\frac{1}{3}(-3\csc 3\phi\cot 3\phi) = \csc 3\phi\cot 3\phi$.

4.9.45 $\int \sec 4\theta\tan 4\theta\, d\theta = \frac{1}{4}\sec 4\theta + C$. Check: $\frac{d}{d\theta}(\frac{1}{4}\sec 4\theta + C) = \frac{1}{4}(4\sec 4\theta\tan 4\theta) = \sec 4\theta\tan 4\theta$.

4.9.46 $\int \csc^2 6x\, dx = \frac{-1}{6}\cot 6x + C$. Check: $\frac{d}{dx}(-\frac{1}{6}\cot 6x + C) = -\frac{1}{6}(-6\csc^2 6x) = \csc^2 6x$.

4.9.47 $\int \frac{1}{2y}\, dy = \frac{1}{2}\int y^{-1}\, dy = \frac{1}{2}\ln|y| + C$. Check: $\frac{d}{dy}(\frac{1}{2}\ln|y| + C) = \frac{1}{2y}$.

4.9.48 $\int (e^{2t} + 2\sqrt{t})\, dt = \frac{1}{2}e^{2t} + 2 \cdot \frac{2}{3}t^{3/2} + C = \frac{1}{2}e^{2t} + \frac{4}{3}t^{3/2} + C$. Check: $\frac{d}{dt}(\frac{1}{2}e^{2t} + \frac{4}{3}t^{3/2} + C) = e^{2t} + 2\sqrt{t}$.

4.9.49 Using Table 4.10 (formula 10, $a = 5$), $\int \frac{6}{\sqrt{25-x^2}}\, dx = 6\sin^{-1}\left(\frac{x}{5}\right) + C$. Check: $\frac{d}{dx}(6\sin^{-1}\left(\frac{x}{5}\right) + C) = \frac{6}{\sqrt{1-(x^2/25)}} \cdot \frac{1}{5} = \frac{6}{\sqrt{25-x^2}}$.

4.9.50 Using Table 4.10 (formula 11, $a = 2$), $\int \frac{3}{4+v^2}\, dv = \frac{3}{2}\tan^{-1}\left(\frac{v}{2}\right) + C$. Check: $\frac{d}{dv}(\frac{3}{2}\tan^{-1}\left(\frac{v}{2}\right) + C) = \frac{3}{2} \cdot \frac{1}{(v^2/4)+1} \cdot \frac{1}{2} = \frac{3}{4+v^2}$.

4.9.51 Using Table 4.10 (formula 12, $a = 10$), $\int \frac{1}{x\sqrt{x^2-100}}\, dx = \frac{1}{10}\sec^{-1}\left|\frac{x}{10}\right| + C$. Check: $\frac{d}{dx}(\frac{1}{10}\sec^{-1}\left|\frac{x}{10}\right| + C) = \frac{1}{10} \cdot \frac{1}{(x/10) \cdot \sqrt{(x^2/100)-1}} \cdot \frac{1}{10} = \frac{1}{x\sqrt{x^2-100}}$.

4.9.52 Using Table 4.10 (formula 11, $a = 5/4$), $\int \frac{2}{16z^2+25}\, dz = \frac{1}{8}\int \frac{1}{z^2+25/16}\, dz = \frac{1}{8} \cdot \frac{4}{5}\tan^{-1}\left(\frac{4}{5}z\right) + C = \frac{1}{10}\tan^{-1}\left(\frac{4}{5}z\right) + C$. Check: $\frac{d}{dz}(\frac{1}{10}\tan^{-1}\left(\frac{4}{5}z\right) + C) = \frac{1}{10} \cdot \frac{1}{(16z^2/25)+1} \cdot \frac{4}{5} = \frac{2}{16z^2+25}$.

4.9.53 Using Table 4.10 (formula 12, $a = 5$), $\int \frac{1}{x\sqrt{x^2-25}}\, dx = \frac{1}{5}\sec^{-1}\left|\frac{x}{5}\right| + C$. Check: $\frac{d}{dx}\left(\sec^{-1}\left|\frac{x}{5}\right| + C\right) = \frac{1}{5} \cdot \frac{5}{x\sqrt{x^2-25}} = \frac{1}{x\sqrt{x^2-25}}$.

4.9.54 $\int (49 - x^2)^{-1/2}\, dx = \sin^{-1}(x/7) + C$. Check: $\frac{d}{dx}(\sin^{-1}(x/7) + C) = \frac{1}{\sqrt{1-(x^2/49)}} \cdot \frac{1}{7} = \frac{1}{\sqrt{49-x^2}}$.

4.9.55 $\int \frac{t+1}{t}\, dt = \int \left(\frac{t}{t} + \frac{1}{t}\right) dt = \int \left(1 + \frac{1}{t}\right) dt = t + \ln|t| + C$. Check: $\frac{d}{dt}(t + \ln|t| + C) = 1 + \frac{1}{t} = \frac{t+1}{t}$.

4.9.56 $\int (22x^{10} - 24e^{12x})\, dx = 2x^{11} - 2e^{12x} + C$. Check: $\frac{d}{dx}(2x^{11} - 2e^{12x} + C) = 22x^{10} - 24e^{12x}$.

4.9.57 $\int e^{x+2}\, dx = \int e^2 e^x\, dx = e^2 \int e^x\, dx = e^2 e^x + C = e^{x+2} + C$. Check $\frac{d}{dx}(e^{x+2} + C) = e^{x+2}$.

4.9.58 $\int \frac{10t^5-3}{t}\,dt = \int \left(\frac{10t^5}{t} - \frac{3}{t}\right)\,dt = \int \left(10t^4 - \frac{3}{t}\right)\,dt = 2t^5 - 3\ln|t| + C$. Check: $\frac{d}{dt}\left(2t^5 - 3\ln|t| + C\right) = 10t^4 - \frac{3}{t} = \frac{10t^5-3}{t}$.

4.9.59 We have $F(x) = \int (x^5 - 2x^{-2} + 1)\,dx = \frac{x^6}{6} + 2x^{-1} + x + C$; substituting $F(1) = 0$ gives $\frac{1}{6} + 2 + 1 + C = 0$, so $C = -\frac{19}{6}$, and thus $F(x) = \frac{x^6}{6} + \frac{2}{x} + x - \frac{19}{6}$.

4.9.60 We have $F(t) = \int \sec^2 t\,dt = \tan t + C$; substituting $F(\pi/4) = 1$ gives $\tan \frac{\pi}{4} + C = 1 + C = 1$, so $C = 0$, and thus $F(t) = \tan t$.

4.9.61 We have $F(v) = \int \sec v \tan v\,dv = \sec v + C$; substituting $F(0) = 2$ gives $\sec 0 + C = 1 + C = 2$, so $C = 1$, and thus $F(v) = \sec v + 1$.

4.9.62 We have $F(x) = \int \left(\frac{4\sqrt{x} + 6/\sqrt{x}}{x^2}\right)\,dx = \int (4x^{-3/2} + 6x^{-5/2})\,dx = 4 \cdot (-2)x^{-1/2} + 6 \cdot \left(-\frac{2}{3}\right)x^{-3/2} + C = -8x^{-1/2} - 4x^{-3/2} + C$; substituting $F(1) = 4$ gives $-8 - 4 + C = 4$, so $C = 16$, and thus $F(x) = -8x^{-1/2} - 4x^{-3/2} + 16$.

4.9.63 We have $F(x) = \int (8x^3 - 2x^{-2})\,dx = 2x^4 + 2x^{-1} + C$; substituting $F(1) = 5$ gives $2 + 2 + C = 5$, so $C = 1$, and thus $F(x) = 2x^4 + 2x^{-1} + 1$.

4.9.64 We have $F(u) = \int (2e^u + 3)\,du = 2e^u + 3u + C$; substituting $F(0) = 8$ gives $2 + 0 + C = 8$, so $C = 6$, and thus $F(u) = 2e^u + 3u + 6$.

4.9.65 We have $F(y) = \int \frac{3y^3+5}{y}\,dy = \int \left(\frac{3y^3}{y} + \frac{5}{y}\right)\,dy = \int \left(3y^2 + \frac{5}{y}\right)\,dy = y^3 + 5\ln|y| + C$; substituting $F(1) = 3$ gives $1 + 0 + C = 3$, so $C = 2$, and thus $F(y) = y^3 + 5\ln|y| + 2$.

4.9.66 $F(\theta) = \int (2\sin 2\theta - 4\cos 4\theta)\,d\theta = -\cos 2\theta - \sin 4\theta + C$; substituting $F(\pi/4) = 2$ gives $0 + 0 + C = 2$, so $C = 2$, and thus $F(\theta) = -\cos 2\theta - \sin 4\theta + 2$.

4.9.67 We have $f(x) = \int (2x - 3)\,dx = x^2 - 3x + C$; substituting $f(0) = 4$ gives $C = 4$, so $f(x) = x^2 - 3x + 4$.

4.9.68 We have $g(x) = \int (7x^6 - 4x^3 + 12)\,dx = x^7 - x^4 + 12x + C$; substituting $g(1) = 24$ gives $1 - 1 + 12 + C = 24$, so $C = 12$, and thus $g(x) = x^7 - x^4 + 12x + 12$.

4.9.69 We have $g(x) = \int 7x\left(x^6 - \frac{1}{7}\right)\,dx = \int (7x^7 - x)\,dx = \frac{7}{8}x^8 - \frac{x^2}{2} + C$; substituting $g(1) = 2$ gives $\frac{7}{8} - \frac{1}{2} + C = 2$, so $C = \frac{13}{8}$, and thus $g(x) = \frac{7}{8}x^8 - \frac{x^2}{2} + \frac{13}{8}$.

4.9.70 We have $h(t) = \int 6\sin 3t\,dt = 6 \cdot \left(-\frac{1}{3}\cos 3t\right) + C = -2\cos 3t + C$; substituting $h(\pi/6) = 6$ gives $-2\cos \frac{\pi}{2} + C = 6$, so $C = 6$, and thus $h(t) = -2\cos 3t + 6$.

4.9.71 We have $f(u) = \int 4(\cos u - \sin 2u)\,du = 4(\sin u + \frac{1}{2}\cos 2u) + C = 4\sin u + 2\cos 2u + C$; substituting $f(\pi/6) = 0$ gives $4\sin \frac{\pi}{6} + 2\cos \frac{\pi}{3} + C = 2 + 1 + C = 0$, so $C = -3$, and thus $f(u) = 4\sin u + 2\cos 2u - 3$.

4.9.72 We have $p(t) = \int 10e^{-t}\,dt = -10e^{-t} + C$; substituting $p(0) = 100$ gives $-10 + C = 100$, so $C = 110$, and thus $p(t) = -10e^{-t} + 110$.

4.9.73 We have $y(t) = \int \left(\frac{3}{t} + 6\right)\,dt = 3\ln|t| + 6t + C$; substituting $y(1) = 8$ gives $0 + 6 + C = 8$, so $C = 2$, and thus $y(t) = 3\ln|t| + 6t + 2$.

4.9.74 We have $u(x) = \int \frac{e^{2x} + 4e^{-x}}{e^x}\,dx = \int \left(\frac{e^{2x}}{e^x} + \frac{4e^{-x}}{e^x}\right)\,dx = \int (e^x + 4e^{-2x})\,dx = e^x - 2e^{-2x} + C$; substituting $u(\ln 2) = 2$ gives $2 - 2(1/4) + C = 2$, so $C = 1/2$, and thus $u(x) = e^x - 2e^{-2x} + \frac{1}{2}$.

4.9.75 We have $y(\theta) = \int \frac{\sqrt{2}\cos^3\theta + 1}{\cos^2\theta}\,d\theta = \int \left(\frac{\sqrt{2}\cos^3\theta}{\cos^2\theta} + \frac{1}{\cos^2\theta}\right)\,d\theta = \int (\sqrt{2}\cos\theta + \sec^2\theta)\,d\theta = \sqrt{2}\sin\theta + \tan\theta + C$; substituting $y(\pi/4) = 3$ gives $1 + 1 + C = 3$, so $C = 1$, and thus $y(\theta) = \sqrt{2}\sin\theta + \tan\theta + 1$.

4.9.76 $v(x) = \int (4x^{1/3} + 2x^{-1/3})\, dx = 3x^{4/3} + 3x^{2/3} + C$, substituting $v(8) = 40$ gives $48 + 12 + C = 40$, so $C = -20$ and thus $v(x) = 3x^{4/3} + 3x^{2/3} - 20$.

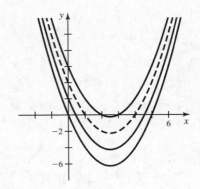

4.9.77 We have $f(x) = \int (2x - 5)\, dx = x^2 - 5x + C$; substituting $f(0) = 4$ gives $C = 4$, so $f(x) = x^2 - 5x + 4$.

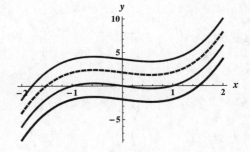

4.9.78 We have $f(x) = \int (3x^2 - 1)\, dx = x^3 - x + C$; substituting $f(1) = 2$ gives $C = 2$, so $f(x) = x^3 - x + 2$.

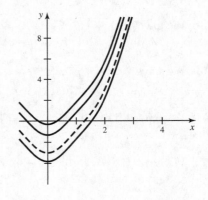

4.9.79 We have $f(x) = \int (3x + \sin \pi x)\, dx = \frac{3x^2}{2} - \frac{\cos \pi x}{\pi} + C$; substituting $f(2) = 3$ gives $6 - \frac{\cos 2\pi}{\pi} + C = 6 - \frac{1}{\pi} + C = 3$, so $C = \frac{1}{\pi} - 3$, and thus $f(x) = \frac{3x^2}{2} - \frac{\cos \pi x}{\pi} + \frac{1 - 3\pi}{\pi}$.

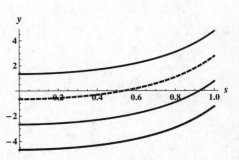

4.9.80 We have $f(s) = \int 4 \sec s \tan s\, ds = 4 \sec s + C$; substituting $f(\pi/4) = 1$ gives $4 \sec \frac{\pi}{4} + C = 4\sqrt{2} + C = 1$, so $C = 1 - 4\sqrt{2}$, and thus $f(s) = 4 \sec s + 1 - 4\sqrt{2}$.

4.9.81 We have $f(t) = \int \frac{1}{t}\,dt = \ln t + C$; substituting $f(1) = 4$ gives $C = 4$, so $f(t) = \ln t + 4$.

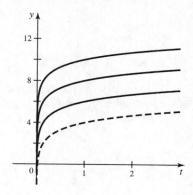

4.9.82 We have $f(x) = \int 2\cos 2x\,dx = 2 \cdot \frac{\sin 2x}{2} + C = \sin 2x + C$; substituting $f(0) = 1$ gives $C = 1$, so $f(x) = \sin 2x + 1$.

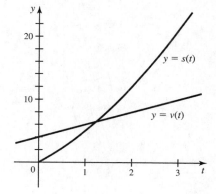

4.9.83 We have $s(t) = \int (2t + 4)\,dt = t^2 + 4t + C$; substituting $s(0) = 0$ gives $C = 0$, so $s(t) = t^2 + 4t$.

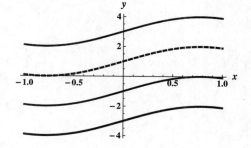

4.9.84 We have $s(t) = \int (e^{-2t} + 4)\,dt = -\frac{1}{2}e^{-2t} + 4t + C$; substituting $s(0) = 2$ gives $-\frac{1}{2} + C = 2$, so $C = \frac{5}{2}$, and thus $s(t) = -\frac{1}{2}e^{-2t} + 4t + \frac{5}{2}$.

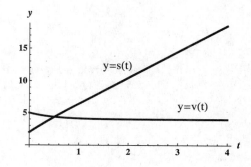

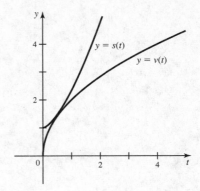

4.9.85 We have $s(t) = \int 2\sqrt{t}\,dt = 2 \cdot \frac{2}{3}t^{3/2} + C = \frac{4}{3}t^{3/2} + C$; substituting $s(0) = 1$ gives $C = 1$, so $s(t) = \frac{4}{3}t^{3/2} + 1$.

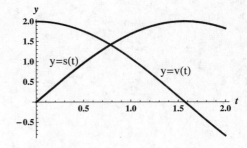

4.9.86 We have $s(t) = \int 2\cos t\,dt = 2\sin t + C$; substituting $s(0) = 0$ gives $C = 0$, so $s(t) = 2\sin t$.

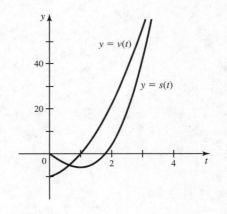

4.9.87 We have $s(t) = \int (6t^2 + 4t - 10)\,dt = 2t^3 + 2t^2 - 10t + C$; substituting $s(0) = 0$ gives $C = 0$, so $s(t) = 2t^3 + 2t^2 - 10t$.

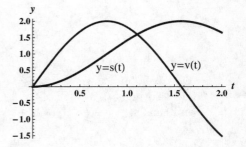

4.9.88 We have $s(t) = \int 2\sin 2t\,dt = -\cos 2t + C$; substituting $s(0) = 0$ gives $-1 + C = 0$, so $C = 1$ and $s(t) = 1 - \cos 2t$.

4.9.89 $v(t) = \int a(t)\,dt = \int -32\,dt = -32t + C_1$. Because $v(0) = 20$, we have $0 + C_1 = 20$, so $v(t) = -32t + 20$.

$s(t) = \int v(t)\,dt = \int (-32t + 20)\,dt = -16t^2 + 20t + C_2$. Because $s(0) = 0$, we have $C_2 = 0$, and thus $s(t) = -16t^2 + 20t$.

4.9.90 $v(t) = \int a(t)\,dt = \int 4\,dt = 4t + C_1$. Because $v(0) = -3$, we have $C_1 = -3$.

$s(t) = \int v(t)\,dt = \int (4t - 3)\,dt = 2t^2 - 3t + C_2$. Because $s(0) = 2$, we have $C_2 = 2$, and thus $s(t) = 2t^2 - 3t + 2$.

4.9.91 $v(t) = \int a(t)\,dt = \int .2t\,dt = .1t^2 + C_1$. Because $v(0) = 0$, we have $C_1 = 0$.

$s(t) = \int v(t)\,dt = \int .1t^2\,dt = \frac{1}{30}t^3 + C_2$. Because $s(0) = 1$, we have $C_2 = 1$, and thus $s(t) = \frac{1}{30}t^3 + 1$.

4.9.92 $v(t) = \int a(t)\,dt = \int 2\cos t\,dt = 2\sin t + C_1$. Because $v(0) = 1$, we have $C_1 = 1$.

$s(t) = \int v(t)\,dt = \int (2\sin t + 1)\,dt = -2\cos t + t + C_2$. Because $s(0) = 0$, we have $-2 + 0 + C_2 = 0$, so $C_2 = 2$. Thus, $s(t) = -2\cos t + t + 2$.

4.9.93 $v(t) = \int a(t)\,dt = \int 3\sin 2t\,dt = (-3/2)\cos 2t + C_1$. Because $v(0) = 1$, we have $-3/2 + C_1 = 1$, so $C_1 = 5/2$.

$s(t) = \int v(t)\,dt = \int [(-3/2)\cos 2t + 5/2]\,dt = (-3/4)\sin 2t + (5/2)t + C_2$. Because $s(0) = 10$, we have $C_2 = 10$, so $s(t) = (-3/4)\sin 2t + (5/2)t + 10$.

4.9.94 $v(t) = \int a(t)\,dt = \int 2e^{-t/6}\,dt = -12e^{-t/6} + C_1$. Because $v(0) = 1$, we have $-12 + C_1 = 1$, so $C_1 = 13$.

$s(t) = \int v(t)\,dt = \int (-12e^{-t/6} + 13)\,dt = 72e^{-t/6} + 13t + C_2$. Because $s(0) = 0$, we have $72 + C_2 = 0$, so $C_2 = -72$. Thus, $s(t) = 72e^{-t/6} + 13t - 72$.

4.9.95 Runner A has position function $s(y) = \int \sin t\,dt = -\cos t + C$; the initial condition $s(0) = 0$ gives $C = 1$, so $s(t) = 1 - \cos t$. Runner B has position function $S(t) = \int \cos t\,dt = \sin t + C$; the initial condition $S(0) = 0$ gives $C = 0$, so $S(t) = \sin t$. The smallest $t > 0$ where $s(t) = S(t)$ is $t = \pi/2$ s.

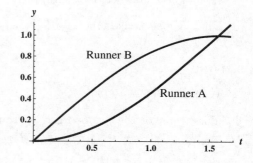

4.9.96 Runner A has position function $s(y) = \int 2e^{-t}\,dt = -2e^{-t} + C$; the initial condition $s(0) = 0$ gives $-2 + C = 0$, so $C = 2$ and $s(t) = 2 - 2e^{-t}$. Runner B has position function $S(t) = \int 4e^{-4t}\,dt = -e^{-4t} + C$; the initial condition $S(0) = 10$ gives $-1 + C = 10$, so $C = 11$ and $S(t) = 11 - e^{-4t}$. Observe that $s(t) < 2$ and $S(t) > 10$ for all $t > 0$, so runner A never catches runner B.

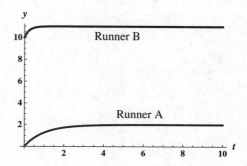

4.9.97

a. We have $v(t) = -9.8t + v_0$ and $v_0 = 30$, so $v(t) = -9.8t + 30$.

b. The height of the softball above ground is given by $s(t) = \int (-9.8t + 30)\,dt = -4.9t^2 + 30t + s_0 = -4.9t^2 + 30t$.

c. The ball reaches its maximum height when $v(t) = -9.8t + 30 = 0$, which gives $t = 30/9.8 \approx 3.06$ s; the maximum height is $s(30/9.8) \approx 45.92$ m.

d. The ball strikes the ground when $s(t) = 0$ (and $t > 0$), which gives $t(30 - 4.9t) = 0$, so $t = 30/4.9 \approx 6.12$ s.

4.9.98

a. We have $v(t) = -9.8t + v_0$ and $v_0 = 30$, so $v(t) = -9.8t + 30$.

b. The height of the stone above ground is given by $s(t) = \int (-9.8t + 30)\, dt = -4.9t^2 + 30t + s_0 = -4.9t^2 + 30t + 200$.

c. The stone reaches its maximum height when $v(t) = -9.8t + 30 = 0$, which gives $t = 30/9.8 \approx 3.06$ s; the maximum height is $s(30/9.8) \approx 245.92$ m.

d. The stone strikes the ground when $s(t) = 0$ (and $t > 0$), which gives $-4.9t^2 + 30t + 200 = 0$, so $t \approx 10.15$ s.

4.9.99

a. We have $v(t) = -9.8t + v_0$ and $v_0 = 10$, so $v(t) = -9.8t + 10$.

b. The height of the payload above ground is given by $s(t) = \int (-9.8t + 10)\, dt = -4.9t^2 + 10t + s_0 = -4.9t^2 + 10t + 400$.

c. The payload reaches its maximum height when $v(t) = -9.8t + 10 = 0$, which gives $t = 10/9.8 \approx 1.02$ s; the maximum height is $s(10/9.8) \approx 405.10$ m.

d. The payload strikes the ground when $s(t) = 0$ (and $t > 0$), which gives $-4.9t^2 + 10t + 400 = 0$, so $t \approx 10.11$ s.

4.9.100

a. We have $v(t) = -9.8t + v_0$ and $v_0 = -10$, so $v(t) = -9.8t - 10$.

b. The height of the payload above ground is given by $s(t) = \int (-9.8t - 10)\, dt = -4.9t^2 - 10t + s_0 = -4.9t^2 - 10t + 400$.

c. Because $v(t) < 0$ for $t > 0$, the maximum height occurs at $t = 0$ and is the initial height 400 m.

d. The payload strikes the ground when $s(t) = 0$ (and $t > 0$), which gives $-4.9t^2 - 10t + 400 = 0$, so $t \approx 8.07$ s.

4.9.101

a. True, because $F'(x) = G'(x)$.

b. False; f is the derivative of F.

c. True; $\int f(x)\, dx$ is the most general antiderivative of $f(x)$, which is $F(x) + C$.

d. False; a function cannot have more than one derivative.

e. False; one can only conclude that $F(x)$ and $G(x)$ differ by a constant.

4.9.102 $\int (\sqrt[3]{x^2} + \sqrt{x^3})\, dx = \int (x^{2/3} + x^{3/2})\, dx = \frac{3}{5}x^{5/3} + \frac{2}{5}x^{5/2} + C$. Check: $\frac{d}{dx}(\frac{3}{5}x^{5/3} + \frac{2}{5}x^{5/2} + C) = \sqrt[3]{x^2} + \sqrt{x^3}$.

4.9.103 $\int \frac{e^{2x} - e^{-2x}}{2}\, dx = \frac{1}{2}\left(\frac{e^{2x}}{2} - \frac{e^{-2x}}{-2}\right) + C = \frac{e^{2x} + e^{-2x}}{4} + C$. Check: $\frac{d}{dx}(\frac{e^{2x} + e^{-2x}}{4} + C) = \frac{e^{2x} - e^{-2x}}{2}$.

4.9.104 $\int (4\cos 4w - 3\sin 3w)\, dw = 4 \cdot \frac{\sin 4w}{4} - 3\left(\frac{-\cos 3w}{3}\right) + C = \sin 4w + \cos 3w + C$. Check: $\frac{d}{dw}(\sin 4w + \cos 3w + C) = 4\cos 4w - 3\sin 3w$.

4.9.105 $\int (\csc^2\theta + 2\theta^2 - 3\theta)\, d\theta = -\cot\theta + \frac{2}{3}\theta^3 - \frac{3}{2}\theta^2 + C$. Check: $\frac{d}{d\theta}\left(-\cot\theta + \frac{2}{3}\theta^3 - \frac{3}{2}\theta^2 + C\right) = \csc^2\theta + 2\theta^2 - 3\theta$.

4.9.106 $\int (\csc^2\theta + 1)\, d\theta = -\cot\theta + \theta + C$. Check: $\frac{d}{d\theta}(-\cot\theta + \theta + C) = \csc^2\theta + 1$.

4.9.107 $\int \frac{1+\sqrt{x}}{x}\, dx = \int (x^{-1} + x^{-1/2})\, dx = \ln|x| + 2x^{1/2} + C = \ln|x| + 2\sqrt{x} + C$. Check: $\frac{d}{dx}(\ln|x| + 2\sqrt{x} + C) = \frac{1}{x} + \frac{1}{\sqrt{x}} = \frac{1+\sqrt{x}}{x}$.

4.9.108 $\int \frac{2+x^2}{1+x^2}\, dx = \int \frac{(1+x^2)+1}{1+x^2}\, dx = \int \left(1 + \frac{1}{1+x^2}\right) dx = x + \tan^{-1}x + C$. Check: $\frac{d}{dx}(x + \tan^{-1}x + C) = 1 + \frac{1}{x^2+1} = \frac{2+x^2}{1+x^2}$.

4.9.109 $\int \sqrt{x}(2x^6 - 4\sqrt[3]{x})\, dx = \int (2x^{13/2} - 4x^{5/6})\, dx = 2\cdot\frac{2}{15}x^{15/2} - 4\cdot\frac{6}{11}x^{11/6} + C = \frac{4}{15}x^{15/2} - \frac{24}{11}x^{11/6} + C$. Check: $\frac{d}{dx}\left(\frac{4}{15}x^{15/2} - \frac{24}{11}x^{11/6} + C\right) = 2x^{13/2} - 4x^{5/6} = \sqrt{x}(2x^6 - 4\sqrt[3]{x})$.

4.9.110 We have $F'(x) = \int 1\, dx = x + C$; $F'(0) = 3$ so $C = 3$. Then $F(x) = \int (x+3)\, dx = \frac{x^2}{2} + 3x + C$; $F(0) = 4$ so $C = 4$ and $F(x) = (1/2)x^2 + 3x + 4$.

4.9.111 We have $F'(x) = \int \cos x\, dx = \sin x + C$; $F'(0) = 3$ so $C = 3$. Then $F(x) = \int (\sin x + 3)\, dx = -\cos x + 3x + C$; $F(\pi) = 4$ gives $1 + 3\pi + C = 4$ so $C = 3 - 3\pi$ and $F(x) = -\cos x + 3x + 3 - 3\pi$.

4.9.112 We have $F''(x) = \int 4x\, dx = 2x^2 + C$; $F''(0) = 0$ so $C = 0$. Next $F'(x) = \int 2x^2\, dx = 2\cdot\frac{x^3}{3} + C$; $F'(0) = 1$ so $C = 1$. Finally $F(x) = \int \left(\frac{2}{3}x^3 + 1\right) dx = \frac{2}{3}\cdot\frac{x^4}{4} + x + C$; $F(0) = 3$ so $C = 3$ and $F(x) = \frac{x^4}{6} + x + 3$.

4.9.113 We have $F''(x) = \int (672x^5 + 24x)\, dx = 672\cdot\frac{x^6}{6} + 24\cdot\frac{x^2}{2} + C$; $F''(0) = 0$ so $C = 0$. Next $F'(x) = \int (112x^6 + 12x^2)\, dx = 112\cdot\frac{x^7}{7} + 12\cdot\frac{x^3}{3} + C$; $F'(0) = 2$ so $C = 2$. Finally $F(x) = \int (16x^7 + 4x^3 + 2)\, dx = 16\cdot\frac{x^8}{8} + 4\cdot\frac{x^4}{4} + 2x + C$; $F(0) = 1$ so $C = 1$ and $F(x) = 2x^8 + x^4 + 2x + 1$.

4.9.114 The velocity is given by $v(t) = \int \sin(\pi t)\, dt = -\frac{\cos\pi t}{\pi} + C$; $v(0) = 3$ implies $-\frac{1}{\pi} + C = 3$, so $C = 3 + \frac{1}{\pi}$. The position s is given by $s(t) = \int \left(-\frac{\cos\pi t}{\pi} + 3 + \frac{1}{\pi}\right) dt = -\frac{\sin\pi t}{\pi^2} + \left(3 + \frac{1}{\pi}\right)t + C$; $s(0) = 0$ implies that $C = 0$, so $s(t) = -\frac{\sin\pi t}{\pi^2} + \left(3 + \frac{1}{\pi}\right)t$.

4.9.115

a. We have $Q(t) = \int 0.1(100 - t^2)\, dt = 0.1\left(100t - \frac{t^3}{3}\right) + C$; $Q(0) = 0$, so $C = 0$ and $Q(t) = 10t - t^3/30$ gal.

b.

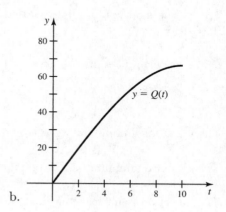

c. $Q(10) = 200/3 \approx 67$ gal.

4.9.116 Object A has position function $s(t)$ given by $s(t) = \int 2at\, dt = at^2 + s_0$, and we are given $s_0 = 0$, so $s(t) = at^2$. Object B has position function $S(t)$ given by $S(t) = \int b\, dt = bt + S_0$, and we are given $S_0 = c > 0$, so $S(t) = bt + c$. Therefore A will overtake B when $s(t) = S(t)$, which gives the quadratic equation $at^2 - bt - c = 0$; this equation has a unique positive root given by $t = \frac{b+\sqrt{b^2+4ac}}{2a}$.

4.9.117 $\int \sin^2 x \, dx = \frac{1}{2} \int (1 - \cos 2x) \, dx = \frac{1}{2} \left(x - \frac{\sin 2x}{2} \right) + C = \frac{x}{2} - \frac{\sin 2x}{4} + C; \int \cos^2 x \, dx = \frac{1}{2} \int (1 + \cos 2x) \, dx = \frac{1}{2} \left(x + \frac{\sin 2x}{2} \right) + C = \frac{x}{2} + \frac{\sin 2x}{4} + C.$

4.9.118 Check that $\frac{d}{dx} (2 \sin \sqrt{x}) = 2 \cos \sqrt{x} \left(\frac{1}{2\sqrt{x}} \right) = \frac{\cos \sqrt{x}}{\sqrt{x}}.$

4.9.119 Check that $\frac{d}{dx} (\sqrt{x^2 + 1}) = \frac{2x}{2\sqrt{x^2+1}} = \frac{x}{\sqrt{x^2+1}}.$

4.9.120 Check that $\frac{d}{dx} \left(\frac{1}{3} \sin x^3 \right) = \frac{1}{3} \cos x^3 (3x^2) = x^2 \cos x^3.$

4.9.121 Check that $\frac{d}{dx} \left(-\frac{1}{2(x^2-1)} \right) = -\frac{1}{2} \frac{d}{dx} (x^2 - 1)^{-1} = -\frac{1}{2}(-1)(x^2 - 1)^{-2}(2x) = \frac{x}{(x^2-1)^2}.$

Chapter Four Review

1

    a. False. The point $(c, f(c))$ is a critical point for f, but is not necessarily a local maximum or minimum. Example: $f(x) = x^3$ at $c = 0$.

    b. False. The fact that $f''(c) = 0$ does not necessarily imply that f changes concavity at c. Example: $f(x) = x^4$ at $c = 0$.

    c. True. Both are antiderivatives of $2x$.

    d. True. The function has a maximum on the closed interval determined by the two local minima, and the only way the maximum can occur at the endpoints is if the function is constant, in which case every point is a local max and min.

    e. True. The slope of the linearization is given by $f'(0) = \cos(0) = 1$, and the line has y-intercept $(0, f(0)) = (0, 0)$.

    f. False. For example, $\lim_{x \to \infty} x^2 = \infty$ and $\lim_{x \to \infty} x = \infty$, but $\lim_{x \to \infty} (x^2 - x) = \infty$.

2

    a. There is a local minimum at $(2, -3)$ and a local maximum at $(-1, 3)$.

    b. The absolute minimum and maximum on $[-3, 3]$ occur at $(-3, -5)$ and $(-1, 3)$ respectively.

    c. The inflection point has coordinates $(1/2, 0)$.

    d. The function has zeros at $x \approx -2.2, 2.8$.

    e. The function is concave up on the interval $(1/2, 3)$.

    f. The function is concave down on the interval $(-3, 1/2)$.

3

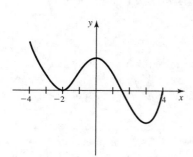

4

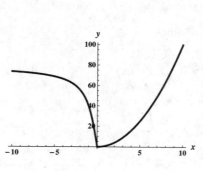

5

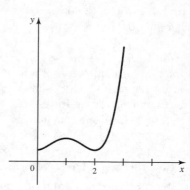

6 The critical points satisfy $f'(x) = 2\cos 2x = 0$, which has solutions $x = \pm\pi/4$ and $x = \pm3\pi/4$ in the interval $(-\pi, \pi)$. We have $f(-\pi) = 3$, $f(-3\pi/4) = 4$, $f(-\pi/4) = 2$, $f(\pi/4) = 4$, $f(3\pi/4) = 2$ and $f(\pi) = 3$; therefore the absolute minimum and maximum values of f on $[-\pi, \pi]$ are 2 and 4 respectively.

7 The critical points satisfy $f'(x) = 6x^2 - 6x - 36 = 6(x-3)(x+2) = 0$, so the critical points are $x = 3, -2$. Because $\lim\limits_{x\to\infty} f(x) = \infty$ and $\lim\limits_{x\to-\infty} f(x) = -\infty$, this function has no absolute max or min on $(-\infty, \infty)$.

8 Observe that $f'(x) = 2x^{-1/2} - \frac{5}{2}x^{3/2}$, so the critical points satisfy $x^2 = 4/5$; hence $x = 2/\sqrt{5} \approx 0.894$ is the only critical point in the interval $(0, 4)$. We have $f(0) = 0$, $f(2/\sqrt{5}) \approx 3.026$, $f(4) = -24$; hence the absolute minimum and maximum values are -24 and ≈ 3.026 respectively.

9 The critical points satisfy $f'(x) = 2\ln x + 2x \cdot \frac{1}{x} = 2\ln x + 2 = 0$, which has solution $x = 1/e$. The Second Derivative Test shows that this critical point is a local minimum, so by Theorem 4.5 the absolute minimum value on the interval $(0, \infty)$ is $f(\frac{1}{e}) = -\frac{2}{e} + 10$. Because $\lim\limits_{x\to\infty} x\ln x = \infty$, this function does not have an absolute maximum on $(0, \infty)$.

10 The critical points satisfy $g'(x) = \frac{x}{\sqrt{1-x^2}} + \sin^{-1} x = 0$. Note that $g'(0) = 0$, so $x = 0$ is a critical point, and this turns out to be the only critical point. This can be seen by noting that for $x < 0$ both $\frac{x}{\sqrt{1-x^2}}$ and $\sin^{-1} x$ are negative, so their sum is negative, and for $x > 0$ both $\frac{x}{\sqrt{1-x^2}}$ and $\sin^{-1} x$ are positive, so their sum is positive. Note that $g(-1) = \frac{\pi}{2} = g(1)$, and $g(0) = 0$, so the absolute maximum of g is $\frac{\pi}{2}$ and the absolute minimum is 0.

11

All points in the interval $[-3, 2]$ are critical points. The absolute max occurs at $(4, 9)$; there are no local maxima. All points $(x, 5)$ for x in the interval $[-3, 2]$ are absolute and local minima.

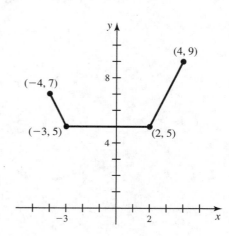

12 Observe that $f''(x) = 40x^3 - 120x^2 + 120x = 40x(x^2 - 3x + 3)$. The quadratic $x^2 - 3x + 3$ has no real roots, so $x = 0$ is the only possible inflection point. The sign of $f''(x)$ changes at $x = 0$ so an inflection point occurs at $(0, 1)$.

13 The derivatives of f are $f'(x) = 2x^3 - 6x + 4$, $f''(x) = 6x^2 - 6$. Observe that $f'(x) = 2(x-1)^2(x+2)$, so we have critical points $x = 1, -2$. Solving $f''(x) = 6(x^2 - 1) = 0$ gives possible inflection points at $x = \pm 1$. Testing the sign of $f'(x)$ shows that f is decreasing on the interval $(-\infty, -2)$ and is increasing on $(-2, \infty)$. The First Derivative Test shows that a local minimum occurs at $x = -2$, and that the critical point $x = 1$ is neither a local max or min.

Testing the sign of $f''(x)$ shows that f is concave down on the interval $(-1, 1)$ and is concave up on the intervals $(-\infty, -1)$ and $(1, \infty)$. Therefore inflection points occur at $x = \pm 1$. Using a numerical solver, we see that the graph has x-intercepts at $x \approx -2.917, -0.215$. We also observe that $\lim\limits_{x \to \pm\infty} f(x) = \infty$, so f has no absolute maximum and an absolute minimum at $x = -2$.

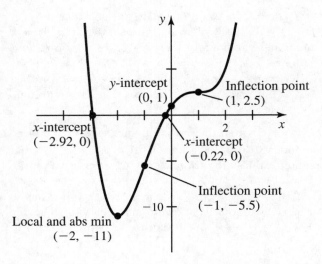

14 The derivatives of f are $f'(x) = 3 \cdot \frac{3 - x^2}{(x^2 + 3)^2}$, $f''(x) = 6 \cdot \frac{x(x^2 - 9)}{(x^2 + 3)^3}$. Solving $f'(x) = 0$ gives critical points $x = \pm\sqrt{3}$, and solving $f''(x) = 0$ gives possible inflection points at $x = 0, \pm 3$. Testing the sign of $f'(x)$ shows that f is decreasing on the intervals $(-\infty, -\sqrt{3})$ and $(\sqrt{3}, \infty)$ and increasing on $(-\sqrt{3}, \sqrt{3})$. The First Derivative Test shows that a local minimum occurs at $x = -\sqrt{3}$ and a local maximum occurs at $x = \sqrt{3}$.

Testing the sign of $f''(x)$ shows that f is concave down on the intervals $(-\infty, -3)$ and $(0, 3)$ and concave up on the intervals $(-3, 0)$ and $(3, \infty)$. Therefore inflection points occur at $x = 0, \pm 3$. The graph has x-intercept at $x = 0$. We also observe that $\lim\limits_{x \to \pm\infty} f(x) = 0$, so f has its absolute maximum and minimum at $x = \sqrt{3}, -\sqrt{3}$ respectively.

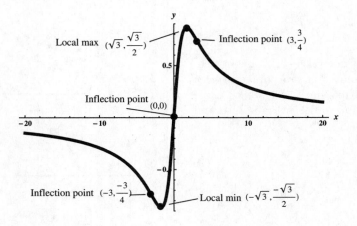

15 The derivatives of f are $f'(x) = -4\pi \sin[\pi(x-1)]$, $f''(x) = -4\pi^2 \cos[\pi(x-1)]$. Solving $f'(x) = 0$ gives critical point $x = 1$, and solving $f''(x) = 0$ gives possible inflection points at $x = 1/2, 3/2$. Testing the sign of $f'(x)$ shows that f is decreasing on the interval $(1, 2)$ and increasing on $(0, 1)$. The First Derivative Test shows that a local maximum occurs at $x = 1$. By Theorem 4.5, this solitary local maximum must be the absolute maximum for f on the interval $[0, 2]$.

Testing the sign of $f''(x)$ shows that f is concave down on the interval $(1/2, 3/2)$ and concave up on the intervals $(0, 1/2)$ and $(3/2, 2)$. Therefore inflection points occur at $x = 1/2, 3/2$. These points are also the x-intercepts of the graph. We also observe that $f(0) = f(2) = -4$, so f takes its absolute minimum at these points.

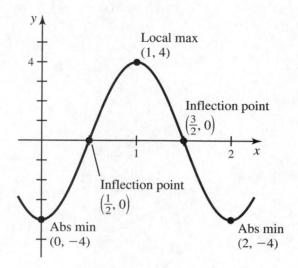

16 The derivatives of f are $f'(x) = \frac{x^2+8x+4}{(x^2-4)^2}$, $f''(x) = -2 \cdot \frac{x^3+12x^2+12x+16}{(x^2-4)^3}$. Solving $f'(x) = 0$ gives critical points $x = -4 \pm 2\sqrt{3} \approx -7.464, -0.536$, and solving $f''(x) = 0$ numerically gives a possible inflection point at $x \approx -11.045$. Also note that f' and f'' are undefined at $x = \pm 2$; f has vertical asymptotes at these points. Testing the sign of $f'(x)$ shows that f is decreasing on the intervals $(-7.464, -2)$ and $(-2, -0.536)$ and increasing on $(-\infty, -7.464)$, $(-0.536, 2)$ and $(2, \infty)$. The First Derivative Test shows that a local minimum occurs at $x \approx -0.536$ and a local maximum occurs at $x \approx -7.464$.

Testing the sign of $f''(x)$ shows that f is concave down on the intervals $(-11.045, -2)$ and $(2, \infty)$ and concave up on the intervals $(-\infty, -11.045)$ and $(-2, 2)$. Therefore an inflection point occurs at $x \approx -11.045$.

The graph has x-intercepts at $x = -1, 0$. Observe that $\lim\limits_{x \to 2^-} \frac{x^2+x}{4-x^2} = \infty$, $\lim\limits_{x \to 2^+} \frac{x^2+x}{4-x^2} = -\infty$; therefore f has no absolute min or max. We also observe that $\lim\limits_{x \to \pm\infty} f(x) = -1$.

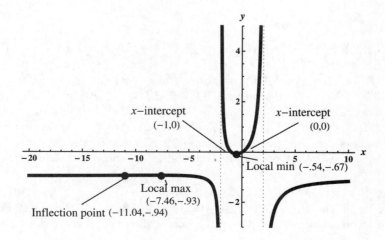

17 Note that the domain of f is the interval $(0, \infty)$. The derivatives of f are $f'(x) = \frac{1}{3}x^{-2/3} - \frac{1}{2}x^{-1/2}$, and $f''(x) = -\frac{2}{9}x^{-5/3} + \frac{1}{4}x^{-3/2}$. Solving $f'(x) = 0$ gives critical point $x = (2/3)^6$, and solving $f''(x) = 0$ gives a possible inflection point at $x = (8/9)^6$. Testing the sign of $f'(x)$ shows that f is increasing on the interval $(0, (2/3)^6)$ and decreasing on the interval $((2/3)^6, \infty)$. The First Derivative Test shows that a local maximum occurs at $x = (2/3)^6$ and By Theorem 4.5 this solitary local maximum must be the absolute maximum of f on the interval $(0, \infty)$.

Testing the sign of $f''(x)$ shows that f is concave down on the interval $(0, (8/9)^6)$ and concave up on the interval $((8/9)^6, \infty)$. Therefore an inflection point occurs at $x = (8/9)^6$. Using a numerical solver, we find that the graph has x-intercept at $x \approx 23.767$. Because $\lim_{x \to \infty} f(x) = -\infty$, f has no absolute minimum on the interval $(0, \infty)$.

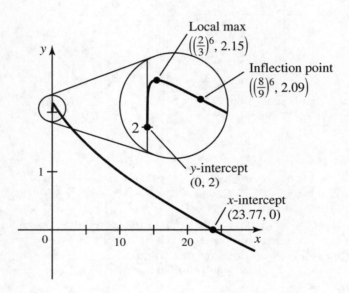

18 Observe that f is an even function, so its graph is symmetric in the y-axis. The derivatives of f are $f'(x) = -\frac{\pi(1+x^2)\sin \pi x + 2x \cos \pi x}{(1+x^2)^2}$, $f''(x) = \frac{4\pi(x^3+x)\sin \pi x + (-\pi^2 x^4 + (6-2\pi^2)x^2 - \pi^2 - 2)\cos \pi x}{(1+x^2)^3}$. Note that $x = 0$ is a critical point; solving $f'(x) = 0$ numerically gives additional critical points $x = \pm 0.902, \pm 1.919$, and solving $f''(x) = 0$ gives possible inflection points at $x \approx \pm 0.382, \pm 1.307$. Testing the sign of f' between critical points shows that f is decreasing on the intervals $(-1.919, -0.902)$, $(0, 0.902)$ and $(1.919, 2)$ and increasing on $(-2, -1.919)$, $(-0.902, 0)$ and $(0.902, 1.919)$. The First Derivative Test shows that local minima occur at $x \approx \pm 0.90$ and local maxima occur at $x = 0$ and $x \approx \pm 1.92$. Comparing the values of f at the critical points and endpoints shows that the absolute maximum occurs at $x = 0$ and the absolute minimum at $x \approx \pm 0.902$.

Testing the sign of $f''(x)$ shows that f is concave down on the intervals $(-2, -1.307)$, $(-0.382, 0.382)$ and $(1.307, 2)$ and concave up on the intervals $(-1.31, -0.38)$ and $(0.38, 1.31)$. Therefore inflection points occur at $x = \pm 0.382, \pm 1.307$. The x-intercepts of the graph occur when $\cos \pi x = 0$, which gives $x = \pm 1/2, \pm 3/2$.

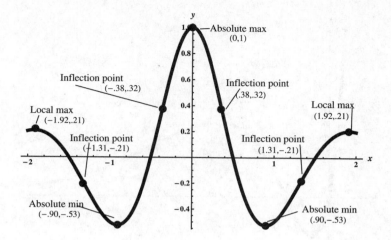

19 The derivatives of f are $f'(x) = \frac{2}{3}x^{-1/3} + \frac{1}{3}(x + 2)^{-2/3}$, $f''(x) = -\frac{2}{9}\left(x^{-4/3} + (x + 2)^{-5/3}\right)$. Solving $f'(x) = 0$ gives critical points $x \approx -2.57, -1.559$; we also have critical points at $x = -2, 0$ because $f'(x)$ is undefined at these points. Solving $f''(x) = 0$ numerically gives a possible inflection point at $x \approx -6.434$. We also have possible inflection points at $x = -2, 0$ because $f''(x)$ is undefined at these points. Testing the sign of $f'(x)$ shows that f is decreasing on the intervals $(-\infty, -2.566)$ and $(-1.559, 0)$ and increasing on $(-2.566, -1.559)$ and $(0, \infty)$. The First Derivative Test shows that local mins occur at $x \approx -2.566$ and $x = 0$ and a local max occurs at $x \approx -1.559$.

Testing the sign of $f''(x)$ shows that f is concave down on the intervals $(-\infty, -6.434)$, $(-2, 0)$ and $(0, \infty)$ and concave up on the interval $(-6.434, -2)$. Therefore inflection points occur at $x \approx -6.434$ and $x = -2$. Because $\lim\limits_{x \to \pm\infty} f(x) = \infty$, f has no absolute maximum. The absolute minimum occurs at $x \approx -2.566$.

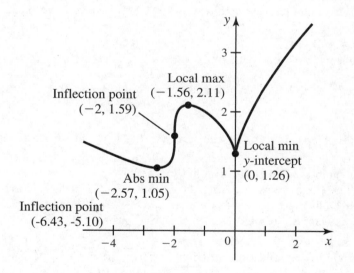

20 The derivatives of f are $f'(x) = -(x^2 - 3x + 1)e^{-x}$, $f''(x) = (x^2 - 5x + 4)e^{-x}$. Solving $f'(x) = 0$ gives critical points $x \approx 0.382, 2.618$, and solving $f''(x) = 0$ gives possible inflection points at $x = 1, 4$. Testing the sign of $f'(x)$ shows that f is decreasing on the intervals $(-\infty, 0.382)$ and $(2.618, \infty)$ and increasing on $(0.382, 2.618)$. The First Derivative Test shows that a local minimum occurs at $x \approx 0.382$ and a local maximum occurs at $x \approx 2.618$.

Testing the sign of $f''(x)$ shows that f is concave up on the intervals $(-\infty, 1)$ and $(4, \infty)$ and concave down on the interval $(1, 4)$. Therefore inflection points occur at $x = 1, 4$. The graph has x-intercepts at $x = 0, 1$. Observe that $\lim\limits_{x \to -\infty} f(x) = \infty$, $\lim\limits_{x \to \infty} f(x) = 0$; therefore f has no absolute max, and the absolute min occurs at $x \approx 0.382$.

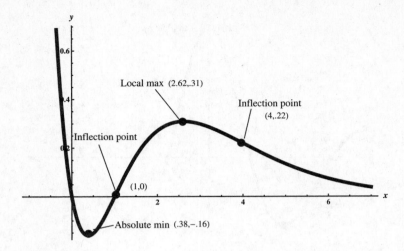

21 The objective function to be maximized is the volume of the cone, given by $V = \pi r^2 h/3$. By the Pythagorean theorem, r and h satisfy the constraint $h^2 + r^2 = 16$, which gives $r^2 = 16 - h^2$. Therefore $V(h) = \frac{\pi}{3}h(16 - h^2) = \frac{\pi}{3}(16h - h^3)$. We must maximize this function for $0 \le h \le 4$. The critical points of $V(h)$ satisfy $V'(h) = \frac{\pi}{3}(16 - 3h^2) = 0$, which has unique solution $h = 4/\sqrt{3} = 4\sqrt{3}/3$ in $(0, 4)$. Because $V(0) = V(4) = 0$, $h = 4\sqrt{3}/3$ gives the maximum value of $V(h)$ on $[0, 4]$. The corresponding value of r satisfies $r^2 = 16 - \frac{16}{3} = \frac{32}{3}$, so $r = \frac{4\sqrt{2}}{\sqrt{3}} = \frac{4\sqrt{6}}{3}$.

22 The rectangle has dimensions x and $\cos x$, so the objective function to be maximized is $A(x) = x \cos x$, where $0 \le x \le \pi/2$. The critical points of this function satisfy $A'(x) = \cos x - x \sin x = 0$, which can be solved numerically to obtain $x \approx 0.860$. Note that $A(0) = A(\pi/2) = 0$, so the maximum area occurs at $x \approx 0.860$; the dimensions of the largest rectangle are 0.860 and $\cos 0.860 \approx 0.652$, which gives maximum area ≈ 0.561.

23 We have that $xy = 98$, and we want to maximize $p = (y-2)(x-1) = (y-2)(98/y-1) = 98 - y - 196/y + 2$. Note that $p'(y) = -1 + 196/y^2$, which is zero when $y^2 = 196$, so $y = \sqrt{196} = 14$. Also note that $p'(13) > 0$ and $p'(15) < 0$, so there is a local (in fact, absolute) maximum at $y = 14$. The value of x when $y = 14$ is $x = 98/14 = 7$.

24 A point on the graph of $y = \frac{5}{2} - x^2$ has the form $(x, \frac{5}{2} - x^2)$; the square of its distance to the origin is given by $Q(x) = x^2 + \left(\frac{5}{2} - x^2\right)^2 = x^4 - 4x^2 + \frac{25}{4}$, which we can take as our objective function to be minimized. The critical points of $Q(x)$ satisfy $Q'(x) = 4x^3 - 8x = 4x(x^2 - 2) = 0$, which has solutions $x = 0$ and $x = \pm\sqrt{2}$. The First Derivative Test shows that $x = 0$ is a local maximum and $x = \pm\sqrt{2}$ are local minima. Note that $Q(x)$ takes the same value at $x = \pm\sqrt{2}$, so the absolute minimum of $Q(x)$ occurs at $x = \pm\sqrt{2}$ and the points closest to the origin on the graph are $(\pm\sqrt{2}, \frac{1}{2})$.

25 The area of the triangle is $\frac{1}{2}pq$, and the constraint is $\sqrt{p^2 + q^2} = 10$, or $p^2 + q^2 = 100$. So we can write the area of the triangle as $A(p) = (1/2)p\sqrt{100 - p^2}$. We have $A'(p) = (1/2)\sqrt{100 - p^2} + \frac{1}{2}p \cdot \frac{-p}{\sqrt{100-p^2}} = \frac{100-p^2-p^2}{2\sqrt{100-p^2}} = \frac{100-2p^2}{2\sqrt{100-p^2}}$. This is zero for $p = \sqrt{50} = 5\sqrt{2}$. An application of the First Derivative Test shows that there is a local (in fact, absolute) maximum at this value of p. The value of q for this value of p is $\sqrt{100 - 50} = 5\sqrt{2}$ as well. So the area of the triangle is maximized when $p = q = 5\sqrt{2}$.

26 The volume of the cistern is $\pi r^2 h$, so our constraint is $\pi r^2 h = 50$, so $h = \frac{50}{\pi r^2}$. The area of the painted surface is given by $A = 2\pi r h + \pi r^2 = 2\pi r \cdot \frac{50}{\pi r^2} + \pi r^2 = \frac{100}{r} + \pi r^2$. Thus we have $A'(r) = \frac{-100}{r^2} + 2\pi r$, which is zero when $2\pi r = \frac{100}{r^2}$, or $r^3 = \frac{50}{\pi}$, so $r = \sqrt[3]{50/\pi}$. This is a minimum because $A'(r) < 0$ for $r < \sqrt[3]{50\pi}$ and $A'(r) > 0$ for $r > \sqrt[3]{50/\pi}$. The dimension of the cistern are $r = \sqrt[3]{50/\pi}$ and $h = \frac{50}{\pi r^2} = \sqrt[3]{50/\pi}$.

27

a. $f'(x) = \frac{2}{3}x^{-1/3}$, so $f'(27) = \frac{2}{3\sqrt[3]{27}} = \frac{2}{9}$. Thus $L(x) - 9 = \frac{2}{9}(x - 27)$, or $L(x) = 9 + \frac{2}{9}(x - 27) = \frac{2}{9}x + 3$.

b. $f(29) \approx L(29) = 9 + \frac{4}{9} \approx 9.44$. This is an overestimate, because $f''(27) < 0$. Note that the calculator value of $f(29)$ is about 9.43913.

28

a. $f'(x) = \frac{1}{\sqrt{1-x^2}}$, so $f'(1/2) = \frac{2}{\sqrt{3}}$. Thus $L(x) - \pi/6 = \frac{2}{\sqrt{3}}(x - 1/2)$, or $L(x) = \frac{\pi}{6} + \frac{2}{\sqrt{3}}(x - 1/2)$.

b. $f(0.48) \approx L(.48) = \frac{\pi}{6} + \frac{2}{\sqrt{3}}(-.02) \approx .5005$. This is an underestimate because $f''(1/2) > 0$. The calculator value of $\sin^{-1}(0.48) \approx 0.500655$.

29 Let $f(x) = 1/x^2$ and let $a = 4$. Then $f'(x) = \frac{-2}{x^3}$ so $f'(4) = \frac{-2}{64} = \frac{-1}{32}$. The linearization is $L(x) = \frac{1}{16} + (-1/32)(x - 4)$. Then $f(4.2) = 1/(4.2)^2 \approx L(4.2) = \frac{1}{16} - \frac{1}{32} \cdot \frac{2}{10} = .05625$.

30 Let $f(x) = \tan^{-1}(x)$ and $a = 1$. Then $f'(x) = \frac{1}{x^2+1}$ so $f'(1) = \frac{1}{2}$. The linearization is $L(x) = \frac{\pi}{4} + \frac{1}{2}(x-1)$. Then $f(1.05) = \tan^{-1}(1.05) \approx L(1.05) = \frac{\pi}{4} + \frac{1}{2} \cdot \frac{1}{20} \approx .8104$.

31 $\Delta h \approx h'(a)\Delta t = -32 \cdot 5 \cdot 0.7 = -112$ feet.

32 $\Delta E \approx E'(a)\Delta M = 25000 \cdot 10^{1.5 \cdot 7} \cdot 1.5(\ln 10) \cdot 0.5 \approx 1.365 \times 10^{15}$ J.

33

a. The average rate of change of $P(t)$ on the interval $[0,8]$ is $\frac{P(8)-P(0)}{8-0} = \frac{800/9-0}{8} = \frac{100}{9}$ cells/week.

b. We solve $P'(t) = \frac{100}{(t+1)^2} = \frac{100}{9}$ which gives $(t+1)^2 = 9$, so $t = 2$ weeks.

34

a. The average rate of change is $\frac{\text{change in growth}}{\text{elapsed time}} = \frac{15}{5} = 3$ cm per hour.

b. 3 cm per hour is equivalent to $30/3600 = 1/120$ mm per second. The Mean Value Theorem tells us that sometime between 10:00 a.m. and 3:00 p.m, there will be a time when the instantaneous growth rate is exactly $1/120$ mm per second.

35 It is possible to note that 1 is a root by inspection. Then by long division by $x - 1$, we have $f(x) = (x - 1)(3x^2 - x - 1)$. We apply Newton's method to the function $g(x) = 3x^2 - x - 1$.

The Newton's method recursion is given by $x_{n+1} = x_n - \frac{3x_n^2-x_n-1}{6x_n-1}$. Applying this recursion to the initial estimates of $-.5$ and $.8$ yields:

n	x_n
0	$-.5$
1	$-.4375$
2	$-.434267$
3	$-.434259$
4	$-.434259$

n	x_n
0	$.8$
1	$.768421$
2	$.767592$
3	$.767592$
4	$.767592$

The roots are thus 1, and approximately -.434259 and .767592.

36 The Newton's method recursion is given by $x_{n+1} = x_n - \frac{e^{-2x_n}+2e^{x_n}-6}{-2e^{-2x_n}+2e^{x_n}}$. Applying this recursion to the initial estimates of -1 and 1 yields:

n	x_n
0	-1
1	$-.848685$
2	$-.817331$
3	$-.816164$
4	$-.816162$
5	$-.816162$

n	x_n
0	1
1	1.08287
2	1.07918
3	1.07917
4	1.07917
5	1.07917

The roots are thus 1, and approximately $-.816162$ and 1.07917.

37 First note that $f'(x) = 10x^4 - 18x^2 - 4$ and $f''(x) = 40x^3 - 36x = 4x(10x^2 - 9)$. This is clearly 0 when $x = 0$, and when $10x^2 - 9 = 0$. Applying Newton's method to the function $g(x) = 10x^2 - 9$ with initial estimates of -1 and 1 yields:

n	x_n
0	-1
1	$-.95$
2	$-.948684$
3	$-.948683$
4	$-.948683$
5	$-.948683$

n	x_n
0	1
1	$.95$
2	$.948684$
3	$.948683$
4	$.948683$
5	$.948683$

Checking the signs of $f''(x)$ on the appropriate intervals leads to the conclusion that these are all the locations of inflection points of f. So the inflection points of f are located at 0 and approximately $\pm.948683$.

38 L'Hôpital's rule gives $\lim\limits_{t \to 2} \dfrac{t^3 - t^2 - 2t}{t^2 - 4} = \lim\limits_{t \to 2} \dfrac{3t^2 - 2t - 2}{2t} = \dfrac{3}{2}$.

39 L'Hôpital's rule gives $\lim\limits_{t \to 0} \dfrac{1 - \cos 6t}{2t} = \lim\limits_{t \to 0} \dfrac{6 \sin 6t}{2} = 0$.

40 If we factor out x^2 from the numerator and denominator, we see that $\dfrac{5x^2 + 2x - 5}{\sqrt{x^4 - 1}} = \dfrac{5 + 2/x - 5/x^2}{\sqrt{1 - 1/x^4}} \to 5$ as $x \to \infty$.

41 Observe that $\lim\limits_{\theta \to 0} \dfrac{3 \sin^2 2\theta}{\theta^2} = 3 \left(\lim\limits_{\theta \to 0} \dfrac{\sin 2\theta}{\theta} \right)^2$; l'Hôpital's rule gives $\lim\limits_{\theta \to 0} \dfrac{\sin 2\theta}{\theta} = \lim\limits_{\theta \to 0} \dfrac{2 \cos 2\theta}{1} = 2$, so $\lim\limits_{\theta \to 0} \dfrac{3 \sin^2 2\theta}{\theta^2} = 3 \cdot 2^2 = 12$.

42 First observe that

$$(\sqrt{x^2 + x + 1} - \sqrt{x^2 - x}) \frac{(\sqrt{x^2 + x + 1} + \sqrt{x^2 - x})}{(\sqrt{x^2 + x + 1} + \sqrt{x^2 - x})} = \frac{2x + 1}{(\sqrt{x^2 + x + 1} + \sqrt{x^2 - x})}.$$

Next, factor out x from both numerator and denominator to obtain

$$\frac{2x + 1}{(\sqrt{x^2 + x + 1} + \sqrt{x^2 - x})} = \frac{2 + 1/x}{(\sqrt{1 + 1/x + 1/x^2} + \sqrt{1 - 1/x})}.$$

This expression converges to $2/2 = 1$ as $x \to \infty$, so $\lim\limits_{x \to \infty} (\sqrt{x^2 + x + 1} - \sqrt{x^2 - x}) = 1$.

43 Observe that $2\theta \cot 3\theta = 2\cos 3\theta \cdot \frac{\theta}{\sin 3\theta}$; $\lim_{\theta \to 0} \frac{\theta}{\sin 3\theta} = \lim_{\theta \to 0} \frac{1}{3\cos 3\theta} = \frac{1}{3}$ by l'Hôpital's rule, so

$$\lim_{\theta \to 0} 2\theta \cot 3\theta = 2 \cdot 1 \cdot \frac{1}{3} = \frac{2}{3}.$$

44 Apply l'Hôpital's rule twice: $\lim_{x \to 0} \frac{e^{-2x} - 1 + 2x}{x^2} = \lim_{x \to 0} \frac{-2e^{-2x} + 2}{2x} = \lim_{x \to 0} \frac{4e^{-2x}}{2} = 2.$

45 Make the change of variables $x = 1/y$; then $\ln^{10} y = (\ln y)^{10} = (-\ln x)^{10} = \ln^{10} x$, and so $\lim_{y \to 0^+} \frac{\ln^{10} y}{\sqrt{y}} = \lim_{x \to \infty} \sqrt{x} \ln^{10} x = \infty.$

46 Apply l'Hôpital's rule: $\lim_{\theta \to 0} \frac{3 \sin 8\theta}{8 \sin 3\theta} = \lim_{\theta \to 0} \frac{24 \cos 8\theta}{24 \cos 3\theta} = 1.$

47 Apply l'Hôpital's rule twice:

$$\lim_{x \to 1} \frac{x^4 - x^3 - 3x^2 + 5x - 2}{x^3 + x^2 - 5x + 3} = \lim_{x \to 1} \frac{4x^3 - 3x^2 - 6x + 5}{3x^2 + 2x - 5} = \lim_{x \to 1} \frac{12x^2 - 6x - 6}{6x + 2} = 0.$$

48 The function $\ln x^{100} = 100 \ln x$ grows more slowly than $\sqrt{x}$ as $x \to \infty$, so $\lim_{x \to \infty} \frac{\ln x^{100}}{\sqrt{x}} = 0.$

49 $\lim_{x \to 0} \csc x \sin^{-1} x = \lim_{x \to 0} \frac{\sin^{-1} x}{\sin x} = \lim_{x \to 0} \frac{1/\sqrt{1 - x^2}}{\cos x} = 1$, by l'Hôpital's rule.

50 The function $\ln^3 x$ grows more slowly than $\sqrt{x}$ as $x \to \infty$, so $\lim_{x \to \infty} \frac{\ln^3 x}{\sqrt{x}} = 0.$

51 Observe that $\lim_{x \to \infty} \frac{x + 1}{x - 1} = 1$, either by l'Hôpital's rule or Theorem 2.7. Hence $\lim_{x \to \infty} \ln\left(\frac{x + 1}{x - 1}\right) = \ln 1 = 0.$

52 Note that $\ln(1 + x)^{\cot x} = \cot x \ln(1 + x) = \frac{\ln(1+x)}{\tan x}$. We evaluate
$L = \lim_{x \to 0^+} \frac{\ln(1 + x)}{\tan x} = \lim_{x \to 0^+} \frac{1/(1 + x)}{\sec^2 x} = 1$ by l'Hôpital's rule. Therefore $\lim_{x \to 0^+} (1 + x)^{\cot x} = e^L = e^1 = e.$

53 Note that $\ln(\sin x)^{\tan x} = \tan x \ln \sin x$, so we evaluate $L = \lim_{x \to \pi/2^-} \tan x \ln \sin x = \lim_{x \to \pi/2^-} \frac{\ln \sin x}{\cot x} = \lim_{x \to \pi/2^-} \frac{\cot x}{-\csc^2 x} = \lim_{x \to \pi/2^-} (-\cos x \sin x) = 0$ by l'Hôpital's rule. Therefore $\lim_{x \to \pi/2^-} (\sin x)^{\tan x} = e^L = 1.$

54 Note that $\ln(\sqrt{x} + 1)^{1/x} = \frac{\ln(\sqrt{x}+1)}{x}$, so we evaluate $L = \lim_{x \to \infty} \frac{\ln(\sqrt{x} + 1)}{x} = \lim_{x \to \infty} \frac{\frac{1}{(\sqrt{x}+1)} \cdot \frac{1}{2\sqrt{x}}}{1} = 0$ by l'Hôpital's rule. Therefore, $\lim_{x \to \infty} (\sqrt{x} + 1)^{1/x} = e^L = e^0 = 1.$

55 Note that for $0 < x < 1$, we have $\ln x < 0$, so $|\ln x| = -\ln x$. Then $|\ln x|^x = (-\ln x)^x$. Consider the natural logarithm of this quantity, $x \ln(-\ln x) = \frac{\ln(-\ln x)}{\frac{1}{x}}$. Using l'Hôpital's rule we have

$$\lim_{x \to 0^+} \frac{\ln(-\ln x)}{\frac{1}{x}} = \lim_{x \to 0^+} \frac{\frac{1}{x \ln x}}{\frac{-1}{x^2}} = \lim_{x \to 0^+} \frac{-x}{\ln x} = 0.$$

Thus $\lim_{x \to 0^+} |\ln x|^x = e^0 = 1.$

56 Note that $\ln x^{1/x} = \ln x / x$, so we evaluate $L = \lim_{x \to \infty} \frac{\ln x}{x} = 0$ because $\ln x$ grows more slowly than x as $x \to \infty$. Therefore $\lim_{x \to \infty} x^{1/x} = e^L = 1.$

57 Note that $\ln\left(1 - \frac{3}{x}\right)^x = x \ln\left(1 - \frac{3}{x}\right) = \frac{\ln(1-3/x)}{1/x}$, so we evaluate

$$L = \lim_{x\to\infty} \frac{\ln(1-3/x)}{1/x} = \lim_{x\to\infty} \frac{(1-3/x)^{-1}(3/x^2)}{-1/x^2} = -3$$

by l'Hôpital's rule. Therefore $\lim_{x\to\infty}\left(1 - \frac{3}{x}\right)^x = e^L = e^{-3}$.

58 Note that $\ln\left(\left(\frac{2}{\pi}\tan^{-1}x\right)^x\right) = x \ln\left(\frac{2}{\pi}\tan^{-1}x\right) = \frac{\ln\left(\frac{2}{\pi}\tan^{-1}x\right)}{1/x}$. We evaluate

$$L = \lim_{x\to\infty} \frac{\ln\left(\frac{2}{\pi}\tan^{-1}x\right)}{1/x} = \lim_{x\to\infty} \frac{\frac{1}{(2/\pi)\tan^{-1}(x)} \cdot \frac{2}{\pi(x^2+1)}}{-1/x^2} = \lim_{x\to\infty} \frac{-x^2}{x^2+1} \cdot \frac{1}{\tan^{-1}(x)} = -\frac{2}{\pi}.$$

Thus, $\lim_{x\to\infty}\left(\frac{2}{\pi}\tan^{-1}x\right)^x = e^L = e^{-2/\pi}$.

59 Let $y = (x-1)^{\sin \pi x}$. Then $\ln y = \sin \pi x \ln(x-1) = \frac{\ln(x-1)}{\csc \pi x}$. Then

$$\lim_{x\to 1}\ln y = \lim_{x\to 1} \frac{\ln(x-1)}{\csc \pi x} = \lim_{x\to 1} \frac{\frac{1}{x-1}}{-\pi \csc \pi x \cot \pi x} = \lim_{x\to 1} \frac{\sin^2 \pi x}{-\pi(x-1)\cos \pi x}$$

$$= \lim_{x\to 1} \frac{1}{-\pi \cos \pi x} \cdot \lim_{x\to 1} \frac{\sin^2 \pi x}{x-1} = \frac{1}{\pi}\lim_{x\to 1} \frac{2\pi \sin \pi x \cos \pi x}{1} = \frac{1}{\pi} \cdot 0 = 0.$$

Then $\lim_{x\to 1} y = \lim_{x\to 1} e^{\ln y} = e^0 = 1$.

60 By Theorem 4.15, 1.1^x grows faster than x^{100} as $x \to \infty$.

61 Observe that $\lim_{x\to\infty} \frac{x^{1/2}}{x^{1/3}} = \lim_{x\to\infty} x^{1/6} = \infty$, so $x^{1/2}$ grows faster than $x^{1/3}$ as $x \to \infty$.

62 Because $\log_{10} x = \ln x / \ln 10$, $\ln x$ and $\log_{10} x$ have comparable growth rates as $x \to \infty$.

63 By Theorem 4.15, $\sqrt{x}$ grows faster than $\ln^{10} x$ as $x \to \infty$.

64 Because $\ln x^2 = 2\ln x$, Theorem 4.15 shows that $10x$ grows faster than $\ln x^2$ as $x \to \infty$.

65 Observe that $\lim_{x\to\infty} \frac{e^x}{3^x} = \lim_{x\to\infty}\left(\frac{e}{3}\right)^x = 0$ because $e/3 < 1$. Therefore 3^x grows faster than e^x as $x \to \infty$.

66 Observe that $\lim_{x\to\infty} \frac{\sqrt{x^6+10}}{x^3} = \lim_{x\to\infty} \sqrt{1 + \frac{10}{x^6}} = 1$, so $\sqrt{x^6+10}$ and x^3 have comparable growth rates as $x \to \infty$.

67 Observe that $4^{x/2} = (4^{1/2})^x = 2^x$, so these functions are identical and hence have comparable growth rates as $x \to \infty$.

68 $\int (x^8 - 3x^3 + 1)\,dx = \frac{x^9}{9} - 3 \cdot \frac{x^4}{4} + x + C = \frac{x^9}{9} - \frac{3}{4}x^4 + x + C$.

69 $\int (2x+1)^2\,dx = \int (4x^2 + 4x + 1)\,dx = \frac{4}{3}x^3 + 2x^2 + x + C$.

70 $\int \frac{x+1}{x}\,dx = \int \left(\frac{x}{x} + \frac{1}{x}\right)dx = \int \left(1 + \frac{1}{x}\right)dx = x + \ln|x| + C$.

71 $\int \left(\frac{1}{x^2} - \frac{2}{x^{5/2}}\right)dx = \int (x^{-2} - 2x^{-5/2})\,dx = -x^{-1} - 2 \cdot \left(-\frac{2}{3}\right)x^{-3/2} = -\frac{1}{x} + \frac{4}{3}x^{-3/2} + C$.

72 $\int \frac{x^4 - 2\sqrt{x} + 2}{x^2}\,dx = \int (x^2 - 2x^{-3/2} + 2x^{-2})\,dx = \frac{x^3}{3} - 2 \cdot (-2x^{-1/2}) - 2x^{-1} + C = \frac{x^3}{3} + \frac{4}{\sqrt{x}} - \frac{2}{x} + C$.

73 Using Table 4.5 (formula 1), $\int (1 + \cos 3\theta)\,d\theta = \theta + \frac{\sin 3\theta}{3} + C$.

74 Using Table 4.5 (formula 3), $\int 2\sec^2\theta\,d\theta = 2\tan\theta + C$.

75 Using Table 4.5 (formula 5), $\int \sec 2x\tan 2x\,dx = \frac{1}{2}\sec 2x + C$.

76 Using Table 4.6 (formula 7), $\int 2e^{2x}\,dx = e^{2x} + C$.

77 Using Table 4.6 (formula 8), $\int \frac{12}{x}\,dx = 12\ln|x| + C$.

78 Using Table 4.6 (formula 9), $\int \frac{dx}{\sqrt{1-x^2}} = \sin^{-1} x + C$.

79 Using Table 4.6 (formula 10), $\int \frac{dx}{x^2+1} = \tan^{-1} x + C$.

80 Note that $\frac{1+\tan\theta}{\sec\theta} = \cos\theta + \sin\theta$, so $\int \frac{1+\tan\theta}{\sec\theta}\,d\theta = \sin\theta - \cos\theta + C$.

81 $\int \left(\sqrt[4]{x^3} + \sqrt{x^5}\right)\,dx = \int (x^{3/4} + x^{5/2})\,dx = \frac{4}{7}x^{7/4} + \frac{2}{7}x^{7/2} + C$.

82 We have $f(x) = \int (3x^2 - 1)\,dx = x^3 - x + C$; $f(0) = C = 10$, so $f(x) = x^3 - x + 10$.

83 We have $f(t) = \int (\sin t + 2t)\,dt = -\cos t + t^2 + C$; $f(0) = -1 + C = 5$, so $C = 6$ and $f(t) = -\cos t + t^2 + 6$.

84 We have $g(t) = \int (t^2 + t^{-2})\,dt = \frac{t^3}{3} - \frac{1}{t} + C$; $g(1) = 1/3 - 1 + C = C - 2/3 = 1$, so $C = 5/3$ and $g(t) = t^3/3 - 1/t + 5/3$.

85 Using the identity $\sin^2 x = (1 - \cos 2x)/2$ and Table 4.5 (formula 1), we see that $h(x) = \frac{1}{2}\int (1 - \cos 2x)\,dx = \frac{1}{2}\left(x - \frac{\sin 2x}{2}\right) + C = \frac{x}{2} - \frac{\sin 2x}{4} + C$. We have $h(1) = \frac{1}{2} - \frac{\sin 2}{4} + C = 1$, so $C = \frac{1}{2} + \frac{\sin 2}{4}$ and so $h(x) = \frac{x}{2} - \frac{\sin 2x}{4} + \frac{1}{2} + \frac{\sin 2}{4}$.

86 The difference in the positions of the objects is given by the function $f(t) = 2\sin t - \sin(t - \pi/2) = 2\sin t + \cos t$. The objects meet when $f(t) = 0$, which occurs at $t = \pi - \tan^{-1}(1/2) \approx 2.673$ and $t = 2\pi - \tan^{-1}(1/2) \approx 5.820$. The objects are furthest apart when f attains its absolute max or min; the critical points of f satisfy $f'(t) = 2\cos t - \sin t = 0$, or $\tan t = 2$; this gives $t = \tan^{-1}(2) \approx 1.11$ and $t = \pi + \tan^{-1} 2 \approx 4.25$. The value of f is $\approx \pm 2.24$ at these points, so the objects are furthest apart at these two times.

87 The velocity of the rocket is given by $v(t) = -9.8t + v_0 = -9.8t + 120$, and the position function of the rocket is $s(t) = \int (-9.8t + 120)\,dt = -4.9t^2 + 120t + s_0 = -4.9t^2 + 120t + 125$. The rocket reaches its maximum height when $v(t) = 0$, which occurs at $t = 120/9.8 \approx 12.24$ s; the maximum height is $s(120/9.8) \approx 859.69$ m. The rocket hits the ground when $s(t) = 0$; solving this quadratic equation gives $t \approx 25.49$ s.

88 We have $\ln(\ln(\ln x)) \ll \ln(\ln x) \ll \ln x$ as $x \to \infty$. For the first relation, make the change of variables $y = \ln(\ln(x))$: then $\lim\limits_{x\to\infty} \frac{\ln(\ln(\ln x))}{\ln(\ln x)} = \lim\limits_{y\to\infty} \frac{\ln y}{y} = 0$; and for the second, let $y = \ln x$: $\lim\limits_{x\to\infty} \frac{\ln(\ln x)}{\ln x} = \lim\limits_{y\to\infty} \frac{\ln y}{y} = 0$.

89

For the second limit, let $y = x^2$: $\lim\limits_{x\to 0} \frac{x^2}{1 - e^{-x^2}} = \lim\limits_{y\to 0} \frac{y}{1 - e^{-y}} = \lim\limits_{y\to 0} \frac{1}{e^{-y}} = 1$ by l'Hôpital's rule. For the first, observe that for $x > 0$ $\frac{x}{\sqrt{1-e^{-x^2}}} = \left(\frac{x^2}{1-e^{-x^2}}\right)^{1/2}$, so $\lim\limits_{x\to 0^+} \frac{x}{\sqrt{1-e^{-x^2}}} = 1$ as well.

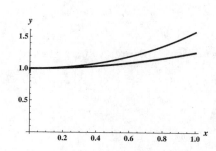

90 Observe that

$$\ln\left(\frac{a^r + b^r + c^r}{3}\right)^{1/r} = \frac{\ln(a^r + b^r + c^r) - \ln 3}{r}.$$

By l'Hôpital's rule, we have

$$L = \lim_{r\to 0} \frac{\ln(a^r + b^r + c^r) - \ln 3}{r} = \lim_{r\to 0} \frac{(a^r + b^r + c^r)^{-1}\left((\ln a)a^r + (\ln b)b^r + (\ln c)c^r\right)}{1}$$

$$= \frac{1}{3}(\ln a + \ln b + \ln c) = \ln(abc)^{1/3};$$

therefore $\displaystyle\lim_{r\to 0}\left(\frac{a^r + b^r + c^r}{3}\right)^{1/r} = e^L = \sqrt[3]{abc}.$

91 Observe that $\displaystyle\lim_{x\to\infty}\frac{2x^5 - x + 1}{5x^6 + x} = 0$ by Theorem 2.7. We can also use l'Hôpital's rule:

$$\lim_{x\to\infty}\frac{2x^5 - x + 1}{5x^6 + x} = \lim_{x\to\infty}\frac{10x^4 - 1}{30x^5 + 1} = \lim_{x\to\infty}\frac{40x^3}{150x^4} = \lim_{x\to\infty}\frac{4}{15x} = 0.$$

92 Observe that $\displaystyle\lim_{x\to\infty}\frac{4x^4 - \sqrt{x}}{2x^4 + x^{-1}} = \lim_{x\to\infty}\frac{4 - x^{-7/2}}{2 + x^{-5}} = \frac{4}{2} = 2.$ We can also apply l'Hôpital's rule four times:

$$\lim_{x\to\infty}\frac{4x^4 - x^{1/2}}{2x^4 + x^{-1}} = \lim_{x\to\infty}\frac{96 + (15/16)x^{-7/2}}{48 + 24x^{-5}} = 2.$$

93 Note that $\displaystyle\lim_{x\to 0^+} x^x = 1$, as shown in Example 6 a. Therefore $\displaystyle\lim_{x\to 0^+} f(x) = \lim_{x\to 0^+}(x^x)^x = 1^0 = 1$, and $\displaystyle\lim_{x\to 0} g(x) = \lim_{x\to 0} x^{(x^x)} = 0^1 = 0.$

94

a. Make the change of variables $y = x^n$ and apply l'Hôpital's rule twice:
$$\lim_{x\to 0}\frac{1 - \cos x^n}{x^{2n}} = \lim_{y\to 0}\frac{1 - \cos y}{y^2} = \lim_{y\to 0}\frac{\cos y}{2} = \frac{1}{2}.$$

b. Apply l'Hôpital's rule: $\displaystyle\lim_{x\to 0}\frac{1 - \cos^n x}{x^2} = \lim_{x\to 0}\frac{n\cos^{n-1} x \sin x}{2x} = \frac{n}{2}\left(\lim_{x\to 0}\cos^{n-1} x\right)\left(\lim_{x\to 0}\frac{\sin x}{x}\right) = \frac{n}{2}\cdot$
$1 \cdot 1 = \dfrac{n}{2}.$

95 First, observe that $\displaystyle\lim_{x\to\infty}\left(1 + \frac{1}{x}\right)^{x+a} = \lim_{x\to\infty}\left(1 + \frac{1}{x}\right)^x\left(1 + \frac{1}{x}\right)^a = e\cdot 1 = e.$ Therefore $\displaystyle\lim_{x\to\infty}\ln g(x) = 1.$ It suffices to determine whether $\ln g(x) - 1$ is positive or negative as $x\to\infty.$ To do this, consider $\displaystyle\lim_{x\to\infty} x(\ln g(x) - 1) = \lim_{t\to 0}\frac{(1 + at)\ln(1 + t) - t}{t^2}$, where we make the change of variables $t = 1/x.$ This limit can be evaluated by using l'Hôpital's rule twice: $\displaystyle\lim_{t\to 0}\frac{(1 + at)\ln(1 + t) - t}{t^2} = a - \frac{1}{2}.$ Therefore when $a > 1/2$ we have $g(x) > e$ as $x\to\infty$, and when $0 < a < 1/2$, $g(x) < e$ as $x\to\infty.$ In the case $a = 1/2$ we consider the limit $\displaystyle\lim_{x\to\infty} x^2(\ln g(x) - 1) = \lim_{t\to 0}\frac{(1 + at)\ln(1 + t) - t}{t^3}$, which can be evaluated by using l'Hôpital's three times: $\displaystyle\lim_{t\to 0}\frac{(1 + t/2)\ln(1 + t) - t}{t^3} = \frac{1}{12}.$ Therefore $g(x) > e$ as $x\to\infty$ in this case as well.

96

a. The domain is the interval $[-a, \infty).$

b. Observe that $\lim\limits_{x \to -a^+} (a+x)^x = \lim\limits_{x \to -a^+} (a+x)^{a+x}(a+x)^{-a} = \lim\limits_{y \to 0+} y^y \lim\limits_{y \to 0+} y^{-a} = 1 \cdot \infty = \infty$. We also have $\lim\limits_{x \to \infty} (a+x)^x = \infty$ because $(a+x)^x > x^x$.

c. Using logarithmic differentiation, we find that $f'(x) = x(a+x)^{x-1} + \ln(a+x)(a+x)^x$.

d. Multiplying $f'(x)$ by $(a+x)^{1-x}$ shows that the critical point z for f satisfies the equation $z + (z+a)\ln(z+a) = 0$, which is equivalent to the equation $\ln(z+a) - \frac{a}{z+a} = -1$. The left side is an increasing function on $(-a, \infty)$ with range $(-\infty, \infty)$, so there exists a unique z satisfying this equation.

e. Graphical analysis shows that as $a \to \infty$, $z \to -\infty$ and $f(z) \to 0$.

Chapter 5

Integration

5.1 Approximating Areas under Curves

5.1.1

In the first 2 seconds, the object moves $15 \cdot 2 = 30$ meters. In the next three seconds, the object moves $25 \cdot 3 = 75$ meters, so the total displacement is $75 + 30 = 105$ meters.

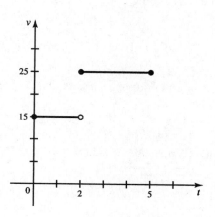

5.1.2 The area under the curve and above the t-axis, between $t = a$ and $t = b$ numerically represents the displacement.

5.1.3 Subdivide the interval from 0 to $\pi/2$ into subintervals. On each subinterval, pick a sample point (like the left endpoint, or the right endpoint, or the midpoint, for example) and call the first sample point x_1 and the second sample point x_2 and so on. For each sample point x_i, calculate the area of the rectangle which lies over the subinterval and has height $f(x_i) = \cos x_i$. Do this for each subinterval, and add the areas of the corresponding rectangles together. This will give an approximation to the area under the curve, with generally a better approximation occurring as n increases – where n is the number of subintervals used.

5.1.4 As the number of subintervals increases, the approximation to the area under the curve improves.

5.1.5 Because the interval $[1, 3]$ has length 2, if we subdivide it into 4 subintervals, each will have length $\Delta x = \frac{2}{4} = \frac{1}{2}$. The grid points will be $x_0 = 1$, $x_1 = 1 + \Delta x = 1.5$, $x_2 = 1 + 2\Delta x = 2$, $x_3 = 1 + 3\Delta x = 2.5$, and $x_4 = 1 + 4\Delta x = 3$.

    If we use the left-hand side of each subinterval, we will use 1, 1.5, 2, and 2.5.

    If we use the right-hand side of each subinterval, we will use 1.5, 2, 2.5, and 3.

    If we use the midpoint of each subinerval, we will use 1.25, 1.75, 2.25, and 2.75.

5.1.6

The left Riemann sum will be $\displaystyle\sum_{k=1}^{4} f(x_{k-1}) \cdot 1 = \sum_{k=1}^{4} (x_{k-1})^2$.

411

The right Riemann sum will be $\sum_{k=1}^{4} f(x_k) \cdot 1 = \sum_{k=1}^{4} (x_k)^2$.

The midpoint Riemann sum will be $\sum_{k=1}^{4} f\left(\frac{x_{k-1} + x_k}{2}\right) \cdot 1 = \sum_{k=1}^{4} \left(\frac{x_{k-1} + x_k}{2}\right)^2$.

5.1.7 It is an underestimate. If we use the right-hand side of each subinterval to determine the height of the rectangles, the height of each rectangle will be the minimum of f over the subinterval, so the sum of the areas of the rectangles will be less than the corresponding area under the curve.

5.1.8 It is an underestimate. If we use the left-hand side of each subinterval to determine the height of the rectangles, the height of each rectangle will be the minimum of f over the subinterval, so the sum of the areas of the rectangles will be less than the corresponding area under the curve.

5.1.9

a. On the first subinterval, the midpoint is .5, and $v(.5) = 1.75$. On the 2nd subinterval, the midpoint is 1.5 and $v(1.5) = 7.75$. Continuing in this manner, we obtain the estimate to the displacement of

$$v(.5) \cdot 1 + v(1.5) \cdot 1 + v(2.5) \cdot 1 + v(3.5) \cdot 1 = 1.75 + 7.75 + 19.75 + 37.75 = 67.$$

b. This time the midpoints are at .25, .75, 1.25 .... Each subinterval has length $\frac{1}{2}$. Thus, the estimate is given by

$$v(.25) \cdot .5 + v(.75) \cdot .5 + v(1.25) \cdot .5 + v(1.75) \cdot .5 + v(2.25) \cdot .5 + v(2.75) \cdot .5 + v(3.25) \cdot .5 + v(3.75) \cdot .5$$
$$= .5(1.1875 + 2.6875 + 5.6875 + 10.1875 + 16.1875 + 23.6875 + 32.6875 + 43.1875)$$
$$= .5(135.5) = 67.75.$$

5.1.10

a. The midpoints are 2, 4, and 6. So the estimate is

$$v(2) \cdot 2 + v(4) \cdot 2 + v(6) \cdot 2 \approx 37.085.$$

b. The midpoints are $\frac{3}{2}$, $\frac{5}{2}$, $\frac{7}{2}$, $\frac{9}{2}$, $\frac{11}{2}$, and $\frac{13}{2}$. So the estimate is

$$v\left(\frac{3}{2}\right) + v\left(\frac{5}{2}\right) + v\left(\frac{7}{2}\right) + v\left(\frac{9}{2}\right) + v\left(\frac{11}{2}\right) + v\left(\frac{13}{2}\right) = \sqrt{15} + 5 + \sqrt{35} + 3\sqrt{5} + \sqrt{55} + \sqrt{65} \approx 36.976.$$

5.1.11

The left-hand grid points are 0 and 4. The length of each subinterval is $8/2 = 4$. So the left Riemann sum is given by $v(0) \cdot 4 + v(4) \cdot 4 = 4 \cdot (1 + 9) = 40$.

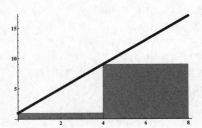

5.1.12

The left-hand grid points are 0, 1 and 2. The length of each subinterval is $3/3 = 1$. So the left Riemann sum is given by $v(0) \cdot 1 + v(1) \cdot 1 + v(2) \cdot 1 = 1 + e + e^2 \approx 11.1$

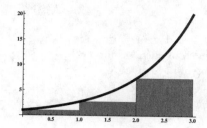

5.1.13

The left-hand grid points are 0, 2, 4, and 6. The length of each subinterval is 2. So the left Riemann sum is given by $v(0) \cdot 2 + v(2) \cdot 2 + v(4) \cdot 2 + v(6) \cdot 2 = 2 \cdot \left(\frac{1}{1} + \frac{1}{5} + \frac{1}{9} + \frac{1}{13} \right) \approx 2.776$.

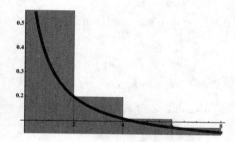

5.1.14

The left-hand grid points are 0, 2, 4, and 6, 8, and 10. The length of each subinterval is 2. So the left Riemann sum is given by $\sum_{k=1}^{6} v(2(k-1)) \cdot 2 = 8 + 12 + 24 + 44 + 72 + 108 = 268$.

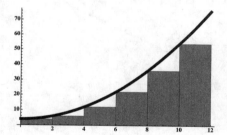

5.1.15

The left-hand grid points are 0, 3, 6, 9, and 12. The length of each subinterval is 3. So the left Riemann sum is given by $\sum_{k=1}^{5} v(3(k-1)) \cdot 3 = 12 + 24 + 12\sqrt{7} + 12\sqrt{10} + 12\sqrt{13} \approx 148.963$.

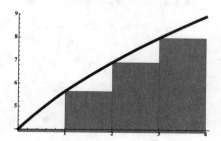

5.1.16

The left-hand grid points are 0, 1, 2, and 3. The length of each subinterval is 1. So the left Riemann sum is given by

$$v(0) + v(1) + v(2) + v(3) = \frac{1}{2} + \frac{2}{3} + \frac{5}{6} + 1 = 3.$$

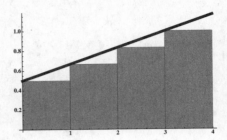

5.1.17 The left Riemann sum is given by $f(1) + f(2) + f(3) + f(4) + f(5) = 2 + 3 + 4 + 5 + 6 = 20.$

The right Riemann sum is given by $f(2) + f(3) + f(4) + f(5) + f(6) = 3 + 4 + 5 + 6 + 7 = 25.$

5.1.18 The left Riemann sum is given by $f(1) + f(2) + f(3) + f(4) = 1 + \frac{1}{2} + \frac{1}{3} + \frac{1}{4} = \frac{25}{12}.$

The right Riemann sum is given by $f(2) + f(3) + f(4) + f(5) = \frac{1}{2} + \frac{1}{3} + \frac{1}{4} + \frac{1}{5} = \frac{77}{60}.$

5.1.19

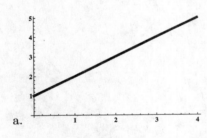

a.

b. We have $\Delta x = \frac{4-0}{4} = 1$. The grid points are $x_0 = 0$, $x_1 = 1$, $x_2 = 2$, $x_3 = 3$, and $x_4 = 4$.

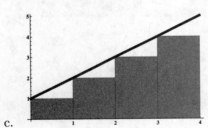

c.

d. The left Riemann sum is $1 \cdot 1 + 2 \cdot 1 + 3 \cdot 1 + 4 \cdot 1 = 10$, which is an underestimate of the area under the curve. The right Riemann sum is $2 \cdot 1 + 3 \cdot 1 + 4 \cdot 1 + 5 \cdot 1 = 14$ which is an overestimate of the area under the curve.

5.1.20

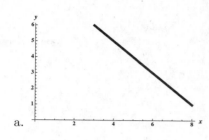

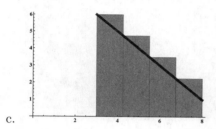

b. We have $\Delta x = \frac{8-3}{5} = 1$. The grid points are $x_0 = 3$, $x_1 = 4$, $x_2 = 5$, $x_3 = 6$, $x_4 = 7$, and $x_5 = 8$.

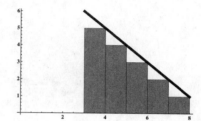

d. The left Riemann sum is $6 \cdot 1 + 5 \cdot 1 + 4 \cdot 1 + 3 \cdot 1 + 2 \cdot 1 = 20$, which is an overestimate of the area under the curve. The right Riemann sum is $5 \cdot 1 + 4 \cdot 1 + 3 \cdot 1 + 2 \cdot 1 + 1 \cdot 1 = 15$ which is an underestimate of the area under the curve.

5.1.21

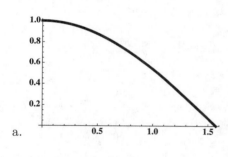

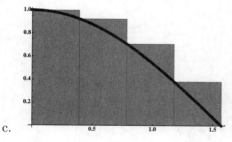

b. We have $\Delta x = \frac{\pi/2 - 0}{4} = \frac{\pi}{8}$. The grid points are $x_0 = 0$, $x_1 = \frac{\pi}{8}$, $x_2 = \frac{\pi}{4}$, $x_3 = \frac{3\pi}{8}$, and $x_4 = \frac{\pi}{2}$.

d. The left Riemann sum is $1 \cdot \frac{\pi}{8} + \cos(\pi/8) \cdot \frac{\pi}{8} + \cos(\pi/4) \cdot \frac{\pi}{8} + \cos(3\pi/8) \cdot \frac{\pi}{8} \approx 1.185$, which is an overestimate of the area under the curve. The right Riemann sum is $\cos(\pi/8) \cdot \frac{\pi}{8} + \cos(\pi/4) \cdot \frac{\pi}{8} + \cos(3\pi/8) \cdot \frac{\pi}{8} + 0 \cdot \frac{\pi}{8} \approx 0.791$ which is an underestimate of the area under the curve.

5.1.22

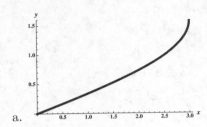

a.

b. We have $\Delta x = \frac{3-0}{6} = \frac{1}{2}$. The grid points are $x_0 = 0$, $x_1 = \frac{1}{2}$, $x_2 = 1$, $x_3 = \frac{3}{2}$, $x_4 = 2$, $x_5 = \frac{5}{2}$, and $x_6 = 3$.

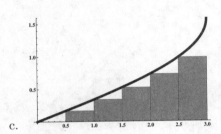

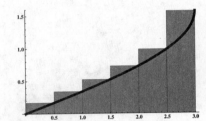

c.

d. The left Riemann sum is

$$\frac{1}{2}\left(0 + \sin^{-1}(1/6) + \sin^{-1}(1/3) + \sin^{-1}(1/2) + \sin^{-1}(2/3) + \sin^{-1}(5/6)\right) \approx 1.373,$$

which is an underestimate of the area under the curve.

The right Riemann sum is

$$\frac{1}{2}\left(\sin^{-1}(1/6) + \sin^{-1}(1/3) + \sin^{-1}(1/2) + \sin^{-1}(2/3) + \sin^{-1}(5/6) + \sin^{-1}1\right) \approx 2.158,$$

which is an overestimate of the area under the curve.

5.1.23

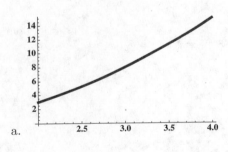

a.

b. We have $\Delta x = \frac{4-2}{4} = \frac{1}{2}$. The grid points are $x_0 = 2$, $x_1 = 2.5$, $x_2 = 3$, $x_3 = 3.5$, and $x_4 = 4$.

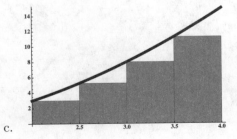

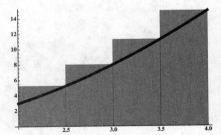

c.

d. The left Riemann sum is $(3 + 5.25 + 8 + 11.25) \cdot 0.5 = 13.75$, which is an underestimate of the area under the curve. The right Riemann sum is $(5.25 + 8 + 11.25 + 15) \cdot 0.5 = 19.75$ which is an overestimate of the area under the curve.

5.1.24

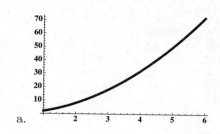

b. We have $\Delta x = \frac{6-1}{5} = 1$. The grid points are $x_0 = 1$, $x_1 = 2$, $x_2 = 3$, $x_3 = 4$, $x_4 = 5$, and $x_5 = 6$.

a.

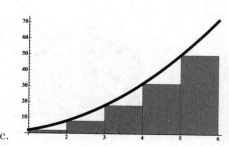

c.

d. The left Riemann sum is $2 + 8 + 18 + 32 + 50 = 110$, which is an underestimate of the area under the curve. The right Riemann sum is $8 + 18 + 32 + 50 + 72 = 180$ which is an overestimate of the area under the curve.

5.1.25

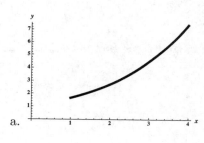

b. We have $\Delta x = \frac{4-1}{6} = \frac{1}{2}$. The grid points are $x_0 = 1$, $x_1 = 1.5$, $x_2 = 2$, $x_3 = 2.5$, $x_4 = 3$, $x_5 = 3.5$, and $x_6 = 4$.

a.

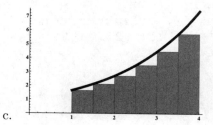

c.

d. The left Riemann sum is $\frac{1}{2}\left(e^{1/2} + e^{3/4} + e + e^{5/4} + e^{3/2} + e^{7/4}\right) \approx 10.105$, which is an underestimate of the area under the curve. The right Riemann sum is $\frac{1}{2}\left(e^{3/4} + e + e^{5/4} + e^{3/2} + e^{7/4} + e^2\right) \approx 12.975$ which is an overestimate of the area under the curve.

5.1.26

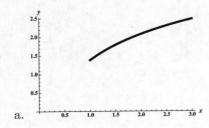

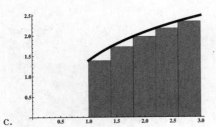

a.

b. We have $\Delta x = \frac{3-1}{5} = \frac{2}{5} = .4$. The grid points are $x_0 = 1$, $x_1 = 1.4$, $x_2 = 1.8$, $x_3 = 2.2$, $x_4 = 2.6$, and $x_5 = 3$.

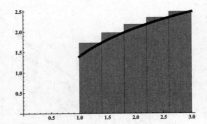

c.

d. The left Riemann sum is

$$.4 \left(\ln 4 + \ln 5.6 + \ln 7.2 + \ln 8.8 + \ln 10.4 \right) \approx 3.840,$$

which is an underestimate of the area under the curve. The right Riemann sum is

$$.4 \left(\ln 5.6 + \ln 7.2 + \ln 8.8 + \ln 10.4 + \ln 12 \right) \approx 4.279,$$

which is an overestimate of the area under the curve.

5.1.27 We have $\Delta x = 2$, so the midpoints are 1, 3, 5, 7, and 9. So the midpoint Riemann sum is $2(f(1) + f(3) + f(5) + f(7) + f(9)) = 670$.

5.1.28 We have $\Delta x = \pi/4$, so the midpoints are $\pi/8$, $3\pi/8$, $5\pi/8$, and $7\pi/8$. So the midpoint Riemann sum is $\frac{\pi}{4} \cdot (f(\pi/8) + f(3\pi/8) + f(5\pi/8) + f(7\pi/8)) \approx 2.013$.

5.1.29

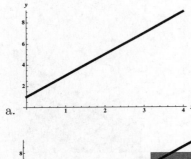

a.

b. We have $\Delta x = \frac{4-0}{4} = 1$. The gridpoints are $x_0 = 0$, $x_1 = 1$, $x_2 = 2$, $x_3 = 3$, and $x_4 = 4$, so the midpoints are .5, 1.5, 2.5, and 3.5.

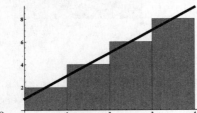

c.

d. The midpoint Riemann sum is $1(2+4+6+8) = 20$.

5.1.30

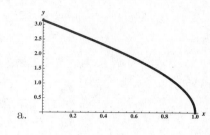

a.

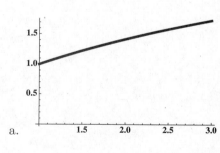

c.

b. We have $\Delta x = \frac{1-0}{5} = .2$. The gridpoints are $x_0 = 0$, $x_1 = .2$, $x_2 = .4$, $x_3 = .6$, $x_4 = .8$, and $x_5 = 1$, so the midpoints are 0.1, 0.3, 0.5, 0.7, and 0.9.

d. The midpoint Riemann sum is $.4(\cos^{-1} 0.1 + \cos^{-1} 0.3 + \cos^{-1} 0.5 + \cos^{-1} 0.7 + \cos^{-1} 0.9) \approx 2.012$.

5.1.31

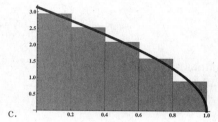

a.

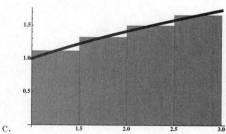

c.

b. We have $\Delta x = \frac{3-1}{4} = \frac{1}{2}$. So the midpoints are 1.25, 1.75, 2.25, and 2.75.

d. The midpoint Riemann sum is $.5(\sqrt{1.25} + \sqrt{1.75} + \sqrt{2.25} + \sqrt{2.75}) \approx 2.800$.

5.1.32

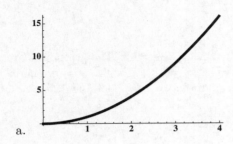

a.

b. We have $\Delta x = \frac{4-0}{4} = 1$. So the midpoints are .5, 1.5, 2.5, and 3.5.

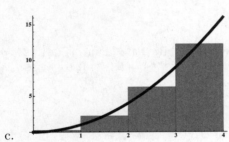

c.

d. The midpoint Riemann sum is $.5^2 + 1.5^2 + 2.5^2 + 3.5^2 = 21$.

5.1.33

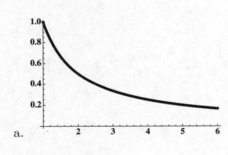

a.

b. We have $\Delta x = \frac{6-1}{5} = 1$. So the midpoints are 1.5, 2.5, 3.5, 4.5, and 5.5.

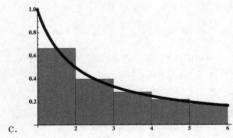

c.

d. The midpoint Riemann sum is $2/3 + 2/5 + 2/7 + 2/9 + 2/11 \approx 1.756$.

5.1.34

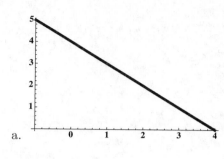

a.

b. We have $\Delta x = \frac{4-(-1)}{5} = 1$. So the midpoints are $-.5, .5, 1.5, 2.5,$ and 3.5.

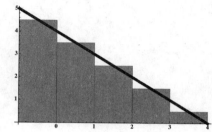

c.

d. The midpoint Riemann sum is $(4-(-.5))+(4-.5)+(4-1.5)+(4-2.5)+(4-3.5) = 20-7.5 = 12.5$.

5.1.35 Note that $\Delta x = \frac{2-0}{4} = .5$. So the left Riemann sum is given by $.5(5+3+2+1) = 5.5$ and the right Riemann sum is given by $.5(3+2+1+1) = 3.5$.

5.1.36 Note that $\Delta x = \frac{5-1}{8} = .5$. So the left Riemann sum is given by $.5(0+2+3+2+2+1+0+2) = 6$ and the right Riemann sum is given by $.5(2+3+2+2+1+0+2+3) = 7.5$.

5.1.37

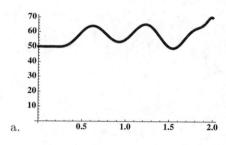

a.

b. With $n = 2$, we have $\Delta x = \frac{2-0}{2} = 1$, so the midpoints are $.5$ and 1.5. So the midpoint Riemann sum is $60 + 50 = 110$. For $n = 4$, we have $\Delta x = \frac{2-0}{4} = \frac{1}{2}$, so the midpoints are $.25, .75, 1.25,$ and 1.75. The midpoint Riemann sum in this case is $0.5(50+60+65+60) = \frac{235}{2} = 117.5$.

5.1.38

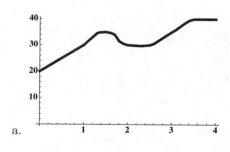

a.

b. With $n = 2$, we have $\Delta x = \frac{4-0}{2} = 2$, so the midpoints are 1 and 3. So the midpoint Riemann sum is $2(30+35) = 130$. For $n = 4$, we have $\Delta x = \frac{4-0}{4} = 1$, so the midpoints are $.5, 1.5, 2.5,$ and 3.5. The midpoint Riemann sum in this case is $25 + 35 + 30 + 40 = 130$.

5.1.39

a. $\displaystyle\sum_{k=1}^{5} k.$

b. $\displaystyle\sum_{k=1}^{6} (k+3).$

c. $\displaystyle\sum_{k=1}^{4} k^2.$

d. $\displaystyle\sum_{k=1}^{4} \frac{1}{k}.$

5.1.40

a. $\displaystyle\sum_{k=1}^{50}(2k-1).$ b. $\displaystyle\sum_{k=1}^{9}(5k-1).$ c. $\displaystyle\sum_{k=1}^{13}(5k-2).$ d. $\displaystyle\sum_{k=1}^{49}\frac{1}{k(k+1)}.$

5.1.41

a. $\displaystyle\sum_{k=1}^{10}k = 1+2+3+\ldots+10 = 55.$ b. $\displaystyle\sum_{k=1}^{6}(2k+1) = 3+5+7+9+11+13 = 48.$

c. $\displaystyle\sum_{k=1}^{4}k^2 = 1+4+9+16 = 30.$ d. $\displaystyle\sum_{n=1}^{5}(1+n^2) = 2+5+10+17+26 = 60.$

e. $\displaystyle\sum_{m=1}^{3}\frac{2m+2}{3} = \frac{4}{3}+\frac{6}{3}+\frac{8}{3} = 6.$ f. $\displaystyle\sum_{j=1}^{3}(3j-4) = -1+2+5 = 6.$

g. $\displaystyle\sum_{p=1}^{5}(2p+p^2) = 3+8+15+24+35 = 85.$ h. $\displaystyle\sum_{n=0}^{4}\sin\frac{n\pi}{2} = 0+1+0+(-1)+0 = 0.$

5.1.42

a. $\displaystyle\sum_{k=1}^{45}k = \frac{45\cdot46}{2} = 45\cdot23 = 1035.$

b. $\displaystyle\sum_{k=1}^{45}(5k-1) = 5\sum_{k=1}^{45}k - \sum_{k=1}^{45}1 = 5\cdot1035 - 45 = 5130.$

c. $\displaystyle\sum_{k=1}^{75}2k^2 = 2\sum_{k=1}^{75}k^2 = 2\cdot\frac{75\cdot76\cdot151}{6} = 286,900.$

d. $\displaystyle\sum_{n=1}^{50}(1+n^2) = \sum_{n=1}^{50}1 + \sum_{n=1}^{50}n^2 = 50 + \frac{50\cdot51\cdot101}{6} = 50+42925 = 42975.$

e. $\displaystyle\sum_{m=1}^{75}\frac{2m+2}{3} = \frac{2}{3}\sum_{m=1}^{75}m + \frac{2}{3}\sum_{m=1}^{75}1 = \frac{2}{3}\cdot\frac{75\cdot76}{2} + \frac{2}{3}\cdot75 = 1900 + 50 = 1950.$

f. $\displaystyle\sum_{j=1}^{20}(3j-4) = 3\sum_{j=1}^{20}j - \sum_{j=1}^{20}4 = 3\cdot\frac{20\cdot21}{2} - 20\cdot4 = 550.$

g. $\displaystyle\sum_{p=1}^{35}(2p+p^2) = 2\sum_{p=1}^{35}p + \sum_{p=1}^{35}p^2 = 2\cdot\frac{35\cdot36}{2} + \frac{35\cdot36\cdot71}{6} = 16170.$

h. $\displaystyle\sum_{n=0}^{40}(n^2+3n-1) = \sum_{n=0}^{40}n^2 + \sum_{n=0}^{40}3n - \sum_{n=0}^{40}1 = \frac{40\cdot41\cdot81}{6} + 3\cdot\frac{40\cdot41}{2} - 41 = 24559.$

5.1.43 Note that $\Delta x = \frac{1}{10}$, and $x_k = a + k\Delta x = \frac{k}{10}$.

a. The left Riemann sum is given by $\displaystyle\sum_{k=0}^{39}\sqrt{k/10}\cdot(1/10) \approx 5.227.$

The right Riemann sum is given by $\displaystyle\sum_{k=1}^{40}\sqrt{k/10}\cdot(1/10) \approx 5.427.$

The midpoint Riemann sum is given by $\sum_{k=0}^{39} \sqrt{(1/20) + (k/10)} \cdot (1/10) \approx 5.335$.

b. It appears that the actual area is about $5 + 1/3$.

5.1.44 Note that $\Delta x = \frac{1}{25}$, and $x_k = -1 + k\Delta x = -1 + (k/25)$. So $f(x_k) = (-1 + (k/25))^2 + 1$.

a. The left Riemann sum is given by $\sum_{k=0}^{49}[(-1 + (k/25))^2 + 1] \cdot (1/25) \approx 2.667$.

The right Riemann sum is given by $\sum_{k=1}^{50}[(-1 + (k/25))^2 + 1] \cdot (1/25) \approx 2.667$.

The midpoint Riemann sum is given by $\sum_{k=0}^{49}[(-(49/50) + (k/25))^2 + 1] \cdot (1/25) \approx 2.666$.

b. It appears that the actual area is about $2 + 2/3$.

5.1.45 Note that $\Delta x = \frac{1}{15}$, and $x_k = 2 + k\Delta x = 2 + (k/15)$. So $f(x_k) = (2 + (k/15))^2 - 1$.

a. The left Riemann sum is given by $\sum_{k=0}^{74}[(2 + (k/15))^2 - 1] \cdot (1/15) \approx 105.170$.

The right Riemann sum is given by $\sum_{k=1}^{75}[(2 + (k/15))^2 - 1] \cdot (1/15) \approx 108.170$.

The midpoint Riemann sum is given by $\sum_{k=0}^{74}[((61/30) + (k/15))^2 - 1] \cdot (1/15) \approx 106.665$.

b. It appears that the actual area is about $106 + 2/3$.

5.1.46 Note that $\Delta x = \frac{\pi}{240}$, and $x_k = k\Delta x = (k\pi/240)$. So $f(x_k) = \cos(k\pi/120)$.

a. The left Riemann sum is given by $\sum_{k=0}^{59} \cos(k\pi/120) \cdot (\pi/240) \approx .507$.

The right Riemann sum is given by $\sum_{k=1}^{60} \cos(k\pi/120) \cdot (\pi/240) \approx .493$.

The midpoint Riemann sum is given by $\sum_{k=0}^{59} \cos((\pi/240) + k\pi/120) \cdot (\pi/240) \approx .500$.

b. It appears that the actual area is about $.5$.

5.1.47 The right Riemann sum is given by $A_n = \sum_{k=1}^{n} f(x_k)\Delta x = \sum_{k=1}^{n} \left(4 - \left(-2 + \frac{4k}{n}\right)^2\right) \cdot \frac{4}{n}$.

n	A_n
10	10.560
30	10.655
60	10.664
80	10.665

It appears that A_n is approaching $10\frac{2}{3}$.

5.1.48 The right Riemann sum is given by $A_n = \sum_{k=1}^{n} f(x_k)\Delta x = \sum_{k=1}^{n} \left(\left(\frac{2k}{n} \right)^2 + 1 \right) \cdot \frac{2}{n}$.

n	A_n
10	5.08
30	4.801
60	4.734
80	4.717

It appears that A_n is approaching $\frac{14}{3}$.

5.1.49 The right Riemann sum is given by $A_n = \sum_{k=1}^{n} f(x_k)\Delta x = \sum_{k=1}^{n} \left(2 - 2\sin\left(\frac{-\pi}{2} + \frac{\pi k}{n} \right) \right) \cdot \frac{\pi}{n}$.

n	A_n
10	5.6549
30	6.0737
60	6.1785
80	6.2046

It appears that A_n is approaching 2π.

5.1.50 The right Riemann sum is given by $A_n = \sum_{k=1}^{n} f(x_k)\Delta x = \sum_{k=1}^{n} 2^{1+\frac{k}{n}} \cdot \frac{1}{n}$.

n	A_n
10	2.98665
30	2.91885
60	2.90209
80	2.897908

It appears that A_n is approaching approximately 2.8.

5.1.51 The right Riemann sum is given by $A_n = \sum_{k=1}^{n} f(x_k)\Delta x = \sum_{k=1}^{n} \ln\left(1 + \frac{k(e-1)}{n} \right) \cdot \frac{e-1}{n}$.

n	A_n
10	1.08436
30	1.02847
60	1.01428
80	1.01071

It appears that A_n is approaching 1.

5.1.52 The right Riemann sum is given by $A_n = \sum_{k=1}^{n} f(x_k)\Delta x = \sum_{k=1}^{n} \sqrt{\frac{3k}{n} + 1} \cdot \frac{3}{n}$.

n	A_n
10	4.8148
30	4.71646
60	4.69161
80	4.68539

It appears that A_n is approaching $\frac{14}{3}$.

5.1.53

a. True. Because the curve is a straight line, the region under the curve and over each subinterval is a trapezoid. The formula for the area of such a trapezoid over $[x_i, x_{i+1}]$ is $\frac{f(x_i)+f(x_{i+1})}{2}$.

$\Delta x = \frac{2x_i + 5 + 2x_{i+1} + 5}{2} \cdot \Delta x = (x_i + x_{i+1} + 5)\Delta x$ and the area given by using the midpoint formula is $f\left(\frac{x_i + x_{i+1}}{2}\right)\Delta x = (x_i + x_{i+1} + 5)\Delta x$. So the area under the curve is exactly given by the midpoint Riemann sum. Note that this holds for any straight line.

b. False. The left Riemann sum will underestimate the area under an increasing function.

c. True. The value of f at the midpoint will always be between the value of f at the endpoints, if f is monotonic increasing or monotonic decreasing.

5.1.54

a. Note that if $y = \sqrt{1 - x^2}$, then $y^2 = 1 - x^2$, so $x^2 + y^2 = 1$, which represents a circle of radius one. Note that for the original function $y > 0$ for all x, so this represents the top semicircle.

b. We have $\sum_{k=1}^{25} f(x_k^*)\frac{2}{25}$ where x_k^* represents the midpoint of the kth subinterval. This sum is

$$\sum_{k=0}^{24} \sqrt{1 - \left(-.96 + \frac{2k}{25}\right)^2} \cdot \frac{2}{25} \approx 1.575.$$

c. We have $\sum_{k=1}^{75} f(x_k^*)\frac{2}{75}$ where x_k^* represents the midpoint of the kth subinterval. This sum is

$$\sum_{k=0}^{74} \sqrt{1 - \left((-.98\overline{6}) + \frac{2k}{75}\right)^2} \cdot \frac{2}{75} \approx 1.572.$$

d. It appears as though the area approaches $\pi/2$ as $n \to \infty$.

5.1.55 $\sum_{k=1}^{50} \left(\frac{2k}{25} + 1\right) \cdot \frac{2}{25} = 12.16.$

5.1.56 $\sum_{k=0}^{39} e^{k(\ln 2)/40} \cdot \frac{\ln 2}{40} \approx 0.991.$

5.1.57 $\sum_{k=0}^{31} \left(3 + \frac{1}{8} + \frac{k}{4}\right)^3 \cdot \frac{1}{4} \approx 3639.125.$

5.1.58 $\sum_{k=0}^{49} \left[1 + \cos\left(\pi\left(\frac{1}{50} + \frac{k}{25}\right)\right)\right] \cdot \frac{1}{25} = 2.$

5.1.59 This is the right Riemann sum for f on the interval $[1, 5]$ for $n = 4$.

5.1.60 This is the right Riemann sum for f on the interval $[2, 6]$ for $n = 4$.

5.1.61 This is the midpoint Riemann sum for f on the interval $[2, 6]$ for $n = 4$.

5.1.62 This is the right Riemann sum for f on the interval $[1.5, 5.5]$ for $n = 8$.

5.1.63 For all of the calculations below, we have $\Delta x = \frac{1}{2}$, and grid points $x_0 = 0$, $x_1 = .5$, $x_2 = 1$, $x_3 = 2.5$, and $x_4 = 2$.

a.

The left Riemann sum is given by $\frac{1}{2}\left(f(0) + f(.5) + f(1) + f(1.5)\right)$ which is equal to $\frac{1}{2}\left(2 + 2.25 + 3 + 4.25\right) = 5.75$.

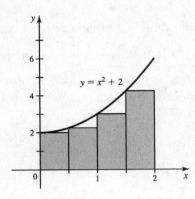

b.

The midpoint Riemann sum is given by $\frac{1}{2}\left(f(.25) + f(.75) + f(1.25) + f(1.75)\right)$ which is equal to $\frac{1}{2}\left(2.0625 + 2.5625 + 3.5625 + 5.0625\right) = 6.625$.

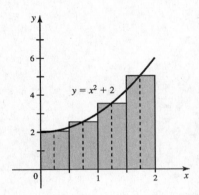

c.

The right Riemann sum is given by $\frac{1}{2}\left(f(.5) + f(1) + f(1.5) + f(2)\right)$ which is equal to $\frac{1}{2}\left(2.25 + 3 + 4.25 + 6\right) = 7.75$.

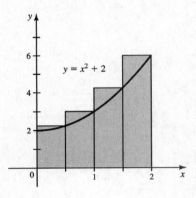

5.1.64 Using 3 subintervals, we have $\Delta x = \frac{6}{3} = 2$. The left Riemann sum is $2(f(0) + f(2) + f(4)) = 2(1 + 6 + 9) = 32$. The right Riemann sum is given by $2(f(2) + f(4) + f(6)) = 2(6 + 9 + 11) = 52$.

5.1.65 We have $\Delta x = \frac{7-1}{6} = 1$. The left Riemann sum is given by $1(10 + 9 + 7 + 5 + 2 + 1) = 34$ and the right Riemann sum is given by $1(9 + 7 + 5 + 2 + 1 + 0) = 24$.

5.1.66

a. The object's velocity decreases during the first second, then remains constant between time $t = 1$ and $t = 3$, and then steadily increases until $t = 4$, and then stays constant after that.

b. The displacement is given by the area under the curve, which between $t = 0$ and $t = 3$ is 35, so the displacement is 35 meters.

c. Between $t = 3$ and $t = 5$ the area under the curve is 50, so the displacement is 50 meters.

d. Between $t = 0$ and $t = 4$ the displacement is 55, and between 4 and t for $t > 4$, the displacement is $30(t - 4)$. So the displacement between 0 and t for $t > 4$ is $55 + 30(t - 4)$.

5.1.67

a. During the first second, the velocity steadily increases from 0 to 20, then it remains constant until $t = 3$. From $t = 3$ until $t = 5$ it steadily decreases, and then remains constant until $t = 6$.

b. Between $t = 0$ and $t = 2$ the area under the curve is $\frac{1}{2} \cdot 1 \cdot 20 + 1 \cdot 20 = 30$.

c. Between $t = 2$ and $t = 5$ the displacement is the sum of the area of a rectangle with area 20 and a trapezoid with area 30, so the displacement is 50 meters.

d. Between $t = 0$ and $t = 5$ the displacement is 80. Between $t = 5$ and any time $t \geq 5$ the displacement is $10(t - 5)$ so the displacement between $t = 0$ and $t \geq 5$ is $80 + 10(t - 5)$.

5.1.68

a. Between 0 and 4, the area under the curve is given by $\frac{1}{2} \cdot 4000 \cdot 4 = 8000$ cubic feet.

b. Between 8 and 10, the area under the curve is given by $2 \cdot 5000 = 10,000$ cubic feet.

c. Between 4 and 6 the amount is 9500 cubic feet, which is more than between 0 and 4.

d. When we multiply $\text{ft}^3/\text{hr} \cdot \text{hr}$ the result is ft^3.

5.1.69

a. Between 0 and 5, the area under the curve is given by the area of a square of area 4 and the area of a trapezoid of area 10.5, so the total area is 14.5.

b. Between 5 and 10, the area under the curve is given by the area of a trapezoid of area 5.5 and the area of a rectangle of area $4 \cdot 6 = 24$, so the total area is 29.5.

c. The mass of the entire rod would be the total area under the curve from 0 to 10, which would be $14.5 + 29.5 = 44$ grams.

d. At $x = \frac{19}{3}$ there is a mass of 22 on each side. Note that from 0 to 6 the mass is 20 grams, so the center of mass is a little greater than 6.

5.1.70 If $0 \leq t \leq 1.5$, the displacement is $40t$. If $1.5 \leq t \leq 3$, the displacement is $60 + 50(t - 1.5)$.

Thus, $d(t) = \begin{cases} 40t & \text{if } 0 \leq t \leq 1.5, \\ 50t - 15 & \text{if } 1.5 \leq t \leq 3. \end{cases}$

5.1.71 If $0 \leq t \leq 2$, the displacement is $30t$. If $2 \leq t \leq 2.5$, the displacement is $60 + 50(t - 2)$. If $2.5 \leq t \leq 3$, the displacement is $85 + 44(t - 2.5)$.

Thus, $d(t) = \begin{cases} 30t & \text{if } 0 \leq t \leq 2, \\ 50t - 40 & \text{if } 2 \leq t \leq 2.5 \\ 44t - 25 & \text{if } 2.5 \leq t \leq 3. \end{cases}$

5.1.72 Using the left Riemann sum

$$\sum_{k=0}^{n-1} \left| 25 - \left(\frac{10k}{n} \right)^2 \right| \cdot \frac{10}{n},$$

we have

n	16	32	64
A_n	234.375	242.188	246.094

It appears that the areas are approaching 250.

5.1.73 Using the left Riemann sum

$$\sum_{k=0}^{n-1} \left| \left(-1 + \frac{2k}{n} \right) \left(\left(-1 + \frac{2k}{n} \right)^2 - 1 \right) \right| \cdot \frac{2}{n},$$

we have

n	16	32	64
A_n	.492188	.498047	.499512

It appears that the areas are approaching .5.

5.1.74 Using the left Riemann sum

$$\sum_{k=0}^{n-1} \left| \cos \left(2 \cdot \frac{\pi k}{n} \right) \right| \cdot \frac{\pi}{n},$$

we have

n	16	32	64
A_n	1.97423	1.99357	1.99839

It appears that the areas are approaching 2.

5.1.75 Using the left Riemann sum

$$\sum_{k=0}^{n-1} \left| 1 - \left(-1 + \frac{3k}{n} \right)^3 \right| \cdot \frac{3}{n},$$

we have

n	16	32	64
A_n	4.33054	4.52814	4.63592

It appears that the areas are approaching 4.75.

5.1.76 Because the function f is constant, its value is c at each grid point. Thus the left Riemann sum is

$$\sum_{k=0}^{n-1} f(x_k) \cdot \frac{b-a}{n} = \sum_{k=0}^{n-1} c \cdot \frac{b-a}{n} = \frac{c(b-a)}{n} \cdot \sum_{k=0}^{n-1} 1 = \frac{c(b-a)}{n} \cdot n = c(b-a).$$

For the right Riemann sum we have $\sum_{k=1}^{n} f(x_k) \cdot \frac{b-a}{n} = \sum_{k=1}^{n} c \cdot \frac{b-a}{n} = \frac{c(b-a)}{n} \cdot \sum_{k=1}^{n} 1 = \frac{c(b-a)}{n} \cdot n = c(b-a).$

For the midpoint Riemann sum we have $\sum_{k=0}^{n-1} f \left(a + \frac{b-a}{2n} + \frac{(b-a)k}{n} \right) \cdot \frac{b-a}{n} = \sum_{k=0}^{n-1} c \cdot \frac{b-a}{n} = \frac{c(b-a)}{n} \cdot$

$\sum_{k=0}^{n-1} 1 = \frac{c(b-a)}{n} \cdot n = c(b-a).$

So all three rules give the exact area of $(b-a) \cdot c$.

5.1.77 The midpoint Riemann sum gives

$$\sum_{k=0}^{n-1} f\left(a + \frac{b-a}{2n} + \frac{k(b-a)}{n}\right) \cdot \frac{b-a}{n} = \sum_{k=0}^{n-1}\left(m\left(a + \frac{b-a}{2n} + \frac{k(b-a)}{n}\right) + c\right) \cdot \frac{b-a}{n} =$$

$$m \cdot a \cdot n \cdot \frac{b-a}{n} + \frac{m(b-a)^2 n}{2n^2} + \frac{(n-1)n}{2} \cdot \frac{m(b-a)^2}{n^2} + \frac{cn(b-a)}{n} =$$

$$m \cdot a \cdot (b-a) + \frac{m(b-a)^2}{2n} + \frac{m(b-a)^2}{2} - \frac{m(b-a)^2}{2n} + c(b-a) =$$

$$m \cdot a \cdot (b-a) + \frac{m(b-a)^2}{2} + c(b-a) = (b-a) \cdot \left(\frac{m(a+b)}{2} + c\right).$$

This proves that the midpoint Riemann sum is independent of n. Because the region in question is a trapezoid, we know that the exact area is given by the width of the subinterval times the average value at the endpoints, which is $(b-a)\left(\frac{f(a)+f(b)}{2}\right) = (b-a)\left(\frac{ma+c+mb+c}{2}\right) = (b-a)\left(\frac{m(a+b)}{2} + c\right)$.

5.1.78 For a function that is concave up and increasing, each rectangle of the left Riemann sum will lie wholly below the curve, since the value of the function at the left edge of the rectangle will be smaller than at any other point in the rectangle. Thus this will be an underestimate. For a function that is concave up and decreasing, however, each rectangle will have its top edge above the curve, since the value of the function at the left edge will be larger than at any other point in the rectangle. Thus this will be an overestimate. For a function that is concave down and increasing, each rectangle of the left Riemann sum will lie wholly below the curve, since the value of the function at the left edge of the rectangle will be smaller than at any other point in the rectangle. Thus this will be an underestimate. Finally, for a function that is concave down and decreasing, each rectangle will have its top edge above the curve, since the value of the function at the left edge will be larger than at any other point in the rectangle. Thus this will be an overestimate. Graphs of each of the four situations are below:

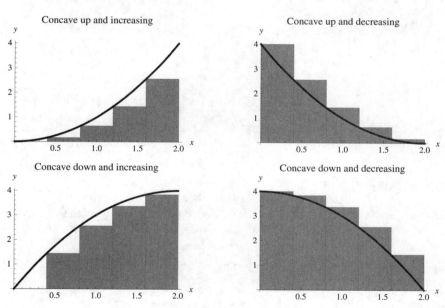

So the answer is

	Increasing on $[a, b]$	Decreasing on $[a, b]$
Concave up on $[a, b]$	Underestimate	Overestimate
Concave down on $[a, b]$	Underestimate	Overestimate

5.1.79 For a function that is concave up and increasing, each rectangle of the right Riemann sum will have its top edge above the curve, since the value of the function at the right edge of the rectangle will be larger than at any other point in the rectangle. Thus this will be an overestimate. For a function that is concave up and decreasing, however, each rectangle will lie wholly below the curve, since the value of the function at the right edge will be smaller than at any other point in the rectangle. Thus this will be an underestimate. For a function that is concave down and increasing, each rectangle of the right Riemann sum will have its top edge above the curve, since the value of the function at the right edge of the rectangle will be larger than at any other point in the rectangle. Thus this will be an overestimate. Finally, for a function that is concave down and decreasing, however, each rectangle will lie wholly below the curve, since the value of the function at the right edge will be smaller than at any other point in the rectangle. Thus this will be an underestimate. Graphs of each of the four situations are below:

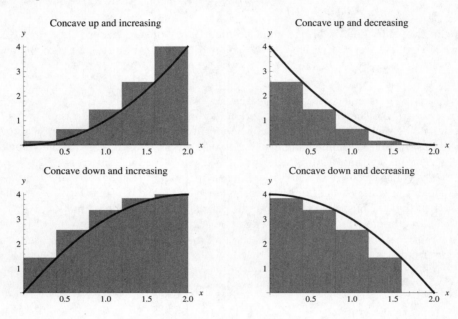

So the answer is

	Increasing on $[a, b]$	Decreasing on $[a, b]$
Concave up on $[a, b]$	Overestimate	Underestimate
Concave down on $[a, b]$	Overestimate	Underestimate

5.2   Definite Integrals

5.2.1 The net area is the difference between the area above the x-axis and below the curve, and below the x-axis and above the curve.

5.2.2 The definite integral $\int_a^b f(x)\, dx$ gives the net area of the function between $x = a$ and $x = b$.

5.2.3 When the function is strictly above the x-axis, the net area is equal to the area. The net area differs from the area when the function dips below the x-axis so that the area below the x-axis and above the curve is nonzero.

5.2.4 In the Riemann sum formulas like $\sum_{k=1}^{n} f(x_k)\Delta x$, the quantity Δx is positive, so if the quantity $f(x_i)$ is negative, we have the sum of n negative numbers, which is a negative number.

5.2.5 Because each of the functions $\sin x$ and $\cos x$ have the same amount of area above the x-axis as below between 0 and 2π, these both have value 0.

5.2.6 The greek letter $\sum$ and the integral sign $\int$ both remind us of the letter S, which stands for sum. The differential dx is analogous to Δx, helping us think of a small width. In both cases, the product of some form of $f(x)$ with either dx or Δx should make us think of an area – a height times a width. So both symbols are evocative of a sum of areas of rectangles, or a limit of such things.

5.2.7 Because a region "from $x = a$ to $x = a$" has no width, its area is zero. This is akin to asking for the area of a one-dimensional object.

5.2.8 $\displaystyle\int_1^6 (2x^3 - 4x)\,dx = \int_1^6 2x^3\,dx - 4\int_1^6 x\,dx.$

5.2.9 This integral represents the area under $y = x$ between $x = 0$ and $x = a$, which is a right triangle. The length of the base of the triangle is a and the height is a, so the area is $\frac{1}{2}\cdot a^2$, so $\displaystyle\int_0^a x\,dx = \frac{a^2}{2}.$

5.2.10 Because the function $|f|$ never goes below the x axis, the definite integral of $|f|$ does represent the area between $|f|$ and the x-axis. If this area is zero, then f must strictly lie on the x axis, so f must be the constant function with value 0.

5.2.11

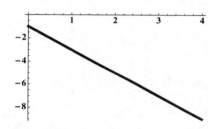

The left Riemann sum is $f(0)\cdot 1 + f(1)\cdot 1 + f(2)\cdot 1 + f(3)\cdot 1 = -1 - 3 - 5 - 7 = -16$.
The right Riemann sum is $f(1)\cdot 1 + f(2)\cdot 1 + f(3)\cdot 1 + f(4)\cdot 1 = -3 - 5 - 7 - 9 = -24$.
The midpoint Riemann sum is $f(.5)\cdot 1 + f(1.5)\cdot 1 + f(2.5)\cdot 1 + f(3.5)\cdot 1 = -2 - 4 - 6 - 8 = -20$.

5.2.12

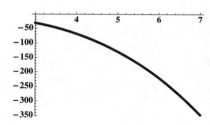

We have $\Delta x = \frac{7-3}{4} = 1$. The left Riemann sum is $f(3)\cdot 1 + f(4)\cdot 1 + f(5)\cdot 1 + f(6)\cdot 1 = -31 - 68 - 129 - 220 = -448$.
The right Riemann sum is $f(4)\cdot 1 + f(5)\cdot 1 + f(6)\cdot 1 + f(7)\cdot 1 = -68 - 129 - 220 - 347 = -764$.
The midpoint Riemann sum is $f(3.5)\cdot 1 + f(4.5)\cdot 1 + f(5.5)\cdot 1 + f(6.5)\cdot 1 = -46.875 - 95.125 - 170.375 - 278.625 = -591$.

5.2.13

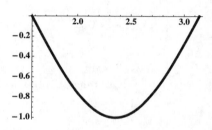

We have $\Delta x = \frac{\pi/2}{4} = \frac{\pi}{8}$. The left Riemann sum is $f(\pi/2)\cdot\frac{\pi}{8} + f(5\pi/8)\cdot\frac{\pi}{8} + f(6\pi/8)\cdot\frac{\pi}{8} + f(7\pi/8)\cdot\frac{\pi}{8} = \left(0 - \sqrt{2}/2 - 1 - \sqrt{2}/2\right)\cdot\frac{\pi}{8} = \frac{\pi}{8}\cdot(-1-\sqrt{2}) \approx -.948$.

The right Riemann sum is $f(5\pi/8)\cdot\frac{\pi}{8} + f(6\pi/8)\cdot\frac{\pi}{8} + f(7\pi/8)\cdot\frac{\pi}{8} + f(\pi)\cdot\frac{\pi}{8} = \left(-\sqrt{2}/2 - 1 - \sqrt{2}/2 - 0\right)\cdot\frac{\pi}{8} = \frac{\pi}{8}\cdot(-1 - \sqrt{2}) \approx -.948$.

The midpoint Riemann sum is $f(9\pi/16)\cdot\frac{\pi}{8} + f(11\pi/16)\cdot\frac{\pi}{8} + f(13\pi/16)\cdot\frac{\pi}{8} + f(15\pi/16)\cdot\frac{\pi}{8} \approx \frac{\pi}{8}\cdot(-0.382683 - .92388 - .92388 - 0.382683) \approx -1.026$.

5.2.14

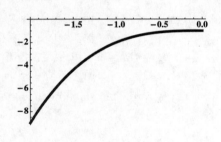

We have $\Delta x = \frac{2}{4} = \frac{1}{2}$. The left Riemann sum is $f(-2) \cdot \frac{1}{2} + f(-1.5) \cdot \frac{1}{2} + f(-1) \cdot \frac{1}{2} + f(-.5) \cdot \frac{1}{2} = .5(-9 - 4.375 - 2 - 1.125) = -8.25$.

The right Riemann sum is $f(-1.5) \cdot \frac{1}{2} + f(-1) \cdot \frac{1}{2} + f(-.5) \cdot \frac{1}{2} + f(0) \cdot \frac{1}{2} = .5(-4.375 - 2 - 1.125 - 1) = -4.25$.

The midpoint Riemann sum is $f(-1.75) \cdot \frac{1}{2} + f(-1.25) \cdot \frac{1}{2} + f(-.75) \cdot \frac{1}{2} + f(-.25) \cdot \frac{1}{2} = .5(-6.35938 - 2.95313 - 1.42188 - 1.10563) \approx -5.875$.

5.2.15

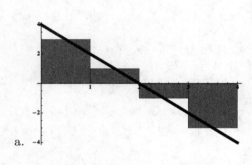

a.

b. The left Riemann sum $\sum_{k=0}^{3} f(x_k) \cdot 1 = 4$.

The right Riemann sum $\sum_{k=1}^{4} f(x_k) \cdot 1 = -4$.

The midpoint Riemann sum $\sum_{k=1}^{4} f(x_k^*) \cdot 1 = 0$.

c. The rectangles whose height is $f(x_k)$ contribute positively when $x_k < 2$ and negatively when $x_k > 2$.

5.2.16

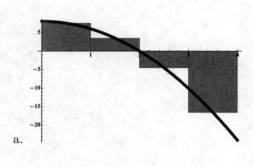

a.

b. The left Riemann sum $\sum_{k=0}^{3} f(x_k) \cdot 1 = 4$.

The right Riemann sum $\sum_{k=1}^{4} f(x_k) \cdot 1 = -28$.

The midpoint Riemann sum $\sum_{k=1}^{4} f(x_k^*) \cdot 1 = -10$.

c. The rectangles whose height is $f(x_k)$ contribute positively when $x_k < 2$ and negatively when $x_k > 2$.

5.2.17

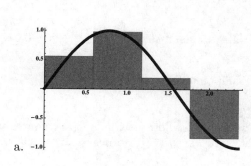

a.

b. The left Riemann sum $\sum_{k=0}^{3} f(x_k) \cdot \frac{3\pi}{16} \approx .7353$.

The right Riemann sum $\sum_{k=1}^{4} f(x_k) \cdot \frac{3\pi}{16} \approx 0.146$.

The midpoint Riemann sum $\sum_{k=1}^{4} f(x_k^*) \cdot \frac{3\pi}{16} \approx 0.530$.

c. The rectangles whose height is $f(x_k)$ contribute positively when $x_k < \frac{\pi}{2}$ and negatively when $x_k > \frac{\pi}{2}$.

5.2.18

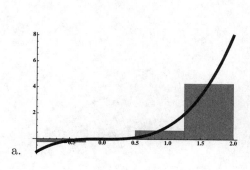

a.

b. The left Riemann sum $\sum_{k=0}^{3} f(x_k) \cdot \frac{3}{4} \approx .797$.

The right Riemann sum $\sum_{k=1}^{4} f(x_k) \cdot \frac{3}{4} \approx 7.547$.

The midpoint Riemann sum $\sum_{k=1}^{4} f(x_k^*) \cdot \frac{3}{4} \approx 3.539$.

c. The rectangles whose height is $f(x_k)$ contribute positively when $x_k > 0$ and negatively when $x_k < 0$.

5.2.19

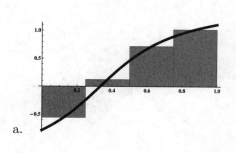

a.

b. The left Riemann sum $\sum_{k=0}^{3} f(x_k) \cdot \frac{1}{4} \approx 0.082$.

The right Riemann sum $\sum_{k=1}^{4} f(x_k) \cdot \frac{1}{4} \approx 0.555$.

The midpoint Riemann sum $\sum_{k=1}^{4} f(x_k^*) \cdot \frac{1}{4} \approx 0.326$.

c. The rectangles whose height is $f(x_k)$ contribute positively when $x_k > 1/3$ and negatively when $x_k < 1/3$.

5.2.20

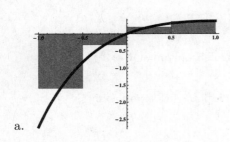

a.

b. The left Riemann sum $\sum_{k=0}^{3} f(x_k) \cdot \frac{1}{2} \approx -1.620$.

The right Riemann sum $\sum_{k=1}^{4} f(x_k) \cdot \frac{1}{2} \approx -0.077$.

The midpoint Riemann sum $\sum_{k=1}^{4} f(x_k^*) \cdot \frac{1}{2} \approx -0.6780$.

c. The rectangles whose height is $f(x_k)$ contribute positively when $x_k > 0$ and negatively when $x_k < 0$.

5.2.21 This is $\int_0^2 \left(x^2 + 1\right) dx$.

5.2.22 This is $\int_{-2}^2 \left(4 - x^2\right) dx$.

5.2.23 This is $\int_1^2 x \ln(x) \, dx$.

5.2.24 This is $\int_{-2}^2 \left|x^2 - 1\right| dx$.

5.2.25

The region in question is a triangle with base 4 and height 8, so the area is $\frac{1}{2} \cdot 8 \cdot 4 = 16$, and this is therefore the value of the definite integral as well.

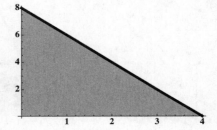

5.2.26

The region in question is a triangle with base 4 and height 8, above the axis, and a triangle with base 2 and height 4 below the axis, so the net area is $\frac{1}{2} \cdot 4 \cdot 8 - \frac{1}{2} \cdot 2 \cdot 4 = 16 - 4 = 12$.

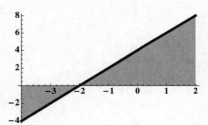

5.2.27

The region consists of two triangles, both below the axis. One has base 1 and height 1, the other has base 2 and height 2, so the net area is $-\frac{1}{2} \cdot 1 \cdot 1 - \frac{1}{2} \cdot 2 \cdot 2 = -2.5$.

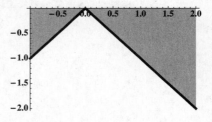

5.2.28

The region consists of two triangles of equal area, one of which is above the axis and one below, so the net area is 0.

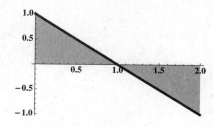

5.2.29

The region consists of a quarter circle of radius 4, situated above the axis. So the net area is $\frac{\pi \cdot 4^2}{4} = 4\pi$.

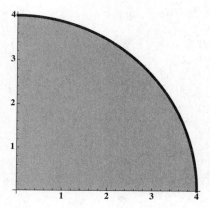

5.2.30

The region consists of a semicircle situated above the axis, of radius 2. The area is thus $\frac{4\pi}{2} = 2\pi$.

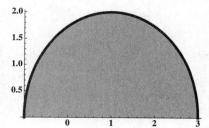

5.2.31

The region consists of a rectangle of area 10 above the axis, and a trapezoid of area 16 above the axis, so the net area is $10 + 16 = 26$.

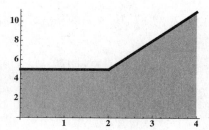

5.2.32

The region consists of a trapezoid of area 6 above the axis, a triangle of area 4 below the axis, and a rectangle of area 56 below the axis. So the net area is $6 - 4 - 56 = -54$.

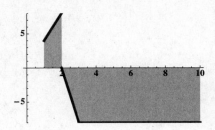

5.2.33 $\displaystyle\int_0^a f(x)\,dx = 16.$ **5.2.34** $\displaystyle\int_0^b f(x)\,dx = 16 - 5 = 11.$

5.2.35 $\displaystyle\int_a^c f(x)\,dx = 11 - 5 = 6.$ **5.2.36** $\displaystyle\int_0^c f(x)\,dx = 16 - 5 + 11 = 22.$

5.2.37 $\displaystyle\int_0^\pi x \sin x\,dx = A(R_1) + A(R_2) = 1 + \pi - 1 = \pi.$ **5.2.38** $\displaystyle\int_0^{3\pi/2} x \sin x\,dx = A(R_1) + A(R_2) - A(R_3) = 1 + \pi - 1 - \pi - 1 = -1.$

5.2.39 $\displaystyle\int_0^{2\pi} x \sin x\,dx = A(R_1) + A(R_2) - A(R_3) - A(R_4) = 1 + \pi - 1 - \pi - 1 - 2\pi + 1 = -2\pi.$ **5.2.40** $\displaystyle\int_{\pi/2}^{2\pi} x \sin x\,dx = A(R_2) - A(R_3) - A(R_4) = \pi - 1 - \pi - 1 - 2\pi + 1 = -2\pi - 1.$

5.2.41

a. $\displaystyle\int_4^0 3x(4 - x)\,dx = -\int_0^4 3x(4 - x)\,dx = -32.$

b. $\displaystyle\int_0^4 x(x - 4)\,dx = \frac{-1}{3}\int_0^4 3x(4 - x)\,dx = \frac{-1}{3}\cdot 32 = \frac{-32}{3}.$

c. $\displaystyle\int_4^0 6x(4 - x)\,dx = -2\cdot\int_0^4 3x(4 - x)\,dx = -2\cdot 32 = -64.$

d. $\displaystyle\int_0^8 3x(4 - x)\,dx = \int_0^4 3x(4 - x)\,dx + \int_4^8 3x(4 - x)\,dx = 32 + \int_4^8 3x(4 - x)\,dx.$ It is not possible to evaluate the given integral from the information given.

5.2.42

a. $\displaystyle\int_1^4 (-3f(x))\,dx = -3\int_1^4 f(x)\,dx = -3\cdot 8 = -24.$

b. $\displaystyle\int_1^4 3f(x)\,dx = 3\int_1^4 f(x)\,dx = 3\cdot 8 = 24.$

c. $\displaystyle\int_6^4 12f(x)\,dx = -12\int_4^6 f(x)\,dx = -12\left(\int_1^6 f(x)\,dx - \int_1^4 f(x)\,dx\right) = -12(5 - 8) = 36.$

d. $\displaystyle\int_4^6 3f(x)\,dx = 3\left(\int_1^6 f(x)\,dx - \int_1^4 f(x)\,dx\right) = 3(5 - 8) = -9.$

5.2.43

a. $\displaystyle\int_0^3 5f(x)\,dx = 5\int_0^3 f(x)\,dx = 5\cdot 2 = 10.$

b. $\int_3^6 (-3g(x))\, dx = -3 \int_3^6 g(x)\, dx = -3 \cdot 1 = -3.$

c. $\int_3^6 (3f(x) - g(x))\, dx = 3 \int_3^6 f(x)\, dx - \int_3^6 g(x)\, dx = 3(-5) - 1 = -16.$

d. $\int_6^3 [f(x) + 2g(x)]\, dx = -\left[\int_3^6 f(x)\, dx + 2 \int_3^6 g(x)\, dx \right] = -[-5 + 2 \cdot 1] = 3.$

5.2.44

a. $\int_0^5 f(x)\, dx = \int_0^2 f(x)\, dx + \int_2^5 f(x)\, dx = 6 + (-8) = -2.$

b. $\int_0^5 |f(x)|\, dx = \int_0^2 f(x)\, dx - \int_2^5 f(x)\, dx = 6 + 8 = 14.$

c. $\int_2^5 4|f(x)|\, dx = 4 \int_2^5 (-f(x))\, dx = 4 \cdot 8 = 32.$

d. $\int_0^5 (f(x) + |f(x)|)\, dx = \int_0^2 (f(x) + f(x))\, dx + \int_2^5 f(x) - f(x)\, dx = 2 \int_0^2 f(x)\, dx = 2 \cdot 6 = 12.$

5.2.45

a. $\int_0^1 (4x - 2x^3)\, dx = -2 \int_0^1 (x^3 - 2x)\, dx = -2 \cdot \dfrac{-3}{4} = \dfrac{3}{2}.$

b. $\int_1^0 (2x - x^3)\, dx = \int_0^1 (x^3 - 2x)\, dx = \dfrac{-3}{4}.$

5.2.46

a. $\int_0^{\pi/2} (2\sin\theta - \cos\theta)\, d\theta = - \int_0^{\pi/2} (\cos\theta - 2\sin\theta)\, d\theta = -(-1) = 1.$

b. $\int_{\pi/2}^0 (4\cos\theta - 8\sin\theta)\, d\theta = -4 \int_0^{\pi/2} (\cos\theta - 2\sin\theta)\, d\theta = -4(-1) = 4.$

5.2.47

$$
\begin{aligned}
\int_0^2 (2x + 1)\, dx &= \lim_{n \to \infty} \sum_{k=1}^n f(x_k) \Delta x = \lim_{n \to \infty} \sum_{k=1}^n \left[2\left(\frac{2k}{n} \right) + 1 \right] \frac{2}{n} \\
&= \lim_{n \to \infty} \left[\frac{8}{n^2} \sum_{k=1}^n k + \frac{2}{n} \sum_{k=1}^n 1 \right] \\
&= \lim_{n \to \infty} \left[\frac{8}{n^2} \cdot \frac{n(n+1)}{2} + \frac{2}{n} \cdot n \right] \\
&= \lim_{n \to \infty} \left[\frac{4(n+1)}{n} + 2 \right] = 4 + 2 = 6.
\end{aligned}
$$

5.2.48

$$\int_1^5 (1-x)\,dx = \lim_{n\to\infty} \sum_{k=1}^{n} f(x_k)\Delta x = \lim_{n\to\infty} \sum_{k=1}^{n} \left[1 - \left(1 + \frac{4k}{n}\right)\right]\frac{4}{n}$$

$$= \lim_{n\to\infty} \left[\frac{-16}{n^2} \sum_{k=1}^{n} k\right]$$

$$= \lim_{n\to\infty} \left[\frac{-16}{n^2} \cdot \frac{n(n+1)}{2}\right]$$

$$= \lim_{n\to\infty} \left[\frac{-8(n+1)}{n}\right] = -8.$$

5.2.49

$$\int_3^7 (4x+6)\,dx = \lim_{n\to\infty} \sum_{k=1}^{n} f(x_k)\Delta x = \lim_{n\to\infty} \sum_{k=1}^{n} \left[4\left(3 + \frac{4k}{n}\right) + 6\right]\frac{4}{n}$$

$$= \lim_{n\to\infty} \left[\frac{64}{n^2} \sum_{k=1}^{n} k + \frac{72}{n} \sum_{k=1}^{n} 1\right]$$

$$= \lim_{n\to\infty} \left[\frac{64}{n^2} \cdot \frac{n(n+1)}{2} + \frac{72}{n} \cdot n\right]$$

$$= \lim_{n\to\infty} \left[\frac{32(n+1)}{n} + 72\right] = 104.$$

5.2.50

$$\int_0^2 (x^2-1)\,dx = \lim_{n\to\infty} \sum_{k=1}^{n} f(x_k)\Delta x = \lim_{n\to\infty} \sum_{k=1}^{n} \left[\left(\frac{2k}{n}\right)^2 - 1\right]\frac{2}{n}$$

$$= \lim_{n\to\infty} \left[\frac{2}{n}\left(\sum_{k=1}^{n} -1\right) + \frac{8}{n^3} \sum_{k=1}^{n} k^2\right]$$

$$= \lim_{n\to\infty} \left[\frac{2}{n} \cdot (-n) + \frac{8}{n^3} \cdot \frac{n(n+1)(2n+1)}{6}\right]$$

$$= \lim_{n\to\infty} \left[-2 + \frac{8n^2 + 12n + 4}{3n^2}\right] = -2 + \frac{8}{3} = \frac{2}{3}.$$

5.2.51

$$\int_1^4 (x^2-1)\,dx = \lim_{n\to\infty} \sum_{k=1}^{n} f(x_k)\Delta x = \lim_{n\to\infty} \sum_{k=1}^{n} \left[\left(1 + \frac{3k}{n}\right)^2 - 1\right]\frac{3}{n}$$

$$= \lim_{n\to\infty} \left[\frac{18}{n^2} \sum_{k=1}^{n} k + \frac{27}{n^3} \sum_{k=1}^{n} k^2\right]$$

$$= \lim_{n\to\infty} \left[\frac{18}{n^2} \cdot \frac{n(n+1)}{2} + \frac{27}{n^3} \cdot \frac{n(n+1)(2n+1)}{6}\right]$$

$$= \lim_{n\to\infty} \left[\frac{9(n+1)}{n} + \frac{18n^2 + 27n + 9}{2n^2}\right] = 9 + 9 = 18.$$

5.2.52

$$\int_0^2 4x^3\,dx = \lim_{n\to\infty}\sum_{k=1}^n f(x_k)\Delta x = \lim_{n\to\infty}\sum_{k=1}^n \left[4\left(\frac{2k}{n}\right)^3\right]\frac{2}{n}$$

$$= \lim_{n\to\infty}\left[\frac{64}{n^4}\sum_{k=1}^n k^3\right]$$

$$= \lim_{n\to\infty}\left[\frac{64}{n^4}\cdot\left(\frac{n(n+1)}{2}\right)^2\right]$$

$$= \lim_{n\to\infty}\left[\frac{16(n^2+2n+1)}{n^2}\right] = 16.$$

5.2.53

a. True. See problem 76 in the previous section for a proof.

b. True. See problem 77 in the previous section for a proof.

c. True. Because both of those function are periodic with period $\frac{2\pi}{a}$, and both have the same amount of area above the axis as below for one period, the net area of each between 0 and $\frac{2\pi}{a}$ is zero.

d. False. For example $\int_0^{2\pi}\sin x\,dx = 0 = \int_{2\pi}^0 \sin x\,dx$, but $\sin x$ is not a constant function.

e. False. Because x is not a constant, it can not be factored outside of the integral. For example $\int_0^1 x\cdot 1\,dx \neq x\int_0^1 1\,dx.$

5.2.54

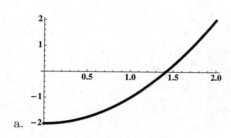

a.

b. $\Delta x = \frac{1}{2}$, so the grid points are at 0, .5, 1, 1.5, and 2.

c. The left Riemann sum is $.5(-2-1.75-1+.25) = -2.25$. The right Riemann sum is $.5(-1.75-1+.25+2) = -0.25$.

d. The left Riemann sum underestimates the true value, while the right Riemann sum overestimates it.

5.2.55

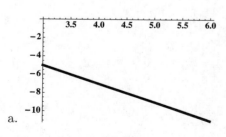

a.

b. $\Delta x = \frac{1}{2}$, so the grid points are at 3, 3.5, 4, 4.5, 5, 5.5, and 6.

c. The left Riemann sum is $.5(-5-6-7-8-9-10) = -22.5$. The right Riemann sum is $.5(-6-7-8-9-10-11) = -25.5$.

d. The left Riemann sum overestimates the true value, while the right Riemann sum underestimates it.

5.2.56

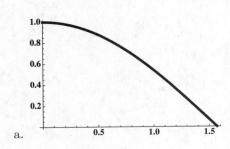

a.

b. $\Delta x = \frac{\pi}{8}$, so the grid points are at 0, $\frac{\pi}{8}$, $\frac{\pi}{4}$, $\frac{3\pi}{8}$, and $\frac{\pi}{2}$.

c. The left Riemann sum is approximately

$$\frac{\pi}{8}\left(1 + 0.92388 + 0.707107 + 0.382683\right) \approx 1.183.$$

The right Riemann sum is about

$$\frac{\pi}{8}\left(0.92388 + 0.707107 + 0.382683 + 0\right) \approx 0.791.$$

d. The left Riemann sum overestimates the true value, while the right Riemann sum underestimates it.

5.2.57

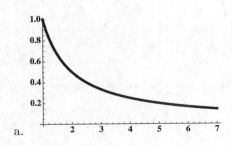

a.

b. $\Delta x = 1$, so the grid points are at 1, 2, 3, 4, 5, 6, and 7.

c. The left Riemann sum is approximately $1 + 0.5 + 0.333333 + 0.25 + -.2 + 0.166666 = 2.45$. The right Riemann sum is approximately $.5 + 0.333333 + 0.25 + 0.2 + 0.166666 + 0.142857 \approx 1.593$.

d. The left Riemann sum overestimates the true value, while the right Riemann sum underestimates it.

5.2.58

a. $\displaystyle\sum_{k=1}^{20} 3\sqrt{4 + \frac{5(k-1)}{20}} \cdot \frac{5}{20} \approx 37.624.$ $\displaystyle\sum_{k=1}^{20} 3\sqrt{4 + \frac{5k}{20}} \cdot \frac{5}{20} \approx 38.374.$

$\displaystyle\sum_{k=1}^{50} 3\sqrt{4 + \frac{5(k-1)}{50}} \cdot \frac{5}{50} \approx 37.850.$ $\displaystyle\sum_{k=1}^{50} 3\sqrt{4 + \frac{5k}{50}} \cdot \frac{5}{50} \approx 38.150.$

$\displaystyle\sum_{k=1}^{100} 3\sqrt{4 + \frac{5(k-1)}{100}} \cdot \frac{5}{100} \approx 37.925.$ $\displaystyle\sum_{k=1}^{100} 3\sqrt{4 + \frac{5k}{100}} \cdot \frac{5}{100} \approx 38.075.$

b. It appears that the integral's value is 38.

5.2.59

a. $\displaystyle\sum_{k=1}^{20} \left(\left(\frac{k-1}{20}\right)^2 + 1\right) \cdot \frac{1}{20} \approx 1.309.$ $\displaystyle\sum_{k=1}^{20} \left(\left(\frac{k}{20}\right)^2 + 1\right) \cdot \frac{1}{20} \approx 1.359.$

$\displaystyle\sum_{k=1}^{50} \left(\left(\frac{k-1}{50}\right)^2 + 1\right) \cdot \frac{1}{50} \approx 1.323.$ $\displaystyle\sum_{k=1}^{50} \left(\left(\frac{k}{50}\right)^2 + 1\right) \cdot \frac{1}{50} \approx 1.343.$

$\displaystyle\sum_{k=1}^{100} \left(\left(\frac{k-1}{100}\right)^2 + 1\right) \cdot \frac{1}{100} \approx 1.328.$ $\displaystyle\sum_{k=1}^{100} \left(\left(\frac{k}{100}\right)^2 + 1\right) \cdot \frac{1}{100} \approx 1.338.$

b. It appears that the integral's value is about $\frac{4}{3}$.

5.2.60

a. $\displaystyle\sum_{k=1}^{20} \ln\left(1 + (k-1)\frac{(e-1)}{20}\right)\cdot\frac{e-1}{20} \approx 0.957.$ $\displaystyle\sum_{k=1}^{20} \ln\left(1 + k\cdot\frac{(e-1)}{20}\right)\cdot\frac{e-1}{20} \approx 1.043.$

$\displaystyle\sum_{k=1}^{50} \ln\left(1 + (k-1)\frac{(e-1)}{50}\right)\cdot\frac{e-1}{50} \approx .983.$ $\displaystyle\sum_{k=1}^{50} \ln\left(1 + k\cdot\frac{(e-1)}{50}\right)\cdot\frac{e-1}{50} \approx 1.017.$

$\displaystyle\sum_{k=1}^{100} \ln\left(1 + (k-1)\frac{(e-1)}{100}\right)\cdot\frac{e-1}{100} \approx 0.991.$ $\displaystyle\sum_{k=1}^{100} \ln\left(1 + k\cdot\frac{(e-1)}{100}\right)\cdot\frac{e-1}{100} \approx 1.009.$

b. It appears that the integral's value is 1.

5.2.61

a. $\displaystyle\sum_{k=1}^{20} \cos^{-1}((k-1)/20)\cdot\frac{1}{20} \approx 1.036.$ $\displaystyle\sum_{k=1}^{20} \cos^{-1}(k/20)\cdot\frac{1}{20} \approx 0.958.$

$\displaystyle\sum_{k=1}^{50} \cos^{-1}((k-1)/50)\cdot\frac{1}{50} \approx 1.015.$ $\displaystyle\sum_{k=1}^{50} \cos^{-1}(k/50)\cdot\frac{1}{50} \approx 0.983.$

$\displaystyle\sum_{k=1}^{100} \cos^{-1}((k-1)/100)\cdot\frac{1}{100} \approx 1.008.$ $\displaystyle\sum_{k=1}^{100} \cos^{-1}(k/100)\cdot\frac{1}{100} \approx 0.992.$

b. It appears that the integral's value is 1.

5.2.62

a. $\displaystyle\sum_{k=1}^{20} \pi\cos\left(\frac{\pi}{2}\left(-1 + \frac{2(k-1)}{20}\right)\right)\cdot\frac{2}{20} \approx 3.992.$ $\displaystyle\sum_{k=1}^{20} \pi\cos\left(\frac{\pi}{2}\left(-1 + \frac{2k}{20}\right)\right)\cdot\frac{2}{20} \approx 3.992.$

$\displaystyle\sum_{k=1}^{50} \pi\cos\left(\frac{\pi}{2}\left(-1 + \frac{2(k-1)}{50}\right)\right)\cdot\frac{2}{50} \approx 3.999.$ $\displaystyle\sum_{k=1}^{50} \pi\cos\left(\frac{\pi}{2}\left(-1 + \frac{2k}{50}\right)\right)\cdot\frac{2}{50} \approx 3.999.$

$\displaystyle\sum_{k=1}^{100} \pi\cos\left(\frac{\pi}{2}\left(-1 + \frac{2(k-1)}{100}\right)\right)\cdot\frac{2}{100} \approx 4.000.$ $\displaystyle\sum_{k=1}^{100} \pi\cos\left(\frac{\pi}{2}\left(-1 + \frac{2k}{100}\right)\right)\cdot\frac{2}{100} \approx 4.000.$

b. It appears that the integral's value is 4.

5.2.63

a. $\displaystyle\sum_{k=1}^{n} 2\sqrt{1 + \frac{3}{2n} + \frac{3(k-1)}{n}}\cdot\frac{3}{n}.$

b.

n	20	50	100
Midpoint Sum	9.3338	9.33341	9.33335

It appears that the integral's value is about $\frac{28}{3}$.

5.2.64

a. $\displaystyle\sum_{k=1}^{n} \sin\left(\frac{\pi}{4}\left(-1 + \frac{3}{2n} + \frac{3(k-1)}{n}\right)\right)\cdot\frac{3}{n}.$

b.

n	20	50	100
Midpoint Sum	.900837	.9004	.900337

It appears that the integral's value is about .9.

5.2.65

a. $\displaystyle\sum_{k=1}^{n}\left(4\left(\frac{2}{n}+\frac{4(k-1)}{n}\right)-\left(\frac{2}{n}+\frac{4(k-1)}{n}\right)^{2}\right)\cdot\frac{4}{n}.$

b.

n	20	50	100
Midpoint Sum	10.68	10.6688	10.6672

It appears that the integral's value is about $\frac{32}{3}$.

5.2.66

a. $\displaystyle\sum_{k-1}^{n}\sin^{-1}\left(\frac{1}{4n}+\frac{k-1}{2n}\right)\cdot\frac{1}{2n}.$

b.

n	20	50	100
Midpoint Sum	.127821	.127824	.127825

It appears that the integral's value is about .12782.

5.2.67

a. $\displaystyle\int_{1}^{4}3f(x)\,dx=3\int_{1}^{4}f(x)\,dx=3\cdot\left(\int_{1}^{6}f(x)\,dx-\int_{4}^{6}f(x)\,dx\right)=3\cdot(10-5)=15.$

b. $\displaystyle\int_{1}^{6}(f(x)-g(x))\,dx=\int_{1}^{6}f(x)\,dx-\int_{1}^{6}g(x)\,dx=10-5=5.$

c. $\displaystyle\int_{1}^{4}(f(x)-g(x))\,dx=\int_{1}^{4}f(x)\,dx-\int_{1}^{4}g(x)\,dx=\left(\int_{1}^{6}f(x)\,dx-\int_{4}^{6}f(x)\,dx\right)-2=(10-5)-2=3.$

d. $\displaystyle\int_{4}^{6}(g(x)-f(x))\,dx=\int_{4}^{6}g(x)\,dx-\int_{4}^{6}f(x)\,dx=\left(\int_{1}^{6}g(x)\,dx-\int_{1}^{4}g(x)\,dx\right)-5=(5-2)-5=-2.$

e. $\displaystyle\int_{4}^{6}8g(x)\,dx=8\left(\int_{1}^{6}g(x)\,dx-\int_{1}^{4}g(x)\,dx\right)=8(5-2)=24.$

f. $\displaystyle\int_{4}^{1}2f(x)\,dx=-2\int_{1}^{4}f(x)\,dx=-2\cdot\left(\int_{1}^{6}f(x)\,dx-\int_{4}^{6}f(x)\,dx\right)=-2(10-5)=-10.$

5.2.68

The region above the axis is a triangle with base $8-2=6$ and height $f(8)=24$, while the region below the axis is a triangle with base $2-(-4)=6$ and height $-f(-4)=24$, so the net area is 0, and the area is 144.

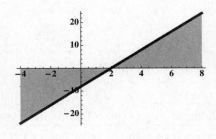

5.2.69

The region above the axis is a triangle with base 2 and height $f(-2) = 6$, and the region below the axis is a triangle with base 2 and height $-f(2) = 6$, so the net area is 0, and the area is 12.

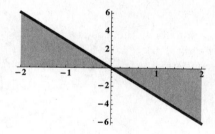

5.2.70

The region above the axis is a triangle with base $6 - 2 = 4$ and height $f(6) = 12$, while the region below the axis is a triangle with base 2 and height $-f(-0) = 6$, so the net area is $\frac{1}{2} \cdot 4 \cdot 12 - \frac{1}{2} \cdot 2 \cdot 6 = 24 - 6 = 18$, while the area is 30.

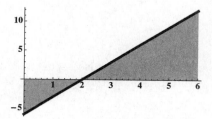

5.2.71

The region above the axis is a triangle with base 2 and height $f(0) = 1$, while the region below the axis consists of two triangles each with base 1 and height 1, so the net area is 0, and the area is 2.

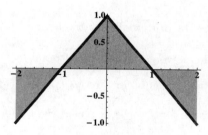

5.2.72

The region in question consists of two triangles above the axis, one with base 1 and height 1, and one with base 4 and height 4, so the net area is $\frac{1}{2} \cdot 1 \cdot 1 + \frac{1}{2} \cdot 4 \cdot 4 = 8.5$.

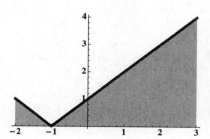

5.2.73

The region in question consists of two triangles above the axis, one with base 1 and height 2, and one with base 4 and height 8, so the net area is $\frac{1}{2} \cdot 1 \cdot 2 + \frac{1}{2} \cdot 4 \cdot 8 = 17$.

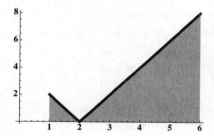

5.2.74

The region above the axis is a triangle with base 4 and height $f(6) = 12$, while the region below the axis consists of a triangle with base 1 and height $-f(1) = 3$, so the net area is $\frac{1}{2} \cdot 4 \cdot 12 - \frac{1}{2} \cdot 1 \cdot 3 = 24 - 1.5 = 22.5$.

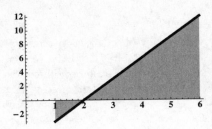

5.2.75

The region in question is a semicircle above the axis with radius 5, so the area is $\frac{1}{2}\pi \cdot 5^2 = \frac{25\pi}{2}$.

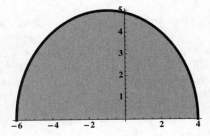

5.2.76 Let the grid points for the interval $[a, c]$ be $x_i = a + i \cdot \frac{c-a}{n}$, where $1 \le i \le n$. Let the grid points for the interval $[c, b]$ be $x_j^* = c + j \cdot \frac{b-c}{m}$ where $1 \le j \le m$. Note that if we take the union of both of these sets of grid points, we get a set of grid points for $[a, b]$.

One Riemann sum for f on $[a, b]$ is $\sum_{k=1}^{n} f(x_k) \cdot \frac{c-a}{n} + \sum_{j=1}^{m} f(x_j^*) \cdot \frac{b-c}{m}$, which naturally splits into a right Riemann sum for f on $[a, c]$ plus a right Riemann sum for f on $[c, b]$.

By the definition of definite integral, taking limits as $m, n \to \infty$ shows that $\int_a^b f(x)\, dx = \int_a^c f(x)\, dx + \int_c^b f(x)\, dx$.

5.2.77 $\int_0^{10} f(x)\, dx = \int_0^5 2\, dx + \int_5^{10} 3\, dx = 10 + 15 = 25$.

5.2.78 $\int_1^6 f(x)\, dx = \int_1^4 2x\, dx + \int_4^6 (10 - 2x)\, dx = 15 + 0 = 15$.

5.2.79 $\int_1^5 x\lfloor x \rfloor\, dx = \int_1^2 x\lfloor x \rfloor\, dx + \int_2^3 x\lfloor x \rfloor\, dx + \int_3^4 x\lfloor x \rfloor\, dx + \int_4^5 x\lfloor x \rfloor\, dx = \int_1^2 x\, dx + \int_2^3 2x\, dx + \int_3^4 3x\, dx + \int_4^5 4x\, dx$. Each of these integrals represents the area of a trapezoid with base 1. The value of the integral is $\frac{1+2}{2} + \frac{4+6}{2} + \frac{9+12}{2} + \frac{16+20}{2} = 35$.

5.2.80 $\int_0^4 \frac{x}{\lceil x \rceil}\, dx = \int_0^1 \frac{x}{\lceil x \rceil}\, dx + \int_1^2 \frac{x}{\lceil x \rceil}\, dx + \int_2^3 \frac{x}{\lceil x \rceil}\, dx + \int_3^4 \frac{x}{\lceil x \rceil}\, dx = \int_0^1 x\, dx + \int_1^2 \frac{x}{2}\, dx + \int_2^3 \frac{x}{3}\, dx + \int_3^4 \frac{x}{4}\, dx$. The first of these represents the area of a triangle with base one and height 1, while the others represent the area of trapezoids with base 1. The value of the integral is $\frac{1}{2} + \frac{\frac{1}{2}+1}{2} + \frac{\frac{2}{3}+1}{2} + \frac{\frac{3}{4}+1}{2} = \frac{71}{24}$.

5.2.81

$$\int_a^b cf(x)\,dx = \lim_{\Delta \to 0} \sum_{k=1}^{n} cf(x_k^*)\Delta x_k$$

$$= \lim_{\Delta \to 0} c \sum_{k=1}^{n} f(x_k^*)\Delta x_k$$

$$= c \lim_{\Delta \to 0} \sum_{k=1}^{n} f(x_k^*)\Delta x_k = c \int_a^b f(x)\,dx.$$

5.2.82 Note that $\int_c^d x\,dx = \frac{d^2-c^2}{2}$, because it represents the area of a trapezoid with base of length $d - c$ and heights c and d. Also note that $\int_c^d b\,dx = b(d-c)$ because it represents the area of a rectangle with base $d - c$ and height b.

Therefore, $\int_c^d (x+b)\,dx = \int_c^d x\,dx + \int_c^d b\,dx = \frac{d^2-c^2}{2} + b(d-c) = (d-c)\cdot\left(\frac{d+c}{2}+b\right)$. Because $c \neq d$, this is zero exactly when $b = -\frac{c+d}{2}$.

5.2.83 Let n be a positive integer. Let $\Delta x = \frac{1}{n}$. Note that each grid point $\frac{k}{n}$ for $0 \leq k \leq n$ where i is an integer is a rational number. So $f(x_k) = 1$ for each grid point. So the right Riemann sum is $\sum_{k=1}^{n} f(x_k)\frac{1}{n} = \frac{1}{n}\sum_{k=1}^{n} 1 = \frac{1}{n}\cdot n = 1$. The left Riemann sum calculation is similar, as is the midpoint Riemann sum calculation (because the grid midpoints are also rational numbers – they are the average of two rational numbers and hence are rational as well).

5.2.84

a. The left Riemann sum for I(p) is $\sum_{k=0}^{n-1} \left(\frac{k}{n}\right)^p \cdot \frac{1}{n}$.

b. We have $I(p) = \int_0^1 x^p\,dx = \lim_{n\to\infty} \sum_{k=0}^{n-1} \left(\frac{k}{n}\right)^p \cdot \frac{1}{n} = \frac{1}{p+1}$.

5.2.85

a. Note that for all values of $k = 1, 2, \ldots, n$, we have $x_{k-1}x_{k-1} \leq x_{k-1}x_k$, so $\sqrt{x_{k-1}x_{k-1}} \leq \sqrt{x_{k-1}x_k}$, and thus $x_{k-1} \leq \sqrt{x_{k-1}x_k}$. Similarly, $x_{k-1}x_k \leq x_k x_k$, so $\sqrt{x_{k-1}x_k} \leq \sqrt{x_k x_k} = x_k$, so $\sqrt{x_{k-1}x_k} \leq x_k$. Thus $x_{k-1} \leq \sqrt{x_{k-1}x_k} \leq x_k$ for all $k = 1, 2, \ldots, n$.

b. $\frac{1}{x_{k-1}} - \frac{1}{x_k} = \frac{x_k}{x_{k-1}x_k} - \frac{x_{k-1}}{x_{k-1}x_k} = \frac{x_k - x_{k-1}}{x_{k-1}x_k} = \frac{\Delta x_k}{x_{k-1}x_k}$, for all $k = 1, 2, \ldots, n$.

c. The Riemann sum is $\sum_{k=1}^{n} \frac{\Delta x_k}{\overline{x_k}^2}$. Using $\overline{x_k} = \sqrt{x_{k-1}x_k}$, we have

$$\sum_{k=1}^{n} \frac{\Delta x_k}{x_{k-1}x_k} = \sum_{k=1}^{n} \left(\frac{1}{x_{k-1}} - \frac{1}{x_k}\right),$$

where the last equality follows from part (b). Now note that the sum telescopes (that is, has many canceling terms).

$$\sum_{k=1}^{n}\left(\frac{1}{x_{k-1}}-\frac{1}{x_k}\right)=\left(\frac{1}{x_0}-\frac{1}{x_1}\right)+\left(\frac{1}{x_1}-\frac{1}{x_2}\right)+\cdots+\left(\frac{1}{x_{n-2}}-\frac{1}{x_{n-1}}\right)+\left(\frac{1}{x_{n-1}}-\frac{1}{x_n}\right)$$

$$=\frac{1}{x_0}+\left(-\frac{1}{x_1}+\frac{1}{x_1}\right)+\left(-\frac{1}{x_2}+\frac{1}{x_2}\right)+\cdots+\left(-\frac{1}{x_{n-1}}+\frac{1}{x_{n-1}}\right)-\frac{1}{x_n}$$

$$=\frac{1}{x_0}-\frac{1}{x_n}$$

$$=\frac{1}{a}-\frac{1}{b}.$$

d. The integral is the limit of the Riemann sum as $n \to \infty$. Thus we have

$$\int_a^b \frac{dx}{x^2}=\lim_{n\to\infty}\sum_{k=1}^{n}\frac{\Delta x_k}{\overline{x_k}^2}=\lim_{n\to\infty}\left(\frac{1}{a}-\frac{1}{b}\right)=\frac{1}{a}-\frac{1}{b}.$$

5.3 Fundamental Theorem of Calculus

5.3.1 A is also an antiderivative of f.

5.3.2 Because F and A are both antiderivatives of f, we have $A(x) = F(x) + C$, where C is a constant.

5.3.3 The fundamental theorem says that $\int_a^b f(x)\,dx = F(b) - F(a)$ where F is any antiderivative of f. So to evaluate $\int_a^b f(x)\,dx$, one could find an antiderivative $F(x)$, and then evaluate this at a and b and then subtract, obtaining $F(b) - F(a)$.

5.3.4 An area function has the form $\int_a^x c\,dt$, and gives the area between a and x and under c, which is the area of a rectangle with base $x - a$ and height c. As x increases, the base $x - a$ increases while the height c remains constant, so the area increases.

5.3.5

$A(x) = \int_0^x (3 - t)\,dt$ represents the area between 0 and x and below this curve. As x increases (but remains less than 3), the trapezoidal region's area increases, so the area function increases until x is 3.

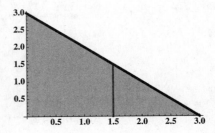

5.3.6 $\int_0^2 3x^2 = x^3\Big|_0^2 = 8 - 0 = 8.$

$\int_{-2}^2 3x^2 = x^3\Big|_{-2}^2 = 8 - -8 = 16.$

5.3.7 $\dfrac{d}{dx}\displaystyle\int_a^x f(t)\,dt = f(x)$, and $\displaystyle\int f'(x)\,dx = f(x) + C.$

5.3.8 It can be omitted because it doesn't change the value of $F(b) - F(a)$. For example, suppose $F(x)$ is an antiderivative of f, and so is $G(x) = F(x) + C$. Then $G(b) - G(a) = F(b) + C - (F(a) + C) = F(b) - F(a)$.

5.3.9 $\dfrac{d}{dx}\displaystyle\int_a^x f(t)\,dt = f(x)$, and $\dfrac{d}{dx}\displaystyle\int_a^b f(t)\,dt = 0$. The latter is the derivative of a constant, the former follows from the Fundamental Theorem.

5.3.10 Because f is an antiderivative of f', the Fundamental Theorem assures us that $\displaystyle\int_a^b f'(x)\,dx = f(b) - f(a)$.

5.3.11

   a. $A(-2) = \int_{-2}^{-2} f(t)\,dt = 0$.

   b. $F(8) = \int_4^8 f(t)\,dt = -9$.

   c. $A(4) = \int_{-2}^4 f(t)\,dt = 8 + 17 = 25$.

   d. $F(4) = \int_4^4 f(t)\,dt = 0$.

   e. $A(8) = \int_{-2}^8 f(t)\,dt = 25 - 9 = 16$.

5.3.12

   a. $A(2) = \int_0^2 f(t)\,dt = 8$.

   b. $F(5) = \int_2^5 f(t)\,dt = -5$.

   c. $A(0) = \int_0^0 f(t)\,dt = 0$.

   d. $F(8) = \int_2^8 f(t)\,dt = -16$.

   e. $A(8) = \int_0^8 f(t)\,dt = 8 - 16 = -8$.

   f. $A(5) = \int_0^5 f(t)\,dt = 8 - 5 = 3$.

   g. $F(2) = \int_2^2 f(t)\,dt = 0$.

5.3.13

   a. $A(x) = \int_0^x f(t)\,dt = \int_0^x 5\,dt = 5x$.

   b. $A'(x) = 5 = f(x)$.

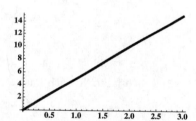

5.3.14

   a. $A(x) = \int_4^x f(t)\,dt = \int_4^x 10\,dt = 10(x - 4)$.

   b. $A'(x) = 10 = f(x)$.

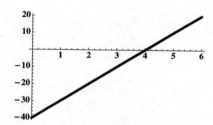

5.3.15

   a. $A(x) = \int_{-5}^x f(t)\,dt = \int_{-5}^x 5\,dt = 5(x + 5)$.

   b. $A'(x) = 5 = f(x)$.

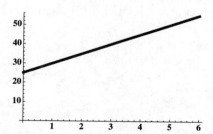

5.3.16

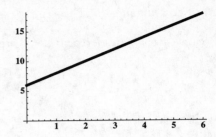

a. $A(x) = \int_{-3}^{x} f(t)\,dt = \int_{-3}^{x} 2\,dt = 2(x+3)$.

b. $A'(x) = 2 = f(x)$.

5.3.17

a. $A(2) = \int_0^2 t\,dt = 2$. $A(4) = \int_0^4 t\,dt = 8$. Because the region whose area is $A(x) = \int_0^x t\,dt$ is a triangle with base x and height x, its value is $\frac{1}{2}x^2$.

b. $F(4) = \int_2^4 t\,dt = 6$. $F(6) = \int_2^6 t\,dt = 16$. Because the region whose area is $A(x) = \int_2^x t\,dt$ is a trapezoid with base $x-2$ and $h_1 = 2$ and $h_2 = x$, its value is $(x-2)\frac{2+x}{2} = \frac{x^2-4}{2} = \frac{x^2}{2} - 2$.

c. We have $A(x) - F(x) = \frac{x^2}{2} - (\frac{x^2}{2} - 2) = 2$, a constant.

5.3.18

a. $A(2) = \int_1^2 (2t-2)\,dt = 1$. $A(3) = \int_1^3 (2t-2)\,dt = 4$. Because the region whose area is $A(x) = \int_1^x (2t-2)\,dt$ is a triangle with base $x-1$ and height $2x-2$, its value is $\frac{1}{2} \cdot (x-1)(2(x-1)) = (x-1)^2$.

b. $F(5) = \int_4^5 (2t-2)\,dt = 7$. $F(6) = \int_4^6 (2t-2)\,dt = 16$. Because the region whose area is $A(x) = \int_2^x t\,dt$ is a trapezoid with base $x-4$ and $h_1 = 6$ and $h_2 = 2x-2$, its value is $(x-4)\left(\frac{6+2x-2}{2}\right) = (x-4)(x+2) = x^2 - 2x - 8$.

c. We have $A(x) - F(x) = x^2 - 2x + 1 - (x^2 - 2x - 8) = 9$, a constant.

5.3.19

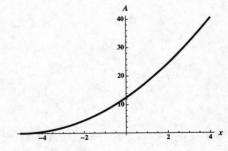

a. The region is a triangle with base $x + 5$ and height $x + 5$, so its area is $A(x) = \frac{1}{2}(x+5)^2$.

b. $A'(x) = x + 5 = f(x)$.

5.3.20

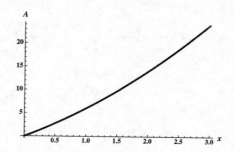

a. The region is a trapezoid with base x and heights $h_1 = f(0) = 5$ and $h_2 = f(x) = 2x+5$, so its area is $A(x) = x \cdot \frac{5+2x+5}{2} = x \cdot (x+5) = x^2 + 5x$.

b. $A'(x) = 2x + 5 = f(x)$.

5.3.21

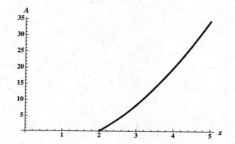

a. The region is a trapezoid with base $x - 2$ and heights $h_1 = f(2) = 7$ and $h_2 = f(x) = 3x+1$, so its area is $A(x) = (x - 2) \cdot \frac{7+3x+1}{2} = (x - 2) \cdot (\frac{3}{2}x + 4) = \frac{3}{2}x^2 + x - 8$.

b. $A'(x) = 3x + 1 = f(x)$.

5.3.22

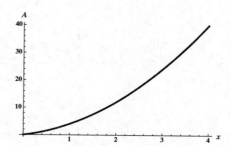

a. The region is a trapezoid with base x and heights $h_1 = f(0) = 2$ and $h_2 = f(x) = 4x+2$, so its area is $A(x) = (x) \cdot \frac{2+4x+2}{2} = (x) \cdot (2x + 2) = 2x^2 + 2x$.

b. $A'(x) = 4x + 2 = f(x)$.

5.3.23 $\int_0^1 (x^2 - 2x + 3)\, dx = \left(\frac{x^3}{3} - x^2 + 3x \right) \Big|_0^1 = \frac{1}{3} - 1 + 3 - (0 - 0 + 0) = \frac{7}{3}$. It does appear that the area is between 2 and 3.

5.3.24 $\int_{-\pi/4}^{7\pi/4} (\sin x + \cos x)\, dx = (-\cos x + \sin x) \Big|_{-\pi/4}^{7\pi/4} = -\sqrt{2}/2 + -\sqrt{2}/2 - (-\sqrt{2}/2 + -\sqrt{2}/2) = 0$. It does appear that the area above the axis is equal to the area below, so the net area is 0.

5.3.25

$$\int_{-2}^{3} (x^2 - x - 6)\, dx = \left(\frac{x^3}{3} - \frac{x^2}{2} - 6x \right) \Big|_{-2}^{3} =$$
$$\frac{-125}{6}.$$

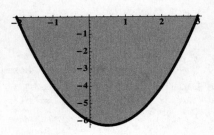

5.3.26

$$\int_{0}^{1} (x - \sqrt{x})\, dx = \left(\frac{x^2}{2} - \frac{2}{3} x^{3/2} \right) \Big|_{0}^{1} = \frac{1}{2} - \frac{2}{3} -$$
$$(0 - 0) = \frac{-1}{6}.$$

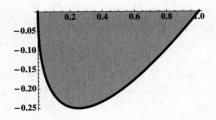

5.3.27

$$\int_{0}^{5} (x^2 - 9)\, dx = \left(\frac{x^3}{3} - 9x \right) \Big|_{0}^{5} = \frac{125}{3} - 45 -$$
$$(0 - 0) = \frac{-10}{3}.$$

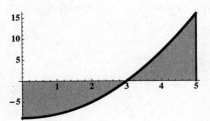

5.3.28

$$\int_{1/2}^{2} \left(1 - \frac{1}{x^2} \right) dx = \left(x + \frac{1}{x} \right) \Big|_{1/2}^{2} = 2 + \frac{1}{2} -$$
$$\left(\frac{1}{2} + 2 \right) = 0.$$

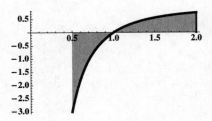

5.3.29 $\displaystyle\int_{0}^{2} 4x^3\, dx = x^4 \Big|_{0}^{2} = 16 - 0 = 16.$

5.3.30 $\displaystyle\int_{0}^{2} (3x^2 + 2x)\, dx = \left(x^3 + x^2 \right) \Big|_{0}^{2} = (8 + 4) - (0 + 0) = 12.$

5.3.31 $\displaystyle\int_{0}^{1} (x + \sqrt{x})\, dx = \left(\frac{x^2}{2} + \frac{2x^{3/2}}{3} \right) \Big|_{0}^{1} = \frac{1}{2} + \frac{2}{3} - (0 + 0) = \frac{7}{6}.$

5.3.32 $\displaystyle\int_{0}^{\pi/4} 2\cos x\, dx = 2\sin x \Big|_{0}^{\pi/4} = \frac{2\sqrt{2}}{2} - 0 = \sqrt{2}.$

5.3.33 $\displaystyle\int_1^9 \frac{2}{\sqrt{x}}\,dx = \int_1^9 2x^{-1/2}\,dx = 4x^{1/2}\,\Big|_1^9 = 12 - 4 = 8.$

5.3.34 $\displaystyle\int_4^9 \frac{2+\sqrt{t}}{t}\,dt = \int_4^9 \left(2t^{-1} + t^{-1/2}\right)dt = \left(2\ln|t| + 2\sqrt{t}\right)\Big|_4^9 = (2\ln 9 + 6) - (2\ln 4 + 4) = 2 + \ln(81/16).$

5.3.35 $\displaystyle\int_{-2}^2 (x^2 - 4)\,dx = \left(\frac{x^3}{3} - 4x\right)\Big|_{-2}^2 = \frac{8}{3} - 8 - \left(\frac{-8}{3} + 8\right) = \frac{16}{3} - 16 = -\frac{32}{3}.$

5.3.36 $\displaystyle\int_0^{\ln 8} e^x\,dx = e^x\,\Big|_0^{\ln 8} = e^{\ln 8} - e^0 = 8 - 1 = 7.$

5.3.37 $\displaystyle\int_{1/2}^1 (x^{-3} - 8)\,dx = \left(\frac{x^{-2}}{-2} - 8x\right)\Big|_{1/2}^1 = \frac{-1}{2} - 8 - (-2 - 4) = -\frac{5}{2}.$

5.3.38 $\displaystyle\int_0^4 x(x-2)(x-4)\,dx = \int_0^4 (x^3 - 6x^2 + 8x)\,dx = \left(\frac{x^4}{4} - 2x^3 + 4x^2\right)\Big|_0^4 = 64 - 128 + 64 - 0 = 0.$

5.3.39 $\displaystyle\int_0^{\pi/4} \sec^2\theta\,d\theta = \tan\theta\,\Big|_0^{\pi/4} = 1 - 0 = 1.$

5.3.40 $\displaystyle\int_0^{1/2} \frac{dx}{\sqrt{1-x^2}} = \sin^{-1}x\,\Big|_0^{1/2} = \sin^{-1}(1/2) - \sin^{-1}0 = \pi/6 - 0 = \pi/6.$

5.3.41 $\displaystyle\int_{-2}^{-1} x^{-3}\,dx = \frac{x^{-2}}{-2}\,\Big|_{-2}^{-1} = \frac{-1}{2x^2}\,\Big|_{-2}^{-1} = \frac{-1}{2} - \left(-\frac{1}{8}\right) = -\frac{3}{8}.$

5.3.42 $\displaystyle\int_0^{\pi} (1 - \sin x)\,dx = (x + \cos x)\,\Big|_0^{\pi} = \pi - 1 - (0 + 1) = \pi - 2.$

5.3.43 $\displaystyle\int_1^4 (1-x)(x-4)\,dx = \int_1^4 (-x^2 + 5x - 4)\,dx = \left(\frac{-x^3}{3} + \frac{5x^2}{2} - 4x\right)\Big|_1^4 = \frac{9}{2}.$

5.3.44 $\displaystyle\int_{-\pi/2}^{\pi/2} (\cos x - 1)\,dx = (\sin x - x)\,\Big|_{-\pi/2}^{\pi/2} = 1 - \frac{\pi}{2} - \left(-1 - \left(-\frac{\pi}{2}\right)\right) = 2 - \pi.$

5.3.45 $\displaystyle\int_1^2 \frac{3}{t}\,dt = 3\ln|t|\,\Big|_1^2 = 3\ln 2 - 3\ln 1 = \ln 8.$

5.3.46

$$\int_4^9 \frac{x - \sqrt{x}}{x^3}\,dx = \int_4^9 \left(\frac{x}{x^3} - \frac{x^{1/2}}{x^3}\right)dx = \int_4^9 \left(x^{-2} - x^{-5/2}\right)dx = \left(\frac{x^{-1}}{-1} - \frac{x^{-3/2}}{-3/2}\right)\Big|_4^9$$

$$= \left(\frac{-1}{x} + \frac{2}{3x^{3/2}}\right)\Big|_4^9 = \frac{-1}{9} + \frac{2}{81} - \left(\frac{-1}{4} + \frac{2}{24}\right) = \frac{-7}{81} - \left(-\frac{1}{6}\right) = \frac{13}{162}.$$

5.3.47 $\displaystyle\int_0^{\pi/8} \cos 2x\,dx = \left(\frac{\sin 2x}{2}\right)\Big|_0^{\pi/8} = \frac{\sqrt{2}/2 - 0}{2} = \frac{\sqrt{2}}{4}.$

5.3.48 $\displaystyle\int_0^1 10e^{2x}\,dx = \left(5e^{2x}\right)\Big|_0^1 = 5(e^2 - 1).$

5.3.49 $\displaystyle\int_1^{\sqrt{3}} \frac{1}{1+x^2}\,dx = \tan^{-1}x \Big|_1^{\sqrt{3}} = \tan^{-1}\sqrt{3} - \tan^{-1}1 = \pi/3 - \pi/4 = \pi/12.$

5.3.50 $\displaystyle\int_{\pi/16}^{\pi/8} 8\csc^2 4x\,dx = (-2\cot 4x)\Big|_{\pi/16}^{\pi/8} = -2\cdot 0 - (-2)\cdot 1 = 2.$

5.3.51

The area (and net area) of this region is given by $\displaystyle\int_1^4 \sqrt{x}\,dx = \frac{2}{3}x^{3/2}\Big|_1^4 = \frac{16}{3} - \frac{2}{3} = \frac{14}{3}.$

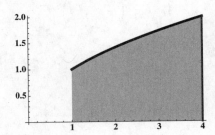

5.3.52

The area (and net area) of this region is given by $\displaystyle\int_{-2}^2 (4-x^2)\,dx = \left(4x - \frac{x^3}{3}\right)\Big|_{-2}^2 = 8 - \frac{8}{3} - \left(-8 + \frac{8}{3}\right) = 16 - \frac{16}{3} = \frac{32}{3}.$

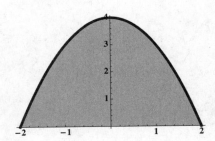

5.3.53

The net area of this region is given by $\displaystyle\int_{-2}^2 (x^4 - 16)\,dx = \left(\frac{x^5}{5} - 16x\right)\Big|_{-2}^2 = \frac{32}{5} - 32 - \left(\frac{-32}{5} + 32\right) = \frac{64}{5} - 64 = \frac{-256}{5}.$ Thus the area is $\dfrac{256}{5}.$

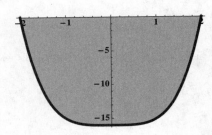

5.3.54

The net area of this region is given by $\displaystyle\int_{-\pi/2}^{\pi} 6\cos x\,dx = 6\sin x\Big|_{-\pi/2}^{\pi} = 0 - -6 = 6.$ The area is given by $\displaystyle\int_{-\pi/2}^{\pi/2} 6\cos x\,dx - \int_{\pi/2}^{\pi} 6\cos x\,dx = 6\sin x\Big|_{-\pi/2}^{\pi/2} - 6\sin x\Big|_{\pi/2}^{\pi} = 6 - -6 - (0 - 6) = 18.$

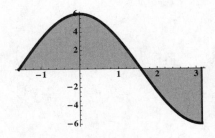

5.3.55 Because this region is below the axis, the area of it is given by $-\int_2^4 (x^2 - 25)\,dx = -\left(\frac{x^3}{3} - 25x\right)\Big|_2^4 = -\left(\frac{64}{3} - 100 - \left(\frac{8}{3} - 50\right)\right) = 50 - \frac{56}{3} = \frac{94}{3}.$

5.3.56 Because the function is below the axis between -1 and 1, and is above the axis between 1 and 2, the area of the bounded region is given by $-\int_{-1}^{1}(x^3-1)\,dx+\int_{1}^{2}(x^3-1)\,dx=-\left(\dfrac{x^4}{4}-x\right)\Big|_{-1}^{1}+\left(\dfrac{x^4}{4}-x\right)\Big|_{1}^{2}=$
$-\left(\dfrac{1}{4}-1-\left(\dfrac{1}{4}+1\right)\right)+\left(4-2-\left(\dfrac{1}{4}-1\right)\right)=2+2.75=4.75.$

5.3.57 Because this region is below the axis, the area of it is given by $-\int_{-2}^{-1}\frac{1}{x}\,dx=-\left(\ln|x|\,\Big|_{-2}^{-1}\right)=$ $\ln 2-\ln 1=\ln 2.$

5.3.58 Because the function is above the axis between -1 and 0 and is below the axis between 0 and 2, the area is given by $\int_{-1}^{0}(x^3-x^2-2x)\,dx-\int_{0}^{2}(x^3-x^2-2x)\,dx=\left(\dfrac{x^4}{4}-\dfrac{x^3}{3}-x^2\right)\Big|_{-1}^{0}-\left(\dfrac{x^4}{4}-\dfrac{x^3}{3}-x^2\right)\Big|_{0}^{2}=$
$\left(0-\left(\dfrac{1}{4}+\dfrac{1}{3}-1\right)\right)-\left(4-\dfrac{8}{3}-4-0\right)=\dfrac{5}{12}+\dfrac{8}{3}=\dfrac{37}{12}.$

5.3.59 The area is given by

$$-\int_{-\pi/4}^{0}\sin x\,dx+\int_{0}^{3\pi/4}\sin x\,dx=\left(\cos x\,\Big|_{-\pi/4}^{0}\right)+\left(-\cos x\,\Big|_{0}^{3\pi/4}\right)=\left(1-\dfrac{\sqrt{2}}{2}\right)+\left(1+\dfrac{\sqrt{2}}{2}\right)=2.$$

5.3.60 Because this region is below the axis, the area is given by $-\int_{\pi/2}^{\pi}\cos x\,dx=-\left(\sin x\,\Big|_{\pi/2}^{\pi}\right)=$ $\sin(\pi/2)-\sin(\pi)=1.$

5.3.61 By a direct application of the Fundamental Theorem, this is $x^2+x+1.$

5.3.62 By a direct application of the Fundamental Theorem, this is $e^x.$

5.3.63 By the Fundamental Theorem and the chain rule, this is $\frac{1}{x^6}\cdot 3x^2=\frac{3}{x^4}.$

5.3.64 This is equal to $-\dfrac{d}{dx}\int_{10}^{x^2}\dfrac{dz}{z^2+1}=\dfrac{-1}{x^4+1}\cdot 2x=\dfrac{-2x}{x^4+1}.$

5.3.65 This is $-\dfrac{d}{dx}\int_{1}^{x}\sqrt{t^4+1}\,dt=-\sqrt{x^4+1}.$

5.3.66 This is $-\dfrac{d}{dx}\int_{0}^{x}\dfrac{dp}{p^2+1}=\dfrac{-1}{x^2+1}.$

5.3.67 This can be written as

$$\frac{d}{dx}\left(\int_{-x}^{0}\sqrt{1+t^2}\,dt+\int_{0}^{x}\sqrt{1+t^2}\,dt\right)=\frac{d}{dx}\left(-\int_{0}^{-x}\sqrt{1+t^2}\,dt+\int_{0}^{x}\sqrt{1+t^2}\,dt\right)$$
$$=-\sqrt{1+(-x)^2}(-1)+\sqrt{1+x^2}=2\sqrt{1+x^2}.$$

5.3.68 This can be written as

$$\frac{d}{dx}\left(\int_{e^x}^{0}\ln(t^2)\,dt+\int_{0}^{e^{2x}}\ln(t^2)\,dt\right)=\frac{d}{dx}\left(-\int_{0}^{e^x}\ln(t^2)\,dt+\int_{0}^{e^{2x}}\ln(t^2)\,dt\right)$$
$$=-\ln((e^x)^2)\cdot e^x+\ln((e^{2x})^2)\cdot 2e^{2x}=-2xe^x+8xe^{2x}=2xe^x(4e^x-1).$$

5.3.69

    (a) matches with (C) – its area function is increasing linearly.

    (b) matches with (B) – its area function increases then decreases.

    (c) matches with (D) – its area function is always increasing on $[0, b]$, although not linearly.

    (d) matches with (A) – its area function decreases at first and then eventually increases.

5.3.70

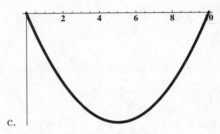

    a. It appears that $A(x) = 0$ for $x = 0$ and $x = 10$.

    b. A has a local minimum at $x = 5$ where the area function changes from decreasing to increasing.

                                         c.

5.3.71

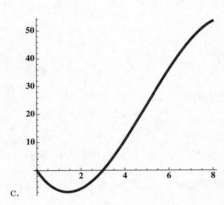

    a. It appears that $A(x) = 0$ for $x = 0$ and at about $x = 3$.

    b. A has a local minimum at about $x = 1.5$ where the area function changes from decreasing to increasing, and a local max at around $x = 8.5$ where the area function changes from increasing to decreasing.

                                         c.

5.3.72

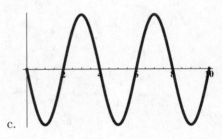

    a. It appears that $A(x) = 0$ for $x = 0$, $x = 2$, $x = 4$, $x = 6$, $x = 8$, and $x = 10$.

    b. A has a local minimum at $x = 1$, $x = 5$, and $x = 9$ where the area function changes from decreasing to increasing, and a local maximum at $x = 3$ and $x = 7$ where the area function changes from increasing to decreasing.

                                         c.

5.3.73

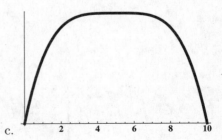

    a. It appears that $A(x) = 0$ for $x = 0$ and $x = 10$.

    b. A has a local maximum at $x = 5$ where the area function changes from increasing to decreasing.

                                         c.

5.3.74 $A(1) = \frac{1}{2} \cdot 1 \cdot 1 = \frac{1}{2}$. $A(2) = \frac{1}{2} \cdot 2 \cdot 2 = 2$. $A(4) = 2 + 2^2 = 6$. $A(6) = 6 + \frac{1}{4}\pi \cdot 2^2 = 6 + \pi$.

5.3.75 $A(2) = -\frac{1}{4}\pi \cdot 2^2 = -\pi$. $A(5) = -\pi + \frac{1}{2} \cdot 3 \cdot 3 = \frac{9}{2} - \pi$. $A(8) = \frac{9}{2} - \pi + \frac{1}{2} \cdot 3 \cdot 3 = 9 - \pi$. $A(12) = 9 - \pi - \frac{1}{2} \cdot 4 \cdot 2 = 5 - \pi$.

5.3.76

a. $A(x) = \int_0^x \sin t \, dt = -\cos t \Big|_0^x = -\cos x - (-1) = 1 - \cos x$.

c. $A(\pi/2) = 1 - \cos(\pi/2) = (1 - 0) = 1$ and $A(\pi) = 1 - \cos \pi = 1 - (-1) = 2$. The area under the curve between 0 and $\pi/2$ is the same as the area under the curve between $\pi/2$ and π.

b.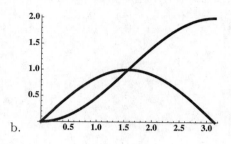

5.3.77

a. $A(x) = \int_0^x e^t \, dt = e^t \Big|_0^x = e^x - (1)$.

c. $A(\ln 2) = e^{\ln 2} - 1 = 2 - 1 = 1$. $A(\ln 4) = e^{\ln 4} - 1 = 4 - 1 = 3$. There is twice as much area under the curve between $\ln 2$ and $\ln 4$ as there is between 0 and $\ln 2$.

b.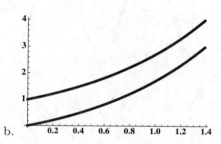

5.3.78

a. $A(x) = \int_0^x -12t(t-1)(t-2) \, dt = \int_0^x -12t^3 + 36t^2 - 24t \, dt = \left(-3t^4 + 12t^3 - 12t^2\right)\Big|_0^x = -3x^4 + 12x^3 - 12x^2$.

c. $A(1) = -3 + 12 - 12 = -3$. $A(2) = -48 + 96 - 48 = 0$. The area bounded between the x-axis and the curve on $[0, 1]$ is equal to the area bounded between the x-axis and the curve on $[1, 2]$.

b.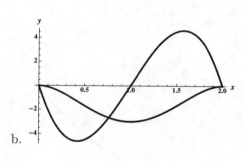

5.3.79

a. $A(x) = \int_0^x \cos \pi t \, dt = \frac{1}{\pi} \sin \pi t \Big|_0^x = \frac{\sin \pi x}{\pi}$.

c. $A(1/2) = \frac{1}{\pi}$. $A(1) = \frac{\sin \pi}{\pi} = 0$. The area bounded between the x-axis and the curve on $[0, 1/2]$ is equal to the area bounded between the x-axis and the curve on $[1/2, 1]$.

b.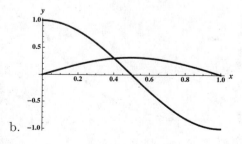

5.3.80

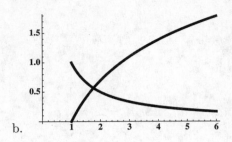

a. $A(x) = \int_1^x 1/t\,dt = \ln t \,\Big|_1^x = \ln x.$

c. $A(4) = \ln 4$ and $A(6) = \ln 6.$

b.

5.3.81

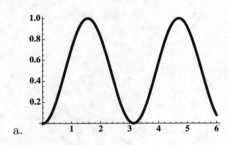

a.

b. $g'(x) = \sin^2 x.$

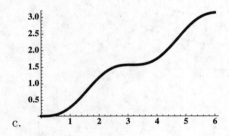

c.

Note that g' is always positive, so g is always increasing. There are inflection points where g' changes from increasing to decreasing, and vice versa.

5.3.82

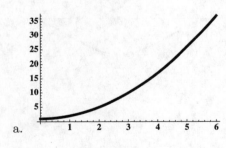

a.

b. $g'(x) = x^2 + 1.$

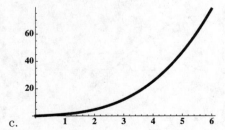

c.

Note that g' is always positive, so g is always increasing. Also g' is always increasing, so g is always concave up.

5.3.83

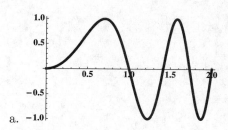

b. $g'(x) = \sin(\pi x^2)$.

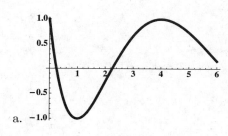

Note that g is increasing where $g' > 0$ and g is decreasing when $g' < 0$. Also, where g' is increasing, g is concave up and where g' is decreasing, g is concave down.

5.3.84

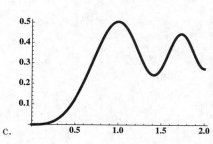

b. $g'(x) = \cos(\pi\sqrt{x})$.

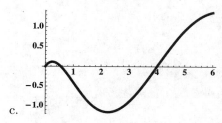

Note that g is increasing where $g' > 0$ and g is decreasing when $g' < 0$. Also, where g' is increasing, g is concave up and where g' is decreasing, g is concave down.

5.3.85

a. True. The net area under the curve increases as x increases, as long as f is above the axis.

b. True. The net area decreases as x increases, as long as f is below the axis.

c. False. These do not have the same derivative, so they are not antiderivatives of the same function.

d. True, because the two functions differ by a constant, and thus have the same derivative.

e. True, because the derivative of a constant is zero.

5.3.86 $\dfrac{1}{2}\displaystyle\int_0^{\ln 2} e^x\, dx = \dfrac{1}{2}\left(e^x\,\Big|_0^{\ln 2}\right) = \dfrac{1}{2}\left(2 - 1\right) = \dfrac{1}{2}.$

5.3.87

$$\int_1^4 \frac{x-2}{\sqrt{x}}\,dx = \int_1^4 \left(\frac{x}{\sqrt{x}} - \frac{2}{\sqrt{x}}\right) dx = \int_1^4 \left(x^{1/2} - 2x^{-1/2}\right) dx$$

$$= \left(\frac{2}{3}x^{3/2} - 4x^{1/2}\right)\Big|_1^4 = \frac{16}{3} - 8 - \left(\frac{2}{3} - 4\right) = \frac{14}{3} - \frac{12}{3} = \frac{2}{3}.$$

5.3.88 $\displaystyle\int_1^2 \left(\frac{2}{s} - \frac{4}{s^3}\right) ds = \left(2\ln|s| + \frac{2}{s^2}\right)\Big|_1^2 = 2\ln 2 + \frac{1}{2} - (0 + 2) = \ln 4 - \frac{3}{2}.$

5.3.89 $\displaystyle\int_0^{\pi/3} \sec x \tan x\,dx = \sec x\,\Big|_0^{\pi/3} = 2 - 1 = 1.$

5.3.90 $\displaystyle\int_{\pi/4}^{\pi/2} \csc^2\theta\,d\theta = -\cot\theta\,\Big|_{\pi/4}^{\pi/2} = 0 + 1 = 1.$

5.3.91 $\displaystyle\int_1^8 \sqrt[3]{y}\,dy = \frac{3}{4}y^{4/3}\,\Big|_1^8 = 12 - \frac{3}{4} = \frac{45}{4}.$

5.3.92 $\displaystyle\int_{\sqrt{2}}^2 \frac{dx}{x\sqrt{x^2-1}} = \sec^{-1}x\,\Big|_{\sqrt{2}}^2 = \frac{\pi}{3} - \frac{\pi}{4} = \frac{\pi}{12}.$

5.3.93 $\displaystyle\int_1^2 \frac{z^2+4}{z}\,dz = \int_1^2 \left(z + \frac{4}{z}\right) dz = \left(\frac{z^2}{2} + 4\ln z\right)\Big|_1^2 = 2 + 4\ln 2 - \left(\frac{1}{2} + 0\right) = \ln 16 + \frac{3}{2}.$

5.3.94 $\displaystyle\int_0^{\sqrt{3}} \frac{3\,dx}{9+x^2} = \tan^{-1}(x/3)\,\Big|_0^{\sqrt{3}} = \tan^{-1}(\sqrt{3}/3) = \pi/6.$

5.3.95

We can use geometry – there is a triangle with base 4 and height 2 and a triangle with base 2 and height 2, so the total area is $\frac{1}{2}\cdot 4\cdot 2 + \frac{1}{2}\cdot 2\cdot 2 = 6.$

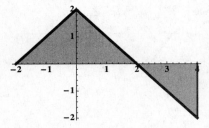

5.3.96

Because the region is above the axis, we can simply compute $\displaystyle\int_{-1/2}^{\sqrt{3}/2} \frac{dx}{\sqrt{1-x^2}} = \sin^{-1}x\,\Big|_{-1/2}^{\sqrt{3}/2} = \frac{\pi}{3} - \left(-\frac{\pi}{6}\right) = \frac{\pi}{2}.$

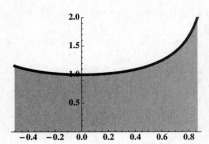

5.3.97

Because the region is below the axis on $[1, \sqrt{2}]$ and above on $[\sqrt{2}, 4]$ we need to compute $\displaystyle\int_{\sqrt{2}}^{4} (x^4 - 4)\, dx - \int_{1}^{\sqrt{2}} (x^4 - 4)\, dx =$

$\displaystyle\left(\frac{x^5}{5} - 4x \right) \Big|_{\sqrt{2}}^{4} - \left(\frac{x^5}{5} - 4x \right) \Big|_{1}^{\sqrt{2}} = \frac{1024}{5} -$

$16 - (4\sqrt{2}/5 - 4\sqrt{2}) - (4\sqrt{2}/5 - 4\sqrt{2}) + \frac{1}{5} - 4 =$

$185 + \dfrac{32\sqrt{2}}{5}$

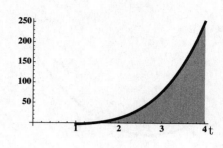

5.3.98

Because the function is below (or touching) the axis on $[-1, 2]$ and above on $[2, 3]$, the area is given by $\displaystyle\int_{2}^{3} (x^3 - 2x^2)\, dx -$

$\displaystyle\int_{-1}^{2} (x^3 - 2x^2)\, dx = \left(\frac{x^4}{4} - \frac{2x^3}{3} \right) \Big|_{2}^{3} -$

$\displaystyle\left(\frac{x^4}{4} - \frac{2x^3}{3} \right) \Big|_{-1}^{2} = \left(\frac{81}{4} - 18 \right) - \left(4 - \frac{16}{3} \right) -$

$\displaystyle\left(4 - \frac{16}{3} \right) + \left(\frac{1}{4} + \frac{2}{3} \right) = \frac{41}{2} - 26 + \frac{34}{3} = \frac{35}{6}.$

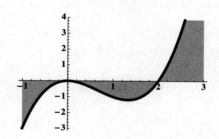

5.3.99 $\displaystyle\int_{3}^{8} f'(t)\, dt = f(8) - f(3).$

5.3.100 $\displaystyle\frac{d}{dx} \int_{0}^{x^2} \frac{1}{t^2 + 4}\, dt = \frac{2x}{x^4 + 4}.$

5.3.101 $\displaystyle\frac{d}{dx} \int_{0}^{\cos x} (t^4 + 6)\, dt = -(\cos^4 x + 6) \sin x.$

5.3.102 $\displaystyle\frac{d}{dx} \int_{x}^{1} e^{t^2}\, dt = -\frac{d}{dx} \int_{1}^{x} e^{t^2}\, dt = -e^{x^2}.$

5.3.103 $\displaystyle\frac{d}{dt} \left(\int_{1}^{t} \frac{3}{x}\, dx - \int_{t^2}^{1} \frac{3}{x}\, dx \right) = \frac{d}{dt} \int_{1}^{t} \frac{3}{x}\, dx + \frac{d}{dt} \int_{1}^{t^2} \frac{3}{x}\, dx = \frac{3}{t} + \frac{6t}{t^2} = \frac{9}{t}.$

5.3.104 $\displaystyle\frac{d}{dt} \left(\int_{0}^{t} \frac{dx}{1 + x^2} + \int_{0}^{1/t} \frac{dx}{1 + x^2} \right) = \frac{1}{1 + t^2} + \frac{1}{1 + (1/t)^2} \left(-\frac{1}{t^2} \right) = \frac{1}{1 + t^2} - \frac{1}{1 + t^2} = 0.$

5.3.105

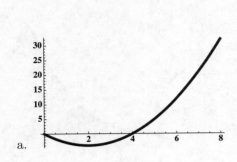

a.

b. We seek b so that $\int_0^b (x^2 - 4x) = 0$ for $b > 0$. We have $\left(\frac{x^3}{3} - 2x^2\right)\Big|_0^b = \frac{b^3}{3} - 2b^2 = 0$, which occurs for $\frac{b}{3} = 2$, or $b = 6$.

c. We seek b so that $\int_0^b (x^2 - ax) = 0$ for $b > 0$. We have $\left(\frac{x^3}{3} - \frac{ax^2}{2}\right)\Big|_0^b = \frac{b^3}{3} - \frac{ab^2}{2} = 0$, which occurs for $\frac{b}{3} = \frac{a}{2}$, or $b = \frac{3a}{2}$.

5.3.106 If $0 < x < a$, then $x > 0$, $x - a < 0$, and $x - b < 0$, so the product of these three quantities is positive. If $a < x < b$, then $x > 0$, $x - a > 0$, and $x - b < 0$, so the product of these three quantities is negative. The region between $x = 0$ and $x = a$, which is above the x-axis, has area

$$\int_0^a x(x-a)(x-b)\,dx = \int_0^a (x^3 - (a+b)x^2 + abx)\,dx = \left(\frac{x^4}{4} - \frac{a+b}{3}x^3 + \frac{ab}{2}x\right)\Big|_0^a = \frac{a^3(2b-a)}{12},$$

while the region between $x = a$ and $x = b$, which is below the x-axis, has area

$$-\int_a^b x(x-a)(x-b)\,dx = -\int_a^b (x^3 - (a+b)x^2 + abx)\,dx = -\left(\frac{x^4}{4} - \frac{a+b}{3}x^3 + \frac{ab}{2}x\right)\Big|_a^b = \frac{(b-a)^3(a+b)}{12}.$$

These are equal when $a^3(2b - a) = (b - a)^3(a + b)$. Divide through by a^4 to obtain

$$2 \cdot \frac{b}{a} - 1 = \left(\frac{b}{a} - 1\right)^3 \left(1 + \frac{b}{a}\right).$$

Let $c = \frac{b}{a}$; then $2c - 1 = (c - 1)^3(c + 1) = c^4 - 2c^3 + 2c - 1$, so that $c^4 - 2c^3 = 0$. Because $b > 0$ we must have $c > 0$, and the only nonzero root is $c = 2$. Thus $c = \frac{b}{a} = 2$, so $b = 2a$.

5.3.107 Because $\frac{d}{db}\int_{-1}^b x^2(3 - x)\,dx = b^2(3 - b)$ we see that this function of b has critical points at $b = 0$ and $b = 3$. Note also that the integrand is positive on $[0, 3]$, but is negative on $[3, \infty)$. So the maximum for this area function occurs at $b = 3$.

5.3.108 The function $f(x) = 8 + 2x - x^2 = (4 - x)(2 + x)$ is 0 for $x = 4$ and $x = -2$, and is positive on $(-2, 4)$ and negative on $(-\infty, -2)$ and on $(4, \infty)$. Thus, the largest possible value for the area $\int_a^b f(x)\,dx$ is when $a = -2$ and $b = 4$.

5.3.109 Differentiating both sides of the given equation yields $f(x) = -2\sin x + 3$.

5.3.110 Suppose that a maximum of A occurs at $x = c$, and that A is not a constant function near c. Then A changes from increasing to decreasing at c. But because A is the net area from 0 to x, the only way for A to change from increasing to decreasing is for f to change from above the axis to below, so it must be the case that $f > 0$ to the left of c and $f < 0$ to the right of c, but because f is continuous, this implies that $f(c) = 0$. An analogous argument holds for the case when A has a minimum at c.

For $f(x) = x^2 - 10x$, note that $A(x) = \int_0^x (t^2 - 10t)\,dt = \frac{x^3}{3} - 5x^2$, and that this function has a minimum at $x = 10$, because $A'(x) = x^2 - 10x = f(x)$ changes from negative to positive at $x = 10$, so that A changes from decreasing to increasing there.

Using a computer or calculator, we obtain:

x	500	1000	1500	2000
$S(x)$	1.5726	1.57023	1.57087	1.57098

5.3.111 This appears to be approaching $\frac{\pi}{2}$.
Note that between 0 and π, the area is approximately half the area of a rectangle with height 1 and base π, and then from π on there is approximately as much area above the axis as below.

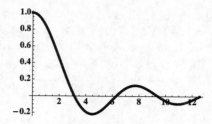

5.3.112 By the Fundamental Theorem, $S'(x) = \dfrac{\sin x}{x}$, so $S''(x) = \dfrac{x \cos x - \sin x}{x^2} = \dfrac{\cos x}{x} - \dfrac{\sin x}{x^2}$. Thus,

$$S'''(x) = \frac{-x \sin x - \cos x}{x^2} - \frac{x^2 \cos x - 2x \sin x}{x^4} = \frac{-\sin x}{x} - \frac{2 \cos x}{x^2} + \frac{2 \sin x}{x^3}.$$

$$xS'(x) + 2S''(x) + xS'''(x) = \sin x + \frac{2 \cos x}{x} - \frac{2 \sin x}{x^2} + -\sin x - \frac{2 \cos x}{x} + \frac{2 \sin x}{x^2} = 0.$$

5.3.113 By the Fundamental Theorem, $S'(x) = \sin x^2$, so $S''(x) = 2x \cos x^2$, so

$$S'(x)^2 + \left(\frac{S''(x)}{2x}\right)^2 = \sin^2 x^2 + \cos^2 x^2 = 1.$$

5.3.114 Note that $\displaystyle\int_{-x}^{x} (t^2 + 1)\, dt = \int_{0}^{x} (t^2 + 1)\, dt - \int_{0}^{-x} (t^2 + 1)\, dt$. Thus, the derivative with respect to x of this expression is

$$(x^2 + 1) - ((-x)^2 + 1) \cdot -1 = 2x^2 + 2.$$

5.3.115

a. By definition of Reimann sums, $\int_{a}^{b} f'(x)\, dx$ is approximated by $\sum_{k=1}^{n} f'(x_{k-1})\Delta x$. But $f'(x_{k-1}) = \lim_{h \to 0} \dfrac{f(x_{k-1} + h) - f(x_{k-1})}{h}$. If $h = \Delta x$, then we have $f'(x_{k-1}) \approx \frac{f(x_{k-1} + \Delta x) - f(x_{k-1})}{\Delta x} = \frac{f(x_k) - f(x_{k-1})}{\Delta x}$, so that

$$\int_{a}^{b} f'(x)\, dx \approx \sum_{k=1}^{n} \frac{f(x_k) - f(x_{k-1})}{\Delta x} \cdot \Delta x.$$

b. Canceling the Δx factors we obtain

$$\int_{a}^{b} f'(x)\, dx \approx \sum_{k=1}^{n} \frac{f(x_k) - f(x_{k-1})}{\Delta x} \cdot \Delta x$$

$$= \sum_{k=1}^{n} (f(x_k) - f(x_{k-1}))$$

$$= (f(x_1) - f(x_0)) + (f(x_2) - f(x_1)) + \cdots + (f(x_{n-1}) - f(x_{n-2})) + (f(x_n) - f(x_{n-1}))$$

$$= f(x_n) - f(x_0) = f(b) - f(a).$$

c. The analogy between the two situations is that both (a) the sum of difference quotients and (b) integral of a derivative are equal to the difference in function values at the endpoints.

5.3.116

a. If m^* is the minimum and M^* is the maximum of f on $[a, b]$, then for every possible subinterval $[x_i, x_{i+1}]$ of $[a, x]$ of width h_i, we have $m^* h_i \leq f(x_i^*) h_i \leq M^* h_i$ where x_i^* is any value on $[x_i, x_{i+1}]$. Adding these up over any partition of $[a, x]$ and taking the limit as $n \to \infty$ gives $m^*(x - a) \leq \int_a^x f(t)\, dt \leq M^*(x - a)$, so $m^*(x - a) \leq A(x) \leq M^*(x - a)$. Now consider $\lim_{x \to a^+} m^*(x - a) = \lim_{x \to a^+} M^*(x - a) = 0$. Thus by the Squeeze Theorem we must have $\lim_{x \to a^+} A(x) = 0 = A(a)$, so A is continuous from the right at $x = a$.

b. First note that $A(b) - A(x) = \int_a^b f(t)\, dt - \int_a^x f(t)\, dt = \int_x^b f(t)\, dt$. Now if m^* is the minimum and M^* is the maximum of f on $[a, b]$, then for every possible subinterval $[x_i, x_{i+1}]$ of $[b, x]$ of width h_i, we have $m^* h_i \leq f(x_i^*) h_i \leq M^* h_i$ where x_i^* is any value on $[x_i, x_{i+1}]$. Adding these up over any partition of $[b, x]$ and taking the limit as $n \to \infty$ gives $m^*(b - x) \leq \int_x^b f(t)\, dt \leq M^*(b - x)$, so $m^*(b - x) \leq A(b) - A(x) \leq M^*(b - x)$. Now consider $\lim_{x \to b^-} m^*(b - x) = \lim_{x \to b^-} M^*(b - x) = 0$. Thus by the Squeeze Theorem we must have $\lim_{x \to b^-}(A(b) - A(x)) = 0$, so $\lim_{x \to b^-} A(x) = A(b)$, and A is continuous from the left at $x = b$.

5.4   Working with Integrals

5.4.1 If f is odd, it is symmetric about the origin, which guarantees that between $-a$ and a, there is as much area above the axis and under f as there is below the axis and above f, so the net area must be 0.

5.4.2 If f is even, it is symmetric about the the y-axis, which guarantees that the region between $-a$ and 0 has the same net area as the region between 0 and a, so $\displaystyle\int_{-a}^0 f(x)\, dx + \int_0^a f(x)\, dx = 2\int_0^a f(x)\, dx$.

5.4.3 $f(x) = x^{12}$ is an even function, because $f(-x) = (-x)^{12} = x^{12} = f(x)$. $g(x) = \sin x^2$ is also even, because $g(-x) = \sin((-x)^2) = \sin x^2 = g(x)$.

5.4.4 The average value of a function f on $[a, b]$ is $\displaystyle\frac{1}{b-a}\int_a^b f(x)\, dx$. This is analogous to "adding up all the value of f and dividing by how many there are" – in the sense that computing the interval is like adding up all the values of the function, and dividing by $b - a$ is like dividing by how many x values there are.

5.4.5 The average value of a continuous function on a closed interval $[a, b]$ will always be between the maximum and the minimum value of f on that interval. Because the function is continuous, the Intermediate Value Theorem assures us that the function will take on each value between the maximum and the minimum somewhere on the interval.

5.4.6   Note that the area of the triangle is $\frac{1}{2} \cdot 2 \cdot 2 = 2$, so the rectangle needs to have a height of 1 and a base of 2 so that its area is 2.

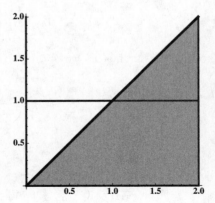

5.4.7 Because x^9 is an odd function, $\displaystyle\int_{-2}^2 x^9\, dx = 0$.

5.4.8 Because $2x^5$ is an odd function, $\displaystyle\int_{-200}^{200} 2x^5\,dx = 0$.

5.4.9 $\displaystyle\int_{-2}^{2} (3x^8 - 2)\,dx = 2\int_{0}^{2} (3x^8 - 2)\,dx = 2\left(\frac{x^9}{3} - 2x\right)\bigg|_{0}^{2} = \left(\frac{1024}{3}\right) - 8 = \frac{1000}{3}$.

5.4.10 $\displaystyle\int_{-\pi/4}^{\pi/4} \cos x\,dx = 2\int_{0}^{\pi/4} \cos x\,dx = 2\,(\sin x)\bigg|_{0}^{\pi/4} = 2\left(\frac{\sqrt{2}}{2}\right) = \sqrt{2}$.

5.4.11 Note that the first two terms of the integrand form an odd function, and the last two terms form an even function. $\displaystyle\int_{-2}^{2} (x^9 - 3x^5 + 2x^2 - 10)\,dx = 2\int_{0}^{2} (2x^2 - 10)\,dx = 2\left(\frac{2x^3}{3} - 10x\right)\bigg|_{0}^{2} = \frac{32}{3} - 40 = -\frac{88}{3}$.

5.4.12 $\displaystyle\int_{-\pi/2}^{\pi/2} 5\sin x\,dx = 0$ because the integrand is an odd function.

5.4.13 $\displaystyle\int_{-10}^{10} \frac{x}{\sqrt{200 - x^2}}\,dx = 0$ because the integrand is an odd function.

5.4.14 Note that the first term of the integrand is an even function, and the other two terms are odd functions. Thus, $\displaystyle\int_{-\pi/2}^{\pi/2} (\cos 2x + \cos x \sin x - 3\sin x^5)\,dx = 2\int_{0}^{\pi/2} \cos 2x\,dx = 2\left(\frac{\sin 2x}{2}\right)\bigg|_{0}^{\pi/2} = 0$.

5.4.15 Because the integrand is an odd function and the interval is symmetric about 0, this integral's value is 0.

5.4.16 $\displaystyle\int_{-1}^{1} (1 - |x|)\,dx = 2\int_{0}^{1} (1 - x)\,dx = 2\left(x - \frac{x^2}{2}\right)\bigg|_{0}^{1} = 2\left(1 - \frac{1}{2}\right) = 1$.

5.4.17

Because the integrand is an odd function and the interval is symmetric about 0, this integral's value is 0.

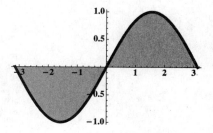

5.4.18

Because of the symmetry of the cosine function, the net area is zero between 0 and 2π.

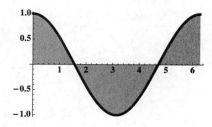

5.4.19

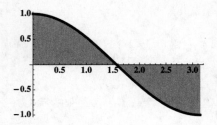

Because of the symmetry of the cosine function, the net area is zero between 0 and π.

5.4.20

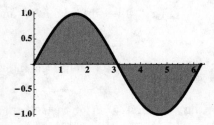

Because of the symmetry of the sine function, the net area is zero between 0 and 2π.

5.4.21

The average value is $\dfrac{1}{1-(-1)}\displaystyle\int_{-1}^{1} x^3\, dx =$ $\dfrac{1}{2}\left(x^4/4\right)\Big|_{-1}^{1} = 0.$

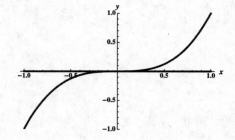

5.4.22

The average value is $\dfrac{1}{2-(-2)}\displaystyle\int_{-2}^{2}(x^2 +$ $1)\, dx = \dfrac{1}{4}\left(x^3/3 + x\right)\Big|_{-2}^{2} =$ $\dfrac{8/3 + 2 - (-8/3 - 2)}{4} = \dfrac{7}{3}.$

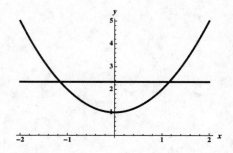

5.4.23

The average value is
$$\frac{1}{1-(-1)} \int_{-1}^{1} \frac{1}{x^2 + 1}\, dx = \frac{1}{2} \tan^{-1} x \,\Big|_{-1}^{1} = \frac{\pi/4 - (-\pi/4)}{2} = \frac{\pi}{4}.$$

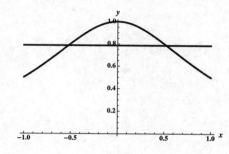

5.4.24

The average value is $\dfrac{1}{\pi/2} \displaystyle\int_{-\pi/4}^{\pi/4} \cos 2x\, dx = $
$$\frac{1}{\pi} \left(\sin 2x\right) \Big|_{-\pi/4}^{\pi/4} = \frac{1}{\pi}[1 - (-1)] = \frac{2}{\pi}.$$

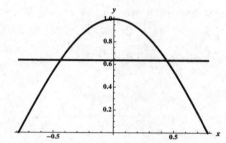

5.4.25

The average value is $\dfrac{1}{e - 1} \displaystyle\int_{1}^{e} \frac{1}{x}\, dx = $
$$\frac{1}{e - 1} \left(\ln |x|\right) \Big|_{1}^{e} = \frac{1}{e - 1} \approx .582.$$

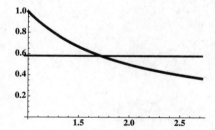

5.4.26

The average value is $\dfrac{1}{\ln 2} \displaystyle\int_{0}^{\ln 2} e^{2x}\, dx = $
$$\frac{1}{\ln 2} \left(\frac{e^{2x}}{2}\right) \Big|_{0}^{\ln 2} = \frac{1}{\ln 2} \cdot \left(2 - \frac{1}{2}\right) = \frac{3}{2 \ln 2} \approx 2.164.$$

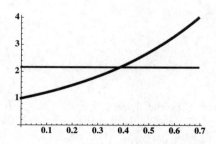

5.4.27

The average value is $\dfrac{1}{\pi}\displaystyle\int_{-\pi/2}^{\pi/2}\cos x\,dx\;=$

$\dfrac{1}{\pi}\left(\sin x\right)\Big|_{-\pi/2}^{\pi/2}=\dfrac{1}{\pi}\cdot(1--1)=\dfrac{2}{\pi}\approx .6366.$

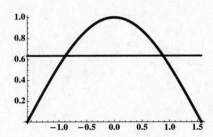

5.4.28

The average value is $\dfrac{1}{1}\displaystyle\int_{0}^{1}(x-x^2)\,dx\;=$

$\left(\dfrac{x^2}{2}-\dfrac{x^3}{3}\right)\Big|_{0}^{1}=\dfrac{1}{2}-\dfrac{1}{3}=\dfrac{1}{6}\approx .1667.$

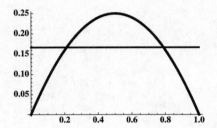

5.4.29

The average value is $\dfrac{1}{1}\displaystyle\int_{0}^{1}x^n\,dx\;=$

$\left(\dfrac{x^{n+1}}{n+1}\right)\Big|_{0}^{1}=\dfrac{1}{n+1}.$ The picture shown is for the case $n=3$.

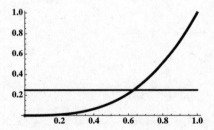

5.4.30

The average value is $\dfrac{1}{1}\displaystyle\int_{0}^{1}x^{1/n}\,dx\;=$

$\left(\dfrac{x^{(n+1)/n}}{(n+1)/n}\right)\Big|_{0}^{1}=\dfrac{n}{n+1}.$ The picture shown is for the case $n=3$.

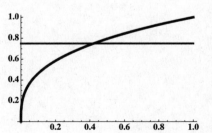

5.4.31 The average distance to the axis is given by $\dfrac{1}{20}\displaystyle\int_{0}^{20}30x(20-x)\,dx.$ This is equal to $\dfrac{1}{20}\displaystyle\int_{0}^{20}(600x-30x^2)\,dx=\dfrac{1}{20}\left(300x^2-10x^3\right)\Big|_{0}^{20}=2000.$

5.4.32

The average value is $\dfrac{1}{4-0}\displaystyle\int_0^4 (x^3 - 5x^2 + 30)\,dx = \dfrac{1}{4}\left(\dfrac{x^4}{4} - \dfrac{5x^3}{3} + 30x\right)\Big|_0^4 = \dfrac{1}{4}(64 - \dfrac{320}{3} + 120) - 0 = \dfrac{58}{3}.$

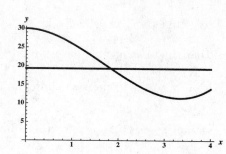

5.4.33 The average height is $\dfrac{1}{\pi}\displaystyle\int_0^\pi 10\sin x\,dx = \dfrac{1}{\pi}\left(-10\cos x\right)\Big|_0^\pi = \dfrac{1}{\pi}\left(10 - -10\right) = \dfrac{20}{\pi}.$

5.4.34 The average height is $\dfrac{1}{2\pi}\displaystyle\int_{-\pi}^\pi (5 + 5\cos x)\,dx = \dfrac{1}{2\pi}\left(5x + 5\sin x\right)\Big|_{-\pi}^\pi = \dfrac{1}{2\pi}\left(5\pi - -5\pi\right) = 5.$

5.4.35 The average value is $\dfrac{1}{4}\displaystyle\int_0^4 (8 - 2x)\,dx = \dfrac{1}{4}\left(8x - x^2\right)\Big|_0^4 = 4.$ The function has a value of 4 when $8 - 2x = 4$, which occurs when $x = 2$.

5.4.36 The average value is $\dfrac{1}{2}\displaystyle\int_0^2 e^x\,dx = \dfrac{1}{2}\left(e^x\right)\Big|_0^2 = \dfrac{e^2 - 1}{2}.$ The function attains this value when $\dfrac{e^2-1}{2} = e^x$, which is when $x = \ln\left(\dfrac{e^2-1}{2}\right) \approx 1.1614.$

5.4.37 The average value is $\dfrac{1}{a}\displaystyle\int_0^a \left(1 - \dfrac{x^2}{a^2}\right)dx = \dfrac{1}{a}\left(x - \dfrac{x^3}{3a^2}\right)\Big|_0^a = \dfrac{2}{3}.$ The function attains this value when $\dfrac{2}{3} = 1 - \dfrac{x^2}{a^2}$, which is when $x^2 = \dfrac{a^2}{3}$, which on the given interval occurs for $x = \sqrt{3}a/3.$

5.4.38 The average value is $\dfrac{1}{\pi}\displaystyle\int_0^\pi \dfrac{\pi}{4}\sin x\,dx = \dfrac{1}{4}\left(-\cos x\right)\Big|_0^\pi = \dfrac{1}{4}\left(1 - -1\right) = \dfrac{1}{2}.$ The function attains this value when $\dfrac{1}{2}\cdot\dfrac{4}{\pi} = \sin x$, which is when $x = \sin^{-1}\dfrac{2}{\pi} \approx .690107$ and for $x \approx 2.45149.$

5.4.39 The average value is $\dfrac{1}{2}\displaystyle\int_{-1}^1 (1 - |x|)\,dx = \dfrac{1}{2}\displaystyle\int_{-1}^0 (1 + x)\,dx + \dfrac{1}{2}\displaystyle\int_0^1 (1 - x)\,dx = \dfrac{1}{2}\left(x + \dfrac{x^2}{2}\right)\Big|_{-1}^0 + \dfrac{1}{2}\left(x - \dfrac{x^2}{2}\right)\Big|_0^1 = \dfrac{1}{4} + \dfrac{1}{4} = \dfrac{1}{2}.$ The function attains this value twice, once on $[-1, 0]$ when $1 + x = \dfrac{1}{2}$ which occurs when $x = -\dfrac{1}{2}$, and once on $[0, 1]$ when $1 - x = \dfrac{1}{2}$ which occurs when $x = \dfrac{1}{2}.$

5.4.40 The average value is given by $\dfrac{1}{3}\displaystyle\int_1^4 1/x\,dx = \dfrac{1}{3}\left(\ln x\right)\Big|_1^4 = \dfrac{1}{3}\left(\ln 4\right).$ The function attains this value when $x = \dfrac{3}{\ln 4} \approx 2.164.$

5.4.41

a. True. Because of the symmetry, the net area between 0 and 4 will be twice the net area between 0 and 2.

b. True. This follows because the symmetry implies that the net area from a to $a + 2$ is the opposite of the net area from $a - 2$ to a.

c. True. If $f(x) = cx + d$ on $[a, b]$ the value at the midpoint is $c \cdot \dfrac{a+b}{2} + d$, and the average value is
$\dfrac{1}{b-a}\displaystyle\int_a^b (cx + d)\,dx = \dfrac{1}{b-a}\left(\dfrac{cx^2}{2} + dx\right)\Big|_a^b = \dfrac{1}{b-a}\left(\dfrac{cb^2}{2} + db - \left(\dfrac{ca^2}{2} + da\right)\right) = \dfrac{c}{2}\cdot(a + b) + d.$

d. False, for example, when $a = 1$, we have that the maximum value of $x - x^2$ on $[0, 1]$ occurs at $\frac{1}{2}$ and is equal to $\frac{1}{4}$, but the average value is $\int_0^1 (x - x^2) \, dx = \left(\frac{x^2}{2} - \frac{x^2}{3} \right) \Big|_0^1 = \frac{1}{2} - \frac{1}{3} = \frac{1}{6}$.

5.4.42 Recall that the tangent function is an odd function, so the value of this integral is 0.

5.4.43 $\sec^2 x$ is even, so the value of this integral is $2 \int_0^{\pi/4} \sec^2 x \, dx = 2 \left(\tan x \right) \Big|_0^{\pi/4} = 2 \cdot (1 - 0) = 2$.

5.4.44 The function $1 - |x|^3$ is even, so the value of this integral is $2 \int_0^2 (1 - x^3) \, dx = 2 \left(x - \frac{x^4}{4} \right) \Big|_0^2 = 2(2 - 4) = -4$.

5.4.45 The integrand is an odd function, so the value of this integral is zero.

5.4.46 Let $T = \frac{2\pi k}{\omega}$ where k is an integer. The RMS is given by $\sqrt{\dfrac{\omega}{2\pi k} \int_0^{2\pi k/\omega} A^2 \sin^2(\omega t) \, dt} =$

$A \sqrt{\dfrac{\omega}{2\pi k} \int_0^{2\pi k/\omega} \dfrac{1 - \cos(2\omega t)}{2} \, dt} = A \sqrt{\dfrac{\omega}{2\pi k} \left[\dfrac{t}{2} - \dfrac{\sin(2\omega t)}{4\omega} \right]_0^{2\pi k/\omega}} = \dfrac{A}{\sqrt{2}}$.

5.4.47 The average height of the arch is given by

$$\frac{1}{630} \int_{-315}^{315} \left(630 - \frac{630}{315^2} x^2 \right) dx = \frac{630}{630} \left(x - \frac{x^3}{3 \cdot 315^2} \right) \Big|_{-315}^{315} = (315 - 105 - (-315 + 105)) = 420 \text{ ft.}$$

5.4.48 The average height of the arch is given by

$$\frac{1}{630} \int_{-315}^{315} \left(1260 - 315 \left(e^{0.00418x} + e^{-.00418x} \right) \right) dx$$

$$= \frac{1}{630} \left(1260x - \frac{315}{0.00418} (e^{0.00418x} - e^{-.00418x}) \right) \Big|_{-315}^{315} \approx 431.514 \text{ ft.}$$

5.4.49

a. $d^2 = x^2 + y^2 = x^2 + b^2(1 - (x^2/a^2))$. The average value of d^2 is $\dfrac{1}{2a} \int_{-a}^{a} \left(b^2 + \left(1 - \dfrac{b^2}{a^2} \right) x^2 \right) dx =$

$\dfrac{1}{2a} \left(b^2 x + \dfrac{\left(1 - (b^2/a^2) \right) x^3}{3} \right) \Big|_{-a}^{a} = \dfrac{1}{2a} \left(b^2 a + \dfrac{a^3}{3} - \dfrac{b^2 a}{3} - \left(-b^2 a - \dfrac{a^3}{3} + \dfrac{b^2 a}{3} \right) \right) = \dfrac{2b^2}{3} + \dfrac{a^2}{3}$.

b. If $a = b = R$, the above becomes $\dfrac{2R^2}{3} + \dfrac{R^2}{3} = R^2$.

c. $D^2 = (x - \sqrt{a^2 - b^2})^2 + y^2 = x^2 - 2x\sqrt{a^2 - b^2} + y^2 + a^2 - b^2 = \left(1 - \dfrac{b^2}{a^2} \right) x^2 - 2\sqrt{a^2 - b^2}\, x + a^2$. So the

average value of D^2 is $\dfrac{1}{2a} \int_{-a}^{a} D^2 \, dx = \dfrac{1}{2a} \int_{-a}^{a} \left[\left(1 - \dfrac{b^2}{a^2} \right) x^2 + a^2 \right] dx - \dfrac{1}{a} \int_{-a}^{a} x\sqrt{a^2 - b^2} \, dx =$

$\dfrac{1}{a} \int_0^a \left[\left(1 - \dfrac{b^2}{a^2} \right) x^2 + a^2 \right] dx + 0 = \dfrac{1}{3}(a^2 - b^2) + a^2 = \dfrac{4a^2 - b^2}{3}$.

5.4.50

a. Note that $\frac{d}{dx} \sin x = \cos x$, which is zero when $x = \pi/2$, and because the derivative is positive on $(0, \pi/2)$ and negative on $(\pi/2, 0)$, there is a maximum at $x = \pi/2$. Similarly, $\frac{d}{dx} \frac{4\pi x - 4x^2}{\pi^2} = \frac{4\pi - 8x}{\pi^2}$, which is zero when $x = \pi/2$, and this function is increasing on $(0, \pi/2)$ and decreasing on $(\pi/2, \pi)$, so it also has a maximum at $\pi/2$. Also, both functions have the value 1 at $x = \pi/2$.

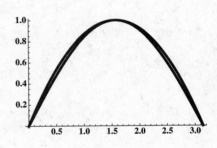

b. On $(0, \pi)$, the sine function is always less than or equal to the other function.

c. The average values are

$$\frac{1}{\pi} \int_0^\pi \sin x \, dx = \frac{1}{\pi} \left(-\cos x \right) \Big|_0^\pi = \frac{2}{\pi}$$

and

$$\frac{1}{\pi} \cdot \frac{4}{\pi^2} \int_0^\pi \pi x - x^2 \, dx = \frac{4}{\pi^3} \left(\frac{\pi x^2}{2} - \frac{x^3}{3} \right) \Big|_0^\pi = \frac{4}{\pi^3} \left(\frac{\pi^3}{2} - \frac{\pi^3}{3} \right) = \frac{2}{3}.$$

5.4.51

a. Because $\int_{-8}^8 f(x) \, dx = 18 = 2 \int_0^8 f(x) \, dx$, we have $\int_0^8 f(x) \, dx = \frac{18}{2} = 9$.

b. Because $x f(x)$ is an odd function when $f(x)$ is even, we have $\int_{-8}^8 x f(x) \, dx = 0$.

5.4.52

a. Because $f(x)$ is odd, $\int_{-4}^0 f(x) \, dx = - \int_0^4 f(x) \, dx$. We have

$$\int_{-4}^8 f(x) \, dx = \int_{-4}^0 f(x) \, dx + \int_0^8 f(x) \, dx = - \int_0^4 f(x) \, dx + \int_0^8 f(x) \, dx = -3 + 9 = 6.$$

b. $\int_{-8}^4 f(x) \, dx = \int_{-8}^0 f(x) \, dx + \int_0^4 f(x) \, dx = -9 + 3 = -6.$

5.4.53 $f(g(-x)) = f(g(x))$, so $f(g(x))$ is an even function, and $\int_{-a}^a f(g(x)) \, dx = 2 \int_0^a f(g(x)) \, dx$.

5.4.54 $f(p(-x)) = f(-p(x)) = f(p(x))$, and thus $f(p(x))$ is an even function. Therefore, $\int_{-a}^a f(p(x)) \, dx = 2 \int_0^a f(p(x)) \, dx.$

5.4.55 $p(g(-x)) = p(g(x))$, so $p(g(x))$ is an even function, and $\int_{-a}^a p(g(x)) \, dx = 2 \int_0^a p(g(x)) \, dx$.

5.4.56 $p(q(-x)) = p(-q(x)) = -p(q(x))$, so $p(q(x))$ is an odd function, and $\int_{-a}^a p(q(x)) \, dx = 0$.

5.4.57

a. The average value is $\int_0^1 (ax - ax^2) \, dx = \left(\frac{ax^2}{2} - \frac{ax^3}{3} \right) \Big|_0^1 = \frac{a}{2} - \frac{a}{3} = \frac{a}{6}$.

b. The function is equal to its average value when $\frac{a}{6} = ax - ax^2$ which occurs when $6x - 6x^2 = 1$, so when $6x^2 - 6x + 1 = 0$. On the given interval, this occurs for $x = \frac{6 \pm \sqrt{12}}{12} = \frac{3 \pm \sqrt{3}}{6}$.

5.4.58 The statement is true for constant functions $f(x) = c$. For these functions, the average value over $[a, b]$ is $\frac{1}{b-a} \int_a^b c \, dx = \frac{c(b-a)}{b-a} = c$, so the square of the average value is c^2, while the average value of the square of the function is $\frac{1}{b-a} \int_a^b c^2 \, dx = \frac{c^2(b-a)}{b-a} = c^2$.

If f is not constant, then the statement does not hold. To see this, suppose f is a polynomial satisfying the given conditions. Let

$$P(t) = \frac{1}{t}\int_0^t f(x)^2\,dx, \qquad Q(t) = \left(\frac{1}{t}\int_0^t f(x)\,dx\right)^2 = \frac{1}{t}^2\left(\int_0^t f(x)\,dx\right)^2.$$

Then P is the average value of the square of f on $[0,t]$ and Q is the square of the average value of f on $[0,t]$. Then P and Q are polynomials that are equal for all values of t and must agree term by term. Suppose f has degree d, so that its highest degree term is cx^d. Then

$$P(t) = \frac{1}{t}\int_0^t f(x)^2\,dx = \frac{1}{t}\int_0^t (cx^d + \dots)^2\,dx = \frac{1}{t}\int_0^t (c^2 x^{2d} + \dots)\,dx$$

$$= \frac{1}{t}\left(\frac{c^2}{2d+1}x^{2d+1} + \dots\right)\Big|_0^t = \frac{c^2}{2d+1}t^{2d} + \dots$$

and

$$Q(t) = \frac{1}{t^2}\left(\int_0^t f(x)\right)^2\,dx = \frac{1}{t^2}\left(\int_0^t (cx^d + \dots)\right)^2\,dx = \frac{1}{t^2}\left(\frac{c}{d+1}t^{d+1} + \dots\right)^2$$

$$= \frac{1}{t^2}\left(\frac{c^2}{(d+1)^2}t^{2d+2} + \dots\right) = \frac{c^2}{(d+1)^2}t^{2d} + \dots$$

In order for P and Q to be the same polynomial, it is necessary that their leading coefficients be equal, so we must have $\frac{c^2}{2d+1} = \frac{c^2}{(d+1)^2}$, or $d^2 + 2d + 1 = 2d + 1$, or $d^2 = 0$, so that $d = 0$ and f has degree zero.

5.4.59

a. The area of the triangle is $\frac{1}{2}\cdot 2a\cdot a^2 = a^3$. The area under the parabola is $\displaystyle\int_{-a}^a (a^2 - x^2)\,dx =$

$\left(a^2 x - \dfrac{x^3}{3}\right)\Big|_{-a}^a = a^3 - \dfrac{a^3}{3} - \left(-a^3 + \dfrac{a^3}{3}\right) =$

$2a^3 - \dfrac{2a^3}{3} = \dfrac{4a^3}{3}$, as desired. The diagram shown is for $a = 2$.

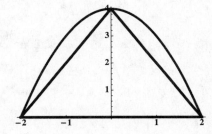

b. The area of the rectangle described is $2a\cdot a^2 = 2a^3$, and $\frac{2}{3}$ of this is $\frac{4a^3}{3}$, which is the area under the parabola derived above.

5.4.60 The area bounded by $c\sin x$ over the stated interval is $\displaystyle\int_0^\pi c\sin x\,dx = (-c\cos x)\Big|_0^\pi = (c - -c) = 2c$. So this is one when $c = \frac{1}{2}$.

5.4.61 $\displaystyle\int_0^c x(x-c)^2\,dx = \int_0^c (x^3 - 2cx^2 + c^2 x)\,dx = \left(\frac{x^4}{4} - 2c\frac{x^3}{3} + \frac{c^2 x^2}{2}\right)\Big|_0^c = \frac{c^4}{4} - \frac{2c^4}{3} + \frac{c^4}{2} = \frac{c^4}{12}$. This is one when $c = \sqrt[4]{12}$.

5.4.62

a. $\displaystyle\int_1^b \frac{1}{x}\,dx = (\ln x)\Big|_1^b = \ln b - 0 = \ln b$. This is equal to one when $b = e$.

b. $\displaystyle\int_1^b x^{-p}\,dx = \left(\frac{x^{1-p}}{1-p}\right)\Big|_1^b = \frac{b^{1-p} - 1}{1-p}$. This is equal to 1 when $b^{1-p} = 2 - p$, which occurs for $b = (2-p)^{1/(1-p)}$. Such a b exists and is bigger than 1 when $1 < p < 2$.

c. $b(p)$ is increasing, because as p gets bigger, the area under $1/x^p$ from 1 to b gets smaller, so b would have to increase in order for the area to remain equal to 1.

5.4.63

a. The left Riemann sum is given by $\dfrac{\pi}{2n} \displaystyle\sum_{k=0}^{n-1} \sin((k\pi)/(2n))$.

b.

$$\lim_{\theta \to 0} \theta \left(\frac{\cos\theta + \sin\theta - 1}{2(1 - \cos\theta)} \right) \left(\frac{1 + \cos\theta}{1 + \cos\theta} \right) = \lim_{\theta \to 0} \frac{\theta}{2} \left(\frac{(1 + \cos\theta)(\cos\theta + \sin\theta - 1)}{\sin^2\theta} \right)$$

$$= \left(\frac{1}{2} \lim_{\theta \to 0} \frac{\theta}{\sin\theta} \cdot \frac{1 + \cos\theta}{1} \right) \left(\lim_{\theta \to 0} \frac{\cos\theta - 1}{\sin\theta} + \lim_{\theta \to 0} \frac{\sin\theta}{\sin\theta} \right)$$

$$= \frac{1}{2} \cdot 1 \cdot 2 \left(\lim_{\theta \to 0} \frac{\frac{\cos - 1}{\theta}}{\frac{\sin\theta}{\theta}} + 1 \right) = 1(0 + 1) = 1.$$

c. Using the previous result, the left Riemann sum is given by $\dfrac{\pi}{2n} \left(\dfrac{\cos(\pi/(2n)) + \sin(\pi/(2n)) - 1}{2(1 - \cos(\pi/(2n)))} \right)$. Let $\theta = \frac{\pi}{2n}$. Then as $n \to \infty$, $\theta \to 0$, and the limit of the left Riemann sum as $n \to \infty$ is 1.

5.4.64

a. $f(0) = \dfrac{\int_a^b x \, dx}{\int_a^b 1 \, dx} = \dfrac{\frac{b^2 - a^2}{2}}{b - a} = \dfrac{a + b}{2}$.

b. $f\left(-\dfrac{3}{2}\right) = \dfrac{\int_a^b x^{-1/2} \, dx}{\int_a^b x^{-3/2} \, dx} = \dfrac{\frac{2}{1}(b^{1/2} - a^{1/2})}{-\frac{2}{1} \cdot (b^{-1/2} - a^{-1/2})} \cdot \dfrac{\sqrt{ab}}{\sqrt{ab}} = \dfrac{b^{1/2} - a^{1/2}}{b^{1/2} - a^{1/2}} \cdot \sqrt{ab} = \sqrt{ab}$.

c. $f(-3) = \dfrac{\int_a^b x^{-2} \, dx}{\int_a^b x^{-3} \, dx} = \dfrac{-(b^{-1} - a^{-1})}{\frac{-1}{2} \cdot (b^{-2} - a^{-2})} \cdot \dfrac{a^2 b^2}{a^2 b^2} = \dfrac{2(a^2 b - b^2 a)}{a^2 - b^2} = \dfrac{2ab(a - b)}{(a - b)(a + b)} = \dfrac{2ab}{a + b}$.

d. $f(-1) = \dfrac{\int_a^b 1 \, dx}{\int_a^b x^{-1} \, dx} = \dfrac{b - a}{\ln b - \ln a}$.

5.4.65 Suppose f is even, so that $f(-x) = f(x)$. Then $f^n(x) = f^n(-x)$, so that f^n is an even function, no matter what the parity of n is.

Suppose g is an odd function, so that $g(-x) = -g(x)$. Then $g^n(-x) = (-1)^n g^n(x)$, so g^n is even when n is even, and is odd when n is odd.

Summarizing, we have:

	f is even	f is odd
n is even	f^n is even	f^n is even
n is odd	f^n is even	f^n is odd

5.4.66 The average value of f' is given by $\dfrac{1}{b - a} \displaystyle\int_a^b f'(x) \, dx = \dfrac{f(b) - f(a)}{b - a}$. This result tells us that for a function with a continuous derivative, the average slope of the tangent line over an interval is the slope of the secant line through the endpoints of the interval.

5.4.67

a. Because of the symmetry, $\displaystyle\int_{c-a}^{c} (f(x) - d) \, dx = \int_c^{c+a} (d - f(x)) \, dx$. Thus, $\displaystyle\int_{c-a}^{c+a} f(x) \, dx = \int_{c-a}^{c} (f(x) -$

$d + d) \, dx + \displaystyle\int_c^{c+a} f(x) \, dx = \int_{c-a}^{c} d \, dx + \int_{c-a}^{c} (f(x) - d) \, dx + \int_c^{c+a} f(x) \, dx = ad + \int_c^{c+a} (d - f(x)) \, dx +$

$\displaystyle\int_c^{c+a} f(x) \, dx = ad + ad + 0 = 2ad.$

b.

The curve is symmetric about $(\pi/4, 1/2)$. To see this, we will show that if $\sin^2(\pi/4 - x) = (1/2) - r$, then $\sin^2(\pi/4 + x) = (1/2) + r$. Using a double angle identity, we have $\sin^2(\pi/4 - x) = \frac{1}{2} - \frac{1}{2}\cos\left(\frac{\pi}{2} - 2x\right) = \frac{1}{2} - \frac{1}{2}\sin 2x$.

On the other hand, $\sin^2(\pi/4 + x) = \frac{1}{2} - \frac{1}{2}\cos\left(\frac{\pi}{2} + 2x\right) = \frac{1}{2} + \frac{1}{2}\sin(2x)$.

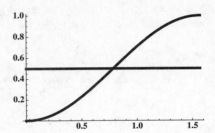

c. Using the idea from part a), the area under f over this interval must be equal to the area of the rectangle over the interval $[0, \pi/2]$ with height $1/2$. Thus the area is $\frac{\pi}{2} \cdot \frac{1}{2} = \frac{\pi}{4}$.

5.4.68

a.

The smallest expression is the area of a rectangle on the x-axis over $[a, b]$ and height given by the value of f at the midpoint of the interval. The biggest expression is the area of a rectangle with that same base, but height equal to the average of the value of the function at the endpoints. The middle quantity represents the area under the curve.

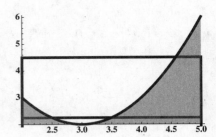

b. After dividing, we have that

$$f\left(\frac{a+b}{2}\right) \le \frac{1}{b-a}\int_a^b f(x)\,dx \le \frac{f(a)+f(b)}{2}.$$

This says that the average value of f over the interval is greater than or equal to the value of f at the average of the endpoints, and is less than or equal to the average of the values of f at the endpoints.

5.4.69

a. Note that h is continuous and differentiable on $[a, b]$, and that $h(a) = (a - b)\int_a^a f(t)\,dt + (a - a)\int_a^b g(t)\,dt = 0 + 0 = 0$. Also, $h(b) = (b - b)\int_a^b f(t)\,dt + (b - a)\int_b^b g(t)\,dt = 0 + 0 = 0$. So by Rolle's theorem, there exists c between a and b so that $h'(c) = 0$. By the Product and Sum Rules, and the Fundamental Theorem of Calculus, we have $h'(x) = \int_a^x f(t)\,dt + (x-b)f(x) + \int_x^b g(t)\,dt - (x-a)g(x)$. So at the promised number c we have $h'(c) = \int_a^c f(t)\,dt + (c-b)f(c) + \int_c^b g(t)\,dt - (c-a)g(c) = 0$, so

$$\int_a^c f(t)\,dt + \int_c^b g(t)\,dt = (b-c)f(c) + (c-a)g(c).$$

b. Given f continuous on $[a, b]$, let g be the constant zero function, that is, $g(x) = 0$ for all x. Applying the result of part (a), we have that there exists a c between a and b with

$$\int_a^c f(t)\,dt + 0 = f(c)(b-c) + 0,$$

so

$$\int_a^c f(t)\,dt = f(c)(b-c),$$

as desired.

c. There exists a rectangle with base from c to b and height $f(c)$ so that the area of the rectangle is equal to the value of the integral of f from a to c.

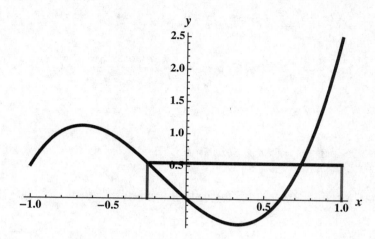

d. Given a function f continuous on $[a, b]$, let $g = f$. Then by part (a) there exists c between a and b so that

$$\int_a^c f(t)\,dt + \int_c^b f(t)\,dt = f(c)(b - c) + f(c)(c - a),$$

so

$$\int_a^b f(t)\,dt = f(c)(b - c + c - a) = f(c)(b - a),$$

so

$$\frac{1}{b-a} \int_a^b f(t)\,dt = f(c).$$

5.5 Substitution Rule

5.5.1 It is based on the Chain Rule for differentiation.

5.5.2 After making a substitution, one obtains an integral in terms of a different variable, so the variable has "changed."

5.5.3 Typically u is substituted for the inner function, so $u = g(x)$.

5.5.4 One can either let $u = \tan x$, which is a good choice because the derivative is then $\sec^2 x$ which is a factor of the integrand, or one can let $u = \sec x$, because then the derivative is $\tan x \sec x$ which is also a factor of the integrand.

5.5.5 The new integral is $\displaystyle\int_{g(a)}^{g(b)} f(u)\,du$.

5.5.6 The new limits of integration are 0 and 12.

5.5.7 Using the identity $\cos^2 x = \frac{1}{2} + \frac{\cos 2x}{2}$, we have $\displaystyle\int \cos^2 x \, dx = \int \left(\frac{1}{2} + \frac{\cos 2x}{2} \right) dx = \frac{x}{2} + \frac{\sin 2x}{4} + C.$

5.5.8 The identity $\sin^2 x = \frac{1}{2} - \frac{\cos 2x}{2}$ could be used.

5.5.9 $\displaystyle\int (x+1)^{12}\,dx = \frac{(x+1)^{13}}{13} + C$, because $\frac{d}{dx}\left(\frac{(x+1)^{13}}{13} + C \right) = (x+1)^{12}.$

5.5.10 $\displaystyle\int e^{3x+1}\,dx = \frac{e^{3x+1}}{3} + C$, because $\displaystyle\frac{d}{dx}\left(\frac{e^{3x+1}}{3} + C\right) = e^{3x+1}$.

5.5.11 $\displaystyle\int \sqrt{2x+1}\,dx = \frac{(2x+1)^{3/2}}{3} + C$, because $\displaystyle\frac{d}{dx}\left(\frac{(2x+1)^{3/2}}{3} + C\right) = \frac{3}{2}\cdot\frac{1}{3}\cdot(2x+1)^{1/2}\cdot 2 = \sqrt{2x+1}$.

5.5.12 $\displaystyle\int \cos(2x+5)\,dx = \frac{\sin(2x+5)}{2} + C$, because $\displaystyle\frac{d}{dx}\left(\frac{\sin(2x+5)}{2} + C\right) = \cos(2x+5)$.

5.5.13 Because $u = x^2 + 1$, $du = 2x\,dx$. Substituting yields $\displaystyle\int u^4\,du = \frac{u^5}{5} + C = \frac{(x^2+1)^5}{5} + C$.

5.5.14 Because $u = 4x^2 + 3$, $du = 8x\,dx$. Substituting yields $\displaystyle\int \cos u\,du = \sin u + C = \sin(4x^2+3) + C$.

5.5.15 Because $u = \sin x$, $du = \cos x\,dx$. Substituting yields $\displaystyle\int u^3\,du = \frac{u^4}{4} + C = \frac{\sin^4(x)}{4} + C$.

5.5.16 Because $u = 3x^2 + x$, $du = 6x + 1\,dx$. Substituting yields $\displaystyle\int \sqrt{u}\,du = \frac{2}{3}\cdot u^{3/2} + C = \frac{2}{3}\cdot\sqrt{(3x^2+x)^3} + C$.

5.5.17 Let $u = x^2 - 1$. Then $du = 2x\,dx$. Substituting yields $\displaystyle\int u^{99}\,du = \frac{u^{100}}{100} + C = \frac{(x^2-1)^{100}}{100} + C$.

5.5.18 Let $u = x^2$. Then $du = 2x\,dx$, so $\frac{1}{2}du = x\,dx$. Substituting yields $\displaystyle\frac{1}{2}\int e^u\,du = \frac{1}{2}\cdot e^u + C = \frac{1}{2}\cdot e^{x^2} + C$.

5.5.19 Let $u = 1 - 4x^3$. Then $du = -12x^2\,dx$, so $\frac{-1}{6}du = 2x^2\,dx$. Substituting yields $\displaystyle\frac{-1}{6}\int \frac{1}{\sqrt{u}}\,du = \frac{-1}{3}\cdot\sqrt{u} + C = \frac{-1}{3}\cdot\sqrt{1-4x^3} + C$.

5.5.20 Let $u = \sqrt{x} + 1$. Then $du = \frac{1}{2\sqrt{x}}\,dx$. Substituting yields $\displaystyle\int u^4\,du = \frac{u^5}{5} + C = \frac{(\sqrt{x}+1)^5}{5} + C$.

5.5.21 Let $u = x^2 + x$. Then $du = 2x + 1\,dx$. Substituting yields $\displaystyle\int u^{10}\,du = \frac{u^{11}}{11} + C = \frac{(x^2+x)^{11}}{11} + C$.

5.5.22 Let $u = 10x - 3$. Then $du = 10\,dx$, so $\frac{1}{10}du = dx$. Substituting yields $\displaystyle\frac{1}{10}\int \frac{1}{u}\,du = \frac{1}{10}\cdot\ln|u| + C = \frac{1}{10}\ln|10x-3| + C$.

5.5.23 Let $u = x^4 + 16$. Then $du = 4x^3\,dx$, so $\frac{1}{4}du = x^3\,dx$. Substituting yields $\displaystyle\frac{1}{4}\int u^6\,du = \frac{1}{4}\cdot\frac{u^7}{7} + C = \frac{(x^4+16)^7}{28} + C$.

5.5.24 Let $u = \sin\theta$. Then $du = \cos\theta\,d\theta$. Substituting yields $\displaystyle\int u^{10}\,du = \frac{u^{11}}{11} + C = \frac{(\sin\theta)^{11}}{11} + C$.

5.5.25 Let $u = 3x$. Then $du = 3\,dx$, so $\frac{1}{3}du = dx$. Substituting yields $\displaystyle\frac{1}{3}\int \frac{1}{\sqrt{1-u^2}}\,du = \frac{1}{3}\sin^{-1}u + C = \frac{1}{3}\sin^{-1}3x + C$.

5.5.26 Let $u = x^{10}$. Then $du = 10x^9\,dx$, so $\frac{1}{10}du = x^9\,dx$. Substituting yields $\displaystyle\frac{1}{10}\int \sin u\,du = \frac{-1}{10}\cos u + C = \frac{-1}{10}\cos x^{10} + C$.

5.5.27 Let $u = x^6 - 3x^2$. Then $du = (6x^5 - 6x)\,dx$, so $\frac{1}{6}du = (x^5 - x)\,dx$. Substituting yields $\frac{1}{6}\int u^4\,du = \frac{1}{6}\cdot\frac{u^5}{5} + C = \frac{(x^6 - 3x^2)^5}{30} + C$.

5.5.28 Let $u = x - 2$, so that $u + 2 = x$. Then $du = dx$. Substituting yields $\int \frac{u+2}{u}\,du = \int\left(1 + \frac{2}{u}\right)du = u + 2\ln|u| + D = x - 2 + 2\ln|x - 2| + D$. The constant $-2 + D$ could be renamed as a different constant C, yielding $x + 2\ln|x - 2| + C$.

5.5.29 Let $u = 2x$, so that $du = 2dx$. Substituting yields $\frac{1}{2}\int\frac{1}{1+u^2}\,du = \frac{1}{2}\tan^{-1}u + C = \frac{1}{2}\tan^{-1}2x + C$.

5.5.30 Let $u = 5y$, so that $du = 5dy$. Substituting yields $\frac{1}{5}\int\frac{1}{1+u^2}\,du = \frac{1}{5}\tan^{-1}u + C = \frac{1}{5}\tan^{-1}5y + C$.

5.5.31 Let $u = 2x$, so that $du = 2dx$. Substituting yields $2\int\frac{1}{u\sqrt{u^2-1}}\,du = 2\sec^{-1}u + C = 2\sec^{-1}2x + C$.

5.5.32 Let $u = 2x^2 + 3x$, so that $du = (4x + 3)\,dx = \frac{1}{2}(8x + 6)\,dx$. Substituting yields $2\int\frac{1}{u}\,du = 2\ln|u| + C = 2\ln|2x^2 + 3x| + C$.

5.5.33 Let $u = x - 4$, so that $u + 4 = x$. Then $du = dx$. Substituting yields $\int\frac{u+4}{\sqrt{u}}\,du = \int\left(\frac{u}{\sqrt{u}} + \frac{4}{\sqrt{u}}\right)du = \int u^{1/2} + 4u^{-1/2}\,du = \frac{2}{3}u^{3/2} + 8u^{1/2} + C = \frac{2}{3}\cdot(x-4)^{3/2} + 8\sqrt{x-4} + C$.

5.5.34 Let $u = y + 1$, so that $u - 1 = y$. Then $du = dy$. Substituting yields $\int\frac{(u-1)^2}{u^4}\,du = \int\frac{u^2 - 2u + 1}{u^4}\,du = \int\left(u^{-2} - 2u^{-3} + u^{-4}\right)du = \frac{-1}{u} + \frac{1}{u^2} - \frac{1}{3u^3} + C = \frac{-1}{y+1} + \frac{1}{(y+1)^2} - \frac{1}{3(y+1)^3} + C$.

5.5.35 Let $u = x + 4$, so that $u - 4 = x$. Then $du = dx$. Substituting yields

$$\int\frac{u-4}{\sqrt[3]{u}}\,du = \int\left(u^{2/3} - 4u^{-1/3}\right)du = \frac{3}{5}u^{5/3} + -6u^{2/3} + C$$
$$= \frac{3}{5}(x+4)^{5/3} - 6(x+4)^{2/3} + C.$$

5.5.36 Let $u = e^x + e^{-x}$. Then $du = (e^x - e^{-x})\,dx$. Substituting yields $\int\frac{1}{u}\,du = \ln|u| + C = \ln(e^x + e^{-x}) + C$.

5.5.37 Let $u = 2x + 1$. Then $du = 2dx$ and $x = \frac{u-1}{2}$. Substituting yields $\frac{1}{2}\int\frac{u-1}{2}\cdot\sqrt[3]{u}\,du = \frac{1}{4}\int(u^{4/3} - u^{1/3})\,du = \frac{1}{4}\left(\frac{3}{7}u^{7/3} - \frac{3}{4}u^{4/3}\right) + C = \frac{3(2x+1)^{7/3}}{28} - \frac{3(2x+1)^{4/3}}{16} + C$.

5.5.38 Let $u = 3z + 2$. Then $du = 3dz$ and $z = \frac{u-2}{3}$. Substituting yields $\frac{1}{3}\int\frac{u+1}{3}\cdot\sqrt{u}\,du = \frac{1}{9}\int(u^{3/2} + u^{1/2})\,du = \frac{1}{9}\left(\frac{2}{5}u^{5/2} + \frac{2}{3}u^{3/2}\right) + C = \frac{2(3z+2)^{5/2}}{45} + \frac{2(3z+2)^{3/2}}{27} + C$.

5.5.39 Let $u = 4 - x^2$. Then $du = -2x\,dx$. Also, when $x = 0$ we have $u = 4$ and when $x = 1$ we have $u = 3$. Substituting yields $-\int_4^3 u\,du = \int_3^4 u\,du = \left(\frac{u^2}{2}\right)\Big|_3^4 = 8 - 4.5 = 3.5$.

5.5.40 Let $u = x^2 + 1$. Then $du = 2x\,dx$. Also, when $x = 0$ we have $u = 1$ and when $x = 2$ we have $u = 5$. Substituting yields $\int_1^5 u^{-2}\,du = \left(\dfrac{-1}{u}\right)\Big|_1^5 = 1 - \dfrac{1}{5} = \dfrac{4}{5}$.

5.5.41 Let $u = \sin\theta$. Then $du = \cos\theta\,d\theta$. Also, when $\theta = 0$ we have $u = 0$ and when $\theta = \pi/2$ we have $u = 1$. Substituting yields $\int_0^1 u^2\,du = \left(\dfrac{u^3}{3}\right)\Big|_0^1 = \dfrac{1}{3}$.

5.5.42 Let $u = \cos x$. Then $du = -\sin x\,dx$. Also, when $x = 0$ we have $u = 1$ and when $x = \pi/4$ we have $u = \sqrt{2}/2$. Substituting yields $-\int_1^{\sqrt{2}/2} \dfrac{1}{u^2}\,du = \int_{\sqrt{2}/2}^1 u^{-2}\,du = \left(\dfrac{-1}{u}\right)\Big|_{\sqrt{2}/2}^1 = \dfrac{2}{\sqrt{2}} - 1 = \sqrt{2} - 1$.

5.5.43 Let $u = x^3 + 1$. Then $du = 3x^2\,dx$. Also, when $x = -1$ we have $u = 0$ and when $x = 2$ we have $u = 9$. Substituting yields $\dfrac{1}{3}\int_0^9 e^u\,du = \left(\dfrac{e^u}{3}\right)\Big|_0^9 = \dfrac{e^9 - 1}{3}$.

5.5.44 Let $u = 9 + p^2$. Then $du = 2p\,dp$. Also, when $p = 0$ we have $u = 9$ and when $p = 4$ we have $u = 25$. Substituting yields $\dfrac{1}{2}\int_9^{25} u^{-1/2}\,du = \sqrt{u}\,\Big|_9^{25} = 5 - 3 = 2$.

5.5.45 Let $u = \sin x$. Then $du = \cos x\,dx$. Also, when $x = \pi/4$ we have $u = \sqrt{2}/2$ and when $x = \pi/2$ we have $u = 1$. Substituting yields $\int_{\sqrt{2}/2}^1 \dfrac{1}{u^2}\,du = \left(\dfrac{-1}{u}\right)\Big|_{\sqrt{2}/2}^1 = \left(-1 - \left(-\dfrac{2}{\sqrt{2}}\right)\right) = \sqrt{2} - 1$.

5.5.46 Let $u = \cos x$. Then $du = -\sin x\,dx$. Also, when $x = 0$ we have $u = 1$ and when $x = \pi/4$ we have $u = \sqrt{2}/2$. Substituting yields $-\int_1^{\sqrt{2}/2} \dfrac{1}{u^3}\,du = \int_{\sqrt{2}/2}^1 u^{-3}\,du = \left(\dfrac{-1}{2u^2}\right)\Big|_{\sqrt{2}/2}^1 = \dfrac{-1}{2} + 1 = \dfrac{1}{2}$.

5.5.47 Let $u = 5x$, so that $du = 5\,dx$. Also, when $x = 2/(5\sqrt{3})$ we have $u = 2/\sqrt{3}$ and when $x = 2/5$ we have $u = 2$. Substituting yields $\int_{2/\sqrt{3}}^2 \dfrac{du}{u\sqrt{u^2-1}} = \sec^{-1} u\,\Big|_{2/\sqrt{3}}^2 = \dfrac{\pi}{3} - \dfrac{\pi}{6} = \dfrac{\pi}{6}$.

5.5.48 Let $u = v^3 + 3v + 4$, so that $du = (3v^2 + 3)\,dv$, so that $\frac{1}{3}\cdot du = (v^2 + 1)\,dv$. Also, when $v = 0$ we have $u = 4$ and when $v = 3$ we have $u = 40$. Substituting yields $\dfrac{1}{3}\int_4^{40} u^{-1/2}\,du = \dfrac{1}{3}\left(2\sqrt{u}\right)\Big|_4^{40} = \dfrac{4\sqrt{10} - 4}{3}$.

5.5.49 Let $u = x^2 + 1$, so that $du = 2x\,dx$. Substituting yields $\dfrac{1}{2}\int_1^{17} \dfrac{1}{u}\,du = \dfrac{1}{2}\ln|u|\,\Big|_1^{17} = \dfrac{\ln 17}{2}$.

5.5.50 Let $u = 1 - 16x^2$, so that $du = -32x\,dx$. Substituting yields $\dfrac{-1}{32}\int_1^0 \dfrac{1}{\sqrt{u}}\,du = \dfrac{1}{16}\sqrt{u}\,\Big|_0^1 = \dfrac{1}{16}$.

5.5.51 Let $u = 3x$, so that $du = 3\,dx$. Substituting yields $\dfrac{4}{3}\int_1^{3/\sqrt{3}} \dfrac{1}{u^2 + 1}\,du = \dfrac{4}{3}\tan^{-1} u\,\Big|_1^{3/\sqrt{3}} = \dfrac{4}{3}\left(\dfrac{\pi}{3} - \dfrac{\pi}{4}\right) = \dfrac{4}{3}\cdot\dfrac{\pi}{12} = \dfrac{\pi}{9}$.

5.5.52 Let $u = 3 + 2e^x$, so that $du = 2e^x\,dx$. Substituting yields $\dfrac{1}{2}\int_5^{11} \dfrac{1}{u}\,du = \dfrac{1}{2}\ln|u|\,\Big|_5^{11} = \dfrac{\ln(11/5)}{2}$.

5.5.53 $\int_{-\pi}^\pi \cos^2 x\,dx = 2\int_0^\pi \dfrac{1 + \cos 2x}{2}\,dx = \left(x + \dfrac{\sin 2x}{2}\right)\Big|_0^\pi = \pi$.

5.5.54 $\displaystyle\int \sin^2 x\, dx = \int \frac{1 - \cos 2x}{2}\, dx = \frac{1}{2}\left(x - \frac{\sin 2x}{2}\right) + C = \frac{x}{2} - \frac{\sin 2x}{4} + C.$

5.5.55 $\displaystyle\int \sin^2\left(\theta + \frac{\pi}{6}\right) d\theta = \frac{1}{2}\int \left(1 - \cos\left(2\theta + \frac{\pi}{3}\right)\right) d\theta = \frac{\theta}{2} - \frac{\sin\left(2\theta + \frac{\pi}{3}\right)}{4} + C.$

5.5.56 $\displaystyle\int_0^{\pi/4} \cos^2 8\theta\, d\theta = \int_0^{\pi/4} \frac{1 + \cos 16\theta}{2}\, d\theta = \left(\frac{\theta}{2} + \frac{\sin 16\theta}{32}\right)\Big|_0^{\pi/4} = \frac{\pi}{8}.$

5.5.57 $\displaystyle\int_{-\pi/4}^{\pi/4} \sin^2 2\theta\, d\theta = 2\int_0^{\pi/4} \sin^2 2\theta\, d\theta = 2\int_0^{\pi/4} \frac{1 - \cos 4\theta}{2}\, d\theta = \left(\theta - \frac{\sin 4\theta}{4}\right)\Big|_0^{\pi/4} = \frac{\pi}{4}.$

5.5.58 Let $u = x^2$, so that $du = 2x\, dx$. Substituting yields

$$\frac{1}{2}\int \cos^2 u\, du = \frac{1}{2}\int \frac{1 + \cos 2u}{2}\, du = \frac{1}{4}\left(u + \frac{\sin 2u}{2}\right) + C$$

$$= \frac{x^2}{4} + \frac{\sin 2x^2}{8} + C.$$

5.5.59 Let $u = \sin^2 y + 2$ so that $du = 2\sin y \cos y\, dy = \sin(2y)\, dy$. Substituting yields $\displaystyle\int_2^{9/4} \frac{1}{u}\, du =$

$(\ln|u|)\Big|_2^{9/4} = \ln(9/4) - \ln 2 = \ln(9/8).$

5.5.60 Because $\sin^4\theta = (\sin^2\theta)^2 = \left(\frac{1 - \cos 2\theta}{2}\right)^2 = \frac{1 - 2\cos 2\theta + \cos^2 2\theta}{4}$, we have

$$\int \sin^4\theta\, d\theta = \int \left(\frac{1 - 2\cos 2\theta + \cos^2 2\theta}{4}\right) d\theta = \frac{1}{4}\theta - \frac{\sin 2\theta}{4} + \frac{1}{4}\int \cos^2 2\theta\, d\theta.$$

Because $\frac{1}{4}\cos^2 2\theta = \frac{1 + \cos 4\theta}{8}$, we have

$$\int \sin^4\theta\, d\theta = \frac{1}{4}\theta - \frac{\sin 2\theta}{4} + \frac{1}{8}\theta + \frac{\sin 4\theta}{32} = \frac{3}{8}\theta - \frac{\sin 2\theta}{4} + \frac{\sin 4\theta}{32}.$$

Thus, $\int_0^{\pi/2} \sin^4\theta\, d\theta = \left(\frac{3}{8}\theta - \frac{\sin 2\theta}{4} + \frac{\sin 4\theta}{32}\right)\Big|_0^{\pi/2} = \frac{3\pi}{16}.$

5.5.61

a. True. This follows by substituting $u = f(x)$ to obtain the integral $\displaystyle\int u\, du = \frac{u^2}{2} + C = \frac{f(x)^2}{2} + C.$

b. True. Again, this follows from substituting $u = f(x)$ to obtain the integral $\displaystyle\int u^n\, du = \frac{u^{n+1}}{n+1} + C = \frac{(f(x))^{n+1}}{n+1} + C$ where $n \neq -1$.

c. False. If this were true, then $\sin 2x$ and $2\sin x$ would have to differ by a constant, which they do not. In fact, $\sin 2x = 2\sin x \cos x$.

d. False. The derivative of the right hand side is $(x^2 + 1)^9 \cdot 2x$ which is not the integrand on the left hand side.

e. False. If we let $u = f'(x)$, then $du = f''(x)\, dx$. Substituting yields $\displaystyle\int_{f'(a)}^{f'(b)} u\, du = \left(\frac{u^2}{2}\right)\Big|_{f'(a)}^{f'(b)} = \frac{(f'(b))^2}{2} - \frac{(f'(a))^2}{2}.$

5.5.62 Let $u = 4w$. Then $du = 4\,dw$. Substituting yields $\dfrac{1}{4}\displaystyle\int \sec u \tan u\,du = \dfrac{1}{4}\sec u + C = \dfrac{1}{4}\sec 4w + C.$

5.5.63 Let $u = 10x$. Then $du = 10\,dw$. Substituting yields $\dfrac{1}{10}\displaystyle\int \sec^2 u\,du = \dfrac{1}{10}\tan u + C = \dfrac{1}{10}\tan 10x + C.$

5.5.64 Let $u = \sin x$. Then $du = \cos x\,dx$. Substituting yields $\displaystyle\int u^5 + 3u^3 - u\,du = \dfrac{u^6}{6} + \dfrac{3u^4}{4} - \dfrac{u^2}{2} + C = $
$\dfrac{\sin^6 x}{6} + \dfrac{3\sin^4 x}{4} - \dfrac{\sin^2 x}{2} + C.$

5.5.65 Let $u = \cot x$. Then $du = -\csc^2 x\,dx$. Substituting yields $-\displaystyle\int u^{-3}\,du = \dfrac{1}{2u^2} + C = \dfrac{1}{2\cot^2 x} + C.$

5.5.66 Let $u = x^{3/2} + 8$. Then $du = \dfrac{3}{2}\cdot\sqrt{x}\,dx$. Substituting gives $\dfrac{2}{3}\displaystyle\int u^5\,du = \dfrac{2}{3}\dfrac{u^6}{6} + C = \dfrac{(x^{3/2}+8)^6}{9} + C.$

5.5.67 Note that $\sin x \sec^8 x = \dfrac{\sin x}{\cos^8 x}$. Let $u = \cos x$, so that $du = -\sin x\,dx$. Substituting yields
$-\displaystyle\int u^{-8}\,du = \dfrac{1}{7u^7} + C = \dfrac{1}{7\cos^7 x} + C = \dfrac{\sec^7 x}{7} + C.$

5.5.68 Let $u = e^{2x} + 1$. Then $du = 2e^{2x}\,dx$. Substituting yields $\dfrac{1}{2}\displaystyle\int \dfrac{1}{u}\,du = \dfrac{\ln|u|}{2} + C = \dfrac{\ln(e^{2x}+1)}{2} + C.$

5.5.69 Let $u = 1 - x^2$. Then $du = -2x\,dx$. Also note that when $x = 0$ we have $u = 1$, and when $x = 1$ we have $u = 0$. Substituting yields $\dfrac{-1}{2}\displaystyle\int_1^0 \sqrt{u}\,du = \dfrac{1}{2}\displaystyle\int_0^1 \sqrt{u}\,du = \left(\dfrac{u^{3/2}}{3}\right)\Big|_0^1 = \dfrac{1}{3}.$

5.5.70 Let $u = \ln p$. Then $du = \dfrac{1}{p}\,dp$. Also note that when $p = 1$ we have $u = 0$, and when $p = e^2$ we have $u = 2$. Substituting yields $\displaystyle\int_0^2 u\,du = \left(\dfrac{u^2}{2}\right)\Big|_0^2 = 2.$

5.5.71 Let $u = x^2 - 1$, so that $du = 2x\,dx$. Also note that when $x = 2$ we have $u = 3$, and when $x = 3$ we have $u = 8$. Substituting yields $\dfrac{1}{2}\displaystyle\int_3^8 u^{-1/3}\,du = \dfrac{1}{2}\left(\dfrac{3u^{2/3}}{2}\right)\Big|_3^8 = \dfrac{3}{4}\left(4 - \sqrt[3]{9}\right).$

5.5.72 Let $u = 5x/6$ so that $du = \dfrac{5}{6}\,dx$. Also note that when $x = 0$ we have $u = 0$ and when $x = 6/5$ we have $u = 1$. Substituting yields $\dfrac{6}{5\cdot 36}\displaystyle\int_0^1 \dfrac{1}{u^2+1}\,du = \dfrac{1}{30}\left(\tan^{-1} u\right)\Big|_0^1 = \dfrac{\pi}{120}.$

5.5.73 Let $u = 16 - x^4$. Then $du = -4x^3\,dx$. Also note that when $x = 0$ we have $u = 16$, and when $x = 2$ we have $u = 0$. Substituting yields $\dfrac{1}{4}\displaystyle\int_0^{16} \sqrt{u}\,du = \dfrac{1}{4}\left(\dfrac{2u^{3/2}}{3}\right)\Big|_0^{16} = \dfrac{32}{3}.$

5.5.74 Let $u = x^2 - 2x$. Then $du = 2(x-1)\,dx$. Also note that when $x = -1$ we have $u = 3$ and when $x = 1$ we have $u = -1$. Substituting yields $\dfrac{1}{2}\displaystyle\int_3^{-1} u^7\,du = \dfrac{1}{16}\left(u^8\right)\Big|_3^{-1} = \dfrac{1}{16}\left(1 - 3^8\right) = \dfrac{-6560}{16} = -410.$

5.5.75 Let $u = 2 + \cos x$ so that $du = -\sin x\,dx$. Note that when $x = -\pi$, $u = 1$ and when $x = 0$, $u = 3$. Substituting yields $\displaystyle\int_1^3 \dfrac{-1}{u}\,du = \left(-\ln|u|\right)\Big|_1^3 = -(\ln 3 - \ln 1) = -\ln 3.$

5.5.76 Let $u = 2v^3 + 9v^2 + 12v + 36$, so that $du = (6v^2 + 18v + 12)\,dv = 6(v+1)(v+2)\,dv$. Note that $u = 36$ when $v = 0$ and $u = 59$ when $v = 1$. Substituting yields $\dfrac{1}{6}\displaystyle\int_{36}^{59} \dfrac{1}{u}\,du = \dfrac{1}{6}\left(\ln|u|\right)\Big|_{36}^{59} = \dfrac{1}{6}(\ln 59 - \ln 36) = \dfrac{1}{6}\ln(59/36).$

5.5.77 Let $u = 3x + 1$ so that $du = 3\,dx$. Note that $9x^2 + 6x + 1 = (3x + 1)^2 = u^2$, and also that when $x = 1$, $u = 4$ and when $x = 2$, $u = 7$. Substituting yields $\dfrac{4}{3}\displaystyle\int_4^7 \dfrac{1}{u^2}\,du = \dfrac{4}{3}\left(\dfrac{-1}{u}\right)\Big|_4^7 = \dfrac{4}{3}\left(\dfrac{-1}{7} - \left(-\dfrac{1}{4}\right)\right) = \dfrac{4}{3}\left(\dfrac{3}{28}\right) = \dfrac{1}{7}$.

5.5.78 Let $u = \sin^2 x$, so that $du = 2\sin x \cos x\,dx = \sin 2x\,dx$. Note that when $x = 0$, $u = 0$, and when $x = \pi/4$, $u = 1/2$. Substituting yields $\displaystyle\int_0^{1/2} e^u\,du = e^u\Big|_0^{1/2} = \sqrt{e} - 1$.

5.5.79 $A(x) = \displaystyle\int_0^{\sqrt{\pi}} x\sin x^2\,dx$. Let $u = x^2$, so that $du = 2x\,dx$. Also, when $x = 0$ we have $u = 0$ and when $x = \sqrt{\pi}$ we have $u = \pi$. Substituting yields $\dfrac{1}{2}\displaystyle\int_0^\pi \sin u\,du = \dfrac{1}{2}\left(-\cos u\right)\Big|_0^\pi = 1$.

5.5.80 $A(x) = \displaystyle\int_0^{\pi/2} \sin x \cos x\,dx$. Let $u = \sin x$, so that $du = \cos x\,dx$. Also, when $x = 0$ we have $u = 0$ and when $x = \pi/2$ we have $u = 1$. Substituting yields $\displaystyle\int_0^1 u\,du = \left(\dfrac{u^2}{2}\right)\Big|_0^1 = \dfrac{1}{2}$.

5.5.81 $A(x) = \displaystyle\int_2^6 (x - 4)^4\,dx = \dfrac{(x - 4)^5}{5}\Big|_2^6 = \dfrac{2^5}{5} - \left(-\dfrac{(2)^5}{5}\right) = \dfrac{64}{5}$.

5.5.82 $A(x) = \displaystyle\int_4^5 \dfrac{x}{\sqrt{x^2 - 9}}\,dx$. Let $u = x^2 - 9$, so that $du = 2x\,dx$. Also, when $x = 4$ we have $u = 7$ and when $x = 5$ we have $u = 16$. Substituting yields $\dfrac{1}{2}\displaystyle\int_7^{16} u^{-1/2}\,du = \sqrt{u}\,\Big|_7^{16} = 4 - \sqrt{7}$.

5.5.83 $A(a) = \displaystyle\int_0^a \left(\dfrac{1}{a} - \dfrac{x^2}{a^3}\right) dx = \left(\dfrac{x}{a} - \dfrac{x^3}{3a^3}\right)\Big|_0^a = 1 - \dfrac{1}{3} = \dfrac{2}{3}$. This is a constant function.

5.5.84

a. Let $u = x^2$, so that $du = 2x\,dx$. Note that when $x = 1$ or $x = -1$, we have $u = 1$. Substituting gives $\dfrac{1}{2}\displaystyle\int_1^1 f(u)\,du = 0$. Alternatively, we could note that when f is even, $xf(x^2)$ is odd, so $\displaystyle\int_{-1}^1 xf(x^2)\,dx = 0$.

b. Let $u = x^3$ so that $du = 3x^2\,dx$. Note that when $x = -2$, $u = -8$, and when $x = 2$, $u = 8$. Substituting yields $\dfrac{1}{3}\displaystyle\int_{-8}^8 f(u)\,du = \dfrac{2}{3}\displaystyle\int_0^8 f(u)\,du = \dfrac{2}{3}\cdot 9 = 6$.

5.5.85

a. Let $u = \sin px$, so that $du = p \cos px \, dx$. Note that when $x = 0$, $u = 0$, and when $x = \pi/2p$, $u = 1$.
Substituting yields $\dfrac{1}{p} \displaystyle\int_0^1 f(u) \, du = \dfrac{\pi}{p}$.

b. Let $u = \sin x$ so that $du = \cos x \, dx$. Note that when $x = -\pi/2$, $u = -1$ and when $x = \pi/2$, $u = 1$.
Substituting yields $\displaystyle\int_{-1}^1 f(u) \, du = 0$, because f is an odd function. Alternatively, we could note that
when f is odd, $\cos x \cdot f(\sin x)$ is also odd, because $\sin x$ is odd and $\cos x$ is even. Thus the given integral
must be zero because it is the definite integral of an odd function over a symmetric interval about 0.

5.5.86

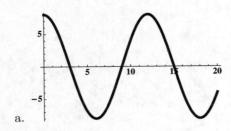

a.

b. $\displaystyle\int_0^t 8 \cos(\pi y/6) \, dy = \left(\dfrac{48}{\pi} \sin(\pi y/6) \right) \Big|_0^t = \dfrac{48}{\pi} \sin(\pi t/6)$.

c. The period is $\dfrac{2\pi}{\pi/6} = 12$.

5.5.87

a. $\displaystyle\int_0^4 \dfrac{200}{(t+1)^2} \, dt = \left(\dfrac{-200}{t+1} \right) \Big|_0^4 = -40 + 200 = 160$.

b. $\displaystyle\int_0^6 \dfrac{200}{(t+1)^3} \, dt = \left(\dfrac{-200}{2(t+1)^2} \right) \Big|_0^6 = \dfrac{-100}{49} + 100 = \dfrac{4800}{49}$.

c. $\Delta P = \displaystyle\int_0^T \dfrac{200}{(t+1)^r} \, dt$. This decreases as r increases, because $\dfrac{200}{(t+1)^r} > \dfrac{200}{(t+1)^{r+1}}$.

d. Suppose $\displaystyle\int_0^{10} \dfrac{200}{(t+1)^r} \, dt = 350$. Then $\left(\dfrac{200(t+1)^{-r+1}}{1-r} \right) \Big|_0^{10} = 350$, so $11^{1-r} - 1 = \dfrac{350(1-r)}{200}$, and thus
$\dfrac{11}{11^r} = \dfrac{7-7r}{4} + \dfrac{4}{4} = \dfrac{11-7r}{4}$, and $11^r = \dfrac{44}{11-7r}$. Using trial and error to find r, we arrive at $r \approx 1.278$.

e. $\displaystyle\int_0^T \dfrac{200}{(t+1)^3} \, dt = \left(\dfrac{-200}{2(t+1)^2} \right) \Big|_0^T = \dfrac{-100}{(T+1)^2} + 100$. As $T \to \infty$, this expression $\to 100$, so in the long
run, the bacteria approaches a finite limit.

5.5.88 The average vertical distance is given by

$$\frac{1}{a} \int_0^a \left(b - \frac{b}{a}x \right) dx = \frac{1}{a} \left(bx - \frac{b}{2a}x^2 \right) \Big|_0^a = \frac{1}{a} \left(ba - \frac{ba^2}{2a} \right) = b - \frac{b}{2} = \frac{b}{2}.$$

5.5.89 $\dfrac{1}{\pi/k - 0} \displaystyle\int_0^{\pi/k} \sin kx \, dx = \dfrac{k}{\pi} \cdot \left(\dfrac{-\cos kx}{k} \right) \Big|_0^{\pi/k} = \dfrac{1}{\pi}(1 - (-1)) = \dfrac{2}{\pi}$.

5.5.90

a. Let $u = \cos x$, so that $du = -\sin x \, dx$. Substituting yields $-\displaystyle\int \dfrac{1}{u} \, du = -\ln|u| + C = -\ln|\cos x| + C$.

b. Let $u = \sin x$ so that $du = \cos x \, dx$. Substituting yields $\displaystyle\int \dfrac{1}{u} \, du = \ln|u| + C = \ln|\sin x| + C$.

5.5.91

a. $\int \sec x \cdot \dfrac{\sec x + \tan x}{\sec x + \tan x} \, dx = \int \dfrac{\sec^2 x + \sec x \tan x}{\sec x + \tan x} \, dx$. Let $u = \sec x + \tan x$ and note that $du = (\sec^2 x + \sec x \tan x) \, dx$. Substituting yields $\int \dfrac{1}{u} \, du = \ln |u| + C = \ln |\sec x + \tan x| + C$.

b. $\int \csc x \cdot \dfrac{\csc x + \cot x}{\csc x + \cot x} \, dx = \int \dfrac{\csc^2 x + \csc x \cot x}{\csc x + \cot x} \, dx$. Let $u = \csc x + \cot x$ and note that $du = -(\csc^2 x + \csc x \cot x) \, dx$. Substituting yields $-\int \dfrac{1}{u} \, du = -\ln |u| + C = -\ln |\csc x + \cot x| + C$.

5.5.92 The area on the left is given by $\displaystyle\int_0^{\pi/2} 2 \sin 2x \, dx$. If we let $u = 2x$ so that $du = 2 \, dx$, we obtain the equivalent integral $\displaystyle\int_0^{\pi} \sin u \, du$ which represents the area on the right.

5.5.93 The area on the left is given by $\displaystyle\int_4^9 \dfrac{(\sqrt{x} - 1)^2}{2\sqrt{x}} \, dx$. If we let $u = \sqrt{x} - 1$ so that $du = \dfrac{1}{2\sqrt{x}} \, dx$, we obtain the equivalent integral $\displaystyle\int_1^2 u^2 \, du$ which represents the area on the right.

5.5.94 Let $u = f(x)$, so that $du = f'(x) \, dx$. Substituting yields $\int (5u^3 + 7u^2 + u) \, du = \dfrac{5u^4}{4} + \dfrac{7u^3}{3} + \dfrac{u^2}{2} + C = \dfrac{5f^4(x)}{4} + \dfrac{7f^3(x)}{3} + \dfrac{f^2(x)}{2} + C$.

5.5.95 Let $u = f(x)$, so that $du = f'(x) \, dx$. Substituting yields

$$\int_4^5 (5u^3 + 7u^2 + u) \, du = \left(\dfrac{5u^4}{4} + \dfrac{7u^3}{3} + \dfrac{u^2}{2} \right) \Bigg|_4^5 = \dfrac{7297}{12}.$$

5.5.96 Let $u = f'(x)$ so that $du = f''(x) \, dx$. Substituting yields $\displaystyle\int_3^2 u \, du = \left(\dfrac{u^2}{2} \right) \Bigg|_3^2 = 2 - \dfrac{9}{2} = -2.5$.

5.5.97 Let $u = f^{(p)}(x)$ so that $du = f^{(p+1)}(x) \, dx$. Substituting yields

$$\int u^n \, du = \dfrac{u^{n+1}}{n+1} + C = \dfrac{1}{n+1} \left(f^{(p)}(x) \right)^{n+1} + C.$$

5.5.98 Let $u = f(x)$ so that $du = f'(x) \, dx$. Substituting yields $2 \int (u^3 + 2u^2) \, du = 2 \left(\dfrac{u^4}{4} + \dfrac{2u^3}{3} \right) + C = \dfrac{f^4(x)}{2} + \dfrac{4f^3(x)}{3} + C$.

5.5.99 If we let $u = \sqrt{x + a}$, then $u^2 = x + a$ and $2u \, du = dx$. Substituting yields $\displaystyle\int_{\sqrt{a}}^{\sqrt{1+a}} (u^2 - a) \cdot u \cdot 2u \, du = \int_{\sqrt{a}}^{\sqrt{1+a}} (2u^4 - 2au^2) \, du = \left(\dfrac{2u^5}{5} - \dfrac{2au^3}{3} \right) \Bigg|_{\sqrt{a}}^{\sqrt{1+a}} = \dfrac{2(\sqrt{1+a})^5}{5} - \dfrac{2a(\sqrt{1+a})^3}{3} - \dfrac{2a^{5/2}}{5} + \dfrac{2a^{5/2}}{3}$.

If we let $u = x + a$, then $u - a = x$ and $du = dx$. Substituting yields $\displaystyle\int_a^{a+1} (u - a)\sqrt{u} \, du = \left(\dfrac{2u^{5/2}}{5} - \dfrac{2au^{3/2}}{3} \right) \Bigg|_a^{a+1} = \dfrac{2(a+1)^{5/2}}{5} - \dfrac{2a(a+1)^{3/2}}{3} - \dfrac{2a^{5/2}}{5} + \dfrac{2a^{5/2}}{3}$.

Note that the two results are the same.

5.5.100 If we let $u = \sqrt[p]{x + a}$, then $u^p = x + a$ and $pu^{p-1}\,du = dx$. Substituting yields

$$p \int_{\sqrt[p]{a}}^{\sqrt[p]{1+a}} (u^{2p} - au^p)\,du = \left(\frac{pu^{2p+1}}{2p+1} - \frac{pau^{p+1}}{p+1} \right) \Bigg|_{\sqrt[p]{a}}^{\sqrt[p]{1+a}}$$

$$= \frac{p(1+a)^2 \sqrt[p]{1+a}}{2p+1} - \frac{ap(1+a)\sqrt[p]{1+a}}{p+1} - \frac{pa^2 \sqrt[p]{a}}{2p+1} + \frac{a^2 p \sqrt[p]{a}}{p+1}.$$

If we let $u = x + a$, then $u - a = x$ and $du = dx$. Substituting yields

$$\int_a^{a+1} (u-a)\sqrt[p]{u}\,du = \int_a^{a+1} \left(u^{(p+1)/p} - au^{1/p} \right) du = \left(\frac{u^{(2p+1)/p}}{(2p+1)/p} - \frac{au^{(p+1)/p}}{(p+1)/p} \right) \Bigg|_a^{a+1}$$

$$= \left(\frac{pu^2 u^{1/p}}{2p+1} - \frac{pau \cdot u^{1/p}}{p+1} \right) \Bigg|_a^{a+1}$$

$$= \frac{p(1+a)^2 \sqrt[p]{1+a}}{2p+1} - \frac{ap(1+a)\sqrt[p]{1+a}}{p+1} - \frac{pa^2 \sqrt[p]{a}}{2p+1} + \frac{a^2 p \sqrt[p]{a}}{p+1}.$$

Note that the two results are the same.

5.5.101 If we let $u = \cos\theta$, then $du = -\sin\theta\,d\theta$. Substituting yields $\int -u^{-4}\,du = \frac{1}{3u^3} + C = \frac{1}{3\cos^3\theta} + C = \frac{\sec^3\theta}{3} + C$.

If we let $u = \sec\theta$, then $du = \sec\theta\tan\theta\,d\theta$. Substituting yields $\int u^2\,du = \frac{u^3}{3} + C = \frac{\sec^3\theta}{3} + C$. Note that the two results are the same.

5.5.102 Let $u = ax$, so that $\frac{1}{a}du = dx$. Substituting yields $\frac{1}{a}\int \sin^2 u\,du = \frac{1}{a}\int \frac{1-\cos 2u}{2}\,du = \frac{1}{2a}\int (1 - \cos 2u)\,du = \frac{1}{2a}\left(u - \frac{\sin 2u}{2} \right) + C = \frac{x}{2} - \frac{\sin 2ax}{4a} + C$.

For the second integral, we use the same substitution to obtain $\frac{1}{a}\int \cos^2 u\,du = \frac{1}{a}\int \frac{1+\cos 2u}{2}\,du = \frac{1}{2a}\int (1 + \cos 2u)\,du = \frac{1}{2a}\left(u + \frac{\sin 2u}{2} \right) + C = \frac{x}{2} + \frac{\sin 2ax}{4a} + C$.

5.5.103

a. Because $\sin 2x = 2\sin x\cos x$, we can write $(\sin x\cos x)^2 = \left(\frac{\sin 2x}{2}\right)^2 = \frac{\sin^2 2x}{4}$. Then we have $I = \frac{1}{4}\int \sin^2 2x\,dx = \frac{1}{4}\left(\frac{x}{2} - \frac{\sin 4x}{8} \right) + C = \frac{x}{8} - \frac{\sin 4x}{32} + C$. Note that we used the result of the previous problem during this derivation.

b. $I = \frac{1}{4}\int (1 - \cos 2x)(1 + \cos 2x)\,dx = \frac{1}{4}\int (1 - \cos^2 2x)\,dx = \frac{1}{4}\int \sin^2 2x\,dx = \frac{1}{4}\left(\frac{x}{2} - \frac{\sin 4x}{8} \right) + C = \frac{x}{8} - \frac{\sin 4x}{32} + C$.

c. The results are consistent. The work involved is similar in each method.

5.5.104

a. Let $u = x + c$. Note that $du = dx$. Substitution yields $\int_a^b f(x+c)\,dx = \int_{a+c}^{b+c} f(u)\,du$.

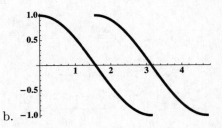

b.

5.5.105

a. Let $u = cx$. Note that $du = c \cdot dx$. Substitution yields $\displaystyle\int_a^b f(cx)\,dx = \frac{1}{c}\int_{ac}^{bc} f(u)\,du$.

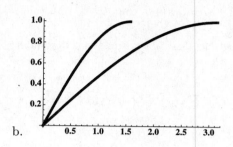

b.

5.5.106 First let $u = x^2$, so that $du = 2x\,dx$. Substituting yields $\displaystyle\frac{1}{2}\int \sin^4 u \cos u\,du$. Now let $v = \sin u$, so that $dv = \cos u\,du$. This substitution yields $\displaystyle\frac{1}{2}\int v^4\,dv = \frac{1}{2}\cdot\frac{v^5}{5} + C = \frac{\sin^5 u}{10} + C = \frac{\sin^5 x^2}{10} + C$.

5.5.107 Let $u = \sqrt{x+1}$ so that $u^2 = x+1$. Then $2u\,du = dx$. Substituting yields $\displaystyle\int 2\cdot\frac{u\,du}{\sqrt{1+u}}$. Now let $v = \sqrt{1+u}$ so that $v^2 = 1+u$ and $2v\,dv = du$. Now a substitution yields $\displaystyle 4\int\frac{(v^2-1)v}{v}\,dv = 4\int(v^2-1)\,dv = \frac{4v^3}{3} - 4v + C = \frac{4}{3}(1+u)^{3/2} - 4\sqrt{1+u} + C = \frac{4}{3}\left(1+\sqrt{x+1}\right)^{3/2} - 4\sqrt{1+\sqrt{x+1}} + C$.

5.5.108 Let $u = 1 - \sqrt{x}$. Then $x = (1-u)^2$ and $dx = 2(1-u)(-du) = 2(u-1)\cdot du$. Then we have

$$\int_0^1 x\sqrt{1-\sqrt{x}}\,dx = \int_1^0 (1-u)^2\sqrt{u}\cdot(-2)(1-u)\,du$$
$$= 2\int_0^1 (1-u)^3\sqrt{u}\,du = 2\int_0^1\left(1-3u+3u^2-u^3\right)\sqrt{u}\,du$$
$$= 2\int_0^1 (u^{1/2} - 3u^{3/2} + 3u^{5/2} - u^{7/2})\,du$$
$$= 2\left(\frac{2u^{3/2}}{3} - \frac{6u^{5/2}}{5} + \frac{6u^{7/2}}{7} - \frac{2u^{9/2}}{9}\right)\bigg|_0^1$$
$$= 2\left(\frac{2}{3} - \frac{6}{5} + \frac{6}{7} - \frac{2}{9}\right) = \frac{64}{315}.$$

5.5.109 Let $u = 1 - \sqrt{x}$. Then $x = (1-u)^2$ and $dx = 2(1-u)(-du) = -2(1-u)\cdot du$. Then we have

$$\int_0^1 \sqrt{x - x\sqrt{x}}\,dx = \int_1^0 (1-u)\sqrt{u}\cdot(-2)(1-u)\,du$$
$$= 2\int_0^1 (1-u)^2\sqrt{u}\,du = 2\int_0^1\left(1-2u+u^2\right)\sqrt{u}\,du$$
$$= 2\int_0^1 (u^{1/2} - 2u^{3/2} + u^{5/2})\,du$$
$$= 2\left(\frac{2u^{3/2}}{3} - \frac{4u^{5/2}}{5} + \frac{2u^{7/2}}{7}\right)\bigg|_0^1$$
$$= 2\left(\frac{2}{3} - \frac{4}{5} + \frac{2}{7}\right) = \frac{32}{105}.$$

5.5.110 Let $u = 4x$, so that $du = 4\,dx$. Substituting yields $\displaystyle\frac{1}{4}\int \tan^{10} u \sec^2 u\,du$. Now let $v = \tan u$, so that $dv = \sec^2 u\,du$. This leads to $\displaystyle\frac{1}{4}\int v^{10}\,dv = \frac{v^{11}}{44} + C = \frac{\tan^{11} 4x}{44} + C$.

5.5.111 Let $u = \cos\theta$, so that $du = -\sin\theta\,d\theta$. This substitution yields $\displaystyle\int_0^1 \frac{u}{\sqrt{u^2 + 16}}\,du$. Now let $v = u^2 + 16$,

so that $dv = 2u\,du$. Now a substitution yields $\displaystyle\frac{1}{2}\int_{16}^{17} v^{-1/2}\,dv = \sqrt{v}\,\Big|_{16}^{17} = \sqrt{17} - 4$.

Chapter Five Review

1

    a. True. The antiderivative of a linear function is a quadratic function.

    b. False. $A'(x) = f(x)$, not $F(x)$.

    c. True, Note that f is an antiderivative of f', so this follows from the Fundamental Theorem.

    d. True. Because $|f(x)| \geq 0$ for all x, this integral must be positive, unless f is constantly 0.

    e. False. For example, the average value of $\sin x$ on $[0, 2\pi]$ is zero.

    f. True. This is equal to $2\int_a^b f(x)\,dx - 3\int_a^b g(x)\,dx = 2\int_a^b f(x)\,dx + 3\int_b^a g(x)\,dx$.

    g. True. The derivative of the right hand side is $f'(g(x))g'(x)$ by the Chain Rule.

2

    a. The distance traveled is given by $\displaystyle\int_0^4 (2t + 5)\,dt = \left(t^2 + 5t\right)\Big|_0^4 = 36$.

    b. The average value is $\displaystyle\frac{1}{4}\int_0^4 (2t + 5)\,dt = \frac{1}{4}\cdot 36 = 9$.

    c. True. If it traveled at a rate of 9 for a time of 4, it would have gone 36 units.

3

    a. This region can be divided up into a 4×2 rectangle and a right triangle with base and height equal to 1. Thus, the integral is equal to $8 + \frac{1}{2} = 8.5$.

    b. $\displaystyle\int_6^4 f(x)\,dx = -\int_4^6 f(x)\,dx$. The region whose area is $\displaystyle\int_4^6 f(x)\,dx$ consists of a 1×3 rectangle, together with a right triangle with base 1 and height 3, so $\displaystyle\int_4^6 f(x)\,dx = 3 + \frac{3}{2} = 4.5$, and $\displaystyle\int_6^4 f(x)\,dx = -4.5$.

    c. $\displaystyle\int_5^7 f(x)\,dx = \int_5^6 f(x)\,dx + \int_6^7 f(x)\,dx$. The region lying over $[5, 6]$ is a right triangle with height 3 and base 1, so its area is $\frac{3}{2}$. The region lying under $[6, 7]$ has the same area, but is below the x-axis, so $\displaystyle\int_6^7 f(x)\,dx = \frac{-3}{2}$. So $\displaystyle\int_5^7 f(x)\,dx = \frac{3}{2} + \frac{-3}{2} = 0$.

    d. Note that $\displaystyle\int_4^5 f(x)\,dx = 3$, because the area represented is that of a 1×3 rectangle. Now by the work above, $\displaystyle\int_0^7 f(x)\,dx = \int_0^4 f(x)\,dx + \int_4^5 f(x)\,dx + \int_5^7 f(x)\,dx = 8.5 + 3 + 0 = 11.5$.

4

    i. We are seeking $\displaystyle\int_0^5 g(t)\,dt$. Because this represents the area of a region which can be divided into a 5×1 rectangle and a right triangle with base 2 and height 2, its value is $5 + 2 = 7$.

ii. We are seeking $\int_3^7 g(t)\,dt$. Because this represents the area of a region which can be divided into a 4×1 rectangle and a right triangle with base 4 and height 2, its value is $4 + 4 = 8$.

iii. We are seeking $\int_0^8 g(t)\,dt = \int_0^3 g(t)\,dt + \int_3^7 g(t)\,dt + \int_7^8 g(t)\,dt = 3 + 8 + 1 = 12$. The first term in this sum is represented by a 1×3 rectangle, the second term is from part ii), and the third is represented by a 1×1 square.

5 $\int_0^4 \sqrt{8x - x^2}\,dx = \int_0^4 \sqrt{16 - (x^2 - 8x + 16)}\,dx = \int_0^4 \sqrt{16 - (x - 4)^2}\,dx$. This represents one quarter of the area inside the circle centered at $(4, 0)$ with radius 4, so its value is $\dfrac{1}{4} \cdot 16\pi = 4\pi$.

6 Using the right Riemann sum, we obtain $(.25)60 + (.25)75 + (.25)60 + (.25)(50) + (.25)40 + (.25)(30) = (.25)(315) = 78.75$. Using the left Riemann sum, we obtain $(.25)(45) + (.25)60 + (.25)75 + (.25)60 + (.25)(50) + (.25)(40) = (.25)(330) = 82.5$.

7

a. The right Riemann sum is $4 \cdot 1 + 7 \cdot 1 + 10 \cdot 1 = 21$.

b. The right Riemann sum is $\displaystyle\sum_{k=1}^{n} \left(3\left(1 + \frac{3k}{n}\right) - 2 \right) \cdot \frac{3}{n}$.

c. The sum evaluates as $\displaystyle\sum_{k=1}^{n} \frac{3}{n} + \sum_{k=1}^{n} \frac{27k}{n^2} = 3 + \frac{27}{n^2} \cdot \frac{n(n+1)}{2}$. As $n \to \infty$, the limit of this expression is $3 + 13.5 = 16.5$.

d.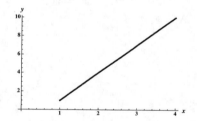

The area consists of a trapezoid with base 3 and heights 1 and 10, so the value is $(3)\left(\frac{1+10}{2}\right) = \frac{33}{2} = 16.5$. The Fundamental Theorem assures us that $\int_1^4 (3x - 2)\,dx = \left(\frac{3x^2}{2} - 2x\right)\Big|_1^4 = (24 - 8) - (3/2 - 2) = 16 + 1/2 = 16.5$.

8 Let $\Delta x = \frac{1-0}{n} = \frac{1}{n}$. Let $x_k = 0 + k\Delta x = \frac{k}{n}$. Then $f(x_k) = \frac{4k}{n} - 2$. Thus,

$$\lim_{n \to \infty} \sum_{k=1}^{n} f(x_k)\Delta x = \lim_{n \to \infty} \sum_{k=1}^{n} \left(\frac{4k}{n} - 2\right) \cdot \frac{1}{n} = \lim_{n \to \infty} \left(\frac{4}{n^2} \sum_{k=1}^{n} k - \frac{2}{n} \sum_{k=1}^{n} 1\right) =$$

$$\lim_{n \to \infty} \left(\frac{4}{n^2}\left(\frac{n^2 + n}{2}\right) - 2\right) = 2 - 2 = 0.$$

9 Let $\Delta x = \frac{2-0}{n} = \frac{2}{n}$. Let $x_k = 0 + k\Delta x = \frac{2k}{n}$. Then $f(x_k) = \frac{4k^2}{n^2} - 4$. Thus,

$$\lim_{n \to \infty} \sum_{k=1}^{n} f(x_k)\Delta x = \lim_{n \to \infty} \sum_{k=1}^{n} \left(\frac{4k^2}{n^2} - 4\right) \cdot \frac{2}{n} = \lim_{n \to \infty} \left(\frac{8}{n^3} \sum_{k=1}^{n} k^2 - \frac{8}{n} \sum_{k=1}^{n} 1\right) =$$

$$\lim_{n \to \infty} \left(\frac{8}{n^3} \cdot \frac{n(n+1)(2n+1)}{6} - 8\right) = \frac{8}{3} - 8 = \frac{-16}{3}.$$

10 Let $\Delta x = \frac{2-1}{n} = \frac{1}{n}$. Let $x_k = 1 + k\Delta x = 1 + \frac{k}{n} = \frac{n+k}{n}$. Then $f(x_k) = 3\frac{(n+k)^2}{n^2} + \frac{n+k}{n}$. Thus,

$$\lim_{n\to\infty} \sum_{k=1}^{n} f(x_k)\Delta x = \lim_{n\to\infty} \sum_{k=1}^{n} \left(3\left(\frac{(n+k)^2}{n^2}\right) + \frac{n+k}{n}\right) \cdot \frac{1}{n} = \lim_{n\to\infty} \sum_{k=1}^{n} \left(\frac{3}{n} + \frac{6k}{n^2} + \frac{3k^2}{n^3} + \frac{1}{n} + \frac{k}{n^2}\right) =$$

$$\lim_{n\to\infty} \left(\frac{4}{n} \sum_{k=1}^{n} 1 + \frac{7}{n^2} \sum_{k=1}^{n} k + \frac{3}{n^3} \sum_{k=1}^{n} k^2\right) = \lim_{n\to\infty} \left(4 + \frac{7}{2} \cdot \frac{n^2+n}{n^2} + \frac{3}{6} \cdot \frac{n(n+1)(2n+1)}{n^3}\right) = 4 + \frac{7}{2} + 1 = 8.5$$

11 Let $\Delta x = \frac{4-0}{n} = \frac{4}{n}$. Let $x_k = 0 + k\Delta x = 0 + \frac{4k}{n}$. Then $f(x_k) = \frac{64k^3}{n^3} - \frac{4k}{n}$. Thus,

$$\lim_{n\to\infty} \sum_{k=1}^{n} f(x_k)\Delta x = \lim_{n\to\infty} \sum_{k=1}^{n} \left(\frac{64k^3}{n^3} - \frac{4k}{n}\right) \cdot \frac{4}{n} = \lim_{n\to\infty} \left(\frac{256}{n^4} \sum_{k=1}^{n} k^3 - \frac{16}{n^2} \sum_{k=1}^{n} k\right) =$$

$$\lim_{n\to\infty} \left(\frac{256}{n^4} \cdot \frac{n^2(n+1)^2}{4} - \frac{16}{n^2} \cdot \frac{n(n+1)}{2}\right) = 64 - 8 = 56.$$

12 The midpoint Riemann sum is $(3 \cdot 3.5 + 4) + (3 \cdot 4.5 + 4) + (3 \cdot 5.5 + 4) + (3 \cdot 6.5 + 4) = 3 \cdot 20 + 16 = 76$. The exact area of the region is given by $\int_3^7 (3x+4)\,dx = \left(\frac{3x^2}{2} + 4x\right)\bigg|_3^7 = \frac{147}{2} + 28 - \left(\frac{27}{2} + 12\right) = 60 + 16 = 76$.

13 This sum is equal to $\int_0^4 (x^5 + 1)\,dx = \left(\frac{x^6}{6} + x\right)\bigg|_0^4 = \frac{4^6}{6} + 4 = \frac{2060}{3}$.

14 The area represented is a triangle with base $x - 2$ and height $2x - 4$, so its area is $\frac{(x-2)(2x-4)}{2} = x^2 - 4x + 4$. If we call this quantity $A(x)$, then $A'(x) = 2x - 4$, as desired.

15 $\int_{-2}^{2} (3x^4 - 2x + 1)\,dx = \left(\frac{3x^5}{5} - x^2 + x\right)\bigg|_{-2}^{2} = \frac{96}{5} - 4 + 2 - \left(-\frac{96}{5} - 4 - 2\right) = \frac{192}{5} + 4 = \frac{212}{5}$.

16 $\int \cos(3x)\,dx = \frac{\sin 3x}{3} + C$.

17 $\int_0^2 (x+1)^3\,dx = \left(\frac{(x+1)^4}{4}\right)\bigg|_0^2 = \frac{81}{4} - \frac{1}{4} = 20$.

18 $\int_0^1 (4x^{21} - 2x^{16} + 1)\,dx = \left(\frac{4x^{22}}{22} - \frac{2x^{17}}{17} + x\right)\bigg|_0^1 = \frac{2}{11} - \frac{2}{17} + 1 = \frac{199}{187}$.

19 $\int (9x^8 - 7x^6)\,dx = x^9 - x^7 + C$.

20 $\int_{-2}^{2} e^{4x+8}\,dx = \left(\frac{1}{4} \cdot e^{4x+8}\right)\bigg|_{-2}^{2} = \frac{1}{4}\left(e^{16} - 1\right)$.

21 $\int_0^1 (x + \sqrt{x})\,dx = \left(\frac{x^2}{2} + \frac{2x^{3/2}}{3}\right)\bigg|_0^1 = \frac{1}{2} + \frac{2}{3} = \frac{7}{6}$.

22 Let $u = y^3 + 27$, and note that $du = 3y^2\,dy$. Substituting yields $\frac{1}{3} \int \frac{1}{u}\,du = \frac{1}{3}\ln|u| + C = \frac{\ln|y^3 + 27|}{3} + C$.

23 $\frac{1}{2} \int_0^1 \frac{dx}{\sqrt{1 - (x/2)^2}} = \sin^{-1}\left(\frac{x}{2}\right)\bigg|_0^1 = \frac{\pi}{6}$.

24 Let $u = 3y^3 + 1$, and note that $du = 9y^2\,dy$. Substituting yields $\dfrac{1}{9}\displaystyle\int u^4\,du = \dfrac{u^5}{45} + C = \dfrac{(3y^3 + 1)^5}{45} + C$.

25 Let $u = 25 - x^2$, and note that $du = -2x\,dx$. Substituting yields $\dfrac{-1}{2}\displaystyle\int_{25}^{16} u^{-1/2}\,du = -\sqrt{u}\,\Big|_{25}^{16} = 5 - 4 = 1$.

26 Let $u = \cos x^2$ and note that $du = -\sin x^2 \cdot 2x\,dx$. Substituting yields $\dfrac{-1}{2}\displaystyle\int u^8\,du = \dfrac{-u^9}{18} + C = \dfrac{-\cos^9 x^2}{18} + C$.

27 $\displaystyle\int_0^\pi \sin^2 5\theta\,d\theta = \int_0^\pi \dfrac{1 - \cos 10\theta}{2}\,d\theta = \left(\dfrac{\theta}{2} - \dfrac{\sin 10\theta}{20}\right)\Big|_0^\pi = \dfrac{\pi}{2}$.

28 $\displaystyle\int_0^\pi (1 - \cos^2 3\theta)\,d\theta = \int_0^\pi \sin^2 3\theta\,d\theta = \int_0^\pi \dfrac{1 - \cos 6\theta}{2}\,d\theta = \left(\dfrac{\theta}{2} - \dfrac{\sin 6\theta}{12}\right)\Big|_0^\pi = \dfrac{\pi}{2}$.

29 Let $u = x^3 + 3x^2 - 6x$, and note that $du = 3x^2 + 6x - 6\,dx = 3(x^2 + 2x - 2)\,dx$. Substituting yields $\dfrac{1}{3}\displaystyle\int_8^{36} \dfrac{1}{u}\,du = \left(\dfrac{1}{3}\ln u\right)\Big|_8^{36} = \dfrac{1}{3}(\ln 36 - \ln 8) = \dfrac{1}{3}\ln\left(\dfrac{9}{2}\right)$.

30 Let $u = e^x$ so that $du = e^x\,dx$. Substituting yields $\displaystyle\int_1^2 \dfrac{1}{1 + u^2}\,du = \tan^{-1}(u)\Big|_1^2 = \tan^{-1} 2 - \dfrac{\pi}{4}$.

31

The area is given by $\displaystyle\int_{-4}^4 (16 - x^2)\,dx = (16x - x^3/3)\,\Big|_{-4}^4 = 64 - 64/3 - (-64 + 64/3) = 256/3$.

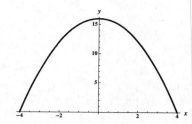

32

The area is given by $\displaystyle\int_{-1}^0 (x^3 - x)\,dx = (x^4/4 - x^2/2)\,\Big|_{-1}^0 = 0 - (1/4 - 1/2) = 1/4$.

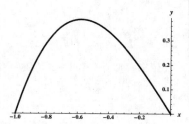

33

The area is given by $2\displaystyle\int_0^{2\pi} \sin(x/4)\,dx = 2\,(-4\cos(x/4))\,\Big|_0^{2\pi} = -8(0 - 1) = 8$.

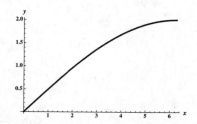

34

The area is given by $\displaystyle\int_{-1}^{\sqrt{3}} \frac{1}{1+x^2}\,dx =$

$\tan^{-1} x \Big|_{-1}^{\sqrt{3}} = \dfrac{\pi}{3} - \left(-\dfrac{\pi}{4}\right) = \dfrac{7\pi}{12}.$

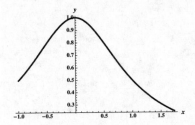

35

i. $\displaystyle\int_{-1}^{1} (x^4 - x^2)\,dx = \left(x^5/5 - x^3/3\right)\Big|_{-1}^{1} =$
$(1/5 - 1/3) - (-1/5 - (-1/3)) = -4/15.$

ii. Because the region lies completely below the x-axis, the area bounded by the curve and the x-axis is $-\displaystyle\int_{-1}^{1} (x^4 - x^2)\,dx = 4/15.$

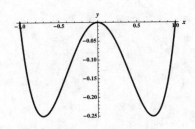

36

i. $\displaystyle\int_{0}^{3} (x^2 - x)\,dx = \left(x^3/3 - x^2/2\right)\Big|_{0}^{3} = 9 - 9/2 = 9/2.$

ii. Because the region is below the x-axis between 0 and 1 and above between 1 and 3, the area bounded by the curve and the x-axis is $-\displaystyle\int_{0}^{1} (x^2 - x)\,dx +$
$\displaystyle\int_{1}^{3} (x^2 - x)\,dx = -\left(x^3/3 - x^2/2\right)\Big|_{0}^{1} +$
$\left(x^3/3 - x^2/2\right)\Big|_{1}^{3} = -(1/3 - 1/2) + (9 - 9/2) - (1/3 - 1/2) = 9/2 + 2(1/2 - 1/3) = 9/2 + 1/3 = 29/6.$

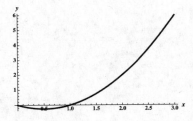

37

a. $\displaystyle\int_{-4}^{4} f(x)\,dx = 2\int_{0}^{4} f(x)\,dx = 2 \cdot 10 = 20.$

b. $\displaystyle\int_{-4}^{4} 3g(x)\,dx = 3 \cdot 0 = 0.$

c. $\displaystyle\int_{-4}^{4} 4f(x) - 3g(x)\,dx = 2 \cdot 4 \cdot \int_{0}^{4} f(x)\,dx - 3 \cdot 0 = 8 \cdot 10 - 0 = 80.$

d. Let $u = 4x^2$, so that $du = 8x\,dx$. Substituting yields $\displaystyle\int_{0}^{4} f(u)\,du = 10.$

e. Because f is an even function, $3xf(x)$ is an odd function. Thus, $\displaystyle\int_{-2}^{2} 3xf(x)\,dx = 0$.

38

a. $\displaystyle\int_{a}^{c} f(x)\,dx = 20 - 12 = 8$.

b. $\displaystyle\int_{b}^{d} f(x)\,dx = 15 - 12 = 3$.

c. $\displaystyle 2\int_{c}^{b} f(x)\,dx = -2\int_{b}^{c} f(x)\,dx = -2(-12) = 24$.

d. $\displaystyle 4\int_{a}^{d} f(x)\,dx = 80 - 48 + 60 = 92$.

e. $\displaystyle 3\int_{a}^{b} f(x)\,dx = 3 \cdot 20 = 60$.

f. $\displaystyle 2\int_{b}^{d} f(x)\,dx = 2(15 - 12) = 6$.

39 $\displaystyle\int_{1}^{4} 3f(x)\,dx = 3\int_{1}^{4} f(x)\,dx = 3 \cdot 6 = 18$.

40 $\displaystyle -\int_{4}^{1} 2f(x)\,dx = 2\int_{1}^{4} f(x)\,dx = 2 \cdot 6 = 12$.

41 $\displaystyle\int_{1}^{4} (3f(x) - 2g(x))\,dx = 3\int_{1}^{4} f(x)\,dx - 2\int_{1}^{4} g(x)\,dx = 3 \cdot 6 - 2 \cdot 4 = 18 - 8 = 10$.

42 There is not enough information to compute this integral.

43 There is not enough information to compute this integral.

44 $\displaystyle\int_{4}^{1} (f(x) - g(x))\,dx = \int_{1}^{4} (g(x) - f(x))\,dx = \int_{1}^{4} g(x)\,dx - \int_{1}^{4} f(x)\,dx = 4 - 6 = -2$.

45 The displacement is $\displaystyle\int_{0}^{2} 5\sin \pi t\,dt = \left(\frac{-5}{\pi} \cos \pi t \right) \bigg|_{0}^{2} = 0$.
The distance traveled is

$$\int_{0}^{2} 5|\sin \pi t|\,dt = 5\int_{0}^{1} \sin \pi t\,dt + 5\int_{1}^{2} (-\sin \pi t)\,dt = \left(\frac{-5}{\pi} \cos \pi t \right) \bigg|_{0}^{1} + \left(\frac{5}{\pi} \cos \pi t \right) \bigg|_{1}^{2} = \frac{10}{\pi} + \frac{10}{\pi} = \frac{20}{\pi}.$$

46 The baseball is in the air for x in the interval $(0, 200)$. The average height is

$$\frac{1}{200} \int_{0}^{200} (2x - 0.01x^2)\,dx = \frac{1}{200} \left(x^2 - \frac{0.01x^3}{3} \right) \bigg|_{0}^{200} = 200 - \frac{400}{3} = \frac{200}{3}.$$

47

a. The average value is 2.5. This is because for a straight line, the average value occurs at the midpoint of the interval, which is at the point $(3.5, 2.5)$, so $c = 3.5$.

b. The average value is 3 over the interval $[2, 4]$ and 3 over the interval $[4, 6]$, so is 3 over the interval $[2, 6]$. The function takes on this value at $c = 3$ and $c = 5$.

48 Differentiating both sides of the given equation gives $12x^3 = f(x)$. To check, we compute $\displaystyle\int_{2}^{x} 12t^3\,dt = 3t^4 \bigg|_{2}^{x} = 3x^4 - 48$, which gives the original equation.

49 Let $u = 2x$, so that $du = 2\,dx$. We have $\displaystyle\frac{1}{2} \int_{2}^{4} f'(u)\,du = \frac{1}{2} \cdot (f(4) - f(2)) = \frac{f(4)}{2} - 2$. Because we are given that this quantity is 10, we have $f(4) = 24$.

50 Note that $H'(x) = \sqrt{4 - x^2}$ by the Fundamental Theorem.

a. $H(0) = \int_0^0 \sqrt{4 - t^2}\, dt = 0.$

b. $H'(1) = \sqrt{3}.$

c. $H'(2) = \sqrt{4 - 4} = 0.$

d. $H(2) = \int_0^2 \sqrt{4 - t^2}\, dt = \dfrac{1}{4} \cdot \pi \cdot 2^2 = \pi.$ This follows because the given area represents $\frac{1}{4}$ of the area inside a circle of radius 2.

e. $H(-x) = \int_0^{-x} \sqrt{4 - t^2}\, dt = -\int_{-x}^0 \sqrt{4 - t^2}\, dt = -H(x)$, because $\sqrt{4 - t^2}$ is an even function. So $s = -1.$

51

By the Fundamental Theorem, $f'(x) = \dfrac{1}{x}$, which is always positive for $x > 1$. Thus f is always increasing. Also, $f(1) = \int_1^1 \dfrac{1}{t}\, dt = 0$. Also, $f''(x) = \dfrac{-1}{x^2}$ which is always negative, so f is always concave down.

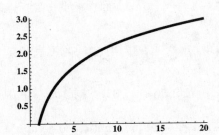

52 It appears that B is the derivative of A, and C is the derivative of B. Thus we must have $A = \int_0^x f(t)\, dt$, $B = f(x)$, and $C = f'(x)$. Note that A is decreasing where B is negative and increasing where B is positive, and has a minimum where B is zero. Note also that B is increasing where C is positive, and is decreasing where C is negative, and has a maximum where C is zero.

53

a.

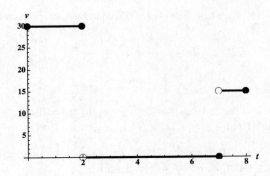

b. The area is $2 \cdot 30 + 0 + 15 \cdot 1 = 75.$

c. The area represents the distance that the diver ascends.

54

a. $F(2) = \int_0^2 f(t)\, dt = \int_0^1 f(t)\, dt + \int_1^2 f(t)\, dt = -1 + 1 = 0.$

$F(-2) = \int_0^{-2} f(t)\, dt = -\int_0^{-2} f(t)\, dt = \dfrac{1}{4} \cdot \pi \cdot 4 = \pi.$

$$F(4) = \int_0^4 f(t)\,dt = \int_0^2 f(t)\,dt + \int_2^4 f(t)\,dt = 0 + \frac{1}{4} \cdot \pi \cdot 4 = \pi.$$

b. $G(-2) = \int_1^{-2} f(t)\,dt = -\int_{-2}^1 f(t)\,dt = -\left(\int_{-2}^0 f(t)\,dt + \int_0^1 f(t)\,dt \right) = \pi + 1.$

$G(0) = \int_1^0 f(t)\,dt = -\int_0^1 f(t)\,dt = 1.$

$G(4) = \int_1^4 f(t)\,dt = \int_1^2 f(t)\,dt + \int_2^4 f(t)\,dt = 1 + \pi.$

c. One can either reason that the two functions differ by $\int_0^1 f(t)\,dt$ which is a constant, or using the Fundamental Theorem of Calculus, that the two functions have the same derivative (namely $f(x)$) and therefore differ by a constant. Note that $F(x) = G(x) - 1$ for $-2 \le x \le 4$.

55

a. $F(-2) = \int_{-1}^{-2} f(t)\,dt = \int_{-1}^{-2} t\,dt = \left. \frac{t^2}{2} \right|_{-1}^{-2} = \frac{3}{2}.$

$F(2) = \int_{-1}^2 f(t)\,dt = \int_{-1}^0 f(t)\,dt + \int_0^2 f(t)\,dt = \int_{-1}^0 t\,dt + \int_0^2 \frac{t^2}{2}\,dt = \left. \frac{t^2}{2} \right|_{-1}^0 + \left. \frac{t^3}{6} \right|_0^2 = \left(0 - \frac{1}{2} \right) + \left(\frac{8}{6} - 0 \right) = \frac{5}{6}.$

b. By the Fundamental Theorem of Calculus, $F'(x) = f(x)$, so for $-2 \le x < 0$ we have $F''(x) = x$.

c. By the Fundamental Theorem of Calculus, $F'(x) = f(x)$, so for $0 \le x < 2$ we have $F''(x) = \frac{x^2}{2}$.

d. $F'(-1) = -1$ and $F'(1) = \frac{1}{2}$. These represent the rate of change of F at the given points. Because the graph in the exercise is the derivative of F, this is just the value of f at the given points.

e. Note that $F''(x) = \begin{cases} 1 & \text{if } -2 \le x < 0, \\ x & \text{if } 0 \le x \le 2. \end{cases}$ Thus we have $F''(-1) = 1$ and $F''(1) = 1$.

f. The difference $F(x) - G(x) = \int_{-1}^{-2} f(t)\,dt = \frac{3}{2}$, as noted in part (a).

56

a. $G(-1) = \int_{-2}^{-1} f(t)\,dt = \int_{-2}^{-1} t\,dt = \left. \frac{t^2}{2} \right|_{-2}^{-1} = -\frac{3}{2}.$

$G(1) = \int_{-2}^1 f(t)\,dt = \int_{-2}^0 f(t)\,dt + \int_0^1 f(t)\,dt = \int_{-2}^0 t\,dt + \int_0^1 \frac{t^2}{2}\,dt = \left. \frac{t^2}{2} \right|_{-2}^0 + \left. \frac{t^3}{6} \right|_0^1 = -\frac{11}{6}.$

b. By the Fundamental Theorem, $G'(x) = f(x)$, so that for $-2 \le x < 0$, we have $G'(x) = f(x) = x.$

c. By the Fundamental Theorem, $G'(x) = f(x)$, so that for $0 \le x \le 2$, we have $G'(x) = f(x) = \frac{x^2}{2}.$

d. $G'(0) = f(0) = 0$ and $G'(1) = f(1) = \frac{1}{2}$. These represent the rate of change of G at the given points. Because the graph in the exercise is the derivative of G, this is just the value of f at the given points.

e. The difference $F(x) - G(x) = \int_{-1}^{-2} f(t)\,dt = \frac{3}{2}$, as noted in part (f) of the previous problem.

57 By L'hôpital's rule, we have

$$\lim_{x \to 2} \frac{\int_2^x e^{t^2}\,dt}{x - 2} = \lim_{x \to 2} \frac{e^{x^2}}{1} = e^4.$$

58 By L'hôpital's rule, we have

$$\lim_{x \to 1} \frac{\int_1^{x^2} e^{t^3}\, dt}{x - 1} = \lim_{x \to 1} \frac{2x e^{x^6}}{1} = 2e.$$

59

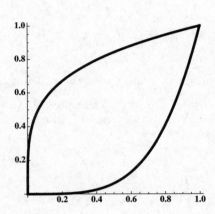

Because x^n and $\sqrt[n]{x}$ are inverse functions of each other, they are symmetric in the square $[0,1] \times [0,1]$ about the line $y = x$. Together, the two regions completely fill up the 1×1 square, so these two areas add to one.

60 If we let $u^3 = x^2 - 1$, then $3u^2\, du = 2x\, dx$, so $x\, dx = \frac{3u^2}{2}\, du$. Also, when $x = 1$ we have $u = 0$ and when $x = 3$ we have $u = 2$. Substituting gives $\displaystyle\int_1^3 x \sqrt[3]{x^2 - 1}\, dx = \frac{3}{2}\int_0^2 u^2 \cdot u\, du = \frac{3}{2}\left(\frac{u^4}{4}\right)\Big|_0^2 = 6.$

61 Factoring out $\frac{1}{b^2}$ gives $\dfrac{1}{b^2}\displaystyle\int \frac{dx}{(ax/b)^2 + 1}$. Now let $u = ax/b$, so that $du = \frac{a}{b}\, dx$. Substituting yields $\dfrac{1}{b^2} \cdot \dfrac{b}{a}\displaystyle\int \frac{du}{u^2 + 1} = \frac{1}{ab}\left(\tan^{-1}(u)\right) + C = \frac{1}{ab}\tan^{-1}(ax/b) + C.$

62 Let $u = 1 + \cos^2 x$. Then $du = -2\sin x \cos x\, dx$. Substituting yields $-\displaystyle\int \frac{1}{u}\, du = -\ln|u| + C = -\ln(1 + \cos^2 x) + C.$

63 Let $u = \frac{1}{x}$. Then $du = \frac{-1}{x^2}\, dx$. Substituting yields $-\displaystyle\int \sin u\, du = \cos u + C = \cos\left(\frac{1}{x}\right) + C.$

64 Let $u = \tan^{-1} x$. Then $du = \frac{1}{1+x^2}\, dx$. Substituting yields $\displaystyle\int u^5\, du = \frac{u^6}{6} + C = \frac{(\tan^{-1} x)^6}{6} + C.$

65 Let $u = \tan^{-1} x$. Then $du = \frac{1}{1+x^2}\, dx$. Substituting yields $\displaystyle\int \frac{1}{u}\, du = \ln|u| + C = \ln|\tan^{-1} x| + C.$

66 Let $u = \sin^{-1} x$. Then $du = \frac{1}{\sqrt{1-x^2}}\, dx$. Substituting yields $\displaystyle\int u\, du = \frac{u^2}{2} + C = \frac{(\sin^{-1} x)^2}{2} + C.$

67 Let $u = e^x + e^{-x}$. Then $du = (e^x - e^{-x})\, dx$. Substituting yields $\displaystyle\int \frac{1}{u}\, du = \ln|u| + C = \ln(e^x + e^{-x}) + C.$

68

a.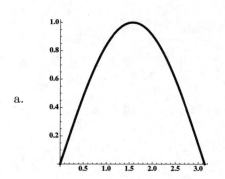

b.
$$\int_0^{\pi/a} \sin(ax)\, dx = \left(\frac{-\cos ax}{a} \right) \Bigg|_0^{\pi/a} = \frac{1}{a} +$$
$$\frac{1}{a} = \frac{2}{a}.$$
This is a decreasing function of a.

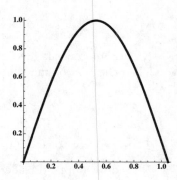

69 This follows by differentiating each side of the equation. $\frac{d}{dx}\left(u(x) + 2\int_0^x u(t)\, dt \right) = u'(x) + 2u(x)$, and $\frac{d}{dx} 10 = 0$. The reverse is not true, because if $u(x) + 2\int_0^x u(t)\, dt = C$ for any constant C, then it would satisfy the second equation, even if $C \neq 10$.

70

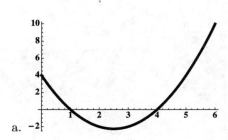

a.

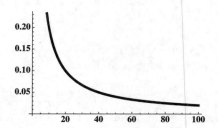

b.

c. The zeros of f are at 1 and 4, and A has a local maximum at $x = 1$ and a local minimum at $x = 4$.

d. Geometric: Because f is above the axis from 0 to 1 and then crosses below the axis at 1, the net area from 0 to x will switch from increasing to decreasing as x moves from the left of 1 to the right of 1. A similar (but opposite) thing can be said near 4, because f switches from below the axis to above, the net area switches from decreasing to increasing at $x = 4$.

Analytic: By the Fundamental Theorem, $A'(x) = f(x)$, so the zeros of f are critical points of A, and in this example, lead to extrema.

e. Because $A(x) = \frac{x}{6} \cdot (2x^2 - 15x + 24)$, the non-zero zeros of A occur at $x = \frac{15 \pm \sqrt{225 - 4 \cdot 2 \cdot 24}}{4} = \frac{15 \pm \sqrt{33}}{4}$. So $x_1 = \frac{15 - \sqrt{33}}{4} \approx 2.31386$ and $x_2 = \frac{15 + \sqrt{33}}{4} \approx 5.18614$.

f. Because $f(x) = A'(x)$, the area bounded by the graph of f and the x-axis on $[0, x_1]$ is

$$\int_0^1 f(x)\,dx - \int_1^{x_1} f(x)\,dx = A(1) - A(0) - (A(x_1) - A(1)) = 2A(1) = \frac{11}{3}.$$

Now, note that the area bounded by the graph of f on $[x_1, 4]$ is $-(A(4) - A(x_1)) = \frac{8}{3}$, so that $b > 4$. Then the area bounded by the graph of f and the x-axis on $[x_1, b]$ is

$$-\int_{x_1}^4 f(x)\,dx + \int_4^b f(x)\,dx = -(A(4) - A(x_1)) + A(b) - A(4) = A(b) - 2A(4) = A(b) + \frac{16}{3}.$$

Thus we want to solve $A(b) = -\frac{5}{3}$; using technology, we obtain $b \approx 4.756$.

g. No. For example, consider the function

$$f(x) = \begin{cases} 1 & \text{if } 0 \le x < 1, \\ -1 & \text{if } 1 \le x \le 2. \end{cases}$$

Then $A(x) = \int_0^x f(t)\,dt$ has a maximum at $x = 1$, even though f is never zero. An extreme point of A can occur at points of discontinuity of f.

71 Note that $f'(x) = (x-1)^{15}(x-2)^9$, and that the zeros of f' are at $x = 1$ and $x = 2$.

a. f' is positive and thus f is increasing on $(-\infty, 1)$ and on $(2, \infty)$, while f' is negative and f is decreasing on $(1, 2)$.

b. $f''(x) = 15(x-1)^{14}(x-2)^9 + (x-1)^{15} \cdot 9(x-2)^8 = 3(x-1)^{14}(x-2)^8(8x - 13)$.

   f is concave up on $\left(\frac{13}{8}, \infty\right)$ and concave down on $\left(-\infty, \frac{13}{8}\right)$.

c. f has a local maximum at $x = 1$ and a local minimum at $x = 2$.

d. f has an inflection point at $x = \frac{13}{8}$.

72

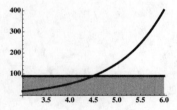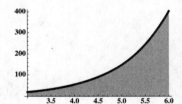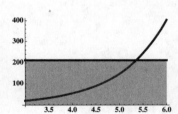

The first graph on the left above shows that the area of the rectangle with height e^m where m is the midpoint of $[a, b]$ is less than the area under the curve of e^x over $[a, b]$. The last graph on the right above shows that the area of the rectangle whose height is the average of e^a and e^b is greater than the area under the curve of e^x over that interval. Note that the area under the curve is $\int_a^b e^x\,dx = \left(e^x\right)\Big|_a^b = e^b - e^a$. Putting these ideas together, we have

$$e^{(a+b)/2}(b-a) < e^b - e^a < \left(\frac{e^a + e^b}{2}\right)(b-a),$$

and dividing through by $(b-a)$ yields

$$e^{(a+b)/2} < \frac{e^b - e^a}{b-a} < \frac{e^a + e^b}{2}.$$

Chapter 6

Applications of Integration

6.1 Velocity and Net Change

6.1.1 The position of an object is the coordinate of the object on the line at a given time, often denoted $s(t)$. The displacement over an interval $[a, b]$ is $s(b) - s(a)$, the difference of the object's ending position and beginning position. It can be written as $\int_a^b v(t)\, dt$ where $v(t)$ is the object's velocity at time t. The distance traveled by the object is $\int_a^b |v(t)|\, dt$, the sum of the distance traveled along the line to the right and the distance traveled along the line to the left over the given time interval.

6.1.2 If velocity is positive, then $|v(t)| = v(t)$, so the distance and displacement are equal.

6.1.3 The displacement is given by $\int_a^b v(t)\, dt$, because this quantity is equal to $s(b) - s(a)$.

6.1.4 The net change of a quantity is given by $\int_a^b f'(t)\, dt$, if $f'(t)$ is the rate of change of the quantity.

6.1.5 The value of Q at time t will be given by $Q(t) = Q(0) + \int_0^t Q'(x)\, dx$.

6.1.6 If $Q'(t)$ is the growth rate of a population Q at time t, then $\int_a^b Q'(t)\, dt = Q(b) - Q(a)$, the net change of the population over the time period $[a, b]$.

6.1.7

    a. The velocity is positive for $0 \le t < 1$ and for $3 < t < 5$, so the object is moving in the positive direction on those intervals.

    b. The displacement is $\displaystyle\int_0^3 v(t)\, dt = 12 - 16 = -4$.

    c. The distance traveled is $\displaystyle\int_1^5 |v(t)|\, dt = 16 + 10 = 26$.

    d. The displacement is $\displaystyle\int_0^5 v(t)\, dt = 12 - 16 + 10 = 6$.

    e. After five hours the object's position is 6 miles from the original position in the positive direction.

6.1.8

    a. The velocity is negative for $0 < t < 2$ and for $4 < t < 6$, so the object is moving in the negative direction on those intervals.

    b. The displacement is $\displaystyle\int_2^6 v(t)\, dt = 14 - 10 = 4$.

c. The distance traveled is $\int_0^6 |v(t)|\, dt = 20 + 14 + 10 = 44.$

d. The displacement is $\int_0^8 v(t)\, dt = -20 + 14 - 10 + 6 = -10.$

e. After eight minutes the object's position is 10 meters from the original position in the negative direction.

6.1.9

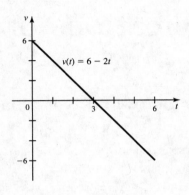

a. The motion is positive for $0 \le t < 3$ and negative for $3 < t \le 6$.

b . The displacement is $\int_0^6 (6 - 2t)\, dt = \left(6t - t^2\right)\big|_0^6 = 0$ m.

c. The distance traveled is $\int_0^3 (6 - 2t)\, dt + \int_3^6 (2t - 6)\, dt = 9 + 9 = 18$ m.

6.1.10

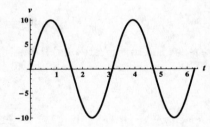

a. The motion is positive for $0 < t < \pi/2$ and $\pi < t < 3\pi/2$, and negative for $\pi/2 < t < \pi$ and for $3\pi/2 < t < 2\pi$.

b. The displacement is $\int_0^{2\pi} 10\sin 2t\, dt = (-5\cos 2t)\big|_0^{2\pi} = 0$ m.

c. Using symmetry, the distance traveled is $4 \cdot \int_0^{\pi/2} 10\sin 2t\, dt = 4\left(-5\cos 2t\right)\big|_0^{\pi/2} = 4 \cdot 10 = 40$ m.

6.1.11

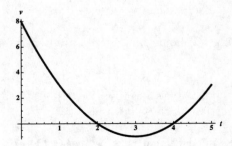

a. The motion is positive for $0 < t < 2$ and $4 < t < 5$, and negative for $2 < t < 4$.

b. The displacement is $\int_0^5 (t^2 - 6t + 8)\,dt = \left(t^3/3 - 3t^2 + 8t\right)\big|_0^5 = 125/3 - 75 + 40 = \dfrac{20}{3}$ m.

c. The distance traveled from time 0 to 2 is $\int_0^2 (t^2 - 6t + 8)\,dt = \left(t^3/3 - 3t^2 + 8t\right)\big|_0^2 = 8/3 - 12 + 16 = \dfrac{20}{3}$.

From time 2 to 4 is $-\int_2^4 (t^2 - 6t + 8)\,dt = -\left(t^3/3 - 3t^2 + 8t\right)\big|_2^4 = -(64/3 - 48 + 32) + (8/3 - 12 + 16) = \dfrac{4}{3}$

m. From time 4 to 5 is $\int_4^5 (t^2 - 6t + 8)\,dt = \left(t^3/3 - 3t^2 + 8t\right)\big|_4^5 = (125/3 - 75 + 40) - (64/3 - 48 + 32) = \dfrac{4}{3}$

m. Thus the total distance traveled is $\dfrac{20}{3} + \dfrac{4}{3} + \dfrac{4}{3} = \dfrac{28}{3}$ m.

6.1.12

a. The motion is positive for $1 < t < 4$, and negative for $0 \le t < 1$ and $4 < t \le 5$.

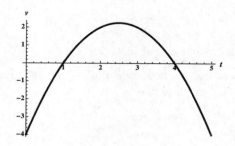

b. The displacement is $\int_0^5 (-t^2 + 5t - 4)\,dt = \left(-t^3/3 + 5t^2/2 - 4t\right)\big|_0^5 = -125/3 + 125/2 - 20 = \dfrac{5}{6}$ m.

c. The distance traveled from time 0 to 1 is $-\int_0^1 (-t^2 + 5t - 4)\,dt = \left(-t^3/3 + 5t^2/2 - 4t\right)\big|_0^1 = -(-1/3 +$

$5/2 - 4) = \dfrac{11}{6}$ m. From time 1 to 4 is $\int_1^4 (-t^2 + 5t - 4)\,dt = \left(-t^3/3 + 5t^2/2 - 4t\right)\big|_1^4 = (-64/3 + 40 -$

$16) - (-1/3 + 5/2 - 4) = \dfrac{9}{2}$ m. From time 4 to 5 is $-\int_4^5 (-t^2 + 5t - 4)\,dt = \left(-t^3/3 + 5t^2/2 - 4t\right)\big|_4^5 =$

$-(-125/3 + 125/2 - 20) + (-64/3 + 40 - 16) = \dfrac{11}{6}$ m. Thus the total distance traveled is $\dfrac{11}{6} + \dfrac{9}{2} + \dfrac{11}{6} = \dfrac{49}{6}$
m.

6.1.13

a. The motion is positive for $0 < t < 2$ and $3 < t \le 5$, and negative for $2 < t < 3$.

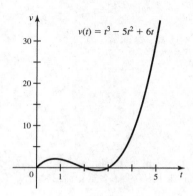

b. The displacement is $\int_0^5 (t^3 - 5t^2 + 6t)\,dt = \left(\dfrac{t^4}{4} - \dfrac{5t^3}{3} + 3t^2\right)\big|_0^5 = \dfrac{275}{12}$ m.

c. The distance traveled is $\int_0^2 v(t)\,dt - \int_2^3 v(t)\,dt + \int_3^5 v(t)\,dt = \left(\frac{t^4}{4} - \frac{5t^3}{3} + 3t^2\right)\Big|_0^2 - \left(\frac{t^4}{4} - \frac{5t^3}{3} + 3t^2\right)\Big|_2^3 +$
$\left(\frac{t^4}{4} - \frac{5t^3}{3} + 3t^2\right)\Big|_3^5 = \frac{8}{3} + \frac{5}{12} + \frac{62}{3} = \frac{95}{4} = 23.75$ m.

6.1.14

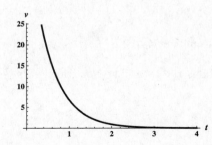

a.   The motion is positive for $0 \le t \le 4$.

b. The displacement is $\int_0^4 50e^{-2t}\,dt = \left(-25e^{-2t}\right)\Big|_0^4 = 25(1 - e^{-8}) \approx 24.992$ m.

c. Because the velocity is positive on the given interval, the distance traveled is the same as the displacement, given above.

6.1.15

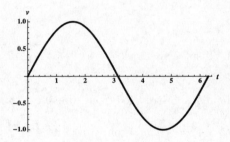

a.   The motion is positive for $0 < t < \pi$, and negative for $\pi < t < 2\pi$.

b. $s(t) = \int \sin t\,dt = -\cos t + C$, and because $s(0) = 1$, we must have $C = 2$. Thus, $s(t) = 2 - \cos t$. Also, $s(t) = s(0) + \int_0^t \sin x\,dx = 1 + (-\cos x)\big|_0^t = 2 - \cos t$.

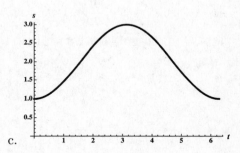

c.

6.1.16

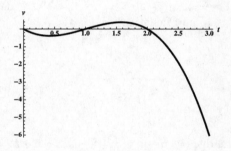

a.   The motion is positive for $1 < t < 2$, and negative for $0 < t < 1$ and $2 < t \le 3$.

b. $s(t) = \int (-t^3 + 3t^2 - 2t)\,dt = -t^4/4 + t^3 - t^2 + C$.
Because $s(0) = 4$, we have $C = 4$, and thus
$s(t) = -t^4/4 + t^3 - t^2 + 4$.
Also, $s(t) = s(0) + \int_0^t (-x^3 + 3x^2 - 2x)\,dx = 4 + \left(-x^4/4 + x^3 - x^2\right)\Big|_0^t = 4 - t^4/4 + t^3 - t^2$.

c.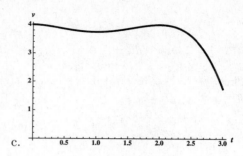

6.1.17

a. The motion is positive for $0 \le t < 3$, and negative for $3 < t \le 5$.

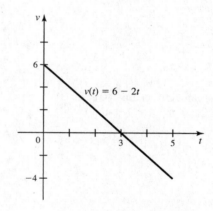

b. $s(t) = \int (6 - 2t)\,dt = 6t - t^2 + C$, and because $s(0) = 0$, we must have $C = 0$. Thus, $s(t) = 6t - t^2$. Also, $s(t) = s(0) + \int_0^t (6 - 2x)\,dx = \left(6x - x^2\right)\Big|_0^t = 6t - t^2$.

c.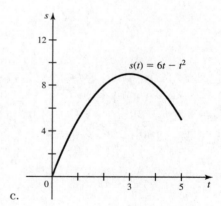

6.1.18

a. The motion is positive for $0 < t < 1$ and $2 < t < 3$, and negative for $1 < t < 2$ and $3 < t < 4$.

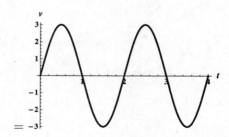

b. $s(t) = \int 3\sin(\pi t)\, dt = -\frac{3}{\pi}\cos(\pi t) + C$, and because $s(0) = 1$, we must have $C = 1 + \frac{3}{\pi}$. Thus, $s(t) = -\frac{3}{\pi}\cos\pi t + 1 + \frac{3}{\pi}$. Also, $s(t) = s(0) + \int_0^t 3\sin(\pi x)\, dx = 1 + \left(-\frac{3}{\pi}\cos(\pi x)\right)\big|_0^t = -\frac{3}{\pi}\cos\pi t + 1 + \frac{3}{\pi}$.

c.

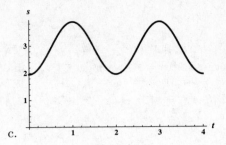

6.1.19

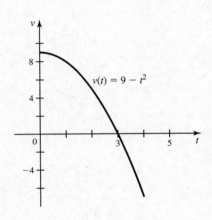

a. The motion is positive for $0 \le t < 3$, and negative for $3 < t \le 4$.

b. $s(t) = \int (9 - t^2)\, dt = 9t - t^3/3 + C$, and because $s(0) = -2$, we must have $C = -2$. Thus, $s(t) = 9t - \frac{t^3}{3} - 2$. Also, $s(t) = s(0) + \int_0^t (9 - x^2)\, dx = -2 + \left(9x - x^3/3\right)\big|_0^t = 9t - \frac{t^3}{3} - 2$.

c.

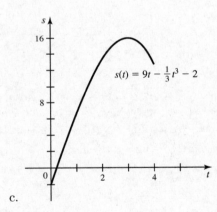

6.1.20

a. The motion is positive for $0 \le t \le 8$.

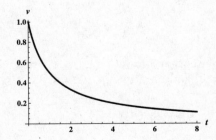

b. $s(t) = \int \frac{1}{t+1}\, dt = \ln(t+1) + C$, and because $s(0) = -4$, we must have $C = -4$. Thus, $s(t) = -\ln(t+1) - 4$. Also, $s(t) = s(0) + \int_0^t \frac{1}{1+x}\, dx = -4 + (\ln(x+1))\big|_0^t = \ln(t+1) - 4$.

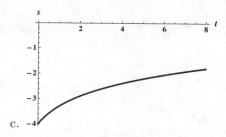

c.

6.1.21

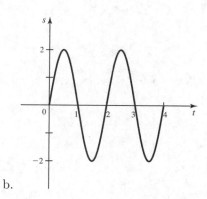

a. $s(t) = s(0) + \int_0^t 2\pi \cos \pi x\, dx = 2\sin \pi x\big|_0^t = 2\sin \pi t$.

b.

c. The mass reaches its lowest point at $t = 1.5$, $t = 3.5$ and $t = 5.5$.

d. The mass reaches its highest point at $t = .5$, $t = 2.5$, and $t = 4.5$.

6.1.22

a. $s(5) = \int_0^5 |400 - 20t|\, dt = \int_0^5 (400 - 20t)\, dt = \left(400t - 10t^2\right)\big|_0^5 = 1750$ m.

b. $s(10) = \int_0^{10} |400 - 20t|\, dt = \int_0^{10} (400 - 20t)\, dt = \left(400t - 10t^2\right)\big|_0^{10} = 3000$ m.

c. Her velocity is 250 when $400 - 20t = 250$, or $t = 7.5$, and thus $s(7.5) = \int_0^{7.5} (400 - 20t)\, dt = \left(400t - 10t^2\right)\big|_0^{7.5} = 2437.5$.

6.1.23

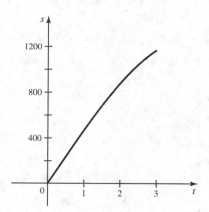

a. $s(t) = s(0) + \int_0^t 30(16 - x^2)\, dx = \left(480x - 10x^3\right)\big|_0^t = 480t - 10t^3 = 10t(48 - t^2)$.

b. Because the velocity is positive, this is given by $s(2) - s(0) = 960 - 80 = 880$ miles.

c. The velocity is 400 when $480 - 30t^2 = 400$, or $t = \sqrt{8/3}$. At this point the plane has traveled
$$s(\sqrt{8/3}) = 480\sqrt{8/3} - 10\sqrt{8/3}^3 \approx 740.290 \text{ miles.}$$

6.1.24

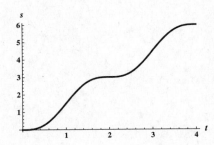

a. $s(t) = s(0) + \int_0^t 3\sin^2(\pi x/2)\,dx =$
$\frac{3}{2}\int_0^t (1 - \cos(\pi x))\,dx = \frac{3}{2}\left(x - \frac{1}{\pi}\sin \pi x\right)\Big|_0^t =$
$\frac{3}{2}\left(t - \frac{1}{\pi}\sin \pi t\right).$

b. Because the velocity is positive, this is given by $s(.25) - s(0) = \frac{3}{2}\left(.25 - \frac{\sin(\pi/4)}{\pi}\right) = \frac{3}{8} - \frac{3\sqrt{2}}{4\pi} \approx .0374$ miles.

c. $s(3) = 4.5$ miles.

6.1.25

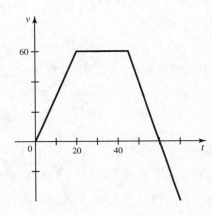

a. The velocity has a maximum of 60 for $20 \leq t \leq 45$. The velocity is 0 at $t = 0$ and at $t = 60$.

b. $\int_0^{20} 3t\,dt + \int_{20}^{30} 60\,dt = 1200$ m.

c. $1200 + \int_{30}^{45} 60\,dt + \int_{45}^{60}(240 - 4t)\,dt = 1200 + 900 + \left(240t - 2t^2\right)\Big|_{45}^{60} = 2550$ m.

d. At time $t = 60$ the automobile is at position 2550. In the following 15 seconds, it moves $\int_{60}^{75}(240 - 4t)\,dt = 450$ feet in the opposite direction, so it is at position $2550 - 450 = 2100$.

6.1.26

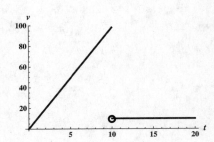

a. The velocity is given by
$$v(t) = \begin{cases} 9.8t & \text{if } 0 \leq t \leq 10, \\ 10 & \text{if } t > 10. \end{cases}$$

b. $s(30) = \int_0^{10} 9.8t\, dt + \int_{10}^{30} 10\, dt = 490 + 200 = 690$ m.

c. We seek t so that $490 + \int_{10}^t 10\, dx = 3000$, which can be written $10t - 100 = 2510$, so $t = 261$ s.

6.1.27 $v(t) = \int a(t)\, dt = \int (-32)\, dt = -32t + C$, and because $v(0) = 70$, we have $C = 70$, so $v(t) = -32t + 70$. $s(t) = \int v(t)\, dt = \int (70 - 32t)\, dt = 70t - 16t^2 + D$, and because $s(0) = 10$, we must have $D = 10$. Thus $s(t) = -16t^2 + 70t + 10$.

6.1.28 $v(t) = \int a(t)\, dt = \int (-32)\, dt = -32t + C$, and because $v(0) = 50$, we have $C = 50$, so $v(t) = -32t + 50$. $s(t) = \int v(t)\, dt = \int (50 - 32t)\, dt = 50t - 16t^2 + D$, and because $s(0) = 0$, we must have $D = 0$. Thus $s(t) = -16t^2 + 50t$.

6.1.29 $v(t) = \int a(t)\, dt = \int (-9.8)\, dt = -9.8t + C$, and because $v(0) = 20$, we have $C = 20$, so $v(t) = -9.8t + 20$.
$s(t) = \int v(t)\, dt = \int (20 - 9.8t)\, dt = 20t - 4.9t^2 + D$, and because $s(0) = 0$, we must have $D = 0$. Thus $s(t) = 20t - 4.9t^2$.

6.1.30 $v(t) = \int a(t)\, dt = \int e^{-t}\, dt = -e^{-t} + C$, and because $v(0) = 60$, we have $C = 61$, so $v(t) = -e^{-t} + 61$.
$s(t) = \int v(t)\, dt = \int (61 - e^{-t})\, dt = 61t + e^{-t} + D$, and because $s(0) = 40$, we must have $D = 39$. Thus $s(t) = 39 + 61t + e^{-t}$.

6.1.31 $v(t) = \int a(t)\, dt = \int (-0.01t)\, dt = -.005t^2 + C$, and because $v(0) = 10$, we have $C = 10$, so $v(t) = 10 - .005t^2$.
$s(t) = \int v(t)\, dt = \int (10 - .005t^2)\, dt = 10t - \frac{1}{600}t^3 + D$, and because $s(0) = 0$, we must have $D = 0$. Thus $s(t) = 10t - \frac{1}{600}t^3$.

6.1.32 $v(t) = \int a(t)\, dt = \int \frac{20}{(t+2)^2}\, dt = -\frac{20}{t+2} + C$, and because $v(0) = 20$, we have $C = 30$, so $v(t) = 30 - \frac{20}{t+2}$.
$s(t) = \int v(t)\, dt = \int \left(30 - \frac{20}{t+2}\right)\, dt = 30t - 20\ln|t + 2| + D$, and because $s(0) = 10$, we must have $D = 10 + 20\ln 2$. Thus $s(t) = 10 + 20\ln 2 + 30t - 20\ln|t + 2|$.

6.1.33 $v(t) = \int a(t)\, dt = \int \cos 2t\, dt = \frac{1}{2}\sin 2t + C$, and because $v(0) = 5$, we have $C = 5$, so $v(t) = \frac{1}{2}\sin 2t + 5$.
$s(t) = \int v(t)\, dt = \int \left(\frac{1}{2}\sin 2t + 5\right)\, dt = \frac{-1}{4}\cos 2t + 5t + D$, and because $s(0) = 7$, we must have $D = \frac{29}{4}$. Thus $s(t) = \frac{-1}{4}\cos 2t + 5t + \frac{29}{4}$.

6.1.34 $v(t) = \int a(t)\, dt = \int \frac{2t}{(t^2+1)^2}\, dt$. Let $u = t^2 + 1$ so that $du = 2t\, dt$. Then we have $\int \frac{1}{u^2}\, du = \frac{-1}{u} + C = \frac{-1}{t^2+1} + C$, and because $v(0) = 0$, we have $C = 1$, so $v(t) = \frac{-1}{t^2+1} + 1$.
$s(t) = \int v(t)\, dt = \int \left(\frac{-1}{t^2+1} + 1\right)\, dt = -\tan^{-1}(t) + t + D$, and because $s(0) = 0$, we must have $D = 0$. Thus $s(t) = -\tan^{-1} t + t$.

6.1.35

a. The velocity is given by $\int 88\, dt = 88t + C$, and $C = 0$ because $v(0) = 0$, so $v(t) = 88t$ ft/s.
The position is given by $\int 88t\, dt = 44t^2 + D$, but $D = 0$ because $s(0) = 0$, so $s(t) = 44t^2$ ft.

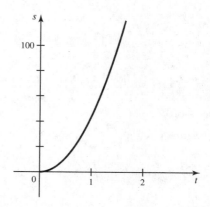

b. The car travels $s(4) = 44 \cdot 16 = 704$ feet.

c. Because a quarter mile is 1320 feet, we need $44t^2 = 1320$, so $t = \sqrt{30} \approx 5.477$ seconds.

d. We need $44t^2 = 300$, so $t \approx 2.611$ seconds.

e. It reaches that speed when $88t = 178$, or $t = 89/44$ seconds. At that time the racer has traveled $s(89/44) = 44(89/44)^2 = 89^2/44 \approx 180.023$ feet.

6.1.36

The velocity is given by $\int (-15)\, dt = -15t + C$, and $C = 60$ because $v(0) = 60$, so $v(t) = -15t + 60$.

a. The position is given by $\int (-15t + 60)\, dt = -7.5t^2 + 60t + D$, but $D = 0$ because $s(0) = 0$, so $s(t) = -7.5t^2 + 60t$.

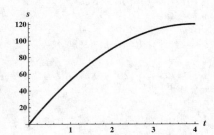

b. The car comes to rest when $v(t) = 0$, which occurs for $t = 4$. At that time $s(4) = 120$ feet.

6.1.37 $v(t) = \int a(t)\, dt = \int -\frac{1280}{(1+8t)^3}\, dt = \frac{80}{(1+8t)^2} + C$, and $C = 0$, because $v(0) = 80$.

$s(t) = \int v(t)\, dt = \int \frac{80}{(1+8t)^2}\, dt = -\frac{10}{1+8t} + D$, but we can take $D = 0$ because the initial position is unspecified. Then in the first .2 seconds the train travels $s(.2) - s(0) = -\frac{10}{2.6} - (-10) = 10 - \frac{50}{13} = \frac{80}{13} \approx 6.154$ miles. Between time 0.2 and 0.4 the train travels $s(.4) - s(.2) = -\frac{10}{4.2} - \left(-\frac{10}{2.6}\right) = \frac{50}{13} - \frac{50}{21} = \frac{400}{273} \approx 1.465$ miles.

6.1.38

a. $Q''(t) = 3t^2 \cdot 2 \cdot (40 - t)(-1) + (40 - t)^2 \cdot 6t = 12t(t - 20)(t - 40)$. This changes from positive to negative at $t = 20$, so Q' is maximized there on the given domain. So the peak extraction rate is at $t = 20$.

b. In the first 10 years, the amount is

$$\int_0^{10} Q'(t)\, dt = \int_0^{10} (3t^4 - 240t^3 + 4800t^2)\, dt = \left(\frac{3t^5}{5} - 60t^4 + 1600t^3\right)\Bigg|_0^{10} = 1,060,000$$

millions of barrels.

In the first 20 years, the amount is

$$\int_0^{20} Q'(t)\, dt = \int_0^{20} (3t^4 - 240t^3 + 4800t^2)\, dt = \left(\frac{3t^5}{5} - 60t^4 + 1600t^3\right)\Bigg|_0^{20} = 5,120,000$$

millions of barrels.

In the first 30 years, the amount is

$$\int_0^{30} Q'(t)\, dt = \int_0^{30} (3t^4 - 240t^3 + 4800t^2)\, dt = \left(\frac{3t^5}{5} - 60t^4 + 1600t^3\right)\Bigg|_0^{30} = 9,180,000$$

millions of barrels.

c. In the first 40 years, the amount is

$$\int_0^{40} Q'(t)\, dt = \int_0^{40} (3t^4 - 240t^3 + 4800t^2)\, dt = \left(\frac{3t^5}{5} - 60t^4 + 1600t^3\right)\Bigg|_0^{40} = 10,240,000$$

millions of barrels.

d. No. The amount extracted in the first 10 years is not 1/4 of the total amount extracted.

6.1.39

a. In the first 35 days the number of barrels produced is $\int_0^{30} 800\, dt + \int_{30}^{35} (2600 - 60t)\, dt = 24000 + 3250 = 27250$.

b. In the first 50 days the number of barrels produced is $27250 + \int_{35}^{40} (2600 - 60t)\, dt + \int_{40}^{50} 200\, dt = 27250 + 1750 + 2000 = 31000$.

c. A constant 200 barrels per day times 20 days yields 4000 barrels.

6.1.40

a. $55 + \int_0^6 (20 - (t/5))\, dt = 55 + \left(20t - \frac{t^2}{10}\right)\Big|_0^6 = \frac{857}{5} \approx 171.4$.

b. $P(200) = 55 + \int_0^{200} \left(20 - \frac{t}{5}\right) dt = 55 + \left(20t - \frac{t^2}{10}\right)\Big|_0^{200} = 55$.

6.1.41

a. $P(20) = 250 + \int_0^{20} (30 + 30\sqrt{t})\, dt = 250 + \left(30t + 20t^{3/2}\right)\Big|_0^{20} = 250 + 600 + 800\sqrt{5} = 850 + 800\sqrt{5} \approx 2639$ people.

b. $P(t) = 250 + \int_0^t (30 + 30\sqrt{x})\, dx = 250 + \left(30x + 20x^{3/2}\right)\Big|_0^t = 250 + 30t + 20t^{3/2}$ people.

6.1.42

a. $P(15) = 35 + \int_0^{15} (5 + 10\sin(\pi t/5))\, dt = 35 + (5t - (50/\pi)\cos(\pi t/5))|_0^{15} = 35 + (75 + (50/\pi)) - (0 - (50/\pi)) = 110 + 100/\pi \approx 142$ foxes.

$P(35) = 35 + \int_0^{35} (5 + 10\sin(\pi t/5))\, dt = 35 + (5t - (50/\pi)\cos(\pi t/5))|_0^{35} = 35 + (175 + (50/\pi)) - (0 - (50/\pi)) = 210 + 100/\pi \approx 242$ foxes.

b. $P(t) = 35 + \int_0^t (5 + 10\sin(\pi x/5))\, dx = 35 + (5x - (50/\pi)\cos(\pi x/5))|_0^t = 35 + 5t - (50/\pi)\cos(\pi t/5) + (50/\pi)$ foxes.

6.1.43

a. $N(20) = 1500 + \int_0^{20} 100e^{-0.25t}\, dt = 1500 + \left(-400e^{-0.25t}\right)\Big|_0^{20} = 1500 + (-400e^{-5} + 400) = 1900 - \frac{400}{e^5} \approx 1897$ cells.

$N(40) = 1500 + \int_0^{40} 100e^{-0.25t}\, dt = 1500 + \left(-400e^{-0.25t}\right)\Big|_0^{40} = 1500 + (-400e^{-10} + 400) = 1900 - \frac{400}{e^{10}} \approx 1900$ cells.

b. $N(t) = 1500 + \int_0^t 100e^{-0.25x}\, dx = 1500 + \left(-400e^{-0.25x}\right)\Big|_0^t = 1500 + (-400e^{-0.25t} + 400) = -400e^{-0.25t} + 1900$ cells.

6.1.44

a. $\int_0^{30} (0.25t^2 + 37.46t + 722.47)\, dt = \left(\frac{0.25}{3}t^3 + \frac{37.46}{2}t^2 + 722.47t\right)\Big|_0^{30} = 40781.1$.

b. $\int_0^{30} (0.90t^2 - 69.06t + 2053.12)\, dt = \left(\frac{0.90}{3}t^3 + \frac{69.06}{2}t^2 + 2053.12t\right)\Big|_0^{30} = 38616.6$.

c. $40781.1 + 38616.6 = 79397.7$ millions of cubic feet, or 7.93977×10^{10} cubic feet. There are $5280^3 = 147197952000$ cubic feet in a cubic mile, so the Spokane River contains $0.67 \cdot 147197952000 = 9.86226 \cdot 10^{10}$ cubic feet of water. So the percentage can be calculated by $\frac{7.93977 \times 10^{10}}{9.86226 \cdot 10^{10}} \approx 80.507\%$.

6.1.45

a. The additional cost is $\int_{100}^{150} (2000 - .5x)\, dx = \left(2000x - \frac{x^2}{4}\right)\Big|_{100}^{150} = 96875$ dollars.

b. The additional cost is $\int_{500}^{550} (2000 - .5x)\, dx = \left(2000x - \frac{x^2}{4}\right)\Big|_{500}^{550} = 86875$ dollars.

6.1.46

a. The additional cost is $\int_{100}^{150} (200 - .05x)\, dx = \left(200x - \frac{x^2}{40}\right)\Big|_{100}^{150} = 9687.5$ dollars.

b. The additional cost is $\int_{500}^{550} (200 - .05x)\, dx = \left(200x - \frac{x^2}{40}\right)\Big|_{500}^{550} = 8687.5$ dollars.

6.1.47

a. The additional cost is $\int_{100}^{150} (300 + 10x - .01x^2)\, dx = \left(300x + 5x^2 - \frac{x^3}{300}\right)\Big|_{100}^{150} = 69583.33$ dollars.

b. The additional cost is $\int_{500}^{550} (300 + 10x - .01x^2)\, dx = \left(300x + 5x^2 - \frac{x^3}{300}\right)\Big|_{500}^{550} = 139583.33$ dollars.

6.1.48

a. The additional cost is $\int_{100}^{150} (3000 - x - .001x^2)\, dx = \left(3000x - .5x^2 - \frac{x^3}{3000}\right)\Big|_{100}^{150} = 142958.33$ dollars.

b. The additional cost is $\int_{500}^{550} (3000 - x - .001x^2)\, dx = \left(3000x - .5x^2 - \frac{x^3}{3000}\right)\Big|_{500}^{550} = 109958.33$ dollars.

6.1.49

a. False. This would only be the case if the motion was all in the same direction. If the object changes direction at all, then the distance traveled is greater than the displacement.

b. True. This is because $v(t) = |v(t)|$ in this case.

c. True. This is because $R(t) > 0$ for $0 < t < 10$, but $R(t) < 0$ for $t > 10$.

d. True. The cost of increasing production from A to B is given by $\int_A^B C'(t)\, dt$, which is geometrically the area under the curve $y = C'(x)$ from A to B. If C' is positive and decreasing, there is more area under the curve from A to $2A$ than from $2A$ to $3A$.

6.1.50

a. The displacement is the net area, which is $3 \cdot 3 + \frac{1}{2} \cdot 3 \cdot 2 = 9 + 3 = 12$.

b. Because $v(t) > 0$ on that interval, the distance traveled is the same as the displacement, so it is 12 also.

c. $s(5) = s(0) + \int_0^5 v(t)\, dt = 0 + 12 = 12$.

d. $s(t) = \begin{cases} 3t & \text{if } 0 \le t \le 3, \\ 9 + \int_3^t \left(-\frac{3}{2}x + \frac{15}{2}\right) dx & \text{if } 3 \le t \le 5 \end{cases} = \begin{cases} 3t & \text{if } 0 \le t \le 3, \\ -\frac{3}{4}t^2 + \frac{15}{2}t - \frac{27}{4} & \text{if } 3 \le t \le 5 \end{cases}$.

6.1.51

a. The displacement is the net area, which is $\frac{1}{2} \cdot 2 \cdot 2 - \frac{1}{2} \cdot \frac{4}{3} \cdot 1 + \frac{1}{2} \cdot \frac{5}{3} \cdot 2 = 3$.

b. The distance traveled is $\frac{1}{2} \cdot 2 \cdot 2 + \frac{1}{2} \cdot \frac{4}{3} \cdot 1 + \frac{1}{2} \cdot \frac{5}{3} \cdot 2 = \frac{13}{3}$

c. $s(5) = s(0) + \int_0^5 v(t)\, dt = 0 + 3 = 3$.

d. $s(t) = \begin{cases} \int_0^t (-x+2)\,dx & \text{if } 0 \le t \le 3, \\ \frac{3}{2} + \int_3^t (3x-10)\,dx & \text{if } 3 < t \le 4, \\ 2 + \int_4^t (-2x+10)\,dx & \text{if } 4 < t \le 5 \end{cases} = \begin{cases} -\frac{t^2}{2} + 2t & \text{if } 0 \le t \le 3, \\ \frac{3t^2}{2} - 10t + 18 & \text{if } 3 < t \le 4, \cdot \\ -t^2 + 10t - 22 & \text{if } 4 < t \le 5. \end{cases}$

6.1.52 The distance traveled is $\int_0^8 (2t+6)\,dt = (t^2 + 6t)\big|_0^8 = 112$. So the same distance could have been traveled over the given time period at a constant velocity of $\frac{112}{8} = 14$.

6.1.53 The distance traveled is $\int_0^4 (1 - (t^2/16))\,dt = (t - (t^3/48))\big|_0^4 = \frac{8}{3}$. So the same distance could have been traveled over the given time period at a constant velocity of $\frac{8/3}{4} = \frac{2}{3}$.

6.1.54 The distance traveled is $\int_0^\pi 2\sin t\,dt = (-2\cos t)\big|_0^\pi = 4$. So the same distance could have been traveled over the given time period at a constant velocity of $\frac{4}{\pi}$.

6.1.55 The distance traveled is $\int_0^5 t\sqrt{25 - t^2}\,dt = \frac{1}{2}\int_0^{25} \sqrt{u}\,du = \left(\frac{1}{3}u^{3/2}\right)\big|_0^{25} = \frac{125}{3}$. So the same distance could have been traveled over the given time period at a constant velocity of $\frac{125/3}{5} = \frac{25}{3}$.

6.1.56

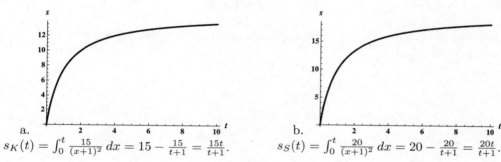

a.
$s_K(t) = \int_0^t \frac{15}{(x+1)^2}\,dx = 15 - \frac{15}{t+1} = \frac{15t}{t+1}.$

b.
$s_S(t) = \int_0^t \frac{20}{(x+1)^2}\,dx = 20 - \frac{20}{t+1} = \frac{20t}{t+1}.$

c. They meet when $\frac{15t}{t+1} + \frac{20t}{t+1} = 20$, which occurs for $t = \frac{4}{3}$. (Which represents 1:20 PM.) At this time, Kelly has gone $s_K(4/3) = \frac{20}{7/3} = \frac{60}{7}$ km, and Sandy has gone $s_S(4/3) = \frac{80}{7}$ km.

d. We would need $\frac{At}{t+1} + \frac{Bt}{t+1} = D$ to have a solution. If we solve for t, we obtain $t = \frac{D}{A+B-D}$, so we need $A + B > D$.

e. The maximum distances are A and B respectively, because $\lim_{t\to\infty} \frac{At}{t+1} = A$ and $\lim_{t\to\infty} \frac{Bt}{t+1} = B$.

6.1.57

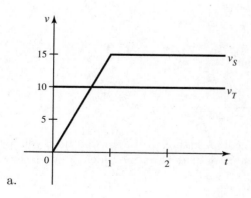

a.

b. After 1 hour, Theo has ridden $1 \cdot 10 = 10$ miles, and Sasha has ridden $\frac{1}{2} \cdot 15 = 7.5$ miles, so Theo has ridden farther.

c. After 2 hours, Theo has ridden $2 \cdot 10 = 20$ miles, and Sasha has ridden $7.5 + 15 \cdot 1 = 22.5$ miles, so Sasha has ridden farther.

d. The times when they arrive at the various mile markers are in the following table:

	10	15	20
Theo	1	3/2	2
Sasha	7/6	3/2	11/6

Note that Theo hits the 10 mile marker first, then they are tied as they hit the 15 mile marker, and Sasha hits the 20 mile marker first. The area under v_S is the same as the area under v_T for $t = 1.5$, for $t < 1.5$ the area under v_T is greater, and for $t > 1.5$, the area under v_S is greater.

e. Theo will then hit the 20 mile mark in $18.8/10 = 1.88$ hours. Sasha hits the 20 mile mark at $t = 11/6 \approx 1.833$ hours, so Sasha will win.

f. A head start of .2 hours is equivalent for Theo of $10 \cdot .2 = 2$ miles. It will take him $18/10 = 1.8$ hours to ride the other 18 miles, while it still takes Sasha about 1.83 hours to cover 20 miles, so Theo will win.

6.1.58

a. $s_A(t) = \int_0^t \frac{4}{x+1}\, dx = \left(4\ln(x+1)\right)\big|_0^t = 4\ln(t+1)$.

$s_B(t) = 2 + \int_0^t \frac{2}{x+1}\, dx = 2 + \left(2\ln(x+1)\right)\big|_0^t = 2 + 2\ln(t+1)$.

b. This would occur if $4\ln(t+1) = 2 + 2\ln(t+1)$, or $\ln(t+1) = 1$, which occurs for $t = e - 1$, which is about 1 hour and 43 minutes.

6.1.59

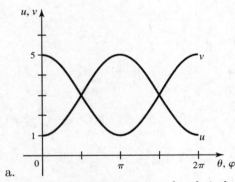

a. Abe starts out running into a headwind, Bess starts out running with a tailwind.

b. The average of Abe's speed function is $\frac{1}{2\pi}\int_0^{2\pi}(3 - 2\cos\varphi)\,d\varphi = \frac{1}{2\pi}\left(3\theta - 2\sin\varphi\right)\big|_0^{2\pi} = 3$ mph, and The average of Bess' speed function is $\frac{1}{2\pi}\int_0^{2\pi}(3 + 2\cos\theta)\,d\theta = \frac{1}{2\pi}\left(3\theta + 2\sin\theta\right)\big|_0^{2\pi} = 3$ mph. They have the same average speed.

c. The track is 1/10 mile in radius. We have $u = \frac{ds}{dt}$ where $s = \frac{1}{10}\varphi$. Thus, $u = \frac{ds}{dt} = \frac{1}{10}\frac{d\varphi}{dt} = 3 - 2\cos\varphi$, so $dt = \frac{d\varphi}{10(3 - 2\cos\varphi)}$. The time T for one lap is then

$$T = \int_0^T dt = \int_0^{2\pi} \frac{d\varphi}{10(3 - 2\cos\varphi)} = \frac{\pi}{5\sqrt{5}} = \frac{\pi\sqrt{5}}{25}.$$

You may need to use a computer algebra system to compute the integral, or wait until you have studied chapter 7. The calculation for Bess' velocity function produces the same time. They tie the race. Both have average speed $\frac{2\pi}{10T} = \sqrt{5}$.

6.1.60

a. $\int_0^{60} 3\sqrt{t}\, dt = \left(2t^{3/2}\right)\big|_0^{60} \approx 929.52$ L.

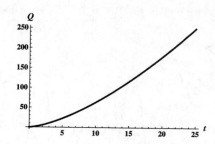

b. $Q(t) = \int_0^t 3\sqrt{x}\,dx = \left(2x^{3/2}\right)\big|_0^t = 2t^{3/2}$ L, where t is measured in minutes.

c. The tank will be full when $2t^{3/2} = 2000$, or $t = \sqrt[3]{1000^2} = 100$ minutes.

6.1.61

a. $Q(t) = \int r(t)\,dt = \int 10^7 e^{-kt}\,dt = \frac{10^7}{-k}e^{-kt} + C$. When $t = 0$ we have $Q(0) = 0$, so $C + \frac{10^7}{-k} = 0$, so $C = \frac{10^7}{k}$. Thus $Q(t) = \frac{10^7(1 - e^{-kt})}{k}$.

b. $\lim_{t\to\infty} Q(t) = \lim_{t\to\infty} \frac{10^7(1 - e^{-kt})}{k} = \frac{10^7}{k}$. This represents the total number of barrels extracted if the nation extracts the oil indefinitely where it is assumed that the nation has at least $\frac{10^7}{k}$ barrels of oil in reserve.

c. We seek k so that $\frac{10^7}{k} = 2 \times 10^9$, which gives $k = \frac{1}{200} = .005$.

d. We want T so that $(2 \times 10^7)\int_0^T e^{-.005t}\,dt = 2 \times 10^9$, so $\left(-200e^{-.005t}\right)\big|_0^T = 100$, so $1 - e^{-T/200} = 1/2$, so $T = 200\ln 2 \approx 138.629$ years.

6.1.62 Let the depth of the snow at time t be t units (adjusting your units as necessary.) The speed of the plow at time t will be $1/t$. Let $t = 0$ be the time the snow started, and let time $T > 0$ represent noon. $\int_T^{T+1} \frac{1}{t}\,dt$ represents the distance the plow goes in the first hour, and this quantity is equal to $\ln(T + 1) - \ln(T) = \ln((T + 1)/T)$. The distance the plow goes in the 2nd hour is $\int_{T+1}^{T+2} \frac{1}{t}\,dt = \ln((T + 2)/(T + 1))$.

Thus we have $\ln((T + 1)/T) = 2\ln((T + 2)/(T + 1))$, so $\left(\frac{T+1}{T}\right) = \left(\frac{T+2}{T+1}\right)^2$, which leads to the equation $(T + 1)^3 = T(T + 2)^2$, so $T^3 + 3T^2 + 3T + 1 = T^3 + 4T^2 + 4T$, so $T^2 + T - 1 = 0$, and $T = \frac{-1+\sqrt{5}}{2} \approx .618$.

So if noon corresponds to the .618 hours after the snow started falling, the snow must have started falling about 37 minutes before noon, so at about 11:23 AM.

6.1.63

a. $\int_0^2 20(1 + \cos(\pi t/12))\,dt = \left(20t + \frac{240}{\pi}\sin(\pi t/12)\right)\big|_0^2 = 40 + \frac{240}{\pi} \cdot \frac{1}{2} = 40 + \frac{120}{\pi} \approx 78.197\,\text{m}^3$.

b.

$Q(t) = \int_0^t 20(1 + \cos(\pi x/12))\,dx$, which is equal to $\left(20x + \frac{240}{\pi}\sin(\pi x/12)\right)\big|_0^t = 20t + \frac{240}{\pi} \cdot \sin(\pi t/12)\,\text{m}^3$.

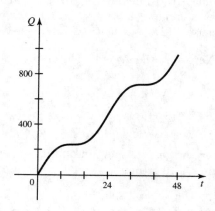

c. The reservoir is full when $20T + \frac{240}{\pi} \sin(\pi T/12) = 2500$, which occurs for $T \approx 122.6$ hours.

6.1.64

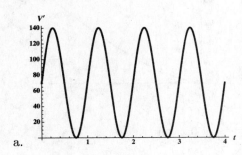

b. $\int_0^1 70(1 + \sin(2\pi t)) \, dt = \left(70t - \frac{35}{\pi} \cos(2\pi t) \right) \big|_0^1 = 70 - \frac{35}{\pi} + \frac{35}{\pi} = 70$ mL.

a.

c. $\int_0^t 70(1 + \sin(2\pi x)) \, dx = \left(70x - \frac{35}{\pi} \cos(2\pi x) \right) \big|_0^t = 70t - \frac{35}{\pi} \cos(2\pi t) + \frac{35}{\pi} = \frac{35}{\pi} + 70t - \frac{35}{\pi} \cos(2\pi t)$ mL.

d. $\int_t^{t+1} 70(1 + \sin(2\pi x)) \, dx = \left(70x - \frac{35}{\pi} \cos(2\pi x) \right) \big|_t^{t+1} = 70t + 70 - \frac{35}{\pi} \cos(2\pi(t+1)) - (70t - \frac{35}{\pi} \cos(2\pi t)) = \frac{35}{\pi} + 70t - \frac{35}{\pi} \cos(2\pi t) = 70$ mL.

6.1.65

a. Note that $\int -\frac{\pi}{2} \sin \frac{\pi t}{2} \, dt = \cos \frac{\pi t}{2} + C$. The value of this function at $t = 0$ is $1 + C = 6$, so we require $C = 5$, and we have

$$V(t) = 5 + \cos \frac{\pi t}{2}.$$

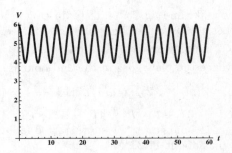

b. Because $\sin \frac{\pi t}{2}$ is periodic with period 4, the breathing cycle repeats every 4 seconds, so there are $\frac{60}{4} = 15$ breaths per minute.

c. The lungs are full at $t = 0$, at which time $V(0) = 6$ L, so this is the capacity of the lungs. The tidal volume is the difference between this amount and the amount in the lungs after each exhalation, which is the minimum value of $V(t)$. This minimum occurs at the first positive zero of $V'(t)$, which is at t=2. Because $V(2) = 4$, the tidal volume is $6 - 4 = 2$L.

6.1.66   Note that the general solution for $N(t)$ is

$$N(t) = \int N'(t) \, dt = \int (A \sin(2\pi t/P) + r) \, dt = -\frac{PA}{2\pi} \cos(2\pi t/P) + rt + C,$$

and $C = N(0) + \frac{PA}{2\pi}$. Thus $N(t) = -\frac{PA}{2\pi} \cos(2\pi t/P) + rt + N(0) + \frac{PA}{2\pi} = N(0) + rt + \frac{PA}{2\pi}(1 - \cos(2\pi t/P))$.

a. Using the general solution above, we have $N(t) = 10 + \frac{100}{\pi}(1 - \cos(\pi t/5))$. This is never 0, because it is always 10 or more.

b. Using the general solution above, we have that $N(t) = 100 + \frac{100}{\pi}(1 - \cos(\pi t/5))$. The population is never extinct, because it is always 100 or more.

c. Using the general solution above, we have $N(t) = 10 + 5t + \frac{250}{\pi}(1 - \cos(\pi t/5))$. Again, for $t \geq 0$ this is always at least 10, so the population never becomes extinct.

d. Using the general solution above, we have $N(t) = N(0) - 5t + \frac{250}{\pi}(1 - \cos(\pi t/5))$. Suppose $t = 5k$ for a positive even integer k. Then $\cos(\pi t/5) = \cos(k\pi) = 1$, so $N(t) = N(0) - 25k + 0$, which grows negatively without bound as $k \to \infty$. Thus, there is no choice of $N(0)$ which will ensure that the population won't become extinct.

6.1.67

a. $E = \int_0^{24}(300 - 200\sin(\pi t/12))\,dt = \left(300t + \frac{2400}{\pi}\cos(\pi t/12)\right)\Big|_0^{24} = 7200$ MWh. This is equivalent to $7.2 \times 10^6 \cdot 3.6 \times 10^6 = 2.592 \times 10^{13}$ Joules.

b. For one day, $\frac{7.2 \times 10^6 \text{ KWh}}{450 \text{ Kwh/kg}} = 16{,}000$ kg coal needed.

For one year, $16000\,\text{kg} \times 365 = 5{,}840{,}000$ kg coal needed.

c. For one day, $\frac{7.2 \times 10^6 \text{ KWh}}{1.6 \times 10^4 \text{ Kwh/g}} = 450$ g U-235 need.

For one year, $450 \times 365 = 164{,}250$ g needed.

d. $\frac{7.2 \times 10^6 \text{ KWh/day}}{(200 \text{ KW/turbine}) \cdot (24 \text{ hours/day})} = 1500$ turbines.

6.1.68

a. $y(t)$ is the position of the projectile, and the derivative of position is velocity, and the derivative of velocity is acceleration. Note that the acceleration force is due to gravity, and only depends on the position y of the projectile.

b. $\frac{1}{2}\frac{d}{dy}\left(v^2\right) = \frac{1}{2} \cdot 2v\frac{dv}{dy} = \frac{dy}{dt} \cdot \frac{dv}{dy} = \frac{dv}{dt}$.

c. Because $\frac{dv}{dt} = a(y)$ and $\frac{dv}{dt} = \frac{1}{2}\frac{d}{dy}(v^2)$, we must have $\frac{1}{2}\frac{d}{dy}(v^2) = a(y)$.

d. $\frac{1}{2}\int \frac{d}{dy}(v^2)\,dy = \int a(y)\,dy$, so $\frac{1}{2}(v^2) = \int -\frac{g}{(1+y/R)^2}\,dy = gR\left(\frac{1}{1+y/R}\right) + D$. Now when $t = 0$, we have $v = v_0$ and $y = 0$, so $\frac{1}{2}v_0^2 = gR + D$, so $D = -gR + \frac{1}{2}v_0^2$, and we can write

$$\frac{1}{2}(v^2 - v_0^2) = gR\left(\frac{1}{1+y/R} - 1\right).$$

e. When $v = 0$ we have $-\frac{1}{2}v_0^2 \cdot \frac{1}{gR} + 1 = \frac{1}{1+y/R}$, so $\frac{1}{1+y/R} = \frac{2gR - v_0^2}{2gR}$, so $1 + y/R = \frac{2gR}{2gR - v_0^2}$, and $y = \frac{2gR^2}{2gR - v_0^2} - R = \frac{2gR^2}{2gR - v_0^2} - \frac{2gR^2 - Rv_0^2}{2gR - v_0^2} = \frac{Rv_0^2}{2gR - v_0^2}$.

f. $y_{\max}(500) \approx 12{,}780$ m.
$y_{\max}(1500) \approx 116{,}893$ m.
$y_{\max}(5000) \approx 1{,}592{,}990$ m.

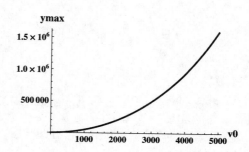

g. The denominator of the expression for $y_{\max}$ is 0 when $2gR = v_0^2$, so when $v_0 = \sqrt{2gR}$. As $v_0 \to \sqrt{2gR}$, $y_{\max} \to \infty$.

6.1.69 Using the Fundamental Theorem, we have

$$\int_a^b f'(x)\,dx = f(b) - f(a) = g(b) - g(a) = \int_a^b g'(x)\,dx.$$

6.1.70 Let $f(t)$ represent the position of the first runner at time t and let $g(t)$ represent the position of the second runner over the time interval $[a, b]$. We are given that $f(a) = g(a)$ and $f(b) = g(b)$. Then by problem 69, we have

$$\int_a^b f'(t)\,dt = \int_a^b g'(t)\,dt,$$

so the displacements of the two runners is the same, even though it might not be the case that $f'(t) = g'(t)$ for every t.

6.1.71 If $f(x)$ is the elevation of trail one at position x and $g(x)$ is the elevation of trail two at position x, then because we are given that $f(a) = g(a)$ and $f(b) = g(b)$, we must have that

$$\int_a^b f'(x)\,dx = \int_a^b g'(x)\,dx,$$

so the two trails have the same net change in elevation.

6.1.72 Let $f(x) = 12\sin(\pi x^2)$ and $g(x) = x^{10}(2 - x)^2$. Note that $f(0) = 0 = g(0)$ and $f(2) = 0 = g(2)$. Thus by problem 69, $\displaystyle\int_0^2 f'(x)\,dx = \int_0^2 g'(x)\,dx$, which is equivalent to the statement we are trying to prove.

6.2   Regions Between Curves

6.2.1   If f and g intersect at $x = a$ and $x = b$ with $a < b$ and if $f(x) \geq g(x)$ on $[a, b]$, then the area between these curves is given by $\int_a^b (f(x) - g(x))\,dx$.

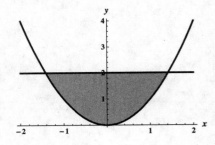

6.2.2   If f and g intersect exactly three times at $x = a$, $x = b$, and $x = c$ with $a < b < c$, and if $f(x) \geq g(x)$ on $[a, b]$ and $g(x) \geq f(x)$ on $[b, c]$, then the area is given by $\int_a^b (f(x) - g(x))\,dx + \int_b^c (g(x) - f(x))\,dx$.

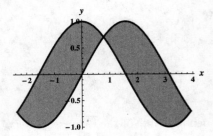

6.2.3

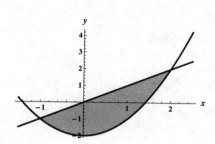

6.2.4

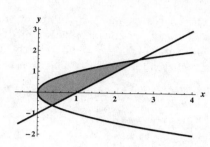

6.2.5 The curves intersect when $x = x^2 - 2$, or $(x+1)(x-2) = 0$, so at $x = -1$ and $x = 2$. The area is
$\int_{-1}^{2}(x - (x^2 - 2)) = \left(2x + x^2/2 - x^3/3\right)\Big|_{-1}^{2} = 4.5$.

6.2.6 The curves intersect when $x = x^3$, or $x(x-1)(x+1) = 0$, so at $x = 0$, $x = -1$ and $x = 1$. The area is given by $\int_{-1}^{0}(x^3 - x)\,dx + \int_{0}^{1}(x - x^3)\,dx = 2\int_{0}^{1}(x - x^3)\,dx = 2\left(x^2/2 - x^4/4\right)\Big|_{0}^{1} = \frac{1}{2}$.

6.2.7 By inspection, the curves intersect at $x = 1$. The area is given by

$$\int_{0}^{1}(3 - x - 2^x)\,dx = \left(3x - x^2/2 - \frac{2^x}{\ln 2}\right)\Big|_{0}^{1} = 3 - (1/2) - \frac{2}{\ln 2} - \left(-\frac{1}{\ln 2}\right) = \frac{5}{2} - \frac{1}{\ln 2}.$$

6.2.8 The curves intersect when $\frac{\sec^2 x}{4} = 4\cos^2 x$, which can be written as $\cos^4 x = \frac{1}{16} = \frac{1}{2^4}$. This occurs when $\cos x = \pm\frac{1}{2}$, which occurs at $-\pi/3$ and $\pi/3$. Using symmetry, the area is given by

$$2\int_{0}^{\pi/3}(4\cos^2 x - (1/4)\sec^2 x)\,dx = 2\int_{0}^{\pi/3}(2(1 + \cos 2x) - (1/4)\sec^2 x)\,dx$$

$$= 2\left(2x + \sin 2x - (1/4)\tan x\right)\Big|_{0}^{\pi/3} = \frac{4\pi}{3} + \sqrt{3} - \frac{\sqrt{3}}{2} = \frac{4\pi}{3} + \frac{\sqrt{3}}{2}.$$

6.2.9 The nonvertical lines intersect when $2x + 2 = 3x + 3$, or $x = -1$. The vertical line $x = 4$ intersects both nonvertical lines when $x = 4$. The area is given by $\int_{-1}^{4}(3x + 3 - (2x + 2))\,dx = \int_{-1}^{4}(x + 1)\,dx = \left(x^2/2 + x\right)\Big|_{-1}^{4} = 8 + 4 - ((1/2) - 1) = 12.5$.

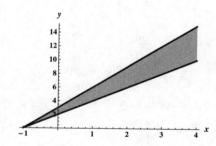

6.2.10 $\cos x = \sin x$ when $\tan x = 1$, or $x = \tan^{-1}(1) = \pi/4$. They also intersect at $\pi/4 + \pi = 5\pi/4$. The area is given by $\int_{\pi/4}^{5\pi/4}(\sin x - \cos x)\,dx = (-(\cos x + \sin x))\Big|_{\pi/4}^{5\pi/4} = -((-\sqrt{2}/2 - \sqrt{2}/2) - (\sqrt{2}/2 + \sqrt{2}/2)) = 2\sqrt{2}$.

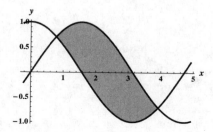

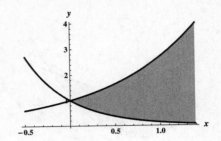

6.2.11 The curves e^x and e^{-2x} intersect when $e^x = e^{-2x}$, or $e^{3x} = 1$, which occurs only for $x = 0$. The vertical line $x = \ln 4$ clearly intersects the curves for $x = \ln 4$. The area is given by

$$\int_0^{\ln 4} (e^x - e^{-2x})\, dx = \left(e^x + e^{-2x}/2\right)\Big|_0^{\ln 4} = 4 + (1/32) - (1 + (1/2)) = 81/32.$$

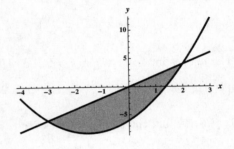

6.2.12 The curves intersect when $2x = x^2 + 3x - 6$, which occurs when $x^2 + x - 6 = 0$. Because $x^2 + x - 6 = (x+3)(x-2)$, the curves intersect at $x = -3$ and $x = 2$. The area is given by

$$\int_{-3}^2 (2x - (x^2 + 3x - 6))\, dx = \int_{-3}^2 (-x^2 - x + 6)\, dx = \left(-x^3/3 - x^2/2 + 6x\right)\Big|_{-3}^2 = -8/3 - 2 + 12 - (9 - 9/2 - 18) = \frac{125}{6}.$$

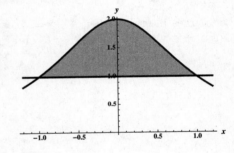

6.2.13 The curves intersect when $\frac{2}{1+x^2} = 1$, or $x^2 + 1 = 2$, or $x^2 - 1 = (x-1)(x+1) = 0$. So the intersections occur when $x = \pm 1$. Using symmetry, the area is $2\int_0^1 \left(\frac{2}{1+x^2} - 1\right) dx = 2\left(2\tan^{-1} x - x\right)\Big|_0^1 = \pi - 2.$

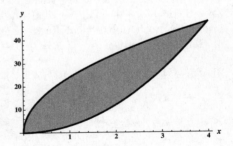

6.2.14 The curves intersect when $24\sqrt{x} = 3x^2$, so when either $x = 0$ or when $8 = x^{3/2}$. Thus happens for $x = 8^{2/3} = 4$. We have

$$\int_0^4 \left(24\sqrt{x} - 3x^2\right) dx = \left(16x^{3/2} - x^3\right)\Big|_0^4 = 128 - 64 = 64.$$

6.2.15 The curves intersect at $\pi/4$, so the area is given by $\int_0^{\pi/4} \sin x\, dx + \int_{\pi/4}^{\pi/2} \cos x\, dx = (-\cos x)\Big|_0^{\pi/4} + (\sin x)\Big|_{\pi/4}^{\pi/2} = (1 - \sqrt{2}/2) + (1 - \sqrt{2}/2) = 2 - \sqrt{2}.$

6.2.16 Note that $\sin 2x = 2\sin x \cos x$, so the curves intersect where $2\sin x \cos x = \sin x$, so the curves intersect at $x = 0$ and $x = \pi$, and $x = \pi/3$, because $\cos \pi/3 = \frac{1}{2}$. The area is given by $\int_0^{\pi/3} (\sin 2x - $

$\sin x)\, dx + \int_{\pi/3}^{\pi}(\sin x - \sin 2x)\, dx = \left. (-\cos(2x)/2 + \cos x) \right|_0^{\pi/3} + \left. (-\cos(x) + \cos(2x)/2) \right|_{\pi/3}^{\pi} = (1/4 + 1/2 - ((-1/2) + 1)) + (1 + (1/2) - ((-1/2) + (-1/4))) = 1/4 + 9/4 = 5/2.$

6.2.17 The curves intersect when $x = 1/x$, or $x^2 = 1$. This occurs in the first quadrant when $x = 1$. The area is given by $\int_0^1 x\, dx + \int_1^2 1/x\, dx = \left. (x^2/2) \right|_0^1 + \left. (\ln x) \right|_1^2 = 1/2 + \ln 2.$

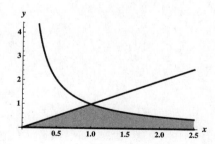

6.2.18 Note that the curves intersect when $4x - x^2 = 4x - 4$, or $x^2 - 4 = 0$. We see that the curves intersect for $x > 0$ when $x = 2$. The line $y = 4x - 4$ intersects the x-axis at $x = 1$. The area is given by $\int_0^1 (4x - x^2)\, dx + \int_1^2 (4x - x^2 - (4x - 4))\, dx = \int_0^1 (4x - x^2)\, dx + \int_1^2 (4 - x^2)\, dx = \left. (2x^2 - x^3/3) \right|_0^1 + \left. (4x - x^3/3) \right|_1^2 = (2 - 1/3) + (8 - 8/3) - (4 - 1/3) = \frac{10}{3}.$

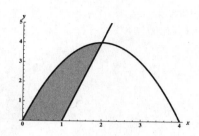

6.2.19 A plot of the region is

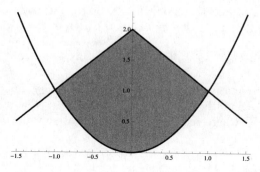

The curves intersect at $x = \pm 1$, and the area is twice the area from 0 to 1, so it is

$$2\int_0^1 (2 - x - x^2)\, dx = 2\left. \left(2x - \frac{1}{2}x^2 - \frac{1}{3}x^2\right) \right|_0^1 = \frac{7}{3}.$$

6.2.20 Using symmetry, the area is $2\int_0^3 (9x - x^3)\, dx = 2\left. \left(9x^2/2 - x^4/4\right) \right|_0^3 = 2(81/2 - 81/4) = 81/2.$

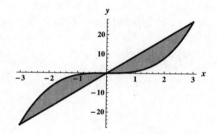

$\int_2^6 (x/2 - |x - 3|) \, dx = \int_2^3 (x/2 - (3 - x)) \, dx + \int_3^6 (x/2 - (x - 3)) \, dx = \int_2^3 (3x/2 - $

6.2.21 $3) \, dx + \int_3^6 (3 - x/2) \, dx = (3x^2/4 - 3x) \Big|_2^3 +$

$(3x - x^2/4) \Big|_3^6 = 27/4 - 9 - (3 - 6) + (18 - $

$9 - (9 - 9/4)) = 3/4 + 9/4 = 3.$

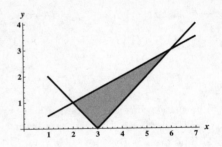

6.2.22

$$\int_{-2}^{2} (12 - 4x - (3x^2 - x^3)) \, dx + \int_{2}^{3} (3x^2 - x^3 - (12 - 4x)) \, dx$$

$$= (12x - 2x^2 - x^3 + x^4/4) \Big|_{-2}^{2} + (x^3 - x^4/4 - 12x + 2x^2) \Big|_{2}^{3}$$

$$= (24 - 8 - 8 + 4 - (-24 - 8 + 8 + 4)) + (27 - 81/4 - 36 + 18 - (8 - 4 - 24 + 8)) = \frac{131}{4}.$$

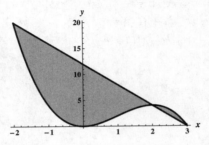

6.2.23 The two curves meet at $x = 0$; at that point $y = 1$. So the integration is from $y = 0$ to $y = 1$. Solving for x gives the curves $x = 2y^2 - 2$ and $x = 1 - y^2$. Thus the area of the region is

$$\int_0^1 ((1 - y^2) - (2y^2 - 2)) \, dy = \int_0^1 (-3y^2 + 3) \, dy = (-y^3 + 3y) \Big|_0^1 = 2.$$

6.2.24 The curves $-\sin 2y$ and $\cos y$ intersect where $-\sin 2y = \cos y$, but $-\sin 2y = -2 \sin y \cos y$, so we must solve $-2 \sin y \cos y = \cos y$. So either $\cos y = 0$ or $\sin y = -\frac{1}{2}$. The first positive value of y satisfying either of these conditions is $y = \frac{\pi}{2}$, where $\cos y = 0$; the first negative value of y is $y = -\frac{\pi}{6}$ where $\sin y = -\frac{1}{2}$. So the area is

$$\int_{-\pi/6}^{\pi/2} (\cos y - (-\sin 2y)) \, dy = \left(\sin y - \frac{1}{2} \cos 2y \right) \Big|_{-\pi/6}^{\pi/2}$$

$$= \sin \frac{\pi}{2} - \frac{1}{2} \cos \pi - \sin \left(-\frac{\pi}{6} \right) + \frac{1}{2} \cos \left(-\frac{\pi}{3} \right)$$

$$= 1 + \frac{1}{2} + \frac{1}{2} + \frac{1}{4} = \frac{9}{4}.$$

6.2.25 The curves $x = y^2 - 3y + 12$ and $x = -2y^2 - 6y + 30$ intersect where $y^2 - 3y + 12 = -2y^2 - 6y + 30$, or $3y^2 + 3y - 18 = 3(y + 3)(y - 2) = 0$. So the points of intersection are $y = -3$ and $y = 2$. Thus the area is

$$\int_{-3}^{2} ((-2y^2 - 6y + 30) - (y^2 - 3y + 12)) \, dy = \int_{-3}^{2} (-3y^2 - 3y + 18) \, dy$$

$$= \left(-y^3 - \frac{3}{2}y^2 + 18y \right) \Big|_{-3}^{2}$$

$$= -8 - 6 + 36 - 27 + \frac{27}{2} + 54 = \frac{125}{2}.$$

6.2.26 These two curves intersect where $y^3 - 4y^2 + 3y = y^2 - y$, or $y^3 - 5y^2 + 4y = y(y-4)(y-1) = 0$. The three intersection points occur where $y = 0$, $y = 4$, and $y = 1$. Note that from $y = 0$ to $y = 1$ we have $y^2 - y \le y^3 - 4y^2 + 3y$; from $y = 1$ to $y = 4$ this is reversed. Thus the area between the curves is

$$\int_0^1 (y^3 - 4y^2 + 3y - (y^2 - y))\, dy + \int_1^4 (y^2 - y - (y^3 - 4y^2 + 3y))\, dy$$

$$= \int_0^1 (y^3 - 5y^2 + 4y)\, dy + \int_1^4 (-y^3 + 5y^2 - 4y)\, dy$$

$$= \left(\frac{1}{4}y^4 - \frac{5}{3}y^3 + 2y^2 \right) \Big|_0^1 + \left(-\frac{1}{4}y^4 + \frac{5}{3}y^3 - 2y^2 \right) \Big|_1^4$$

$$= \frac{1}{4} - \frac{5}{3} + 2 - 64 + \frac{320}{3} - 32 + \frac{1}{4} - \frac{5}{3} + 2 = \frac{71}{6}.$$

6.2.27

a. The area is given by $\int_{-\sqrt{2}}^{-1} (-(x^2 - 2))\, dx + \int_{-1}^0 (-x)\, dx$.

b. The area can also be written as $\int_{-1}^0 (y - (-\sqrt{y+2}))\, dy$.

6.2.28

a. The area is given by $\int_0^2 (-(x^2 - 4x))\, dx + \int_2^4 (-(2x - 8))\, dx$.

b. The area can also be written as $\int_{-4}^0 (y/2 + 4 - (2 - \sqrt{y+4}))\, dy$. Note that in order to solve $y = x^2 - 4x$ for x, we needed to complete the square to obtain $y + 4 = x^2 - 4x + 4 = (x-2)^2$, so $\sqrt{y+4} + |x-2|$, and the part of this we need is $x = 2 - \sqrt{y+4}$.

6.2.29

a. The area is given by $\int_{-3}^{-2} (\sqrt{x+3} - (-\sqrt{x+3}))\, dx + \int_{-2}^6 (\sqrt{x+3} - x/2)\, dx$.

b. The area can also be written $\int_{-1}^3 (2y - (y^2 - 3))\, dy$.

6.2.30

a. The area is given by $\int_0^1 (\sqrt{x} - x^3)\, dx$.

b. The area can also be written $\int_0^1 (\sqrt[3]{y} - y^2)\, dy$.

6.2.31 The region is plotted below.

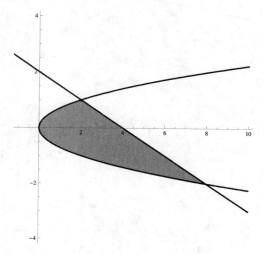

Note that the two curves intersect where $y = 2 - \frac{x}{2} = 2 - y^2$, so for $y^2 + y - 2 = (y+2)(y-1) = 0$. So they intersect at the points $(2, 1)$ and $(8, -2)$.

a. Integrating with respect to x, we must solve the second equation for y to obtain $y = \pm\sqrt{\frac{x}{2}}$. Then the integral must be split into two integrals, and the area is

$$\int_0^2 \left(\sqrt{\frac{x}{2}} - \left(-\sqrt{\frac{x}{2}}\right)\right) dx + \int_2^8 \left(2 - \frac{x}{2} - \left(-\sqrt{\frac{x}{2}}\right)\right) dx$$

$$= \frac{2}{\sqrt{2}} \int_0^2 x^{1/2} \, dx + \int_2^8 \left(2 - \frac{x}{2} + \frac{1}{\sqrt{2}} x^{1/2}\right) dx$$

$$= \frac{2}{\sqrt{2}} \left(\frac{2}{3} x^{3/2}\right)\Big|_0^2 + \left(2x - \frac{x^2}{4} + \frac{2}{3\sqrt{2}} x^{3/2}\right)\Big|_2^8$$

$$= \sqrt{2} \cdot \frac{2}{3} \cdot 2\sqrt{2} + 16 - 16 + \frac{2}{3\sqrt{2}} \cdot 16\sqrt{2} - 4 + 1 - \frac{2}{3\sqrt{2}} \cdot 2\sqrt{2}$$

$$= \frac{3}{2} + \frac{32}{3} - 3 - \frac{4}{3} = 9.$$

b. With respect to y, we have

$$\int_{-2}^1 (4 - 2y - 2y^2) \, dy = \left(4y - y^2 - \frac{2}{3} y^3\right)\Big|_{-2}^1 = \left(4 - 1 - \frac{2}{3}\right) - \left(-8 - 4 + \frac{16}{3}\right) = 9.$$

6.2.32 The region is plotted below.

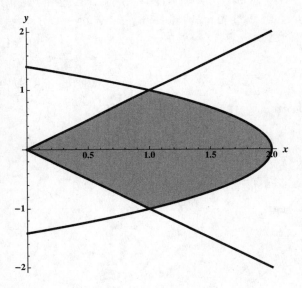

Note that the curves intersect at $(1, 1)$ and $(1, -1)$.

a. Using symmetry, the area is given by

$$2\int_0^1 x \, dx + 2 \int_1^2 \sqrt{2 - x} \, dx = \left(x^2\right)\Big|_0^1 + 2\left((-2/3)(2-x)^{3/2}\right)\Big|_1^2 = 1 + (0 - (-4/3)) = 7/3.$$

b. Using symmetry, we have

$$2\int_0^1 ((2 - y^2) - y) \, dy = 2\left(2y - y^3/3 - y^2/2\right)\Big|_0^1 = 2(2 - 1/3 - 1/2) = 3 - 2/3 = 7/3.$$

6.2.33

The area is given by $\int_0^8 (4 - x^{2/3})\,dx =$ $\left. \left(4x - 3x^{5/3}/5\right) \right|_0^8 = 32 - 96/5 = 64/5.$

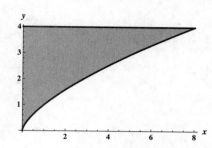

6.2.34

The area is given by $\int_0^{\pi/2} (2 - 2\sin x)\,dx =$ $\left. \left(2x + 2\cos x\right) \right|_0^{\pi/2} = \pi - 2.$

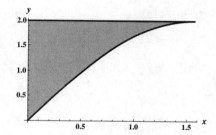

6.2.35

The area is given by $\int_0^{\ln 2} (2e^{-x} + 1 - e^x)\,dx =$ $\left. \left(-2e^{-x} + x - e^x\right) \right|_0^{\ln 2} = -1 + \ln 2 - 2 - (-2 - 1) = \ln 2.$

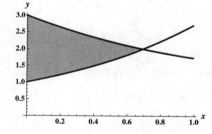

6.2.36

The area is given by $\int_0^{\pi/4} (2 - \sec^2 x)\,dx =$ $\left. \left(2x - \tan x\right) \right|_0^{\pi/4} = \frac{\pi}{2} - 1.$

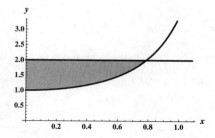

6.2.37

The area is given by $\int_0^{\sqrt{3}/2}(2x\sqrt{1-x^2} - x)\,dx = \left(-\frac{2}{3}(1-x^2)^{3/2} - \frac{x^2}{2}\right)\Big|_0^{\sqrt{3}/2} = \frac{-2}{24} - \frac{3}{8} + \frac{2}{3} = \frac{5}{24}.$

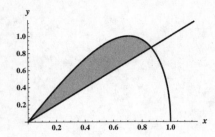

6.2.38

The area is given by $\int_{-1}^{4}(3y - (y^2 - 4))\,dy = (3y^2/2 - y^3/3 + 4y)\Big|_{-1}^{4} = 24 - 64/3 + 16 - (3/2 + 1/3 - 4) = 44 - 65/3 - 3/2 = \frac{125}{6}.$

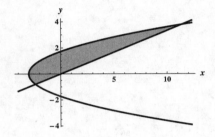

6.2.39

a. False. This can be done either with respect to x or with respect to y. For the latter, the relevant integral is $\int_0^1(y - y^2)\,dy$.

b. False. On the interval $(0, \pi/4)$ the cosine function is greater, but on $(\pi/4, \pi/2)$ the sine function is greater. The area is $\int_0^{\pi/4}(\cos x - \sin x)\,dx + \int_{\pi/4}^{\pi/2}(\sin x - \cos x)\,dx.$

c. True. They both represent the area of the region in the first quadrant under $y = x$ and above $y = x^2$.

6.2.40

The area is given by $\int_0^{\pi}(\sin x - x^2 + \pi x)\,dx = \left(-\cos x - x^3/3 + \pi x^2/2\right)\Big|_0^{\pi} = 1 - \pi^3/3 + \pi^3/2 - (-1) = 2 + \pi^3/6.$

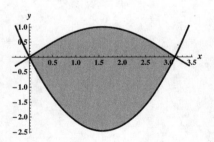

6.2.41

The area is given by $\int_4^5(7x - 19 - (x - 1)^2)\,dx = \left(7x^2/2 - 19x - (x-1)^3/3\right)\Big|_4^5 = (175/2 - 95 - 64/3) - (56 - 76 - 9) = -\frac{173}{6} + 29 = \frac{1}{6}.$

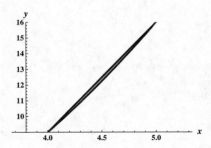

6.2.42

Using symmetry, the area is given by $2\int_0^{\sqrt{3}/2}\left(2-\frac{1}{\sqrt{1-x^2}}\right)dx =$
$2\left(2x-\sin^{-1}(x)\right)\Big|_0^{\sqrt{3}/2} = 2\sqrt{3}-2\pi/3.$

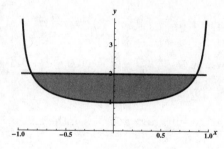

6.2.43

The area is given by $\int_2^5(5x-9-(x-1)^2)\,dx =$
$\left(5x^2/2-9x-(x-1)^3/3\right)\Big|_2^5 = 125/2-45-$
$64/3-(10-18-(1/3)) = 4.5.$

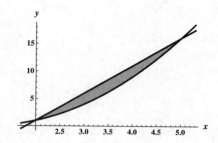

6.2.44 Using symmetry, this is $2\int_0^1(-y(y-1))\,dy = 2\left(-y^3/3+y^2/2\right)\Big|_0^1 = 1/3.$

6.2.45 This is given by $\int_0^4(3y-(y^2-y))\,dy = \int_0^4(4y-y^2)\,dy = \left(2y^2-y^3/3\right)\Big|_0^4 = 32-64/3 = 32/3.$

6.2.46 The area is given by

$$\int_{-1}^0((7/3)x+10/3-(-x^3))\,dx + \int_0^2((7/3)x+10/3-x^3)\,dx$$

$$= \left(7x^2/6+10x/3+x^4/4\right)\Big|_{-1}^0 + \left(7x^2/6+10x/3-x^4/4\right)\Big|_0^2$$

$$= (-7/6+10/3-1/4)+(14/3+20/3-4) = \frac{37}{4}.$$

6.2.47 The area is given by $\int_0^3(y/2+7.5-y^2)\,dy = \left(y^2/4+7.5y-y^3/3\right)\Big|_0^3 = (2.25+22.5-9) = 15.75.$

6.2.48 The region above the axis can be divided into a triangle over $[-1,2]$ with height $15/4$, plus the other region. The area of the triangle is $\frac{1}{2}\cdot 3\cdot 15/4 = 45/8$. The area of the remaining region is given by
$\int_2^3(5x/4+5/4-x^2+4)\,dx = \left(5x^2/8+21x/4-x^3/3\right)\Big|_2^3 = 49/24.$ The total area is thus $\frac{49}{24}+\frac{45}{8} = \frac{184}{24} = \frac{23}{3}.$

6.2.49 This area is given by $\int_{1/2}^2(5/2-1/x-x)\,dx = \left(5x/2-\ln x-x^2/2\right)\Big|_{1/2}^2 = 5-\ln 2-2-(5/4-\ln(1/2)-1/8) = 15/8-2\ln 2.$

6.2.50 This area is given by $\int_0^{1/2}(4x-x/4)\,dx + \int_{1/2}^2(1/x-x/4)\,dx = \left(15x^2/8\right)\Big|_0^{1/2} + \left(\ln x-x^2/8\right)\Big|_{1/2}^2 =$
$15/32+\ln 2-1/2-(\ln 1/2-1/32) = 2\ln 2.$

6.2.51

a. The area of R_1 is $\int_0^1 (x - x^p)\, dx = \left(x^2/2 - \frac{x^{p+1}}{p+1}\right)\Big|_0^1 = \frac{1}{2} - \frac{1}{p+1} = \frac{p-1}{2p+2}.$

The area of R_2 is $\int_0^1 (x^{1/q} - x)\, dx = \left(\frac{q}{q+1}x^{(q+1)/q} - x^2/2\right)\Big|_0^1 = \frac{q}{q+1} - \frac{1}{2} = \frac{q-1}{2q+2}.$

Clearly, if $q = p$ then $R_1 = R_2$.

b. Using the results above, if $p > q$, then $R_1 - R_2 = \frac{(p-1)(2q+2)-(q-1)(2p+2)}{(2p+2)(2q+2)} = \frac{4p-4q}{(2p+2)(2q+2)} = \frac{p-q}{(p+1)(q+1)} >$ 0, so $R_1 > R_2$.

c. If $p < q$, then $R_1 - R_2$ computed above is less than 0, so $R_1 < R_2$.

6.2.52

$$A = \int_{1/2}^1 \left(4\sqrt{2x} - (-4x + 6)\right) dx + \int_1^2 \left(4\sqrt{2x} - 2x^2\right) dx$$

$$= \left(\frac{8\sqrt{2}}{3}x^{3/2} + 2x^2 - 6x\right)\Big|_{1/2}^1 + \left(\frac{8\sqrt{2}}{3}x^{3/2} - 2x^3/3\right)\Big|_1^2 = 19/6.$$

6.2.53 $y = 8x$ and $y = 9 - x^2$ intersect when $x^2 + 8x - 9 = (x + 9)(x - 1) = 0$, so at $x = 1$ in the first quadrant. $y = \frac{5}{2}x$ and $y = 9 - x^2$ intersect when $x^2 + \frac{5}{2}x - 9 = 0$, or $2x^2 + 5x - 18 = (2x + 9)(x - 2) = 0$, so at $x = 2$ in the first quadrant. Thus the area of the region is

$$A = \int_0^1 \left(8x - \frac{5}{2}x\right) dx + \int_1^2 \left(9 - x^2 - \frac{5}{2}x\right) dx$$

$$= \int_0^1 \frac{11}{2}x\, dx + \int_1^2 \left(9 - x^2 - \frac{5}{2}x\right) dx$$

$$= \left(\frac{11}{4}x^2\right)\Big|_0^1 + \left(9x - \frac{x^3}{3} - \frac{5}{4}x^2\right)\Big|_1^2$$

$$= \frac{11}{4} + 18 - \frac{8}{3} - 5 - 9 + \frac{1}{3} + \frac{5}{4} = \frac{17}{3}.$$

6.2.54 Let y_1 be the y coordinate of the lower points where the curves cross, and let y_2 be the y coordinate of the higher point where the curves cross. Note that $y_1 \approx .705$ and $y_2 \approx 2.12$. We have $A = \int_0^{y_1} (\sqrt{y} - 2\sin^2 y)\, dy + \int_{y_1}^{y_2} (2\sin^2 y - \sqrt{y})\, dy = (2y^{3/2}/3 - y + \sin(2y)/2)\Big|_0^{y_1} + (y - \sin(2y)/2 - 2y^{3/2}/3)\Big|_{y_1}^{y_2} = 2y_1^{3/2}/3 - y_1 + \sin(2y_1)/2 + (y_2 - \sin(2y_2)/2 - 2y_2^{3/2}/3) - (y_1 - \sin(2y_1)/2 - 2y_1^{3/2}/3)$. Note that this is approximately equal to .8738.

6.2.55 $A = \int_{-4}^5 (8 - y - (y-2)^2/3)\, dy = \left(8y - y^2/2 - (y-2)^3/9\right)\Big|_{-4}^5 = 40 - 25/2 - 3 - (-32 - 8 + 24) = 40.5.$

6.2.56 $A_n = \int_0^1 (x - x^n)\, dx = \left(x^2/2 - x^{n+1}/(n+1)\right)\Big|_0^1 = \frac{1}{2} - \frac{1}{n+1} = \frac{n-1}{2n+2}.$

6.2.57 $A_n = \int_0^1 (x^{1/n} - x)\, dx = \left(\frac{nx^{(n+1)/n}}{n+1} - x^2/2\right)\Big|_0^1 = \frac{n}{n+1} - \frac{1}{2} = \frac{n-1}{2n+2}.$

6.2.58 $A_n = \int_0^1 (x^{1/n} - x^n)\, dx = \left(\frac{nx^{(n+1)/n}}{n+1} - \frac{x^{n+1}}{n+1}\right)\Big|_0^1 = \frac{n}{n+1} - \frac{1}{n+1} = \frac{n-1}{n+1}.$

6.2.59 Using the result of the previous problem, $\lim_{n\to\infty} A_n = \lim_{n\to\infty} \frac{n-1}{n+1} = 1$. As $n \to \infty$, the region in question approaches the 1×1 square over the interval $[0, 1]$, which has area 1.

6.2.60 R is a right triangle with both legs equal to 1, so its area is $\frac{1}{2}$. Integrating with respect to y, we are looking for k so that $\int_0^k (1 - y)\, dy$ is half the area of the triangle, or $\frac{1}{4}$. Now,

$$\int_0^k (1 - y)\, dy = \left(y - \frac{y^2}{2}\right)\bigg|_0^k = k - \frac{k^2}{2}.$$

Setting $k - \frac{k^2}{2} = \frac{1}{4}$, we have $2k^2 - 4k + 1 = 0$, which has roots $k = \frac{2\pm\sqrt{2}}{2}$. Only the negative sign choice gives a value between 0 and 1, so we want $k = \frac{2-\sqrt{2}}{2} = 1 - \frac{\sqrt{2}}{2}$.

6.2.61 This is a triangle with base 2 and height 1, so it has area 1. Note that for $0 \le x \le 1$ the line which forms the top of the triangle is $y = x$, and for $1 \le x \le 2$, the line is $y = 2 - x$. Integrating with respect to y, we are looking for k so that $\int_0^k (2 - y - y)\, dy = \frac{1}{2}$. Now,

$$\int_0^k (2 - 2y)\, dy = \left(2y - y^2\right)\bigg|_0^k = 2k - k^2.$$

Setting $2k - k^2 = \frac{1}{2}$, we have $2k^2 - 4k + 1 = 0$, which has roots $k = \frac{2\pm\sqrt{2}}{2}$. Only the negative sign choice gives a value between 0 and 1, so we want $k = \frac{2-\sqrt{2}}{2} = 1 - \frac{\sqrt{2}}{2}$.

6.2.62 The parabola intersects the x-axis at $x = \pm 2$, so the total area under the parabola is

$$\int_{-2}^2 (4 - x^2)\, dx = \left(4x - \frac{1}{3}x^3\right)\bigg|_{-2}^2 = \frac{32}{3}.$$

Solving for x gives $x = \pm\sqrt{4 - y}$, so we want to find k such that $\int_0^k (\sqrt{4 - y} - (-\sqrt{4 - y}))\, dy$ is half the area under the parabola, or $\frac{16}{3}$. Now the integral is

$$\int_0^k 2(4 - y)^{1/2}\, dy = 2\left(-\frac{2}{3}(4 - y)^{3/2}\right)\bigg|_0^k = -\frac{4}{3}((4 - k)^{3/2} - 8).$$

Setting this equal to $\frac{16}{3}$ and simplifying gives $4 = (4 - k)^{3/2}$, and raising both sides to the 2/3 power gives $4 - k = 4^{2/3}$. Thus $k = 4 - 4^{2/3}$.

6.2.63 Using the result of Exercise 57, the total area bounded by these two curves is $\frac{2-1}{2\cdot 2+2} = \frac{1}{6}$. We are looking for k so that $\int_0^k (y - y^2)\, dy = \frac{1}{12}$. Now,

$$\int_0^k (y - y^2)\, dy = \left(\frac{1}{2}y^2 - \frac{1}{3}y^3\right)\bigg|_0^k = \frac{1}{2}k^2 - \frac{1}{3}k^3.$$

Setting this equal to $\frac{1}{12}$ and simplifying gives $4k^3 - 6k^2 + 1 = 0$. The root $k = \frac{1}{2}$ can be found by inspection or through the use of a computer algebra system. By long division, we can see that $4k^3 - 6k^2 + 1 = (2k - 1)(2k^2 - 2k - 1)$, so the other roots are $k = \frac{1\pm\sqrt{3}}{2}$. The only root in the interval $(0, 1)$ is $k = \frac{1}{2}$.

6.2.64

a. The proportion of the whole board which has the desired property is the same as the proportion of each "quarter board" with the desired property, so we can consider only the quarter board rather than the whole board.

b. Let $P(x, y)$ be a point on the curve C. Let Q be the point on line segment $\overline{AB}$ so that $\overline{QP} \perp \overline{AB}$. Then, because the distance from O to P is the same as the distance from P to Q, we must have $\sqrt{x^2 + y^2} = 1 - y$, so $y = \frac{1}{2}(1 - x^2)$.

c. The area of the region R is 1, and the area of $R_1 - R$ is

$$2\int_0^{\sqrt{2}-1} \left(\frac{1}{2}(1 - x^2) - x\right) dx = \left.\left(x - x^3/3 - x^2\right)\right|_0^{\sqrt{2}-1}$$
$$= \sqrt{2} - 1 - (\sqrt{2} - 1)^3/3 - (\sqrt{2} - 1)^2 = \sqrt{2} - 1 + 7/3 - (5/3)\sqrt{2} + 2\sqrt{2} - 34\sqrt{2}/3 - 5/3.$$

So the probability of landing in R_2 is $1 - (4\sqrt{2}/3 - 5/3) = \frac{8 - 4\sqrt{2}}{3} \approx .781$.

6.2.65

a. The point (n, n) on the curve $y = x$ would represent the notion that the lowest $p\%$ of the society owns $p\%$ of the wealth, which would represent a form of equality.

b. The function must be increasing and concave up because the poorest $p\%$ cannot own more than $p\%$ of the wealth.

c. $y = x^{1.1}$ is closest to $y = x$, and $y = x^4$ is furthest from $y = x$.

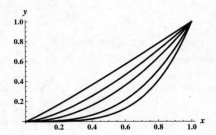

d. Note that $B = \int_0^1 L(x)\, dx$, and $A + B = 1/2$, so $A = \frac{1}{2} - \int_0^1 L(x)\, dx$. Then $G = \frac{A}{A+B} = \frac{A}{1/2} = 2A = 1 - 2\int_0^1 L(x)\, dx$.

e. For $L(x) = x^p$, we have $G = 1 - 2\int_0^1 x^p\, dx = 1 - 2\left.\left(\frac{x^{p+1}}{p+1}\right)\right|_0^1 = 1 - \frac{2}{p+1} = \frac{p-1}{p+1}$. So we have

p	1.1	1.5	2	3	4
G	1/21	1/5	1/3	1/2	3/5

f. For $p = 1$ we have $G = 0$. Because $\lim_{p \to \infty} \frac{p-1}{p+1} = 1$, the largest possible value of G approaches 1.

g. For $L(x) = 5x^2/6 + x/6$, note that $L(0) = 0$, $L(1) = 1$, $L'(x) = 5x/3 + 1/6 > 0$ on $[0, 1]$, and $L''(x) = 5/3 > 0$ as well. The Gini index is

$$G = 1 - 2\int_0^1 (5x^2/6 + x/6)\, dx = 1 - 2\left.\left(5x^3/18 + x^2/12\right)\right|_0^1 = 1 - 2(5/18 + 1/12) = 1 - 5/9 - 1/6 = 5/18.$$

6.2.66

a. In this case l_Q is $y = 2ax - a^2$, l_R is $y = 0$, and l_P is the line $y = -2ax - a^2$. We have $P' = (a/2, 0)$, $R' = (0, -a^2)$, and $Q' = (-a/2, 0)$. The area of triangle PQR is $\frac{1}{2} \cdot 2a \cdot a^2 = a^3$ and the area of triangle $P'Q'R'$ is $\frac{1}{2} \cdot (2(a/2)) \cdot (a^2) = a^3/2$.

b. In this case l_Q is $y = 2bx - b^2$, l_R is $y = 0$, and l_P is $y = -2ax - a^2$. We have $P' = (b/2, 0)$, $R' = ((b - a)/2, -ab)$, and $Q' = (-a/2, 0)$. The area of triangle PQR is $ab(a + b)$, and the area of $P'Q'R'$ is $ab \cdot \frac{a+b}{2}$.

c. Let the coordinates of R be (c, c^2). Assume $0 < a < c < b$ (the other cases can be handled similarly.)

In this case l_Q is $y = 2bx - b^2$, l_P is $y = -2ax - a^2$, and l_R is $y = 2cx - c^2$. We have $P' = ((b+c)/2, bc)$, $Q' = ((c-a)/2, -ca)$, and $R' = ((b-a)/2, -ab)$. The area of PQR is $\frac{1}{2}(a^2b + b^2c + ab^2 - ac^2 - a^2c - bc^2)$. The area of triangle $P'Q'R'$ is $\frac{1}{4}(a^2b + b^2c + ab^2 - ac^2 - a^2c - bc^2)$.

6.2.67

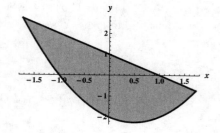

Some experimental data:

a	-2	-1	0	1
Approximate Area	7.812	6.928	7.812	10.667

The area seems to be minimized for $a = -1$.

This can be confirmed using an computer algebra system. Note that $y = (x+1)(x-2)$ and $y = ax+1$ intersect at $(1/2)(1 + a \pm \sqrt{a^2 + 2a + 13})$. Then

$$\int_{(1/2)(1+a-\sqrt{a^2+2a+13})}^{(1/2)(1+a+\sqrt{a^2+2a+13})} [ax + 1 - (x+1)(x-2)]\, dx = (1/6)(a^2 + 2a + 13)^{3/2}.$$

Let $f(a) = (1/6)(a^2 + 2a + 13)^{3/2}$. Then $f'(a) = (1/2)(a+1)\sqrt{a^2 + 2a + 13}$, which is zero for $a = -1$. Also, $f''(-1) = \sqrt{3} > 0$, so by the Second Derivative test, there is a minimum for $a = -1$.

6.2.68

$$A(a) = \int_0^{a^{-4/5}} (x^{1/2} - a^2 x^3)\, dx =$$
$$\left(\frac{2}{3}x^{3/2} - \frac{1}{4}a^2 x^4 \right)\Big|_0^{a^{-4/5}} = \frac{2}{3}a^{-6/5} - \frac{1}{4}a^{-6/5} =$$
$$\frac{5}{12}\frac{1}{a\sqrt[5]{a}}. \quad \text{Note that} \quad A(a) = 16 \quad \text{when}$$
$$a^{6/5} = \frac{5}{192}, \text{ so } a = \left(\frac{5}{192} \right)^{5/6} \approx .048.$$

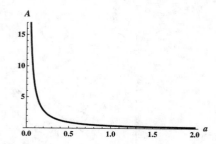

6.2.69 $A = 2\int_0^1 y^2 \sqrt{1 - y^3}\, dy = \frac{2}{3}\int_0^1 \sqrt{u}\, du$ (where $u = 1 - y^3$). So $A = \frac{2}{3}\left(\frac{2}{3}u^{3/2} \right)\Big|_0^1 = \frac{4}{9}$.

6.2.70 Suppose $x = \frac{1}{2y} - \sqrt{\frac{1}{4y^2} - 1} = \frac{1}{2y} - \frac{\sqrt{1-4y^2}}{2y} = \frac{1 - \sqrt{1-4y^2}}{2y}$. Then $\frac{1}{x} = \frac{2y}{1 - \sqrt{1-4y^2}}$. Now note that

$$x + \frac{1}{x} = \frac{1 - \sqrt{1-4y^2}}{2y} + \frac{2y}{1 - \sqrt{1-4y^2}} = \frac{1 - 2\sqrt{1-4y^2} + (1-4y^2) + 4y^2}{2y(1 - \sqrt{1-4y^2})} = \frac{1}{y}.$$

So $y = \frac{x}{x^2+1}$. The area we seek is $\int_0^1 \frac{x}{x^2+1}\, dx = \frac{1}{2}\int_1^2 \frac{1}{u}\, du = \frac{\ln 2}{2}$.

6.2.71

a.

$$F(a) = \int_0^b x(x-a)(x-b)\,dx = \int_0^b (abx - ax^2 - bx^2 + x^3)\,dx$$

$$= \left(abx^2/2 - ax^3/3 - bx^3/3 + x^4/4\right)\Big|_0^b = ab^3/2 - ab^3/3 - b^4/3 + b^4/4 = ab^3/6 - b^4/12.$$

So $F(a) = \frac{b^3}{6}\left(a - \frac{b}{2}\right)$ and $F(a) = 0$ when $a = \frac{b}{2}$ or when $b = 0$. If $b = 0$, then because $0 \le a \le b$, we have $a = 0$ as well. In either case, we have $a = \frac{b}{2}$.

b. Note that $f(x) \ge 0$ for $x \in [0, a]$ and $f(x) \le 0$ for $x \in [a, b]$. So the area under the curve is

$$A(a) = \int_0^a x(x-a)(x-b)\,dx - \int_a^b x(x-a)(x-b)\,dx$$

$$= \left(abx^2/2 - ax^3/3 - bx^3/3 + x^4/4\right)\Big|_0^a - \left(abx^2/2 - ax^3/3 - bx^3/3 + x^4/4\right)\Big|_a^b$$

$$= -\frac{a^4}{6} + \frac{a^3 b}{3} - \frac{ab^3}{6} + \frac{b^4}{12}$$

$$A'(a) = -\frac{2}{3}a^3 + a^2 b - \frac{1}{6}b^3 = -\frac{1}{6}(2a - b)(2a^2 - 2ab - b^2).$$

$$A''(a) = -2a^3 + 2ab.$$

Note that $A'(b/2) = 0$, and $A''(b/2) = -b^2/2 + b^2 > 0$, so there is a minimum at $a = b/2$. The other critical numbers are $a = \frac{2b \pm \sqrt{4b^2 - 4\cdot 2\cdot(-b^2)}}{4} = \frac{b \pm \sqrt{3b^2}}{2} = \left(\frac{1 \pm \sqrt{3}}{2}\right)b$ are not on the interval $(0, b)$. The maximum value of A is $b^4/12$ which occurs at $a = 0$ and $a = b$.

6.2.72 Given $\int_{-a}^a (f(x) - g(x))\,dx = 10$, we have (by symmetry) that $\int_0^a (f(x) - g(x))\,dx = 5$. Then, $\int_0^{\sqrt{a}} x(f(x^2) - g(x^2))\,dx = \frac{1}{2}\int_0^a (f(u) - g(u))\,du = \frac{5}{2}$. (Where we used the substitution $u = x^2$.)

6.2.73

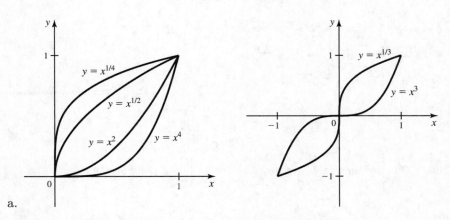

a.

b. $A_n(x)$ is the net area of the region between the graphs of f and g from 0 to x.

c. Note that $\int_0^1 (f(s) - g(s))\,ds = \left(\frac{s^{n+1}}{n+1} - \frac{s^{(1/n)+1}}{(1/n)+1}\right)\Big|_0^1 = \frac{1}{n+1} - \frac{n}{n+1} = \frac{1-n}{n+1} < 0$. So we seek the smallest c so that $\int_1^c (f(s) - g(s))\,ds = \frac{n-1}{n+1}$. This occurs when $\left(\frac{s^{n+1}}{n+1} - \frac{s^{(1/n)+1}}{(1/n)+1}\right)\Big|_1^c = \frac{n-1}{n+1}$, or $\frac{c^{n+1}}{n+1} = \frac{c^{(n+1)/n}}{(n+1)/n}$, or $c^{n+1} = nc^{(n+1)/n}$, or $c^{n-(1/n)} = n$, so $c = n^{n/(n^2-1)}$. As n increases, this root increases as well.

6.2.74

a.

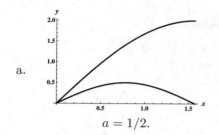
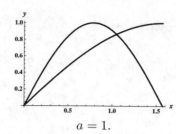
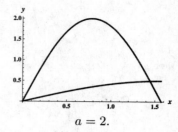

$$a = 1/2. \qquad\qquad a = 1. \qquad\qquad a = 2.$$

b. We seek a root of $a \sin 2x = (\sin x)/a$, or $2 \sin x \cos x = \frac{\sin x}{a^2}$, so $\cos x = \frac{1}{2a^2}$. This has a solution as long as $\frac{1}{2a^2} \le 1$, which occurs when $a \ge \sqrt{1/2}$.

c.

$$A = \int_0^{x^\star} (\sin 2x - \sin x)\, dx = \left(\cos x - \frac{1}{2} \cos 2x \right) \Big|_0^{x^\star}$$

$$= \left(\cos x - \frac{1}{2}(2\cos^2 x - 1) \right) \Big|_0^{x^\star} = \left(\cos x - \cos^2 x + \frac{1}{2} \right) \Big|_0^{x^\star}$$

$$= \cos x^\star - \cos^2 x^\star + \frac{1}{2} - \left(1 - 1 + \frac{1}{2} \right) = \frac{1}{2a^2} - \frac{1}{4a^4} = \frac{2a^2 - 1}{4a^4}.$$

When $a = 1$ this is equal to $\frac{1}{4}$.

d. Using the result of the previous calculation, we simply note that $\frac{2a^2-1}{4a^4} \to 0$ as $a \to 1/\sqrt{2}$.

6.3   Volume by Slicing

6.3.1 $A(x)$ is the area of the cross section through the solid at the point x.

6.3.2 The general slicing method would be used.

6.3.3 $V = \pi \int_0^2 (4x^2 - x^4)\, dx$.

6.3.4 $V = \pi \int_0^4 (y - \frac{y^2}{4})\, dy$.

6.3.5 The cross sections are disks and $A(x)$ is the area of a disk.

6.3.6 The inner radius is 2, and the outer radius is $2 + f(x)$.

6.3.7 The curves intersect when $2 - x^2 = x^2$, or $x = \pm 1$.
$A(x) = ((2 - x^2) - x^2)^2 = (2(1 - x^2))^2 = 4(1 - 2x^2 + x^4)$. The volume is given by

$$\int_{-1}^1 4(1 - 2x^2 + x^4)\, dx = 4\left(x - 2x^3/3 + x^5/5 \right) \Big|_{-1}^1 = 4((1 - 2/3 + 1/5) - (-1 + 2/3 - 1/5)) = 64/15.$$

6.3.8 The curves intersect when $\sqrt{1 - x^2} = 0$, or $x = \pm 1$.
$A(x) = (\sqrt{1 - x^2})^2 = 1 - x^2$. The volume is given by

$$\int_{-1}^1 (1 - x^2)\, dx = \left(x - x^3/3 \right) \Big|_{-1}^1 = (1 - 1/3) - (-1 + 1/3) = 4/3.$$

6.3.9 The curves intersect when $\sqrt{\cos x} = 0$, or $x = \pm\pi/2$. $A(x) = \frac{1}{2}\left(\sqrt{\cos x}\right)^2 = \frac{\cos x}{2}$. The volume is given by

$$\int_{-\pi/2}^{\pi/2} \frac{\cos x}{2}\,dx = \frac{\sin x}{2}\bigg|_{-\pi/2}^{\pi/2} = 1/2 - (-1/2) = 1.$$

6.3.10 $A(y) = \frac{1}{2}\cdot 2\sqrt{25 - y^2}\left(\frac{\sqrt{3}}{2}\cdot 2\sqrt{25 - y^2}\right) = \sqrt{3}(25 - y^2)$.

$$V = \int_0^5 A(y)\,dy = 2\sqrt{3}\int_0^5 (25 - y^2)\,dy = 2\sqrt{3}\left(25y - y^3/3\right)\bigg|_0^5 = \frac{500\sqrt{3}}{3}.$$

6.3.11 $A(x) = (2\sqrt{25 - x^2})^2 = 100 - 4x^2$.

$$V = \int_0^5 A(x)\,dx = \int_0^5 (100 - 4x^2)\,dx = \left(100x - 4x^3/3\right)\bigg|_0^5 = 500 - \frac{500}{3} = \frac{1000}{3}.$$

6.3.12 $A(y) = (2\sqrt{y})^2 = 4y$.

$$V = \int_0^1 A(y)\,dy = \int_0^1 4y\,dy = 2y^2\bigg|_0^1 = 2.$$

6.3.13 For each value of x, the height of the triangle is $2 - x$, which is the diameter of the semicircle, so the area of that semicircle is

$$A(x) = \frac{\pi}{2}\left(\frac{2 - x}{2}\right)^2 = \frac{\pi}{8}(4 - 4x + x^2).$$

Thus the volume is

$$V = \int_0^2 A(x)\,dx = \int_0^2 \frac{\pi}{8}(4 - 4x + x^2)\,dx = \frac{\pi}{8}\left(4x - 2x^2 + x^3/3\right)\bigg|_0^2 = \frac{\pi}{3}.$$

6.3.14 Place the z-axis along the axis of the pyramid; then for each z, sing similarity, the side length of the cross-section of the pyramid at that height is $4\left(\frac{2-z}{z}\right) = 2(2 - z)$, so the area is $A(z) = 4(z^2 - 4z + 4)$. Thus the volume is

$$V = \int_0^2 A(z)\,dx = \int_0^2 4(4 - 4z + z^2)\,dz = 4\left(4z - 2z^2 + z^3/3\right)\bigg|_0^2 = \frac{32}{3}.$$

6.3.15 The relationship between the height h of tetrahedron and the edge length l is $h = l\sqrt{2/3}$, which can be deduced using triangle geometry and the Pythagorean theorem.

Let z be the distance from the top vertex of the tetrahedron down toward the base perpendicularly. The cross sections perpendicular to this axis are all equilateral triangles with height z, so their side length is $\sqrt{3/2}z$, and their area is

$$A(z) = \frac{\sqrt{3}}{4}\left(z\sqrt{\frac{3}{2}}\right)^2 = \frac{3\sqrt{3}z^2}{8}.$$

The volume is thus

$$\int_0^{4\sqrt{2/3}} \frac{3\sqrt{3}}{8}z^2\,dz = \frac{3\sqrt{3}}{8}\left(z^3/3\right)\bigg|_0^{4\sqrt{2/3}} = \frac{16\sqrt{2}}{3}.$$

6.3.16 Because the cross sections are all circles with area πr^2, the volume is $\int_0^h \pi r^2\,dz = \pi r^2 h$. The 45 degree angle does not affect the volume.

6.3.17 $V = \pi\int_0^3 4x^2\,dx = 4\pi\left(x^3/3\right)\bigg|_0^3 = 36\pi.$

6.3.18 $V = \pi \int_0^1 (2-2x)^2 \, dx = 4\pi \left(x - x^2 + x^3/3 \right) \Big|_0^1 = \frac{4\pi}{3}$.

6.3.19 $V = \pi \int_0^{\ln 4} e^{-2x} \, dx = \frac{-\pi}{2} \left(e^{-2x} \right) \Big|_0^{\ln 4} = \frac{-\pi}{2}((1/16) - 1) = \frac{15\pi}{32}$.

6.3.20 $V = \pi \int_0^{\pi/2} \cos^2 x \, dx = \frac{\pi}{2} \int_0^{\pi/2} (1 + \cos 2x) \, dx = \frac{\pi}{2} \left(x + \frac{\sin 2x}{2} \right) \Big|_0^{\pi/2} = \frac{\pi^2}{4}$.

6.3.21 $V = \pi \int_0^{\pi} \sin^2 x \, dx = \frac{\pi}{2} \int_0^{\pi} (1 - \cos 2x) \, dx = \frac{\pi}{2} \left(x - \frac{\sin 2x}{2} \right) \Big|_0^{\pi} = \frac{\pi^2}{2}$.

6.3.22 Using symmetry, $V = 2\pi \int_0^5 (\sqrt{25 - x^2})^2 \, dx = 2\pi \left(25x - x^3/3 \right) \Big|_0^5 = \frac{500\pi}{3}$. The volume of a sphere of radius 5 is $\frac{4}{3}\pi \cdot 5^3 = \frac{500\pi}{3}$.

6.3.23 $V = \pi \int_0^{1/2} \frac{1}{\sqrt{1-x^2}} \, dx = \pi \sin^{-1} x \Big|_0^{1/2} = \frac{\pi^2}{6}$.

6.3.24 $V = \pi \int_0^{\pi/4} \sec^2 x \, dx = \pi \tan x \Big|_0^{\pi/4} = \pi$.

6.3.25 $V = \pi \int_{-1}^1 \left(\frac{1}{\sqrt{1+x^2}} \right)^2 dx = \pi \tan^{-1} x \Big|_{-1}^1 = \pi(\pi/4 + \pi/4) = \pi^2/2$.

6.3.26 $V = \pi \int_{-1/2}^{1/2} \left(\frac{1}{\sqrt[4]{1-x^2}} \right)^2 dx = \pi \int_{-1/2}^{/2} \frac{1}{\sqrt{1-x^2}} \, dx = \pi \sin^{-1} x \Big|_{-1/2}^{1/2} = \pi(\pi/6 + \pi/6) = \frac{\pi^2}{3}$.

6.3.27 $V = \pi \int_0^4 ((2\sqrt{x})^2 - x^2) \, dx = \pi \left(2x^2 - x^3/3 \right) \Big|_0^4 = \pi(32 - 64/3) = \frac{32\pi}{3}$.

6.3.28 The curves intersect at $x = 0$ and $x = 1$. We have $V = \pi \int_0^1 ((\sqrt[4]{x^2}) - x^2) \, dx = \pi \int_0^1 (\sqrt{x} - x^2) \, dx = \pi \left(2x^{3/2}/3 - x^3/3 \right) \Big|_0^1 = \pi(2/3 - 1/3) = \pi/3$.

6.3.29 $V = \pi \int_{\ln 2}^{\ln 3} ((e^{x/2})^2 - (e^{-x/2})^2) \, dx = \pi \int_{\ln 2}^{\ln 3} (e^x - e^{-x}) \, dx = \pi \left(e^x + e^{-x} \right) \Big|_{\ln 2}^{\ln 3} = \pi((3 + 1/3) - (2 + 1/2)) = 5\pi/6$.

6.3.30 $V = \pi \int_0^4 ((x+2)^2 - x^2) \, dx = \pi \int_0^4 (4x + 4) \, dx = \pi \left(2x^2 + 4x \right) \Big|_0^4 = 48\pi$.

6.3.31 $V = \pi \int_{-1}^2 ((x+3)^2 - (x^2+1)^2) \, dx = \pi \int_{-1}^2 (x^2 + 6x + 9 - x^4 - 2x^2 - 1) \, dx = \pi \int_{-1}^2 (-x^4 - x^2 + 6x + 8) \, dx = \pi \left(-x^5/5 - x^3/3 + 3x^2 + 8x \right) \Big|_{-1}^2 = \pi(-32/5 - 8/3 + 12 + 16 - (1/5 + 1/3 + 3 - 8)) = \frac{117\pi}{5}$.

6.3.32 $V = \pi \int_0^{\pi/2} (1 - \sin x) \, dx = \pi \left(x + \cos x \right) \Big|_0^{\pi/2} = \pi(\pi/2 - 1)$.

6.3.33 $V = \pi \int_0^{\pi/2} (\sin x - \sin^2 x) \, dx = \pi \int_0^{\pi/2} (\sin x - \frac{1}{2}(1 - \cos(2x))) \, dx = \pi \left(\sin(2x)/4 - \cos x - x/2 \right) \Big|_0^{\pi/2} = \pi(1 - \pi/4) = \frac{4\pi - \pi^2}{4}$.

6.3.34 Note that the curves intersect at $x = \pm 1$. We have $V = \pi \int_{-1}^{0}((2 - x^2)^2 - (-x)^2)\, dx + \pi \int_{0}^{1}((2 - x^2)^2 - x^2)\, dx = \pi \int_{-1}^{1}(4 - 4x^2 + x^4 - x^2)\, dx = \pi \int_{-1}^{1}(4 - 5x^2 + x^4)\, dx = \pi \left(4x - 5x^3/3 + x^5/5\right)\Big|_{-1}^{1} = \pi((4 - 5/3 + 1/5) - (-4 + 5/3 - 1/5)) = 76\pi/15$.

6.3.35 $V = \pi \int_{0}^{6}(y^2 - y^2/4)\, dy = \frac{3\pi}{4}\left(y^3/3\right)\Big|_{0}^{6} = 54\pi$.

6.3.36 $V = \pi \int_{0}^{2} e^{2y}\, dy = \frac{\pi(e^4 - 1)}{2}$.

6.3.37 $V = \pi \int_{0}^{8}(4 - y^{2/3})\, dy = \pi \left(4y - (3/5)y^{5/3}\right)\Big|_{0}^{8} = \frac{64\pi}{5}$.

6.3.38 $V = \pi \int_{0}^{2}(16 - y^4)\, dy = \pi \left(16y - y^5/5\right)\Big|_{0}^{2} = \frac{128\pi}{5}$.

6.3.39 $V = \pi \int_{-2}^{2}(\sqrt{4 - y^2})^2\, dy = \pi \left(4y - y^3/3\right)\Big|_{-2}^{2} = \pi((8 - 8/3) - (-8 + 8/3)) = \frac{32\pi}{3}$.

6.3.40 $V = \pi \int_{0}^{\pi/4} \sin^2 y\, dy = \frac{\pi}{2}\int_{0}^{\pi/4}(1 - \cos(2y))\, dy = \frac{\pi}{2}\left(y - \sin(2y)/2\right)\Big|_{0}^{\pi/4} = \frac{\pi}{2}\left(\frac{\pi}{4} - \frac{1}{2}\right) = \frac{\pi(\pi - 2)}{8}$.

6.3.41 About the x-axis: $V_x = \pi \int_{0}^{5} 4x^2\, dx = \pi \left(4x^3/3\right)\Big|_{0}^{5} = \frac{500\pi}{3}$.

About the y-axis: $V_y = \pi \int_{0}^{10}(25 - y^2/4)\, dy = \pi \left(25y - y^3/12\right)\Big|_{0}^{10} = \frac{500\pi}{3}$.

The volumes are the same.

6.3.42 About the x-axis: $V_x = \pi \int_{0}^{2}(4 - 2x)^2\, dx = 4\pi \left(4x - 2x^2 + x^3/3\right)\Big|_{0}^{2} = \frac{32\pi}{3}$.

About the y-axis: $V_y = \pi \int_{0}^{4}(2 - (y/2))^2\, dy = \pi \left(4y - y^2 + y^3/12\right)\Big|_{0}^{4} = \frac{16\pi}{3}$.

The volume V_x is bigger.

6.3.43 About the x-axis: $V_x = \pi \int_{0}^{1}(1 - x^3)^2\, dx = \pi \int_{0}^{1}(1 - 2x^3 + x^6)\, dx = \pi \left(x - x^4/2 + x^7/7\right)\Big|_{0}^{1} = \frac{9\pi}{14}$.

About the y-axis: $V_y = \pi \int_{0}^{1}(\sqrt[3]{1 - y})^2\, dy = -\pi \left(\frac{3}{5}(1 - y)^{5/3}\right)\Big|_{0}^{1} = -\pi(0 - 3/5) = \frac{3\pi}{5}$. The volume V_x is bigger.

6.3.44 About the x-axis: $V_x = \pi \int_{0}^{2}(8x - x^4)\, dx = \pi \left(4x^2 - x^5/5\right)\Big|_{0}^{2} = \frac{48\pi}{5}$.

About the y-axis: $V_y = \pi \int_{0}^{4}(y - y^4/64)\, dy = \pi \left(y^2/2 - y^5/320\right)\Big|_{0}^{4} = \frac{24\pi}{5}$.

The volume V_x is bigger.

6.3.45 Using the disk method, a disk located at x has a radius of $1 - \sqrt{x}$ when revolved about the line $y = 1$, so the volume is

$$V = \pi \int_{0}^{1}(1 - \sqrt{x})^2\, dx = \pi \int_{0}^{1}(1 - 2\sqrt{x} + x)\, dx = \pi \left(x - \frac{4}{3}x^{3/2} + \frac{1}{2}x^2\right)\Big|_{0}^{1} = \pi \left(1 - \frac{4}{3} + \frac{1}{2}\right) = \frac{\pi}{6}.$$

6.3.46 We use the washer method. Note that $x = y^2$, and for each value of y, the washer has outer radius 4 and inner radius $4 - y^2$, so that the volume is

$$V = \pi \int_0^2 (4^2 - (4 - y^2)^2)\, dy = \pi \int_0^2 (8y^2 - y^4)\, dy = \pi \left(\frac{8}{3}y^3 - \frac{1}{5}y^5 \right) \Big|_0^2 = \pi \left(\frac{64}{3} - \frac{32}{5} \right) = \frac{224}{15}\pi.$$

6.3.47 We use the washer method. For each x, the washer has outer radius $2 + 2\sin x$ and inner radius 2, so the volume is

$$V = \pi \int_0^\pi \left((2 + 2\sin x)^2 - 2^2 \right) dx = \pi \int_0^\pi (8\sin x + 4\sin^2 x)\, dx$$

$$= \pi \int_0^\pi (8\sin x + 2(1 - \cos 2x))\, dx = \pi(-8\cos x + 2x - \sin 2x) \Big|_0^\pi$$

$$= \pi(8 + 2\pi + 8) = 2\pi(\pi + 8).$$

6.3.48 We use the washer method. First solve for x to obtain $x = e^y$; then for each value of y, the outer radius of a washer is $e^y + 1$ and the inner radius is 1, so the volume is

$$V = \pi \int_0^1 \left((e^y + 1)^2 - 1^2 \right) dy = \pi \int_0^1 (2e^y + e^{2y})\, dy = \pi \left(2e^y + \frac{1}{2}e^{2y} \right) \Big|_0^1$$

$$= \pi \left(2e + \frac{1}{2}e^2 - \frac{5}{2} \right) = \frac{\pi}{2} \left(e^2 + 4e - 5 \right).$$

6.3.49 We use the washer method. For each x, the outer radius is $1 + \sin x$ and the inner radius is $1 + (1 - \sin x) = 2 - \sin x$. Thus the volume is

$$V = \pi \int_{\pi/6}^{5\pi/6} \left((1 + \sin x)^2 - (2 - \sin x)^2 \right) dx = \pi \int_{\pi/6}^{5\pi/6} (6\sin x - 3)\, dx$$

$$= \pi(-6\cos x - 3x) \Big|_{\pi/6}^{5\pi/6} = \pi \left(3\sqrt{3} - \frac{5\pi}{2} + 3\sqrt{3} + \frac{\pi}{2} \right) = \pi \left(6\sqrt{3} - 2\pi \right).$$

6.3.50 The lines $y = 1 + \frac{x}{2}$ and $y = x$ meet at the point $(2, 2)$. For each x, we obtain a washer with outer radius $3 - x$ and inner radius $3 - \left(1 + \frac{x}{2} \right) = 2 - \frac{x}{2}$. Hence the volume is

$$V = \pi \int_0^2 \left((3 - x)^2 - \left(2 - \frac{x}{2} \right)^2 \right) dx = \pi \int_0^2 \left(5 - 4x + \frac{3}{4}x^2 \right) dx = \pi \left(5x - 2x^2 + \frac{1}{4}x^3 \right) \Big|_0^2 = 4\pi.$$

6.3.51 The lines $x = 2 - y$ and $x = 1 - \frac{y}{2}$ meet at the point $(0, 2)$. For each y, we obtain a washer whose outer radius is $3 - \left(1 - \frac{y}{2} \right) = 2 + \frac{y}{2}$ and whose inner radius is $3 - (2 - y) = y + 1$. Thus the volume is

$$V = \pi \int_0^2 \left(\left(2 + \frac{y}{2} \right)^2 - (y + 1)^2 \right) dy = \pi \int_0^2 \left(-\frac{3}{4}y^2 + 3 \right) dy = \pi \left(-\frac{1}{4}y^3 + 3y \right) \Big|_0^2 = 4\pi.$$

6.3.52 We would expect the volume to be greater when revolved about the line $y = 2$, because the wider portion of the figure then moves through a larger radius, so it traces out a larger volume. When revolving about $y = 0$, we obtain a disk with radius $2x(2 - x)$, so the volume is

$$V = \pi \int_0^2 (2x(2 - x))^2\, dx = \pi \int_0^2 (16x^2 - 16x^3 + 4x^4)\, dx = \left(\frac{16}{3}x^3 - 4x^4 + \frac{4}{5}x^5 \right) \Big|_0^2 = \frac{64\pi}{15}.$$

When revolving about the line $y = 2$, we have washers with outer radius 2 and inner radius $2 - 2x(2 - x)$, so the volume is

$$V = \pi \int_0^2 \left(4 - (2 - 2x(2 - x))^2 \right) dx = \pi \int_0^2 (8x(2 - x) - 4x^2(2 - x)^2)\, dx$$

$$= \pi \int_0^2 (-4x^4 + 16x^3 - 24x^2 + 16x)\, dx = \pi \left(-\frac{4}{5}x^5 + 4x^4 - 8x^3 + 8x^2 \right) \Big|_0^2 = \frac{32}{5}\pi.$$

The second calculation yields a larger result.

6.3.53

a. False. The cross sections are not disks or washers.

b. True. It is given by $V = \pi \int_0^R (R^2 - x^2)\, dx$.

c. True. This is because if we shift the sine function horizontally by $\pi/2$ units, we obtain the cosine function.

6.3.54

$$V = \pi \int_1^2 \left(\frac{\ln x}{\sqrt{x}}\right)^2 dx$$

$$= \pi \int_1^2 \frac{\ln^2 x}{x}\, dx = \pi/3 \left(\ln^3 x\right)\Big|_1^2$$

$$= \frac{\pi \ln^3 2}{3}.$$

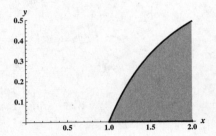

6.3.55 $\quad V = \pi \int_2^6 \left(\frac{1}{\sqrt{x}}\right)^2 dx = \pi \left(\ln x\right)\Big|_2^6 = \pi \ln 3.$

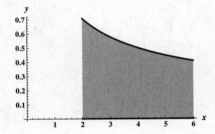

6.3.56

$$V = \pi \int_{-1}^1 \left(\frac{1}{x^2+1} - \frac{1}{2}\right) dx$$

$$= \pi \left(\tan^{-1}(x) - x/2\right)\Big|_{-1}^1$$

$$= \pi((\pi/4 - 1/2) - (-\pi/4 + 1/2))$$

$$= \pi^2/2 - \pi.$$

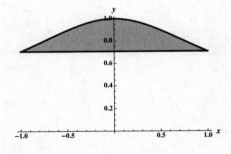

6.3.57

$$V = \pi \int_0^2 e^{2x}\, dx = \pi/2 \left(e^{2x}\right)\Big|_0^2$$

$$= (\pi/2)(e^4 - 1)$$

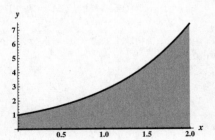

6.3.58

$$V = \pi \int_0^{\ln 4} (e^{2x} - e^{-2x})\, dx$$

$$= \pi/2 \left(e^{2x} + e^{-2x}\right) \Big|_0^{\ln 4}$$

$$= (\pi/2)(16 + (1/16) - 2) = \frac{225\pi}{32}.$$

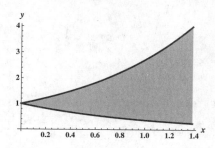

6.3.59

$$V = \pi \int_0^{\ln 8} (e^{2y} - e^y)\, dy$$

$$= \pi \left(e^{2y}/2 - e^y\right) \Big|_0^{\ln 8}$$

$$= \pi(32 - 8 - (1/2 - 1)) = 24.5\pi.$$

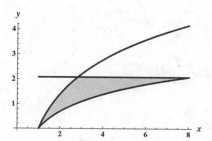

6.3.60 $V(p) = \pi \int_0^p e^{-2x}\, dx = -\frac{\pi}{2}\left(e^{-2x}\right)\Big|_0^p = \frac{\pi}{2}\left(1 - e^{-2p}\right)$. The volume is bounded by $\pi/2$ as $p \to \infty$.

6.3.61 The volume V_S is $\pi \int_0^{\sqrt{a}} (y^2 - a)^2\, dy = \pi \left(y^5/5 - 2ay^3/3 + a^2 y\right)\Big|_0^{\sqrt{a}} = \frac{8\pi}{15} a^{5/2}$.

The volume V_T is $\frac{1}{3}\pi a^2 \cdot a^{1/2} = \frac{1}{3}\pi a^{5/2}$. The ratio of $V_S/V_T = \frac{8/15}{1/3} = \frac{8}{5}$.

6.3.62 $V = \pi \int_0^2 x^2\, dx + \pi \int_2^5 (2x - 2)^2\, dx + \pi \int_5^6 (18 - 2x)^2\, dx = \frac{8}{3}\pi + 84\pi + \frac{148\pi}{3} = 136\pi.$

6.3.63

a. This comes from revolving the region in the first quadrant bounded by $\sin x$ and the line $y = 0$ between $x = 0$ and $x = \pi$ around the x axis.

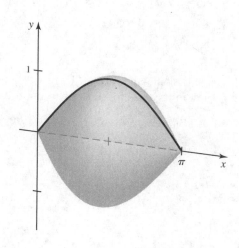

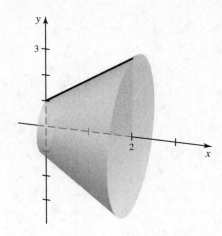

b. This comes from revolving the region in the first quadrant bounded by $y = x + 1$ and the line $y = 0$ between $x = 0$ and $x = 2$ around the x axis.

6.3.64 The volume is approximately

$$\pi \left((12.6/2)^2 + (14.0/2)^2 + (16.8/2)^2 + (25.2/2)^2 + (36.4/2)^2 + (42.0/2)^2\right) \left(\frac{50}{6}\right) \approx 28542.7 \, \text{cm}^3.$$

6.3.65

a. Think of the cone as being obtained by revolving the region under $y = x$ in the first quadrant from $x = 0$ to $x = R$ around the x-axis. The volume is $\pi \int_0^R x^2 \, dx = \pi R^3/3 = \frac{1}{3} V_C$.

b. Think of the hemisphere as being obtained by revolving the region under $y = \sqrt{R^2 - x^2}$ between $x = 0$ and $x = R$ around the x-axis. The volume is $\pi \int_0^R (R^2 - x^2) \, dx = \pi \left(R^2 x - x^3/3\right) \Big|_0^R = \frac{2\pi R^3}{3} = \frac{2}{3} V_C$.

6.3.66 $V(h) = \pi \int_{-8}^{-8+h} (\sqrt{64 - y^2})^2 \, dy = \pi \left(64y - y^3/3\right) \Big|_{-8}^{-8+h} = 8\pi h^2 - \frac{\pi h^3}{3}$. Note that $V(0) = 0$ and $V(8) = \frac{2\pi}{3} 8^3$.

6.3.67 $V = \pi \int_{-2}^{2} \left((3 + \sqrt{4 - y^2})^2 - (3 - \sqrt{4 - y^2})^2\right) dy = 24\pi \int_0^2 \sqrt{4 - y^2} \, dy = 24\pi(\pi) = 24\pi^2$. Note that the last integral evaluated represents $1/4$ the area of a circle of radius 2

6.3.68 Around the x-axis: $V_x = \pi \int_0^1 (x - x^4) \, dx = \pi \left(x^2/2 - x^5/5\right) \Big|_0^1 = \pi(1/2 - 1/5) = \frac{3\pi}{10}$.

Around the line $y = 1$: $V_1 = \pi \int_0^1 ((1 - x^2)^2 - (1 - \sqrt{x})^2) \, dx = \pi \int_0^1 (x^4 - 2x^2 - x + 2\sqrt{x}) \, dx = \pi \left(x^5/5 - 2x^3/3 - x^2/2 + 4x^{3/2}/3\right) \Big|_0^1 = \pi(1/5 - 2/3 - 1/2 + 4/3) = \frac{11\pi}{30}$. Note that $V_1 > V_x$.

6.3.69

a. By the general slicing method, $V(x) = \int_a^b A(x) \, dx$. Because the two figures have the same cross sections $A(x)$, they must therefore have the same volumes.

b. We are seeking the value of r so that $10\pi r^2 = 40$, so $r^2 = \frac{4}{\pi}$, and $r = \frac{2}{\sqrt{\pi}}$ meters.

6.3.70

a.

$$V(n) = \pi \int_0^1 (x^{2/n} - x^{2n}) \, dx = \pi \left(\frac{n}{n+2} x^{(n+2)/n} - \frac{1}{2n+1} x^{2n+1}\right) \Big|_0^1$$

$$= \pi \left(\frac{n}{n+2} - \frac{1}{2n+1}\right) = \frac{2\pi(n+1)(n-1)}{(n+2)(2n+1)} = \frac{2\pi(n^2 - 1)}{(n+2)(2n+1)}.$$

b. $\lim_{n\to\infty} V(n) = \lim_{n\to\infty} \frac{2n^2-2}{2n^2+5n+2} \cdot \pi = \pi$.

6.4   Volume by Shells

6.4.1 $V = 2\pi \int_a^b x(f(x) - g(x)) \, dx$.

6.4.2 ...revolved about the y axis. ...using the disk/washer method and integrating with respect to $\underline{y}$ or using the shell method and integrating with respect to $\underline{x}$.

6.4.3 ...revolved about the x axis. ...using the disk/washer method and integrating with respect to $\underline{x}$ or using the shell method and integrating with respect to $\underline{y}$.

6.4.4 No, it depends on the function. There are examples where the disk/washer method leads to easier-to-compute integrals, and examples where the shell method leads to easier-to-compute integrals.

6.4.5 $V = 2\pi \int_0^1 x(x - x^2) \, dx = 2\pi \int_0^1 (x^2 - x^3) \, dx = 2\pi \left. \left(x^3/3 - x^4/4 \right) \right|_0^1 = 2\pi (1/3 - 1/4) = \pi/6$.

6.4.6 $V = 2\pi \int_1^4 x((-x^2 + 4x + 2) - (x^2 - 6x + 10)) \, dx = 2\pi \int_1^4 (-2x^3 + 10x^2 - 8x) \, dx =$
$2\pi \left. \left(-x^4/2 + 10x^3/3 - 4x^2 \right) \right|_1^4 = 2\pi((-128 + 640/3 - 64) - (-1/2 + 10/3 - 4)) = 45\pi$.

6.4.7 $V = 2\pi \int_0^2 \frac{x}{1+x^2} \, dx = \pi \ln(1 + x^2) \left. \right|_0^2 = \pi \ln 5$.

6.4.8 $V = 2\pi \int_2^4 x(6 - x) \, dx = 2\pi \left. \left(3x^2 - x^3/3 \right) \right|_2^4 = \frac{104\pi}{3}$.

6.4.9 $V = 2\pi \int_0^1 x(3 - 3x) \, dx = 2\pi \left. \left(3x^2/2 - x^3 \right) \right|_0^1 = \pi$.

6.4.10 $V = 2\pi \int_0^1 x(1 - x^2) \, dx = 2\pi \int_0^1 (x - x^3) \, dx = 2\pi \left. \left(x^2/2 - x^4/4 \right) \right|_0^1 = 2\pi (1/2 - 1/4) = \pi/2$.

6.4.11 Note that the line $y = 1$ intersects the curve $y = x^3 - x^8 + 1$ at $x = 0$ and $x = 1$. $V = 2\pi \int_0^1 x(x^3 - x^8 + 1 - 1) \, dx = 2\pi \int_0^1 (x^4 - x^9) \, dx = 2\pi \left. \left(x^5/5 - x^{10}/10 \right) \right|_0^1 = 2\pi(1/5 - 1/10) = \pi/5$.

6.4.12 $V = 2\pi \int_0^1 x\sqrt{x} \, dx = 2\pi \left. \left(2x^{5/2}/5 \right) \right|_0^1 = \frac{4\pi}{5}$.

6.4.13 $V = 2\pi \int_0^{\sqrt{\pi/2}} x \cos(x^2) \, dx = \pi \left. \left(\sin(x^2) \right) \right|_0^{\sqrt{\pi/2}} = \pi$.

6.4.14 $V = 2\pi \int_0^{\sqrt{2}} x\sqrt{4 - 2x^2} \, dx = -\pi \left. \left((\sqrt{4 - 2x^2})^3/3 \right) \right|_0^{\sqrt{2}} = -\pi(0 - (8/3)) = \frac{8\pi}{3}$.

6.4.15 $V = 2\pi \int_0^2 y(4 - y^2) \, dy = 2\pi \left. \left(2y^2 - y^4/4 \right) \right|_0^2 = 8\pi$.

6.4.16 $V = 2\pi \int_2^6 y(y - 2)/2 \, dy + 2\pi \int_6^8 2y \, dy = \pi \left. \left(y^3/3 - y^2 \right) \right|_2^6 + 2\pi \left. \left(y^2 \right) \right|_6^8 = \frac{112\pi}{3} + 56\pi = \frac{280\pi}{3}$.

6.4.17 $V = 2\pi \int_2^4 y(4-y)\, dy = 2\pi \left(2y^2 - y^3/3\right) \Big|_2^4 = \frac{32\pi}{3}.$

6.4.18 $V = 2\pi \int_1^{\sqrt{3}} y\left(\frac{4}{y+y^3} - \frac{1}{\sqrt{3}}\right) dy = 2\pi \int_1^{\sqrt{3}} \left(\frac{4}{1+y^2} - \frac{y}{\sqrt{3}}\right) dy = 2\pi \left(4\tan^{-1} y - \frac{y^2}{2\sqrt{3}}\right) \Big|_1^{\sqrt{3}} =$
$2\pi \left(\left(\frac{4\pi}{3} - \frac{3}{2\sqrt{3}}\right) - \left(\pi - \frac{1}{2\sqrt{3}}\right)\right) = 2\pi \left(\frac{\pi}{3} - \frac{1}{\sqrt{3}}\right) = \frac{2\pi}{3}\left(\pi - \sqrt{3}\right).$

6.4.19 Note that the lines intersect at $(0,0)$, $(2,0)$ and $(1,1)$.

$V = 2\pi \int_0^1 y((2-y) - y)\, dy = 2\pi \int_0^1 (2y - 2y^2)\, dy = 2\pi \left(y^2 - 2y^3/3\right) \Big|_0^1 = 2\pi/3.$

6.4.20 Note that the line $x = 4$ intersects the curve $x = y^2$ at $(4,2)$. $V = 2\pi \int_0^2 y(4-y^2)\, dy = 2\pi \int_0^2 (4y - y^3)\, dy = 2\pi \left(2y^2 - y^4/4\right) \Big|_0^2 = 8\pi.$

6.4.21 $V = 2\pi \int_0^3 y(y^2)\, dy = 2\pi \int_0^3 y^3\, dy = 2\pi \left(y^4/4\right) \Big|_0^3 = 81\pi/2.$

6.4.22 $V = 2\pi \int_0^1 y(\sqrt[3]{y})\, dy = 2\pi \left(\frac{3}{7} y^{7/3}\right) \Big|_0^1 = \frac{6\pi}{7}.$

6.4.23 $V = 2\pi \int_2^{16} y(2/y)^{2/3}\, dy = 2^{5/3}\pi \int_2^{16} y^{1/3}\, dy = 2^{5/3}\pi \left(3y^{4/3}/4\right) \Big|_2^{16} = 2^{5/3}\pi(3 \cdot 2^{10/3} - 3 \cdot 2^{-2/3}) = 3\pi(2^5 - 2) = 90\pi.$

6.4.24 $V = 2\pi \int_0^{\sqrt{\pi/2}} y \sin y^2\, dy = -\pi \cos y^2 \Big|_0^{\sqrt{\pi/2}} = -\pi(0-1) = \pi.$

6.4.25 Note that $y = \sqrt{\cos^{-1} x}$ intersects the axes at $(0, \sqrt{\pi/2})$ and $(1,0)$. $V = 2\pi \int_0^{\sqrt{\pi/2}} y \cos y^2\, dy = \pi \sin y^2 \Big|_0^{\sqrt{\pi/2}} = \pi(1-0) = \pi.$

6.4.26 $V = 2\pi \int_0^{5\sqrt{2}} y\sqrt{(50-y^2)/2}\, dy = \sqrt{2}\pi \int_0^{5\sqrt{2}} y\sqrt{50-y^2}\, dy = \sqrt{2}\pi \cdot \frac{1}{2} \int_0^{50} u^{1/2}\, du$, where $u = 50 - y^2$.
Thus, $V = \frac{\sqrt{2}\pi}{2} \left(2u^{3/2}/3\right) \Big|_0^{50} = \frac{\sqrt{2}\pi}{2} \left(2 \cdot 50 \cdot 5\sqrt{2}/3\right) = \frac{500\pi}{3}.$

6.4.27 Consider the region in the first quadrant bounded by the coordinate axes and the line $y = 8 - (8/3)x$. We can generate the desired cone by revolving this region around the y-axis. We then have $V = 2\pi \int_0^3 x(8 - (8/3)x)\, dx = \frac{16\pi}{3} \int_0^3 (3x - x^2)\, dx = \frac{16\pi}{3} \left(3x^2/2 - x^3/3\right) \Big|_0^3 = 24\pi.$

6.4.28 Consider the rectangle in the first quadrant bounded by $x = 2$, $x = 4$, $y = 6$ and $y = 0$. The solid in question is formed by revolving this region around the y-axis. The volume is $V = 2\pi \int_2^4 6x\, dx = 2\pi \left(3x^2\right) \Big|_2^4 = 72\pi.$

6.4.29 Consider the triangle in the first quadrant bounded by $y = 0$, $x = 3$, and $y = 9 - (3/2)x$. The solid in question is formed by revolving this region around the y-axis. The volume is $V = 2\pi \int_3^6 x(9 - (3/2)x)\, dx = 2\pi \left(9x^2/2 - x^3/2\right) \Big|_3^6 = 54\pi.$

6.4.30 Consider the region in the first and second quadrants bounded by $x = 3$, the circle $x^2 + y^2 = 36$. The solid in question is formed by revolving this region around the y-axis. The volume is $V = 4\pi \int_3^6 x\sqrt{36 - x^2}\, dx$. This integral can be computing using the substitution $u = 36 - x^2$. We then have $V = 2\pi \int_0^{27} u^{1/2}\, du = 2\pi \left(2u^{3/2}/3\right)\Big|_0^{27} = 108\sqrt{3}\pi$.

6.4.31 Consider the part of the ellipse which lies in the first quadrant. We can obtain half the ellipsoid by revolving this region around the y-axis. So the volume of the whole ellipsoid is $V = 4\pi \int_0^2 x\sqrt{2 - (x^2/2)}\, dx$. Let $u = 2 - x^2/2$. Then $V = 4\pi \int_0^2 u^{1/2}\, du = 8\pi/3 \left(u^{3/2}\right)\Big|_0^2 = \frac{16\pi\sqrt{2}}{3}$.

6.4.32 $V = 2\pi \int_r^R x \cdot 6(1 - x^2/R^2)\, dx = 12\pi \left(x^2/2 - x^4/4R^2\right)\Big|_r^R = \frac{3\pi(R^2 - r^2)^2}{R^2}$.

6.4.33 $V = 2\pi \int_0^1 (x + 2)x^2\, dx = 2\pi \left(x^4/4 + 2x^3/3\right)\Big|_0^1 = \frac{11\pi}{6}$.

6.4.34 $V = 2\pi \int_0^1 (1 - x)x^2\, dx = 2\pi \left(x^3/3 - x^4/4\right)\Big|_0^1 = \frac{\pi}{6}$.

6.4.35

$$V = 2\pi \int_0^1 (y + 2)(1 - \sqrt{y})\, dy = 2\pi \int_0^1 \left(y + 2 - y^{3/2} - 2y^{1/2}\right) dy = 2\pi \left(y^2/2 + 2y - 2y^{5/2}/5 - 4y^{3/2}/3\right)\Big|_0^1$$
$$= 2\pi(1/2 + 2 - 2/5 - 4/3) = \frac{23\pi}{15}.$$

6.4.36

$$V = 2\pi \int_0^1 (1 - \sqrt{y})(2 - y)\, dy = 2\pi \int_0^1 \left(2 - y - 2y^{1/2} + y^{3/2}\right) dy = 2\pi \left(2y - \frac{y^2}{2} - \frac{4y^{3/2}}{3} + \frac{2y^{5/2}}{5}\right)\Big|_0^1 = \frac{17\pi}{15}.$$

6.4.37 Using washers, we have

$$V = \pi \int_0^1 (3^2 - (x^2 + 2)^2)\, dx = \pi \int_0^1 (9 - x^4 - 4x^2 - 4)\, dx = \pi \int_0^1 (5 - x^4 - 4x^2)\, dx$$
$$= \pi \left(5x - \frac{x^5}{5} - \frac{4x^3}{3}\right)\Big|_0^1 = \pi \left(5 = \frac{1}{5} - \frac{4}{3}\right) = \frac{52\pi}{15}.$$

6.4.38 Using washers, we have

$$V = \pi \int_0^1 ((\sqrt{y} + 1)^2 - 1^2)\, dy = \pi \int_0^1 (y + 2\sqrt{y})\, dy = \pi \left(\frac{y^2}{2} + \frac{4y^{3/2}}{3}\right)\Big|_0^1 = \frac{11\pi}{6}.$$

6.4.39 Using washers, we have

$$V = \pi \int_0^1 ((6 - x^2)^2 - 5^2)\, dx = \pi \int_0^1 (x^4 - 12x^2 + 11)\, dx = \pi \left(\frac{x^5}{5} - 4x^3 + 11x\right)\Big|_0^1 = \frac{36\pi}{5}.$$

6.4.40 Using washers, we have

$$V = \pi \int_0^1 (4 - (2 - \sqrt{y})^2)\, dy = \pi \int_0^1 (4\sqrt{y} - y)\, dy = \pi \left(\frac{8y^{3/2}}{3} - \frac{y^2}{2}\right)\Big|_0^1 = \frac{13\pi}{6}.$$

6.4.41 With washers we have

$$V = \pi \int_0^1 (x^{2/3} - x^2)\, dx = \pi \left(\frac{3x^{5/3}}{5} - \frac{x^3}{3} \right) \Bigg|_0^1 = \frac{4\pi}{15}.$$

With shells we have

$$V = 2\pi \int_0^1 y(y - y^3)\, dy = 2\pi \left(\frac{y^3}{3} - \frac{y^5}{5} \right) \Bigg|_0^1 = 2\pi \left(\frac{1}{3} - \frac{1}{5} \right) = \frac{4\pi}{15}.$$

The two methods are equally easy to apply.

6.4.42 The curves intersect when $x^2 = 2 - x$, or $x^2 + x - 2 = (x - 1)(x + 2) = 0$, so for $x = 1$ and $x = -2$. Only $x = 1$ is in the first quadrant; the corresponding y coordinate is $y = 1$. Also, $2 - x \geq x^2$ on $[0, 1]$. Using disks, we must split this up into two integrals: one from $y = 0$ to $y = 1$ with radius $\sqrt{y}$, and one from $y = 1$ to $y = 2$ with radius $2 - y$. The volume is thus

$$V = \pi \int_0^1 (\sqrt{y})^2\, dy + \pi \int_1^2 (2 - y)^2\, dy = \pi \int_0^1 y\, dy + \pi \int_1^2 (4 - 4y + y^2)\, dy$$

$$= \pi \left(\frac{1}{2} y^2 \right) \Bigg|_0^1 + \pi \left(4y - 2y^2 + \frac{y^3}{3} \right) \Bigg|_1^2 = \pi \left(\frac{1}{2} + 8 - 8 + \frac{8}{3} - 4 + 2 - \frac{1}{3} \right) = \frac{5\pi}{6}.$$

Using shells, the height of each shell is $2 - x - x^2$, so the volume is

$$V = 2\pi \int_0^1 x(2 - x - x^2)\, dx = 2\pi \left(x^2 - \frac{x^3}{3} - \frac{x^4}{4} \right) \Bigg|_0^1 = \frac{5\pi}{6}.$$

The shell method is clearly easier to apply.

6.4.43 Using washers we have

$$V = \pi \int_0^2 \left(\left(1 - \frac{x}{3} \right)^2 - \frac{1}{(x+1)^2} \right) dx = \pi \left(x - \frac{x^2}{3} + \frac{x^3}{27} + \frac{1}{(x+1)} \right) \Bigg|_0^2 = \frac{8\pi}{27}.$$

Using shells we have

$$V = 2\pi \int_{1/3}^1 y \left(3 - 3y - \left(\frac{1}{y} - 1 \right) \right) dy = 2\pi \int_{1/3}^1 (4y - 3y^2 - 1)\, dy = 2\pi \left(2y^2 - y^3 - y \right) \Bigg|_{1/3}^1$$

$$= 2\pi \left(0 - \left(\frac{2}{9} - \frac{1}{27} - \frac{1}{3} \right) \right) = \frac{8\pi}{27}.$$

The shell method seems a little easier to apply.

6.4.44 Using washers we have

$$V = \pi \int_{-10}^{25} (\sqrt[3]{y + 2} + 2)^2\, dy = \pi \int_{-8}^{27} (u^{1/3} + 2)^2\, du = \pi \int_{-8}^{27} (u^{2/3} + 4u^{1/3} + 4)\, du$$

$$= \pi \left(3u^{5/3}/5 + 3u^{4/3} + 4u \right) \Bigg|_{-8}^{27} = \pi(3^6/5 + 3^5 + 108 - (-96/5 + 48 - 32)) = \pi \left(\frac{2484}{5} + \frac{16}{5} \right) = 500\pi.$$

Using shells we have

$$V = 2\pi \int_0^5 x(25 - (x - 2)^3 + 2)\, dx = 2\pi \int_0^5 (27x - x(x - 2)^3)\, dx = 2\pi \int_0^5 -x^4 + 6x^3 - 12x^2 + 35x\, dx$$

$$= 2\pi \left(-\frac{x^5}{5} + \frac{3x^4}{2} - 4x^3 + \frac{35x^2}{2} \right) \Bigg|_0^5 = 500\pi$$

The disk/washer method seems a little easier to apply.

6.4.45 Using washers we have

$$V = \pi \int_1^{\sqrt{e}} (\ln x^2 - \ln x)\, dx + \pi \int_{\sqrt{e}}^{e} (1 - \ln x)\, dx = \pi \int_1^{\sqrt{e}} \ln x\, dx + \pi \int_{\sqrt{e}}^{e} (1 - \ln x)\, dx.$$

This integral requires techniques that we won't learn until Chapter 7. So we must use shells.

Using shells we have

$$V = 2\pi \int_0^1 y(e^{y^2} - e^{y^2/2})\, dy = 2\pi \left(e^{y^2}/2 - e^{y^2/2} \right)\Big|_0^1 = \pi(e - 2\sqrt{e} - (1 - 2)) = \pi(\sqrt{e} - 1)^2.$$

6.4.46 First, note that the curve and the line intersect at the points $(-1, 3)$ and $(0, 2)$.

Using washers we have

$$V = \pi \int_{-1}^0 \left((2 - x)^2 - \frac{36}{(x + 3)^2} \right)\, dx = \pi \int_{-1}^0 \left(4 - 4x + x^2 - \frac{36}{(x + 3)^2} \right)\, dx$$

$$= \pi \left(4x - 2x^2 + \frac{x^3}{3} + \frac{36}{x + 3} \right)\Big|_{-1}^0 = \pi \left(12 - \left(-4 - 2 + \frac{1}{3} + 18 \right) \right) = \frac{\pi}{3}.$$

For shells, first solve $y = 2 - x$ and $y = \frac{6}{x+3}$ to get $x = 2 - y$ and $x = \frac{6}{y} - 3$. Then

$$V = 2\pi \int_2^3 y \left((2 - y) - \left(\frac{6}{y} - 3 \right) \right)\, dy = 2\pi \int_2^3 (2y - y^2 - 6 + 3y)\, dy$$

$$= 2\pi \left(\frac{5y^2}{2} - \frac{y^3}{3} - 6y \right)\Big|_2^3 = 2\pi \cdot \frac{1}{6} = \frac{\pi}{3}.$$

The shell method is easier to apply.

6.4.47 First, note that the curve and the line intersect at $(0, 0)$ and $(1, 0)$.

Washers:

$$V = \pi \int_0^1 (x - x^4)^2\, dx = \pi \int_0^1 (x^2 - 2x^5 + x^8)\, dx$$

$$= \pi \left(x^3/3 - x^6/3 + x^9/9 \right)\Big|_0^1 = \pi/9$$

Shells: It isn't practical to even attempt the shell method, as it is not easy to write x in terms of y for the given expression.

6.4.48 First, note that the curve and the line intersect at $(0, 0)$ and $(1, 0)$.

Washers: It isn't practical to even attempt the washer method, as it is not easy to write x in terms of y for the given expression.

Shells:

$$V = 2\pi \int_0^1 x(x - x^4)\, dx = 2\pi \int_0^1 (x^2 - x^5)\, dx$$

$$= 2\pi \left(x^3/3 - x^6/6 \right)\Big|_0^1 = 2\pi(1/3 - 1/6) = \pi/3.$$

6.4.49

a. True. Otherwise, we wouldn't have shells!

b. False. Either method can be used when revolving around either axis.

c. True.

6.4.50

$$V = 2\pi \int_1^3 (\ln x)/x \, dx = 2\pi \left((\ln x)^2/2 \right) \Big|_1^3$$
$$= \pi (\ln 3)^2.$$

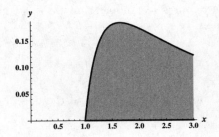

6.4.51

$$V = 2\pi \int_2^8 1/x \, dx = 2\pi \ln x \Big|_2^8 = 2\pi \ln 4$$
$$= 4\pi \ln 2.$$

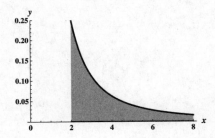

6.4.52

$$V = 2\pi \int_1^4 x/(x^2 + 1) \, dx = \pi \ln(x^2 + 1) \Big|_1^4$$
$$= \pi (\ln(17) - \ln(2)) = \pi \ln(17/2).$$

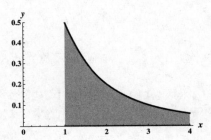

6.4.53

$$V = 2\pi \int_1^2 x(e^x/x) \, dx = 2\pi \, e^x \Big|_1^2$$
$$= 2\pi (e^2 - e).$$

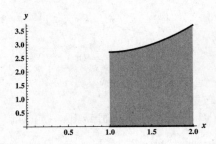

6.4.54

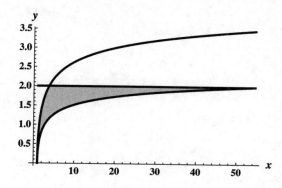

$$V = 2\pi \int_0^2 y(e^{y^2} - e^{y^2/3})\,dy = \pi\left(e^{y^2} - 3e^{y^2/3}\right)\Big|_0^2 = \pi(e^4 - 3e^{4/3} - (1-3)) = \pi(2 + e^4 - 3e^{4/3}).$$

6.4.55 $V = 2\pi \int_0^1 ((2-x^2)^2 - (x^2)^2)\,dx = 2\pi \int_0^1 (4 - 4x^2)\,dx = 2\pi\left(4x - 4x^3/3\right)\Big|_0^1 = \frac{16\pi}{3}.$

6.4.56

$$V = \pi \int_{\pi/6}^{5\pi/6} (\sin^2 x - (1 - \sin x)^2)\,dx = \pi \int_{\pi/6}^{5\pi/6} (2\sin x - 1)\,dx$$

$$= -\pi\left(2\cos x + x\right)\Big|_{\pi/6}^{5\pi/6} = 2\sqrt{3}\pi - \frac{2\pi^2}{3}.$$

6.4.57 $V = 2\pi \int_2^6 x(2x + 2 - x)\,dx = 2\pi \int_2^6 (x^2 + 2x)\,dx = 2\pi\left(x^3/3 + x^2\right)\Big|_2^6 = \frac{608\pi}{3}.$

6.4.58 $V = \pi \int_0^2 (x^3)^2\,dx = \pi\left(x^7/7\right)\Big|_0^2 = \frac{128\pi}{7}.$

6.4.59 $V = \int_0^1 A(y)\,dy = \int_0^1 \frac{\pi}{2}(\sqrt{y})^2\,dy = \frac{\pi}{2}\left(y^2/2\right)\Big|_0^1 = \frac{\pi}{4}.$

6.4.60 $V = 2\pi \int_0^6 x(2x + 2 - 2)\,dx = 2\pi\left(2x^3/3\right)\Big|_0^6 = 288\pi.$

6.4.61 By symmetry, $V = 2\int_0^1 \frac{\pi}{2}(1-x)^2\,dx = \pi \int_0^1 (1 - 2x + x^2)\,dx = \pi\left(x - x^2 + x^3/3\right)\Big|_0^1 = \frac{\pi}{3}.$

6.4.62 $V = \pi \int_0^4 (\sqrt{x})^2\,dx = \pi\left(x^2/2\right)\Big|_0^4 = 8\pi.$

6.4.63

a. $V_1 = \pi \int_0^1 (ax^2 + 1)^2\,dx = \pi \int_0^1 (a^2x^4 + 2ax^2 + 1)\,dx = \pi(a^2/5 + 2a/3 + 1).$

   $V_2 = 2\pi \int_0^1 x(ax^2 + 1)\,dx = 2\pi(a/4 + 1/2) = \pi a/2 + \pi.$

b. These are equal when $\pi a/2 + \pi = \pi a^2/5 + 2a\pi/3 + \pi$, or when $\pi a^2/5 + a\pi/6 = 0$, which occurs when $a = 0$ and when $a = -5/6$.

6.4.64

a. $V = \pi \int_0^r (r^2 - x^2)\, dx = \pi \left(r^2 x - x^3/3 \right) \Big|_0^r = \frac{2\pi r^3}{3}.$

b. $V = 2\pi \int_0^r y\sqrt{r^2 - y^2}\, dy = -2\pi/3 \left((\sqrt{r^2 - y^2})^3 \right) \Big|_0^r = \frac{-2\pi}{3}(0 - r^3) = \frac{2\pi r^3}{3}.$

c. $A(y) = \frac{\pi}{2}(r^2 - y^2). \ V = \int_{-r}^r A(y)\, dy = 2\int_0^r \frac{1}{2}\pi(r^2 - y^2)\, dy = \pi\left(r^2 y - y^3/3 \right) \Big|_0^r = \frac{2\pi r^3}{3}.$

6.4.65

a. $V = \pi \int_0^h (rx/h)^2\, dx = \frac{\pi r^2}{h^2} \left(x^3/3 \right) \Big|_0^h = \frac{\pi r^2 h}{3}.$

b. $V = 2\pi \int_0^r y(h - (h/r)y)\, dy = 2\pi h \left(y^2/2 - y^3/(3r) \right) \Big|_0^r = \frac{\pi r^2 h}{3}.$

6.4.66

a. $V = \pi \int_{r-h}^r (r^2 - y^2)\, dy = \pi \left(r^2 y - y^3/3 \right) \Big|_{r-h}^r = \pi(2r^3/3 - (r^2(r - h) - (r - h)^3/3)) = \frac{\pi h^2}{3}(3r - h).$

b.

$$V = 2\pi \int_0^{\sqrt{2rh - h^2}} x(\sqrt{r^2 - x^2} - (r - h))\, dx = 2\pi \left(\frac{-1}{3}(\sqrt{r^2 - x^2})^3 - (r - h)x^2/2 \right) \Big|_0^{\sqrt{2rh - h^2}}$$

$$= 2\pi \left(\frac{-1}{3}(\sqrt{r^2 - 2rh + h^2})^3 - (r - h)(2rh - h^2)\frac{1}{2} + \frac{1}{3}r^3 \right)$$

$$= 2\pi \left(-(r - h)^3/3 - r^2 h + rh^2/2 + rh^2 - h^3/2 + r^3/3 \right) = \pi h^2 r - \frac{\pi h^3}{3}.$$

c. If we take slices perpendicular to the y-axis, we have circles whose area $A(y) = \pi(r^2 - y^2)$. So $V = \pi \int_{r-h}^r (r^2 - y^2)\, dy$, which is exactly the integral computed in part (a) above.

Note that all three approaches led to the same result, and the result is consistent with other formulas. For example, when $h = 0$ we have no figure, so our volume is 0. When $h = r$, we have $V = \frac{2\pi r^3}{3}$, the volume of a hemisphere.

6.4.67 The bowl is the surface of revolution when $y = -\sqrt{64 - x^2}$ for $0 \le x \le 8$ is revolved boy the y-axis. The volume of water in the bowl up to height h is the volume integral for the bowl evaluated from -8 (the bottom) to $-8 + h$ (h above the bottom). Using shells, each shell has height $(-8 + h) - (-\sqrt{64 - x^2}) = h - 8 + \sqrt{64 - x^2}$. Further, the quarter-circle meets the line $y = h - 8$ when $h - 8 = -\sqrt{64 - x^2}$, so that $x = \sqrt{16h - h^2}$. Thus the bounds of integration are $x = 0$ to $x = \sqrt{16h - h^2}$. We have

$$V = 2\pi \int_0^{\sqrt{16h - h^2}} x(h - 8 + \sqrt{64 - x^2})\, dx = 2\pi \left(hx^2/2 - 4x^2 - \frac{1}{3}\left(64 - x^2 \right)^{3/2} \right) \Big|_0^{\sqrt{16h - h^2}}$$

$$= \pi(16h^2 - h^3 - 8(16h - h^2) - \frac{2}{3}(8 - h)^3 - (0 - 0 - 1024/3)) = \frac{1}{3}(24 - h)\pi h^2.$$

Note that when $h = 0$ the bowl is empty, and in fact the formula above gives $V = 0$. When $h = 8$ the bowl is full, so we have a hemisphere of radius 8, which has volume $\frac{2}{3}\pi \cdot 8^3 = \frac{1024}{3}\pi$; evaluating the expression above at $h = 8$ gives $\frac{1}{3}(24 - 8)\pi \cdot 64 = \frac{1024}{3}\pi$ as well.

6.4.68 Vertical slices of the wedge are triangles with area $\frac{1}{2}xh$, where x is the base and h is the height. Note that $h = x\tan\theta$, so the triangles have area $\frac{1}{2}x^2\tan\theta$. Now if we think of the curved part of the base of the wedge as having equation $x^2 + y^2 = a^2$, then we have $x^2 = a^2 - y^2$. So the volume of the wedge is given by

$$\int_{-a}^{a} \frac{1}{2}\tan\theta(a^2 - y^2)\,dy = \int_0^a \tan\theta(a^2 - y^2)\,dy = \tan\theta\left(a^2 y - y^3/3\right)\Big|_0^a = \frac{2a^3}{3}\tan\theta.$$

6.4.69

$$V = 2\pi \int_0^2 ((3 + \sqrt{4 - x^2})^2 - (3 - \sqrt{4 - x^2})^2)\,dx = 24\pi \int_0^2 \sqrt{4 - x^2}\,dx = 24\pi(\pi) = 24\pi^2.$$

The last integral can be computed with a computer, or one can note that it represents $1/4$ of the area of the circle of radius 2 centered at the origin, so its value is $(1/4)\pi \cdot 4 = \pi$.

6.4.70

a. As in figure 6.44 in the text, the result of revolving a slice around the line $x = x_0$ is a shell with the same height as before, but with the radius being $\overline{x}_k - x_0$ rather than $\overline{x}_k$. Thus, when the volumes of the shells are added and the limit is taken, the resulting integral is $\int_a^b 2\pi(x - x_0)(f(x) - g(x))\,dx$ instead of $\int_a^b 2\pi(x)(f(x) - g(x))\,dx$.

b. When $x_0 > b$, the radius of a typical shell is given by $x_0 - \overline{x}_k$, so the volume is given by $\int_a^b 2\pi(x_0 - x)(f(x) - g(x))\,dx$.

6.4.71

a. The cross sections of such an object are washers, with inner radius given b $g(x) - y_0$ and outer radius given by $f(x) - y_0$, so the volume is given by $\pi \int_a^b ((f(x) - y_0)^2 - (g(x) - y_0)^2)\,dx$.

b. The cross section of this object are also washers, and this time the inner radius is $y_0 - f(x)$ and the outer radius is $y_0 - g(x)$, so the volume is given by $\pi \int_a^b ((y_0 - g(x))^2 - (y_0 - f(x))^2)\,dx$.

6.4.72

a. $V = 2\pi \int_0^a y^2\,dx = 2\pi \int_0^a b^2(1 - (x^2/a^2))\,dx = 2\pi b^2\left(x - x^3/(3a^2)\right)\Big|_0^a = \frac{4\pi ab^2}{3}$.

b. $V = 2 \cdot 2\pi \int_0^a (xb\sqrt{1 - (x^2/a^2)})\,dx = \frac{4\pi b}{a} \int_0^a x\sqrt{a^2 - x^2}\,dx = \frac{4\pi b}{a}\left(\frac{-1}{3}(a^2 - x^2)^{3/2}\right)\Big|_0^a = \frac{4\pi b}{a}\left(\frac{-1}{3}(0 - a^3)\right) = \frac{4\pi ba^2}{3}$.

c. The ellipsoids generated are different when $a \neq b$, so there isn't any reason to expect them to have the same volumes.

6.4.73 $V = 2\pi \int_0^2 xf(x^2)\,dx = \pi \int_0^4 f(u)\,du$, where $u = x^2$. Thus, $V = 10\pi$.

6.4.74

a. Consider the region in the first quadrant bounded by the coordinate axes and $y = 8 - 2x$. The integral on the left represents the volume of the solid obtained when this region is revolved around the x-axis, using the disk/washer method, and the integral on the right represents the same volume calculated using the shell method. Hence, they are equal.

b. Consider the region in the first quadrant bounded by the line $x = 0$, the line $y = 5$, and the curve $y + x^2 + 1$. The integral on the left represents $\frac{1}{\pi}$ times the volume of the solid obtained when this region is revolved around the x-axis, using the disk/washer method, and the integral on the right represents $\frac{1}{\pi}$ times the same volume calculated using the shell method. Hence, they are equal.

6.4.75

a. The longest diagonal of the cube is equal to the diameter of the sphere, which is $\sqrt{r^2 + r^2 + r^2} = \sqrt{3}r$. Thus, if R is the radius of the sphere, we must have $R = \frac{\sqrt{3}}{2}r$.

Now analyzing the cone which contains the sphere, we see that the height h of the cone is $3R$, so $h = \frac{3\sqrt{3}}{2}r$.

Now the volume of the cylinder is $V = \pi \left(\frac{3r}{2}\right)^2 \left(\frac{3\sqrt{3}r}{2}\right) = \frac{27\sqrt{3}\pi r^3}{8}$.

b. Imagine the cone with its vertex up. Consider the plane which contains the vertex of the cone and two non-adjacent vertices of the cube's bottom face. The cross section of this plane with the cone and cube consists of an $r \times \sqrt{2}r$ rectangle (where r is the side length of the cube) and an isosceles triangle of base 2 and height 3, with the rectangle inscribed in the triangle, and the longer side of the rectangle lying on the base of the triangle. Using similar triangles, we have $\frac{r}{3} = \frac{1-(r/\sqrt{2})}{1}$, so $r = \frac{3\sqrt{2}}{3+\sqrt{2}}$, and the volume of the cube is $\frac{54\sqrt{2}}{(3+\sqrt{2})^3}$.

c. Imagine the sphere with the hole as being obtained by revolving the region pictured around the x-axis, where the relevant curves are $y = r$ and $y = \sqrt{R^2 - x^2}$ where r is the radius of the hole and R is the radius of the sphere. Note that if you draw the triangle with vertices $(0,0)$, $(5,0)$, and $(5,r)$, you have a right triangle with legs of length 5 and r, and hypotenuse of length R, so $25 + r^2 = R^2$.

The volume we are interested in is

$$V = 2\pi \int_0^5 \left((R^2 - x^2) - r^2\right) dx = 2\pi \int_0^5 (25 - x^2)\, dx = 2\pi \left(25x - x^3/3\right)\Big|_0^5 = \frac{500\pi}{3}.$$

Note that (surprisingly!), the result doesn't depend on the radius of the original sphere.

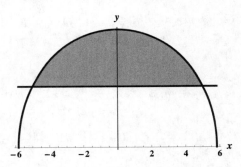

6.5   Length of Curves

6.5.1 Given $f(x)$ and a and b, compute $f'(x)$ and then compute $\int_a^b \sqrt{1 + f'(x)^2}\, dx$.

6.5.2 Given $g(y)$ and c and d, compute $g'(y)$ and then compute $\int_c^d \sqrt{1 + g'(y)^2}\, dy$.

6.5.3 Because $f'(x) = 3x^2$, the arc length is $\int_{-2}^5 \sqrt{1 + f'(x)^2}\, dx = \int_{-2}^5 \sqrt{1 + 9x^4}\, dx$.

6.5.4 Because $f'(x) = -6\sin 3x$, the arc length is $\int_{-\pi}^{\pi} \sqrt{1 + f'(x)^2}\, dx = \int_{-\pi}^{\pi} \sqrt{1 + 36\sin^2 3x}\, dx$.

6.5.5 Because $f'(x) = -2e^{-2x}$, the arc length is $\int_0^2 \sqrt{1 + f'(x)^2}\, dx = \int_0^2 \sqrt{1 + 4e^{-4x}}\, dx$.

6.5.6 Because $f'(x) = \frac{1}{x}$, the arc length is $\int_1^{10} \sqrt{1 + f'(x)^2}\, dx = \int_1^{10} \sqrt{1 + \frac{1}{x^2}}\, dx = \int_1^{10} \frac{\sqrt{x^2+1}}{x}\, dx$.

6.5.7 $L = \int_1^5 \sqrt{1 + 2^2}\, dx = 4\sqrt{5}$.

6.5.8 $L = \int_{-3}^2 \sqrt{1 + (y')^2} = \int_{-3}^2 \sqrt{1 + (-3)^2}\, dx = \int_{-3}^2 \sqrt{10}\, dx = 5\sqrt{10}$.

6.5.9 $L = \int_{-2}^6 \sqrt{1 + (y')^2}\, dx = \int_{-2}^6 \sqrt{1 + (-8)^2}\, dx = \int_{-2}^6 \sqrt{65}\, dx = 8\sqrt{65}$.

6.5.10 $y' = \frac{1}{2}(e^x - e^{-x})$, so $1 + (y')^2 = 1 + \frac{1}{4}\left(e^{2x} - 2 + e^{-2x}\right) = \left(\frac{1}{2}(e^x + e^{-x})\right)^2$. Thus,

$$L = \int_{-\ln 2}^{\ln 2} \frac{1}{2}(e^x + e^{-x})\, dx = \frac{1}{2}\left(e^x - e^{-x}\right)\Big|_{-\ln 2}^{\ln 2} = \frac{1}{2}(2 - 1/2 - (1/2 - 2)) = \frac{3}{2}.$$

6.5.11 $y' = \sqrt{x}/2$, so $1 + (y')^2 = 1 + x/4$. Thus,

$$L = \int_0^{60} \sqrt{1 + (x/4)}\, dx = \int_0^{60} \frac{1}{2}\sqrt{x + 4}\, dx = \left(\frac{1}{3}(x+4)^{3/2}\right)\Big|_0^{60} = \frac{504}{3} = 168.$$

6.5.12 $y' = 3/x - x/(12)$, so $1 + (y')^2 = 1 + \frac{9}{x^2} - \frac{1}{2} + \frac{x^2}{144} = \left(\frac{3}{x} + \frac{x}{12}\right)^2$. Thus,

$$L = \int_1^6 \left(\frac{3}{x} + \frac{x}{12}\right) dx = \left(3\ln x + x^2/24\right)\Big|_1^6 = 3\ln 6 + \frac{35}{24}.$$

6.5.13 $y' = x(x^2 + 2)^{1/2}$, so $1 + (y')^2 = 1 + x^2(x^2 + 2) = x^4 + 2x^2 + 1 = (x^2 + 1)^2$. Thus,

$$L = \int_0^1 (x^2 + 1)\, dx = \left(x^3/3 + x\right)\Big|_0^1 = \frac{4}{3}.$$

6.5.14 $y' = \sqrt{x}/2 - 1/(2\sqrt{x})$, so $1 + (y')^2 = 1 + \frac{x}{4} - \frac{1}{2} + \frac{1}{4x} = \left(\frac{\sqrt{x}}{2} + \frac{1}{2\sqrt{x}}\right)^2$. Thus,

$$L = \int_4^{16} (x^{1/2}/2 + (1/2)x^{-1/2})\, dx = \left(x^{3/2}/3 + x^{1/2}\right)\Big|_4^{16} = 64/3 + 4 - (8/3 + 2) = 2 + 56/3 = \frac{62}{3}.$$

6.5.15 $y' = x^3 - \frac{1}{4x^3}$, so $1 + (y')^2 = 1 + x^6 - \frac{1}{2} + \frac{1}{16x^6} = \left(x^3 + \frac{1}{4x^3}\right)^2$. Thus,

$$L = \int_1^2 (x^3 + \frac{1}{4x^3})\, dx = \left(x^4/4 + \frac{-1}{8}x^{-2}\right)\Big|_1^2 = 4 - (1/32) - (1/4 - (1/8)) = \frac{123}{32}.$$

6.5.16 $y' = x^{1/2} - (1/(4x^{1/2}))$, so $1 + (y')^2 = 1 + x - 1/2 + \frac{1}{16x} = \left(x^{1/2} + \frac{1}{4x^{1/2}}\right)^2$. Thus,

$$L = \int_1^9 \left(x^{1/2} + \frac{1}{4x^{1/2}}\right) dx = \left(2x^{3/2}/3 + \sqrt{x}/2\right)\Big|_1^9 = 18 + 3/2 - (2/3 + 1/2) = \frac{55}{3}.$$

6.5.17

a. $y' = 2x$, so $1 + (y')^2 = 1 + 4x^2$, so $L = \int_{-1}^1 \sqrt{1 + 4x^2}\, dx$.

b. $L = \int_{-1}^1 \sqrt{1 + 4x^2}\, dx \approx 2.958$.

6.5.18

a. $y' = \cos x$, so $1 + (y')^2 = 1 + \cos^2 x$, so $L = \int_0^\pi \sqrt{1 + \cos^2 x}\, dx$.

b. $L = \int_0^\pi \sqrt{1 + \cos^2 x}\, dx \approx 3.820$.

6.5.19

  a. $y' = 1/x$, so $1 + (y')^2 = 1 + (1/x)^2 = \frac{x^2+1}{x^2}$, so $L = \int_1^4 \frac{\sqrt{x^2+1}}{x}\, dx$.

  b. $L = \int_1^4 \frac{\sqrt{x^2+1}}{x}\, dx \approx 3.343$.

6.5.20

  a. $y' = x^2$, so $1 + (y')^2 = 1 + x^4$, so $L = \int_{-1}^1 \sqrt{1+x^4}\, dx$.

  b. $L = \int_{-1}^1 \sqrt{1+x^4}\, dx \approx 2.179$.

6.5.21

  a. $y' = \frac{1}{2\sqrt{x-2}}$, so $1 + (y')^2 = 1 + \frac{1}{4(x-2)} = \frac{4x-7}{4x-8}$, so $L = \int_3^4 \sqrt{\frac{4x-7}{4x-8}}\, dx$.

  b. $L = \int_3^4 \sqrt{\frac{4x-7}{4x-8}}\, dx \approx 1.083$.

6.5.22

  a. $y' = -\frac{16}{x^3}$, so $1 + (y')^2 = 1 + \frac{16^2}{x^6} = \frac{x^6+16^2}{x^6}$, so $L = \int_1^4 \sqrt{\frac{x^6+16^2}{x^6}}\, dx$.

  b. $L = \int_1^4 \frac{\sqrt{x^6+16^2}}{x^3}\, dx \approx 8.708$.

6.5.23

  a. $y' = -2\sin(2x)$, so $1 + (y')^2 = 1 + 4\sin^2(2x)$, so $L = \int_0^\pi \sqrt{1+4\sin^2(2x)}\, dx$.

  b. $L = \int_0^\pi \sqrt{1+4\sin^2(2x)}\, dx \approx 5.270$.

6.5.24

  a. $y' = 4 - 2x$, so $1 + (y')^2 = 1 + 16 - 16x + 4x^2 = 4x^2 - 16x + 17$, so $L = \int_0^4 \sqrt{4x^2 - 16x + 17}\, dx$.

  b. $L = \int_0^4 \sqrt{4x^2 - 16x + 17}\, dx \approx 9.294$.

6.5.25

  a. $y' = -1/x^2$, so $1 + (y')^2 = 1 + \frac{1}{x^4} = \frac{x^4+1}{x^4}$. Thus, $L = \int_1^{10} \frac{\sqrt{x^4+1}}{x^2}\, dx$.

  b. $L = \int_1^{10} \frac{\sqrt{x^4+1}}{x^2}\, dx \approx 9.153$.

6.5.26

  a. $y' = \frac{-2x}{(x^2+1)^2}$, so $1 + (y')^2 = 1 + \frac{4x^2}{(x^2+1)^4} = \frac{(x^2+1)^4+4x^2}{(x^2+1)^4}$, so $L = \int_{-5}^5 \frac{\sqrt{(x^2+1)^4+4x^2}}{(x^2+1)^2}\, dx$.

  b. $L = \int_{-5}^5 \frac{\sqrt{(x^2+1)^4+4x^2}}{(x^2+1)^2}\, dx \approx 10.369$.

6.5.27 $\frac{dx}{dy} = 2$, so $1 + \left(\frac{dx}{dy}\right)^2 = 1 + 4 = 5$, so $L = \int_{-3}^4 \sqrt{5}\, dy = 7\sqrt{5}$.

6.5.28 $y = \ln(x - \sqrt{x^2-1})$, so $e^y = x - \sqrt{x^2-1}$, and $e^{-y} = \frac{1}{x-\sqrt{x^2-1}} = \frac{x+\sqrt{x^2-1}}{x^2-(x^2-1)} = x + \sqrt{x^2-1}$. Thus $\frac{e^y+e^{-y}}{2} = x$.

We have $\frac{dx}{dy} = \frac{e^y-e^{-y}}{2}$, so $1 + \left(\frac{dx}{dy}\right)^2 = 1 + e^{2y}/4 - 1/2 + e^{-2y}/4 = \left(\frac{e^y+e^{-y}}{2}\right)^2$. Thus,

$$L = \int_{\ln(\sqrt{2}-1)}^0 \frac{e^y + e^{-y}}{2}\, dy = \left(\frac{e^y - e^{-y}}{2}\right)\Bigg|_{\ln(\sqrt{2}-1)}^0 = 0 - \frac{\sqrt{2}-1-\frac{1}{\sqrt{2}-1}}{2}\cdot\frac{\sqrt{2}-1}{\sqrt{2}-1} = \frac{-2+2\sqrt{2}-1+1}{2(\sqrt{2}-1)} = 1.$$

6.5.29 $\frac{dx}{dy} = y^3 - 1/(4y^3)$, so $1 + \left(\frac{dx}{dy}\right)^2 = 1 + y^6 - 1/2 + 1/(16y^6) = \left(y^3 + \frac{1}{4y^3}\right)^2$. So $L = \int_1^2 (y^3 + \frac{1}{4} \cdot y^{-3})\, dy = \left(y^4/4 - \frac{1}{8y^2}\right)\Big|_1^2 = 4 - (1/32) - (1/4 - 1/8) = \frac{123}{32}$.

6.5.30 $\frac{dx}{dy} = 2\sqrt{2}e^{\sqrt{2}y} - \frac{\sqrt{2}}{16}e^{-\sqrt{2}y}$, so $1 + \left(\frac{dx}{dy}\right)^2 = 1 + 8e^{2\sqrt{2}y} - (1/2) + \frac{2}{16^2}e^{-2\sqrt{2}y} = \left(2\sqrt{2}e^{\sqrt{2}y} + \frac{\sqrt{2}}{16}e^{-\sqrt{2}y}\right)^2$.

So $L = \int_0^{(\ln 2)/\sqrt{2}} (2\sqrt{2}e^{\sqrt{2}y} + \frac{\sqrt{2}}{16}e^{-\sqrt{2}y})\, dy = \left(2e^{\sqrt{2}y} - \frac{1}{16}e^{-\sqrt{2}y}\right)\Big|_0^{(\ln 2)/\sqrt{2}} = (4 - (1/32)) - (2 - (1/16)) = \frac{65}{32}$.

6.5.31

a. False. For example, if $f(x) = x^2$, the first integrand is $\sqrt{1 + 4x^2}$ and the second is $1 + 2x$, which clearly yield different values for (for example) $a = 0$ and $b = 1$.

b. True. They are both equal to $\int_a^b \sqrt{1 + f'(x)^2}\, dx$.

c. False. Because $\sqrt{1 + f'(x)^2} > 0$, arc length can't be negative.

6.5.32 $y' = m$, so $1 + (y')^2 = 1 + m^2$, and $L = \int_a^b \sqrt{1 + m^2}\, dx = (b - a)\sqrt{1 + m^2}$.

To see that this is the same result as the one given by the distance formula, consider the points $(a, ma + c)$ and $(b, mb + c)$. The distance between them is $\sqrt{(b - a)^2 + (mb + c - (ma + c))^2} = \sqrt{(b - a)^2 + m^2(b - a)^2} = \sqrt{(b - a)^2}\sqrt{1 + m^2} = (b - a)\sqrt{1 + m^2}$.

6.5.33

a. We are seeking functions $f(x)$ so that $f'(x) = \pm 4x^2$, so any function of the form $f(x) = \pm 4x^3/3 + C$ will work.

b. We are seeking functions $f(x)$ so that $f'(x) = \pm 6\cos(2x)$, so any function of the form $f(x) = \pm 3\sin(2x) + C$ will work.

6.5.34 Because $f'(x) = \pm 4x^{-3}$, we have $f(x) = \frac{\pm 2}{x^2} + C$. Because $f(1) = 5$, we must have either $f(x) = 7 - \frac{2}{x^2}$ or $f(x) = 3 + \frac{2}{x^2}$.

6.5.35 The length of the parabola is $\int_{-1}^1 \sqrt{1 + 4x^2}\, dx \approx 2.9597$.

The length of the given cosine function is $\int_{-1}^1 \sqrt{1 + \frac{\pi^2}{4}\sin^2(\pi x/2)}\, dx \approx 2.924$, so the parabola is longer.

6.5.36 $f'(x) = \sin x$, so the arc length is given by $\int_0^\pi \sqrt{1 + \sin^2 x}\, dx$.

6.5.37 $f'(x) = 0.00074x$, so $L = \int_{-640}^{640} \sqrt{1 + (0.00074x)^2}\, dx \approx 1326.4$ meters.

6.5.38 $f'(x) = \frac{-630}{239.2}\sinh(x/239.2)$, where $\sinh(x) = \frac{e^x - e^{-x}}{2}$.

So $L = \int_{-315}^{315} \sqrt{1 + \left(\frac{630}{239.2}\sinh(x/239.2)\right)^2}\, dx \approx 1472.17$ ft.

6.5.39

a. Let $u = 2x$. Then the given integral is equal to $\frac{1}{2}\int_a^b \sqrt{1 + f'(u)^2}\, du = \frac{L}{2}$.

b. Let $u = cx$. Then the given integral is equal to $\frac{1}{c}\int_a^b \sqrt{1 + f'(u)^2}\, du = \frac{L}{c}$.

6.5.40 If f is odd, then the symmetry of f assures that the portion of the curve from 0 to b matches exactly the portion of the curve from $-b$ to 0, as can be seen by rotating the original curve about the y-axis and then about the x-axis. The same is true for f even, although the two portions match up after just rotating about the y-axis.

Suppose f is even, and recall that this means that f' is odd. Consider $L_- = \int_{-b}^{0} \sqrt{1 + f'(x)^2}\, dx$. Let $u = -x$. The integral becomes

$$L_- = \int_0^b \sqrt{1 + f'(-x)^2}\, dx = \int_0^b \sqrt{1 + (-f'(x))^2}\, dx = \int_0^b \sqrt{1 + f'(x)^2}\, dx = L_+.$$

If f is odd, so that f' is even, we have $L_- = \int_{-b}^{0} \sqrt{1 + f'(x)^2}\, dx$. Let $u = -x$. Then the integral becomes

$$L_- = \int_0^b \sqrt{1 + f'(-x)^2}\, dx = \int_0^b \sqrt{1 + f'(x)^2}\, dx = L_+.$$

6.5.41

a. $f'(x) = Aae^{ax} - \frac{1}{4Aa}e^{-ax}$, so $1 + f'(x)^2 = 1 + (Aae^{ax})^2 - \frac{1}{2} + \left(\frac{1}{4Aa}e^{-ax}\right)^2 = (Aae^{ax})^2 + \frac{1}{2} + \left(\frac{1}{4Aa}e^{-ax}\right)^2 = \left(Aae^{ax} + \frac{1}{4Aa}e^{-ax}\right)^2$. So the arc length for $c \le x \le d$ is $L = \int_c^d \left(Aae^{ax} + \frac{1}{4Aa}e^{-ax}\right) dx = \left(Ae^{ax} - \frac{1}{4Aa^2}e^{-ax}\right)\Big|_c^d$.

b. Applying the previous result with $c = 0$ and $d = \ln 2$, we have $L = \left(Ae^{ax} - \frac{1}{4Aa^2}e^{-ax}\right)\Big|_0^{\ln 2} = A2^a - \frac{1}{4Aa^2}2^{-a} - A + \frac{1}{4Aa^2} = A(2^a - 1) - \frac{1}{4a^2 A}(2^{-a} - 1)$.

6.5.42

a. $y' = \frac{2n+1}{2n}x^{1/(2n)}$, so $1 + (y')^2 = 1 + \left(\frac{2n+1}{2n}\right)^2 x^{1/n}$.

So $L = \int_0^a \sqrt{1 + \left(\frac{2n+1}{2n}\right)^2 x^{1/n}}\, dx$.

b. For the sake of simplicity, let $r = \frac{2n+1}{2n}$, and let $d = \sqrt{1 + r^2 a^{1/n}}$. If we let $u^2 = 1 + r^2 x^{1/n}$, then $x = \left(\frac{u^2-1}{r^2}\right)^n$, and $dx = \frac{n}{r^{2n}}(u^2-1)^{n-1} \cdot 2u\, du$, and our integral becomes $\int_1^d u \cdot \frac{n}{r^{2n}}(u^2-1)^{n-1} \cdot 2u\, du = \frac{2n}{r^{2n}}\int_1^d u^2(u^2-1)^{n-1}\, du$.

c. The binomial theorem assures us that

$$(u^2-1)^{n-1} = u^{2n-2} - \binom{n-1}{1}u^{2n-4} + \binom{n-1}{2}u^{2n-6} - \cdots + (-1)^{n-1}.$$

Thus $u^2(u^2-1)^{n-1} = u^2\left(u^{2n-2} - \binom{n-1}{1}u^{2n-4} + \binom{n-1}{2}u^{2n-6} - \cdots + (-1)^{n-1}\right) = u^{2n} - \binom{n-1}{1}u^{2n-2} + \binom{n-1}{2}u^{2n-4} - \cdots + (-1)^{n-1}u^2$. Then

$$L = \frac{2n}{r^{2n}}\left(u^{2n+1}/(2n+1) - \binom{n-1}{1}u^{2n-1}/(2n-1)\right.$$
$$\left. + \binom{n-1}{2}u^{2n-3}/(2n-3) - \cdots + (-1)^{n+1}u^3/3\right)\Bigg|_1^d.$$

d. For $n = 2$ and $a = 1$ we have $r = (5/4)$ and $d = \sqrt{41}/4$. Using the previous result, we have $L = \frac{4^5}{5^4}\left(u^5/5 - u^3/3\right)\Big|_1^{\sqrt{41}/4} = \frac{2048}{9375} + \frac{1763\sqrt{41}}{9375} \approx 1.423$.

For $n = 3$ and $a = 1$ we have $r = 7/6$ and $d = \sqrt{85}/6$. Using the previous results, we have $L = \frac{6^7}{7^6}\left(u^7/7 - 2u^5/5 + u^3/3\right)\Big|_1^{\sqrt{85}/6} = \frac{142885\sqrt{85}}{823543} - \frac{746496}{4117715} \approx 1.418$.

e.

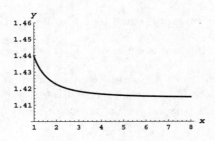

6.6 Surface Area

6.6.1 $S = \pi r \sqrt{r^2 + h^2} = 3\pi\sqrt{9+16} = 15\pi$.

6.6.2 By the formula developed in the section: $S = \pi(4)(6^2 - 2^2)\sqrt{1+4^2} = 128\sqrt{17}\pi$. Or it can be computed via integration:

$$S = 2\pi \int_2^6 4x\sqrt{1+4^2}\,dx = 8\sqrt{17}\pi\,\left(x^2/2\right)\,\Big|_2^6 = 8\sqrt{17}\pi(18-2) = 128\sqrt{17}\pi.$$

6.6.3 Evaluate $\int_a^b 2\pi f(x)\sqrt{1 + f'(x)^2}\,dx$.

6.6.4 Evaluate $\int_c^d 2\pi g(y)\sqrt{1 + g'(y)^2}\,dy$.

6.6.5 $S = 2\pi \int_0^6 (3x+4)\sqrt{1+9}\,dx = 2\sqrt{10}\pi\,\left(3x^2/2 + 4x\right)\,\Big|_0^6 = 2\sqrt{10}\pi(54+24) = 156\sqrt{10}\pi$.

6.6.6 $S = 2\pi \int_1^3 (12-3x)\sqrt{1+9}\,dx = 2\sqrt{10}\pi\,\left(12x - 3x^2/2\right)\,\Big|_1^3 = 2\sqrt{10}\pi(36-27/2 - (12-3/2)) = 24\sqrt{10}\pi$.

6.6.7 $S = 2\pi \int_9^{20} 8\sqrt{x}\sqrt{1+(16/x)}\,dx = 16\pi \int_9^{20}\sqrt{x+16}\,dx = 16\pi\left(\frac{2(x+16)^{3/2}}{3}\right)\Big|_9^{20} = \frac{32\pi}{3}\left(216-125\right) = \frac{2912\pi}{3}$.

6.6.8 $S = 2\pi \int_0^1 x^3\sqrt{1+9x^4}\,dx$. Let $u = 1 + 9x^4$ so that $du = 36x^3\,dx$. Substituting gives
$S = \frac{\pi}{18}\int_1^{10}\sqrt{u}\,du = \frac{\pi}{18}\left(\frac{2u^{3/2}}{3}\right)\Big|_1^{10} = \frac{\pi}{27}(10\sqrt{10}-1)$.

6.6.9 $S = 2\pi\int_1^2\left(x^{3/2} - \frac{\sqrt{x}}{3}\right)\sqrt{1 + (3\sqrt{x}/2 - x^{-1/2}/6)^2}\,dx = 2\pi\int_1^2(x^{3/2} - \sqrt{x}/3)\sqrt{1 + \left(\frac{9x-1}{6\sqrt{x}}\right)^2}\,dx =$
$2\pi\int_1^2(x^{3/2} - \sqrt{x}/3)\sqrt{\frac{36x + 81x^2 - 18x + 1}{36x}}\,dx = 2\pi\int_1^2(x^{3/2} - \sqrt{x}/3)\sqrt{\left(\frac{(1+9x)^2}{36x}\right)}\,dx =$
$2\pi\int_1^2\left(\frac{(1+9x)x}{6} - \frac{1+9x}{18}\right)\,dx = \frac{2\pi}{18}\int_1^2(3x + 27x^2 - 1 - 9x)\,dx = \frac{2\pi}{18}\int_1^2(27x^2 - 6x - 1)\,dx = \frac{\pi}{9}\left(9x^3 - 3x^2 - x\right)\Big|_1^2 =$
$\frac{\pi}{9}(72 - 12 - 2 - (9 - 3 - 1)) = \frac{53\pi}{9}$.

6.6.10 $S = 2\pi\int_0^5\sqrt{4x+6}(\sqrt{1 + (2/\sqrt{4x+6})^2})\,dx = 2\pi\int_0^5\sqrt{4x+6}\sqrt{\left(\frac{4x+6+4}{4x+6}\right)}\,dx = 2\pi\int_0^5\sqrt{4x+10}\,dx =$
$\frac{4\pi}{3}\left((4x+10)^{3/2}/4\right)\Big|_0^5 = \frac{\pi}{3}(30\sqrt{30} - 10\sqrt{10}) = \frac{10\sqrt{10}\pi}{3}(3\sqrt{3} - 1)$.

6.6.11 $S = 2\pi\int_{-2}^2 (1/4)(e^{2x} + e^{-2x})\sqrt{1 + \frac{(2e^{2x} - 2e^{-2x})^2}{16}}\,dx = \frac{\pi}{2}\int_{-2}^2(e^{2x} + e^{-2x})\sqrt{\frac{16 + 4e^{4x} - 8 + 4e^{-4x}}{16}}\,dx =$
$\frac{\pi}{8}\int_{-2}^2(e^{2x} + e^{-2x})\sqrt{(2e^{2x} + 2e^{-2x})^2}\,dx = \frac{\pi}{8}\int_{-2}^2(e^{2x} + e^{-2x})(2e^{2x} + 2e^{-2x})\,dx = \frac{\pi}{4}\int_{-2}^2(e^{4x} + 2 + e^{-4x})\,dx =$
$\frac{\pi}{4}\left(e^{4x}/4 + 2x - e^{-4x}/4\right)\Big|_{-2}^2 = \frac{\pi}{4}(e^8/4 + 4 - e^{-8}/4 - (e^{-8}/4 - 4 - e^8/4)) = \frac{\pi}{4}(e^8/2 + 8 - e^{-8}/2)$.

6.6.12 $S = 2\pi\int_1^2(x^4/8 + x^{-2}/4)\sqrt{1 + (x^3/2 - x^{-3}/2)^2}\,dx =$
$2\pi\int_1^2(x^4/8 + x^{-2}/4)\sqrt{1 + x^6/4 - 1/2 + x^{-6}/4}\,dx =$
$2\pi\int_1^2(x^4/8 + x^{-2}/4)\sqrt{x^6/4 + 1/2 + x^{-6}/4}\,dx = 2\pi\int_1^2(x^4/8 + x^{-2}/4)\sqrt{(x^3/2 + x^{-3}/2)^2}\,dx = 2\pi\int_1^2(x^4/8 + x^{-2}/4)(x^3/2 + x^{-3}/2)\,dx = 2\pi\int_1^2(x^7/16 + x/16 + x/8 + x^{-5}/8)\,dx = \frac{\pi}{8}\int_1^2(x^7 + 3x + 2x^{-5})\,dx =$
$\frac{\pi}{8}\left(x^8/8 + 3x^2/2 - x^{-4}/2\right)\Big|_1^2 = \frac{\pi}{8}(32 + 6 - (1/32) - (1/8 + 3/2 - 1/2)) = \frac{1179\pi}{256}$.

6.6.13 $S = 2\pi \int_{1/2}^{2} (x^3/3 + x^{-1}/4)\sqrt{1 + (x^2 - x^{-2}/4)^2}\, dx =$

$2\pi \int_{1/2}^{2} (x^3/3 + x^{-1}/4)\sqrt{1 + x^4 - 1/2 + x^{-4}/16}\, dx = 2\pi \int_{1/2}^{2} (x^3/3 + x^{-1}/4)\sqrt{x^4 + 1/2 + x^{-4}/16}\, dx =$

$2\pi \int_{1/2}^{2} (x^3/3 + x^{-1}/4)\sqrt{(x^2 + x^{-2}/4)^2}\, dx = 2\pi \int_{1/2}^{2} (x^3/3 + x^{-1}/4)(x^2 + x^{-2}/4)\, dx = 2\pi \int_{1/2}^{2} (x^5/3 + x/12 +$

$x/4 + x^{-3}/16)\, dx = 2\pi \int_{1/2}^{2} (x^5/3 + x/3 + x^{-3}/16)\, dx = 2\pi \left(x^6/18 + x^2/6 - x^{-2}/32 \right)\Big|_{1/2}^{2} = 2\pi(32/9 + 2/3 -$

$1/128 - (1/1152 + 1/24 - 1/8)) = \frac{275\pi}{32}$.

6.6.14 $S = 2\pi \int_{1}^{4} \sqrt{5x - x^2}\sqrt{1 + \frac{(5 - 2x)^2}{4(5x - x^2)}}\, dx = 2\pi \int_{1}^{4} \sqrt{5x - x^2}\sqrt{\frac{20x - 4x^2 + 25 - 20x + 4x^2}{4(5x - x^2)}}\, dx =$

$2\pi \int_{1}^{4} \sqrt{5x - x^2}\sqrt{\frac{25}{4(5x - x^2)}}\, dx = 2\pi \int_{1}^{4} 5/2\, dx = 5\pi \, (x)\, \Big|_{1}^{4} = 15\pi$.

6.6.15 $S = 2\pi \int_{1}^{7} \sqrt{8x - x^2}\sqrt{1 + \frac{(8 - 2x)^2}{4(8x - x^2)}}\, dx = 2\pi \int_{1}^{7} \sqrt{8x - x^2}\sqrt{\frac{32x - 4x^2 + 64 - 32x + 4x^2}{4(8x - x^2)}}\, dx =$

$2\pi \int_{1}^{7} \sqrt{8x - x^2}\sqrt{\frac{64}{4(8x - x^2)}}\, dx = 2\pi \int_{1}^{7} 4\, dx = 8\pi(7 - 1) = 48\pi$. Because the surface area is 48π square meters, the volume of paint required to cover the surface to a thickness of .0015 meters is $48\pi(.0015) \approx .226$ cubic meters. This is about 59.75 gallons.

6.6.16 $S = 2\pi \int_{-8}^{8} \sqrt{100 - x^2}\sqrt{1 + \frac{(-2x)^2}{4(100 - x^2)}}\, dx = 2\pi \int_{-8}^{8} \sqrt{100 - x^2}\sqrt{\frac{400 - 4x^2 + 4x^2}{4(100 - x^2)}}\, dx = 2\pi \int_{-8}^{8} 10\, dx =$

$20\pi(8 - (-8)) = 320\pi$. Because the surface area is 320π square meters, the volume of paint required to cover the surface to a thickness of .0015 meters is $320\pi(.0015) \approx 1.5$ cubic meters. This is about 398.36 gallons.

6.6.17 Note that $x = y^3/3$ for $0 \le y \le 2$. The surface area is $S = 2\pi \int_{0}^{2} (y^3/3)\sqrt{1 + y^4}\, dy$. Let $u = 1 + y^4$ so that $du = 4y^3\, dy$. Substituting yields $S = 2\pi \int_{1}^{17} \frac{1}{12} u^{1/2}\, du = \frac{\pi}{9} \left(u^{3/2} \right)\Big|_{1}^{17} = \frac{\pi}{9}(17\sqrt{17} - 1)$.

6.6.18 Note that $x = 2\sqrt{y}$ for $1 \le y \le 4$. The surface area is $S = 2\pi \int_{1}^{4} 2\sqrt{y}\sqrt{1 + 1/y}\, dy =$

$4\pi \int_{1}^{4} \sqrt{1 + y}\, dy = \frac{8\pi}{3} \left((1 + y)^{3/2} \right)\Big|_{1}^{4} = \frac{8\pi}{3}(5\sqrt{5} - 2\sqrt{2})$.

6.6.19 Note that $x = \frac{y+1}{4}$ for $3 \le y \le 15$. The surface area is $S = 2\pi \int_{3}^{15} \frac{y+1}{4}\sqrt{1 + \frac{1}{16}}\, dy = \frac{\pi\sqrt{17}}{8} \int_{3}^{15} (y + 1)\, dy = \frac{\pi\sqrt{17}}{8} \left(y^2/2 + y \right)\Big|_{3}^{15} = \frac{\pi\sqrt{17}}{8}(225/2 + 15 - (9/2 + 3)) = \frac{\pi\sqrt{17}}{8}(120) = 15\sqrt{17}\pi$.

6.6.20 We can rewrite the given curve as $2x + \sqrt{4x^2 - 1} = e^{2y}$. Squaring yields $4x^2 + 4x\sqrt{4x^2 - 1} + 4x^2 - 1 = e^{4y}$. So $e^{4y} + 1 = 8x^2 + 4x\sqrt{4x^2 - 1} = 4x(2x + \sqrt{4x^2 - 1}) = 4x(e^{2y})$. Thus $x = \frac{e^{4y} + 1}{4e^{2y}} = \frac{e^{2y} + e^{-2y}}{4}$. The portion of the curve in question is for $0 \le y \le \ln 2$.

The surface area is $S = 2\pi \int_{0}^{\ln 2} \frac{e^{2y} + e^{-2y}}{4}\sqrt{1 + (e^{2y}/2 - e^{-2y}/2)^2}\, dy =$

$2\pi \int_{0}^{\ln 2} \frac{e^{2y} + e^{-2y}}{4}\sqrt{e^{4y}/4 + 1/2 + e^{-2y}/4}\, dy = 2\pi \int_{0}^{\ln 2} \frac{e^{2y} + e^{-2y}}{4} \frac{\sqrt{(e^{2y} + e^{-2y})^2}}{2}\, dy = \frac{\pi}{4} \int_{0}^{\ln 2} (e^{4y} + 2 + e^{-4y})\, dy =$

$\frac{\pi}{4} \left(e^{4y}/4 + 2y - e^{-4y}/4 \right)\Big|_{0}^{\ln 2} = \frac{\pi}{4}(4 + 2\ln 2 - 1/64 - (1/4 + 0 - 1/4)) = \frac{\pi}{4} \left(\frac{255}{64} + 2\ln 2 \right)$.

6.6.21

a. False. One would need to find $x = f^{-1}(y)$ and compute the corresponding integral using f^{-1}.

b. False. For example, the curve given in number 14 above isn't one-to-one on the given interval, but the surface is still defined.

c. True. Because the curve is symmetric about the y-axis, the surface generated by revolving half the curve is half the surface generated by revolving the whole curve.

d. False. This curve is symmetric about the y-axis, so the surface generated by revolving the whole curve is the same as the surface generated by revolving the portion over $[0, 4]$.

6.6.22 $S = 2\pi \int_2^{10} \sqrt{12y - y^2}\sqrt{1 + \frac{(12-2y)^2}{4(12y-y^2)}}\,dy = 2\pi \int_2^{10} \sqrt{12y - y^2}\sqrt{\frac{48y - 4y^2 + 144 - 48y + 4y^2}{4(12y-y^2)}}\,dy =$
$2\pi \int_2^{10} 6\,dy = 12\pi(10-2) = 96\pi$.

6.6.23 $S = 2\pi \int_1^4 (4y^{3/2} - y^{1/2}/12)\sqrt{1 + (6y^{1/2} - y^{-1/2}/24)^2}\,dy =$
$2\pi \int_1^4 (4y^{3/2} - y^{1/2}/12)\sqrt{1 + 36y - 1/2 + 1/(576y)}\,dy = 2\pi \int_1^4 (4y^{3/2} - y^{1/2}/12)\sqrt{36y + 1/2 + 1/(576y)}\,dy =$
$2\pi \int_1^4 (4y^{3/2} - y^{1/2}/12)\sqrt{(6y^{1/2} + y^{-1/2}/24)^2}\,dy = 2\pi \int_1^4 (4y^{3/2} - y^{1/2}/12)(6y^{1/2} + y^{-1/2}/24)\,dy =$
$2\pi \int_1^4 (24y^2 - y/3 - 1/288)\,dy = 2\pi \left(8y^3 - y^2/6 - y/288\right)\Big|_1^4 = 2\pi(512 - 8/3 - 1/72 - (8 - 1/6 - 1/288)) = \frac{48143\pi}{48}$.

6.6.24 Note that $x = \sqrt{1 - (y-1)^2} = \sqrt{1 - (y^2 - 2y + 1)} = \sqrt{2y - y^2}$.
$S = 2\pi \int_1^{3/2} \sqrt{2y - y^2}\sqrt{1 + \frac{(2-2y)^2}{4(2y-y^2)}}\,dy = 2\pi \int_1^{3/2} \sqrt{2y - y^2}\sqrt{\frac{8y - 4y^2 + 4 - 8y + 4y^2}{4(2y-y^2)}}\,dy = 2\pi \int_1^{3/2} 1\,dy =$
$2\pi(3/2 - 1) = \pi$.

6.6.25

$$S = 2\pi \int_1^8 (9x^{2/3} - x^{4/3}/32)\sqrt{1 + (6x^{-1/3} - x^{1/3}/24)^2}\,dx$$

$$= 2\pi \int_1^8 (9x^{2/3} - x^{4/3}/32)\sqrt{1 + 36x^{-2/3} - 1/2 + x^{2/3}/576}\,dx$$

$$= 2\pi \int_1^8 (9x^{2/3} - x^{4/3}/32)\sqrt{36x^{-2/3} + 1/2 + x^{2/3}/576}\,dx$$

$$= 2\pi \int_1^8 (9x^{2/3} - x^{4/3}/32)\sqrt{(6x^{-1/3} + x^{1/3}/24)^2}\,dx = 2\pi \int_1^8 (9x^{2/3} - x^{4/3}/32)(6x^{-1/3} - x^{1/3}/24)\,dx$$

$$= 2\pi \int_1^8 54x^{1/3} + 3x/16 - x^{5/3}/768\,dx = 2\pi \left(\frac{81x^{4/3}}{2} + \frac{3x^2}{32} - \frac{x^{8/3}}{2048}\right)\Big|_1^8$$

$$= 2\pi(648 + 6 - 1/8 - (81/2 + 3/32 - 1/2048)) = \frac{1256001\pi}{1024}$$

6.6.26

a. $S = 2\pi \int_0^1 x^5 \sqrt{1 + 25x^8}\,dx$.

b. $S = \approx 3.362$.

6.6.27

a. $S = 2\pi \int_0^{\pi/2} \cos x \sqrt{1 + \sin^2 x}\,dx$.

b. $S \approx 7.21$.

6.6.28

a. $S = 2\pi \int_1^{\sqrt{e}} \ln x^2 \sqrt{1 + 4/x^2}\,dx$.

b. $S \approx 3.845$.

6.6.29

a. $S = 2\pi \int_0^{\pi/4} \tan x \sqrt{1 + \sec^4 x}\,dx$.

b. $S \approx 3.84$.

6.6.30 The surface area of the described cylinder is $2\pi r h$. The surface area of the described cone is $\pi r \sqrt{h^2 + r^2}$. The cone's area is $\frac{2h}{\sqrt{h^2 + r^2}}$ of the cylinder's.

6.6.31 Let $y = f(x) = (a^{2/3} - x^{2/3})^{3/2}$. Note that $f'(x) = -x^{-1/3}\sqrt{a^{2/3} - x^{2/3}}$, so

$$\sqrt{1 + f'(x)^2} = \sqrt{1 + \frac{a^{2/3} - x^{2/3}}{x^{2/3}}} = \sqrt{\frac{x^{2/3} + a^{2/3} - x^{2/3}}{x^{2/3}}} = \frac{a^{1/3}}{x^{1/3}}.$$

Thus (using symmetry) $S = 4\pi \int_0^a (a^{2/3} - x^{2/3})^{3/2}(a^{1/3}x^{-1/3})\,dx$. Let $u = (a^{2/3} - x^{2/3})$, so that $du = (-2x^{-1/3}/3)\,dx$. Substituting gives $S = -6\pi a^{1/3} \int_{a^{2/3}}^0 u^{3/2}\,du = 6\pi a^{1/3} \int_0^{a^{2/3}} u^{3/2}\,du = $

$\frac{12\pi}{5} a^{1/3} \left(u^{5/2}\right)\Big|_0^{a^{2/3}} = \frac{12\pi a^2}{5}.$

6.6.32 Let $y = f(x) = a + \sqrt{r^2 - x^2}$. Revolving this curve around the x-axis will give a portion of the surface of the torus. The other comes from revolving $y = g(x) = a - \sqrt{r^2 - x^2}$ around the x-axis. We will compute the surface area for the first portion first.

Note that $\sqrt{1 + f'(x)^2} = \sqrt{1 + \left(\frac{-x}{\sqrt{r^2 - x^2}}\right)^2} = \sqrt{\frac{r^2 - x^2 + x^2}{r^2 - x^2}} = \frac{r}{\sqrt{r^2 - x^2}}$. So (using symmetry) the surface area for this portion of the torus is $4\pi \int_0^r (a + \sqrt{r^2 - x^2})\left(\frac{r}{\sqrt{r^2 - x^2}}\right)\,dx = 4\pi a r \int_0^r \frac{1}{\sqrt{r^2 - x^2}}\,dx + 4\pi r \int_0^r 1\,dx =$

$4\pi a r \left(\sin^{-1}(x/r)\right)\Big|_0^r + 4\pi r^2 = 4\pi a r\,(\pi/2 - 0) + 4\pi r^2 = 2\pi^2 a r + 4\pi r^2.$

If we revolve $y = g(x) = a - \sqrt{r^2 - x^2}$ around the x-axis, the surface area will be $2\pi^2 a r - 4\pi r^2$ by a very similar calculation. Thus, the total surface area of the torus is

$$S = 2\pi^2 a r + 4\pi r^2 + 2\pi^2 a r - 4\pi r^2 = 4\pi^2 a r.$$

6.6.33 Let $y = f(x) = \sqrt{r^2 - x^2}$, and imagine the surface obtained by revolving this curve around the x-axis for $a \le x \le a + h$. The surface area is $S = 2\pi \int_a^{a+h} \sqrt{r^2 - x^2}\sqrt{1 + \left(\frac{-x}{\sqrt{r^2 - x^2}}\right)^2}\,dx$. This can be written as

$2\pi \int_a^{a+h} \sqrt{r^2 - x^2}\sqrt{\frac{r^2 - x^2 + x^2}{r^2 - x^2}}\,dx = 2\pi \int_a^{a+h} \sqrt{r^2 - x^2}\frac{\sqrt{r^2}}{\sqrt{r^2 - x^2}}\,dx = 2\pi \int_a^{a+h} r\,dx = 2\pi r(a + h - a) = 2\pi r h.$

6.6.34

a. Let $y = f(x) = \frac{b}{a}\sqrt{a^2 - x^2}$. Then $f'(x) = \frac{b}{a} \cdot \frac{-x}{\sqrt{a^2 - x^2}}$, so $\sqrt{1 + f'(x)^2} = \sqrt{1 + \frac{b^2}{a^2} \cdot \frac{x^2}{a^2 - x^2}} = \sqrt{\frac{a^4 - a^2 x^2 + b^2 x^2}{a^2} \cdot \frac{1}{a^2 - x^2}}$. Thus $f(x)\sqrt{1 + f'(x)^2}$ is

$$\frac{b}{a}\sqrt{a^2 - x^2}\sqrt{\frac{a^4 - a^2 x^2 + b^2 x^2}{a^2}} \cdot \frac{1}{\sqrt{a^2 - x^2}} = \frac{b}{a}\sqrt{a^2 - \frac{(a^2 - b^2)x^2}{a^2}} = \frac{b}{a}\sqrt{a^2 - \left(1 - \frac{b^2}{a^2}\right)x^2}.$$

Letting $c^2 = 1 - \frac{b^2}{a^2}$ and using symmetry gives

$$S = \frac{4\pi b}{a}\int_0^a \sqrt{a^2 - c^2 x^2}\,dx.$$

b. Let $u = cx$, so that $du = c\,dx$, Note that when $x = 0$, u is also 0, and when $x = a$, we have $u = ca = \sqrt{1 - \frac{b^2}{a^2}}\sqrt{a^2} = \sqrt{a^2 - b^2}$. Thus,

$$S = \frac{4\pi b}{ac}\int_0^{\sqrt{a^2 - b^2}} \sqrt{a^2 - u^2}\,du = \frac{4\pi b}{\sqrt{a^2 - b^2}}\int_0^{\sqrt{a^2 - b^2}} \sqrt{a^2 - u^2}\,du.$$

c. S is

$$\frac{2\pi b}{\sqrt{a^2 - b^2}} \left(u\sqrt{a^2 - u^2} + a^2 \sin^{-1}(u/a) \right) \Big|_0^{\sqrt{a^2 - b^2}} = \frac{2\pi b}{\sqrt{a^2 - b^2}} \left(b\sqrt{a^2 - b^2} + a^2 \sin^{-1}\left(\frac{\sqrt{a^2 - b^2}}{a} \right) \right).$$

Multiplying through by the factor of $\sqrt{a^2 - b^2}$ in the denominator gives

$$S = 2\pi b \left(b + \frac{a^2}{\sqrt{a^2 - b^2}} \sin^{-1}\left(\frac{\sqrt{a^2 - b^2}}{a} \right) \right).$$

d. S would be measured in square meters.

e. Returning to our work in the first part of this problem, if $a = b$ then $f(x)\sqrt{1 + f'(x)^2} = \frac{b}{a}\sqrt{a^2 - 0} = b$. So the surface area is $S = 4\pi \int_0^a b\, dx = 4\pi b(a - 0) = 4\pi ab = 4\pi a^2$.

6.6.35

a. The ratio is $\frac{6a^2}{a^3} = \frac{6}{a}$.

b. The ratio is $\frac{4\pi a^2}{(4/3)\pi a^3} = \frac{3}{a}$.

c. The ratio is $\dfrac{2\pi \left(1 + \frac{a^2}{\sqrt{a^2 - 1}} \sin^{-1}\left(\frac{\sqrt{a^2 - 1}}{a} \right) \right)}{(4/3)\pi a} = \frac{3}{2a} + \frac{3a}{2\sqrt{a^2 - 1}} \sin^{-1}\left(\frac{\sqrt{a^2 - 1}}{a} \right).$

d.

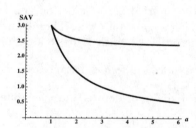

The lower curve is for the sphere and the upper for the ellipsoid.

e. More spherical is better for minimizing heat loss.

6.6.36 Let $c = \frac{g(b) - g(a)}{b - a}$.

The slant height l can be written as $\sqrt{(g(b) - g(a))^2 + (b - a)^2}$, so the quantity $\pi(g(b) + g(a))l$ can be written as

$$\frac{b - a}{\sqrt{(b - a)^2}} \pi(g(b) + g(a))\sqrt{(g(b) - g(a))^2 + (b - a)^2} = (b - a)\pi(g(b) + g(a))\sqrt{c^2 + 1}.$$

We will show that the surface area of the frustrum is this quantity.

The line between $(a, g(a))$ and $(b, g(b))$ has slope $\frac{g(b) - g(a)}{b - a} = c$. Then the equation of the line is $y = f(x) = g(a) + c(x - a)$. The surface area is $S = 2\pi \int_a^b (g(a) + c(x - a))\sqrt{1 + c^2}\, dx = 2\pi\sqrt{1 + c^2} \int_a^b (g(a) + c(x - a))\, dx = 2\pi\sqrt{1 + c^2} \left(g(a)x + \frac{c(x-a)^2}{2} \right) \Big|_a^b = 2\pi\sqrt{1 + c^2} \left(g(a)(b - a) + \frac{c(b-a)^2}{2} \right) = \pi\sqrt{1 + c^2} \left(2g(a)(b - a) + (g(b) - g(a))(b - a) \right) = \pi\sqrt{1 + c^2}(b - a)(2g(a) + g(b) - g(a)) = \pi\sqrt{1 + c^2}(b - a)(g(a) + g(b))$, as desired.

6.6.37

a. Note that $g(x) = cf(x)$, so that $g'(x) = cf'(x)$.

$2\pi \int_a^b g(x)\sqrt{c^2 + g'(x)^2}\, dx = 2\pi \int_a^b cf(x)\sqrt{c^2 + c^2 f'(x)^2}\, dx = 2c^2\pi \int_a^b f(x)\sqrt{1 + f'(x)^2}\, dx = c^2 A.$

b. Note that $h'(x) = cf'(cx)$. Consider

$$2\pi \int_{a/c}^{b/c} f(cx)\sqrt{c^2 + c^2 f'(cx)^2}\, dx = 2c\pi \int_{a/c}^{b/c} f(cx)\sqrt{1 + f'(cx)^2}\, dx.$$

Let $u = cx$ so that $du = c\, dx$. Then our integral is equal to

$$2\pi \int_a^b f(u)\sqrt{1 + f'(u)^2}\, du = A.$$

6.6.38 The area obtained by revolving $f(x) + C$ around the x-axis is $2\pi \int_a^b (f(x) + C)\sqrt{1 + f'(x)^2}\, dx = 2\pi \int_a^b f(x)\sqrt{1 + f'(x)^2}\, dx + 2\pi C \int_a^b \sqrt{1 + f'(x)^2}\, dx = S + 2\pi CL$, as desired.

6.7   Physical Applications

6.7.1 $m = \rho_1 \cdot l_1 + \rho_2 \cdot l_2 = 1\,\text{g/cm} \cdot 50\,\text{cm} + 2\,\text{g/cm} \cdot 50\,\text{cm} = 150$ g.

6.7.2 The mass is given by $m = \int_a^b \rho(x)\, dx$.

6.7.3 The work is the product of 5 Newtons and 5 meters, which is 25 J.

6.7.4 If the force is not constant, the interval must be divided up into pieces, and on each small piece the work can be approximated by assuming a constant force. These approximations are then added up and then the sum is refined through a limiting process, which leads to a definite integral.

6.7.5 Different volumes of water are moved different distances.

6.7.6 Different parts of the dam have different depths and thus different amount of pressure.

6.7.7 $F = \rho gh = 1000 \cdot 9.8 \cdot 4 = 39,200$ N/m^2.

6.7.8 Along a thin horizontal strip, the pressure is the same, because the depth is constant.

6.7.9 $m = \int_0^\pi (1 + \sin x)\, dx = (x - \cos x)\Big|_0^\pi = \pi - (-1) - (0 - 1) = \pi + 2.$

6.7.10 $m = \int_0^1 (1 + x^3)\, dx = \left(x + x^4/4\right)\Big|_0^1 = \frac{5}{4}.$

6.7.11 $= \int_0^2 (2 - x/2)\, dx = \left(2x - x^2/4\right)\Big|_0^2 = 3.$

6.7.12 $m = \int_0^4 5e^{-2x}\, dx = \left((-5/2)e^{-2x}\right)\Big|_0^4 = \frac{5}{2}(1 - e^{-8}).$

6.7.13 $m = \int_0^1 x\sqrt{2 - x^2}\, dx = \left(\frac{-1}{3}(2 - x^2)^{3/2}\right)\Big|_0^1 = (-1/3) + (2\sqrt{2}/3) = \frac{2\sqrt{2}-1}{3}.$

6.7.14 $m = \int_0^2 1\, dx + \int_2^3 2\, dx = 2 + 2 = 4.$

6.7.15 $m = \int_0^2 1\, dx + \int_2^4 (1+x)\, dx = 2 + \left(x + x^2/2 \right) \Big|_2^4 = 2 + (4+8) - (2+2) = 10.$

6.7.16 $m = \int_0^1 x^2\, dx + \int_1^2 x(2-x)\, dx = \left(x^3/3 \right) \Big|_0^1 + \left(x^2 - x^3/3 \right) \Big|_1^2 = \frac{1}{3} + 4 - 8/3 - (1 - 1/3) = 1.$

6.7.17 $W = \int_0^3 2x\, dx = x^2 \Big|_0^3 = 9$ J.

6.7.18 $W = \int_1^3 2/x^2\, dx = (-2/x) \Big|_1^3 = \frac{-2}{3} - (-2) = \frac{4}{3}$ J.

6.7.19

    a. Because $f(.2) = .2k = 30$, we have $k = 150$.

    b. $W = \int_0^{-.4} 150x\, dx = 75x^2 \Big|_0^{-.4} = 75 \cdot 0.16 = 12$ J.

    c. $W = \int_0^{.3} 150x\, dx = 75x^2 \Big|_0^{.3} = 75 \cdot 0.09 = 6.75$ J.

    d. $W = \int_{.2}^{.4} 150x\, dx = 75x^2 \Big|_{.2}^{.4} = 75(0.16 - 0.04) = 9$ J.

6.7.20

    a. $f(.25) = .25k = 15$, so $k = 60$.

    b. $W = \int_0^{-.2} 60x\, dx = 30x^2 \Big|_0^{-.2} = 30 \cdot 0.04 = 1.2$ J.

    c. $W = \int_{.25}^{.55} 60x\, dx = 30x^2 \Big|_{.25}^{.55} = 30(.3025 - .0625) = 30 \cdot 0.24 = 7.2$ J.

6.7.21

    a. $f(x) = kx$, and $f(.5) = 50$, so $k(.5) = 50$, so $k = 100$.

       Therefore $W = \int_0^{1.5} 100x\, dx = \left(50x^2 \right) \Big|_0^{1.5} = 112.5$ J.

    b. $\int_0^{-.5} 100x\, dx = \left(50x^2 \right) \Big|_0^{-.5} = 12.5$ J.

6.7.22 $f(x) = kx$, and $f(.02) = .02k = 500 \cdot 9.8 = 4900$, so $k = 245000$.

    $W = \int_0^{.04} 245000x\, dx = \left(122500x^2 \right) \Big|_0^{.04} = 196$ J.

6.7.23

    a. $f(.2) = .2k = 50$, so $k = 250$. $W = \int_0^{.5} 250x\, dx = 125x^2 \Big|_0^{.5} = 125 \cdot 0.25 = 31.25$ J.

    b. $\int_0^{.2} kx\, dx = kx^2/2 \Big|_0^{.2} = .02k = 50$, so $k = 2500$. $W = \int_0^{.5} 2500x\, dx = 1250x^2 \Big|_0^{.5} = 1250 \cdot 0.25 = 312.5$
       J.

6.7.24

　a. $f(.1) = .1k = 50$, so $k = 500$. $W = \int_0^{.4} 500x\,dx = 250x^2 \Big|_0^{.4} = 250 \cdot 0.16 = 40$ J.

　b. $\int_0^{.1} kx\,dx = kx^2/2 \Big|_0^{.1} = .005k = 2$, so $k = 400$. $W = \int_0^{.4} 400x\,dx = 200x^2 \Big|_0^{.4} = 200 \cdot 0.16 = 32$ J.

6.7.25

　a. We have $\int_0^{0.5} kx\,dx = \frac{k}{2}x^2 \Big|_0^{0.5} = 0.125k = 100$, so that $k = 800$. Then

$$W = \int_0^{1.25} 800x\,dx = 400x^2 \Big|_0^{1.25} = 625\,\text{J}.$$

　b. $f(0.5) = 0.5k = 250$, so $k = 500$ and thus

$$W = \int_0^{1.25} 500x\,dx = 250x^2 \Big|_0^{1.25} = 390.625\,\text{J}.$$

6.7.26
$$W(x) = \int_0^x 25t\,dt = \left(25t^2/2\right)\Big|_0^x = 25x^2/2.$$
Note that W is an even function, so that $W(-x) = W(x)$, and thus the work is the same to compress or stretch the spring a given distance from its equilibrium position.

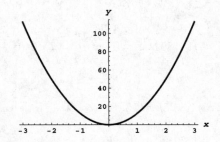

6.7.27 $W = \int_0^{2.5} \rho g A(y)(2.5 - y)\,dy = 1000 \cdot 9.8 \cdot 25 \cdot 15 \int_0^{2.5}(2.5 - y)\,dy = 3675000\left(2.5y - y^2/2\right)\Big|_0^{2.5} = 3675000 \cdot (2.5)^2/2 = 11,484,375$ J.

6.7.28

　a. $W = \int_0^8 \rho g \pi \cdot 2^2 (8 - y)\,dy = 4\pi\rho g\left(8y - y^2/2\right)\Big|_0^8 \approx 3.941 \times 10^6$ J.

　b. Not true. For pumping half the water from a full tank the work is

$$\int_4^8 4\rho\pi g(8 - y)\,dy = 4\pi\rho g\left(8y - y^2/2\right)\Big|_4^8 = 32\pi\rho g \approx 985203\,\text{J}.$$

　To empty a half-full tank, the work is

$$\int_0^4 4\rho\pi g(8 - y)\,dy = 4\pi\rho g\left(8y - y^2/2\right)\Big|_0^4 = 96\pi\rho g \approx 2.95561 \times 10^6\,\text{J}.$$

6.7.29 $W = \int_0^4 \rho\pi g 2^2 (10 - y)\,dy = 4\pi\rho g\left(10y - y^2/2\right)\Big|_0^4 = 4\pi\rho g(40 - 8) = 128\pi\rho g \approx 3.941 \times 10^6$ J.

6.7.30 $W = \int_0^2 \rho g A(y)(3 - y)\,dy = 1000 \cdot 9.8 \cdot 25 \cdot 15 \int_0^2 (3 - y)\,dy = 3675000\left(3y - y^2/2\right)\Big|_0^2 = (3675000) \cdot 4 = 1.47 \times 10^7$ J.

6.7.31

a. Let the vertex of the cone be at $(0,0)$, with the y-axis vertically oriented. Note that the area of a horizontal slice at height y is $\pi y^2/16$, and it must move $6 - y$ meters to get to the top.

$$W = \int_0^6 \rho g \pi \frac{y^2}{16}(6-y)\,dy = \frac{\pi\rho g}{16}\int_0^6 (6y^2 - y^3)\,dy = \frac{\pi\rho g}{16}\left(2y^3 - y^4/4\right)\bigg|_0^6 = (\pi\rho g/16)(108) = 66,150\pi \text{ J.}$$

b. Not true.

$$\int_0^3 \rho g \pi \frac{y^2}{16}(6-y)\,dy = \frac{\pi\rho g}{16}\int_0^3 (6y^2 - y^3)\,dy = \frac{\pi\rho g}{16}\left(2y^3 - y^4/4\right)\bigg|_0^3 = (\pi\rho g/16)\cdot 33.75 \approx 20672\pi \text{ J,}$$

less than half the amount from part (a). Note that while the water must be raised further than water in the top half, due to the shape of the tank, there is far less water in the bottom half than in the top.

6.7.32 Orient the y-axis vertically, with the point $(10,0)$ representing a point on the bottom of the pool in one corner of the deep end, and $(-10,1)$ representing a point on the bottom of the pool in the shallow end on the same side of the pool. Note that the straight line between these two points is given by $y = \frac{1}{20}(10-x)$. So in the first 1 meter of depth, at a height of y the length of the pool is $10 - x = 20y$, so the area of a slice is $20y \cdot 10$. In the 2nd meter of depth, the slices are uniformly of area 200 square meters.

$$W = \int_0^1 \rho g 200 y(2.2 - y)\,dy + \int_1^2 \rho g 200(2.2 - y)\,dy = 200\rho g\left(\left(1.1y^2 - y^3/3\right)\bigg|_0^1 + \left(2.2y - y^2/2\right)\bigg|_1^2\right)$$

$$= 200\rho g\left(1.1 - (1/3) + (4.4 - 2 - (2.2 - 1/2))\right) = \frac{880}{3}\rho g \approx 2.87467 \times 10^6 \text{ J.}$$

6.7.33

a. Orient the axes so that the south pole of the tank is at $(0,0)$ and the north pole is at $(0,16)$. The cross section of the tank which contains the xy plane intersects the tank in the circle centered at $(0,8)$ with radius 8, so the curve is $x^2 + (y-8)^2 = 8^2$. A slice at height y has area $\pi x^2 = \pi(16y - y^2)$.

$$W = \int_0^{16} \rho g \pi (16y - y^2)\,dy = \pi\rho g\left(8y^2 - y^3/3\right)\bigg|_0^{16} = \pi\rho g \frac{16^3}{6} = 200704000 \cdot \pi/3 \approx 2.102 \times 10^8 \text{ J.}$$

b. The total weight of the water lifted up for 18 meters is

$$W = \frac{4\pi}{3}R^3 \rho g h = \frac{4\pi}{3}8^3 \cdot 1000 \cdot 9.8 \cdot 18 = 120422400\pi \approx 3.783 \times 10^8 \text{ J.}$$

6.7.34

a. Orient the axes so that $(0,0)$ is the south pole of the semicircle at one end of the trough. The equation of the semicircle is $x^2 + (y - (1/4))^2 = (1/4)^2$. At a height of y, a slice has area $2x \cdot 3 = 6\sqrt{(1/2)y - y^2}$. The distance it must travel to the top is $1/4 - y$.

$W = \int_0^{1/4} \rho g 6\sqrt{(1/2)y - y^2}((1/4) - y)\,dy$. Let $u = (1/2)y - y^2$, so that $du = ((1/2) - 2y)\,dy = 2((1/4) - y)\,dy$. Then we have $W = 3\rho g \int_0^{1/16} u^{1/2}\,du = 2\rho g\left(u^{3/2}\right)\bigg|_0^{1/16} = \rho g/32 = 306.25$ J.

b. Yes. If we double the length of the trough, the area of a slice is doubled, and the work integral is doubled.

c. No. If the radius is doubled, the work is more than doubled. (There are "more slices," and each must travel farther to get to the top of the tank.)

6.7.35

a. Orient the axes so that the lower corners of the trough are at $(-0.25, 0)$ and at $(.25, 0)$. Then the upper corners are at $(-.5, 1)$ and at $(.5, 1)$. Note that the line between $(.25, 0)$ and $(.5, 1)$ is given by $y = 4x - 1$. The area of a slice at height y is $2x \cdot 10 = 20 \cdot \frac{1}{4}(y + 1) = 5(y + 1)$. Thus, $W = \rho g \int_0^1 5(y + 1)(1 - y)\, dy = 5\rho g \int_0^1 (1 - y^2)\, dy = 5\rho g \left(y - y^3/3 \right) \Big|_0^1 = \frac{10\rho g}{3} \approx 32,667$ J.

b. Yes. If the length is doubled, the area of each slice is doubled, so the work integral is doubled as well.

6.7.36 Note that this tank is full of water, rather than gasoline.

$W = 1000 \cdot 9.8 \int_{-5}^5 20\sqrt{25 - y^2}(10 - y)\, dy = 196,000 \int_{-5}^5 \sqrt{25 - y^2}(10 - y)\, dy$. The integral can be divided into two integrals as in the example. We have $10 \int_{-5}^5 \sqrt{25 - y^2}\, dy - \int_{-5}^5 y\sqrt{25 - y^2}\, dy$. The first represents 10 times the area of a half-circle of radius 5, so the value is $(10)\frac{25\pi}{2} = 125\pi$. The second integral can be computed with the substitution $u = 25 - y^2$, $du = -2y\, dy$. The resulting integral is $\frac{1}{2} \int_0^0 \sqrt{u}\, du = 0$. So the total work is $W = 196000 \cdot 125\pi \approx 7.697 \times 10^7$ J.

6.7.37 Let the vertex of the cone be at $(0, 0)$, with the y-axis vertically oriented. Note that the area of a horizontal slice at height y is $\pi y^2/16$, and it must move $3 - y$ meters to get to the point 1 meter above the top. $W = \int_0^2 \rho g \pi \frac{y^2}{16}(3 - y)\, dy = (\pi \rho g/16) \int_0^2 (3y^2 - y^3)\, dy = (\pi \rho g/16)\left(y^3 - y^4/4 \right) \Big|_0^2 = (\pi \rho g/16)(4) = \frac{\pi \rho g}{4} \approx$ 7696.9 J.

6.7.38 $F = \int_0^{10} \rho g(10 - y) \cdot 40\, dy = 40\rho g \left(10y - y^2/2 \right) \Big|_0^{10} = 200\rho g = 1.960 \times 10^6$ N.

6.7.39 Orient the axes so that the lower corners of the trapezoid are at $(5, 0)$ and $(-5, 0)$, and the upper corners are at $(10, 15)$ and $(-10, 15)$. Note that the line between the corners for $x > 0$ is given by $y = 3(x - 5)$, so at level y, we have a width of $2x = \frac{2y}{3} + 10$.

$F = \rho g \int_0^{15}(15 - y)\left(\frac{2y + 30}{3} \right) dy = \frac{2\rho g}{3} \int_0^{15}(225 - y^2)\, dy = \frac{2\rho g}{3}\left(225y - y^3/3 \right) \Big|_0^{15} = \frac{2\rho g}{3} \cdot 2250 = 1500\rho g = 1.470 \times 10^7$ N.

6.7.40 Orient the axes so that $(0, 0)$ is at the "south pole" of the semicircle. The center of the circle is $(0, 20)$ and the radius is 20, so the equation is $x^2 + (y - 20)^2 = 20^2$, so $x = \sqrt{40y - y^2}$. The width is $2x = 2\sqrt{40y - y^2}$.

$F = 2\rho g \int_0^{20}(20 - y)\sqrt{40y - y^2}\, dy$. Let $u = 40y - y^2$, so that $du = 2(20 - y)\, dy$. Then $F = \rho g \int_0^{400} \sqrt{u}\, du = \rho g \left(2u^{3/2}/3 \right) \Big|_0^{400} = \frac{16000}{3}\rho g = 5.227 \times 10^7$ N.

6.7.41 Orient the axes so that the bottom vertex is at $(0, 0)$. The other vertices are at $(\pm 10, 30)$, and the line between $(0, 0)$ and $(10, 30)$ is given by $y = 3x$. Thus, a slice at height y has width $2x = 2y/3$.

$F = \int_0^{30} \rho g(30 - y)\frac{2y}{3}\, dy = \frac{2\rho g}{3}\left(15y^2 - y^3/3 \right) \Big|_0^{30} = \frac{2\rho g}{3}(4500) = 3000\rho g = 2.940 \times 10^7$ N.

6.7.42 At a height of y, the width of a slice is $2x = 2(4\sqrt{y}) = 8y^{1/2}$. This gives

$$F = 8\rho g \int_0^{25}(25 - y)y^{1/2}\, dy = 8\rho g \left(50y^{3/2}/3 - 2y^{5/2}/5 \right) \Big|_0^{25} = 8\rho g \left(\frac{2500}{3} \right) = 6.533 \times 10^7 \text{ N}.$$

6.7.43 The width of the plate at depth y is $2 - y$, so the force on the plate is

$$F = \int_1^2 \rho g(2 - y)y\, dy = \rho g \left(y^2 - \frac{y^3}{3} \right) \Big|_1^2 = \rho g \cdot \frac{2}{3} \approx 6533 \text{ N}.$$

6.7.44 Arrange the axes so that the origin is in the center of the circular end of the tank. The equation of the circle is $x^2 + y^2 = 25$, so the width of the tank at height y is $2\sqrt{25 - y^2}$, and the depth is $5 - y$. Thus the force is given by

$$\rho g \int_{-5}^{5} (4 - y) 2\sqrt{25 - y^2}\, dy = 14445.2 \int_{-5}^{5} (5 - y)\sqrt{25 - y^2}\, dy$$

$$= 14445. \left(\int_{-5}^{5} 5\sqrt{25 - y^2}\, dy + \int_{-5}^{5} y\sqrt{25 - y^2}\, dy \right).$$

The first integral is five times the area of a semicircle of radius 5, while the second integral is zero since it is a symmetric integral of an odd function. So the total force is $14445.2 \cdot \frac{125\pi}{2} \approx 2.836 \times 10^6$ N.

6.7.45 $F = \int_0^{50} (150 + 2y) \cdot 80\, dy = 80 \left(150y + y^2 \right) \Big|_0^{50} = 8 \times 10^5$ N.

6.7.46 $F = \int_0^{1/2} \rho g (4 - y) \cdot 0.5\, dy = \rho g \left(2y - y^2/4 \right) \Big|_0^{1/2} = \frac{15\rho g}{16} = 9187.5$ N.

6.7.47 $F = \int_1^{1.5} \rho g (4 - y) \cdot 0.5\, dy = \rho g \left(2y - y^2/4 \right) \Big|_1^{1.5} = \frac{11\rho g}{16} = 6737.5$ N.

6.7.48 Orient the axes so that $(0, 0)$ is at the bottom of the circle at the bottom of the pool. Then the equation of the circle is $x^2 + (y - 1/2)^2 = (1/2)^2$, so the width of a slice at a height of y is $2x = 2\sqrt{y - y^2}$. Thus,

$$F = 2\rho g \int_0^1 (4 - y)(\sqrt{y - y^2})\, dy = 2\rho g \int_0^1 \frac{7}{2} \sqrt{y - y^2}\, dy + 2\rho g \int_0^1 (\frac{1}{2} - y)\sqrt{y - y^2}\, dy$$

$$= 7\rho g \left(\frac{\pi}{8} \right) + 2\rho g \left(\frac{1}{3}(y - y^2)^{3/2} \right) \Big|_0^1 = \frac{7\pi\rho g}{8} + 0 \approx 2.694 \times 10^4$ N.

6.7.49

    a. True. $m = \int_a^b \rho(x)\, dx = \frac{1}{b-a} \int_a^b \rho(x)\, dx \cdot (b - a) = \bar{\rho} \cdot L$.

    b. True. $\int_0^L kx\, dx = \frac{kL^2}{2} = \int_0^{-L} kx\, dx$.

    c. True. This follows because work is force times distance.

    d. False. Although they have the same geometry, they are placed at different depths of the water, so the force is different.

6.7.50

    a. $m_1 = \int_0^L 4e^{-x}\, dx = (-4e^{-x}) \Big|_0^L = 4(1 - e^{-L})$.

        $m_2 = \int_0^L 6e^{-2x}\, dx = (-3e^{-2x}) \Big|_0^L = 3(1 - e^{-2L})$.

        These are the same when $3(e^{-L})^2 - 4e^{-L} + 1 = 0$, or $(e^{-L} - 1)(3e^{-L} - 1) = 0$, so $L = \ln 3$. m_2 is bigger on $(0, \ln 3)$ and m_1 is bigger for $L > \ln 3$.

    b. No. $\lim_{L \to \infty} m_1 = 4$ and $\lim_{L \to \infty} m_2 = 3$.

6.7.51

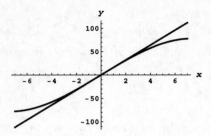

a. Compared to the linear spring $F(x) = 16x$, the restoring force is less for large displacements.

b. $W = \int_0^{1.5} (16x - 0.1x^3)\, dx = \left(8x^2 - .025x^4\right)\Big|_0^{1.5} = 17.87$ J.

c. $W = \int_0^{-2} (16x - 0.1x^3)\, dx = \left(8x^2 - .025x^4\right)\Big|_0^{-2} = 31.6$ J.

6.7.52

a. $f(x) = kx$, and $f(2) = 2k = 10g$, so $k = 5g$. To compress the spring: $W = g\int_{1.5}^{2} 5x\, dx = g\left(5x^2/2\right)\Big|_{1.5}^{2} = g(10 - 45/8) = 35g/8 = 42.875$ J. To move the mass: $10 \cdot .5 \cdot 9.8 = 49$ J. So the total work is $42.875 + 49 = 91.875$ J.

b. To stretch the spring: $W = g\int_{2}^{2.5} 5x\, dx = g\left(5x^2/2\right)\Big|_{2}^{2.5} = g(125/8 - 10) = 45g/8 = 55.125$ J. To move the mass: $10 \cdot .5 \cdot 9.8 = 49$ J. So the total work is $55.125 + 49 = 104.125$ J.

6.7.53 Orient the axes so that $(0,0)$ is in the middle of the bottom of the cup. Note that the line between $(0.02, 0)$ and $(0.025, 0.15)$ is given by $y = 30x - 3/5$, so $x = \frac{y}{30} + \frac{1}{50}$. The area of a cross section at height y is given by $\pi x^2 = \pi\left(\frac{5y+3}{150}\right)^2$. Note that the distance the slice must travel is $0.2 - y$, because it must go 0.05 above the top of the glass. Thus, $W = \pi\rho g \int_0^{0.15} \left(\frac{5y+3}{150}\right)^2 (.2 - y)\, dy = \frac{\pi\rho g}{5\cdot 150^2} \int_0^{0.15} (5y+3)^2 (1 - 5y)\, dy = \frac{\pi\rho g}{5\cdot 150^2} \int_0^{0.15} (-125y^3 - 125y^2 - 15y + 9)\, dy = \frac{\pi\rho g}{5\cdot 150^2}\left(-125y^4/4 - 125y^3/3 - 15y^2/2 + 9y\right)\Big|_0^{0.15} = \frac{\pi\rho g}{5\cdot 150^2} \cdot 1.0248 \approx 0.280$ J.

6.7.54

a. $W = \pi\rho g \int_4^8 9(10-y)\, dy = \pi\rho g\left(90y - 9y^2/2\right)\Big|_4^8 = (720 - 288 - 360 + 72)\pi\rho g = 144\pi\rho g \approx 4.433 \times 10^6$ J.

b. $W = \pi\rho g \int_0^4 9(10-y)\, dy = \pi\rho g\left(90y - 9y^2/2\right)\Big|_0^4 = (360 - 72)\pi\rho g = 288\pi\rho g \approx 4.43342 \times 10^6 \approx 8.867 \times 10^6$ J.

c. The water in the lower part of the tank has to travel farther, so it requires more work to pump it out.

6.7.55

a.

$$W = \int_0^{2500000} \frac{GMm}{(x+R)^2}\, dx = GMm\left(\frac{-1}{x+R}\right)\Big|_0^{2500000}$$

$$= GMm\left(\frac{1}{R} - \frac{1}{R + 2500000}\right) = \frac{GMm\,2500000}{R(R + 2500000)} \approx 8.87435 \times 10^9 \text{ J.}$$

b. $W(x) = \int_0^x \frac{GMm}{(t+R)^2}\, dt = GMm\left(\frac{-1}{t+R}\right)\Big|_0^x = GMm\left(\frac{1}{R} - \frac{1}{R+x}\right) = \frac{GMmx}{R(R+x)} = \frac{500GMx}{R(R+x)}.$

c. $\displaystyle\lim_{x\to\infty} \frac{GMmx}{R(R+x)} = \lim_{x\to\infty} \frac{GMm}{R\left(\left(\frac{R}{x}\right)+1\right)} = \frac{GMm}{R}.$

d. Suppose $\frac{GMmx}{R(R+x)} = \frac{1}{2}mv^2$, then $v^2 = \frac{2GMx}{R(R+x)}$, and as $x \to \infty$ we have $v^2 = \frac{2GM}{R}$, so $v = \sqrt{\frac{2GM}{R}}$.

6.7.56

a. $W = \int_{x_0}^{x_f} mx''\, dx = \int_0^{x(5)} 2 \cdot 8\, dx = 16(x(5)) = 1600$ J.

b. $W = \int_{x_0}^{x_f} mx''\, dx = \int_0^5 2 \cdot 8 \frac{dx}{dt}\, dt = \int_0^5 16 \cdot 8t\, dt = \left(64t^2\right)\Big|_0^5 = 64 \cdot 25 = 1600$ J.

6.7.57

a. $W_1 = \int_0^{30} \rho g(30 - y)\, dy = 5g\left(30y - y^2/2\right)\Big|_0^{30} = 2250g$ J.

b. $W = W_1 + W_2$, where W_2 is the work to just lift the block. $W_2 = 50g \cdot 30 = 1500g$, so $W = 2250g + 1500g = 3750g$ J.

6.7.58 $W = \int_0^{60} \frac{55}{1000} g(60 - y)\, dy = \frac{55g}{1000}\left(60y - y^2/2\right)\Big|_0^{60} = 99g$ J.

6.7.59

a. The acceleration due to gravity is $F = mg$, and is in the vertical direction. The tangent direction to the curve is perpendicular to the normal, which makes an angle of θ with the the vertical. If we form a right triangle with hypotenuse of length mg, and angle θ, then the two legs must have lengths $mg\sin\theta$ (parallel to the curve) and $mg\cos\theta$ (normal to the curve).

b. Note that the angle t is $t = S/L$, where S is arc length. Then $S = Lt$ and $dS = L\, dt$. So $W = \int_0^\theta F\, ds = \int_0^\theta mg\sin\theta \cdot L\, d\theta = mgL\left(-\cos\theta\right)\Big|_0^\theta = mg(L - L\cos\theta) = mgh.$

6.7.60 The plate pictured on the left should have more force, because it has its wider part lower in the pool.

For each plate, orient the axes so that the vertical line through the vertex pointing up (or down) is the y-axis, and the x-axis lies along the horizontal base of the triangle. For the plate on the left, the line through $(1/2, 0)$ and $(0, \sqrt{3}/2)$ is given by $y = \sqrt{3}((1/2) - x)$, so $x = \frac{1}{2} - (\sqrt{3}/3)y$, and the width at height y is given by $1 - \frac{2\sqrt{3}}{3}y$.

For the plate on the left,

$$
\begin{aligned}
F &= \int_0^{\sqrt{3}/2} \rho g(1 + (\sqrt{3}/2) - y)(1 - \frac{2}{\sqrt{3}}y)\, dy \\
&= \rho g \int_0^{\sqrt{3}/2} \left(\frac{2y^2}{\sqrt{3}} - \frac{2y}{\sqrt{3}} - 2y + \frac{\sqrt{3}}{2} + 1\right) dy \\
&= \rho g \left(\frac{1}{6}\left(\frac{4y^3}{\sqrt{3}} - 2(3 + \sqrt{3})y^2 + 3\left(2 + \sqrt{3}\right)y\right)\right)\Big|_0^{\sqrt{3}/2} = \frac{1}{4} + \frac{\sqrt{3}}{4} \approx 0.683\,\text{N}.
\end{aligned}
$$

For the plate on the right, the line through $(0, 0)$ and $(1/2, \sqrt{3}/2)$ is given by $y = \sqrt{3}x$, so $x = \frac{y}{\sqrt{3}}$, and the width at height y is $\frac{2y}{\sqrt{3}}$.

Thus,

$$F = \int_0^{\sqrt{3}/2} \rho g(1 + \sqrt{3}/2 - y)\frac{2y}{\sqrt{3}}\,dy = \rho g \int_0^{\sqrt{3}/2}\left(-\frac{2y^2}{\sqrt{3}} + \frac{2y}{\sqrt{3}} + y\right)dy$$

$$= \rho g\left(-\frac{2y^3}{3\sqrt{3}} + \frac{y^2}{\sqrt{3}} + \frac{y^2}{2}\right)\Bigg|_0^{\sqrt{3}/2} = \frac{1 + 2\sqrt{3}}{8} \approx 0.558\,\text{N}.$$

6.7.61   The plate on the left has more than half of its area below the horizontal line which is 3/2 below the surface, while the plate on the right has exactly half its area below that line, so the plate on the left should have more force than the plate on the right.

   a. Note that the line in the first quadrant forom $(0,0)$ to $(\sqrt{2}/2, \sqrt{2}/2)$ is given by $y = x$, while the line from $(\sqrt{2}/2, \sqrt{2}/2)$ to $(0, \sqrt{2})$ is given by $y = -x + \sqrt{2}$. So the width of a slice at height y in the lower part of the region is $2y$, and in the upper part of the region is $2(\sqrt{2} - y)$.

$F = \rho g \int_0^{\sqrt{2}/2}(\sqrt{2}+1-y)(2y)\,dy + \rho g \int_{\sqrt{2}/2}^{\sqrt{2}}(\sqrt{2}+1-y)2(\sqrt{2}-y)\,dy = \rho g \int_0^{\sqrt{2}/2}(-2y^2+2\sqrt{2}y+2y)\,dy +$

$\rho g \int_{\sqrt{2}/2}^{\sqrt{2}}(2y^2 - 4\sqrt{2}y - 2y + 2\sqrt{2} + 4)\,dy = \rho g\left(-\frac{2y^3}{3} + \sqrt{2}y^2 + y^2\right)\Bigg|_0^{\sqrt{2}/2}$

$+ \rho g\left(2\left(\frac{y^3}{3} - \frac{1}{2}\left(1+2\sqrt{2}\right)y^2 + \sqrt{2}y + 2y\right)\right)\Bigg|_{\sqrt{2}/2}^{\sqrt{2}} = \rho g\left(\frac{1}{2} + \frac{\sqrt{2}}{3} + \frac{1}{2} + \frac{1}{3\sqrt{2}}\right) = \rho g\left(1 + \frac{\sqrt{2}}{2}\right)$ N. This is 16,730 N.

   b. $F = \int_0^1 \rho g(2-y)\cdot 1\,dy = \rho g\left(2y - y^2/2\right)\Big|_0^1 = \frac{3\rho g}{2}$ N. This is 14,700 N.

6.7.62 $W = \rho g \int_0^{.1}\frac{\pi}{24^2}(1.1 - y)\,dy = \frac{\rho g\pi}{576}\left(1.1y - y^2/2\right)\Big|_0^{.1} = \frac{\rho g\pi}{576}(.105) = \frac{1000\cdot 9.8\cdot\pi}{576}(.105) \approx 5.61232$ J. Unfortunately, you do not come close to burning off all the calories when drinking this milkshake.

6.7.63

   a. $F = \int_1^3 \rho g(4-y)\cdot 2\,dy = \rho g\left(8y - y^2\right)\Big|_1^3 = 8\rho g = 78,400$ N. This is less than 90,000 N., so the window can withstand the force.

   b. $F(h) = \int_1^3 \rho g(h - y)\cdot 2\,dy = \rho g\left(2hy - y^2\right)\Big|_1^3 = \rho g(6h - 9 - (2h-1)) = 4\rho g(h-2)$. This is less than or equal to 90,000 Newtons when $h \leq 4.296$ meters.

6.7.64 When the box is fully submerged in the water, the buoyant force is $8g\rho_w$. The force required is $F = 8g\rho_w - 8g\rho = 8g\rho_w - 8g(\rho_w/2) = 4g\rho_w = 39,200$ N.

6.8   Logarithmic and Exponential Functions Revisited

6.8.1 The domain is $(0,\infty)$ and the range is $(-\infty,\infty)$.

6.8.2 This represents the area under the function $\frac{1}{t}$ and above the t axis between the vertical line $t = 1$ and the vertical line $t = x$.

6.8.3 $\int 4^x\,dx = \int e^{x\ln 4}\,dx = \frac{1}{\ln 4}e^{x\ln 4} + C = \frac{4^x}{\ln 4} + C.$

6.8.4 The inverse is $y = e^x$, whose domain is $(-\infty,\infty)$ and whose range is $(0,\infty)$.

6.8.5 $3^x = e^{x\ln 3}$. $x^\pi = e^{\pi\ln x}$. $x^{\sin x} = e^{\sin x\cdot\ln x}$.

6.8.6 $\frac{d}{dx}3^x = \frac{d}{dx}e^{x\ln 3} = e^{x\ln 3}\cdot\ln 3 = \ln 3\cdot 3^x.$

6.8.7 $\frac{d}{dx}(x\ln(x^3)) = x\cdot\frac{1}{x^3}\cdot 3x^2 + \ln(x^3),$ so $\frac{d}{dx}(x\ln(x^3))\Big|_{x=1} = 3 + 0 = 3.$

6.8.8 $\frac{d}{dx}(\ln(\ln(x))) = \frac{1}{\ln x}\cdot\frac{1}{x}.$

6.8.9 $\frac{d}{dx}\sin(\ln x) = \cos(\ln x)\cdot\frac{1}{x} = \frac{\cos(\ln x)}{x}.$

6.8.10 $\frac{d}{dx}\ln(\cos^2 x) = \frac{1}{\cos^2 x}\cdot(2\cos x)(-\sin x) = -\frac{2\sin x}{\cos x}.$

6.8.11 $\frac{d}{dx}((\ln 2x)^{-5}) = -5(\ln 2x)^{-6}(1/x) = \frac{-5}{x\ln^6 2x}.$

6.8.12 $\frac{d}{dx}(\ln^3(3x^2+2)) = 3\ln^2(3x^2+2)\left(\frac{1}{3x^2+2}\right)(6x) = \frac{18x\ln^2(3x^2+2)}{3x^2+2}.$

6.8.13 $\int_0^3\frac{2x-1}{x+1}\,dx = \int_0^3\left(2 - \frac{3}{x+1}\right)dx = (2x - 3\ln(x+1))\Big|_0^3 = 6(1 - \ln 2).$

6.8.14 $\int\tan 10x\,dx = \int -\frac{1}{10}\frac{1}{u}\,du = -\frac{1}{10}\ln|u| + C,$ where $u = \cos x.$ So the original integral is equal to $-\frac{1}{10}\ln|\cos x| + C.$

6.8.15 Let $u = \ln x$ so that $du = \frac{1}{x}\,dx.$ Then $\int_e^{e^2}\frac{dx}{x\ln^3 x}\,dx = \int_1^2 u^{-3}\,du = \frac{-1}{2}\left(u^{-2}\right)\Big|_1^2 = \frac{-1}{2}(1/4 - 1) = \frac{3}{8}.$

6.8.16 Let $u = 1 + \cos x$ so that $du = -\sin x\,dx.$ Then $\int_0^{\pi/2}\frac{\sin x}{1+\cos x}\,dx = \int_1^2\frac{1}{u}\,du = (\ln u)\Big|_1^2 = \ln 2.$

6.8.17 Let $u = 4 + e^{2x}$ so that $du = 2e^{2x}\,dx.$ Substituting gives $\frac{1}{2}\int\frac{du}{u} = \frac{1}{2}\ln|u| + C = \frac{1}{2}\ln(4 + e^{2x}) + C.$

6.8.18 Let $u = \ln(\ln x)$ so that $du = \frac{1}{x\ln x}\,dx.$ Substituting yields $\int\frac{1}{u}\,du = \ln|u| + C = \ln|\ln(\ln x)| + C.$

6.8.19 Let $u = \ln(\ln x)$ so that $du = \frac{1}{x\ln x}\,dx.$ Substituting yields $\int_{\ln 2}^{\ln 3}\frac{1}{u^2}\,du = \left(\frac{-1}{u}\right)\Big|_{\ln 2}^{\ln 3} = \frac{1}{\ln 2} - \frac{1}{\ln 3}.$

6.8.20 Let $u = \ln(y^2 + 1)$ so that $du = \frac{2y}{y^2+1}\,dy.$ Substituting yields $\frac{1}{2}\int_0^{\ln 2}u^4\,du = \frac{1}{2}\left(u^5/5\right)\Big|_0^{\ln 2} = (\ln 2)^5/10.$

6.8.21 Let $u = -x^2/2$ so that $du = -x\,dx.$ Substituting yields $-4\int_0^{-2}e^u\,du = 4\int_{-2}^0 e^u\,du = 4\left(e^u\right)\Big|_{-2}^0 = 4(1 - e^{-2}) = 4 - \frac{4}{e^2}.$

6.8.22 Let $u = \sin x$ so that $du = \cos x\,dx.$ Then $\int\frac{e^{\sin x}}{\sec x}\,dx = \int e^{\sin x}\cos x\,dx = \int e^u\,du = e^u + C = e^{\sin x} + C.$

6.8.23 Let $u = \sqrt{x}$ so that $du = \frac{1}{2\sqrt{x}}\,dx.$ Then $\int\frac{e^{\sqrt{x}}}{\sqrt{x}}\,dx = 2\int e^u\,du = 2e^u + C = 2e^{\sqrt{x}} + C.$

6.8.24 Let $u = e^{z/2} + 1,$ so that $du = \frac{1}{2}e^{z/2}\,dz.$

Then $\int_{-2}^2\frac{e^{z/2}}{e^{z/2}+1}\,dz = \int_{(1/e)+1}^{e+1}\frac{2}{u}\,du = (2\ln u)\Big|_{(1/e)+1}^{e+1} = 2\ln\left(\frac{e+1}{e^{-1}+1}\right) = 2\ln(e) = 2.$

6.8.25 Let $u = e^x - e^{-x}$ so that $du = e^x + e^{-x}\,dx.$ Then we have $\int\frac{e^x+e^{-x}}{e^x-e^{-x}}\,dx = \int\frac{1}{u}\,du = \ln|u| + C = \ln|e^x - e^{-x}| + C.$

6.8.26 Note that the denominator of the integrand is $(e^x - e^{-x})^2$. Let $u = e^x - e^{-x}$ so that $du = (e^x + e^{-x})\,dx$. Substituting gives $\int_{3/2}^{8/3} u^{-2}\,du = (-1/u)\Big|_{3/2}^{8/3} = -3/8 + 2/3 = \frac{-9+16}{24} = \frac{7}{24}$.

6.8.27 $\int_{-1}^{1} 10^x\,dx = \left(\frac{10^x}{\ln 10}\right)\Big|_{-1}^{1} = \frac{10 - 10^{-1}}{\ln 10} = \frac{99}{10\ln 10}$.

6.8.28 Let $u = \sin x$ so that $du = \cos x\,dx$. Then $\int_0^{\pi/2} 4^{\sin x}\cos x\,dx = \int_0^1 4^u\,du = \left(\frac{4^u}{\ln 4}\right)\Big|_0^1 = \frac{3}{\ln 4}$.

6.8.29 $\int_1^2 (1 + \ln x)x^x\,dx = (x^x)\Big|_1^2 = 4 - 1 = 3$.

6.8.30 Let $u = 1/p$, so that $du = -\frac{1}{p^2}\,dp$. Then $\int_{1/3}^{1/2} \frac{10^{1/p}}{p^2}\,dp = \int_2^3 10^u\,du = \left(\frac{10^u}{\ln 10}\right)\Big|_2^3 = \frac{900}{\ln 10}$.

6.8.31 Let $u = x^3 + 8$ so that $du = 3x^2\,dx$. Substituting gives $\frac{1}{3}\int 6^u\,du = \frac{6^u}{3\ln 6} + C = \frac{6^{x^3+8}}{3\ln 6} + C$.

6.8.32 Let $u = \cot x$ so that $du = -\csc^2 x\,dx = \frac{-1}{\sin^2 x}\,dx$. Substituting yields $-\int 4^u\,du = \frac{-4^u}{\ln 4} + C = \frac{-4^{\cot x}}{\ln 4} + C$.

6.8.33 $f(x) = e^{4x\ln(2x)}$ so $f'(x) = e^{4x\ln(2x)}\left(4x\cdot(1/x) + \ln(2x)\cdot 4\right) = (2x)^{4x}(4 + 4\ln(2x)) = 4^{2x+1}x^{4x}(1 + \ln 2x)$.

6.8.34 $f'(x) = \pi x^{\pi - 1}$.

6.8.35 $y' = 2^{x^2}\cdot\ln 2\cdot(2x) = 2^{x^2+1}x\ln 2$.

6.8.36 $\ln(h(t)) = \sqrt{t}\ln(\sin t)$, so $\frac{1}{h(t)}h'(t) = \sqrt{t}\cot t + \ln(\sin t)\cdot\frac{1}{2\sqrt{t}}$, and thus

$$h'(t) = (\sin t)^{\sqrt{t}}\left(\sqrt{t}\cot t + \ln(\sin t)\cdot\frac{1}{2\sqrt{t}}\right) = (\sin t)^{\sqrt{t}}\left(\frac{2t\cot t + \ln(\sin t)}{2\sqrt{t}}\right).$$

6.8.37 $\ln(H(x)) = 2x\ln(x+1)$, so $\frac{1}{H(x)}H'(x) = \frac{2x}{x+1} + 2\ln(x+1)$, and thus $H'(x) = (x+1)^{2x}\left(\frac{2x}{x+1} + 2\ln(x+1)\right)$.

6.8.38 $\ln(p(x)) = -\ln(x)\cdot\ln(x) = -\ln^2(x)$, so $\frac{p'(x)}{p(x)} = -\frac{2\ln x}{x}$, and thus $p'(x) = x^{-\ln x}\cdot -\frac{2\ln x}{x}$.

6.8.39 $\ln(G(y)) = \sin y\ln y$, so $G'(y)/G(y) = \cos y\ln y + \frac{\sin y}{y}$. Thus, $G'(y) = y^{\sin y}\left(\cos y\ln y + \frac{\sin y}{y}\right)$.

6.8.40 $\ln(Q(t)) = \frac{\ln t}{t}$, so $Q'(t)/Q(t) = \frac{t(1/t) - \ln t}{t^2}$, so $Q'(t) = t^{1/t}\left(\frac{1 - \ln t}{t^2}\right)$.

6.8.41

a. True. This follows because $e^{\ln xy} = xy = e^{\ln x}e^{\ln y} = e^{\ln x + \ln y}$, and because the exponential function is one-to-one.

b. False. Zero is not in the domain of the natural logarithm function.

c. False. For example, $\ln(1 + 1) = \ln 2 \neq \ln(1) + \ln(1) = 0$.

d. False. $e^{2\ln x} = e^{\ln x^2} = x^2 \neq 2^x$.

e. False. $\int_0^e \frac{1}{x}\,dx = \lim_{b\to 0^+}\int_b^e \frac{1}{x}\,dx = \lim_{b\to 0^+}(\ln x)\Big|_b^e = 1 - \lim_{b\to 0^+}\ln b$, which does not exist.

6.8.42 $\ln(x/y) = \int_1^{x/y} \frac{1}{t}\,dt = \int_1^x \frac{1}{t}\,dt + \int_x^{x/y} \frac{1}{t}\,dt$. For the second integral, let $u = x/t$ so that $du = \frac{1}{t}\,dx$. Then we have $\ln(x) + \int_1^{1/y} \frac{1}{u}\,du = \ln(x) + \ln(1/y)$. All that remains is to prove that $\ln(1/y) = -\ln(y)$.

In the text it was proved that $\ln xy = \ln x + \ln y$, so if we apply this rule to $0 = \ln(1) = \ln(y(1/y)) = \ln(y) + \ln(1/y)$, we see that $\ln(1/y) = -\ln(y)$.

6.8.43

h	$(1+2h)^{1/h}$	h	$(1+2h)^{1/h}$
10^{-1}	6.1917	-10^{-1}	9.3132
10^{-2}	7.2446	-10^{-2}	7.5404
10^{-3}	7.3743	-10^{-3}	7.4039
10^{-4}	7.3876	-10^{-4}	7.3905
10^{-5}	7.3889	-10^{-5}	7.3892
10^{-6}	7.3890	-10^{-6}	7.3891

Let $y = (1+2h)^{1/h}$. Then $\ln y = \frac{\ln(1+2h)}{h}$. $\lim_{h \to 0} \ln y = \lim_{h \to 0} \frac{\ln(1+2h)}{h} = \lim_{h \to 0} \frac{2}{1+2h} = 2$, so the limit of y as $h \to 0$ is e^2.

6.8.44

h	$(1+3h)^{2/h}$	h	$(1+3h)^{2/h}$
10^{-1}	190.0496	-10^{-1}	1253.25
10^{-2}	369.3558	-10^{-2}	442.2350
10^{-3}	399.8214	-10^{-3}	407.0834
10^{-4}	403.0659	-10^{-4}	403.7921
10^{-5}	403.3925	-10^{-5}	403.4651
10^{-6}	403.4252	-10^{-6}	403.4324
10^{-7}	403.4284	-10^{-7}	403.4288
10^{-8}	403.4288	-10^{-8}	403.4388
10^{-9}	403.4290	-10^{-9}	403.4290

Let $y = (1+3h)^{2/h}$. Then $\ln y = \frac{2\ln(1+3h)}{h}$. $\lim_{h \to 0} \ln y = \lim_{h \to 0} \frac{2\ln(1+3h)}{h} = \lim_{h \to 0} \frac{6}{1+3h} = 6$, so the limit of y as $h \to 0$ is e^6.

6.8.45

x	$\frac{2^x-1}{x}$	x	$\frac{2^x-1}{x}$
10^{-1}	.71773	-10^{-1}	.66967
10^{-2}	.69556	-10^{-2}	.69075
10^{-3}	.69339	-10^{-3}	.69291
10^{-4}	.69317	-10^{-4}	.69312
10^{-5}	.69315	-10^{-5}	.69314
10^{-6}	.69315	-10^{-6}	.69315

$\lim_{x \to 0} \frac{2^x-1}{x} = \lim_{x \to 0} \frac{2^x \ln 2}{1} = \ln 2.$

6.8.46

x	$\frac{\ln(1+x)}{x}$	x	$\frac{\ln(1+x)}{x}$
10^{-1}	.9531	-10^{-1}	1.0536
10^{-2}	.9950	-10^{-2}	1.0050
10^{-3}	.9995	-10^{-3}	1.0005
10^{-4}	1.0000	-10^{-4}	1.0001
10^{-5}	1.0000	-10^{-5}	1.0000
10^{-6}	1.0000	-10^{-6}	1.0000

$\lim_{x \to 0} \frac{\ln(1+x)}{x} = \lim_{x \to 0} \frac{1/(1+x)}{1} = 1.$

6.8.47

a. No. Let $h(a) = \int_{1-a}^{1+a} \frac{1-x}{x}\, dx = \int_{1-a}^{1} \frac{1-x}{x}\, dx + \int_{1}^{1+a} \frac{1-x}{x}\, dx = -\int_{1}^{1-a} \frac{1-x}{x}\, dx + \int_{1}^{1+a} \frac{1-x}{x}\, dx$. Then $h'(a) = \frac{1-(1-a)}{1-a} + \frac{1-(1+a)}{1+a} = \frac{a}{1-a} - \frac{a}{1+a} = \frac{a+a^2+(-a)+a^2}{1-a^2} = \frac{2a^2}{1-a^2} > 0$. Also, $h(a) = 0$. Because h is increasing on $(0,1)$, there are no other numbers on that interval where h is zero.

b. No. Let $g(a) = \int_{1/a}^{a} f(x)\, dx = \int_{1/a}^{1/2} f(x)\, dx + \int_{1/2}^{a} f(x)\, dx = -\int_{1/2}^{1/a} f(x)\, dx + \int_{1/2}^{a} f(x)\, dx$. Then $g'(a) = -f(1/a) \cdot -\frac{1}{a^2} + f(a) = \frac{1-(1/a)}{a} + \frac{1-a}{a} = \frac{2-(a+1/a)}{a} < 0$ because $a + 1/a > 2$ for $a > 1$. Because g has value 0 at $a = 1$ and is decreasing on $(1,\infty)$ it is never 0 on that interval.

6.8.48 Each has limit 0 as $x \to 0^+$ (by L'Hôpital's rule), and each has value 0 at $x = 1$. Each is negative on $(0,1)$. Note that $\frac{d}{dx} x^p \ln x = x^{p-1} + px^{p-1}\ln x = x^{p-1}(1 + p\ln x)$, which is 0 on $(0,1)$ for $x = e^{-1/p}$. This critical point leads to a minimum in each case, but the location of the minimums increases as p increases, and the value of the minimum increases as well.

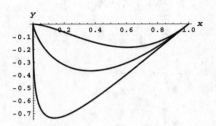

6.8.49 The average value is given by $\frac{1}{p-1}\int_{1}^{p} \frac{1}{x}\, dx = \frac{1}{p-1}\left(\ln x\right)\Big|_{1}^{p} = \frac{\ln p}{p-1}$. Note that

$$\lim_{p\to\infty} \frac{\ln p}{p-1} = \lim_{p\to\infty} \frac{1/p}{1} = 0.$$

6.8.50 $\frac{d}{dx} x^{2x} = \frac{d}{dx} e^{2x\ln x} = e^{2x\ln x}(2 + 2\ln x) = 2x^{2x}(1 + \ln x)$.

6.8.51 $\frac{d}{dx} e^{-10x^2} = e^{-10x^2} \cdot -20x = -20xe^{-10x^2}$.

6.8.52 $\frac{d}{dx} x^{\tan x} = \frac{d}{dx} e^{\tan x \ln x} = e^{\tan x \ln x}((\tan x)/x + \sec^2 x \ln x) = x^{\tan x}((\tan x)/x + \sec^2 x \ln x)$.

6.8.53 $\frac{d}{dx}(1/x)^x = \frac{d}{dx} e^{x\ln(1/x)} = \frac{d}{dx} e^{-x\ln x} = e^{-x\ln x}(-1 - \ln x) = (1/x)^x(-1 - \ln x)$.

6.8.54 $\frac{d}{dx}(x^e + e^x) = ex^{e-1} + e^x$.

6.8.55 $\frac{d}{dx}(1 + (4/x))^x = \frac{d}{dx} e^{x\ln(1+(4/x))} = e^{x\ln(1+(4/x))}\left(\ln(1 + (4/x)) + \frac{x}{1+(4/x)} \cdot -\frac{4}{x^2}\right) = (1 + (4/x))^x\left(\ln(1 + (4/x)) - \frac{4}{x+4}\right)$.

6.8.56 $\frac{d}{dx}(x^{x^{10}}) = \frac{d}{dx} e^{x^{10}\ln x} = e^{x^{10}\ln x}(x^9 + 10x^9\ln x) = x^{x^{10}}(x^9)(1 + 10\ln x)$.

6.8.57 $\frac{d}{dx}\cos(x^{2\sin x}) = \frac{d}{dx}\cos(e^{2\sin x \ln x}) = -\sin(x^{2\sin x}) \cdot e^{2\sin x \ln x} \cdot ((2\sin x)/x + 2\cos x \ln x) = -\sin(x^{2\sin x}) \cdot x^{2\sin x} \cdot ((2\sin x)/x + 2\cos x \ln x)$.

6.8.58 $\int 7^{2x}\, dx = \int e^{2x\ln 7}\, dx = e^{2x\ln 7} \cdot \frac{1}{2\ln 7} + C = \frac{7^{2x}}{2\ln 7} + C$.

6.8.59 $\int 3^{-2x}\, dx = \int e^{-2x\ln 3}\, dx = e^{-2x\ln 3} \cdot \frac{1}{-2\ln 3} + C = -\frac{3^{-2x}}{2\ln 3} + C = \frac{-1}{9^x\ln 9} + C$.

6.8.60 $\int_{0}^{5} 5^{5x}\, dx = \left(\frac{5^{5x}}{5\ln 5}\right)\Big|_{0}^{5} = \frac{5^{25}-1}{5\ln 5}$.

6.8.61 Let $u = x^3$, so that $du = 3x^2\, dx$. Then we have $\int \frac{1}{3} 10^u\, du = \frac{10^u}{3\ln 10} + C = \frac{10^{x^3}}{3\ln 10} + C$.

6.8.62 Let $u = \sin x$ so that $du = \cos x\, dx$. Then we have $\int_0^0 2^u\, du = \left(\frac{2^u}{\ln 2}\right)\Big|_0^0 = 0$.

6.8.63 Let $u = \ln x$ so that $du = \frac{1}{x}\, dx$. Then we have $\int_0^{\ln(2)+1} 3^u\, du = \left(\frac{3^u}{\ln 3}\right)\Big|_0^{\ln(2)+1} = \frac{3 \cdot 3^{\ln 2}-1}{\ln 3}$.

6.8.64 Let $u = \ln x$ so that $du = \frac{1}{x}\, dx$. Then we have $\int \frac{1}{4}\sin u\, du = -\frac{1}{4}\cos u + C = -\frac{1}{4}\cos(\ln x) + C$.

6.8.65 Let $u = \ln x$ so that $du = \frac{1}{x}\, dx$. Then we have $\int_0^2 u^5\, du = \left(\frac{u^6}{6}\right)\Big|_0^2 = \frac{32}{3}$.

6.8.66 Let $u = \ln x$ so that $du = \frac{1}{x}\, dx$. Then we have $\int (u^2 + 2u - 1)\, du = u^3/3 + u^2 - u + C = (\ln x)^3/3 + (\ln x)^2 - \ln x + C$.

6.8.67 Let $u = e^{3x} + e^{-3x}$ so that $du = 3(e^{3x} - e^{-3x})\, dx$. Substituting gives $\frac{1}{3}\int_2^{65/8} \frac{1}{u}\, du = \frac{1}{3}(\ln u)\Big|_2^{65/8} = \frac{1}{3}(\ln(65/8) - \ln 2) = \frac{1}{3}\ln(65/16)$.

6.8.68 Note that $4^{2x} = (4^2)^x = 16^x$. So we are computing $\int_0^1 1\, dx = 1$.

6.8.69 Note that the area of the triangle described is $\frac{1}{2}xy$, so if $xy \geq \frac{1}{2}$, then $\frac{1}{2}xy \geq \frac{1}{4}$, which is not what we are seeking. However, if $xy < 1/2$, then the triangle formed will give us what we want.

Note that for any choice of x with $0 < x < 1/2$ and any choice of possible y, we have $xy < 1/2$ because $0 < y < 1$. Thus because there is a probability of $\frac{1}{2}$ of choosing $0 < x < 1/2$, the probability we seek is at least $1/2$. In addition, for $1/2 < x < 1$, if $y < \frac{1}{2x}$, then $xy < \frac{1}{2}$. So we should add $\int_{1/2}^1 \frac{1}{2x}\, dx = \left(\frac{1}{2}\ln x\right)\Big|_{1/2}^1 = (\ln 2)/2$. Thus the probability we seek is $\frac{1}{2}(1 + \ln 2)$.

6.8.70 For $x > 0$, $\frac{d}{dx}\ln x = \frac{1}{x}$. For $x < 0$, $\frac{d}{dx}\ln(-x) = \frac{1}{-x}\cdot(-1) = \frac{1}{x}$. So $\frac{d}{dx}\ln|x| = \frac{1}{x}$.

6.8.71

a. Let $\exp 0 = z$. Then $\ln \exp 0 = \ln z$, so $\ln z = 0$. Then because $\ln z = \ln 1$, we have $z = 1$, so $\exp 0 = 1$.

b. $\ln\left(\frac{\exp x}{\exp y}\right) = \ln(\exp x) - \ln(\exp y) = x - y$. Thus, $\exp(x - y) = \frac{\exp x}{\exp y}$.

c. $\ln((\exp x)^p) = p\ln(\exp x) = px$, so $\exp px = (\exp x)^p$.

6.8.72

a. The region under $1/x$ and above the x-axis between $x = 1$ and $x = 2$ has area $\int_1^2 1/x\, dx = (\ln x)\Big|_1^2 = \ln 2$.

b. Because the region bounded by the x-axis and the lines $y = 1/2$ and $x = 1$ and $x = 2$ has area $1/2$, and because this region is encompassed by the region under $y = 1/x$ and above the x-axis between $x = 1$ and $x = 2$, we must have $\ln 2 > 1/2$.

c. Let $n > 0$. Because of the result of part b), we must have $n\ln 2 > n/2$, so $\ln 2^n > n/2$. Also, $-n\ln 2 < -n/2$, so $\ln(2^{-n}) < -n/2$.

d. Because $n/2 \to \infty$ as $n \to \infty$, and because $2^n > 2/n$, we must have $\ln(2^n) \to \infty$ as $n \to \infty$. So $\ln x \to \infty$ as $x \to \infty$.

Also because $\ln(2^{-n}) \to -\infty$ as $n \to \infty$ (because $\ln(2^{-n}) < -n/2$), we must have that $\ln x \to -\infty$ as $x \to 0^+$.

6.8.73 Because $1/x$ is decreasing, we know that the left Riemann sum is an overestimate. Using $n = 2$ subintervals, we have $\int_1^2 1/x\,dx = \ln 2 < \frac{1}{1} \cdot \frac{1}{2} + \frac{1}{3/2} \cdot \frac{1}{2} = \frac{5}{6} < 1$.

Because $1/x$ is decreasing, we know that the right Riemann sum is an underestimate. We will use $n = 8$ subintervals. We have $\int_1^3 1/x\,dx = \ln 3 > 2 \left(\frac{1}{9} + \frac{1}{11} + \cdots + \frac{1}{21} \right) > 1$.

6.8.74 With y fixed, we have $\frac{d}{dx}\ln(xy) = \frac{1}{xy} \cdot y = \frac{1}{x} = \frac{d}{dx}\ln(x)$.

Thus, $\ln(xy) = \ln(x) + C$. If we let $x = 1$, we see that $\ln(y) = 0 + C$, so $C = \ln(y)$, and $\ln(xy) = \ln(x) + \ln(y)$.

6.8.75 Because $1/x$ is decreasing, the left Riemann sum is an overestimate to the integral. Over the interval $[1, n + 1]$ with n subdivisions, we must have $\int_1^{n+1} \frac{1}{x}\,dx = \ln(n + 1) < \frac{n+1-1}{n}\left(1 + \frac{1}{2} + \frac{1}{3} + \cdots + \frac{1}{n}\right) = \sum_{i=1}^n \frac{1}{i}$. Because $\ln(n+1) \to \infty$ as $n \to \infty$, it must follow that the harmonic partial sum $\left(1 + \frac{1}{2} + \frac{1}{3} + \cdots + \frac{1}{n}\right) \to \infty$ as well.

6.9   Exponential Models

6.9.1 Exponential growth occurs for a constant relative growth rate.

6.9.2 The initial value, and the relative growth rate.

6.9.3 It is the time it takes the population to double in size.

6.9.4 It is the time it takes for the population to become half its size.

6.9.5 For exponential growth modeled by $y = y_0 e^{kt}$, the doubling time T_2 is $T_2 = \frac{\ln 2}{k}$, where $k > 0$ is the growth constant.

6.9.6 For exponential decay modeled by $y = y_0 e^{-kt}$, the half-life $T_{1/2}$ is $T_{1/2} = \frac{\ln 2}{k}$, where $k > 0$ is the decay constant.

6.9.7 Compound interest and world population growth.

6.9.8 Radioactive decay and depreciation of durable goods.

6.9.9 For $f(t)$, $\frac{df}{dt} = 10.5$, so the absolute growth rate is constant. For $g(t)$, $\frac{dg}{dt} = 100 e^{t/10} \cdot \frac{1}{10} = 10 e^{t/10}$, so the growth rate is not constant but the relative growth rate $\frac{1}{g(t)} g'(t) = \frac{1}{10}$ is constant.

6.9.10 For $f(t)$, $\frac{df}{dt} = 400$, so the absolute growth rate is constant. For $g(t)$, $\frac{dg}{dt} = 400 \cdot 2^{t/20} \cdot \frac{\ln 2}{20}$, so the growth rate is not constant but the relative growth rate $\frac{1}{g(t)} g'(t) = \frac{\ln 2}{20}$ is constant.

6.9.11 The growth is modeled by $p(t) = 90,000 e^{kt}$, with $t = 0$ corresponding to 2010, and time measured in years. Because $(1.024)(90,000) = 90,000 e^k$, we have $k = \ln(1.024)$. The doubling time is $T_2 = \frac{\ln 2}{\ln(1.024)} \approx 29.2263$, so it should reach 180,000 around the year 2039.

6.9.12 The growth is modeled by $p(t) = 2 e^{kt}$ where $t = 0$ corresponds to 2013 and time is measured in years and $k = \ln(1.045)$. The year 2020 corresponds to $t = 7$, so the population should be about $p(7) = 12 e^{\ln(1.045) \cdot 7} \approx 2.72172$ million people.

6.9.13 The growth is modeled by $p(t) = 50000 e^{kt}$. When $t = 10$, we have $p(10) = 50000 e^{10k} = 55000$, so $k = \ln(11/10)/10$. Thus in 20 years, the population should be about $50000 e^{2 \ln(11/10)} = 50000(1.1)^2 = 60,500$.

6.9.14 Our model is given by $y(t) = 1500 e^{kt}$, and $y(1) = 1500 \cdot 1.031 = 1500 e^k$, so $k = \ln(1.031)$. Now we seek t so that $2500 = 1500 e^{\ln(1.031)t}$. Thus $\ln(5/3) = \ln(1.031)t$, so $t = \frac{\ln(5/3)}{\ln(1.031)} \approx 16.7$ years.

6.9.15 The price of a cart of groceries is modeled by $p(t) = 100e^{kt}$ where $t = 0$ corresponds to 2005, and t is measured in years and $k = \ln(1.03)$. The price of the groceries in 2018 when $t = 13$ should be about $p(13) = 100e^{13\ln(1.03)} \approx \$146.85$.

6.9.16 The number of cells is modeled by $y(t) = 8e^{(\ln 2 \cdot t)/6}$ where t is measured in weeks. The population will reach 1500 cells when $\ln(1500/8) = \frac{\ln 2}{6}t$, so when $t = \frac{6\ln(1500/8)}{\ln 2} \approx 45.3$ weeks.

6.9.17

a. The population is modeled by $P(t) = 309e^{t\ln(1.008)}$. The doubling time is $\frac{\ln 2}{\ln 1.008} \approx 87$ years. The population in 2050 will be about $P(40) = 309e^{40\ln(1.008)} \approx 425$ million.

b. If the growth rate is .6%, the doubling time is $\frac{\ln 2}{\ln 1.006} \approx 115.9$ years and the population in 2050 will be about $309e^{40\ln(1.006)} \approx 392.5$ million. If the growth rate is 1%, the doubling time will is $\frac{\ln 2}{\ln 1.01} \approx 69.7$ and the population in 2050 will be about $309e^{40\ln(1.01)} \approx 460.1$ million.

c. A growth rate swing of just .2% produces large differences in population growth.

6.9.18

a. $P(t)$ has the form $P(t) = 2000e^{kt}$, and because $P(1) = 1.013 \cdot 2000$, we have $k = \ln(1.013)$. Thus $P(t) = 2000e^{t\ln(1.013)}$.

b. This is given by $\int_0^4 P(t)\, dt = \left.\frac{2000}{\ln(1.013)}e^{t\ln(1.013)}\right|_0^4 \approx 8210.3$.

c. This is given by $\int_0^t P(s)\, ds = \left.\frac{2000}{\ln(1.013)}e^{s\ln(1.013)}\right|_0^t = -154844 + 154844e^{t\ln(1.013)}$.

6.9.19 The growth is modeled by $p(t) = 20.9e^{kt}$. When $t = 10$, we have $p(10) = 20.9e^{10k} = 25.1$, so $k = \ln(25.1/20.9)/10 \approx .0183$. Thus $p(25) = 20.9e^{.0183(25)} \approx 33$ million people.

6.9.20

a. Note that $k = \ln(1.015)$. The amount consumed over the year would be

$$\int_0^1 1.2e^{\ln(1.015)t}\, dt = \left.\left(\frac{1.2}{\ln(1.015)}e^{\ln(1.015)t}\right)\right|_0^1 \approx 1.20898$$

million barrels of oil.

b. $\int_0^t 1.2e^{\ln(1.015)x}\, dx = \left.\left(\frac{1.2}{\ln(1.015)}e^{\ln(1.015)x}\right)\right|_0^t = \frac{1.2}{\ln(1.015)}(e^{\ln(1.015)t} - 1)$ million barrels.

c. This will occur when $\frac{1.2}{\ln(1.015)}(e^{\ln(1.015)t} - 1) = 10$, or $e^{\ln(1.015)t} = \frac{10\ln(1.015)}{1.2} + 1$, or

$$t = \ln\left(\frac{10\ln(1.015)}{1.2} + 1\right) / (\ln(1.015)) \approx 7.85551\,\text{years}.$$

6.9.21 The homicide rate is modeled by $H(t) = 800e^{-kt}$, where $t = 0$ corresponds to 2010, and time is measured in years, and $-k = \ln(.97) \approx -.03$. The rate will reach 600 when $6/8 = e^{-.03t}$, or $t = \frac{\ln(6/8)}{-.03} \approx 9.6$ years. So it should achieve this rate in 2019.

6.9.22 The amount of drug in the body is modeled by $y(t) = y_0 e^{-kt}$, where y_0 is the initial dose and time is measured in hours and $k = -\ln(.85)$. The amount in the body should be 10 percent of the initial dose when $.1 = e^{\ln(.85)t}$, or $t = \frac{\ln(.1)}{\ln(.85)} \approx 14.1681$ hours.

6.9.23 The amount of Valium in the bloodstream is modeled by $a(t) = 20e^{-kt}$. If the half-life is 36 hours, then $36 = \frac{\ln 2}{k}$, so $k = \frac{\ln 2}{36}$. So $a(12) = 20e^{-12\ln(2)/36} = 20e^{-\ln(2)/3} \approx 15.87$ mg.

The concentration of Valium will reach 2 mg when $.1 = e^{-\ln(2)t/36}$, which is when $t = \frac{-36\ln(.1)}{\ln 2} \approx 119.59$ hours.

6.9.24 The population is modeled by $p(t) = 1.2e^{\ln(.995)t}$. After 50 years, the population should be about $p(50) = 1.2e^{\ln(.995)\cdot 50} \approx .933975$ billion people (or about 934 million people). This rate is not sufficient to meet the goal of 700 million people.

6.9.25 The population is modeled by $p(t) = 9.94e^{kt}$, and $p(10) = 9.94e^{10k} = 9.88$, so $k = \ln(9.88/9.94)/10 \approx -.0006$. We have $p(20) = 9.94e^{(-.0006)(20)} \approx 9.82$ million people. The population decline is likely due to economic factors which may change if the economy (especially manufacturing) improves.

6.9.26

a. The value after t years is given by $V(t) = 2.5e^{-kt}$. Because $V(1) = 2.5 \cdot .932)$, we have $-k = \ln(.932)$. Thus, after 10 years, we have $V(10) = 2.5e^{10\ln(.932)} \approx 1.2$ million dollars.

b. The value is 10 percent of the original when $.10 = e^{t\ln(.932)}$, which occurs when $t = \frac{\ln(.10)}{\ln(.932)} \approx 32.7$ years.

6.9.27 Let $y = 1000e^{-kx}$ model the pressure at x feet above sea level. We know that $\frac{1}{3} = e^{-30000k}$, so $k = \frac{\ln(1/3)}{-30000}$. We want to know for what x does $\frac{1}{2} = e^{-kx}$, so we are seeking $x = \frac{\ln 2}{k} = \frac{30000\ln(2)}{\ln 3} \approx 18,928$ feet above sea level.

The pressure is $1/100$th of the sea-level pressure when $x = \frac{30000\ln(100)}{\ln 3} \approx 125,754$ feet.

6.9.28

a. The decay is modeled by $a(t) = a_0e^{-kt}$ with $k = \frac{\ln 2}{5730}$. We seek t so that $.77a_0 = a_0e^{-kt}$, so $t = \frac{\ln(.77)}{-k} = \frac{\ln(.77)(-5730)}{\ln 2} \approx 2160.6$. So the cloth was painted about 2160.6 year ago.

b. In a similar manner to part (a) we have $t = \frac{\ln(.062)(-5730)}{\ln 2} \approx 22,986.4$, so the wood was cut about 23,000 year ago.

6.9.29 The amount of U-238 in the rock is modeled by $a(t) = a_0e^{-kt}$ with $k = \frac{\ln 2}{4.5}$, where time is measured in billions of years. We seek t so that $a_0 = a_0e^{-kt}$, so $t = \frac{\ln(.85)}{-k} = \frac{\ln(.85)(-4.5)}{\ln 2} \approx 1.055$. So the cloth was painted about 1.055 billion years ago.

6.9.30

a. After t days there would be $y = 100e^{(-t\ln 2)/8}$ millicuries after t days.

b. We seek t so that $10 = 100e^{(-t\ln 2)/8}$, so $t = \frac{-8\ln(.1)}{\ln 2} \approx 26.58$ days.

c. We seek t so that $10 = 105e^{(-t\ln 2)/8}$, so $t = \frac{-8\ln(2/21)}{\ln 2} \approx 27.1385$ days.

6.9.31

a. False. If that was the correct formula, then $y(1) = y_0e^{.06} = (1.06184)y_0 \neq (1.06)y_0$.

b. False. If it increases by ten precent per year, then after 3 years it increases by a factor of $(1.1)^3 = 1.331$ which corresponds to 33.1 percent.

c. True. The relative decay rate is constant, so the decay is exponential.

d. True. This follows because the doubling time is related to k by the equation $T_2 = \frac{\ln 2}{k}$.

e. True. This time would be the constant $\frac{\ln 10}{k}$.

6.9.32 The time required to increase p-fold occurs when $py_0 = y_0e^{kt}$, or when $t = \frac{\ln p}{k}$. Thus, the tripling time is $\frac{\ln 3}{k}$.

6.9.33 As in the previous problem, the doubling time is $\frac{\ln 2}{k}$ which is constant as a function of t.

6.9.34

a. We are seeking t so that $500,000e^{\ln(1.03)t} = 300,000e^{\ln(1.05)t}$. This occurs when $\frac{5}{3} = e^{(\ln(1.05)-\ln(1.03))t}$, so $\ln(5/3) = (\ln(1.05) - \ln(1.03))t$, so $t = \frac{\ln(5/3)}{(\ln(1.05)-\ln(1.03))} \approx 26.5621$ years.

b. We are seeking y_0 and p so that $500,000e^{\ln(1.03)10} = y_0e^{\ln(1+p)10}$. This occurs when

$$y_0 = 500,000e^{(10(\ln(1.03)-\ln(1+p)))} = 500,000\left(\frac{1.03}{1+p}\right)^{10}.$$

6.9.35

a. After 5 hours, Abe has run $\int_0^5 \frac{4}{t+1}\, dt = (4\ln(t+1))\big|_0^5 = 4\ln 6 \approx 7.17$ miles. After 5 hours, Bob has run $\int_0^5 4e^{-t/2}\, dt = \left(8e^{-t/2}\right)\big|_5^0 = 8(1 - e^{-5/2}) \approx 7.34$. So after 5 hours, Bob is ahead.

After 10 hours, Abe has run $\int_0^{10} \frac{4}{t+1}\, dt = (4\ln(t+1))\big|_0^{10} = 4\ln 11 \approx 9.59$ miles. After 10 hours, Bob has run $\int_0^{10} 4e^{-t/2}\, dt = \left(8e^{-t/2}\right)\big|_{10}^0 = 8(1 - e^{-5}) \approx 7.95$. So after 10 hours, Abe is ahead.

b. Bob's distance function is given by $8(1-e^{t/2})$ and is bounded above by 8. Abe's distance function is given by $4\ln(t+1)$ and is unbounded.

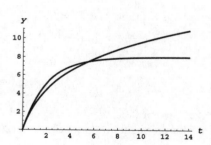

6.9.36 $T_2 = \frac{\ln 2}{k} = \frac{\ln 2}{\ln(1+.0p)} \approx \frac{.693}{\ln(1+.0p)} \approx \frac{70}{p}$. The approximation is best when $\ln(1 + .0p) \approx .0p$, which occurs when p is small.

6.9.37 $(1 + .008)^{12} - 1 \approx 10.034\%$, which is more than $12 \cdot .008 \approx 9.6\%$.

6.9.38

a. If $\frac{dv}{dt} = -kv$, then $\int \frac{1}{v}\frac{dv}{dt}\, dt = \int -k\, dt$, so $\ln(v(t)) = -kt + C$, so $v(t) = v_0e^{-kt} = 10e^{-kt}$.

b. $s(t) = \int 10e^{-kt}\, dt = \frac{10}{-k}e^{-kt} + C = \frac{10}{-k}e^{-kt} + \frac{10}{k}$. (Because $s(0) = 0$.)

c. $dv/dt = \frac{dv}{ds}\frac{ds}{dt}$, so $-kv = \frac{dv}{ds} \cdot v$, so $\frac{dv}{ds} = -k$. Thus $v = -ks + C$ for some constant C, and because $v(0) = 10$, we have $v = 10 - ks$.

6.9.39 As in the previous problem, $s(t) = \frac{v_0}{k}(1 - e^{-kt})$. Consider the equations $s(t_2) - s(t_1) = 1200 = \frac{v_0}{k}(e^{-kt_1} - e^{-kt_2})$ and $v(t_2) - v(t_1) = -100 = v_0(e^{-kt_2} - e^{-kt_1})$. Dividing these two equations yields $k = \frac{1}{12}$.

Now $v(t_1) = 1000 = v_0e^{-t_1/12}$ and $v(t_2) = 900 = v_0e^{-t_2/12}$, so $\frac{1000}{900} = e^{(-1/12)(t_1-t_2)}$, so $t_1 - t_2 = -12\ln(10/9) \approx -1.2643$ seconds. The deceleration takes about 1.2643 seconds to occur.

6.9.40

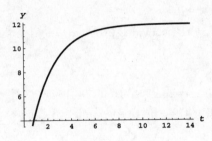

a. The runner's velocity approaches but does not attain 12 meters per second.

b. The position function is $s(t) = \int_0^t 12(1 - e^{-x/2})\, dx = \left(12(x + 2(e^{-x/2}))\right)\big|_0^t = 12t + 24e^{-t/2} - 24$.

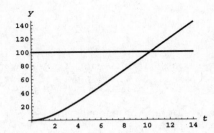

c. $s = 100$ when $12t + 24e^{-t/2} - 24 = 100$, which occurs when $t \approx 10.325$ seconds.

6.9.41 The initial volume is $V_0 = \frac{4\pi}{3}\left(\frac{5}{10000}\right)^3 = \frac{\pi}{6 \times 10^9}$ cubic cm. $k = \frac{\ln 2}{35}$. Suppose $0.5 = V_0 e^{kt} = \frac{\pi}{6 \times 10^9} e^{(t \ln 2)/35}$. Then $\frac{t \ln 2}{35} = \ln\left(\frac{3 \times 10^9}{\pi}\right)$, and $t = \frac{35}{\ln 2} \ln\left(\frac{3 \times 10^9}{\pi}\right) \approx 1044$ days.

6.9.42

a. For China, we have $V_C(t) = 8.2e^{\ln(1.09)t}$, and for the U.S., $V_U = 5.8e^{\ln(1.04)t}$.

b. $V_C = 2V_U$ when $8.2e^{\ln(1.09)t} = 11.6e^{\ln(1.04)t}$. This occurs when $e^{(\ln(1.09/1.04))t} = \frac{11.6}{8.2}$, or for $t \approx 7.387$. So this should occur in approximately 2017.

c. For 2010, the amount per capita for China is $\frac{8.2}{1.3} \approx 6.308$ metric tons per person. For the U.S., it is $\frac{5.8}{0.309} \approx 18.77$ metric tons per person.

d. For China, the population function is $P_C(t) = 1.3e^{\ln(1.005)t}$ and for the U.S. it is $P_U(t) = 0.309e^{\ln(1.007)t}$. So the per capita function for China is $\frac{V_C(t)}{P_C(t)} = \frac{8.2e^{\ln(1.09)t}}{1.3e^{\ln(1.005)t}} \approx 6.308e^{0.081t}$. For the U.S, it is $\frac{V_U(t)}{P_U(t)} = \frac{5.8e^{\ln(1.04)t}}{0.309e^{\ln(1.007)t}} \approx 18.770e^{0.032t}$.

e. Setting the above two equations equal and solving for t yields $t \approx 22.280$, so this should occur in approximately 2032.

6.9.43 Revenue is given by $R(x) = 40xe^{-x/50}$. So $R'(x) = 40xe^{-x/50} \cdot \left(\frac{-1}{50}\right) + 40e^{-x/50} = 40e^{-x/50}(1 - (x/50))$. The critical number is $x = 50$, and this number yields a maximum, because $R'(x) > 0$ on $(0, 50)$, while $R'(x) < 0$ for $x > 50$. Thus, she should charge \$50.00.

6.9.44 If $y(p) = \sqrt{y(m)y(n)}$, then $y_0 e^{kp} = \sqrt{y_0^2 e^{mk} e^{nk}}$, so $e^{kp} = e^{(m+n)k/2}$, so $p = \frac{m+n}{2}$.

6.9.45 If $y_0 e^{kt} = y_0(1 + r)^t$, then $(e^k)^t = (1 + r)^t$, so $e^k = 1 + r$, and $k = \ln(1 + r)$. If $y_0 e^{kt} = y_0 2^{t/T_2}$, then $(e^k)^t = (2^{1/T_2})^t$, so $e^k = 2^{1/T_2}$, and $k = \frac{\ln 2}{T_2}$, or $T_2 = \frac{\ln 2}{k}$. Also, we have $T_2 = \frac{\ln 2}{k} = \frac{\ln 2}{\ln(1+r)}$, so $T_2 \ln(1 + r) = \ln 2$. Then $(1 + r)^{T_2} = 2$, so $r = 2^{1/T_2} - 1$.

6.9.46 $R_T = \frac{y(t+T) - y(t)}{y(t)} = \frac{y_0 e^{k(t+T)} - y_0 e^{kt}}{y_0 e^{kt}} = \frac{y_0 e^{kt}(e^{kT} - 1)}{y_0 e^{kt}} = e^{kT} - 1$. Hence, R_T is constant for all t.

6.10 Hyperbolic Functions

6.10.1 $\cosh x = \frac{e^x + e^{-x}}{2}$; $\sinh x = \frac{e^x - e^{-x}}{2}$.

6.10.2 From left to right, $y = \cosh x$ (an even function), $y = \sinh x$ (an odd function), and $y = \tanh x$ (an odd function). Only $y = \tanh x$ has asymptotes: they are $y = 1$ and $y = -1$.

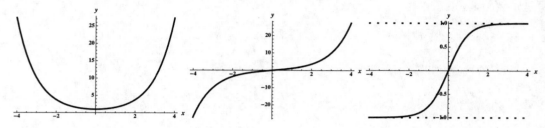

6.10.3 $\cosh^2 x - \sinh^2 x = 1$.

6.10.4 They have a very similar basic form, but the plus and minus signs appear in spots that aren't completely analogous.

6.10.5 $\sinh^{-1} x = \ln(x + \sqrt{x^2 + 1})$.

6.10.6 The domain is $\{x : 0 < x \le 1\}$. $\operatorname{sech}^{-1} x = \cosh^{-1}(1/x)$.

6.10.7 Evaluate $\sinh^{-1}(1/5)$, which has the same value.

6.10.8 This is valid on the domain of the inverse hyperbolic tangent, which is the interval $(-1, 1)$.

6.10.9 $\int \frac{dx}{16 - x^2} = \frac{1}{4}\coth^{-1}(x/4) + C$ for $|x| > 4$; in this case, the values in the interval of integration satisfy $|x| > 4$.

6.10.10 As a increases, the curves become wider and less steep. The value of the minimum at $x = 0$ increases.

6.10.11 $\tanh x = \frac{\sinh x}{\cosh x} = \frac{\frac{e^x - e^{-x}}{2}}{\frac{e^x + e^{-x}}{2}} = \frac{e^x - e^{-x}}{e^x + e^{-x}} \cdot \frac{e^x}{e^x} = \frac{e^{2x} - 1}{e^{2x} + 1}$.

6.10.12 $\tanh(-x) = \frac{\sinh(-x)}{\cosh(-x)} = \frac{\frac{e^{-x} - e^x}{2}}{\frac{e^{-x} + e^x}{2}} = \frac{-\sinh x}{\cosh x} = -\tanh x$.

6.10.13 $\cosh^2 x + \sinh^2 x = \left(\frac{e^x + e^{-x}}{2}\right)^2 + \left(\frac{e^x - e^{-x}}{2}\right)^2 = \frac{e^{2x} + 2 + e^{-2x}}{4} + \frac{e^{2x} - 2 + e^{-2x}}{4} = \frac{2e^{2x} + 2e^{-2x}}{4} = \frac{e^{2x} + e^{-2x}}{2} = \cosh(2x)$.

6.10.14 $2\sinh \ln \sec x = 2\left(\frac{e^{\ln \sec x} - e^{-\ln \sec x}}{2}\right) = \sec x - \cos x = \frac{1 - \cos^2 x}{\cos x} = \frac{\sin^2 x}{\cos x} = \sin x \tan x$.

6.10.15 $\cosh x + \sinh x = \frac{e^x + e^{-x}}{2} + \frac{e^x - e^{-x}}{2} = \frac{2e^x}{2} = e^x$.

6.10.16 $\coth^2 x - 1 = \frac{\cosh^2 x}{\sinh^2 x} - \frac{\sinh^2 x}{\sinh^2 x} = \frac{\cosh^2 x - \sinh^2 x}{\sinh^2 x} = \frac{1}{\sinh^2 x} = \operatorname{csch}^2 x$.

6.10.17 $\frac{1 + \cosh 2x}{2} = \frac{1 + \cosh^2 x + \sinh^2 x}{2} = \frac{\cosh^2 x + (\sinh^2 x + 1)}{2} = \frac{\cosh^2 x + \cosh^2 x}{2} = \cosh^2 x$. $\frac{\cosh 2x - 1}{2} = \frac{\cosh^2 x + \sinh^2 x - 1}{2} = \frac{\sinh^2 x + (\cosh^2 x - 1)}{2} = \frac{\sinh^2 x + \sinh^2 x}{2} = \sinh^2 x$.

6.10.18 $\cosh(2x) = \cosh(x + x) = \cosh x \cosh x + \sinh x \sinh x = \cosh^2 x + \sinh^2 x$.

6.10.19 $\frac{d}{dx}(\coth x) = \frac{d}{dx}\frac{\cosh x}{\sinh x} = \frac{\sinh^2 x - \cosh^2 x}{\sinh^2 x} = \frac{-1}{\sinh^2 x} = -\operatorname{csch}^2 x$.

6.10.20 $\frac{d}{dx}(\operatorname{sech} x) = \frac{d}{dx}\frac{1}{\cosh x} = \frac{\cosh x \cdot 0 - \sinh x}{\cosh^2 x} = -\operatorname{sech} x \tanh x.$

6.10.21 $\frac{d}{dx}(\operatorname{csch} x) = \frac{d}{dx}\frac{1}{\sinh x} = \frac{\sinh x \cdot 0 - \cosh x}{\sinh^2 x} = -\operatorname{csch} x \coth x.$

6.10.22 $y' = 4\cosh 4x.$

6.10.23 $y' = 2(\cosh x)(\sinh x).$

6.10.24 $y' = -3(\sinh^2 4x)(\cosh 4x)(4) = -12(\sinh^2 4x)(\cosh 4x).$

6.10.25 $y' = 2(\tanh x)(\operatorname{sech}^2 x).$

6.10.26 $y' = \frac{1}{2\sqrt{\coth 3x}}\left(-\operatorname{csch}^2(3x)\right)(3) = \frac{-3\operatorname{csch}^2(3x)}{2\sqrt{\coth(3x)}}.$

6.10.27 $y' = \frac{1}{\operatorname{sech} 2x}(-\operatorname{sech} 2x \tanh 2x)(2) = -2\tanh 2x.$

6.10.28 $y' = \tanh x + x\operatorname{sech}^2 x.$

6.10.29 $y' = 2x\cosh^2 3x + x^2(2\cosh(3x)\sinh(3x)(3) = 2x\cosh(3x)(\cosh(3x) + 3x\sinh(3x)).$

6.10.30 $y' = \frac{\operatorname{csch} x + x\operatorname{csch} x \coth x}{\operatorname{csch}^2 x} = \frac{1}{\operatorname{csch} x} + \frac{x\coth x}{\operatorname{csch} x} = \sinh x + x\cosh x.$

6.10.31 $\int \cosh 2x \, dx = \frac{1}{2}\sinh 2x + C.$

6.10.32 Let $u = \tanh x$ so that $du = \operatorname{sech}^x dx$. Then we have $\int \operatorname{sech}^2 x \tanh x \, dx = \int u \, du = u^2/2 + C = \frac{\tanh^2 x}{2} + C$. Note: It is also possible to let $u = \operatorname{sech} x$ and obtain a different-looking but equivalent answer.

6.10.33 Let $u = 1 + \cosh x$ so that $du = \sinh x \, dx$. Substituting gives $\int \frac{1}{u} \, du = \ln|u| + C = \ln|1 + \cosh x| + C.$

6.10.34 Let $u = \coth x$ so that $du = -\operatorname{csch}^2 x \, dx$. Substituting gives $\int -u^2 \, du = -u^3/3 + C = -(\coth x)^3/3 + C.$

6.10.35 Recall that $\tanh^2 x = 1 - \operatorname{sech}^2 x$. So we have $\int(1 - \operatorname{sech}^2 x) \, dx = x - \tanh x + C.$

6.10.36 Recall that $\sinh^2 x = \frac{\cosh 2x - 1}{2}$. Thus we have $\frac{1}{2}\int(\cosh 2x - 1) \, dx = \frac{1}{2}\left(\frac{\sinh 2x}{2} - x\right) + C = \frac{\sinh 2x}{4} - \frac{x}{2} + C.$

6.10.37 Let $u = \cosh 3x$ so that $du = 3\sinh 3x \, dx$. Substituting gives $\frac{1}{3}\int_1^{\cosh 3} u^3 \, du = \left.\left(u^4/12\right)\right|_1^{\cosh 3} = \cosh^4 3/12 - 1/12 \approx 856.034.$

6.10.38 Let $u = \sqrt{x}$ so that $du = \frac{1}{2\sqrt{x}} \, dx$. Substituting yields $2\int_0^2 \operatorname{sech}^2 u \, du = 2\left.(\tanh u)\right|_0^2 = 2(\tanh(2) - 0) = 2\tanh(2) \approx 1.93.$

6.10.39 $\int_0^{\ln 2} \tanh x \, dx = \int_0^{\ln 2} \frac{\sinh x}{\cosh x} \, dx.$ Let $u = \cosh x$ so that $du = \sinh x \, dx$. Substituting gives $\int_1^{5/4} \frac{1}{u} \, du = \left.(\ln u)\right|_1^{5/4} = \ln(5/4).$

6.10.40 We use the formula in Theorem 6.9: $\int \operatorname{csch} y \, dy = \ln|\tanh(y/2)| + C$. We have $\int_{\ln 2}^{\ln 3} \operatorname{csch} y \, dy = \left.(\ln|\tanh(y/2)|)\right|_{\ln 2}^{\ln 3} = \ln(\tanh((\ln 3)/2)) - \ln(\tanh((\ln 2)/2)) \approx 0.405.$

6.10.41

a. Note that $\sinh \ln x = \frac{e^{\ln x} - e^{-\ln x}}{2} = \frac{x - 1/x}{2} = x/2 - 1/(2x)$. So $\int \frac{\sinh \ln x}{x} = \int (1/2 - x^{-2}/2) \, dx = x/2 + x^{-1}/2 + C = \frac{x^2 + 1}{2x} + C$.

b. Let $u = \ln x$, so that $du = \frac{1}{x} \, dx$. Substituting gives $\int \sinh u \, du = \cosh u + C = \cosh \ln x + C = \frac{e^{\ln x} + e^{-\ln x}}{2} + C = \frac{x + 1/x}{2} + C = \frac{x^2 + 1}{2x} + C$.

6.10.42

a. Note that $\cosh \ln x = \frac{e^{\ln x} + e^{-\ln x}}{2} = \frac{x + 1/x}{2} = \frac{x^2 + 1}{2x}$. Thus $\operatorname{sech} \ln x = \frac{1}{\cosh \ln x} = \frac{2x}{x^2 + 1}$. We have $\int_1^{\sqrt{3}} \frac{\sinh \ln x}{x} \, dx = \int_1^{\sqrt{3}} \frac{2}{x^2 + 1} \, dx = \left. \left(2 \tan^{-1} x \right) \right|_1^{\sqrt{3}} = 2(\pi/3 - \pi/4) = \pi/6$.

b. Let $u = \ln x$, so that $du = \frac{1}{x} \, dx$. Substituting gives $\int_0^{\ln \sqrt{3}} \operatorname{sech} u \, du = \left. \left(\tan^{-1} | \sinh(u) | \right) \right|_0^{\ln \sqrt{3}} = \tan^{-1}(\frac{\sqrt{3} - (1/\sqrt{3})}{2}) - 0 = \tan^{-1}(1/\sqrt{3}) = \pi/6$.

6.10.43

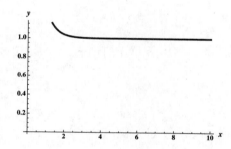

a. The values of $\coth x$ on the interval $[5, 10]$ are very close to 1. So the area under the curve is very close to that of a 5×1 rectangle.

b. $\int_5^{10} \coth x \, dx = \int_5^{10} \frac{\cosh x}{\sinh x} \, dx = \left. (\ln | \sinh x |) \right|_5^{10} = \ln \sinh 10 - \ln \sinh 5 \approx 5.0000454$. The absolute value of the error is about $.0000454$.

6.10.44 Let $u = \sinh x$ so that $du = \cosh x \, dx$. Then $\int \coth x \, dx = \int \frac{\cosh x}{\sinh x} \, dx = \int \frac{1}{u} \, du = \ln |u| + C = \ln | \sinh x | + C$.

6.10.45

a. The curves intersect when $\frac{1}{\cosh x} = \frac{\sinh x}{\cosh x}$, or when $\sinh x = 1$, so at $x = \sinh^{-1}(1) = \ln(1 + \sqrt{2})$.

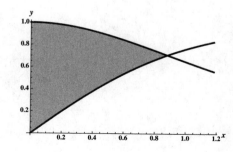

b. We need to compute $A = \int_0^{\ln(1 + \sqrt{2})} \operatorname{sech} x - \tanh x \, dx$. Recall that $\int \operatorname{sech} x \, dx = \tan^{-1} | \sinh x | + C$ and $\int \tanh x \, dx = \ln \cosh x + C$. Thus, $A = \left. \left(\tan^{-1} \sinh x - \ln \cosh x \right) \right|_0^{\ln(1 + \sqrt{2})} = \tan^{-1} \sinh(\ln(1 + \sqrt{2})) - \ln \cosh(\ln(1 + \sqrt{2})) - (0 - 0) \approx .44$.

6.10.46

a. The curves intersect when $\sinh x = \frac{\sinh x}{\cosh x}$, or when $\sinh x = 0$, (or $\cosh x = 1$), so at $x = 0$.

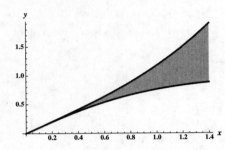

b. We need to compute $\int_0^{\ln 3} \sinh x - \tanh x\, dx =$

$(\cosh x - \ln \cosh x)\Big|_0^{\ln 3} = \cosh(\ln 3) -$

$\ln\cosh\ln(3) - 1 = 5/3 - \ln(5/3) - 1 =$
$2/3 - \ln(5/3) \approx .156.$

6.10.47 $f'(x) = \frac{1}{\sqrt{16x^2-1}} \cdot 4 = \frac{4}{\sqrt{16x^2-1}}.$

6.10.48 $f'(t) = \frac{2}{1-t}\left(\frac{1}{2\sqrt{t}}\right) = \frac{1}{\sqrt{t}(1-t)}.$

6.10.49 $f'(v) = \frac{1}{\sqrt{v^4+1}} \cdot (2v) = \frac{2v}{\sqrt{v^4+1}}.$

6.10.50 $f'(x) = \frac{-1}{|2/x|\sqrt{1+4/x^2}}\left(\frac{-2}{x^2}\right) = \frac{1}{|x|\sqrt{1+4/x^2}} = \frac{1}{\sqrt{x^2+4}}.$

6.10.51 $f'(x) = \sinh^{-1}(x) + \frac{x}{\sqrt{x^2+1}} - \frac{x}{\sqrt{x^2+1}} = \sinh^{-1}(x).$

6.10.52 $f'(u) = \frac{1}{\sqrt{\tan^2 u+1}} \cdot \sec^2 u = \frac{1}{\sqrt{\sec^2 u}} \cdot \sec^2 u = \frac{\sec^2 u}{|\sec u|} = |\sec u|.$

6.10.53 We have $\frac{1}{8}\int \frac{dx}{1-(x/\sqrt{8})^2}\, dx$. Let $u = x/\sqrt{8}$ so that $du = \frac{dx}{\sqrt{8}}$. Substituting gives $\frac{1}{\sqrt{8}}\int \frac{du}{1-u^2} = \frac{1}{\sqrt{8}}\coth^{-1}(u) + C = \frac{1}{\sqrt{8}}\coth^{-1}(x/\sqrt{8}) + C.$

6.10.54 $\frac{1}{4}\int \frac{dx}{\sqrt{(x/4)^2-1}}$. Let $u = x/4$ so that $du = dx/4$. Substituting gives $\int \frac{du}{\sqrt{u^2-1}} = \cosh^{-1}(u) + C = \cosh^{-1}(x/4) + C.$

6.10.55 We have $\frac{1}{36}\int \frac{e^x}{1-(e^x/6)^2}\, dx$.

Let $u = e^x/6$ so that $du = e^x/6\, dx$. Substituting gives $\frac{1}{6}\int \frac{du}{1-u^2} = \frac{1}{6}\tanh^{-1}(u) + C = \frac{1}{6}\tanh^{-1}(e^x/6) + C.$

6.10.56 This can be computed using part 5 of Theorem 6.12. We have $\int \frac{1}{x\sqrt{4^2+x^2}}\, dx = \frac{-1}{4}\mathrm{csch}^{-1}\left(\frac{|x|}{4}\right) + C.$

6.10.57 We have $\frac{1}{2}\int \frac{dx}{x\sqrt{1-(x^4/2)^2}}$. Let $u = x^4/2$ so that $du = 2x^3\, dx$. Substituting gives $\frac{1}{2}\int \frac{du}{4u\sqrt{1-u^2}} = \frac{-1}{8}\mathrm{sech}^{-1}u + C = \frac{-1}{8}\mathrm{sech}^{-1}(x^4/2) + C.$

6.10.58 Let $u = x^2$ so that $du = 2x\, dx$. Substituting gives $\int \frac{du}{2u\sqrt{1+u^2}} = \frac{-1}{2}\mathrm{csch}^{-1}|u| + C = \frac{-1}{2}\mathrm{csch}^{-1}x^2 + C.$

6.10.59 Let $u = \ln x$ so that $du = \frac{dx}{x}$. Substituting gives $\int_0^2 \frac{du}{\sqrt{u^2+1}} = \left(\sinh^{-1}u\right)\Big|_0^2 = \sinh^{-1}(2) - 0 = \ln(2+\sqrt{5}).$

6.10.60 $\int_5^{3\sqrt{5}} \frac{dx}{\sqrt{x^2-3^2}} = \left(\cosh^{-1}(x/3)\right)\Big|_5^{3\sqrt{5}} = \cosh^{-1}(\sqrt{5}) - \cosh^{-1}(5/3) = \ln(\sqrt{5}+2) - \ln(5/3+4/3) = \ln\left(\frac{\sqrt{5}+2}{3}\right).$

6.10.61 $\int_{-2}^{2} \frac{dt}{t^2-3^2} = \frac{-1}{3} \left(\tanh^{-1}(x/3) \right) \Big|_{-2}^{2} = \frac{-1}{3} \left(\tanh^{-1}(2/3) - \tanh^{-1}(-2/3) \right) = $

$\frac{-1}{3} \left(\frac{1}{2} \ln((5/3)/(1/3)) - \frac{1}{2} \ln((1/3)/(5/3)) \right) = \frac{-1}{3} \ln 5 \approx -.54.$

6.10.62 Let $u = 2t$ so that $du = 2\,dt$. Substituting gives $\int_{1/3}^{1/2} \frac{du}{u\sqrt{1-u^2}} = \left(-\text{sech}^{-1}u \right) \Big|_{1/3}^{1/2} = \text{sech}^{-1}(1/3) - $

$\text{sech}^{-1}(1/2) = \cosh^{-1}(3) - \cosh^{-1}(2) = \ln(3 + \sqrt{8}) - \ln(2 + \sqrt{3}) = \ln((3 + \sqrt{8})/(2 + \sqrt{3})) \approx .45.$

6.10.63 Let $u = x^{1/3}$ so that $du = \frac{1}{3}x^{-2/3}\,dx$. Substituting gives $\int_{1/2}^{1} \frac{3u^2\,du}{u^3\sqrt{1+u^2}} = 3\int_{1/2}^{1} \frac{du}{u\sqrt{1+u^2}} = $

$-3 \left(\text{csch}^{-1}x \right) \Big|_{1/2}^{1} = 3(\text{csch}^{-1}(1/2) - \text{csch}^{-1}(1)) = 3(\sinh^{-1}(2) - \sinh^{-1}(1)) = 3(\ln(2 + \sqrt{5}) - \ln(1 + \sqrt{2}) \approx$
1.69.

6.10.64 Let $u = \sinh x$ so that $du = \cosh x\,dx$. Substituting gives $\int_{12/5}^{40/9} \frac{du}{4-u^2} = \frac{1}{2} \left(\coth^{-1}(u/2) \right) \Big|_{12/5}^{40/9} = $

$\frac{1}{2} \left(\coth^{-1}(20/9) - \coth^{-1}(6/5) \right) = \frac{1}{2} \left(\tanh^{-1}(9/20) - \tanh^{-1}(5/6) \right) = $
$\frac{1}{4} \left(\ln((29/20)/(11/20)) - \ln((11/6)/(1/6)) \right) = \frac{1}{4} \left(\ln(29/121) \right) \approx -0.36.$

6.10.65 By symmetry, we compute $I = 2\int_{0}^{\cosh^{-1}(17/15)} (17/15 - \cosh x)\,dx$ and divide by $2\cosh^{-1}(17/15)$.

The value of I is $2\left((17/15)x - \sinh x \right) \Big|_{0}^{\cosh^{-1}(17/15)} = 2\left((17/15)\cosh^{-1}(17/15) - \sinh(\cosh^{-1}(17/15)) \right) = $

$(34/15)\cosh^{-1}(17/15) - 16/15.$ When we divide by $2\cosh^{-1}(17/15)$ we obtain $17/15 - \frac{8}{15\cosh^{-1}(17/15)} \approx 0.09.$

6.10.66 $L = \int_{0}^{a} \sqrt{1 + \sinh^2 x}\,dx = \int_{0}^{a} \cosh x\,dx = (\sinh x) \Big|_{0}^{a} = \sinh a.$

6.10.67

a. Let a be the value that produces a sag of 10 feet. Note that $f(0) + \text{sag} = f(50)$, so $a + \text{sag} = a\cosh(50/a)$, and dividing by a yields $1 + \frac{\text{sag}}{a} = \cosh(50/a)$, which can be written as $\cosh(50/a) - 1 = 10/a.$

b. If $t = 10/a$, we have $\cosh(5t) - 1 = t$. Solving for t yields $t \approx 0.08.$

c. If $0.08 = 10/a$, then $a = 10/0.08 = 125$. The length of the power line is $2\int_{0}^{50} \sqrt{1 + \sinh^2(x/125)}\,dx = $

$2\int_{0}^{50} \cosh(x/125)\,dx = 250\,(\sinh(x/125)) \Big|_{0}^{50} = 250\sinh(50/125) = 250\sinh(2/5) \approx 102.7 \text{ feet.}$

6.10.68 We have a right triangle with hypotenuse 50.5 and side adjacent to θ of length 50, so $\cos\theta = 50/50.5$, so $\theta = \cos^{-1}(50/50.5) \approx .14$ radians.

6.10.69 We are seeking λ so that $7 = \sqrt{\frac{9.8\lambda}{2\pi}} \tanh\left(\frac{20\pi}{\lambda}\right)$. A computer algebra system finds the approximate root to be 32.81 meters.

6.10.70

a. If $\lambda = 50$ and $d = 20$ then $v = \sqrt{\frac{(9.8)(50)}{2\pi}} \tanh\left(\frac{40\pi}{50}\right) \approx 8.77$ meters per second.

b. If $4.5 = \sqrt{\frac{(9.8)(15)}{2\pi}} \tanh\left(\frac{2\pi d}{15}\right)$, then $d \approx 3.14$ meters.

6.10.71

a. $f'(x) = \text{sech}^2(x)$, so $f'(0) = 1$. The point of tangency is $(0, \tanh 0) = (0,0)$, so the linearization is $L(x) = 0 + 1(x - 0) = x.$

b. When $d/\lambda < 0.05$, $2\pi d/\lambda$ is small. Because $\tanh x \approx x$ for small values of x, $\tanh(2\pi d/\lambda) \approx 2\pi d/\lambda$. Thus,

$$v = \sqrt{\frac{g\lambda}{2\pi}\tanh\left(\frac{2\pi d}{\lambda}\right)} \approx \sqrt{\frac{g\lambda}{2\pi}\cdot\frac{2\pi d}{\lambda}} = \sqrt{gd}.$$

c. $v = \sqrt{gd}$ is a function of depth only. As $d \to 0$, $v \to 0$ as well.

6.10.72 With $\lambda = 150$ km which is 150,000 meters, we still have $d/\lambda = \frac{4000}{150000} \approx .027$, which is less than .05. The conclusions from the previous solution (part b) still apply.

6.10.73

a. False. $\sinh(\ln 3)$ is a constant, so its derivative is zero.

b. False. $\frac{d}{dx}\cosh x = \sinh x$, not $-\sinh x$.

c. False. This velocity equation is not a function of time.

d. True. Note that $-\ln(\sqrt{2}-1) = \ln\left(\frac{1}{\sqrt{2}-1}\right) = \ln\left(\frac{1}{\sqrt{2}-1}\cdot\frac{\sqrt{2}+1}{\sqrt{2}+1}\right) = \ln(\sqrt{2}+1)$.

e. False. $\int\frac{dx}{2^2-x^2} = \frac{1}{2}\tanh^{-1}(x/2)$ for $|x| < 2$.

6.10.74

a. $\coth(4) \approx 1.00067$

b. Does not exist

c. $\operatorname{csch}^{-1}(5) \approx 0.19869$

d. $\operatorname{csch}\Big|_{1/2}^{2} \approx -1.64331$

e. $\ln|\tanh(x/2)|\Big|_{1}^{10} \approx .771846$

f. $\tan^{-1}(\sinh x)\Big|_{-3}^{3} \approx 2.94261$

g. $\frac{1}{4}\coth^{-1}(x/4)\Big|_{20}^{36} \approx -0.0227902$

6.10.75

a. $\cosh(0) = 1$

b. $\tanh(0) = 0$

c. Does not exist

d. $\operatorname{sech}(0) = 1$

e. $\coth(\ln 5) = \frac{5+1/5}{5-1/5} = \frac{13}{12}$

f. $\sinh(\ln 9) = \frac{9-1/9}{2} = \frac{40}{9}$

g. $\left(\frac{e+(1/e)}{2}\right)^2 = \left(\frac{e^2+1}{2e}\right)^2$

h. Does not exist

i. $\ln(17/8 + \sqrt{\frac{17^2-8^2}{8^2}}) = \ln 4$

j. $\sinh^{-1}\left(\frac{e^1-e^{-1}}{2}\right) = 1$

6.10.76 $f'(x) = \cosh x > 0$ for all x, so f is increasing on $(-\infty, \infty)$. $f''(x) = \sinh x$, which is zero only for $x = 0$. Note that f'' is positive on $(0, \infty)$ and negative on $(-\infty, 0)$, so f is concave up on $(0, \infty)$ and concave down on $(-\infty, 0)$. There are no extrema, but there is an inflection point at $(0, 0)$.

6.10.77 $f'(x) = 2\sinh x\cosh x\cosh x + \sinh^2 x\sinh x = \sinh x(2\cosh^2 x + \sinh^2 x)$. Note that $\sinh x = 0$ for $x = 0$, while $2\cosh^2 x + \sinh^2 x > 0$ for all x. So the only critical point is $x = 0$.

6.10.78

a. $f'(x) = \frac{x\sinh x - \cosh x}{x^2}$. This is zero when $x\sinh x = \cosh x$, or $x = \coth x$.

b. Using a computer algebra system, we find that $x = \pm 1.2$ are critical points of f.

6.10.79 $f'(x) = 2\tanh x \operatorname{sech}^2 x = \frac{2\sinh x}{\cosh^3 x}$. $f''(x) = \frac{2\cosh^4 x - 2(\sinh x)(3\cosh^2 x)(\sinh x)}{\cosh^6 x} = \frac{2\cosh^2 x - 6\sinh^2 x}{\cosh^4 x}$. This is zero for $\tanh^2 x = 1/3$, or $x = \tanh^{-1}(\pm\sqrt{1/3}) = \pm\tanh^{-1}(\sqrt{1/3})$.

6.10.80 $f'(x) = -\operatorname{sech} x \tanh x$. $f''(x) = (\operatorname{sech} x \tanh x)\tanh x - \operatorname{sech} x \operatorname{sech}^2 x = \operatorname{sech} x(\tanh^2 x - \operatorname{sech}^2 x)$. Because $\operatorname{sech} x > 0$ for all x, this quantity is zero when $\tanh x = \pm\operatorname{sech} x$, which occurs for $\sinh x = \pm 1$, or $x = \sinh^{-1}(\pm 1)$. The potential inflection points occur at $\ln(\sqrt{2}+1)$ and $\ln(\sqrt{2}-1)$. A check of the sign of f'' on the relevant intervals confirms that there are inflection points at these x-values.

6.10.81 This area would be the area under $\operatorname{sech} x$ between 0 and 1, minus the area of a quarter circle. Thus we have $\int_0^1 \operatorname{sech} x \, dx - \frac{\pi}{4} = \left(\tan^{-1}|\sinh x|\right)\Big|_0^1 - \frac{\pi}{4} = \tan^{-1}(\sinh(1)) - \frac{\pi}{4} \approx 0.08$.

6.10.82 $V = \pi\int_0^1 (\operatorname{sech}^2 x - (1-x^2))\,dx = \pi\left(\tanh x - x + x^3/3\right)\Big|_0^1 = \tanh(1) - 1 + 1/3 \approx .095$ cubic units.

6.10.83 Applying L'Hôpital's rule twice brings you back to the initial limit. If we write $\frac{\sinh x}{\cosh x} = \frac{(\sinh x)e^x}{(\cosh x)e^x} = \frac{e^{2x}-1}{e^{2x}+1}$, then applying L'Hôpital's rule once shows that the limit is 1.

6.10.84 $\lim_{x\to\infty}\frac{1-\coth x}{1-\tanh x} = \lim_{x\to\infty}\frac{\operatorname{csch}^2 x}{-\operatorname{sech}^2 x} = -\lim_{x\to\infty}\frac{\cosh^2 x}{\sinh^2 x} = -1$.

6.10.85 $\lim_{x\to 0}\frac{\tanh^{-1}x}{\tan(\pi x/2)} = \lim_{x\to 0}\frac{\frac{1}{1-x^2}}{(\pi/2)\sec^2(\pi x/2)} = \frac{2}{\pi}\lim_{x\to 0}\frac{\cos^2(\pi x/2)}{1-x^2} = \frac{2}{\pi}$.

6.10.86 $\lim_{x\to 1}\frac{\tanh^{-1}x}{\tan(\pi x/2)} = \lim_{x\to 1}\frac{\frac{1}{1-x^2}}{(\pi/2)\sec^2(\pi x/2)} = \frac{2}{\pi}\lim_{x\to 1}\frac{\cos^2(\pi x/2)}{1-x^2} = \frac{2}{\pi}\lim_{x\to 1}\frac{2\cos(\pi x/2)(-\sin(\pi x/2))(\pi/2)}{-2x} = \frac{2}{\pi}\cdot\frac{0}{-2} = 0$.

6.10.87 Let $y = (\tanh x)^x$. Then $\ln y = x\ln(\tanh x) = \frac{\ln\tanh x}{1/x}$. Note that $\lim_{x\to 0}\frac{\ln\tanh x}{1/x} = \lim_{x\to 0}\frac{1/(\sinh x \cosh x)}{-1/x^2} = \lim_{x\to 0}\frac{-x^2}{\sinh x\cosh x} = \lim_{x\to 0}\frac{-2x}{\sinh^2 x + \cosh^2 x} = 0$. Thus, $\lim_{x\to 0}y = \lim_{x\to 0}(\tanh x)^x = e^0 = 1$.

6.10.88

a. Note that $y = -x$ is also a slant asymptote, by symmetry.

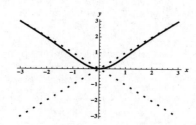

b. Because $\lim_{x\to\infty}\tanh x = 1$, we expect $x\tanh x$ to behave like $x\cdot 1$ as x gets large.

c. Note that $x\tanh x - x = x\left(\frac{e^{2x}-1}{e^{2x}+1} - 1\right) = x\left(\frac{e^{2x}-1-(e^{2x}+1)}{e^{2x}+1}\right) = \frac{-2x}{e^{2x}+1}$. So $\lim_{x\to\infty}x\tanh x - x = \lim_{x\to\infty}\frac{-2x}{e^{2x}+1} = \lim_{x\to\infty}\frac{-2}{2e^{2x}} = 0$.

6.10.89 $\int\frac{\cosh z}{\sinh^2 z}\,dz = \int\coth z \operatorname{csch} z \, dx = -\operatorname{csch} z + C$.

6.10.90 Let $u = \sin\theta$ so that $du = \cos\theta\,d\theta$. Substituting gives

$$\int\frac{du}{3^2 - u^2} = \frac{1}{3}\tanh^{-1}(u/3) + C = \frac{1}{3}\tanh^{-1}((\sin\theta)/3) + C.$$

6.10.91 Let $u = \sinh^{-1} x$ so that $du = \frac{dx}{\sqrt{x^2+1}}$. Substituting gives $\int_{\sinh^{-1}(5/12)}^{\sinh^{-1}(3/4)} u\,du = \left(u^2/2\right)\Big]\Big|_{\sinh^{-1}(5/12)}^{\sinh^{-1}(3/4)} =$

$\frac{1}{2}\left(\left(\sinh^{-1}(3/4)\right)^2 - \left(\sinh^{-1}(5/12)\right)^2\right) \approx .158$.

6.10.92 Consider $\int_{25}^{225} \frac{dx}{\sqrt{x}\sqrt{\sqrt{x^2+25}}}$, and let $u = \sqrt{x}$, so that $du = \frac{dx}{2\sqrt{x}}$. Substituting gives $2\int_{5}^{15} \frac{du}{\sqrt{u^2+5^2}} =$

$2\left(\sinh^{-1}(u/5)\right)\Big|_{5}^{15} = 2(\sinh^{-1}(3) - \sinh^{-1}(1)) = 2(\ln(3+\sqrt{10}) - \ln(1+\sqrt{2})) \approx 1.874$.

6.10.93 Let A be the area under $3 - \cosh x$ between $\cosh^{-1}(-3)$ and $\cosh^{-1}(3)$. Then the volume of the

kiln will be $6A$. By symmetry, $A = 2\int_{0}^{\cosh^{-1}(3)} (3 - \cosh x)\,dx = 2\,(3x - \sinh x)\Big|_{0}^{\cosh^{-1}(3)} = 6\cosh^{-1}(3) -$

$2\sinh(\cosh^{-1}(3)) \approx 4.92$. So the volume of the kiln is about $6 \cdot 4.92 \approx 29.5$

6.10.94 Note that f has odd symmetry, so nonzero critical points should come in positive, negative pairs. $f'(x) = \operatorname{sech} x - x\operatorname{sech} x \tanh x = \operatorname{sech} x(1 - x\tanh x)$. Because $\operatorname{sech} x > 0$ for all x, any roots must come from solutions to the equation $1 - x\tanh x = 0$. Let $g(x) = 1 - x\tanh x$. Applying Newton's method with the recursion $x_{n+1} = x_n - \frac{g(x_n)}{g'(x_n)} = x_n - \frac{1 - x_n\tanh x_n}{-\tanh x_n - x_n\operatorname{sech}^2 x_n}$ starting with $x_0 = 1$ yields $x_1 = 1.20177$, $x_2 = 1.9968$, $x_3 = 1.9968$ and so on, so the local extreme values for f occur at ± 1.9968.

6.10.95

a. $d(10) = \frac{75}{.2}\ln\left(\cosh\left(\sqrt{\frac{(.2)(9.8)}{75}} \cdot 10\right)\right) \approx 360.8$.

b. We need to solve $100 = \frac{75}{.2}\ln\left(\cosh\left(\sqrt{\frac{(.2)(9.8)}{75}} \cdot t\right)\right)$ for t. We have $t = \cosh^{-1}(e^{\frac{100 \cdot .2}{75}}) \cdot \sqrt{\frac{75}{(.2)(9.8)}} \approx$

4.72 seconds. The first 200 feet take $t = \cosh^{-1}(e^{\frac{200 \cdot .2}{75}}) \cdot \sqrt{\frac{75}{(.2)(9.8)}} \approx 6.97$ seconds, which means that the second 100 feet took about $6.97 - 4.72 = 2.25$ seconds. The average velocity over the first 100 feet is $\frac{100}{4.72} \approx 21.2$ meters per second, while over the second 100 feet is $\frac{100}{2.25} \approx 44.5$ meters per second.

6.10.96

a. $d'(t) = \frac{m}{k}\frac{1}{\cosh\left(\sqrt{\frac{kg}{m}}t\right)}\sinh\left(\sqrt{\frac{kg}{m}}t\right)\sqrt{\frac{kg}{m}} = \sqrt{\frac{mg}{k}}\tanh\left(\sqrt{\frac{kg}{m}}t\right)$.

b. $d'(10) = \sqrt{\frac{(75)(9.8)}{.2}}\tanh\left(\sqrt{\frac{(75)(9.8)}{.2}}(10)\right) \approx 56.02$ meters per second.

c. We seek t so that $d'(t) = \sqrt{\frac{mg}{k}}\tanh\left(\sqrt{\frac{kg}{m}}t\right) = 45$. This can be written as

$60.6218\tanh(0.161658t) = 45$, so $t \approx \tanh^{-1}\left(\frac{45}{60.618}\right) \cdot \frac{1}{0.161658} \approx 5.911$ seconds.

6.10.97

a. $\sqrt{\frac{mg}{k}}\lim_{t\to\infty}\tanh\left(\sqrt{\frac{kg}{m}}t\right) = \sqrt{\frac{mg}{k}} \cdot 1 = \sqrt{\frac{mg}{k}}$.

b. $\sqrt{\frac{(75)(9.8)}{.2}} \approx 60.6$ meters per second.

c. We seek t so that $v(t) = \sqrt{\frac{mg}{k}}\tanh\left(\sqrt{\frac{kg}{m}}t\right) = .95\sqrt{\frac{mg}{k}}$.

So $\tanh\left(\sqrt{\frac{kg}{m}}t\right) = .95$, and $t = \tanh^{-1}(.95)\sqrt{\frac{m}{kg}}$.

d. It takes $\tanh^{-1}(.95)\sqrt{\frac{75}{(.2)(9.8)}} \approx 11.33$ seconds to achieve 95 percent of terminal velocity. It takes $d(11.33) \approx 436.5$ feet to achieve this. So the cliff should be at least $436.5 + 300 = 736.5$ feet high.

6.10.98

a. $a(t) = \frac{d}{dt}\sqrt{\frac{mg}{k}}\tanh\left(\sqrt{\frac{kg}{m}}t\right) = \sqrt{\frac{mg}{k}}\operatorname{sech}^2\left(\sqrt{\frac{kg}{m}}t\right)\sqrt{\frac{kg}{m}} = g\operatorname{sech}^2\left(\sqrt{\frac{kg}{m}}t\right).$

b. $\lim_{t\to\infty} g\operatorname{sech}^2\left(\sqrt{\frac{kg}{m}}t\right) = g\left(\lim_{t\to\infty}\operatorname{sech}\left(\sqrt{\frac{kg}{m}}t\right)\right)^2 = g(0)^2 = 0.$ Once terminal velocity is achieved, the velocity is constant, so the acceleration is zero.

6.10.99 For $y = A\sinh kx$, we have $y' = kA\cosh kx$ and $y'' = k^2 A\sinh kx$. So $y'' - k^2 y = k^2 A\sinh kx - k^2 A\sinh kx = 0$.

For $y = B\cosh kx$, we have $y' = kB\sinh kx$ and $y'' = k^2 B\cosh kx$. So $y'' - k^2 y = k^2 B\cosh kx - k^2 B\cosh kx = 0$.

6.10.100 Using symmetry, $A = 4\pi\int_0^{\ln 2}\cosh x\sqrt{1 + \sinh^2 x}\,dx = 4\pi\int_0^{\ln 2}\cosh^2 x\,dx = 4\pi\int_0^{\ln 2}\frac{1+\cosh 2x}{2}\,dx = 2\pi\left(x + (1/2)\sinh 2x\right)\Big|_0^{\ln 2} = 2\pi(\ln 2 + 15/16) = \pi(\ln 4 + 15/8) \approx 10.25.$

6.10.101

$$\sinh(\cosh^{-1}(x)) = \sinh(\ln(x + \sqrt{x^2 - 1})) = \frac{e^{\ln(x+\sqrt{x^2-1})} - \frac{1}{e^{\ln(x+\sqrt{x^2-1})}}}{2}$$

$$= \frac{1}{2}\left(x + \sqrt{x^2 - 1} - \frac{1}{x + \sqrt{x^2 - 1}}\right).$$

Multiplying the last term by $\frac{x - \sqrt{x^2-1}}{x - \sqrt{x^2-1}}$ gives

$$\frac{1}{2}\left((x + \sqrt{x^2 - 1}) - (x - \sqrt{x^2 - 1})\right) = \sqrt{x^2 - 1}.$$

6.10.102

$$\cosh(\sinh^{-1}(x)) = \cosh(\ln(x + \sqrt{x^2 + 1})) = \frac{e^{\ln(x+\sqrt{x^2+1})} + \frac{1}{e^{\ln(x+\sqrt{x^2+1})}}}{2}$$

$$= \frac{1}{2}\left(x + \sqrt{x^2 + 1} + \frac{1}{x + \sqrt{x^2 + 1}}\right).$$

Multiplying the last term by $\frac{x - \sqrt{x^2+1}}{x - \sqrt{x^2+1}}$ gives

$$\frac{1}{2}\left((x + \sqrt{x^2 + 1}) - (x - \sqrt{x^2 + 1})\right) = \sqrt{x^2 + 1}.$$

6.10.103 $\cosh(x + y) = \frac{e^{x+y} + e^{-(x+y)}}{2} = \frac{2e^{x+y} + 2e^{-(x+y)}}{4}$. This can be written as

$$\frac{1}{4}\left(e^{x+y} + e^{x-y} + e^{y-x} + e^{-(x+y)} + e^{x+y} - e^{x-y} - e^{y-x} + e^{-(x+y)}\right)$$

$$= \left(\frac{e^x + e^{-x}}{2}\right)\left(\frac{e^y + e^{-y}}{2}\right) + \left(\frac{e^x - e^{-x}}{2}\right)\left(\frac{e^y - e^{-y}}{2}\right)$$

$$= \cosh x\cosh y + \sinh x\sinh y$$

6.10.104 $\sinh(x+y) = \frac{e^{x+y}-e^{-(x+y)}}{2} = \frac{2e^{x+y}-2e^{-(x+y)}}{4}$. This can be written as

$$\frac{1}{4}\left(e^{x+y} + e^{x-y} - e^{y-x} - e^{-(x+y)} + e^{x+y} - e^{x-y} + e^{y-x} - e^{-(x+y)}\right)$$

$$= \left(\frac{e^x-e^{-x}}{2}\right)\left(\frac{e^y+e^{-y}}{2}\right) + \left(\frac{e^x+e^{-x}}{2}\right)\left(\frac{e^y-e^{-y}}{2}\right)$$

$$= \sinh x \cosh y + \cosh x \sinh y$$

6.10.105 First suppose $x \geq 0$. Then $\cosh^{-1}(\cosh x) = \ln(\cosh x + \sqrt{1 + \cosh^2 x}) = \ln(\cosh x + \sqrt{\sinh^2 x}) = \ln(\cosh x + \sinh x) = \ln e^x = x$.

Now suppose $x < 0$. Then $\cosh^{-1}(\cosh x) = \ln(\cosh x + \sqrt{1 + \cosh^2 x}) = \ln(\cosh x + \sqrt{\sinh^2 x}) = \ln(\cosh x - \sinh x) = \ln e^{-x} = -x$.

Thus $\cosh^{-1}(\cosh x) = |x|$.

6.10.106

    a. Let $y = \cosh^{-1}(x)$. Then $x = \cosh y$, so $1 = \sinh y \cdot \frac{dy}{dx}$. Thus $\frac{dy}{dx} = \frac{1}{\sinh y} = \frac{1}{\sinh(\cosh^{-1}(x))} = \frac{1}{\sqrt{x^2-1}}$.

    b. $\frac{d}{dx}\ln(x + \sqrt{x^2+1}) = \frac{1}{x+\sqrt{x^2+1}}\left(1 + \frac{2x}{2\sqrt{x^2+1}}\right) = \frac{1}{x+\sqrt{x^2+1}}\left(\frac{x+\sqrt{x^2+1}}{\sqrt{x^2+1}}\right) = \frac{1}{\sqrt{x^2+1}}$.

6.10.107

    a. $\int \operatorname{sech} x \, dx = \int \frac{\cosh x}{1+\sinh^2 x}\,dx$. Let $u = \sinh x$ so that $du = \cosh x \, dx$. Then we have $\int \frac{1}{1+u^2}\,du = \tan^{-1}(u) + C = \tan^{-1}(\sinh x) + C$.

    b. Note that $\operatorname{sech} x = \frac{\operatorname{sech}^2 x}{\sqrt{\operatorname{sech}^2 x}} = \frac{\operatorname{sech}^2 x}{\sqrt{1-\tanh^2 x}}$. So $\int \operatorname{sech} x \, dx = \int \frac{\operatorname{sech}^2 x}{\sqrt{1-\tanh^2 x}}\,dx$. Let $u = \tanh x$ so that $du = \operatorname{sech}^2 x \, dx$. Substituting gives $\int \frac{1}{\sqrt{1-u^2}}\,du = \sin^{-1}(u) + C = \sin^{-1}(\tanh x) + C$.

    c. $\frac{d}{dx}(2\tan^{-1}(e^x) + C) = 2\left(\frac{1}{1+e^{2x}}\right)e^x + 0 = \frac{2e^x}{1+e^{2x}} \cdot \frac{e^{-x}}{e^{-x}} = \frac{2}{e^{-x}+e^x} = \frac{1}{\cosh x} = \operatorname{sech} x$.

6.10.108

    a. Consider $I = \int \operatorname{csch} x \, dx$ and let $u = x/2$, so that $du = dx/2$. Substituting gives $I = 2\int \operatorname{csch} 2u \, du = \int \frac{2\,du}{\sinh 2u}$.

    b. Because $\sinh 2x = 2\sinh x \cosh x$, we have $I = \int \frac{2\,du}{2\sinh u \cosh u} = \int \frac{1}{\sinh u \cosh u} \cdot \frac{\frac{1}{\cosh^2 u}}{\frac{1}{\cosh^2 u}}\,du = \int \frac{\operatorname{sech}^2 u}{\tanh u}\,du$.

    c. Let $w = \tanh u$ so that $dw = \operatorname{sech}^2 u \, du$. Substituting gives $I = \int \frac{1}{w}\,dw = \ln|w| + C = \ln|\tanh u| + C = \ln|\tanh(x/2)| + C$.

6.10.109 $L = \int_{\ln 2}^{\ln 8} \sqrt{1 + \operatorname{csch}^2 x}\,dx = \int_{\ln 2}^{\ln 8} \sqrt{\coth^2 x}\,dx = \int_{\ln 2}^{\ln 8} \coth x \, dx = \int_{\ln 2}^{\ln 8} \frac{\cosh x}{\sinh x}\,dx$. Let $u = \sinh x$ so that $du = \cosh x \, dx$. Substituting gives $\int_{3/4}^{63/16} \frac{1}{u}\,du = (\ln u)\Big|_{3/4}^{63/16} = \ln(63/16) - \ln(3/4) = \ln(21/4) \approx 1.66$.

6.10.110 Let $x = \tanh y$ so that $x = \frac{e^y-e^{-y}}{e^y+e^{-y}} \cdot \frac{e^y}{e^y} = \frac{e^{2y}-1}{e^{2y}+1}$. Then $xe^{2y} + x = e^{2y} - 1$, so $x + 1 = e^{2y} - xe^{2y}$, and $x + 1 = e^{2y}(1 - x)$. Dividing through by $1 - x$ gives $\frac{x+1}{1-x} = e^{2y}$, so $\ln\left(\frac{x+1}{1-x}\right) = 2y$, and $y = \frac{1}{2}\ln\left(\frac{x+1}{1-x}\right)$.

6.10.111 Suppose $r > 0$ and $0 < x < 1$. If $u = x^r$, then $du = rx^{r-1}\,dx$. Substituting gives $\int \frac{du}{ru\sqrt{1-u^2}} = \frac{-1}{r}(\operatorname{sech}^{-1}(u)) + C = \frac{-1}{r}(\operatorname{sech}^{-1}(x^r)) + C$.

6.10.112

a. Consider the triangle with vertices $(0,0)$, $(x,0)$ and (x,y). Twice the area of the shaded region is twice the area of the triangle less twice the area under the curve $y = \sqrt{z^2 - 1}$ between $z = 1$ and $z = x$. The area of the triangle is $\frac{1}{2}xy$ and the area under the curve is given by $\int_1^x \sqrt{z^2 - 1}\,dz$. Thus, twice the area is given by

$$t = 2\left(\frac{1}{2}xy - \int_1^x \sqrt{z^2 - 1}\,dz\right) = x\sqrt{x^2 - 1} - 2\int_1^x \sqrt{z^2 - 1}\,dz.$$

b. Given the formula, we have $\int_1^x \sqrt{z^2 - 1}\,dz = \left(\frac{z}{2}\sqrt{z^2 - 1} - \frac{1}{2}\ln|z + \sqrt{z^2 - 1}|\right)\Big|_1^x = \frac{x}{2}\sqrt{x^2 - 1} - \frac{1}{2}\ln|x + \sqrt{x^2 - 1}| - (0 - 0) = \frac{x}{2}\sqrt{x^2 - 1} - \frac{1}{2}\ln(x + \sqrt{x^2 - 1})$. The absolute values can be dropped because $x > 1$ so $x + \sqrt{x^2 - 1} > 0$.

Now using the previous part of this problem, we have

$$t = x\sqrt{x^2 - 1} - 2\left(\frac{x}{2}\sqrt{x^2 - 1} - \frac{1}{2}\ln(x + \sqrt{x^2 - 1})\right) = \ln(x + \sqrt{x^2 - 1}).$$

c. Because $t = \ln(x + \sqrt{x^2 - 1})$, we have $e^t = x + \sqrt{x^2 - 1}$, so $e^{-t} = \frac{1}{x + \sqrt{x^2 - 1}} = \frac{1}{x + \sqrt{x^2 - 1}} \cdot \frac{x - \sqrt{x^2 - 1}}{x - \sqrt{x^2 - 1}} = x - \sqrt{x^2 - 1}$. Thus $e^t + e^{-t} = 2x$, so $x = \frac{e^t + e^{-t}}{2}$.

d. We have $y = \sqrt{x^2 - 1} = \sqrt{\frac{e^{2t} + 2 + e^{-2t}}{4} - \frac{4}{4}} = \sqrt{\frac{e^{2t} - 2 + e^{-2t}}{4}} = \sqrt{\left(\frac{e^t - e^{-t}}{2}\right)^2} = \frac{e^t - e^{-t}}{2}$.

Chapter Six Review

1

a. True. A vertical slice would lead to shells, while a horizontal slice would lead to either disks or washers.

b. True. In order to find position, you would also need to know either its initial position, or at least its position at some time.

c. True. If dV/dt is constant, then V is a linear function of time.

d. False. For example, when t goes from 2 to 3, the value of y goes from 3 to 4, which is not doubling.

e. False. It grows from A to $A \cdot e^{.1} \approx 1.10517A$, so the growth is about 10.517%.

f. False. For example, if $x = e$ and $y = 1$, this equation would imply that $\ln(e \cdot 1) = (\ln e)(\ln 1)$, which is not true because $1 \neq 0$.

g. True. $\sinh(\ln x) = \frac{e^{\ln x} - e^{-\ln x}}{2} = \frac{x - 1/x}{2} \cdot \frac{x}{x} = \frac{x^2 - 1}{2x}$.

2 The displacement is $\int_0^{1.5} 20\cos \pi t\,dt = \left(\frac{20}{\pi}\sin \pi t\right)\Big|_0^{1.5} = \frac{-20}{\pi}$.

3 The position $s(t)$ and the displacement are the same, because the projective started on the ground at position 0. $s(t) = \int_0^t v(x)\,dx = \int_0^t (20 - 10x)\,dx = \left(20x - 5x^2\right)\Big|_0^t = 20t - 5t^2$. Note that the projectile is moving up for $0 < t < 2$ and down for $2 < t < 4$. Thus the distance traveled is equal to the position for $0 < t < 2$, but for $2 < t < 4$ the distance traveled is $20 + (20 - (20t - 5t^2)) = 40 - 20t + 5t^2$.

4 $a(t) = -5$, so $v(t) = -5t + C$, and because $v(0) = 80$, we have $v(t) = 80 - 5t$. The position function $s(t) = \int v(t)\,dt = \int(80 - 5t)\,dt = 80t - 5t^2/2 + D$, and because $s(0) = 0$ we have $D = 0$. Thus, $s(t) = 80t - 5t^2/2$.

5

a. $v(t) = \int a(t)\,dt = \int 2\sin(\pi t/4)\,dt = \frac{-8}{\pi}\cos(\pi t/4) + C$, and because $v(0) = \frac{-8}{\pi}$, we have $C = 0$. Thus, $v(t) = \frac{-8}{\pi}\cos(\pi t/4)$.

$s(t) = \int v(t)\,dt = \int \frac{-8}{\pi}\cos(\pi t/4)\,dt = \frac{-32}{\pi^2}\sin(\pi t/4) + D$, and because $s(0) = 0$ we have $D = 0$. Thus, $s(t) = \frac{-32}{\pi^2}\sin(\pi t/4)$.

b. s is periodic with period 8, so we only consider $0 \le t \le 8$. There are critical numbers for s at $t = 2$ and $t = 6$. There is a maximum for s of $\frac{32}{\pi^2}$ at $t = 6$ and a minimum of $\frac{-32}{\pi^2}$ at $t = 2$.

c. The average velocity is $\frac{1}{8}\int_0^8 \frac{-8}{\pi}\cos(\pi t/4)\,dt = \frac{-4}{\pi^2}\left(\sin(\pi t/4)\right)\Big|_0^8 = 0$.

The average position is $\frac{1}{8}\int_0^8 \frac{-32}{\pi^2}\sin(\pi t/4)\,dt = \frac{16}{\pi^3}\left(\cos(\pi t/4)\right)\Big|_0^8 = 0$.

6

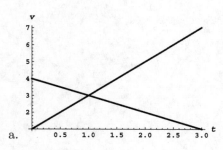

a.

b. Anna runs $\int_0^1 (2t + 1)\,dt = \left(t^2 + t\right)\Big|_0^1 = 2$ miles, while Benny runs $\int_0^1 (4 - t)\,dt = \left(4t - t^2/2\right)\Big|_0^1 = (4 - 1/2) = 3.5$ miles. Note that the area under Anna's graph from 0 to 1 is smaller than the corresponding area under Benny's graph.

c. $s_A(t) = t^2 + t$, which is 6 for $t = 2$. $s_B(t) = 4t - t^2/2$ which is 6 for $t = 2$, so they both take exactly two hours to run 6 miles. At $t = 2$, both velocity function have the same area under them, namely 6.

7

a. For $0 \le t \le 8$ we have $R'(t) = 4t^{1/3}$, so $R(t) = 3t^{4/3} + C$, but $C = 0$, so $R(t) = 3t^{4/3}$.

b. Note that $R(8) = 48$, so for $t > 8$, $R(t) = 48 + \int_8^t 2\,dx = 48 + 2(t - 8)$.

We have $R(t) = \begin{cases} 3t^{4/3} & \text{if } 0 \le t \le 8; \\ 2t + 32 & \text{if } t > 8. \end{cases}$

c. The fuel runs out when $150 = 48 + 2(t - 8)$, which occurs for $t = 59$.

8 Let $V'(t) = -\frac{15}{t+1}$. Then $V(t) = -15\ln(t + 1) + C$, and because $V(0) = 75$, we have $C = 75$. Thus, $V(t) = 75 - 15\ln(t + 1)$. This is 0 when $\ln(t + 1) = 5$, which occurs when $t = e^5 - 1 \approx 147.413$ hours, so don't try to hold your breath while the tank is emptying.

9

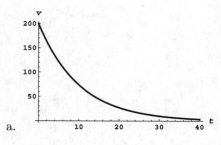

a.

b. The velocity is 50 when $200e^{-t/10} = 50$, which occurs when $e^{t/10} = 4$, so when $t = 10\ln 4$.

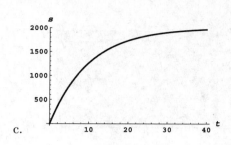

c.

The position is given by $\int_0^t 200e^{-x/10}\,dx =$
$-2000e^{-x/10}\,\Big|_0^t = 2000(1 - e^{-t/10})$.

d. No. $\lim_{t \to \infty} s(t) = 2000 < 2500$.

10

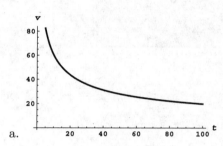

a.

b.

The position is given by $\int_0^t 200/\sqrt{x+1}\,dx =$
$\left(400\sqrt{x+1}\right)\,\Big|_0^t = 400(\sqrt{t+1} - 1)$.

c. Yes, the position is 2500 when $400\sqrt{t+1} = 2900$, which occurs when $t + 1 = \left(\frac{29}{4}\right)^2$, so
$t = \left(\frac{29}{4}\right)^2 - 1 = 51.5625$.

11

a. Tom's position function is given by
$\int_0^t 20e^{-2x}\,dx = \left(-10e^{-2x}\right)\,\Big|_0^t = 10(1 - e^{-2t})$.
Sue's position is given by $\int_0^t 15e^{-x}\,dx =$
$\left(-15e^{-x}\right)\,\Big|_0^t = 15(1 - e^{-t})$.

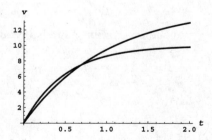

b. We are looking for t so that $10(1 - e^{-2t}) = 15(1 - e^{-t})$, which occurs when $10(e^{-t})^2 - 15e^{-t} + 5 = 0$, or
$2u^2 - 3u + 1 = 0$ where $u = e^{-t}$. This quadratic factors as $(2u - 1)(u - 1)$, so if $e^{-t} = 1$ or $e^{-t} = 1/2$,
so $t = 0$ or $t = \ln 2$.

c. Sue takes the lead and doesn't relinquish it at $t = \ln 2$.

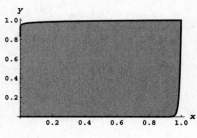

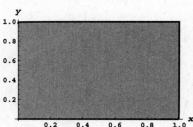

$\int_0^1 (x^{1/p} - x^p)\, dx$ is evaluated as

12 $\left(\frac{p}{p+1} x^{(p+1)/p} - \frac{1}{p+1} x^{p+1} \right) \Big|_0^1 = \frac{p}{p+1} - \frac{1}{p+1} = $ $\frac{p-1}{p+1}$. For $p = 100$ the area is $99/101$, and for $p = 1000$ the area is $999/1001$.

13 These two curves meet when $4x = x\sqrt{25 - x^2}$, so at $x = 0$ and when $4 = \sqrt{25 - x^2}$, which occurs for $x = 3$. A plot of the region is

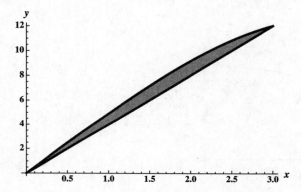

On $[0, 3]$, we have $x\sqrt{25 - x^2} > 4x$ (for example check at $x = 1$), so the area is

$$A = \int_0^3 \left(x\sqrt{25 - x^2} - 4x \right) dx.$$

Note that $\int_0^3 -4x\, dx = -2x^2 \Big|_0^3 = -18$. For the first term, use the substitution $u = 25 - x^2$, so that $du = -2x\, dx$ and the integration bounds become $u = 25$ to $u = 16$. Then we have

$$A = -\frac{1}{2} \int_{25}^{16} u^{1/2}\, du - 18 = -\frac{1}{2} \left(\frac{2}{3} u^{3/2} \right) \Big|_{25}^{16} - 18 = -\frac{64}{3} + \frac{125}{3} - 18 = \frac{7}{3}.$$

14 The area of R_1 is

$$\int_0^{8/5} (16 - x^2)\, dx + \int_{8/5}^3 (16 - x^2 - (5x - 8))\, dx = \left(16x - x^3/3 \right) \Big|_0^{8/5} + \left(24x - 5x^2/2 - x^3/3 \right) \Big|_{8/5}^3 = \frac{341}{10} = 34.1.$$

The area of R_2 is

$$\int_{8/5}^3 (5x - 8)\, dx + \int_3^4 (16 - x^2)\, dx = \left(5x^2/2 - 8x \right) \Big|_{8/5}^3 + \left(16x - x^3/3 \right) \Big|_3^4 = \frac{257}{30}.$$

15 Note that (by inspection followed by an easy calculation) $2\sqrt{x}$ and $x(x-3)$ meet at $(0,0)$ and at $(4,4)$. Also, $2\sqrt{x}$ and $3-x$ meet at $(1,2)$ and $x(x-3)$ and $3-x$ meet at $(-1,4)$ and $(3,0)$. So the area of R_1 is

$$\int_{-1}^{0} ((3-x) - (x^2 - 3x))\,dx + \int_{0}^{1} (3 - x - 2\sqrt{x})\,dx$$

$$= \int_{-1}^{0} (3 + 2x - x^2)\,dx + \int_{0}^{1} (3 - x - 2\sqrt{x})\,dx$$

$$= (3x + x^2 - x^3/3)\Big|_{-1}^{0} + \left(3x - x^2/2 - 4x^{3/2}/3\right)\Big|_{0}^{1}$$

$$= 0 - \left(-3 + 1 + \frac{1}{3}\right) + \left(3 - \frac{1}{2} - \frac{4}{3}\right) - 0 = \frac{17}{6}.$$

The area of R_2 is

$$\int_{0}^{1} (2\sqrt{x} - (x^2 - 3x))\,dx + \int_{1}^{3} ((3-x) - (x^2 - 3x))\,dx$$

$$= \int_{0}^{1} (2\sqrt{x} - x^2 + 3x)\,dx + \int_{1}^{3} (3 + 2x - x^2)\,dx$$

$$= \left(4x^{3/2}/3 - x^3/3 + 3x^2/2\right)\Big|_{0}^{1} + (3x + x^2 - x^3/3)\Big|_{1}^{3}$$

$$= \left(\frac{4}{3} - \frac{1}{3} + \frac{3}{2}\right) - 0 + (9 + 9 - 9) - \left(3 + 1 - \frac{1}{3}\right) = \frac{47}{6}.$$

The area of R_3 is

$$\int_{1}^{3} (2\sqrt{x} - (3-x))\,dx + \int_{3}^{4} (2\sqrt{x} - (x^2 - 3x)\,dx$$

$$= \left(4x^{3/2}/3 - 3x + x^2/2\right)\Big|_{1}^{3} + \left(4x^{3/2}/3 - x^3/3 + 3x^2/2\right)\Big|_{3}^{4}$$

$$= \left(4\sqrt{3} - 9 + \frac{9}{2}\right) - \left(\frac{4}{3} - 3 + \frac{1}{2}\right) + \left(\frac{32}{3} - \frac{64}{3} + 24\right) - \left(4\sqrt{3} - 9 + \frac{27}{2}\right) = \frac{11}{2}.$$

16 $\displaystyle \int_{0}^{2\pi} (x - \sin x)\,dx = \left(x^2/2 + \cos x\right)\Big|_{0}^{2\pi}$

$= 2\pi^2 + 1 - (0 + 1) = 2\pi^2.$

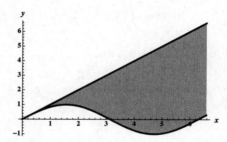

17

$$\int_0^2 x^2 \, dx + \int_2^4 (x^2 - 2x^2 + 4x) \, dx$$

$$= (x^3/3) \Big|_0^2 + (-x^3/3 + 2x^2) \Big|_2^4$$

$$= (8/3) + -64/3 + 32 - (-8/3 + 8) = 8.$$

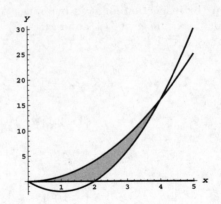

18

$$\int_0^1 (1 - \sqrt{x})^2 \, dx = \int_0^1 (1 - 2\sqrt{x} + x) \, dx$$

$$= \left(x - 4x^{3/2}/3 + x^2/2 \right) \Big|_0^1 = \frac{1}{6}.$$

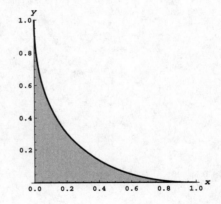

19

$$\int_0^2 (x/2 - x/6) \, dx + \int_2^3 (2 - x/2 - x/6) \, dx$$

$$= (x^2/6) \Big|_0^2 + (2x - x^2/3) \Big|_2^3$$

$$= \frac{2}{3} + (6 - 3) - (4 - 4/3) = 1.$$

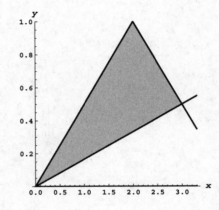

20

a.

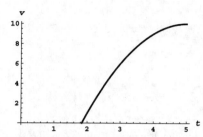

The diagram shown is for $a \approx 1.9$ and $c \approx 5$.

b. $R(x) = \int_a^x (f(t) - g(t))\, dt$, and $R'(x) = f(x) - g(x)$.

21 $A(a) = \int_0^{\sqrt[3]{a}} \left(\sqrt{x/a} - x^2/a \right) dx = \left(\frac{2}{3} \frac{x^{3/2}}{\sqrt{a}} - \frac{x^3}{3a} \right) \Big|_0^{\sqrt[3]{a}} = \frac{1}{3}$.

22

a. $V = \pi \int_0^4 (\sqrt{4-y})^2\, dy = \pi \int_0^4 (4-y)\, dy = \pi \left(4y - y^2/2 \right) \Big|_0^4 = \pi(16 - 8 - (0 - 0)) = 8\pi$.

b. $V = 2\pi \int_0^2 x(4 - x^2)\, dx = 2\pi \int_0^2 (4x - x^3)\, dx = 2\pi \left(2x^2 - x^4/4 \right) \Big|_0^2 = 2\pi \left(8 - 4 - (0 - 0) \right) = 8\pi$.

23 From $x = 0$ to $x = 1$ the area function is $A(x) = (\sqrt{x})^2 = x$, while from $x = 1$ to $x = 2$ it is $A(x) = (2 - x)^2$.

$$\int_0^1 x\, dx + \int_1^2 (2-x)^2\, dx = \frac{1}{2}x^2 \Big|_0^1 - \frac{1}{3}(2-x)^3 \Big|_1^2 = \frac{1}{2} + \frac{1}{3} = \frac{5}{6}.$$

24 The region is the same as in the previous exercise. From $x = 0$ to $x = 1$ the slices are semicircles with diameter $\sqrt{x}$, so their area is $\frac{\pi(\sqrt{x})^2}{8} = \frac{\pi}{8}x$. From $x = 1$ to $x = 2$, the slices are semicircles with diameter $2 - x$, so their area is $\frac{\pi}{8}(2 - x)^2$. Thus by the general slicing method, the volume is

$$\frac{\pi}{8} \left(\int_0^1 x\, dx + \int_1^2 (2-x)^2\, dx \right) = \frac{\pi}{8} \left(\frac{1}{2}x^2 \Big|_0^1 - \frac{1}{3}(2-x)^3 \Big|_1^2 \right) = \frac{\pi}{8} \left(\frac{1}{2} + \frac{1}{3} \right) = \frac{5\pi}{48}.$$

25 Because the cross sections are parallel to the x-axis, solve for x to get $x = y^2$ and $x = 2 - y$. Then from $y = 0$ to $y = 1$ the area function is $A(y) = (y^2)^2 = y^4$ and from $y = 1$ to $y = 2$ it is $A(y) = (2 - y)^2$. The by the general slicing method, the volume is

$$\int_0^1 y^4\, dy + \int_1^2 (2-y)^2\, dy = \frac{y^5}{5} \Big|_0^1 - \frac{1}{3}(2-y)^3 \Big|_1^2 = \frac{1}{5} + \frac{1}{3} = \frac{8}{15}.$$

26

$$V = \pi \int_0^2 ((-x^2 + 2x + 2)^2 - (2x^2 - 4x + 2)^2)\, dx = \pi \int_0^2 (24x - 24x^2 + 12x^3 - 3x^4)\, dx$$

$$= \pi \left(12x^2 - 8x^3 + 3x^4 - 3x^5/5 \right) \Big|_0^2 = \frac{64\pi}{5}.$$

27

a. $V = 2\pi \int_0^1 x((1+\sqrt{x}) - (1-\sqrt{x}))\, dx = 4\pi \int_0^1 x^{3/2}\, dx = 4\pi \cdot \frac{2x^{5/2}}{5}\Big|_0^1 = \frac{8\pi}{5}.$

b. $V = \pi \int_0^2 (1^2 - ((1-y)^2)^2)\, dy = \pi \int_0^2 (1 - (y^4 - 4y^3 + 6y^2 - 4y + 1))\, dy = \pi \int_0^2 (-y^4 + 4y^3 - 6y^2 + 4y)\, dy =$
$\pi \left(-\frac{y^5}{5} + y^4 - 2y^3 + 2y^2\right)\Big|_0^2 = \frac{8\pi}{5}.$

28 $V = \pi \int_0^{(\ln 2)/2} ((2e^{-x})^2 - (e^x)^2)\, dx = \pi \left(-2e^{-2x} - \frac{1}{2}e^{2x}\right)\Big|_0^{(\ln 2)/2} = \frac{\pi}{2}.$

29 It appears to be easiest to use shells, because then we won't have to split the integral up, and also the functions will integrate more easily. Solving for y we have $y = e^{x^2}$ and $y = e^{2-x^2}$. The height of each shell is then $e^{2-x^2} - e^{x^2}$ and the volume is

$$2\pi \int_0^1 x(e^{2-x^2} - e^{x^2})\, dx = 2\pi \left(-\frac{1}{2}e^{2-x^2} - \frac{1}{2}e^{x^2}\right)\Big|_0^1 = \pi(-e - e + e^2 + 1) = \pi(e^2 - 2e + 1) = \pi(e-1)^2.$$

30 Using washers, we have

$$\pi \int_0^{\pi/3} (4 - \sec^2 x)\, dx = \pi (4x - \tan x)\Big|_0^{\pi/3} = \pi \left(4\pi/3 - \sqrt{3} - (0-0)\right) = 4\pi^2/3 - \pi\sqrt{3}.$$

31 We use the shell method. $V = 2\pi \int_0^{\sqrt{3}/2} \frac{x}{\sqrt{1-x^2}}\, dx.$ Let $u = 1 - x^2$ so that $du = -2x\, dx$. Substituting gives $V = 2\pi \int_1^{1/4} \frac{-1}{2\sqrt{u}}\, du = \pi \int_{1/4}^1 u^{-1/2}\, du = 2\pi \sqrt{u}\Big|_{1/4}^1 = 2\pi \left(1 - \frac{1}{2}\right) = \pi.$

32 Use the shell method. Then each shell has height $4 - x^2$ and the radius of the shell at x is $x - (-2) = x + 2$. The volume is then

$$V = 2\pi \int_{-2}^2 (x+2)(4 - x^2)\, dx = 2\pi \int_{-2}^2 (-x^3 - 2x^2 + 4x + 8)\, dx$$

$$= 2\pi \left(-\frac{x^4}{4} - \frac{2}{3}x^3 + 2x^2 + 8x\right)\Big|_{-2}^2 = 2\pi \left(-\frac{32}{3} + 32\right) = \frac{128\pi}{3}.$$

33 We use the disk method. The radius of each disk is $4 - (x-2)^2 = 4x - x^2$, so the volume is

$$V = \pi \int_0^4 (4x - x^2)^2\, dx = \pi \int_0^4 (x^4 - 8x^3 + 16x^2)\, dx$$

$$= \pi \left(\frac{x^5}{5} - 2x^4 + \frac{16}{3}x^3\right)\Big|_0^4 = \pi \left(\frac{1024}{5} - 512 + \frac{1024}{3}\right) = \frac{512\pi}{15}.$$

34 The curves intersect when $6x = x^2 + 5$, or when $x^2 - 6x + 5 = (x-1)(x-5) = 0$, thus at $x = 1$ and $x = 5$. To revolve about the line $y = -1$, we use the washer method; the outer radius of each washer is $6x - (-1) = 6x + 1$ and the inner radius is $x^2 + 5 - (-1) = x^2 + 6$. The volume is thus

$$V = \pi \int_1^5 ((6x+1)^2 - (x^2+6)^2)\, dx = \pi \int_1^5 (-x^4 + 24x^2 + 12x - 35)\, dx$$

$$= \pi \left(-\frac{x^5}{5} + 8x^3 + 6x^2 - 35x\right)\Big|_1^5 = \pi \left(-625 + 1000 + 150 - 175 + \frac{1}{5} - 8 - 6 + 35\right)$$

$$= \pi \left(371 + \frac{1}{5}\right) = \frac{1856\pi}{5}.$$

To revolve about the line $x = -1$, we use the shell method. The height of each shell is $6x - (x^2 + 5) = 6x - x^2 - 5$, and the radius at x is $x - (-1) = x + 1$. The volume is thus

$$V = 2\pi \int_1^5 (x+1)(6x - x^2 - 5)\,dx = 2\pi \int_1^5 (-x^3 + 5x^2 + x - 5)\,dx = 2\pi \left(-\frac{x^4}{4} + \frac{5}{3}x^2 + \frac{1}{2}x^2 - 5x \right)\Big|_1^5$$

$$= 2\pi \left(-\frac{625}{4} + \frac{625}{3} + \frac{25}{2} - 25 + \frac{1}{4} - \frac{5}{3} - \frac{1}{2} + 5 \right) = \frac{256\pi}{3}.$$

35 The two non-horizontal lines intersect at $(2, 4)$. To revolve about $y = -2$, we use the shell method. First solve for x to obtain $x = \frac{y}{2}$ and $x = 6 - y$; then the height of each shell is $6 - y - \frac{y}{2} = 6 - \frac{3}{2}y$, and the radius at y is $y - (-2) = y + 2$. The volume is

$$2\pi \int_0^4 (y+2)\left(6 - \frac{3}{2}y \right)\,dy = 2\pi \int_0^4 \left(12 + 3y - \frac{3}{2}y^2 \right)\,dy = 2\pi \left(12y + \frac{3}{2}y^3 - \frac{1}{2}y^3 \right)\Big|_0^4 = 80\pi.$$

To revolve about $x = -2$, we use the washer method. With the equations above, the outer radius of each asher is $6 - y - (-2) = 8 - y$ and the inner radius is $\frac{y}{2} - (-2) = 2 + \frac{y}{2}$. The volume is

$$V = \pi \int_0^4 \left((8-y)^2 - \left(2 + \frac{y}{2} \right)^2 \right)\,dy = \pi \int_0^4 \left(\frac{3}{4}y^2 - 18y + 60 \right)\,dy$$

$$= \pi \left(\frac{1}{4}y^3 - 9y^2 + 60y \right)\Big|_0^4 = \pi(16 - 144 + 240) = 112\pi.$$

36

a. $A = \displaystyle\int_0^2 ((4+y) - (y^2 + 2))\,dy.$

b. $V = 2\pi \displaystyle\int_0^2 y\left[(4+y) - (y^2 + 2) \right]\,dy.$

c. $V = \pi \displaystyle\int_0^2 \left[(4+y)^2 - (y^2 + 2)^2 \right]\,dy.$

d. $V = \displaystyle\int_0^2 A(y)\,dy = \frac{\pi}{2} \int_0^2 \left(\frac{(4+y) - (y^2 + 2)}{2} \right)^2 dy.$

37

a. $V_x = \pi \displaystyle\int_1^2 \frac{1}{x^2}\,dx = \pi\left(-1/x \right)\Big|_1^2 = \frac{\pi}{2}.$

   $V_y = 2\pi \displaystyle\int_1^2 x \cdot x^{-1}\,dx = 2\pi$, so $V_y > V_x.$

b. $V_x = \pi \displaystyle\int_1^4 \frac{1}{x^6}\,dx = \pi\left(-x^{-5}/5 \right)\Big|_1^4 = \frac{\pi}{5}\left(1 - \frac{1}{1024} \right).$

   $V_y = 2\pi \displaystyle\int_1^4 x \cdot x^{-3}\,dx = 2\pi\left(-1/x \right)\Big|_1^4 = \frac{3\pi}{2}$, so $V_y > V_x.$

c. $V_x = \pi \displaystyle\int_1^a \frac{1}{x^{2p}}\,dx = \begin{cases} \frac{\pi}{1-2p}(-1 + a^{1-2p}) & \text{if } p \neq 1/2, \\ \pi \ln a & \text{if } p = 1/2. \end{cases}$

d. $V_y = 2\pi \displaystyle\int_1^a \frac{1}{x^{p-1}}\,dx = \begin{cases} \frac{2\pi(a^{2-p}-1)}{2-p} & \text{if } p \neq 2, \\ 2\pi \ln a & \text{if } p = 2. \end{cases}$

e. Using part d, let $h = 2 - p$, and note that V_y is continuous. So $\lim_{h \to 0} V_y = \lim_{p \to 2} \frac{2\pi(a^{2-p}-1)}{2-p} = \lim_{h \to 0} \frac{2\pi(a^h-1)}{h} = 2\pi \ln a$, so $\lim_{h \to 0} \frac{(a^h-1)}{h} = \ln a$. A similar calculation can be done with the result of part c.

f. No, $V_y > V_x$ for all values of a and p, because $\frac{1}{x^{2p}} < \frac{1}{x^{p-1}}$ for $x > 1$ and $p > 0$.

38 Substituting x for y^2 in the equation $x = (2 - y^2)^2$, we obtain $x = (2 - x)^2$, which can be written as $x = 4 - 4x + x^2$ or $x^2 - 5x + 4 = (x - 4)(x - 1) = 0$, so the curves intersect at $x = 4$ and $x = 1$. The points of intersection are $(1, \pm 1)$ and $(4, \pm 2)$. It will be easier to integrate with respect to y. Note that between $y = -2$ and $y = -1$ and then again between $y = 1$ and $y = 2$ we have $y^2 > (2 - y^2)^2$, while between $y = -1$ and $y = 1$ the reverse is true. Thus the area is given by

$$A = \int_{-2}^{-1} (y^2 - (2 - y^2)^2)\, dy + \int_{-1}^{1} ((2 - y^2)^2) - y^2)\, dy + \int_{1}^{2} (y^2 - (2 - y^2)^2)\, dy$$

$$= \int_{-2}^{-1} (-y^4 + 5y^2 - 4)\, dy + \int_{-1}^{1} (y^4 - 5y^2 + 4)\, dy + \int_{1}^{2} (-y^4 + 5y^2 - 4)\, dy$$

$$= \left(-\frac{y^5}{5} + \frac{5y^3}{3} - 4y \right) \Big|_{-2}^{-1} + \left(\frac{y^5}{5} - \frac{5y^3}{3} + 4y \right) \Big|_{-1}^{1} + \left(-\frac{y^5}{5} + \frac{5y^3}{3} - 4y \right) \Big|_{1}^{2}$$

$$= \left(\frac{38}{15} - \frac{16}{15} \right) + \left(\frac{38}{15} + \frac{38}{15} \right) + \left(\frac{-16}{15} + \frac{38}{15} \right) = \frac{120}{15} = 8.$$

39 We use disks when revolving about the x-axis. The volume is

$$\pi \int_{0}^{1} c^2 x^2 (1 - x)^2\, dx = \pi c^2 \int_{0}^{1} (x^2 - 2x^3 + x^4)\, dx = \pi c^2 \left(\frac{1}{3}x^3 - \frac{1}{2}x^4 + \frac{1}{5}x^5 \right) \Big|_{0}^{1} = \pi c^2 \left(\frac{1}{3} - \frac{1}{2} + \frac{1}{5} \right) = \frac{\pi c^2}{30}.$$

We use shells when revolving about the y-axis. The volume is

$$2\pi \int_{0}^{1} x \cdot cx(1 - x)\, dx = 2\pi c \int_{0}^{1} (x^2 - x^3)\, dx = 2\pi c \left(\frac{1}{3}x^3 - \frac{1}{4}x^4 \right) \Big|_{0}^{1} = \frac{\pi c}{6}.$$

These are equal when $\frac{\pi c^2}{30} = \frac{\pi c}{6}$, which for $c \neq 0$ occurs when $c = 5$.

40 $L = \int_{-2}^{2} \sqrt{1 + 4}\, dx = \sqrt{5}(2 - (-2)) = 4\sqrt{5}$.

41 $L = \int_{\sqrt{2}}^{\sqrt{5}} \sqrt{1 + \frac{1}{x^2 - 1}}\, dx = \int_{\sqrt{2}}^{\sqrt{5}} \frac{x}{\sqrt{x^2 - 1}}\, dx$. Let $u = x^2 - 1$ so that $du = 2x\, dx$. Substituting gives $\frac{1}{2} \int_{1}^{4} u^{-1/2}\, du = (\sqrt{u}) \Big|_{1}^{4} = 2 - 1 = 1$.

42 Note that $y' = x^2/2 - 1/(2x^2)$, so $1 + y'^2 = (x^2/2 + 1/(2x^2))^2$. $L = \int_{1}^{2} \sqrt{1 + y'^2}\, dy = \int_{1}^{2} (x^2/2 + 1/(2x^2))\, dx = (x^3/6 - 1/(2x)) \Big|_{1}^{2} = \frac{17}{12}$.

43 Note that $y' = 1/(2\sqrt{x}) - \sqrt{x}/2$, so $1 + y'^2 = (1/(2\sqrt{x}) + \sqrt{x}/2)^2$. $L = \int_{1}^{3} \sqrt{1 + y'^2}\, dy = \int_{1}^{3} 1/(2\sqrt{x}) + \sqrt{x}/2\, dx = (\sqrt{x} + x^{3/2}/3) \Big|_{1}^{3} = 2\sqrt{3} - 4/3$.

44 Note that $y' = x^2 + 2x + 1 + \frac{-4}{(4x+4)^2} = (x + 1)^2 - \frac{1}{4(x+1)^2}$, so $L = \int_{0}^{4} \sqrt{\left((x+1)^2 - \frac{1}{4(x+1)^2} \right)^2 + 1}\, dx$. Let $u = x + 1$, so that $L = \int_{1}^{5} \sqrt{\left(u^2 - \frac{1}{(2u)^2} \right)^2 + 1}\, du = \int_{1}^{5} u^2 + \frac{1}{(2u)^2}\, du = (u^3/3 - 1/(4u)) \Big|_{1}^{5} = \frac{623}{15}$.

45 Note that $y' = 1/x$, so $1 + y'^2 = \frac{x^2+1}{x^2}$, and $\sqrt{1+y'^2} = \frac{\sqrt{x^2+1}}{x}$.

So $L = \int_1^b \frac{\sqrt{x^2+1}}{x}\, dx = \left(\sqrt{x^2+1} - \ln\left(\frac{1+\sqrt{x^2+1}}{x}\right)\right)\Big|_1^b = \sqrt{b^2+1} - \sqrt{2} + \ln\left(\frac{(\sqrt{b^2+1}-1)(1+\sqrt{2})}{b}\right)$. Using a computer algebra system, we see that this has value 2 for $b \approx 2.715$.

46

a. $S = 2\pi \int_0^2 (x^3/3)\sqrt{1+x^4}\, dx$. Let $u = 1 + x^4$, so that $du = 4x^3\, dx$. Substituting gives $\frac{\pi}{6}\int_1^{17} u^{1/2}\, du = \frac{\pi}{9}\left(u^{3/2}\right)\Big|_1^{17} = \frac{\pi}{9}\left(17^{3/2}-1\right)$.

b. $V = 2\pi \int_0^2 x(x^3/3)\, dx = 2\pi \int_0^2 x^4/3\, dx = 2\pi\left(x^5/15\right)\Big|_0^2 = 2\pi(32/15 - 0) = 64\pi/15$.

c. $V = \pi \int_0^2 x^6/9\, dx = \pi\left(x^7/63\right)\Big|_0^2 = \pi(128/63) = 128\pi/63$.

47

a. $S = 2\pi \int_0^3 \sqrt{3x-x^2}\sqrt{1 + \frac{(3-2x)^2}{4(3x-x^2)}}\, dx = 2\pi \int_0^3 \sqrt{3x-x^2}\sqrt{\frac{12x-4x^2+9-12x+4x^2}{4(3x-x^2)}}\, dx = \pi \int_0^3 3\, dx = 3\pi(3-0) = 9\pi$.

b. $V = \pi \int_0^3 (3x-x^2)\, dx = \pi\left(3x^2/2 - x^3/3\right)\Big|_0^3 = \pi(27/2 - 9) = 9\pi/2$.

48 Consider the line $y = x/2$ over the interval $[0, 8]$. If we revolve this around the x-axis, we generate a cone with radius 4 and height 8. The surface of this cone is $2\pi \int_0^8 (x/2)\sqrt{1+1/4}\, dx = \sqrt{5}\pi/2\left(x^2/2\right)\Big|_0^8 = 16\sqrt{5}\pi$.

49

a. $S = 2\pi \int_1^2 \left(\frac{x^4}{2} + \frac{1}{16x^2}\right)\sqrt{1 + (2x^3 - (1/8x^3))^2}\, dx =$
$2\pi \int_1^2 \left(\frac{x^4}{2} + \frac{1}{16x^2}\right)\sqrt{1 + (4x^6 - 1/2 + (64/x^6))}\, dx = 2\pi \int_1^2 \left(\frac{x^4}{2} + \frac{1}{16x^2}\right)\sqrt{4x^6 + 1/2 + 64/x^6}\, dx =$
$2\pi \int_1^2 \left(\frac{x^4}{2} + \frac{1}{16x^2}\right)\sqrt{(2x^3 + (1/8x^3))^2}\, dx = 2\pi \int_1^2 \left(\frac{x^4}{2} + \frac{1}{16x^2}\right)\left(2x^3 + \frac{1}{8x^3}\right)\, dx = 2\pi \int_1^2 (x^7 + x/16 +$
$x/8 + x^{-5}/128)\, dx = 2\pi \int_1^2 (x^7 + 3x/16 + x^{-5}/128)\, dx = 2\pi\left(x^8/8 + 3x^2/32 - x^{-4}/512\right)\Big|_1^2 = 2\pi((32 +$
$3/8 - 1/8192) - (1/8 + 3/32 - 1/512)) = \frac{263439\pi}{4096}$.

b. Using the fact that $\sqrt{1 + f'(x)^2} = 2x^3 + 1/(8x^3)$ which was discovered during the previous calculation, we have $L = \int_1^2 (2x^3 + x^{-3}/8)\, dx = \left(x^4/2 - x^{-2}/16\right)\Big|_1^2 = (8 - 1/64) - (1/2 - 1/16) = \frac{483}{64}$.

c. $V = 2\pi \int_1^2 (x^5/2 + x^{-1}/16)\, dx = 2\pi\left(x^6/12 + (1/16)\ln x\right)\Big|_1^2 = 2\pi(16/3 + (\ln 2)/16 - (1/12 + 0)) = \frac{21\pi}{2} + \frac{\pi \ln 2}{8}$.

d. $V = \pi \int_1^2 (x^4/2 + x^{-2}/16)^2\, dx = \pi \int_1^2 (x^8/4 + x^2/16 + x^{-4}/256)\, dx = \pi\left(x^9/36 + x^3/48 - x^{-3}/768\right)\Big|_1^2 = \pi(512/36 + 8/48 - 1/6144 - (1/36 + 1/48 - 1/768)) = \frac{264341\pi}{18432}$.

50 $m = \int_0^9 (3 + 2\sqrt{x})\, dx = \left(3x + 4x^{3/2}/3\right)\Big|_0^9 = 63$ gm.

51 $m = \int_0^3 150 e^{-x/3}\, dx = \left(-450 e^{-x/3}\right)\Big|_0^3 = 450(1 - e^{-1})$ gm.

52 $m = \int_0^2 dx + \int_2^4 2\, dx + \int_4^6 4\, dx = 2 + 4 + 8 = 14.$

53

a. Because $50 = \int_0^{.2} kx\, dx = \dfrac{kx^2}{2}\Big|_0^{0.2} = \dfrac{k}{50}$, we must have $k = 2500$.

$$W = \int_{0.2}^{0.7} 2500x\, dx = 1250x^2\Big|_{0.2}^{0.7} = 562.5 \text{ J.}$$

b. $f(0.2) = 0.2k = 50$, so $k = 250$, and thus

$$W = \int_{0.2}^{0.7} 250x\, dx = 125x^2\Big|_{0.2}^{0.7} = 56.25 \text{ J.}$$

54 $W = \int_0^6 \pi\rho g \cdot 16(6 - y)\, dy = 16\pi\rho g\left(6y - y^2/2\right)\Big|_0^6 = 288\pi\rho g \approx 8,866,830$ N.

55 Orient the semicircle so that the center is at the point $(0, 20)$. Then the force is given by $\int_0^{20} \rho g(20 - y)(2)\sqrt{40y - y^2}\, dy$. Let $u = 40y - y^2$ so that $du = (40 - 2y)\, dy$. Then we have $\rho g \int_0^{400} u^{1/2}\, du = \rho g\left(\frac{2}{3} u^{3/2}\right)\Big|_0^{400} \approx 5.2 \times 10^7$.

56 Let $u = 4e^x + 6$ so that $du = 4e^x\, dx$. Then we have $\frac{1}{4}\int \frac{1}{u}\, du = \frac{1}{4}\ln|u| + C = \frac{1}{4}\ln(4e^x + 6) + C$.

57 Let $u = \ln x$ so that $du = \frac{1}{x}\, dx$. Then we have $\int_2^8 \frac{1}{u}\, du = (\ln u)\Big|_2^8 = \ln 4$.

58 Let $u = \sqrt{x}$ so that $du = \frac{1}{2\sqrt{x}}\, dx$. Then we have $2\int_1^2 10^u\, du = 2\left(10^u/(\ln 10)\right)\Big|_1^2 = \frac{2}{\ln 10}\cdot 90 = \frac{180}{\ln 10}$.

59 Let $u = x^2 + 8x + 25$ so that $du = (2x + 8)\, dx = 2(x + 4)\, dx$. Then we have $\frac{1}{2}\int \frac{1}{u}\, du = \frac{1}{2}\ln|u| + C = \frac{1}{2}\ln(x^2 + 8x + 25) + C$.

60 $\int_{\ln 2}^{\ln 3} \frac{\cosh s}{\sinh s}\, ds = (\ln(\sinh s))\Big|_{\ln 2}^{\ln 3} = \ln(4/3) - \ln(3/4) = \ln(16/9)$.

61 $\int \frac{dx}{\sqrt{x^2 - 9}} = \cosh^{-1}(x/3) + C = \ln(x + \sqrt{x^2 - 9}) + C$.

62 Let $u = e^x$ so that $du = e^x\, dx$. Then we have $\int \frac{du}{\sqrt{u^2 + 4}} = \sinh^{-1}(u/2) + C = \sinh^{-1}(e^x/2) + C$.

63 Let $u = x^3$ so that $du = 3x^2\, dx$. Substituting gives $\frac{1}{3}\int_0^1 \frac{du}{3^2 - u^2} = \frac{1}{9}\left(\tanh^{-1}(u/3)\right)\Big|_0^1 = \frac{1}{9}\tanh^{-1}(1/3) \approx 0.0385$.

64 Because the half-life is 1500 years, we know that $k = \frac{\ln 2}{1500}$. We are seeking t so that $.7y_0 = y_0 e^{-kt}$, so $\ln(.7) = -kt$, and thus $t = \frac{-\ln(.7)}{k} = \frac{-\ln(.7)\cdot 1500}{\ln 2} \approx 771.86$ years ago.

65 Growth is modeled by $p(t) = 150,000 e^{kt}$ where $k = \ln(1.04)$. The population reaches $1,000,000$ when $1,000,000 = 150,000 e^{\ln(1.04)t}$, or when $\ln(20/3) = \ln(1.04)t$, so when $t = \frac{\ln(20/3)}{\ln(1.04)} \approx 48.37$ years.

66

   a. The balance at time t years is given by $1500(1.054)^t$.

   b. The balance doubles when $(1.054)^t = 2$, which occurs for $t = \frac{\ln 2}{\ln 1.054} \approx 13.18$ years.

   c. The balance reaches \$5000 when $5000 = 1500(1.054)^t$, which occurs when $t = \frac{\ln(10/3)}{\ln(1.054)} \approx 22.89$ years.

67 The domain of f is the set of all real numbers. Note that $\lim_{x\to\infty} f(x) = \infty$ and $\lim_{x\to-\infty} f(x) = 0$.

   $f'(x) = e^x(2x-1) + (x^2-x)e^x = e^x(x^2 + x - 1)$, which is 0 for $x = \frac{-1\pm\sqrt{5}}{2}$. Note that $f'(x) > 0$ on the interval $(-\infty, (-1-\sqrt{5})/2)$ and on $((-1+\sqrt{5})/2, \infty)$, so f is increasing on those intervals, while $f'(x) < 0$ (and so f is decreasing) on $((-1-\sqrt{5})/2, (-1+\sqrt{5})/2)$. There is a local maximum at $(-1-\sqrt{5})/2$ and a local minimum at $(-1+\sqrt{5})/2$.

   Note that $f''(x) = e^x(2x+1) + (x^2+x-1)e^x = e^x(x^2+3x)$, which is 0 for $x = 0$ and $x = -3$. $f''(x) > 0$ on $(-\infty, -3)$ and on $(0, \infty)$, so f is concave up on those intervals, while $f''(x) < 0$ on $(-3, 0)$, so f is concave down there. There are inflection points at $x = -3$ and at $x = 0$.

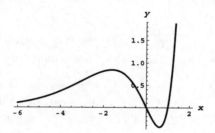

68 The domain of f is $(0, \infty)$, and has x-intercepts where $\ln x(1 - \ln x) = 0$, so at $x = 1$ and $x = e$. Note that $\lim_{x\to\infty} f(x) = -\infty$ and $\lim_{x\to 0^+} f(x) = -\infty$.

   $f'(x) = \frac{1 - 2\ln x}{x}$, which is 0 for $x = \sqrt{e}$. Note that $f'(x) > 0$ on the interval $(0, \sqrt{e})$, so f is increasing on that interval, while $f'(x) < 0$ (and so f is decreasing) on $(\sqrt{e}, \infty)$. There is a local maximum at $x = \sqrt{e}$.

   Note that $f''(x) = \frac{-2 - (1 - 2\ln x)}{x^2} = \frac{2\ln x - 3}{x^2}$, which is 0 for $x = e^{3/2}$. Note that $f''(x) < 0$ on $(0, e^{3/2})$, so f is concave down on that interval, while $f''(x) > 0$ on $(e^{3/2}, \infty)$ so f is concave up there. The point at $x = e^{3/2}$ is an inflection point.

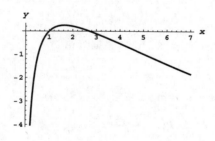

69

a.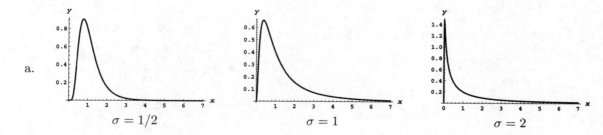

   It appears that $\lim_{x\to 0} f(x) = 0$.

b. Let $x = e^y$, so that $y = \ln x$ and as $x \to 0$ we have $y \to -\infty$. Then $\lim_{x \to 0} f(x) = \lim_{y \to -\infty} \frac{e^{-y^2/2\sigma^2}}{\sigma\sqrt{2\pi}e^y} = \frac{1}{\sigma\sqrt{2\pi}} \lim_{y \to -\infty} \frac{1}{e^y \cdot e^{y^2/2\sigma^2}} = 0$.

c. Write f as $f(x) = \frac{1}{\sigma\sqrt{2\pi}} \left(\frac{1}{xe^{(\ln^2 x)/2\sigma^2}} \right)$. Then

$$f'(x) = \frac{-1}{\sigma\sqrt{2\pi}} \left(\frac{1}{x^2 e^{(\ln^2 x)/\sigma^2}} \right) \left(e^{(\ln^2 x)/2\sigma^2} + xe^{(\ln^2 x)/2\sigma^2} \cdot \frac{1}{\sigma^2} \ln x \cdot \frac{1}{x} \right) =$$

$$\frac{-1}{\sigma\sqrt{2\pi}} \left(\frac{1}{x^2} \right) \left(1 + \frac{\ln x}{\sigma^2} \right).$$

This quantity is 0 only when $1 + \frac{\ln x}{\sigma^2} = 0$, which occurs for $x^* = e^{-\sigma^2}$, and this critical number yields a maximum.

d. $f(e^{-\sigma^2}) = \frac{1}{\sigma\sqrt{2\pi}} \left(\frac{1}{(e^{-\sigma^2}e^{(\ln^2(e^{-\sigma^2}))/2\sigma^2})} \right) = \frac{1}{\sigma\sqrt{2\pi}} \left(\frac{1}{e^{-\sigma^2}e^{\sigma^2/2}} \right) = \frac{e^{\sigma^2/2}}{\sigma\sqrt{2\pi}}$.

e. Let $g(\sigma) = \frac{e^{\sigma^2/2}}{\sigma\sqrt{2\pi}}$. Then $g'(\sigma) = \frac{e^{\frac{\sigma^2}{2}}(\sigma^2-1)}{\sqrt{2\pi}\sigma^2}$, so there is a critical point at $\sigma = 1$. Note that g is decreasing on $(0, 1)$ and increasing on $(1, \infty)$, so g has a minimum at $\sigma = 1$.

70 The equation of L_1 is $y = (2ap + b)(x - p) + f(p)$, which can be written $y = (2ap + b)x - ap^2 + c$. The equation of L_2 is $y = (2aq + b)(x - q) + f(q)$, which can be written $y = (2aq + b)x - aq^2 + c$. If we set these equal to each other and solve to find the point of intersection, we find $s = \frac{p+q}{2}$. Thus, the area $R_1 = \int_p^s f(x) - ((2ap + b)x - ap^2 + c) \, dx = \int_p^s ax^2 - 2apx + ap^2 \, dx = \left(ax^3/3 - apx^2 + ap^2x \right) \Big|_p^s = \frac{as^3}{3} - aps^2 + ap^2s - \frac{ap^3}{3} = \frac{a}{24}(q - p)^3$. Similarly, the area $R_2 = \int_s^q f(x) - ((2aq + b)x - aq^2 + c) \, dx = \int_s^q ax^2 - 2aqx + aq^2 \, dx = \left(ax^3/3 - aqx^2 + aq^2x \right) \Big|_s^q = \frac{aq^3}{3} - \frac{as^3}{3} + aqs^2 - aq^2s = \frac{aq^3}{3} - \frac{as}{3}(s^2 - 3qs + 3q^2) = \frac{a}{24}(q - p)^3$.

71

a. Because $\frac{d}{dx} \cosh x = \sinh x$ and $\frac{d}{dx} \sinh x = \cosh x$, we see that every nth derivative of $\cosh x$ where n is even is equal to $\cosh x$. So $\frac{d^6}{dx^6} \cosh x = \cosh x$.

b. $\frac{d}{dx} x \operatorname{sech} x = \operatorname{sech} x - x \operatorname{sech} x \tanh x = \operatorname{sech} x(1 - x \tanh x)$.

72 Note that the curves intersect when $\frac{8}{\cosh^2 x} = \cosh x$, which occurs when $\cosh^3 x = 8$ or $\cosh x = 2$, which is $x = \cosh^{-1}(2)$. by symmetry, we are seeking $2 \int_0^{\cosh^{-1}(2)} (8 \operatorname{sech}^2 x - \cosh x) \, dx =$

$2 \left(8 \tanh x - \sinh x \right) \Big|_0^{\cosh^{-1}(2)} = 2(4\sqrt{3} - \sqrt{3}) = 6\sqrt{3}$.

73 $f'(\ln 3) = \sinh(\ln 3) = 4/3$. So the linearization is $L(x) = 5/3 + (4/3)(x - \ln 3)$. Using this approximation, we have $\cosh(1) \approx L(1) = (5/3) + (4/3)(1 - \ln 3) \approx 1.535$.

74 Let $y = (\tanh x)^x$. Then we have $\ln y = x \ln(\tanh x)$. So

$$\lim_{x \to \infty} \ln y = \lim_{x \to \infty} \frac{\ln \tanh x}{1/x} = \lim_{x \to \infty} \frac{\operatorname{sech}^2 x / \tanh x}{-1/x^2} = \lim_{x \to \infty} \frac{-x^2}{\sinh x \cosh x}$$

$$= \lim_{x \to \infty} \frac{-2x}{\sinh^2 x + \cosh^2 x} = \lim_{x \to \infty} \frac{-2x}{\cosh 2x} = \lim_{x \to \infty} \frac{-2}{2 \sinh 2x} = 0.$$

Because $\lim_{x \to \infty} \ln y = 0$, we have $\lim_{x \to \infty} y = e^0 = 1$.

Chapter 7

Integration Techniques

7.1 Basic Approaches

7.1.1 Let $u = 4 - 7x$. Then $du = -7\,dx$ and we obtain $-\frac{1}{7}\int u^{-6}\,du$.

7.1.2 Expand the binomial to standard polynomial form: $x^8 + 4x^4 + 4$.

7.1.3 $\sin^2 x = \frac{1 - \cos 2x}{2}$.

7.1.4 Divide the numerator by the denominator by long division, in order to write the integrand as the sum of a polynomial and a rational function.

7.1.5 Complete the square in the denominator to get $\int \dfrac{10}{(x-2)^2 + 1}\,dx$. The integral now matches item 12 in Table 7.1.

7.1.6 Rewrite the integrand as the sum of four terms, each with denominator $3x^3$.

7.1.7 Let $u = 3 - 5x$ so that $du = -5\,dx$. Substituting gives $\frac{-1}{5}\int u^{-4}\,du = \frac{1}{15}u^{-3} + C = \frac{1}{15(3-5x)^3} + C$.

7.1.8 Let $u = 9x - 2$ so that $du = 9\,dx$. Substituting gives $\frac{1}{9}\int u^{-3}\,du = \frac{-1}{18}u^{-2} + C = \frac{-1}{18(9x-2)^2} + C$.

7.1.9 Let $u = 2x - \pi/4$ so that $du = 2\,dx$. Substituting gives

$$\frac{1}{2}\int_{-\pi/4}^{\pi/2} \sin u\,du = \frac{1}{2}\left(-\cos u\right)\Big|_{-\pi/4}^{\pi/2} = \frac{1}{2}\left(0 + \sqrt{2}/2\right) = \frac{\sqrt{2}}{4}.$$

7.1.10 Let $u = 3 - 4x$ so that $du = -4\,dx$. Substituting gives $\frac{-1}{4}\int e^u\,du = \frac{-1}{4}e^u + C = \frac{-1}{4}e^{3-4x} + C$.

7.1.11 Let $u = \ln(2x)$ so that $du = \frac{dx}{x}$. Substituting gives $\int u\,du = u^2/2 + C = \frac{1}{2}\ln^2 2x + C$.

7.1.12 Let $u = 4 - x$ so that $du = -dx$. Substituting gives

$$-\int_9^4 u^{-1/2}\,du = \int_4^9 u^{-1/2}\,du = 2\sqrt{u}\Big|_4^9 = 6 - 4 = 2.$$

7.1.13 Let $u = e^x + 1$ so that $du = e^x\,dx$ Substituting gives $\int \frac{1}{u}\,du = \ln|u| + C = \ln(e^x + 1) + C$.

7.1.14 Let $u = 2\sqrt{y} + 1$ so that $du = dy/\sqrt{y}$. Substituting gives $\int e^u\,du = e^u + C = e^{2\sqrt{y}+1} + C$.

7.1.15 We rewrite the integral by multiplying the numerator and denominator of the integrand by e^x. We have $\int \frac{e^x}{e^x - 2e^{-x}}\,dx = \int \frac{e^x}{e^x - 2e^{-x}} \cdot \frac{e^x}{e^x}\,dx = \int \frac{e^{2x}}{e^{2x} - 2}\,dx$. Now let $u = e^{2x} - 2$ so that $du = 2e^{2x}\,dx$. Substituting gives $\frac{1}{2}\int \frac{du}{u} = \frac{1}{2}\ln|u| + C = \frac{1}{2}\ln|e^{2x} - 2| + C$.

7.1.16 $\int \frac{e^{2z}}{e^{2z}-4e^{-z}} \cdot \frac{e^z}{e^z} \, dz = \int \frac{e^{3z}}{e^{3z}-4} \, dz$. Let $u = e^{3z} - 4$ so that $du = 3e^{3z} \, dz$. Substituting gives $\frac{1}{3} \int \frac{du}{u} = \frac{1}{3} \ln|u| + C = \frac{1}{3} \ln|e^{3z} - 4| + C$.

7.1.17 Let $u = \ln x^2 = 2\ln x$. Then $du = \frac{2}{x} \, dx$. Substituting gives $\frac{1}{2} \int_0^4 u^2 \, du = \left. (u^3/6) \right|_0^4 = 32/3$.

7.1.18 The integral can be written as $\tan^3 x \sec^2 x \, dx$. Let $u = \tan x$ so that $du = \sec^2 x \, dx$. Substituting gives $\int u^3 \, du = u^4/4 + C = (\tan^4 x)/4 + C$.

7.1.19 The integral can be written as $\cot^4 x \csc^2 x \, dx$. Let $u = \cot x$ so that $du = -\csc^2 x \, dx$. Substituting gives $-\int u^4 \, du = -u^5/5 + C = -(\cot^5 x)/5 + C$.

7.1.20 Let $u = x^3 + x^2 + 4$ so that $du = 3x^2 + 2x \, dx = x(3x+2) \, dx$. Substituting gives $\int_4^{16} \frac{du}{\sqrt{u}} = \left. (2\sqrt{u}) \right|_4^{16} = 8 - 4 = 4$.

7.1.21 $\int \frac{dx}{x^{-1}+1} = \int \frac{1}{x^{-1}+1} \cdot \frac{x}{x} \, dx = \int \frac{x}{x+1} \, dx$. Using long division, we have $\frac{x}{x+1} = 1 - \frac{1}{x+1}$. Then $\int \left(1 - \frac{1}{x+1}\right) dx = x - \ln|x+1| + C$.

7.1.22 $\int \frac{dy}{y^{-1}+y^{-3}} = \int \frac{1}{y^{-1}+y^{-3}} \cdot \frac{y^3}{y^3} \, dy = \int \frac{y^3}{y^2+1} \, dy$. Using long division, we have $\frac{y^3}{y^2+1} = y - \frac{y}{y^2+1}$. Thus our integral is equal to $\int \left(y - \frac{y}{y^2+1}\right) dy = y^2/2 - \int \frac{y}{y^2+1} \, dy$. To compute this last integral, let $u = y^2 + 1$ so that $du = 2y \, dy$. We have $y^2/2 - \frac{1}{2} \int \frac{1}{u} \, du = y^2/2 - \frac{1}{2} \ln|u| + C = y^2/2 - \frac{1}{2} \ln|y^2 + 1| + C$.

7.1.23 $\int \frac{x}{x^2+4} \, dx + 2 \int \frac{1}{x^2+4} \, dx = \frac{1}{2} \ln(x^2 + 4) + \tan^{-1}(x/2) + C$.

7.1.24 $\int_4^9 x \, dx - \int_4^9 x^{-1} \, dx = \left. x^2/2 \right|_4^9 - \left. \ln x \right|_4^9 = 81/2 - 16/2 - (\ln 9 - \ln 4) = 65/2 - \ln(9/4)$.

7.1.25
$$\int \frac{\sin t}{\cos^2 t} \, dt + \int \frac{\tan t}{\cos^2 t} \, dt = \int \tan t \sec t \, dt + \int \frac{\sin t}{\cos^3 t} \, dt = \sec t + \int \frac{\sin t}{\cos^3 t} \, dt.$$
Now let $u = \cos t$ so that $du = -\sin t \, dt$. We have
$$\sec t - \int u^{-3} \, du = \sec t + u^{-2}/2 + C = \sec t + \frac{1}{2\cos^2 t} + C = \sec t + \frac{1}{2} \sec^2 t + C.$$

7.1.26 $\int 4e^{-3x} \, dx + \int e^{-5x} \, dx = (-4/3)e^{-3x} + (-1/5)e^{-5x} + C$.

7.1.27
$$\int \frac{2}{\sqrt{1-x^2}} \, dx - 3 \int \frac{x}{\sqrt{1-x^2}} \, dx = 2\sin^{-1} x - 3 \int \frac{x}{\sqrt{1-x^2}} \, dx.$$
Let $u = 1 - x^2$ so that $du = -2x \, dx$. Substituting gives
$$2\sin^{-1} x + \frac{3}{2} \int u^{-1/2} \, du = 2\sin^{-1} x + 3\sqrt{u} + C = 2\sin^{-1} x + 3\sqrt{1-x^2} + C.$$

7.1.28
$$\int \frac{3x}{\sqrt{4-x^2}} \, dx + \int \frac{1}{\sqrt{4-x^2}} \, dx = \int \frac{3x}{\sqrt{4-x^2}} \, dx + \sin^{-1}(x/2).$$
Let $u = 4 - x^2$ so that $du = -2x \, dx$. Substituting gives
$$-\frac{3}{2} \int u^{-1/2} \, du + \sin^{-1}(x/2) = -3\sqrt{u} + \sin^{-1}(x/2) + C = -3\sqrt{4-x^2} + \sin^{-1}(x/2) + C.$$

7.1.29 Note that long division gives $\frac{x+2}{x+4} = 1 - \frac{2}{x+4}$. Thus our integral is equal to

$$\int \left(1 - \frac{2}{x+4}\right)\, dx = x - 2\ln|x+4| + C.$$

7.1.30 Note that long division gives $\frac{x^2+2}{x-1} = x + 1 + \frac{3}{x-1}$. Thus we have

$$\int_2^4 \left(x + 1 + \frac{3}{x-1}\right)\, dx = \left(x^2/2 + x + 3\ln|x-1|\right)\Big|_2^4 = 8 + 4 + 3\ln 3 - (2 + 2 + 0) = 8 + 3\ln 3.$$

7.1.31 Note that long division gives $\frac{t^3-2}{t+1} = t^2 - t + 1 - \frac{3}{t+1}$. Our integral is therefore

$$\int \left(t^2 - t + 1 - \frac{3}{t+1}\right)\, dt = t^3/3 - t^2/2 + t - 3\ln|t+1| + C.$$

7.1.32

$$\int \frac{6}{x^2+4}\, dx - \int \frac{x^4}{x^2+4}\, dx = \int \frac{6}{x^2+4}\, dx - \int \left(x^2 - 4 + \frac{16}{x^2+4}\right)\, dx$$

$$= -x^3/3 + 4x - 10\int \frac{1}{x^2+4}\, dx = -x^3/3 + 4x - 5\tan^{-1}(x/2) + C.$$

7.1.33 Note that $x^2 - 2x + 10 = (x^2 - 2x + 1) + 9 = (x-1)^2 + 9$. So we have $\int \frac{dx}{(x-1)^2+3^2} = \frac{1}{3}\tan^{-1}((x-1)/3) + C$.

7.1.34 Note that $x^2 + 4x + 8 = (x+2)^2 + 4$. Thus we have $\int_0^2 \frac{(x+2)-2}{(x+2)^2+4}\, dx = \int_2^4 \frac{u}{u^2+4}\, du - \int_2^4 \frac{2}{u^2+4}\, du$ where $u = x + 2$. This is equal to $\left(\frac{1}{2}\ln|u^2+4| - \tan^{-1}(u/2)\right)\Big|_2^4 = \frac{1}{2}\ln(5/2) + \frac{\pi}{4} - \tan^{-1}2$.

7.1.35 Note that $27 - 6\theta - \theta^2 = -(\theta^2 + 6\theta + 9 - 36) = -((\theta+3)^2 - 36) = 36 - (\theta+3)^2$. Thus our integral is $\int \frac{d\theta}{\sqrt{36-(\theta+3)^2}} = \sin^{-1}((\theta+3)/6) + C$.

7.1.36 The integral can be written $\int \frac{x}{(x^2+1)^2}\, dx$. Let $u = x^2 + 1$ so that $du = 2x\, dx$. Substitution gives $\frac{1}{2}\int u^{-2}\, du = \frac{-1}{2u} + C = \frac{-1}{2(x^2+1)} + C$.

7.1.37 $\int \frac{1}{1+\sin\theta} \cdot \frac{1-\sin\theta}{1-\sin\theta}\, d\theta = \int \frac{1-\sin\theta}{1-\sin^2\theta}\, d\theta = \int \frac{1-\sin\theta}{\cos^2\theta}\, d\theta = \int \sec^2\theta\, d\theta - \int \frac{\sin\theta}{\cos^2\theta}\, d\theta = \tan\theta - \int \frac{\sin\theta}{\cos^2\theta}\, d\theta$. Let $u = \cos\theta$ so that $du = -\sin\theta\, d\theta$. Substituting gives $\tan\theta + \int u^{-2}\, du = \tan\theta - \frac{1}{u} + C = \tan\theta - \sec\theta + C$.

7.1.38 $\int \frac{1-x}{1-\sqrt{x}} \cdot \frac{1+\sqrt{x}}{1+\sqrt{x}}\, dx = \int \frac{(1-x)(1+\sqrt{x})}{1-x}\, dx = \int (1 + \sqrt{x})\, dx = x + 2x^{3/2}/3 + C$.

7.1.39 $\int \frac{1}{\sec x - 1} \cdot \frac{\sec x + 1}{\sec x + 1}\, dx = \int \frac{\sec x + 1}{\sec^2 x - 1}\, dx = \int \frac{\sec x + 1}{\tan^2 x}\, dx = \int \frac{\sec x}{\tan^2 x}\, dx + \int \cot^2 x\, dx = \int \cot x\csc x\, dx + \int \cot^2 x\, dx = -\csc x + \int (\csc^2 x - 1)\, dx = -\csc x - \cot x - x + C$.

7.1.40 $\int \frac{1}{1-\csc\theta} \cdot \frac{1+\csc\theta}{1+\csc\theta}\, d\theta = \int \frac{1+\csc\theta}{1-\csc^2\theta}\, d\theta = \int \frac{1+\csc\theta}{-\cot^2\theta}\, d\theta = \int \frac{-\csc\theta}{\cot^2\theta}\, d\theta - \int \frac{1}{\cot^2\theta}\, d\theta = \int -\tan\theta\sec\theta\, d\theta - \int \tan^2\theta\, d\theta = -\sec\theta - \int (\sec^2\theta - 1)\, d\theta = -\sec\theta - \tan\theta + \theta + C$.

7.1.41

   a. False. This seem to use the untrue "identity" that $\frac{a}{b+c} = \frac{a}{b} + \frac{a}{c}$.

   b. False. The degree of the numerator is already less than the degree of the denominator, so long division won't help.

   c. False. This is false because $\frac{d}{dx}\ln|\sin x + 1| + C \neq \frac{1}{\sin x + 1}$. The substitution $u = \sin x + 1$ can't be carried out because $du = \cos x\, dx$ can't be accounted for.

d. False. In fact, $\int e^{-x}\,dx = -e^{-x} + C \neq \ln e^x + C$.

7.1.42 Let $u = \sqrt{x}$ so that $du = \frac{1}{2\sqrt{x}}\,dx$, or $dx = 2u\,du$. Substituting gives $\int_2^3 \frac{2u}{1-u}\,du = -\int_2^3 \frac{2u}{u-1}\,du$. By long division, $\frac{2u}{u-1} = 2 + \frac{2}{u-1}$. Thus we have

$$-\int_2^3 \left(2 + \frac{2}{u-1}\right)\,du = (-2u - 2\ln|u-1|)\,\Big|_2^3 = -6 - 2\ln 2 - (-4 - 0) = -2 - 2\ln 2.$$

7.1.43 $\int_{-1}^0 \frac{x}{x^2+2x+2}\,dx = \int_{-1}^0 \frac{x}{(x+1)^2+1}\,dx$. Let $u = x + 1$ so that $du = dx$. Substituting gives $\int_0^1 \frac{u-1}{u^2+1}\,du =$
$\int_0^1 \frac{u}{u^2+1}\,du - \int_0^1 \frac{1}{u^2+1}\,du = \left((1/2)\ln(u^2+1) - \tan^{-1}(u)\right)\,\Big|_0^1 = (1/2)\ln 2 - \frac{\pi}{4} = \frac{1}{4}(\ln 4 - \pi)$.

7.1.44 Let $u = 1 + \sqrt{x}$ so that $du = \frac{1}{2\sqrt{x}}\,dx$, or $dx = 2\sqrt{x}\,du = 2(u-1)\,du$. Substituting gives

$$2\int_1^2 \sqrt{u}(u-1)\,du = 2\int_1^2 (u^{3/2} - u^{1/2})\,du = 2\left(2u^{5/2}/5 - 2u^{3/2}/3\right)\,\Big|_1^2$$
$$= 2(8\sqrt{2}/5 - 4\sqrt{2}/3 - (2/5 - 2/3)) = \frac{8}{15}\left(1 + \sqrt{2}\right).$$

7.1.45 Using the identity $\sin 2x = 2\sin x\cos x$, we have $2\int \sin^2 x\cos x\,dx$. Let $u = \sin x$ so that $du = \cos x\,dx$. We have $2\int u^2\,du = 2u^3/3 + C = 2(\sin^3 x)/3 + C$.

7.1.46 Using the double angle identity $\cos 2x = 2\cos^2 x - 1$, we have

$$\int_0^{\pi/2} \sqrt{2\cos^2 x}\,dx = \int_0^{\pi/2} \sqrt{2}\cos x\,dx = \sqrt{2}\sin x\,\Big|_0^{\pi/2} = \sqrt{2}(1 - 0) = \sqrt{2}.$$

7.1.47 Rewrite the integral as $\int \frac{1}{\sqrt{x}} \cdot \frac{1}{1+(\sqrt{x})^2}\,dx$ and let $u = \sqrt{x}$. Then $du = \frac{1}{2\sqrt{x}}\,dx$, and substituting gives

$$2\int \frac{1}{1+u^2}\,du = 2\tan^{-1} u + C = 2\tan^{-1}\sqrt{x} + C.$$

7.1.48 Let $u = \sqrt{p}$ so that $u^2 = p$ and $2u\,du = dp$. Substituting gives $\int_0^1 \frac{2u}{4-u}\,du = 2\int_0^1 \left(-1 - \frac{4}{u-4}\right)\,du$

$$= 2\left(-u - 4\ln|u-4|\right)\,\Big|_0^1 = 2(-1 - 4\ln 3 - (0 - 4\ln 4)) = 2(\ln(256/81) - 1).$$

7.1.49 Note that $x^2 + 6x + 13 = (x^2 + 6x + 9) + 4 = (x+3)^2 + 4$. Also note that we can write the numerator $x - 2 = x + 3 - 5 = \frac{1}{2}(2x+6) - 5$. We have $\int \frac{\frac{1}{2}(2x+6)}{x^2+6x+13}\,dx - \int \frac{5}{(x+3)^2+4}\,dx$. For the first integral, let $u = x^2 + 6x + 13$ so that $du = (2x+6)\,dx$. We have (for just the first integral) $\frac{1}{2}\int \frac{1}{u}\,du = \frac{1}{2}\ln|u| + C = \frac{1}{2}\ln(x^2+6x+13) + C$. The second integrand has antiderivative equal to $\frac{5}{2}\tan^{-1}((x+3)/2)$, so the original integral is equal to

$$\frac{1}{2}\ln(x^2 + 6x + 13) - \frac{5}{2}\tan^{-1}((x+3)/2) + C.$$

7.1.50 $3\int_0^{\pi/4} \sqrt{1+\sin 2x} \cdot \frac{\sqrt{1-\sin 2x}}{\sqrt{1-\sin 2x}}\,dx = 3\int_0^{\pi/4} \frac{\cos 2x}{\sqrt{1-\sin 2x}}\,dx$. Let $u = 1 - \sin 2x$ so that $du = -2\cos 2x\,dx$. Substituting gives

$$\frac{-3}{2}\int_1^0 u^{-1/2}\,du = 3\sqrt{u}\,\Big|_0^1 = 3.$$

7.1.51 Let $u = e^x$ so that $du = e^x\,dx$. Substituting gives $\int \frac{1}{u^2+2u+1}\,du = \int (u+1)^{-2}\,du = -\frac{1}{u+1} + C = -\frac{1}{e^x+1} + C$.

7.1.52 One of the double angle identities allows us to write $\cos 4x = \cos(2 \cdot 2x) = 1 - 2\sin^2 2x$. Thus we have

$$\int_0^{\pi/8} \sqrt{2\sin^2 2x}\, dx = \sqrt{2} \int_0^{\pi/8} \sin 2x\, dx = -\frac{\sqrt{2}}{2} \cdot \cos 2x \Big|_0^{\pi/8} = -\frac{\sqrt{2}}{2}\left(\frac{\sqrt{2}}{2} - 1\right) = \frac{\sqrt{2} - 1}{2}.$$

7.1.53 The denominator factors as $(x+1)^2$. $\int_1^3 \frac{2}{(x+1)^2}\, dx = -2\left(\frac{1}{x+1}\right)\Big|_1^3 = -2(1/4 - 1/2) = 1/2.$

7.1.54 The denominator factors as $(s+1)^3$. $\int_0^2 \frac{2}{(s+1)^3}\, ds = -(s+1)^{-2}\Big|_0^2 = -(1/9 - 1) = 8/9.$

7.1.55

a. If $u = \tan x$ then $du = \sec^2 x\, dx$. Substituting gives $\int u\, du = u^2/2 + C = (\tan^2 x)/2 + C$.

b. If $u = \sec x$, then $du = \sec x \tan x\, dx$. Substituting gives $\int u\, du = u^2/2 + C = (\sec^2 x)/2 + C$.

c. The seemingly different answers are the same, since $(\tan^2 x)/2$ and $(\sec^2 x)/2$ differ by a constant. In fact, $(\tan^2 x)/2 - (\sec^2 x)/2 = \frac{-1}{2}$.

7.1.56

a. If $u = \cot x$, then $du = -\csc^2 x\, dx$. Substituting gives $-\int u\, du = -u^2/2 + C = -(\cot^2 x)/2 + C$.

b. If $u = \csc x$, then $du = -\csc x \cot x\, dx$. Substituting gives $-\int u\, du = -u^2/2 + C = -(\csc^2 x)/2 + C$.

c. The seemingly different answers are the same, since $-(\cot^2 x)/2$ and $-(\csc^2 x)/2$ differ by a constant. In fact, $-(\cot^2 x)/2 - (-(\csc^2 x)/2) = \frac{1}{2}$.

7.1.57

a. Let $u = x + 1$ so that $du = dx$. Note that $x = u - 1$, so that $x^2 = (u-1)^2$. Substituting gives $\int \frac{u^2 - 2u + 1}{u}\, du = \int (u - 2 + (1/u))\, du = u^2/2 - 2u + \ln|u| + C = (x+1)^2/2 - 2(x+1) + \ln|x+1| + C.$

b. By long division, $\frac{x^2}{x+1} = x - 1 + \frac{1}{x+1}$. Thus, $\int \frac{x^2}{x+1}\, dx = \int \left(x - 1 + \frac{1}{x+1}\right) dx = x^2/2 - x + \ln|x+1| + C.$

c. The seemingly different answers are the same, because they differ by a constant. In fact, $(x+1)^2/2 - 2(x+1) + \ln|x+1| - (x^2/2 - x + \ln|x+1|) = -\frac{3}{2}$.

7.1.58

a. Note that $x - x^2 = -(x^2 - x + 1/4 - 1/4) = -((x - 1/2)^2 - 1/4) = 1/4 - (x - 1/2)^2$. We can write our integral as $\int \frac{dx}{\sqrt{1/4 - (x-1/2)^2}} = 2\int \frac{dx}{\sqrt{1 - (2x-1)^2}}$. Let $u = 2x - 1$. Then $du = 2\, dx$. Substituting gives $\int \frac{du}{\sqrt{1-u^2}} = \sin^{-1} u + C = \sin^{-1}(2x - 1) + C.$

b. We can write our integral as $\int \frac{dx}{\sqrt{x}\sqrt{1-x}}$. Let $u = \sqrt{x}$ so that $du = \frac{1}{2\sqrt{x}}\, dx$. Substituting gives $2\int \frac{du}{\sqrt{1-u^2}} = 2\sin^{-1} u + C = 2\sin^{-1}\sqrt{x} + C.$

c. By parts a and b, it follows that both $\sin^{-1}(2x - 1)$ and $2\sin^{-1}(\sqrt{x})$ are antiderivatives of $\frac{1}{\sqrt{x-x^2}}$. Therefore, $2\sin^{-1}\sqrt{x} - \sin^{-1}(2x - 1) = C$ for some constant C. To determine C, we let $x = 0$, giving $2\sin^{-1}(0) - \sin^{-1}(-1) = C$. Thus $0 - \left(-\frac{\pi}{2}\right) = C$, so $C = \frac{\pi}{2}$.

7.1.59 $A = \int_2^4 \frac{x^2 - 1}{x^3 - 3x}\, dx$. Let $u = x^3 - 3x$ so that $du = 3x^2 - 3\, dx$. Substituting gives $A = \frac{1}{3}\int_2^{52} \frac{1}{u}\, du = \frac{1}{3}\ln u \Big|_2^{52} = \frac{1}{3}(\ln 52 - \ln 2) = \ln(26)/3.$

7.1.60 The curves intersect when $x^3 = 8x$, so at $x = 0$ and $x = \pm\sqrt{8}$. By symmetry, we have $A = 2\int_0^{\sqrt{8}} \frac{8x-x^3}{x^2+1}\,dx$. Using long division, we can write $\frac{8x-x^3}{x^2+1} = -x + \frac{9x}{x^2+1}$. Thus, $A = 2\int_0^{\sqrt{8}}\left(-x + \frac{9x}{x^2+1}\right)dx = 2\int_0^{\sqrt{8}}(-x)\,dx + 2\int_0^{\sqrt{8}} \frac{9x}{x^2+1}\,dx = -2\,x^2/2\,\Big|_0^{\sqrt{8}} + 2\int_0^{\sqrt{8}} \frac{9x}{x^2+1}\,dx = -8 + 2\int_0^{\sqrt{8}} \frac{9x}{x^2+1}\,dx$. To compute this last integral, let $u = x^2+1$ so that $du = 2x\,dx$. Then we have $A = -8 + 9\int_1^9 \frac{1}{u}\,du = -8 + 9\ln u\,\Big|_1^9 = -8 + 9\ln 9 \approx 11.775$.

7.1.61

a. $V = \pi\int_0^2 (x^2+1)\,dx = \pi\left(x^3/3 + x\right)\Big|_0^2 = \pi(8/3 + 2) = 14\pi/3$.

b. $V = 2\pi\int_0^2 x\sqrt{x^2+1}\,dx$. Let $u = x^2+1$ so that $du = 2x\,dx$. Substituting gives $\pi\int_1^5 u^{1/2}\,du = \pi\left(2u^{3/2}/3\right)\Big|_1^5 = \pi(10\sqrt{5}/3 - 2/3)$.

7.1.62

a. $V = \pi\int_0^3 \frac{1}{(x+2)^2}\,dx = \pi\left(\frac{-1}{x+2}\right)\Big|_0^3 = \pi(-1/5 + 1/2) = 3\pi/10$.

b. $V = 2\pi\int_0^3 \frac{x}{x+2}\,dx = 2\pi\int_0^3\left(1 - \frac{2}{x+2}\right)dx = 2\pi\left(x - 2\ln(x+2)\right)\Big|_0^3 = 2\pi(3 - 2\ln 5 - (0 - 2\ln 2)) = 2\pi(3 + 2\ln(5/2))$.

7.1.63 $L = \int_0^1 \sqrt{1 + \frac{25x^{1/2}}{16}}\,dx$. Let $u^2 = 1 + \frac{25x^{1/2}}{16}$. Then $2u\,du = \frac{25}{32\sqrt{x}}\,dx$. Note that $\sqrt{x} = \frac{16}{25}(u^2-1)$, and that $dx = \frac{64\sqrt{x}}{25}u\,du = \frac{1024}{625}(u^3-u)\,du$. Substituting gives

$$L = \int_1^{\sqrt{41/16}} \frac{1024}{625}(u^4 - u^2)\,du = \frac{1024}{625}\left(u^5/5 - u^3/3\right)\Big|_1^{\sqrt{41/16}}$$

$$= \frac{1024}{625}((\sqrt{41/16})^5/5 - (\sqrt{41/16})^3/3 - (1/5 - 1/3)) = \frac{1024}{625}\left(\frac{2}{15} + \frac{1763\sqrt{41}}{15360}\right)$$

$$= \frac{2048 + 1763\sqrt{41}}{9375} \approx 1.423.$$

7.1.64 $A = 2\pi\int_0^{\ln 2}(e^x + e^{-x}/4)\sqrt{1 + (e^x - e^{-x}/4)^2}\,dx$. Note that $1 + (e^x - e^{-x}/4)^2 = 1 + e^{2x} - 1/2 + e^{-2x}/16 = e^{2x} + 1/2 + e^{-2x}/16 = (e^x + e^{-x}/4)^2$. Thus we have $2\pi\int_0^{\ln 2}(e^x + e^{-x}/4)^2\,dx = 2\pi\int_0^{\ln 2}(e^{2x} + 1/2 + e^{-2x}/16)\,dx = 2\pi\left(e^{2x}/2 + x/2 - e^{-2x}/32\right)\Big|_0^{\ln 2} = 2\pi(2 + (\ln 2)/2 - 1/128 - (1/2 - 1/32)) = \pi\left(\frac{195}{64} + \ln 2\right)$.

7.1.65 $A = 2\pi\int_0^1 \sqrt{x+1}\sqrt{1 + \frac{1}{4(x+1)}}\,dx = 2\pi\int_0^1 \sqrt{x + 5/4}\,dx = 2\pi\left((2/3)(x+5/4)^{3/2}\right)\Big|_0^1 = \frac{4\pi}{3}(27/8 - 5\sqrt{5}/8) = \frac{9\pi}{2} - \frac{5\sqrt{5}\pi}{6}$.

7.1.66

$$d(t) = \int_0^t v(y)\,dy = \int_0^t v_T\left(\frac{e^{ay}-1}{e^{ay}+1}\right)dy = v_T\int_0^t \frac{e^{ay}}{e^{ay}+1}\,dy + -v_T\int_0^t \frac{1}{e^{ay}+1}\,dy.$$

The first integral can be computed by letting $u = e^{ay} + 1$ so that $du = ae^{ay}\,dy$. The first integral is then equal to $(v_T/a)\int_2^{e^{at}+1} \frac{1}{u}\,du = (v_T/a)(\ln(e^{at}+1) - \ln(2))$. The second integral is $-v_T\int_0^t \frac{1}{e^{ay}+1}\cdot\frac{e^{ay}}{e^{ay}}\,dy$. Again, let $u = e^{ay} + 1$ and note that $du = ae^{ay}\,dy$. Substitution gives

$$-(v_T/a)\int_2^{e^{at}+1} \frac{1}{u(u-1)}\,du = -(v_T/a)\int_2^{e^{at}+1}\left(\frac{1}{u-1} - \frac{1}{u}\right)dy$$

$$= -(v_T/a)\left(\ln(u-1) - \ln(u)\right)\Big|_2^{e^{at}+1} = -(v_T/a)(at - \ln(e^{at}+1) - (0 - \ln 2)).$$

Adding the results of the two integrations gives

$$d(t) = (v_T/a)(\ln(e^{at}+1) - \ln(2)) + -(v_T/a)(at - \ln(e^{at}+1) - (0 - \ln 2)) = (v_T/a)(2\ln(e^{at}+1) - at - \ln 4)$$

7.2 Integration by Parts

7.2.1 It is based on the product rule. In fact, the rule can be obtained by writing down the product rule, then integrating both sides and rearranging the terms in the result.

7.2.2 It is generally a good idea to let dv be something easy to integrate. In this case, we would let $dv = e^{ax}\,dx$, leaving $u = x^n$. Note that differentiating x^n results in something simpler (lower degree,) while integrating it make it more complicated (higher degree.) However, differentiating or integrating e^{ax} yields essentially the same thing (a constant times the function e^{ax}).

7.2.3 It is generally a good idea to let u be something easy to differentiate, keeping in mind that whatever is left for dv is something which you will need to be able to integrate. In this case, it would be prudent to let $u = x^n$ and $dv = \cos(ax)\,dx$. Note that differentiating x^n results in something simpler (lower degree,) while integrating it make it more complicated (higher degree.) However, differentiating or integrating $\cos(ax)$ yields essentially the same thing (a constant times the sine function).

7.2.4 One can use integration by parts for definite integrals via the formula

$$\int_a^b u(x)v'(x)\,dx = u(x)v(x)\,\Big|_a^b - \int_a^b v(x)u'(x)\,dx.$$

7.2.5 Those for which the choice for dv is easily integrated and when the resulting new integral is no more difficult than the original.

7.2.6 Let $u = \tan^{-1}x$ and let $dv = dx$.

7.2.7 Let $u = x$ and $dv = \cos x\,dx$. Then $du = dx$ and $v = \sin x$. Then $\int x\cos x\,dx = x\sin x - \int \sin x\,dx = x\sin x + \cos x + C$.

7.2.8 Let $u = x$ and $dv = \sin 2x\,dx$. Then $du = dx$ and $v = -\frac{1}{2}\cos(2x)$. Then $\int x\sin 2x\,dx = -\frac{1}{2}x\cos 2x + \frac{1}{2}\int \cos 2x\,dx = -\frac{1}{2}x\cos 2x + \frac{1}{4}\sin 2x + C$.

7.2.9 Let $u = t$ and $dv = e^t\,dt$. Then $du = dt$ and $v = e^t$. Then $\int te^t\,dt = te^t - \int e^t\,dt = te^t - e^t + C$.

7.2.10 Let $u = 2x$ and $dv = e^{3x}\,dx$. Then $du = 2\,dx$ and $v = \frac{e^{3x}}{3}$. Then $\int 2xe^{3x}\,dx = \frac{2xe^{3x}}{3} - \frac{2}{3}\int e^{3x}\,dx = \frac{2xe^{3x}}{3} - \frac{2e^{3x}}{9} + C$.

7.2.11 Let $u = x$ and $dv = \frac{dx}{\sqrt{x+1}}$. Then $du = dx$ and $v = 2\sqrt{x+1}$. Then $\int \frac{x}{\sqrt{x+1}}\,dx = 2x\sqrt{x+1} - \int 2\sqrt{x+1}\,dx. = 2x\sqrt{x+1} - \frac{4}{3}(x+1)^{3/2} + C = \frac{2}{3}\sqrt{x+1}(x-2) + C$.

7.2.12 Let $u = s$ and $dv = e^{-2s}\,ds$. Then $du = ds$ and $v = -\frac{1}{2}e^{-2s}$. Then $\int se^{-2s}\,ds = -\frac{1}{2}se^{-2s} + \frac{1}{2}\int e^{-2s}\,ds = -\frac{1}{2}se^{-2s} - \frac{1}{4}e^{-2s} + C$.

7.2.13 Let $u = \ln x^3 = 3\ln x$ and let $dv = x^2\,dx$. Then $du = \frac{3\,dx}{x}$ and $v = x^3/3$. Then $\int x^2 \ln x^3\,dx = x^3 \ln x - \int x^2\,dx = x^3 \ln x - x^3/3 + C$.

7.2.14 Let $u = \theta$ and $dv = \sec^2\theta\,d\theta$. Then $du = d\theta$ and $v = \tan\theta$. Then $\int \theta \sec^2\theta\,d\theta = \theta\tan\theta - \int \tan\theta\,d\theta = \theta\tan\theta + \ln|\cos\theta| + C$.

7.2.15 Let $u = \ln x$ and $dv = x^2\,dx$. Then $du = \frac{1}{x}\,dx$ and $v = \frac{x^3}{3}$. Then $\int x^2 \ln x\,dx = \frac{x^3}{3}\ln x - \frac{1}{3}\int x^2\,dx = \frac{x^3}{3}\ln x - \frac{x^3}{9} + C = \frac{x^3}{9}(3\ln x - 1) + C$.

7.2.16 Let $u = \ln x$ and $dv = x\,dx$. Then $du = \frac{1}{x}\,dx$ and $v = \frac{x^2}{2}$. Then $\int x \ln x\,dx = \frac{x^2}{2}\ln x - \frac{1}{2}\int x\,dx = \frac{x^2}{2}\ln x - \frac{x^2}{4} + C$.

7.2.17 Let $u = \ln x$ and $dv = x^{-10}\,dx$. Then $du = \frac{1}{x}\,dx$ and $v = -\frac{1}{9}x^{-9}$. Then $\int \frac{\ln x}{x^{10}}\,dx = -\frac{1}{9x^9}\ln x + \frac{1}{9}\int x^{-10}\,dx = -\frac{1}{9x^9}\ln x + -\frac{1}{81x^9} + C$.

7.2.18 Let $u = \sin^{-1}x$ and $dv = dx$. Then $du = \frac{1}{\sqrt{1-x^2}}\,dx$ and $v = x$. Then $\int \sin^{-1}x\,dx = x\sin^{-1}(x) - \int \frac{x}{\sqrt{1-x^2}}\,dx = x\sin^{-1}x + \sqrt{1-x^2} + C$. The fact that $-\int \frac{x}{\sqrt{1-x^2}}\,dx = \sqrt{1-x^2} + C$ follows from the ordinary substitution $u = 1 - x^2$.

7.2.19 Let $u = \tan^{-1}x$ and $dv = dx$. Then $du = \frac{1}{1+x^2}\,dx$ and $v = x$. Then $\int \tan^{-1}x\,dx = x\tan^{-1}x - \int \frac{x}{1+x^2}\,dx = x\tan^{-1}x - \frac{1}{2}\ln(1+x^2) + C$. The fact that $-\int \frac{x}{1+x^2}\,dx = -\frac{1}{2}\ln(1+x^2) + C$ follows from the ordinary substitution $u = 1 + x^2$.

7.2.20 Let $u = \sec^{-1}(x)$ and $dv = x\,dx$. Then $du = \frac{1}{|x|\sqrt{x^2-1}}\,dx$ and $v = \frac{x^2}{2}$. Then $\int x\sec^{-1}(x)\,dx = \frac{x^2}{2}\sec^{-1}(x) - \frac{1}{2}\int \frac{|x|}{\sqrt{x^2-1}}\,dx$.

Now to compute this last integral, we make the ordinary substitution $u = x^2 - 1$, so that $du = 2x\,dx$. Then $\int \frac{|x|}{\sqrt{x^2-1}}\,dx = \pm\frac{1}{2}\int u^{-1/2}\,du = \pm u^{1/2} + C = \frac{x}{|x|}\sqrt{x^2-1} + C$, where $\frac{x}{|x|}$ is a nice expression to represent $+1$ for $x > 0$ and -1 for $x < 0$.

Combining these results yields $\int x\sec^{-1}(x) = \frac{1}{2}x^2\sec^{-1}(x) - \frac{1}{2}\frac{x}{|x|}\sqrt{x^2-1} + C$.

7.2.21 $\int x\sin x\cos x\,dx = \frac{1}{2}\int x\cdot(2\sin x\cos x)\,dx = \frac{1}{2}\int x\sin 2x\,dx$. Now using the result of problem 8, we have
$\int x\sin x\cos x\,dx = \frac{1}{2}\cdot\left(-\frac{1}{2}x\cos 2x + \frac{1}{4}\sin 2x\right) + C = -\frac{1}{4}x\cos 2x + \frac{1}{8}\sin 2x + C$.

7.2.22 Let $u = x^2$, so that $du = 2x\,dx$. Substituting yields $\dfrac{1}{2} \displaystyle\int \tan^{-1} u\,du$. Now the result of problem 19 gives $\displaystyle\int \tan^{-1}(u)\,du = u\tan^{-1}(u) - \dfrac{1}{2}\ln(1+u^2) + C$, so $\displaystyle\int x\tan^{-1}(x^2)\,dx = \dfrac{1}{2}x^2\tan^{-1}(x^2) - \dfrac{1}{4}\ln(1+x^4) + C$.

7.2.23 Let $u = t^2$ and $dv = e^{-t}\,dt$. Then $du = 2t\,dt$ and $v = -e^{-t}$. We have $\displaystyle\int t^2 e^{-t}\,dt = -t^2 e^{-t} + 2\displaystyle\int te^{-t}\,dt$. To compute this last integral, we let $u = t$ and $dv = e^{-t}\,dt$. Then $\displaystyle\int te^{-t}\,dt = -te^{-t} + \displaystyle\int e^{-t}\,dt = -te^{-t} - e^{-t} + C$.

Putting these results together, we obtain

$$\int t^2 e^{-t}\,dt = -t^2 e^{-t} + 2(-te^{-t} - e^{-t}) + C = -e^{-t}(t^2 + 2t + 2) + C.$$

7.2.24 Let $u = \cos 2x$ and $dv = e^{3x}\,dx$. Then $du = -2\sin 2x\,dx$ and $v = \frac{1}{3}e^{3x}$. We have $\displaystyle\int e^{3x}\cos 2x\,dx = \dfrac{1}{3}e^{3x}\cos 2x + \dfrac{2}{3}\displaystyle\int e^{3x}\sin 2x\,dx$.

Now in order to compute the integral which comprises this last term, we let $u = \sin 2x$ and $dv = e^{3x}\,dx$. Then $du = 2\cos 2x\,dx$ and $v = \frac{1}{3}e^{3x}$. Thus, $\displaystyle\int e^{3x}\sin 2x\,dx = \dfrac{1}{3}e^{3x}\sin 2x - \dfrac{2}{3}\displaystyle\int e^{3x}\cos 2x\,dx$.

Putting these results together gives

$$\int e^{3x}\cos 2x\,dx = \frac{1}{3}e^{3x}\cos 2x + \frac{2}{9}e^{3x}\sin 2x - \frac{4}{9}\int e^{3x}\cos 2x\,dx$$

$$\frac{13}{9}\int e^{3x}\cos 2x\,dx = \frac{1}{3}e^{3x}\left(\cos 2x + \frac{2}{3}\sin 2x\right) + C$$

$$\int e^{3x}\cos 2x\,dx = \frac{3}{13}e^{3x}\left(\cos 2x + \frac{2}{3}\sin 2x\right) + C.$$

7.2.25 Let $u = \sin 4x$ and $dv = e^{-x}\,dx$. Then $du = 4\cos 4x\,dx$ and $v = -e^{-x}$. We have $\displaystyle\int e^{-x}\sin 4x\,dx = -e^{-x}\sin 4x + 4\displaystyle\int e^{-x}\cos 4x\,dx$.

Now in order to compute the integral which comprises this last term, we let $u = \cos 4x$ and $dv = e^{-x}\,dx$. Then $du = -4\sin 4x\,dx$ and $v = -e^{-x}$. Thus, $\displaystyle\int e^{-x}\cos 4x\,dx = -e^{-x}\cos 4x - 4\displaystyle\int e^{-x}\sin 4x\,dx$.

Putting these results together gives

$$\int e^{-x}\sin 4x\,dx = -e^{-x}\sin 4x - 4e^{-x}\cos 4x - 16\int e^{-x}\sin 4x\,dx$$

$$17\int e^{-x}\sin 4x\,dx = -e^{-x}\sin 4x - 4e^{-x}\cos 4x + C$$

$$\int e^{-x}\sin 4x\,dx = -\frac{e^{-x}}{17}(\sin 4x + 4\cos 4x) + C.$$

7.2.26 Let $u = \ln^2 x$ and $dv = x^2\,dx$. Then $du = \frac{2\ln x}{x}$ and $v = \frac{x^3}{3}$. We have $\displaystyle\int x^2 \ln^2 x\,dx = \dfrac{1}{3}x^3 \ln^2 x - \dfrac{2}{3}\displaystyle\int x^2 \ln x\,dx$. Note that we already computed $\displaystyle\int x^2 \ln x\,dx$ in problem 15, obtaining $\dfrac{x^3}{9}(3\ln x - 1) + C$. Thus, $\displaystyle\int x^2 \ln^2 x\,dx = \dfrac{x^3}{3}\ln^2 x - \dfrac{2x^3}{27}(3\ln x - 1) + C = \dfrac{x^3}{27}(9\ln^2 x - 6\ln x + 2) + C$.

7.2.27 Let $u = \cos x$ and $dv = e^x\,dx$. Then $du = -\sin x\,dx$ and $v = e^x$. We have $\displaystyle\int e^x \cos x\,dx = e^x \cos x + \displaystyle\int e^x \sin x\,dx$.

Now in order to compute the integral which comprises this last term, we let $u = \sin x$ and $dv = e^x\,dx$. Then $du = \cos x\,dx$ and $v = e^x$. Thus, $\displaystyle \int e^x \sin x\,dx = e^x \sin x - \int e^x \cos x\,dx$.

Putting these results together gives

$$\int e^x \cos x\,dx = e^x \cos x + e^x \sin x - \int e^x \cos x\,dx$$

$$2 \int e^x \cos x\,dx = e^x(\cos x + \sin x) + C$$

$$\int e^x \cos x\,dx = \frac{e^x}{2}(\cos x + \sin x) + C.$$

7.2.28 Let $u = \sin 6\theta$ and $dv = e^{-2\theta}\,d\theta$. Then $du = 6\cos 6\theta\,d\theta$ and $v = -\frac{1}{2}e^{-2\theta}$. We have $\displaystyle \int e^{-2\theta} \sin 6\theta\,d\theta = -\frac{1}{2}e^{-2\theta}\sin 6\theta + 3 \int e^{-2\theta}\cos 6\theta\,d\theta$.

Now in order to compute the integral which comprises this last term, we let $u = \cos 6\theta$ and $dv = e^{-2\theta}\,d\theta$. Then $du = -6\sin 6\theta\,d\theta$ and $v = -\frac{1}{2}e^{-2\theta}$. Thus, $\displaystyle \int e^{-2\theta}\cos 6\theta\,d\theta = -\frac{1}{2}e^{-2\theta}\cos 6\theta - 3 \int e^{-2\theta}\sin 6\theta\,d\theta$.

Putting these results together gives

$$\int e^{-2\theta}\sin 6\theta\,d\theta = -\frac{1}{2}e^{-2\theta}\sin 6\theta - \frac{3}{2}e^{-2\theta}\cos 6\theta - 9\int e^{-2\theta}\sin 6\theta\,d\theta$$

$$10 \int e^{-2\theta}\sin 6\theta\,d\theta = -\frac{1}{2}e^{-2\theta}(\sin 6\theta + 3\cos 6\theta) + C$$

$$\int e^{-2\theta}\sin 6\theta\,d\theta = -\frac{e^{-2\theta}}{20}(\sin 6\theta + 3\cos 6\theta) + C.$$

7.2.29 Let $u = x^2$ and $dv = \sin 2x\,dx$. Then $du = 2x\,dx$ and $v = -\frac{1}{2}\cos 2x$. Then $\displaystyle \int x^2 \sin 2x\,dx = -\frac{1}{2}x^2 \cos 2x + \int x \cos 2x\,dx$.

Now we consider computing this last term $\displaystyle \int x\cos 2x\,dx$ as a new problem. Let $u = x$ and $dv = \cos 2x\,dx$. Then $du = dx$ and $v = \frac{1}{2}\sin 2x$. So $\displaystyle \int x \cos 2x\,dx = \frac{1}{2}x\sin 2x - \frac{1}{2}\int \sin 2x\,dx = \frac{1}{2}x\sin 2x + \frac{1}{4}\cos 2x + C$.

Combining these results we have $\displaystyle \int x^2 \sin 2x\,dx = -\frac{1}{2}x^2 \cos 2x + \frac{1}{2}x \sin 2x + \frac{1}{4}\cos 2x + C$.

7.2.30 Let $u = x^2$ and $dv = e^{4x}\,dx$. Then $du = 2x\,dx$ and $v = \frac{e^{4x}}{4}$. Then $\displaystyle \int x^2 e^{4x}\,dx = \frac{1}{4}x^2 e^{4x} - \frac{1}{2}\int xe^{4x}\,dx$.

Now we consider computing this last integral $\int xe^{4x}\,dx$ as a new problem. Let $u = x$ and $dv = e^{4x}\,dx$. Then $du = dx$ and $v = \frac{e^{4x}}{4}$. Then $\displaystyle \int xe^{4x}\,dx = \frac{1}{4}xe^{4x} - \frac{1}{4}\int e^{4x}\,dx = \frac{1}{4}xe^{4x} - \frac{1}{16}e^{4x} + C$. Combining these results gives $\displaystyle \int x^2 e^{4x}\,dx = \frac{1}{4}x^2 e^{4x} - \frac{1}{8}xe^{4x} + \frac{1}{32}e^{4x} + C = e^{4x}\left(\frac{x^2}{4} - \frac{x}{8} + \frac{1}{32}\right) + C.$

7.2.31 Let $u = x$ and $dv = \sin x\,dx$. Then $du = dx$ and $v = -\cos x$. Then $\displaystyle \int_0^\pi x \sin x\,dx = -x\cos x \Big|_0^\pi + \int_0^\pi \cos x\,dx = \pi - 0 + \sin x \Big|_0^\pi = \pi - 0 + 0 - 0 = \pi.$

7.2.32 First note that $\displaystyle \int_1^e \ln 2x\,dx = \int_1^e \ln 2\,dx + \int_1^e \ln x\,dx = \ln 2(e - 1) + \int_1^e \ln x\,dx.$

Let $u = \ln x$ and $dv = dx$. Then $du = \frac{1}{x}\,dx$ and $v = x$. Then $\int_1^e \ln x\,dx = x\ln x\,\Big|_1^e - \int_1^e dx = e - (e-1) = 1$.

Thus $\int_1^e \ln 2x\,dx = \ln 2(e-1) + 1$.

7.2.33 Let $u = x$ and $dv = \cos 2x\,dx$. Then $du = dx$ and $v = \frac{1}{2}\sin 2x$. Then $\int_0^{\pi/2} x\cos 2x\,dx =$

$\frac{1}{2}x\sin 2x\,\Big|_0^{\pi/2} - \frac{1}{2}\int_0^{\pi/2}\sin 2x\,dx = 0 - \left(\frac{1}{2}\cdot\frac{(-\cos 2x)}{2}\right)\Big|_0^{\pi/2} = -\frac{1}{4} - \frac{1}{4} = -\frac{1}{2}$.

7.2.34 Let $u = x$ and $dv = e^x\,dx$. Then $du = dx$ and $v = e^x$. Then $\int_0^{\ln 2} xe^x\,dx = xe^x\,\Big|_0^{\ln 2} - \int_0^{\ln 2} e^x\,dx =$

$2\ln 2 - (e^x)\,\Big|_0^{\ln 2} = 2\ln 2 - (2-1) = 2\ln 2 - 1$.

7.2.35 Let $u = \ln x$ and $dv = x^2\,dx$. Then $du = \frac{1}{x}\,dx$ and $v = \frac{x^3}{3}$. Then $\int_1^{e^2} x^2\ln x\,dx = \frac{1}{3}x^3\ln x\,\Big|_1^{e^2} -$

$\frac{1}{3}\int_1^{e^2} x^2\,dx = \frac{2}{3}e^6 - \frac{1}{9}x^3\,\Big|_1^{e^2} = \frac{2}{3}e^6 - \frac{1}{9}\left(e^6 - 1\right) = \frac{5}{9}e^6 + \frac{1}{9}$.

7.2.36 By problem 22, we have $\int y\tan^{-1}(y^2)\,dy = \frac{1}{2}y^2\tan^{-1} y^2 - \frac{1}{4}\ln(1+y^4) + C$. Thus,

$$\int_0^{1/\sqrt{2}} y\tan^{-1} y^2\,dy = \left(\frac{1}{2}y^2\tan^{-1} y^2 - \frac{1}{4}\ln(1+y^4)\right)\Big|_0^{1/\sqrt{2}}$$

$$= \frac{1}{4}\tan^{-1}(1/2) - \frac{1}{4}\ln(5/4).$$

7.2.37 By problem 18, $\int \sin^{-1} x\,dx = x\sin^{-1} x + \sqrt{1-x^2}$. Thus,

$$\int_{1/2}^{\sqrt{3}/2} \sin^{-1} x\,dx = \left(x\sin^{-1} x + \sqrt{1-x^2}\right)\Big|_{1/2}^{\sqrt{3}/2}$$

$$= \left(\frac{\sqrt{3}}{2}\cdot\frac{\pi}{3} + \frac{1}{2}\right) - \left(\frac{1}{2}\cdot\frac{\pi}{6} + \frac{\sqrt{3}}{2}\right)$$

$$= \frac{\pi}{6}\left(\sqrt{3} - \frac{1}{2}\right) + \frac{1}{2}\left(1 - \sqrt{3}\right).$$

7.2.38 Let $u = \sec^{-1} z$ and $dv = z\,dz$. Then $du = \frac{1}{|z|\sqrt{z^2-1}}\,dz$ and $v = \frac{z^2}{2}$. Then

$$\int_{2/\sqrt{3}}^2 z\sec^{-1} z\,dz = \left(\frac{z^2}{2}\sec^{-1} z\right)\Big|_{2/\sqrt{3}}^2 - \frac{1}{2}\int_{2/\sqrt{3}}^2 \frac{z}{\sqrt{z^2-1}}\,dz.$$

We can compute this last integral via a regular substitution. Let $u = z^2 - 1$ so that $du = 2z\,dz$. Then

$$\int_{2/\sqrt{3}}^2 \frac{z}{\sqrt{z^2-1}}\,dz = \frac{1}{2}\int_{1/3}^3 u^{-1/2}\,du = \sqrt{u}\,\Big|_{1/3}^3 = \sqrt{3} - \frac{\sqrt{3}}{3} = \frac{2\sqrt{3}}{3}.$$

Thus,

$$\int_{2/\sqrt{3}}^2 z\sec^{-1} z\,dz = \frac{2\pi}{3} - \frac{2\pi}{18} - \frac{\sqrt{3}}{3} = \frac{5\pi}{9} - \frac{\sqrt{3}}{3}.$$

7.2.39 Using shells, we have $\dfrac{V}{2\pi} = \displaystyle\int_0^{\ln 2} xe^{-x}\,dx$. Let $u = x$ and $dv = e^{-x}\,dx$, so that $du = dx$ and $v = -e^{-x}$. Then

$$\frac{V}{2\pi} = -xe^{-x}\bigg|_0^{\ln 2} + \int_0^{\ln 2} e^{-x}\,dx = -\frac{1}{2}\ln 2 - e^{-x}\bigg|_0^{\ln 2} = -\frac{\ln 2}{2} - \left(\frac{1}{2} - 1\right) = \frac{1}{2}\left(1 - \ln 2\right).$$

Thus $V = \pi(1 - \ln 2)$.

7.2.40 Using shells, we have $\dfrac{V}{2\pi} = \displaystyle\int_0^{\pi} x\sin x\,dx$. Let $u = x$ and $dv = \sin x\,dx$, so that $du = dx$ and $v = -\cos x$. Then

$$\frac{V}{2\pi} = -x\cos x\bigg|_0^{\pi} + \int_0^{\pi} \cos x\,dx = \pi + \sin x\bigg|_0^{\pi} = \pi.$$

Thus $V = 2\pi^2$.

7.2.41 Using disks, we have $\dfrac{V}{\pi} = \displaystyle\int_1^{e^2} x^2\ln^2 x\,dx$. By problem 26, we have $\displaystyle\int x^2\ln^2 x\,dx = \frac{1}{3}x^3\ln^2 x - \frac{2}{9}x^3\ln x + \frac{2}{27}x^3 + C$. Thus,

$$\frac{V}{\pi} = \left(\frac{1}{3}x^3\ln^2 x - \frac{2}{9}x^3\ln x + \frac{2}{27}x^3\right)\bigg|_1^{e^2} = \left(\frac{4}{3}e^6 - \frac{4}{9}e^6 + \frac{2}{27}e^6\right) - \left(\frac{2}{27}\right) = \frac{26}{27}e^6 - \frac{2}{27}.$$

Thus, $V = \dfrac{\pi}{27}\left(26e^6 - 2\right)$.

7.2.42 Using shells, we have $\dfrac{V}{2\pi} = \displaystyle\int_0^{\ln 2} (\ln 2 - x)e^{-x}\,dx = \ln 2\int_0^{\ln 2} e^{-x}\,dx - \int_0^{\ln 2} xe^{-x}\,dx$.

In the course of solving problem 39, we deduced that $\displaystyle\int_0^{\ln 2} xe^{-x}\,dx = \frac{1 - \ln 2}{2}$. Thus,

$$\frac{V}{2\pi} = \ln 2\left(-e^{-x}\right)\bigg|_0^{\ln 2} - \frac{1 - \ln 2}{2} = \ln 2\left(-\frac{1}{2} + 1\right) - \frac{1 - \ln 2}{2} = \ln 2 - \frac{1}{2}.$$

Thus, $V = 2\pi\left(\ln 2 - \frac{1}{2}\right) = \pi(\ln 4 - 1)$.

7.2.43

a. False. For example, suppose $u = x$ and $dv = x\,dx$. Then $\displaystyle\int uv'\,dx = \int x^2\,dx = \frac{x^3}{3} + C$, but $\displaystyle\int u\,dx\int v'\,dx = \left(\int x\,dx\right)^2 = \left(\frac{x^2}{2} + C\right)^2$.

b. True. This is one way to write the integration by parts formula.

c. True. This is the integration by parts formula with the roles of u and v reversed.

7.2.44 Let $u = x^n$ and $dv = e^{ax}\,dx$. Then $du = nx^{n-1}\,dx$ and $v = \dfrac{e^{ax}}{a}$. Then $\displaystyle\int x^n e^{ax}\,dx = \frac{x^n e^{ax}}{a} - \frac{n}{a}\int x^{n-1}e^{ax}\,dx$.

7.2.45 Let $u = x^n$ and $dv = \cos ax\,dx$. Then $du = nx^{n-1}\,dx$ and $v = \dfrac{\sin ax}{a}$. Then $\displaystyle\int x^n\cos ax\,dx = \frac{x^n\sin ax}{a} - \frac{n}{a}\int x^{n-1}\sin ax\,dx$.

7.2.46 Let $u = x^n$ and $dv = \sin ax\, dx$. Then $du = nx^{n-1}\, dx$ and $v = -\frac{\cos ax}{a}$. Then $\int x^n \sin ax\, dx =$
$-\frac{x^n \cos ax}{a} + \frac{n}{a} \int x^{n-1} \cos ax\, dx$.

7.2.47 Let $u = \ln^n x$ and $dv = dx$. Then $du = \frac{n \ln^{n-1}(x)}{x}\, dx$ and $v = x$. Then $\int \ln^n(x)\, dx = x \ln^n x -$
$n \int \ln^{n-1}(x)\, dx$.

7.2.48

$$\int x^2 e^{3x}\, dx = \frac{x^2 e^{3x}}{3} - \frac{2}{3} \int x e^{3x}\, dx$$

$$= \frac{x^2 e^{3x}}{3} - \frac{2}{3} \left(\frac{x e^{3x}}{3} - \frac{1}{3} \int e^{3x}\, dx \right)$$

$$= \frac{1}{3} \left(x^2 e^{3x} - \frac{2}{3} x e^{3x} + \frac{2}{9} e^{3x} \right) + C$$

$$= \frac{e^{3x}}{3} \left(x^2 - \frac{2}{3} x + \frac{2}{9} \right) + C.$$

7.2.49

$$\int x^2 \cos 5x\, dx = \frac{x^2 \sin 5x}{5} - \frac{2}{5} \int x \sin 5x\, dx$$

$$= \frac{x^2 \sin 5x}{5} - \frac{2}{5} \left(-\frac{x \cos 5x}{5} + \frac{1}{5} \int \cos 5x\, dx \right)$$

$$= \frac{1}{5} \left(x^2 \sin 5x + \frac{2}{5} x \cos 5x - \frac{2}{25} \sin 5x \right) + C.$$

7.2.50

$$\int x^3 \sin x\, dx = -x^3 \cos x + 3 \int x^2 \cos x\, dx$$

$$= -x^3 \cos x + 3 \left(x^2 \sin x - 2 \int x \sin x\, dx \right)$$

$$= -x^3 \cos x + 3x^2 \sin x - 6 \left(-x \cos x + \int \cos x\, dx \right)$$

$$= -x^3 \cos x + 3x^2 \sin x + 6x \cos x - 6 \sin x + C.$$

7.2.51

$$\int \ln^4 x\, dx = x \ln^4 x - 4 \int \ln^3 x\, dx$$

$$= x \ln^4 x - 4 \left(x \ln^3 x - 3 \int \ln^2 x\, dx \right)$$

$$= x \ln^4 x - 4x \ln^3 x + 12 \left(x \ln^2 x - 2 \int \ln x\, dx \right)$$

$$= x \ln^4 x - 4x \ln^3 x + 12x \ln^2 x - 24 \left(x \ln x - x \right) + C.$$

7.2.52 Let $u = \sin x$ so that $du = \cos x\, dx$. Then $\int \cos x \ln(\sin x)\, dx = \int \ln u\, du = u \ln u - u + C =$
$\sin x \ln(\sin x) - \sin x + C$.

7.2.53 Let $u = \tan x + 2$, so that $du = \sec^2 x\, dx$. Then $\displaystyle\int \sec^2 x \ln(\tan x + 2)\, dx = \int \ln u\, du = u \ln u - u + C =$ $(\tan x + 2) \ln(\tan x + 2) - \tan x + C$.

7.2.54

a. Let $u = x^2$, so that $du = 2x\, dx$. Then

$$\int x \ln x^2\, dx = \frac{1}{2} \int \ln u\, du = \frac{1}{2}(u \ln u - u) + C = \frac{1}{2}\left(x^2 \ln(x^2) - x^2\right) + C.$$

b. Let $u = \ln x$ and $dv = x\, dx$. Then $du = \frac{1}{x}\, dx$ and $v = \frac{x^2}{2}$. Then $\displaystyle\int x \ln x^2\, dx = 2 \int x \ln x\, dx =$

$2\left(\dfrac{x^2}{2} \ln x - \dfrac{1}{2} \displaystyle\int x\, dx\right) = x^2 \ln x - \dfrac{x^2}{2} + C.$

c. The answer to the first part is $\frac{1}{2}\left(x^2 \ln(x^2) - x^2\right) + C = x^2 \ln(x) - \frac{x^2}{2} + C$. which is the answer to the second part.

7.2.55 Using the change of base formula, we have $\displaystyle\int \log_b x\, dx = \int \frac{\ln x}{\ln b}\, dx = \frac{1}{\ln b}(x \ln x - x) + C.$

7.2.56 By parts: Let $u = \sin x$ and $dv = \cos x\, dx$, so that $du = \cos x\, dx$ and $v = \sin x$. Then

$$\int \sin x \cos x\, dx = \sin^2 x - \int \sin x \cos x\, dx,$$

so $\displaystyle\int \sin x \cos x\, dx = \frac{\sin^2 x}{2} + C.$

By substitution: Let $u = \sin x$, so that $du = \cos x\, dx$. Then we have $\displaystyle\int \sin x \cos x\, dx = \int u\, du =$

$\dfrac{u^2}{2} + C = \dfrac{\sin^2 x}{2} + C.$

The two answers are the same.

7.2.57 Let $z = \sqrt{x}$, so that $dz = \frac{1}{2\sqrt{x}}\, dx$. Substituting yields $2 \displaystyle\int \frac{\sqrt{x} \cos \sqrt{x}}{2\sqrt{x}}\, dx = 2 \int z \cos z\, dz$. Now let $u = z$ and $dv = \cos z\, dz$. then $du = dz$ and $v = \sin z$. Then by Integration by Parts, we have $2 \displaystyle\int z \cos z\, dz = 2\left(z \sin z - \int \sin z\, dz\right) = 2z \sin z + 2 \cos z + C$. Thus, the original given integral is equal to $2(\sqrt{x} \sin \sqrt{x} + \cos \sqrt{x}) + C$.

7.2.58 Let $z = \sqrt{x}$, so that $dz = \frac{1}{2\sqrt{x}}\, dx$. Substituting yields $\displaystyle\int_0^{\pi^2/4} \sin \sqrt{x}\, dx = 2 \int_0^{\pi/2} z \sin z\, dz$. Now let $u = z$ and $dv = \sin z\, dz$. Then $du = dz$ and $v = -\cos z$. Then by Integration by Parts, we have $2 \displaystyle\int_0^{\pi/2} z \sin z\, dz = 2(-z \cos z)\Big|_0^{\pi/2} + 2 \int_0^{\pi/2} \cos z = 0 + 2 \sin z\Big|_0^{\pi/2} = 2.$

7.2.59 By the Fundamental Theorem, $f'(x) = \sqrt{\ln^2 x - 1}$. So the arc length is $\displaystyle\int_e^{e^3} \sqrt{1 + (f'(x))^2}\, dx =$

$\displaystyle\int_e^{e^3} \ln x\, dx = (x \ln x - x)\Big|_e^{e^3} = 3e^3 - e^3 - (e - e) = 2e^3.$

7.2.60

a. This is given by $\displaystyle\int_0^4 xe^{-x}\, dx$. Let $u = x$ and $dv = e^{-x}\, dx$. Then $du = dx$ and $v = -e^{-x}$. Then

$$\int_0^4 xe^{-x}\, dx = -xe^{-x}\Big|_0^4 + \int_0^4 e^{-x}\, dx = -\frac{4}{e^4} + \left(-e^{-x}\right)\Big|_0^4 = -\frac{4}{e^4} - \frac{1}{e^4} + 1 = 1 - \frac{5}{e^4}.$$

b. This is given by $\int_0^4 xe^{-ax}\,dx$. Let $u = x$ and $dv = e^{-ax}\,dx$. Then $du = dx$ and $v = -\frac{1}{a}e^{-ax}$. Then

$$\int_0^4 xe^{-ax}\,dx = -\frac{1}{a}xe^{-ax}\Big|_0^4 + \frac{1}{a}\int_0^4 e^{-ax}\,dx = -\frac{4}{ae^{4a}} + \left(-\frac{1}{a^2}e^{-ax}\right)\Big|_0^4 = -\frac{4}{ae^{4a}} - \frac{1}{a^2}\cdot\left(\frac{1}{e^{4a}}-1\right) =$$
$$\frac{1}{a^2}\left(1 - \frac{4a+1}{e^{4a}}\right).$$

c. This is given by $\int_0^b xe^{-ax}\,dx$. Let $u = x$ and $dv = e^{-ax}\,dx$. Then $du = dx$ and $v = -\frac{1}{a}e^{-ax}$. Then

$$\int_0^b xe^{-ax}\,dx = -\frac{1}{a}xe^{-ax}\Big|_0^b + \frac{1}{a}\int_0^b e^{-ax}\,dx = -\frac{b}{ae^{ba}} + \left(-\frac{1}{a^2}e^{-ax}\right)\Big|_0^b = -\frac{b}{ae^{ba}} - \frac{1}{a^2}\cdot\left(\frac{1}{e^{ba}}-1\right) =$$
$$\frac{1}{a^2}\left(1 - \frac{ba+1}{e^{ba}}\right).$$

d. $A(1,\ln b) = 1 - \frac{\ln b+1}{e^{\ln b}} = 1 - \frac{\ln b+1}{b}$.

$A(2,(\ln b)/2) = \frac{1}{4}\left(1 - \frac{\ln b+1}{e^{\ln b}}\right) = \frac{1}{4}\left(1 - \frac{\ln b+1}{b}\right) = \frac{1}{4}A(1,\ln b)$. So $A(1,\ln b) = 4A(2,(\ln b)/2)$.

e. Yes. $A(a,(\ln b)/a) = \frac{1}{a^2}\left(1 - \frac{\ln b+1}{e^{\ln b}}\right) = \frac{1}{a^2}\left(1 - \frac{\ln b+1}{b}\right) = \frac{1}{a^2}A(1,\ln b)$.

So $A(1,\ln b) = a^2 A(a,(\ln b)/a)$.

7.2.61 Using shells, we have $\dfrac{V}{2\pi} = \displaystyle\int_0^{\pi/2} x\cos x\,dx$. Let $u = x$ and $dv = \cos x\,dx$, so that $du = dx$ and $v = \sin x$. We have $\dfrac{V}{2\pi} = x\sin x\Big|_0^{\pi/2} - \displaystyle\int_0^{\pi/2}\sin x\,dx = \dfrac{\pi}{2} - 1$.

Thus, $V = \pi(\pi - 2)$.

7.2.62 We are looking to compute $\displaystyle\int_0^{1/2}(\sin^{-1}x - \sin x)\,dx = \int_0^{1/2}\sin^{-1}x\,dx + \cos 1 - \cos(1/2)$.

Consider $\int \sin^{-1}x$. Let $u = \sin^{-1}x$ and $dv = dx$. Then $du = \frac{1}{\sqrt{1-x^2}}\,dx$ and $v = x$. Then $\int\sin^{-1}x\,dx = x\sin^{-1}x - \int\frac{x}{\sqrt{1-x^2}}\,dx$. Now we perform the ordinary substitution $u = 1 - x^2$, so that $du = -2x\,dx$. We have $x\sin^{-1}x + \frac{1}{2}\int u^{-1/2}\,du = x\sin^{-1}x + \sqrt{1-x^2} + C$.

Thus $\displaystyle\int_0^{1/2}\sin^{-1}x\,dx = \left(\frac{\pi}{12} + \frac{\sqrt{3}}{2}\right) - 1$, and $\displaystyle\int_{1/2}^1(\sin^{-1}x - \sin x)\,dx = \frac{\pi}{12} + \frac{\sqrt{3}}{2} - 1 - (\cos(1/2) - 1) =$
$\frac{\pi}{12} + \frac{\sqrt{3}}{2} + \cos(1/2) - 2$.

7.2.63 Let V_1 be the volume generated when R is revolved about the x-axis, and V_2 the volume generated when R is revolved about the y-axis.

Using disks, we have

$$\frac{V_1}{\pi} = \int_0^\pi \sin^2 x\,dx = \frac{1}{2}\int_0^\pi(1 - \cos 2x)\,dx = \frac{1}{2}\left(\pi - \frac{1}{2}\int_0^\pi 2\cos 2x\,dx\right) = \frac{1}{2}\left(\pi - \frac{1}{2}\int_0^{2\pi}\cos u\,du\right) = \frac{\pi}{2},$$

where the ordinary substitution $u = 2x$ was made. So $V_1 = \frac{\pi^2}{2}$.

Using shells to compute V_2, we have $\dfrac{V_2}{2\pi} = \displaystyle\int_0^\pi x\sin x\,dx$. Letting $u = x$ and $dv = \sin x\,dx$, we have $du = dx$ and $v = -\cos x$. Thus, $\dfrac{V_2}{2\pi} = -x\cos x\Big|_0^\pi + \displaystyle\int_0^\pi \cos x\,dx = \pi$. Thus, $V_2 = 2\pi^2$, and $V_2 > V_1$.

7.2.64 Suppose $m \neq -1$ and let $u = \ln x$ and $dv = x^m \, dx$. Then $du = \frac{1}{x} \, dx$ and $v = \frac{x^{m+1}}{m+1}$. Then

$$\int x^m \ln x \, dx = \frac{x^{m+1}}{m+1} \ln x - \frac{1}{m+1} \int x^m \, dx = \frac{x^{m+1}}{m+1} \left(\ln x - \frac{1}{m+1} \right) + C.$$

For the case $m = -1$ we are computing $\int \frac{1}{x} \ln x \, dx$, so letting $u = \ln x$ so that $du = \frac{1}{x} \, dx$ yields

$$\int u \, du = \frac{u^2}{2} + C = \frac{\ln^2 x}{2} + C.$$

7.2.65

a. Let $u = x$ and $dv = f'(x) \, dx$. Then $du = dx$ and $v = f(x)$. So $\int x f'(x) \, dx = x f(x) - \int f(x) \, dx$.

b. Letting $f'(x) = e^{3x}$ we have $\int x e^{3x} \, dx = \frac{1}{3} x e^{3x} - \frac{1}{9} e^{3x} + C$.

7.2.66

a. Let $y = f^{-1}(x)$, so that $dy = \frac{1}{f'(y)} \, dx$, $f'(y) \neq 0$. Then $\int f^{-1}(x) \, dx = \int f'(y) f^{-1}(x) \frac{1}{f'(y)} \, dx = \int y f'(y) \, dy$.

b. Using the result of exercise 65, $\int f^{-1}(x) \, dx = \int y f'(y) \, dy = y f(y) - \int f(y) \, dy$.

c. $\int \ln x \, dx = x \ln x - \int e^y \, dy = x \ln x - e^y + C = x \ln x - x + C$.

d. $\int \sin^{-1} x \, dx = x \sin^{-1} x - \int \sin y \, dy = x \sin^{-1} x + \cos y + C = x \sin^{-1} x + \sqrt{1 - x^2} + C$.

e. $\int \tan^{-1} x \, dx = x \tan^{-1} x - \int \tan y \, dy = x \tan^{-1} x + \ln|\cos y| + C = x \tan^{-1} x + \ln\left(1/\sqrt{1+x^2}\right) + C = x \tan^{-1} x - \frac{1}{2} \ln(1 + x^2) + C$.

7.2.67 Let $u = \sec x$ and $dv = \sec^2 x \, dx$, so that $du = \sec x \tan x \, dx$ and $v = \tan x$. Then $\int \sec^3 x \, dx =$

$\sec x \tan x - \int \sec x \tan^2 x \, dx = \sec x \tan x - \int \sec x \left(\sec^2 x - 1 \right) \, dx = \sec x \tan x - \int \sec^3 x \, dx + \int \sec x \, dx$.

Thus $2 \int \sec^3 x \, dx = \sec x \tan x + \int \sec x \, dx$, so $\int \sec^3 x \, dx = \frac{1}{2} \sec x \tan x + \frac{1}{2} \int \sec x \, dx$.

7.2.68 Let $u = \sin bx$ and $dv = e^{ax} \, dx$ so that $du = b \cos bx \, dx$ and $v = \frac{e^{ax}}{a}$. Then $\int e^{ax} \sin bx \, dx =$

$\frac{e^{ax}}{a} \sin bx - \frac{b}{a} \int e^{ax} \cos bx \, dx$. Now let $u = \cos bx$ and $dv = e^{ax}$, so that $du = -b \sin bx$ and $v = \frac{e^{ax}}{a}$. Then

$\int e^{ax} \cos bx \, dx = \frac{e^{ax}}{a} \cos bx + \frac{b}{a} \int e^{ax} \sin bx \, dx$. Putting these together yields

$$\int e^{ax} \sin bx \, dx = \frac{e^{ax}}{a} \sin bx - \frac{b}{a} \left(\frac{e^{ax}}{a} \cos bx + \frac{b}{a} \int e^{ax} \sin bx \, dx \right).$$

Multiplying through by a^2 and combining like terms yields

$$(a^2 + b^2) \int e^{ax} \sin bx \, dx = e^{ax} \left(a \sin bx - b \cos bx \right) + C,$$

so $\int e^{ax} \sin bx \, dx = \frac{e^{ax}}{a^2 + b^2} \left(a \sin bx - b \cos bx \right) + C$ as desired.

Now, returning to the integral mentioned above, and incorporating this last result, we have

$$\int e^{ax} \cos bx \, dx = \frac{e^{ax}}{a} \cos bx + \frac{b}{a} \cdot e^{ax} \cdot \frac{a \sin bx - b \cos bx}{a^2 + b^2} + C = \frac{e^{ax}}{a} \cdot \frac{(a^2 + b^2) \cos bx + b(a \sin bx - b \cos bx)}{a^2 + b^2} + C$$

$$= e^{ax} \cdot \frac{a \cos bx + b \sin bx}{a^2 + b^2} + C.$$

7.2.69

a. We have $s(t) = 0$ when $\sin t = 0$, which occurs for $t = k\pi$, where k is an integer.

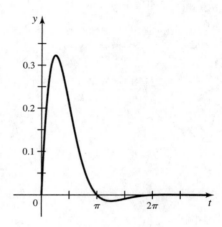

b. This is given by $\frac{1}{\pi} \int_0^{\pi} e^{-t} \sin t \, dt$. Using the previous problem, this is equal to

$$\frac{1}{\pi} e^{-t} \cdot \frac{-\sin t - \cos t}{2} \Big|_0^{\pi} = \frac{1}{2\pi}(e^{-\pi} + 1).$$

c. This is given by $\frac{1}{\pi} \int_{n\pi}^{(n+1)\pi} e^{-t} \sin t \, dt$. Using the previous problem, this is equal to

$$\frac{1}{\pi} e^{-t} \cdot \frac{-\sin t - \cos t}{2} \Big|_{n\pi}^{(n+1)\pi} = \frac{1}{2\pi} \left(e^{-(n+1)\pi} \left(-\sin(n+1)\pi - \cos(n+1)\pi \right) - e^{-n\pi} \left(-\sin n\pi - \cos n\pi \right) \right)$$

$$= \frac{1}{2\pi} \left(-e^{-(n+1)\pi} \cos(n+1)\pi + e^{-n\pi} \cos n\pi \right) = \frac{e^{-n\pi}}{2\pi} \left(\cos n\pi - e^{-\pi} \cos(n+1)\pi \right)$$

$$= \frac{e^{-n\pi}}{2\pi} \left((-1)^n - e^{-\pi}(-1)^{n+1} \right) = (-1)^n \frac{e^{-n\pi}}{2\pi} \left(1 + e^{-\pi} \right).$$

d. Each a_n is $e^{-\pi}$ times a_{n-1}.

7.2.70 The fallacy comes from thinking that $\int \frac{dx}{x}$ represents a unique quantity, as opposed to a family of functions which differ by a constant. When we subtract this quantity from both sides, we should write the arbitrary constant, giving $0 + C_1 = 1 + C_2$, which is a valid statement.

7.2.71

a. If $u = f(x)$ then $du = f'(x) \, dx$, and if $dv = g(x) \, dx$, then $v = G_1(x)$. The integration by parts formula gives

$$\int f(x) g(x) \, dx = f(x) G_1(x) - \int f'(x) G_1(x) \, dx.$$

b. Letting $u = f'(x)$ yields $du = f''(x)\,dx$ and letting $dv = G_1(x)\,dx$ yields $v = G_2(x)$. Then continuing from part (a) we have

$$\int f(x)g(x)\,dx = f(x)G_1(x) - \left(f'(x)G_2(x) - \int f''(x)G_2(x)\,dx \right)$$

$$= f(x)G_1(x) - f'(x)G_2(x) + \int f''(x)G_2(x)\,dx.$$

Note that we end up with three terms which consist of products as indicated by the arrows, with the last product inside an integral sign. The signs alternate as indicated on the chart.

c. For the trailing integral from part (b), we let $u = f''(x)$ so that $du = f'''(x)\,dx$, and let $dv = G_2(x)\,dx$ so that $v = G_3(x)$. Then we have

$$\int f(x)g(x)\,dx = f(x)G_1(x) - f'(x)G_2(x) + \int f''(x)G_2(x)\,dx$$

$$= f(x)G_1(x) - f'(x)G_2(x) + f''(x)G_3(x) - \int f'''(x)G_3(x)\,dx.$$

f and its derivatives	g and its integrals
$f(x)$ $\quad$ +	$g(x)$
$f'(x)$ $\quad$ −	$G_1(x)$
$f''(x)$ $\quad$ +	$G_2(x)$
$f'''(x)$ $\quad$ −	$G_3(x)$

d. The table is as follows:

f and its derivatives	g and its integrals
x^2 $\quad$ +	$e^{0.5x}$
$2x$ $\quad$ −	$2e^{0.5x}$
2 $\quad$ +	$4e^{0.5x}$
0 $\quad$ −	$8e^{0.5x}$

So

$$\int x^2 e^{0.5x}\,dx = 2x^2 e^{0.5x} - 8xe^{0.5x} + 16e^{0.5x} + C.$$

Note that the last integral is $\int 0 \cdot 8e^{0.5x}\,dx = \int 0\,dx = C$.

e. We have:

f and its derivatives		g and its integrals
x^3	+	$\cos x$
$3x^2$	−	$\sin x$
$6x$	+	$-\cos x$
6	−	$-\sin x$
0	+	$\cos x$

So $\int x^3 \cos x\,dx = x^3 \sin x + 3x^2 \cos x - 6x \sin x - 6\cos x + C$.

f. $\frac{d^k}{dx^k}(p_n(x)) = 0$ for $k \geq n+1$, so the process will end.

7.2.72

a. The chart looks like this:

f and its derivatives		g and its integrals
x^4	$+$	e^x
$4x^3$	$-$	e^x
$12x^2$	$+$	e^x
$24x$	$-$	e^x
24	$+$	e^x

Thus $\int x^4 e^x \, dx = x^4 e^x - 4x^3 e^x + 12x^2 e^x - 24xe^x + 24e^x + C$.

b. The chart looks like this:

f and its derivatives		g and its integrals
$7x$	$+$	e^{3x}
7	$-$	$\frac{1}{3}e^{3x}$
0	$+$	$\frac{1}{9}e^{3x}$

Thus $\int 7xe^{3x} \, dx = \frac{7}{3}xe^{3x} - \frac{7}{9}e^{3x} + C$.

c. The chart looks like this:

f and its derivatives		g and its integrals
$2x^2$	$+$	$\sqrt{x+1}$
$4x$	$-$	$\frac{2}{3}(x+1)^{3/2}$
4	$+$	$\frac{4}{15}(x+1)^{5/2}$
0	$-$	$\frac{8}{105}(x+1)^{7/2}$

Thus $\int 2x^2\sqrt{x+1} \, dx = \frac{4}{3}x^2(x+1)^{3/2} - \frac{16}{15}x(x+1)^{5/2} + \frac{32}{105}(x+1)^{7/2} + C$. Evaluating at -1 and 0 gives

$$\int_{-1}^{0} 2x^2\sqrt{x+1} = \frac{32}{105}.$$

d. The chart looks like this:

f and its derivatives		g and its integrals
$x^3 - 2x$	$+$	$\sin 2x$
$3x^2 - 2$	$-$	$-\frac{1}{2}\cos 2x$
$6x$	$+$	$-\frac{1}{4}\sin 2x$
6	$-$	$\frac{1}{8}\cos 2x$
0	$+$	$\frac{1}{16}\sin 2x$

Thus $\int (x^3 - 2x)\sin 2x \, dx = -\frac{1}{2}(x^3 - 2x)\cos 2x + \frac{1}{4}(3x^2 - 2)\sin 2x + \frac{3}{4}x\sin 2x - \frac{3}{8}\sin 2x + C$.

e. The chart looks like this:

f and its derivatives		g and its integrals
$2x^2 - 3x$	$+$	$(x-1)^{-3}$
$4x - 3$	$-$	$-\frac{1}{2}(x-1)^{-2}$
4	$+$	$\frac{1}{2}(x-1)^{-1}$
0	$-$	$\frac{1}{2}\ln|x-1|$

Thus $\int \frac{2x^2-3x}{(x-1)^3}\,dx = -\frac{1}{2}(2x^2-3x)(x-1)^{-2} - \frac{4x-3}{2}(x-1)^{-1} + 2\ln|x-1| + C.$

f. The chart looks like this:

f and its derivatives		g and its integrals
$x^2 + 3x + 4$	$+$	$(2x+1)^{-1/3}$
$2x + 3$	$-$	$\frac{3}{4}(2x+1)^{2/3}$
2	$+$	$\frac{9}{40}(2x+1)^{5/3}$
0	$-$	$\frac{27}{640}(2x+1)^{8/3}$

Thus $\int \frac{x^2+3x+4}{\sqrt[3]{2x+1}}\,dx = \frac{3}{4}(x^2+3x+4)(2x+1)^{2/3} - \frac{9}{40}(2x+3)(2x+1)^{5/3} + \frac{27}{320}(2x+1)^{8/3} + C.$

g. The chart looks like this:

f and its derivatives		g and its integrals
x	$+$	$\frac{1}{\sqrt{1-x^2}}$
1	$-$	$\sin^{-1} x$
0	$+$	$x\sin^{-1} x + \sqrt{1-x^2}$

So $\int \frac{x}{\sqrt{1-x^2}}\,dx = x\sin^{-1} x - (x\sin^{-1} x + \sqrt{1-x^2}) + C = -\sqrt{1-x^2} + C.$ However, this is a little ridiculous because finding the integrals in the 2nd column of the table is more difficult than just integrating the given function using the substitution $u = 1 - x^2$. This gives $du = -2x\,dx$, so we have $-\frac{1}{2}\int u^{-1/2}\,du = -\sqrt{u} + C = -\sqrt{1-x^2} + C.$

7.2.73

a. $\int e^x \cos x\,dx = e^x \sin x + e^x \cos x - \int e^x \cos x\,dx.$

b. Adding $\int e^x \cos x\,dx$ to both sides of the previous equation gives $2\int e^x \cos x\,dx = e^x \sin x + e^x \cos x$, so

$$\int e^x \cos x\,dx = \frac{e^x \sin x + e^x \cos x}{2} + C.$$

c. The chart looks like this:

f and its derivatives		g and its integrals
e^{-2x}	$+$	$\sin 3x$
$-2e^{-2x}$	$-$	$-\frac{1}{3}\cos 3x$
$4e^{-2x}$	$+$	$-\frac{1}{9}\sin 3x$

So we have

$$\int e^{-2x}\sin 3x = -\frac{1}{3}e^{-2x}\cos 3x - \frac{2}{9}e^{-2x}\sin 3x - \frac{4}{9}e^{-2x}\sin 3x.$$

Adding $\frac{4}{9} \int e^{-2x} \sin 3x \, dx$ to both sides gives

$$\frac{13}{9} \int e^{-2x} \sin 3x \, dx = -\frac{1}{3} e^{-2x} \cos 3x - \frac{2}{9} e^{-2x} \sin 3x + D,$$

where D is an arbitrary constant so

$$\int e^{-2x} \sin 3x \, dx = -\frac{3}{13} e^{-2x} \cos 3x - \frac{2}{13} e^{-2x} \sin 3x + C.$$

7.2.74 Let $u = f(x)$ and $dv = f'(x)\,dx$. Then $du = f'(x)\,dx$ and $v = f(x)$. We have

$$\int_a^b f(x)f'(x)\,dx = f(x)^2 \Big|_a^b - \int_a^b f(x)f'(x)\,dx.$$

Thus, $2 \int_a^b f(x)f'(x)\,dx = f(x)^2 \Big|_a^b$, so $\int_a^b f(x)f'(x)\,dx = \frac{1}{2} f(x)^2 \Big|_a^b = \frac{1}{2}\left(f(b)^2 - f(a)^2\right).$

7.2.75 Let $u = x$ and $dv = f''(x)\,dx$. Then $du = dx$ and $v = f'(x)$. We have $\displaystyle\int_a^b x f''(x)\,dx = x f'(x) \Big|_a^b -$

$\displaystyle\int_a^b f'(x)\,dx = (0 - 0) - f(x) \Big|_a^b = -(f(b) - f(a)) = f(a) - f(b).$

7.2.76 Let $u = g(x)$ and $dv = f''(x)\,dx$. Then $du = g'(x)\,dx$ and $v = f'(x)$. Then $\displaystyle\int_0^1 f''(x)g(x)\,dx =$

$f'(x)g(x) \Big|_0^1 - \displaystyle\int_0^1 f'(x)g'(x)\,dx = -\int_0^1 f'(x)g'(x)\,dx.$

Now let $u = g'(x)$ and $dv = f'(x)\,dx$. Then $du = g''(x)\,dx$ and $v = f(x)$. Then $\displaystyle\int_0^1 f'(x)g'(x)\,dx =$

$f(x)g'(x) \Big|_0^1 - \displaystyle\int_0^1 f(x)g''(x)\,dx = -\int_0^1 f(x)g''(x)\,dx.$

Thus, $\displaystyle\int_0^1 f''(x)g(x)\,dx = \int_0^1 f(x)g''(x)\,dx.$

7.2.77

a. To compute I_1, we let $u = -x^2$, so that $du = -2x\,dx$. Then an ordinary substitution yields

$$-\frac{1}{2} \int e^u \, du = -\frac{1}{2} e^u + C = -\frac{1}{2} e^{-x^2} + C.$$

b. To compute I_3, we let $u = x^2$ and $dv = xe^{-x^2}\,dx$, so that $du = 2x\,dx$ and $v = -\frac{1}{2}e^{-x^2}$ (by part (a)).
Then $I_3 = -\frac{1}{2}x^2 e^{-x^2} + \int xe^{-x^2}\,dx = -\frac{1}{2}x^2 e^{-x^2} - \frac{1}{2}e^{-x^2} + C = -\frac{1}{2}e^{-x^2}(x^2 + 1) + C.$

c. To compute I_5, we let $u = x^4$ and $dv = xe^{-x^2}\,dx$. Then $du = 4x^3\,dx$ and $v = -\frac{1}{2}e^{-x^2}$. Then
$I_5 = -\frac{1}{2}x^4 e^{-x^2} + 2\int x^3 e^{-x^2}\,dx = -\frac{1}{2}x^4 e^{-x^2} + 2I_3 = -\frac{1}{2}e^{-x^2}(x^4 + 2x^2 + 2).$

d. Suppose that n is odd and that it is true that $I_n = -\frac{1}{2}e^{-x^2}p_{n-1}(x)$ where $p_{n-1}(x)$ is an even polynomial of degree $n - 1$. We will show that I_{n+2} also has this property, so the result will follow by induction. Let $u = x^{n+1}$ and let $dv = xe^{-x^2}\,dx$, so that $du = (n+1)x^n\,dx$ and $v = -\frac{1}{2}e^{-x^2}$. Then $I_{n+2} = -\frac{1}{2}x^{n+1}e^{-x^2} + \frac{n+1}{2}I_n = -\frac{1}{2}e^{-x^2}(x^{n+1} + \frac{n+1}{2}p_{n-1}(x)) + C = -\frac{1}{2}e^{-x^2}p_{n+1}(x) + C.$ Note that if $p_{n-1}(x)$ is an even polynomial of degree $n - 1$ then $\frac{n+1}{2}p_{n-1}(x) + x^{n+1}$ is an even polynomial of degree $n + 1$.

e. Note that $I_2 = -\frac{1}{2}xe^{-x^2} + \frac{1}{2}I_0$. (Using a similar technique to that above.) Now if I_2 were expressible in terms of elementary functions, then I_0 would be as well, but we are given that it isn't. Similarly, we can express I_{2k} in terms of I_{2k-2} using Integration by Parts, and if any of these were expressible in terms of elementary functions, then the even numbered one below it would be. So the inability to express I_0 that way implies the inability to express I_2 that way, which implies the inability to express I_4 that way, and so on.

7.2.78

a. Let $u = f'(t)$ and $dv = dt$. Then $du = f''(t)\,dt$ and $v = t - x$. We have

$$f(x) = f(0) + \int_0^x f'(t)\,dt$$

$$= f(0) + (t-x)f'(t)\Big|_0^x - \int_0^x (t-x)f''(t)\,dt$$

$$= f(0) + xf'(0) + \int_0^x f''(t)(x-t)\,dt.$$

b. Using integration by parts again, we let $u = f''(t)$ and $dv = (x-t)\,dt$, so that $du = f'''(t)\,dt$ and $v = -\frac{(x-t)^2}{2}$. We then have

$$f(x) = f(0) + xf'(0) + \int_0^x f''(t)(x-t)\,dt$$

$$= f(0) + xf'(0) - \frac{(x-t)^2}{2}f''(t)\Big|_0^x + \frac{1}{2}\int_0^x f'''(t)(x-t)^2\,dt$$

$$= f(0) + xf'(0) + \frac{1}{2}x^2 f''(0) + \frac{1}{2}\int_0^x f'''(t)(x-t)^2\,dt.$$

To see the pattern more clearly, we iterate one more time. Let $u = f'''(t)$ and $dv = (x-t)^2\,dt$, so that $du = f^{(4)}(t)\,dt$ and $v = \frac{(x-t)^3}{3}$. Then

$$f(x) = f(0) + xf'(0) + \frac{1}{2}x^2 f''(0) + \frac{1}{2}\int_0^x f'''(t)(x-t)^2\,dt$$

$$= f(0) + xf'(0) + \frac{1}{2}x^2 f''(0) - \frac{1}{2\cdot 3}f'''(t)(x-t)^3\Big|_0^x + \frac{1}{2\cdot 3}\int_0^x f^{(4)}(t)(x-t)^3\,dt$$

$$= f(0) + xf'(0) + \frac{1}{2}x^2 f''(0) + \frac{1}{2\cdot 3}x^3 f'''(0) + \frac{1}{2\cdot 3}\int_0^x f^{(4)}(t)(x-t)^3\,dt.$$

The general pattern can now be seen to be as given in the statement of the problem.

7.3 Trigonometric Integrals

7.3.1 The half-angle identities for sine and cosine:

$$\sin^2 x = \frac{1-\cos 2x}{2} \quad \text{and} \quad \cos^2 x = \frac{1+\cos 2x}{2},$$

which are conjugates.

7.3.2 The Pythagorean Identities:

$$\cos^2 x + \sin^2 x = 1 \quad \text{and} \quad 1 + \tan^2 x = \sec^2 x \quad \text{and} \quad \cot^2 x + 1 = \csc^2 x,$$

where the second follows from the first by dividing through by $\cos^2 x$, and the third follows from the first by dividing through by $\sin^2 x$.

7.3.3 To integrate $\sin^3 x$, write $\sin^3 x = \sin x \sin^2 x = \sin x(1 - \cos^2 x)$, and let $u = \cos x$ so that $du = -\sin x\, dx$.

7.3.4 To integrate $\sin^m x \cos^n x$ where m is even and n is odd, write $\sin^m x \cos^n x = \sin^m x \cos^{n-1} x \cos x = \sin^m x(1 - \sin^2 x)^{(n-1)/2} \cos x$ and let $u = \sin x$ so that $du = \cos x\, dx$.

7.3.5 A reduction formula is a recursive formula involving integrals. Using it, one can rewrite an integral of a certain type in a simpler form – which can then perhaps be evaluated or further reduced.

7.3.6 One would compute this integral by writing $\cos^2 x \sin^3 x$ as $\cos^2 x(\sin^2 x)\sin x = \cos^2 x(1 - \cos^2 x)\sin x$ and then performing the ordinary substitution $u = \cos x$.

7.3.7 One would compute this integral by letting $u = \tan x$, so that $du = \sec^2 x\, dx$. This substitution leads to the integral $\int u^{10}\, du$, which can easily be evaluated.

7.3.8 One would compute this integral by letting $u = \sec x$, so that $du = \sec x \tan x\, dx$. This substitution leads to the integral $\int u^{11}\, du$, which can easily be evaluated.

7.3.9 $\displaystyle\int \sin^2 x\, dx = \frac{1}{2}\int(1 - \cos 2x)\, dx = \frac{1}{2}\left(x - \frac{1}{2}\sin 2x\right) + C.$

7.3.10 $\displaystyle\int \sin^3 x\, dx = \int \sin x(1 - \cos^2 x)\, dx. = \int(\sin x - \sin x \cos^2 x)\, dx = -\cos x - \int \sin x \cos^2 x\, dx.$ Let $u = \cos x$ so that $du = -\sin x\, dx$ Substituting gives $-\cos x + \int u^2\, du = -\cos x + u^3/3 + C = -\cos x + (\cos^3 x)/3 + C.$

7.3.11 $\displaystyle\int \cos^3 x\, dx = \int \cos x(1 - \sin^2 x)\, dx = \int \cos x\, dx - \int \cos x \sin^2 x\, dx = \sin x - \int \cos x \sin^2 x\, dx.$ Let $u = \sin x$ so that $du = \cos x\, dx$. Substituting gives $\sin x - \int u^2\, du = \sin x - u^3/3 + C = \sin x - (\sin^3 x)/3 + C.$

7.3.12

$$\int \cos^4 2\theta\, d\theta = \int\left(\frac{1 + \cos 4\theta}{2}\right)^2 d\theta = \int \frac{1}{4}(1 + 2\cos 4\theta + \cos^2 4\theta)\, d\theta$$

$$= \frac{1}{4}\int 1 + 2\cos 4\theta + \frac{1 + \cos 8\theta}{2}\, d\theta = \frac{1}{4}\int \frac{3}{2} + 2\cos 4\theta + \frac{1}{2}\cos 8\theta\, d\theta$$

$$= \frac{1}{4}\left(\frac{3\theta}{2} + \frac{\sin 4\theta}{2} + \frac{\sin 8\theta}{16}\right) + C = \frac{1}{8}\left(3\theta + \sin 4\theta + \frac{1}{8}\sin 8\theta\right) + C.$$

7.3.13 $\displaystyle\int \sin^5 x\, dx = \int(\sin^2 x)^2 \sin x\, dx = \int(1 - \cos^2 x)^2 \sin x\, dx.$ Let $u = \cos x$ so that $du = -\sin x\, dx$. Substituting yields $-\int(1 - u^2)^2\, du = \int(-u^4 + 2u^2 - 1)\, du = \frac{-u^5}{5} + \frac{2u^3}{3} - u + C = \frac{-\cos^5 x}{5} + \frac{2\cos^3 x}{3} - \cos x + C.$

7.3.14 $\displaystyle\int \cos^3 20x\, dx = \int \cos^2 20x \cos 20x\, dx = \int(1 - \sin^2 20x)\cos 20x\, dx.$ Let $u = \sin 20x$, so that $du = 20\cos 20x\, dx$. Substituting yields $\frac{1}{20}\int(1 - u^2)\, du = \frac{1}{20}\left(u - \frac{u^3}{3}\right) + C = \frac{1}{20}\left(\sin 20x - \frac{\sin^3 20x}{3}\right) + C.$

7.3.15

$$\int \sin^2 x \cos^2 x\, dx = \int\left(\frac{1 - \cos 2x}{2}\right)\left(\frac{1 + \cos 2x}{2}\right) dx = \frac{1}{4}\int 1 - \cos^2 2x\, dx$$

$$= \frac{1}{4}\int\left(1 - \frac{1 + \cos 4x}{2}\right) dx = \frac{1}{4}\int\left(\frac{1}{2} - \frac{1}{2}\cos 4x\right) dx = \frac{1}{4}\left(\frac{x}{2} - \frac{\sin 4x}{8}\right) + C.$$

7.3.16 $\int \sin^3 x \cos^5 x \, dx = \int (\sin^3 x)(1 - \sin^2 x)^2 \cos x \, dx.$ Let $u = \sin x$ so that $du = \cos x \, dx.$ Then substituting yields $\int u^3 (1 - u^2)^2 \, du = \int u^3 - 2u^5 + u^7 \, du = \dfrac{u^4}{4} - \dfrac{u^6}{3} + \dfrac{u^8}{8} + C = \dfrac{\sin^4 x}{4} - \dfrac{\sin^6 x}{3} + \dfrac{\sin^8 x}{8} + C.$

7.3.17 $\int \sin^3 x \cos^2 x \, dx = \int \sin x (1 - \cos^2 x)(\cos^2 x) \, dx.$ Let $u = \cos x$ so that $du = -\sin x \, dx.$ Substituting gives $\int (u^4 - u^2) \, du = u^5/5 - u^3/3 + C = (\cos^5 x)/5 - (\cos^3 x)/3 + C.$

7.3.18 $\int \sin^2 \theta \cos^5 \theta \, d\theta = \int (\sin^2 \theta)(1 - \sin^2 \theta)^2 \cos \theta \, d\theta.$ Let $u = \sin \theta$ so that $du = \cos \theta \, d\theta.$ Substituting gives $\int u^2 (1 - u^2)^2 \, du = \int (u^2 - 2u^4 + u^6) \, du = u^3/3 - 2u^5/5 + u^7/7 + C = (\sin^3 \theta)/3 - 2(\sin^5 \theta)/5 + (\sin^7 \theta)/7 + C.$

7.3.19 $\int \cos^3 x \sqrt{\sin x} \, dx = \int \cos x (1 - \sin^2 x) \sqrt{\sin x} \, dx.$ Let $u = \sin x$ so that $du = \cos x \, dx.$ Substituting gives $\int (1 - u^2) u^{1/2} \, du = \int (u^{1/2} - u^{5/2}) \, du = 2u^{3/2}/3 - 2u^{7/2}/7 + C = 2(\sin^{3/2} x)/3 - 2(\sin^{7/2} x)/7 + C.$

7.3.20 $\int \dfrac{\sin^3 \theta}{\cos^2 \theta} \, d\theta = \int (\sin \theta) \left(\dfrac{1 - \cos^2 \theta}{\cos^2 \theta} \right) d\theta.$ Let $u = \cos \theta$ so that $du = -\sin \theta \, d\theta.$ Substituting gives $\int \dfrac{u^2 - 1}{u^2} \, du = \int (1 - u^{-2}) \, du = u + \dfrac{1}{u} + C = \cos \theta + \sec \theta + C.$

7.3.21 $\int \sin^5 x \cos^{-2} x \, dx = \int (\sin x) \left(\dfrac{(1 - \cos^2 x)^2}{\cos^2 x} \right) dx.$ Let $u = \cos x$ so that $du = -\sin x \, dx.$ Substituting yields $-\int \dfrac{(1 - u^2)^2}{u^2} \, du = \int -u^{-2} + 2 - u^2 \, du = \dfrac{1}{u} + 2u - \dfrac{u^3}{3} + C = \sec x + 2\cos x - \dfrac{\cos^3 x}{3} + C.$

7.3.22 $\int \sin^{-3/2} x \cos^3 x \, dx = \int \sin^{-3/2} \cos^2 x \cos x \, dx = \int (\sin^{-3/2} x)(1 - \sin^2 x) \cos x \, dx.$ Let $u = \sin x$ so that $du = \cos x \, dx.$ Then a substitution yields $\int u^{-3/2}(1 - u^2) \, du = \int u^{-3/2} - u^{1/2} \, du = \dfrac{-2}{u^{1/2}} - \dfrac{2u^{3/2}}{3} + C = \dfrac{-2}{\sqrt{\sin x}} - \dfrac{2\sin^{3/2} x}{3} + C.$

7.3.23 $\int \sin^2 x \cos^4 x \, dx = \int \left(\dfrac{1 - \cos 2x}{2} \right) \left(\dfrac{1 + \cos 2x}{2} \right)^2 dx = \dfrac{1}{8} \int (1 - \cos^2 2x)(1 + \cos 2x) \, dx = \dfrac{1}{8} \int 1 + \cos 2x - \cos^2 2x - \cos^3 2x \, dx = \dfrac{1}{8} \int 1 + \cos 2x - \dfrac{1 + \cos 4x}{2} - \cos^3 2x \, dx = \dfrac{1}{8} \int \dfrac{1}{2} + \cos 2x - \dfrac{1}{2} \cos 4x \, dx - \dfrac{1}{8} \int (1 - \sin^2 2x) \cos 2x \, dx = \dfrac{x}{16} + \dfrac{\sin 2x}{16} - \dfrac{\sin 4x}{64} - \dfrac{1}{8} \int (1 - \sin^2 2x) \cos 2x \, dx.$ To compute this last integral, we let $u = \sin 2x,$ so that $du = 2 \cos 2x \, dx.$ Then $\int (1 - \sin^2 2x) \cos 2x \, dx = \dfrac{1}{2} \int (1 - u^2) \, du = \dfrac{1}{2} \left(u - \dfrac{u^3}{3} \right) + C = \dfrac{1}{2} \left(\sin 2x - \dfrac{\sin^3 2x}{3} \right) + C.$

Thus, our original given integral is equal to $\dfrac{x}{16} + \dfrac{\sin 2x}{16} - \dfrac{\sin 4x}{64} - \dfrac{1}{8} \left(\dfrac{1}{2} \left(\sin 2x - \dfrac{\sin^3 2x}{3} \right) \right) + C = \dfrac{x}{16} - \dfrac{\sin 4x}{64} + \dfrac{\sin^3 2x}{48} + C.$

7.3.24 $\int \sin^3 x \cos^{3/2} x \, dx = \int (\sin x)(1 - \cos^2 x) \cos^{3/2} x \, dx.$ Let $u = \cos x$ so that $du = -\sin x \, dx.$ Then substituting yields $-\int (1 - u^2) u^{3/2} \, du = \int u^{7/2} - u^{3/2} \, du = \dfrac{2u^{9/2}}{9} - \dfrac{2u^{5/2}}{5} + C = \dfrac{2 \cos^{9/2} x}{9} - \dfrac{2 \cos^{5/2} x}{5} + C.$

7.3.25 $\displaystyle\int \tan^2 x\,dx = \int (\sec^2 x - 1)\,dx = \tan x - x + C.$

7.3.26 $\displaystyle\int 6\sec^4 x\,dx = \int 6\sec^2 x(\tan^2 x + 1)\,dx.$ Let $u = \tan x$, so that $du = \sec^2 x\,dx$. Then we have $6\displaystyle\int (u^2 + 1)\,du = 2u^3 + 6u + C = 2\tan^3 x + 6\tan x + C.$

7.3.27 $\displaystyle\int \cot^4 x\,dx = \int \cot^2 x(\csc^2 x - 1)\,dx = \int (\cot^2 x \csc^2 x - (\csc^2 x - 1))\,dx = \int \cot^2 x \csc^2 x\,dx + \cot x +$ $x.$ Let $u = \cot x$ so that $du = -\csc^2 x\,dx$. Substituting gives $-\displaystyle\int u^2\,du + \cot x + x = -u^3/3 + \cot x + x + C = -(\cot^3 x)/3 + \cot x + x + C.$

7.3.28 $\displaystyle\int \tan^3 \theta\,d\theta = \int \tan\theta(\sec^2 \theta - 1)\,d\theta = \int (\tan\theta \sec^2 \theta - \tan\theta)\,d\theta = \int \tan\theta \sec^2 \theta\,d\theta + \ln|\cos\theta|.$ Let $u = \tan\theta$ so that $du = \sec^2 \theta\,d\theta$. Substituting gives $\displaystyle\int u\,du + \ln|\cos\theta| = u^2/2 + \ln|\cos\theta| + C = (\tan^2 \theta)/2 + \ln|\cos\theta| + C.$ Note that this can also be written as $\sec^2 \theta/2 + \ln|\cos\theta| + C$, because $\sec^2 \theta$ and $\tan^2 \theta$ differ by a constant.

7.3.29

$$\int 20\tan^6 x\,dx = 20\int (\tan^4 x)(\sec^2 x - 1)\,dx = 20\int ((\tan^4 x)\sec^2 x - (\tan^2 x)(\sec^2 x - 1))\,dx$$

$$= 20\int (\tan^4 x \sec^2 x - \tan^2 x \sec^2 x + \sec^2 x - 1)\,dx.$$

Let $u = \tan x$ so that $du = \sec^2 x\,dx$. We have $20\left(\displaystyle\int (u^4 - u^2)\,du + \tan x - x\right) + C = 4u^5 - \dfrac{20u^3}{3} + 20\tan x - 20x + C = 4\tan^5 x - \dfrac{20\tan^3 x}{3} + 20\tan x - 20x + C.$

7.3.30

$$\int \cot^5 3x\,dx = \int (\cot^3 3x)(\csc^2 3x - 1)\,dx = \int (\cot^3 3x \csc^2 3x - (\cot 3x)(\csc^2 3x - 1))\,dx$$

$$= \cot^3 3x \csc^2 3x - \cot 3x \csc^2 3x\,dx + \frac{\ln|\sin 3x|}{3} + C.$$

Now let $u = \cot 3x$, so that $du = -3\csc^2 3x\,dx$. Substituting gives

$$\frac{-1}{3}\int (u^3 - u)\,du + \frac{\ln|\sin 3x|}{3} + C = \frac{-u^4}{12} + \frac{u^2}{6} + \frac{\ln|\sin 3x|}{3} + C$$

$$= \frac{-\cot^4 3x}{12} + \frac{\cot^2 3x}{6} + \frac{\ln|\sin 3x|}{3} + C.$$

7.3.31 Let $u = \tan x$ so that $du = \sec^2 x\,dx$. Substituting gives $\displaystyle\int 10u^9\,du = u^{10} + C = \tan^{10} x + C.$

7.3.32 $\displaystyle\int \tan^9 x(\tan^2 x + 1)\sec^2 x\,dx.$ Let $u = \tan x$ so that $du = \sec^2 x\,dx$. Substituting gives $\displaystyle\int u^9(u^2 + 1)\,du = \int (u^{11} + u^9)\,du = u^{12}/12 + u^{10}/10 + C = (\tan^{12} x)/12 + (\tan^{10} x)/10 + C.$

7.3.33 Let $u = \sec x$ so that $du = \sec x \tan x\,dx$. Substituting gives $\displaystyle\int u^2\,du = u^3/3 + C = (\sec^3 x)/3 + C.$

7.3.34 $\int \sqrt{\tan x} \sec^4 x \, dx = \int \sqrt{\tan x}(\tan^2 x + 1)(\sec^2 x) \, dx$. Let $u = \tan x$ so that $du = \sec^2 x \, dx$. Substituting gives $\int \sqrt{u}(u^2+1) \, du = \int (u^{5/2}+u^{1/2}) \, du = 2u^{7/2}/7 + 2u^{3/2}/3 + C = 2(\tan^{7/2} x)/7 + 2(\tan^{3/2} x)/3 + C$.

7.3.35

$$\int \tan^3 4x \, dx = \int (\tan 4x)(\sec^2 4x - 1) \, dx = \int (\tan 4x) \sec^2 4x \, dx - \int \tan 4x \, dx$$

$$= \int (\tan 4x) \sec^2 4x \, dx + \frac{\ln|\cos 4x|}{4} + C.$$

Let $u = \tan 4x$ so that $du = 4 \sec^2 4x \, dx$. Substituting gives

$$\frac{1}{4} \int u \, du + \frac{\ln|\cos 4x|}{4} + C = \frac{u^2}{8} + \frac{\ln|\cos 4x|}{4} + C = \frac{\tan^2 4x}{8} + \frac{\ln|\cos 4x|}{4} + C.$$

7.3.36 Let $u = \tan x$ so that $du = \sec^2 x \, dx$. Substituting gives $\int u^{-5} \, du = -u^{-4}/4 + C = \dfrac{-1}{4 \tan^4 x} + C$.

7.3.37 Let $u = \tan x$ so that $du = \sec^2 x \, dx$. Then

$$\int \sec^2 x \tan^{1/2} x \, dx = \int u^{1/2} \, du = \frac{2}{3} u^{3/2} + C = \frac{2}{3} \tan^{3/2} x + C.$$

7.3.38

$$\int \sec^{-2} x \tan^3 x \, dx = \int \sec^{-2}(\sec^2 x - 1) \tan x \, dx = \int (\tan x - \sec^{-2} x \tan x) \, dx$$

$$= \int \left(\frac{\sin x}{\cos x} - \cos x \sin x \right) dx.$$

Let $u = \cos x$ so that $du = -\sin x \, dx$. Then we have

$$\int \left(\frac{-1}{u} + u \right) du = -\ln|u| + \frac{u^2}{2} + C = -\ln|\cos x| + \frac{1}{2} \cos^2 x + C.$$

7.3.39 $\int \dfrac{\csc^4 x}{\cot^2 x} \, dx = \int (\csc^2 x) \left(\dfrac{\cot^2 x + 1}{\cot^2 x} \right) dx$. Let $u = \cot x$ so that $du = -\csc^2 x \, dx$. Substituting gives $-\int \dfrac{u^2 + 1}{u^2} \, du = \int -1 - u^{-2} \, du = -u + \dfrac{1}{u} + C = -\cot x + \tan x + C$.

7.3.40 Let $u = \csc x$ so that $du = -\csc x \cot x \, dx$. Substituting gives $-\int u^9 \, du = -u^{10}/10 + C = -(\csc^{10} x)/10 + C$.

7.3.41 $\int_0^{\pi/4} \sec^4 \theta \, d\theta = \int_0^{\pi/4} (\sec^2 \theta)(1 + \tan^2 \theta) \, d\theta$. Let $u = \tan \theta$ so that $du = \sec^2 \theta \, d\theta$. Note that when $\theta = 0$ we have $u = 0$ and when $\theta = \frac{\pi}{4}$ we have $u = 1$. So the original integral is equal to $\int_0^1 (1 + u^2) \, du = \left(u + \dfrac{u^3}{3} \right) \Big|_0^1 = 1 + \dfrac{1}{3} = \dfrac{4}{3}$.

7.3.42 $\int \tan^5 \theta \sec^4 \theta \, d\theta = \int (\tan^5 \theta)(\tan^2 \theta + 1)(\sec^2 \theta) \, d\theta$. Let $u = \tan \theta$ so that $du = \sec^2 \theta \, d\theta$. Substituting yields $\int u^7 + u^5 \, du = \dfrac{u^8}{8} + \dfrac{u^6}{6} + C = \dfrac{\tan^8 \theta}{8} + \dfrac{\tan^6 \theta}{6} + C$.

7.3.43 $\displaystyle\int_{\pi/6}^{\pi/3} \cot^3\theta\,d\theta = \int_{\pi/6}^{\pi/3}(\cot\theta)(\csc^2\theta - 1)\,d\theta = \int_{\pi/6}^{\pi/3}\cot\theta\csc^2\theta\,d\theta - \int_{\pi/6}^{\pi/3}\dfrac{\cos\theta}{\sin\theta}\,d\theta.$ For the first integral, let $u = \cot\theta$ so that $du = -\csc^2\theta\,d\theta$. For the second integral, let $w = \sin\theta$ so that $dw = \cos\theta\,d\theta$. Substituting gives

$$-\int_{\sqrt{3}}^{1/\sqrt{3}} u\,du - \int_{1/2}^{\sqrt{3}/2}\frac{1}{w}\,dw = -\frac{u^2}{2}\Big|_{\sqrt{3}}^{1/\sqrt{3}} - \ln w\,\Big|_{1/2}^{\sqrt{3}/2}$$

$$= -\frac{1}{2}\left(\frac{1}{3} - 3\right) - \left(\ln\sqrt{3} - \ln 2 - \ln 1 + \ln 2\right) = \frac{4}{3} - \frac{\ln 3}{2}.$$

7.3.44 $\displaystyle\int_0^{\pi/4}\tan^3\theta\sec^2\theta\,d\theta.$ Let $u = \tan\theta$ so that $du = \sec^2\theta\,d\theta$. Substituting yields $\displaystyle\int_0^1 u^3\,du = \dfrac{u^4}{4}\Big|_0^1 = \dfrac{1}{4}.$

7.3.45

    a. True. We have $\displaystyle\int_0^\pi\cos^{2m+1}x\,dx = \int_0^\pi(\cos^2 x)^m\cos x\,dx = \int_0^\pi(1 - \sin^2 x)^m\cos x\,dx.$ Let $u = \sin x$ so that $du = \cos x\,dx$. Substituting yields $\displaystyle\int_0^0(1 - u^2)^m\,du = 0.$

    b. False. For example, suppose $m = 1$. Then $\displaystyle\int_0^\pi\sin x\,dx = -\cos x\,\Big|_0^\pi = -(-1 - 1) = 2 \neq 0.$

7.3.46 $\displaystyle\int\cot x\,dx = \int\dfrac{\cos x}{\sin x}\,dx.$ Let $u = \sin x$ so that $du = \cos x\,dx$. We then have $\displaystyle\int\frac{1}{u}\,du = \ln|u| + C = \ln|\sin x| + C.$

7.3.47 $\displaystyle\int\csc x\,dx = \int(\csc x)\left(\dfrac{\csc x + \cot x}{\csc x + \cot x}\right)dx = \int\dfrac{\csc^2 x + \csc x\cot x}{\csc x + \cot x}\,dx.$ Let $u = \csc x + \cot x$ so that $du = -\csc^2 x - \csc x\cot x\,dx$. Substituting then yields $\displaystyle-\int\frac{1}{u}\,du = -\ln|u| + C = -\ln|\csc x + \cot x| + C.$

7.3.48 $R_1 = \displaystyle\int_0^{\pi/3}\tan x\,dx = -\ln|\cos x|\,\Big|_0^{\pi/3} = -\ln(1/2) = \ln 2.$

$R_2 = \displaystyle\int_0^{\pi/6}\sec x\,dx = \ln|\sec x + \tan x|\,\Big|_0^{\pi/6} = \ln\sqrt{3} = \dfrac{\ln 3}{2}.$

$R_1 \approx .693$ and $R_2 \approx .549$ so $R_1 > R_2$.

7.3.49 $A = \displaystyle\int_0^{\pi/4}\sec x - \tan x\,dx = \ln|\sec x + \tan x| + \ln|\cos x|\,\Big|_0^{\pi/4} = \ln\left(\sqrt{2} + 1\right) + \ln\left(\dfrac{\sqrt{2}}{2}\right) - (0 + 0) = \ln\left(1 + \sqrt{2}/2\right).$

7.3.50 $\displaystyle\int_0^{\sqrt{\pi/2}} x\sin^3(x^2)\,dx = \frac{1}{2}\int_0^{\pi/2}\sin^3 u\,du,$ where $u = x^2$ and $du = 2x\,dx$. Now $\dfrac{1}{2}\displaystyle\int_0^{\pi/2}\sin^3 u\,du = \frac{1}{2}\int_0^{\pi/2}(\sin u)(1 - \cos^2 u)\,du.$ Now let $w = \cos u$ so that $dw = -\sin u\,du$. We then have $\dfrac{-1}{2}\displaystyle\int_1^0 1 - w^2\,dw = \frac{1}{2}\left(w - \frac{w^3}{3}\right)\Big|_0^1 = \frac{1}{3}.$

7.3.51 Let $u = \ln\theta$ so that $du = \frac{1}{\theta}\,d\theta$. Substituting yields $\displaystyle\int\sec^4 u\,du = \int(\sec^2 u)(1 + \tan^2 u)\,du.$ Let $w = \tan u$ so that $dw = \sec^2 u\,du$. Substituting again gives $\displaystyle\int(1 + w^2)\,dw = w + \frac{w^3}{3} + C = \tan(\ln(\theta)) + \dfrac{\tan^3(\ln(\theta))}{3} + C.$

7.3.52 $\int_{\pi/6}^{\pi/2} (\csc y)\, dy = -\ln|\csc y + \cot y|\ \Big|_{\pi/6}^{\pi/2} = -\ln|1+0| + \ln|2+\sqrt{3}| = \ln(2+\sqrt{3})$.

7.3.53

$$\int_{-\pi/3}^{\pi/3} \sqrt{\sec^2\theta - 1}\, d\theta = 2\int_0^{\pi/3} \sqrt{\sec^2\theta - 1}\, d\theta = 2\int_0^{\pi/3} \tan\theta\, d\theta$$

$$= -2\ln|\cos\theta|\ \Big|_0^{\pi/3} = -2\ln(1/2) + 2\ln(1) = 2\ln 2.$$

7.3.54 Note that $\tan^3 x \sec^2 x$ is an odd function. Thus, $\int_{-\pi/4}^{\pi/4} \tan^3 x \sec^2 x\, dx = 0$.

7.3.55 $\int_0^\pi (1 - \cos 2x)^{3/2}\, dx = \int_0^\pi (2\sin^2 x)^{3/2}\, dx = 2\sqrt{2}\int_0^\pi \sin^3 x\, dx = 2\sqrt{2}\int_0^\pi (\sin x)(1 - \cos^2 x)\, dx$. Let $u = \cos x$ so that $du = -\sin x\, dx$. Substituting yields $-2\sqrt{2}\int_1^{-1}(1 - u^2)\, du = 2\sqrt{2}\int_{-1}^{1}(1 - u^2)\, du = 4\sqrt{2}\int_0^1 (1 - u^2)\, du = 4\sqrt{2}\left(u - \dfrac{u^3}{3}\right)\Big|_0^1 = \dfrac{8\sqrt{2}}{3}$.

7.3.56 $\int \csc^{10} x \cot^3 x\, dx = \int \csc^9 x \cot^2 x \csc x \cot x\, dx = \int \csc^9 x (\csc^2 x - 1) \csc x \cot x\, dx$. Let $u = \csc x$ so that $du = -\csc x \cot x\, dx$. Substituting gives $-\int u^9(u^2 - 1)\, du = -\int (u^{11} - u^9)\, du = -(u^{12}/12 - u^{10}/10) + C = \dfrac{-\csc^{12} x}{12} + \dfrac{\csc^{10} x}{10} + C$.

7.3.57 Let $u = e^x + 1$ so that $du = e^x\, dx$. Substituting gives $\int \sec u\, du = \ln|\sec u + \tan u| + C = \ln|\sec(e^x + 1) + \tan(e^x + 1)| + C$.

7.3.58 $\int_{-\pi/4}^{\pi/4} \sqrt{1 + \cos 4x}\, dx = 2\int_0^{\pi/4} \sqrt{1 + \cos 4x}\, dx = 2\sqrt{2}\int_0^{\pi/4} \cos 2x\, dx$. Let $u = 2x$, so that $du = 2\, dx$. Substituting yields $\sqrt{2}\int_0^{\pi/2} \cos u\, du = \sqrt{2}\sin u\ \Big|_0^{\pi/2} = \sqrt{2}$.

7.3.59 $\int_0^{\pi/2} \sqrt{1 - \cos 2x}\, dx = \sqrt{2}\int_0^{\pi/2} \sin x\, dx = -\sqrt{2}\cos x\ \Big|_0^{\pi/2} = \sqrt{2}$.

7.3.60 $\int_0^{\pi/8} \sqrt{1 - \cos 8x}\, dx = \sqrt{2}\int_0^{\pi/8} \sin 4x\, dx = -\sqrt{2}\cdot \dfrac{\cos 4x}{4}\ \Big|_0^{\pi/8} = \dfrac{\sqrt{2}}{4}$.

7.3.61 $\int_0^{\pi/4} (1 + \cos 4x)^{3/2}\, dx = \int_0^{\pi/4} (2\cos^2 2x)^{3/2}\, dx = 2\sqrt{2}\int_0^{\pi/4} \cos^3 2x\, dx = 2\sqrt{2}\int_0^{\pi/4} (\cos 2x)(1 - \sin^2 2x)\, dx$. Let $u = \sin 2x$ so that $du = 2\cos 2x\, dx$. Substituting gives

$$\sqrt{2}\int_0^1 (1 - u^2)\, du = \sqrt{2}\left(u - \frac{u^3}{3}\right)\Big|_0^1 = \frac{2\sqrt{2}}{3}.$$

7.3.62 Using the disk method, we have

$$\frac{V}{\pi} = \int_0^\pi \sin^2 x\, dx = \frac{1}{2}\int_0^\pi (1 - \cos 2x)\, dx = \frac{\pi}{2} - \frac{1}{2}\int_0^\pi \cos 2x\, dx = \frac{\pi}{2} - \left(\frac{\sin 2x}{4}\right)\Big|_0^\pi = \frac{\pi}{2}.$$

Thus, $V = \frac{\pi^2}{2}$.

7.3.63 If $y = \ln(\sec x)$ then $\frac{dy}{dx} = \tan x$. Thus, $L = \int_0^{\pi/4} \sqrt{1 + \tan^2 x}\, dx = \int_0^{\pi/4} \sec x\, dx$

$= \ln|\sec x + \tan x| \Big|_0^{\pi/4} = \ln(\sqrt{2} + 1)$.

7.3.64 $\int \sin^n x\, dx = \int \sin^{n-1} x \sin x\, dx$. Let $u = \sin^{n-1} x$ and $dv = \sin x\, dx$. Then we have $du = (n-1)\sin^{n-2} x \cos x\, dx$ and $v = -\cos x$. We have $\int \sin^n x\, dx = -\sin^{n-1} x \cos x + (n-1)\int (\sin^{n-2} x)(1 - \sin^2 x)\, dx = -\sin^{n-1} x \cos x + (n-1)\int \sin^{n-2} x\, dx - (n-1)\int \sin^n x\, dx$. Adding the appropriate quantity to both sides of this last equation gives $n\int \sin^n x\, dx = -\sin^{n-1} x \cos x + (n-1)\int \sin^{n-2} x\, dx$, so $\int \sin^n x\, dx = \dfrac{-\sin^{n-1} x \cos x}{n} + \dfrac{n-1}{n}\int \sin^{n-2} x\, dx$.

Thus, $\int \sin^6 x\, dx = \dfrac{-\sin^5 x \cos x}{6} + \dfrac{5}{6}\left(\dfrac{-\sin^3 x \cos x}{4} + \dfrac{3}{4}\left(\dfrac{x}{2} - \dfrac{\sin 2x}{4}\right)\right) + C$.

7.3.65 For $n \neq 1$, $\int \tan^n x\, dx = \int (\tan^{n-2} x)(\sec^2 x - 1)\, dx = \int \tan^{n-2} x \sec^2 x\, dx - \int \tan^{n-2} x\, dx$. Let $u = \tan x$ so that $du = \sec^2 x\, dx$. Then substituting in the first of these last two integrals yields $\int u^{n-2}\, du - \int \tan^{n-2} x\, dx = \dfrac{u^{n-1}}{n-1} - \int \tan^{n-2} x\, dx = \dfrac{\tan^{n-1} x}{n-1} - \int \tan^{n-2} x\, dx$.

Thus $\int_0^{\pi/4} \tan^3 x\, dx = \dfrac{\tan^2 x}{2} \Big|_0^{\pi/4} - \int_0^{\pi/4} \tan x\, dx = \dfrac{1}{2} + \ln|\cos x| \Big|_0^{\pi/4} = \dfrac{1}{2} - \dfrac{\ln 2}{2}$.

7.3.66 $\int \sec^n x\, dx = \int \sec^{n-2} x \sec^2 x\, dx$. Let $u = \sec^{n-2} x$ and $dv = \sec^2 x\, dx$. Then $du = (n-2)\sec^{n-2} x \tan x\, dx$ and $v = \tan x$. Integration by Parts gives us $\sec^{n-2} x \tan x - (n-2)\int \sec^{n-2} x \tan^2 x\, dx = \sec^{n-2} x \tan x - (n-2)\int (\sec^{n-2} x)(\sec^2 x - 1)\, dx = \sec^{n-2} x \tan x - (n-2)\int \sec^n x\, dx + (n-2)\int \sec^{n-2} x\, dx$. Combining like terms then gives $(n-1)\int \sec^n x\, dx = \sec^{n-2} x \tan x + (n-2)\int \sec^{n-2} x\, dx$, so as long as $n \neq 1$ we have $\int \sec^n x\, dx = \dfrac{\sec^{n-2} x \tan x}{n-1} + \dfrac{n-2}{n-1}\int \sec^{n-2} x\, dx$.

7.3.67 $\int \sin 3x \cos 7x\, dx = \dfrac{1}{2}\left(\int \sin(-4x)\, dx + \int \sin 10x\, dx\right) = \dfrac{1}{2}\left(\dfrac{\cos(-4x)}{4} - \dfrac{\cos 10x}{10}\right) + C = \dfrac{\cos 4x}{8} - \dfrac{\cos 10x}{20} + C$.

7.3.68 $\int \sin 5x \sin 7x\, dx = \dfrac{1}{2}\left(\int \cos(-2x)\, dx - \int \cos 12x\, dx\right) = \dfrac{1}{2}\left(\int \cos 2x\, dx - \int \cos 12x\, dx\right) = \dfrac{1}{2}\left(\dfrac{\sin 2x}{2} - \dfrac{\sin 12x}{12}\right) + C = \dfrac{\sin 2x}{4} - \dfrac{\sin 12x}{24} + C$.

7.3.69 $\int \sin 3x \sin 2x\, dx = \dfrac{1}{2}\left(\int \cos x\, dx - \int \cos 5x\, dx\right) = \dfrac{\sin x}{2} - \dfrac{\sin 5x}{10} + C$.

7.3.70 $\int \cos x \cos 2x\, dx = \dfrac{1}{2}\left(\int \cos(-x)\, dx + \int \cos 3x\, dx\right) = \dfrac{\sin x}{2} + \dfrac{\sin 3x}{6} + C$.

7.3.71

a. $\int_0^\pi \sin mx \sin nx\, dx = \frac{1}{2}\left(\int_0^\pi \cos(m-n)x\, dx - \int_0^\pi \cos(m+n)x\, dx\right) =$

$\frac{1}{2}\left(\frac{1}{m-n}\int_0^{(m-n)\pi} \cos u\, du - \frac{1}{m+n}\int_0^{(m+n)\pi} \cos v\, dv\right)$ where $u = (m-n)x$ and $v = (m+n)x$. But

this yields $\frac{1}{2}\left(\frac{1}{m-n}\sin u\Big|_0^{(m-n)\pi} - \frac{1}{m+n}\sin v\Big|_0^{(m+n)\pi}\right) = \frac{1}{2}(0-0) = 0.$

b. $\int_0^\pi \cos mx \cos nx\, dx = \frac{1}{2}\left(\int_0^\pi \cos(m-n)x\, dx + \int_0^\pi \cos(m+n)x\, dx\right) = 0$ by the previous part of this problem,

c. $\int_0^\pi \sin mx \cos nx\, dx = \frac{1}{2}\left(\int_0^\pi \sin(m-n)x\, dx + \int_0^\pi \sin(m+n)x\, dx\right) =$

$\frac{1}{2}\left(\frac{1}{m-n}\int_0^{(m-n)\pi} \sin u\, du + \frac{1}{m+n}\int_0^{(m+n)\pi} \sin v\, dv\right)$ where $u = (m-n)x$ and $v = (m+n)x$. This

quantity is equal to $\frac{-1}{2}\left(\frac{1}{m-n}\cos u\Big|_0^{(m-n)\pi} + \frac{1}{m+n}\cos v\Big|_0^{(m+n)\pi}\right) =$

$\frac{-1}{2}\left(\frac{1}{m-n}(\cos(m-n)\pi - 1) + \frac{1}{m+n}(\cos(m+n)\pi - 1)\right) =$

$\begin{cases} 0 & \text{if } m \text{ and } n \text{ are both even or both odd;} \\ \frac{1}{m-n}+\frac{1}{m+n} = \frac{2m}{m^2-n^2} & \text{otherwise.} \end{cases}$

7.3.72 Note that the function is equivalent to $\ln|\sec\theta + \tan\theta|$. Its derivative is $\sec\theta$ which is positive on the interval $[0, \pi/2)$ as its second derivative $\sec\theta\tan\theta$, so it is increasing and concave up on the given interval.

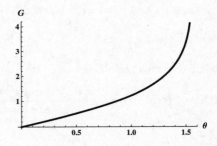

7.3.73

a. $\int_0^\pi \sin^2 x\, dx = \frac{1}{2}\int_0^\pi (1-\cos 2x)\, dx =$
$\frac{1}{2}\left(x - \frac{\sin 2x}{2}\right)\Big|_0^\pi = \frac{\pi}{2}.$

$\int_0^\pi \sin^2 2x\, dx = \frac{1}{2}\int_0^\pi (1-\cos 4x)\, dx =$
$\frac{1}{2}\left(x - \frac{\sin 4x}{4}\right)\Big|_0^\pi = \frac{\pi}{2}.$

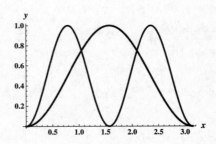

$$\int_0^\pi \sin^2 3x\, dx \;=\; \frac{1}{2}\int_0^\pi (1-\cos 6x)\, dx \;=$$
$$\frac{1}{2}\left(x-\frac{\sin 6x}{6}\right)\Big|_0^\pi = \frac{\pi}{2}.$$

b.
$$\int_0^\pi \sin^2 4x\, dx \;=\; \frac{1}{2}\int_0^\pi (1-\cos 8x)\, dx \;=$$
$$\frac{1}{2}\left(x-\frac{\sin 8x}{8}\right)\Big|_0^\pi = \frac{\pi}{2}.$$

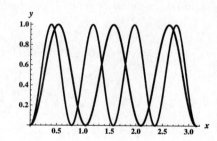

c. $\displaystyle\int_0^\pi \sin^2 nx\, dx = \frac{1}{2}\int_0^\pi (1-\cos 2nx)\, dx = \frac{1}{2}\left(x-\frac{\sin 2nx}{2n}\right)\Big|_0^\pi = \frac{\pi}{2}.$

d. Yes. $\displaystyle\int_0^\pi \cos^2 nx\, dx = \frac{1}{2}\int_0^\pi (1+\cos 2nx)\, dx = \frac{1}{2}\left(x+\frac{\sin 2nx}{2n}\right)\Big|_0^\pi = \frac{\pi}{2}.$

e. Claim: The corresponding integrals are all equal to $\frac{3\pi}{8}$. Proof:

$$\int_0^\pi \sin^4 nx\, dx = \int_0^\pi \left(\frac{1-\cos 2nx}{2}\right)^2 dx$$

$$= \int_0^\pi \frac{1-2\cos 2nx+\cos^2 2nx}{4}\, dx = \int_0^\pi \frac{1}{4}\, dx - \frac{1}{2}\int_0^\pi \cos 2nx\, dx + \frac{1}{4}\int_0^\pi \cos^2 2nx\, dx$$

$$= \frac{\pi}{4} - \frac{1}{2}\left(\frac{\sin 2nx}{2n}\right)\Big|_0^\pi + \frac{1}{4}\cdot\frac{\pi}{2} = \frac{\pi}{4} - 0 + \frac{\pi}{8} = \frac{3\pi}{8}.$$

f. The proof is by strong induction. The base step ($m=1$) follows by part (a) of this problem. Now suppose the result holds for all positive integer values less than m. Now

$$\int_0^\pi \sin^{2m} x\, dx = -\frac{\sin^{2m-1} x\cos x}{2m}\Big|_0^\pi + \frac{2m-1}{2m}\int_0^\pi \sin^{2m-2} x\, dx$$

$$= \frac{2m-1}{2m}\int_0^\pi \sin^{2(m-1)} x\, dx$$

$$= \frac{2m-1}{2m}\cdot \pi \cdot \frac{1\cdot 3\cdot 5\cdots(2m-3)}{2\cdot 4\cdot 6\cdots 2(m-1)} = \pi\cdot\frac{1\cdot 3\cdot 5\cdots(2m-1)}{2\cdot 4\cdot 6\cdots 2m}.$$

Thus the result holds for all positive numbers m. Note the use of the reduction formula from problem number 64.

To see that the same result holds for $\displaystyle\int_0^\pi \cos^{2m} x\, dx$ first note that $\displaystyle\int_{\pi/2}^\pi \sin^{2m} x\, dx = -\int_{\pi/2}^0 \sin^{2m}(\pi-u)\, du = \int_0^{\pi/2} \sin^{2m} u\, du$ (using the substitution $x=\pi-u$.)

Thus, $\displaystyle\int_0^\pi \cos^{2m} x\, dx = -\int_{\pi/2}^{-\pi/2}\cos^{2m}(\pi/2-u)\, du.$ (Via the substitution $x=\pi/2-u$.) This last integral can be written as $\displaystyle\int_{-\pi/2}^{\pi/2} \sin^{2m} u\, du = 2\int_0^{\pi/2} \sin^{2m} u\, du = \int_0^{\pi/2} \sin^{2m} u\, du + \int_{\pi/2}^\pi \sin^{2m} u\, du = \int_0^\pi \sin^{2m} x\, dx.$

7.4 Trigonometric Substitutions

7.4.1 This would suggest $x=3\sec\theta$, because then $\sqrt{x^2-9}=3\sqrt{\sec^2\theta-1}=3\sqrt{\tan^2\theta}=3\tan\theta$, for $\theta\in[0,\pi/2)$.

7.4.2 This would suggest $x = 6\tan\theta$, because then $\sqrt{x^2 + 36} = 6\sqrt{\tan^2\theta + 1} = 6\sqrt{\sec^2\theta} = 6\sec\theta$, for $|\theta| < \frac{\pi}{2}$.

7.4.3 This would suggest $x = 10\sin\theta$, because then $\sqrt{100 - x^2} = 10\sqrt{1 - \sin^2\theta} = 10\sqrt{\cos^2\theta} = 10\cos\theta$, for $|\theta| \leq \frac{\pi}{2}$.

7.4.4

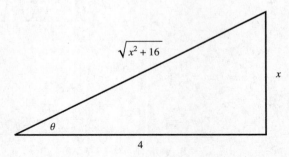

If $\tan\theta = \frac{x}{4}$, then $16\tan^2\theta = x^2$, so $16(\sec^2\theta - 1) = x^2$. Thus $\sec^2\theta = \frac{x^2 + 16}{16}$ and $\cos^2\theta = 1 - \sin^2\theta = \frac{16}{x^2 + 16}$. Thus $\sin^2\theta = \frac{x^2}{16 + x^2}$ and we have $\sin\theta = \frac{x}{\sqrt{16 + x^2}}$, for $|\theta| < \frac{\pi}{2}$.

7.4.5

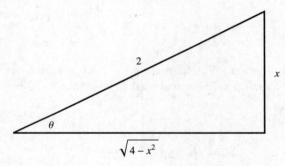

If $x = 2\sin\theta$ then $\frac{x^2}{4} = \sin^2\theta = \frac{1}{\csc^2\theta}$. Then $\cot^2\theta = \csc^2\theta - 1 = \frac{4}{x^2} - 1 = \frac{4 - x^2}{x^2}$. So $\cot\theta = \frac{\sqrt{4 - x^2}}{x}$ for $0 < |\theta| \leq \frac{\pi}{2}$.

7.4.6

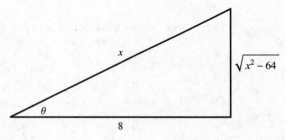

If $x = 8\sec\theta$, the $\tan^2\theta = \sec^2\theta - 1 = \frac{x^2}{64} - 1 = \frac{x^2 - 64}{64}$. Thus $\tan\theta = \begin{cases} \sqrt{x^2 - 64}/8 & \text{if } x \geq 8, \\ -\sqrt{x^2 - 64}/8 & \text{if } x \leq -8. \end{cases}$

7.4.7 Let $x = 5\sin\theta$, so that $dx = 5\cos\theta\,d\theta$. Note that $\sqrt{25 - x^2} = 5\cos\theta$. Then $\displaystyle\int_0^{5/2} \frac{1}{\sqrt{25 - x^2}}\,dx = \int_0^{\pi/6} \frac{5\cos\theta}{5\cos\theta}\,d\theta = \frac{\pi}{6}$.

7.4.8 Let $x = 3\sin\theta$ so that $dx = 3\cos\theta\,d\theta$. Note that $\sqrt{9 - x^2} = 3\cos\theta$. Then $\displaystyle\int_0^{3/2} \frac{1}{(9 - x^2)^{3/2}}\,dx =$
$\displaystyle\int_0^{\pi/6} \frac{3\cos\theta}{27\cos^3\theta}\,d\theta = \frac{1}{9}\int_0^{\pi/6} \sec^2\theta\,d\theta = \frac{1}{9}\tan\theta\,\Big|_0^{\pi/6} = \frac{1}{9}\left(\frac{1}{\sqrt{3}} - 0\right) = \frac{\sqrt{3}}{27}$.

7.4.9 Let $x = 10\sin\theta$ so that $dx = 10\cos\theta\,d\theta$. Note that $\sqrt{100 - x^2} = 10\cos\theta$. Then $\displaystyle\int_5^{10} \sqrt{100 - x^2}\,dx =$
$\displaystyle 100\int_{\pi/6}^{\pi/2} \cos^2\theta\,d\theta = 50\int_{\pi/6}^{\pi/2} (1 + \cos 2\theta)\,d\theta = 50\left(\theta + \frac{\sin 2\theta}{2}\right)\Big|_{\pi/6}^{\pi/2} = 50\left(\frac{\pi}{2} + 0 - \left(\frac{\pi}{6} + \frac{\sqrt{3}}{4}\right)\right) = \frac{50\pi}{3} -$
$\dfrac{25\sqrt{3}}{2}$.

7.4.10 Let $x = 2\sin\theta$, so that $dx = 2\cos\theta\,d\theta$. Note that $\sqrt{4 - x^2} = 2\cos\theta$. Thus, $\displaystyle\int_0^{\sqrt{2}} \frac{x^2}{\sqrt{4 - x^2}}\,dx =$
$\displaystyle\int_0^{\pi/4} \frac{4\sin^2\theta \cdot 2\cos\theta}{2\cos\theta}\,d\theta = 4\int_0^{\pi/4} \sin^2\theta\,d\theta = 2\left(\frac{\pi}{4} - \int_0^{\pi/4}\cos 2\theta\,d\theta\right) = \frac{\pi}{2} - 2\left(\frac{\sin 2\theta}{2}\right)\Big|_0^{\pi/4} = \frac{\pi}{2} - 1$.

7.4.11 Let $x = \sin\theta$ so that $dx = \cos\theta\,d\theta$. Note that $\sqrt{1 - x^2} = \sqrt{1 - \sin^2\theta} = \cos\theta$. Substituting gives
$\displaystyle\int_0^{\pi/6} \sin^2\theta\,d\theta = \int_0^{\pi/6} \frac{1 - \cos 2\theta}{2}\,d\theta = \frac{\theta}{2}\Big|_0^{\pi/6} - \frac{\sin 2\theta}{4}\Big|_0^{\pi/6} = \frac{\pi}{12} - \frac{\sqrt{3}}{8}$.

7.4.12 Let $x = \sin\theta$ so that $dx = \cos\theta\,d\theta$. Note that $\sqrt{1 - x^2} = \sqrt{1 - \sin^2\theta} = \cos\theta$. Substituting gives
$\displaystyle\int_{\pi/6}^{\pi/2} \cot^2\theta\,d\theta = \int_{\pi/6}^{\pi/2} (\csc^2\theta - 1)\,d\theta = (-\cot\theta - \theta)\Big|_{\pi/6}^{\pi/2} = 0 - \pi/2 - (-\sqrt{3} - \pi/6) = \sqrt{3} - \pi/3$.

7.4.13 Let $x = 4\sin\theta$ so that $dx = 4\cos\theta\,d\theta$. Note that $\sqrt{16 - x^2} = 4\cos\theta$. Thus, $\displaystyle\int \frac{1}{\sqrt{16 - x^2}}\,dx =$
$\displaystyle\int \frac{4\cos\theta}{4\cos\theta}\,d\theta = \theta + C = \sin^{-1}\left(\frac{x}{4}\right) + C$.

7.4.14 Let $t = 6\sin\theta$ so that $dt = 6\cos\theta\,d\theta$ and $\sqrt{36 - t^2} = 6\cos\theta$. Then

$$\int \sqrt{36 - t^2}\,dt = \int 36\cos^2\theta\,d\theta = 18\int (1 + \cos 2\theta)\,d\theta = 18\left(\theta + \frac{\sin 2\theta}{2}\right) + C = 18\,(\theta + \sin\theta\cos\theta)$$

$$= 18\left(\sin^{-1}\left(\frac{t}{6}\right) + \frac{t}{6}\cdot\frac{\sqrt{36 - t^2}}{6}\right) + C = 18\sin^{-1}\left(\frac{t}{6}\right) + \frac{t\sqrt{36 - t^2}}{2} + C.$$

7.4.15 Let $x = 3\sin\theta$ so that $dx = 3\cos\theta\,d\theta$ and $\sqrt{9 - x^2} = 3\cos\theta$. Then

$$\int \frac{\sqrt{9 - x^2}}{x}\,dx = \int \frac{3\cos\theta\cdot 3\cos\theta}{3\sin\theta}\,d\theta = 3\int \frac{1 - \sin^2\theta}{\sin\theta}\,d\theta$$

$$= 3\left(\int \csc\theta\,d\theta - \int \sin\theta\,d\theta\right)\,d\theta = 3\,(-\ln|\csc\theta + \cot\theta| + \cos\theta)$$

$$= -3\ln\left|\frac{3}{x} + \frac{\sqrt{9 - x^2}}{x}\right| + \sqrt{9 - x^2} + C.$$

7.4.16 Let $x = 2\sin\theta$ so that $dx = 2\cos\theta\,d\theta$ and $\sqrt{4 - x^2} = 2\cos\theta$. Then $\displaystyle\int (36 - 9x^2)^{-3/2}\,dx =$
$\dfrac{1}{27}\displaystyle\int \frac{1}{(4 - x^2)^{3/2}}\,dx = \frac{1}{27}\int \frac{2\cos\theta}{8\cos^3\theta}\,d\theta = \frac{1}{108}\int \sec^2\theta\,d\theta = \frac{1}{108}\tan\theta + C = \frac{x}{108\sqrt{4 - x^2}} + C$.

7.4.17 Let $x = 8\sin\theta$ so that $dx = 8\cos\theta\,d\theta$ and $\sqrt{64 - x^2} = 8\cos\theta$. Then,

$$\int \sqrt{64 - x^2}\,dx = \int 64\cos^2\theta\,d\theta = 32\int(1 + \cos 2\theta)\,d\theta = 32\theta + 16\sin 2\theta + C$$

$$= 32\theta + 32\sin\theta\cos\theta + C = 32\sin^{-1}\left(\frac{x}{8}\right) + \frac{x\sqrt{64 - x^2}}{2} + C.$$

7.4.18 Let $x = 7\sec\theta$ where $\theta \in (0, \pi/2)$. Then $dx = 7\sec\theta\tan\theta\,d\theta$ and $\sqrt{x^2 - 49} = 7\tan\theta$. Then

$$\int \frac{1}{\sqrt{x^2 - 49}}\,dx = \int \frac{7\sec\theta\tan\theta}{7\tan\theta}\,d\theta = \int \sec\theta\,d\theta = \ln|\sec\theta + \tan\theta| + C = \ln\left|\frac{x}{7} + \frac{\sqrt{x^2 - 49}}{7}\right| + C.$$ (Note

also that the absolute value signs can be omitted because $x > 7$, and if we replace $-\ln(7) + C$ by a different arbitrary constant D, we can write the result as $\ln(x + \sqrt{x^2 - 49}) + D$.

7.4.19 Let $x = \sin\theta$ so that $dx = \cos\theta\,d\theta$. Note that $\sqrt{1 - x^2} = \sqrt{1 - \sin^2\theta} = \cos\theta$. Substituting gives
$\int \sec^2\theta\,d\theta = \tan\theta + C = \tan(\sin^{-1}(x)) + C = \dfrac{x}{\sqrt{1 - x^2}} + C.$

7.4.20 Let $x = \tan\theta$ so that $dx = \sec^2\theta\,d\theta$. Note that $\sqrt{1 + x^2} = \sqrt{1 + \tan^2\theta} = \sec\theta$. Substituting gives
$\int \dfrac{1}{\sec\theta}\,d\theta = \int \cos\theta\,d\theta = \sin\theta + C = \sin(\tan^{-1}(x)) + C = \dfrac{x}{\sqrt{x^2 + 1}} + C.$

7.4.21 Let $x = 3\tan\theta$ so that $dx = 3\sec^2\theta\,d\theta$. Note that $\sqrt{x^2 + 9} = \sqrt{9(\tan^2\theta + 1)} = 3\sec\theta$. Substituting gives $\int \dfrac{1}{9}\cot\theta\csc\theta\,d\theta = -\dfrac{1}{9}\csc\theta + C = -\dfrac{1}{9}\csc(\tan^{-1}(x/3)) + C = \dfrac{-\sqrt{x^2 + 9}}{9x} + C.$

7.4.22 Let $t = 3\sin\theta$, so that $dt = 3\cos\theta\,d\theta$. Note that $\sqrt{9 - t^2} = \sqrt{9(\cos^2\theta)} = 3\cos\theta$. Substituting gives
$\int \dfrac{1}{9}\csc^2\theta\,d\theta = -\dfrac{1}{9}\cot\theta + C = -\dfrac{1}{9}\cot(\sin^{-1}(t/3)) + C = -\dfrac{\sqrt{9 - t^2}}{9t} + C.$

7.4.23 Let $x = 6\sin\theta$ so that $dx = 6\cos\theta\,d\theta$ and $\sqrt{36 - x^2} = 6\cos\theta$. Then $\int \dfrac{1}{\sqrt{36 - x^2}}\,dx = \int \dfrac{6\cos\theta}{6\cos\theta}\,d\theta = \theta + C = \sin^{-1}\left(\dfrac{x}{6}\right) + C.$

7.4.24 Let $x = 2\tan\theta$, $dx = 2\sec^2\theta\,d\theta$ and $\sqrt{16 + 4x^2} = 4\sec\theta$. Then $\int \dfrac{1}{\sqrt{16 + 4x^2}}\,dx = \int \dfrac{2\sec^2\theta}{4\sec\theta}\,d\theta = \dfrac{1}{2}\int \sec\theta\,d\theta = \dfrac{1}{2}\ln|\sec\theta + \tan\theta| + C = \dfrac{1}{2}\ln\left|\dfrac{\sqrt{4 + x^2}}{2} + \dfrac{x}{2}\right| + C.$

7.4.25 Let $x = 9\sec\theta$ with $\theta \in (0, \pi/2)$. Then $dx = 9\sec\theta\tan\theta\,d\theta$ and $\sqrt{x^2 - 81} = 9\tan\theta$. Then
$\int \dfrac{1}{\sqrt{x^2 - 81}}\,dx = \int \dfrac{9\sec\theta\tan\theta}{9\tan\theta}\,d\theta = \int \sec\theta\,d\theta = \ln|\sec\theta + \tan\theta| + C = \ln\left|\dfrac{x}{9} + \dfrac{\sqrt{x^2 - 81}}{9}\right| + C.$
Note that because $x > 9$, the absolute value signs are unnecessary, and the final result can be written as $\ln(\sqrt{x^2 - 81} + x) + C$.

7.4.26 Let $x = (1/\sqrt{2})\sin\theta$ so that $dx = (1/\sqrt{2})\cos\theta\,d\theta$ and $\sqrt{1 - 2x^2} = \cos\theta$. Then $\int \dfrac{1}{\sqrt{1 - 2x^2}}\,dx = \dfrac{1}{\sqrt{2}}\int \dfrac{\cos\theta}{\cos\theta}\,d\theta = \dfrac{1}{\sqrt{2}}\cdot\theta + C = \dfrac{1}{\sqrt{2}}\sin^{-1}(\sqrt{2}x) + C.$

7.4.27 Let $x = \dfrac{\tan\theta}{2}$ so that $dx = \dfrac{\sec^2\theta}{2}\,d\theta$ and $\sqrt{1 + 4x^2} = \sec\theta$. Then $\int \dfrac{1}{(1 + 4x^2)^{3/2}}\,dx = \dfrac{1}{2}\int \dfrac{\sec^2\theta}{\sec^3\theta}\,d\theta = \dfrac{1}{2}\int \cos\theta\,d\theta = \dfrac{\sin\theta}{2} + C = \dfrac{x}{\sqrt{1 + 4x^2}} + C.$

7.4.28 Let $x = 6 \sec \theta$ with $\theta \in (0, \pi/2)$. Then $dx = 6 \sec \theta \tan \theta \, d\theta$, and $\sqrt{x^2 - 36} = 6 \tan \theta$. Then $\int \frac{1}{(x^2 - 36)^{3/2}} \, dx = \int \frac{6 \sec \theta \tan \theta}{6^3 \tan^3 \theta} \, d\theta = \frac{1}{36} \int \frac{\sec \theta}{\tan^2 \theta} \, d\theta = \frac{1}{36} \int \frac{\cos \theta}{\sin^2 \theta} \, d\theta$. Let $u = \sin \theta$ so that $du = \cos \theta \, d\theta$. Then we have $\frac{1}{36} \int u^{-2} \, du = -\frac{1}{36u} + C = -\frac{1}{36 \sin \theta} + C = -\frac{x}{36 \sqrt{x^2 - 36}} + C$.

7.4.29 Let $x = 4 \sin \theta$ so that $dx = 4 \cos \theta \, d\theta$. Note that $\sqrt{16 - x^2} = 4 \cos \theta$. Then $\int \frac{x^2}{\sqrt{16 - x^2}} \, dx = \int \frac{16 \sin^2 \theta \cdot 4 \cos \theta}{4 \cos \theta} \, d\theta = 16 \int \sin^2 \theta \, d\theta = 8 \int (1 - \cos 2\theta) \, d\theta = 8 \left(\theta - \frac{\sin 2\theta}{2} \right) + C = 8\theta - 8 \sin \theta \cos \theta + C = 8 \sin^{-1} \left(\frac{x}{4} \right) - \frac{x \sqrt{16 - x^2}}{2} + C$.

7.4.30 Let $x = 9 \tan \theta$. Then $dx = 9 \sec^2 \theta \, d\theta$ and $81 + x^2 = 81(\sec^2 \theta)$. Then

$$\int \frac{dx}{(81 + x^2)^2} = \int \frac{9 \sec^2 \theta}{9^4 \sec^4 \theta} \, d\theta = \frac{1}{729} \int \cos^2 \theta \, d\theta = \frac{1}{1458} \int 1 + \cos 2\theta \, d\theta$$

$$= \frac{1}{1458} \left(\theta + \frac{\sin 2\theta}{2} \right) + C = \frac{1}{1458} \left(\theta + \sin \theta \cos \theta \right) + C = \frac{1}{1458} \left(\tan^{-1} \left(\frac{x}{9} \right) + \frac{9x}{81 + x^2} \right) + C.$$

7.4.31 Let $x = 3 \sec \theta$ where $\theta \in (0, \pi/2)$. Then $dx = 3 \sec \theta \tan \theta$ and $\sqrt{x^2 - 9} = 3 \tan \theta$. Thus we have $\int \frac{\sqrt{x^2 - 9}}{x} \, dx = \int \frac{3 \sec \theta \tan \theta \cdot 3 \tan \theta}{3 \sec \theta} \, d\theta = 3 \int \tan^2 \theta \, d\theta = 3 \int \sec^2 \theta - 1 \, d\theta = 3 \left(\tan \theta - \theta \right) + C = \sqrt{x^2 - 9} - 3 \tan^{-1} \left(\frac{\sqrt{x^2 - 9}}{3} \right) + C = \sqrt{x^2 - 9} - 3 \sec^{-1}(x/3) + C$.

7.4.32 Let $x = \frac{3}{2} \sin \theta$, so that $dx = \frac{3}{2} \cos \theta \, d\theta$. Note that $\sqrt{9 - 4x^2} = 3 \cos \theta$. Thus $\int \sqrt{9 - 4x^2} \, dx = \frac{3}{2} \int \cos \theta \cdot 3 \cos \theta \, d\theta = \frac{9}{2} \int \cos^2 \theta \, d\theta = \frac{9}{4} \int 1 + \cos 2\theta \, d\theta = \frac{9}{4} \left(\theta + \frac{\sin 2\theta}{2} \right) + C = \frac{9\theta}{4} + \frac{9 \sin \theta \cos \theta}{4} + C = \frac{9 \sin^{-1}(2x/3)}{4} + \frac{x \sqrt{9 - 4x^2}}{2} + C$.

7.4.33 Let $x = 2 \tan \theta$ so that $dx = 2 \sec^2 \theta \, d\theta$. Note that $\sqrt{4 + x^2} = 2 \sec \theta$. Then $\int \frac{x^2}{\sqrt{4 + x^2}} \, dx = \int \frac{4 \tan^2 \theta \cdot 2 \sec^2 \theta}{2 \sec \theta} \, d\theta = 4 \int \tan^2 \theta \sec \theta \, d\theta = 4 \int (\sec^2 \theta - 1) \sec \theta \, d\theta = 4 \left(\int \sec^3 \theta \, d\theta - \int \sec \theta \, d\theta \right) = 4 \left(\frac{1}{2} \left(\sec \theta \tan \theta + \int \sec \theta \, d\theta \right) - \int \sec \theta \, d\theta \right) = 2 \sec \theta \tan \theta - 2 \int \sec \theta \, d\theta = 2 \sec \theta \tan \theta - 2 \ln |\sec \theta + \tan \theta| + C = \frac{x \sqrt{4 + x^2}}{2} - 2 \ln \left| \frac{\sqrt{4 + x^2}}{2} + \frac{x}{2} \right| + C$. This can be written as $\frac{x \sqrt{4 + x^2}}{2} - 2 \ln(x + \sqrt{4 + x^2}) + C$.

7.4.34 Let $x = \frac{1}{2} \sec \theta$ where $\theta \in [0, \pi/2)$. Then $dx = \frac{1}{2} \sec \theta \tan \theta \, d\theta$ and $\sqrt{4x^2 - 1} = \tan \theta$. Thus, $\int \frac{\sqrt{4x^2 - 1}}{x^2} \, dx = \int \frac{\tan \theta \cdot \frac{1}{2} \sec \theta \tan \theta}{\frac{1}{4} \cdot \sec^2 \theta} \, d\theta = 2 \int \frac{\tan^2 \theta}{\sec \theta} \, d\theta = 2 \int \frac{\sec^2 \theta - 1}{\sec \theta} \, d\theta = 2 \int \sec \theta - \cos \theta \, d\theta = 2 \left(\ln |\sec \theta + \tan \theta| - \sin \theta \right) + C = 2 \ln(2x + \sqrt{4x^2 - 1}) - \frac{\sqrt{4x^2 - 1}}{x} + C$.

7.4.35 $\int \frac{1}{\sqrt{3 - 2x - x^2}} \, dx = \int \frac{1}{\sqrt{4 - (x + 1)^2}} \, dx = \int \frac{1}{\sqrt{4 - u^2}} \, du$ where $u = x + 1$. Then let $u = 2 \sin \theta$ so that $du = 2 \cos \theta \, d\theta$. We have $\int \frac{2 \cos \theta}{2 \cos \theta} \, d\theta = \theta + C = \sin^{-1} \left(\frac{x + 1}{2} \right) + C$.

7.4.36 Let $y = \tan\theta$ so that $dy = \sec^2\theta\,d\theta$. Note that $1 + y^2 = \sec^2\theta$. Thus,

$$\int \frac{y^4}{1+y^2}\,dy = \int \frac{\tan^4\theta\sec^2\theta}{\sec^2\theta}\,d\theta = \int \tan^4\theta\,d\theta$$

$$= \int (\tan^2\theta)(\sec^2\theta - 1)\,d\theta = \int \tan^2\theta\sec^2\theta - \tan^2\theta\,d\theta$$

$$= \int \tan^2\theta\sec^2\theta + 1 - \sec^2\theta\,d\theta = \int \tan^2\theta\sec^2\theta\,d\theta + \theta - \tan\theta.$$

Now recall that $y = \tan\theta$, so we have $\displaystyle\int y^2\,dy + \theta - \tan\theta = \frac{y^3}{3} + \theta - \tan\theta = \frac{y^3}{3} + \tan^{-1}(y) - y + C.$

7.4.37 Let $x = \frac{5}{3}\sec\theta$ where $\theta \in [0, \pi/2)$. Then $dx = \frac{5}{3}\sec\theta\tan\theta d\theta$ and $\sqrt{9x^2 - 25} = 5\tan\theta$. Thus,
$\displaystyle\int \frac{\sqrt{9x^2-25}}{x^3}\,dx = \int \frac{5\tan\theta \cdot \frac{5}{3}\cdot\sec\theta\tan\theta}{\frac{125}{27}\sec^3\theta}\,d\theta = \frac{9}{5}\int \frac{\tan^2\theta}{\sec^2\theta}\,d\theta = \frac{9}{5}\int \frac{\sec^2\theta - 1}{\sec^2\theta}\,d\theta = \frac{9}{5}\int 1 - \cos^2\theta\,d\theta =$
$\frac{9}{5}\int \sin^2\theta\,d\theta = \frac{9}{10}\int 1 - \cos 2\theta\,d\theta = \frac{9\theta}{10} - \frac{9\sin 2\theta}{20} + C = \frac{9\theta}{10} - \frac{9\sin\theta\cos\theta}{10} = \frac{9\cos^{-1}(5/3x)}{10} - \frac{\sqrt{9x^2-25}}{2x^2} + C.$

7.4.38 Let $x = 3\sin\theta$ so that $dx = 3\cos\theta\,d\theta$. Note that $\sqrt{9 - x^2} = 3\cos\theta$. Thus, $\displaystyle\int \frac{\sqrt{9-x^2}}{x^2}\,dx =$
$\displaystyle\int \frac{3\cos\theta \cdot 3\cos\theta}{9\sin^2\theta}\,d\theta = \int \cot^2\theta\,d\theta = \int \csc^2 - 1\,d\theta = -\cot\theta - \theta + C = -\frac{\sqrt{9-x^2}}{x} - \sin^{-1}(x/3) + C.$

7.4.39 Let $x = 5\tan\theta$ so that $dx = 5\sec^2\theta\,d\theta$. Note that $25 + x^2 = 25\sec^2\theta$. Thus, $\displaystyle\int \frac{x^2}{(25+x^2)^2}\,dx =$
$\displaystyle\int \frac{25\tan^2\theta \cdot 5\sec^2\theta}{25^2\sec^4\theta}\,d\theta = \frac{1}{5}\int \frac{\tan^2\theta}{\sec^2\theta}\,d\theta = \frac{1}{5}\int \frac{\sec^2\theta - 1}{\sec^2\theta}\,d\theta = \frac{1}{5}\int (1 - \cos^2\theta)\,d\theta = \frac{1}{5}\int \sin^2\theta\,d\theta =$
$\frac{1}{10}\int 1 - \cos 2\theta\,d\theta = \frac{1}{10}\left(\theta - \frac{\sin 2\theta}{2}\right) + C = \frac{1}{10}(\theta - \sin\theta\cos\theta) + C = \frac{1}{10}\left(\tan^{-1}(x/5) - \frac{5x}{25+x^2}\right) + C.$

7.4.40 Let $x = \frac{1}{3}\sec\theta$, where $\theta \in (0, \pi/2)$. Then $dx = \frac{1}{3}\sec\theta\tan\theta\,d\theta$. Note that $\sqrt{9x^2 - 1} = \tan\theta$. Then

$$\int \frac{1}{x^2\sqrt{9x^2-1}}\,dx = \int \frac{\frac{1}{3}\sec\theta\tan\theta}{\frac{1}{9}\sec^2\theta\tan\theta}\,d\theta = 3\int \cos\theta\,d\theta = 3\sin\theta + C = \frac{\sqrt{9x^2-1}}{x} + C.$$

7.4.41 Let $x = 10\sin\theta$ so that $dx = 10\cos\theta\,d\theta$. Note that $\sqrt{100 - x^2} = 10\cos\theta$. Thus,

$$\int \frac{x^2}{(100-x^2)^{3/2}}\,dx = \int \frac{100\sin^2\theta \cdot 10\cos\theta}{1000\cos^3\theta}\,d\theta = \int \tan^2\theta\,d\theta$$

$$= \int (\sec^2\theta - 1)\,d\theta = \tan\theta - \theta + C = \frac{x}{\sqrt{100-x^2}} - \sin^{-1}(x/10) + C.$$

7.4.42 Let $x = 10\sec\theta$ where $\theta \in (0, \pi/2)$. Then $dx = 10\sec\theta\tan\theta\,d\theta$ and $\sqrt{x^2 - 100} = 10\tan\theta$. Thus,

$$\int \frac{1}{x^3\sqrt{x^2-100}}\,dx = \int \frac{10\sec\theta\tan\theta}{10^3\sec^3\theta \cdot 10\tan\theta}\,d\theta = \frac{1}{1000}\int \cos^2\theta\,d\theta$$

$$= \frac{1}{2000}\int (1 + \cos 2\theta)\,d\theta = \frac{\theta}{2000} + \frac{\sin 2\theta}{4000} + C = \frac{\theta}{2000} + \frac{\sin\theta\cos\theta}{2000} + C$$

$$= \frac{\tan^{-1}(\sqrt{x^2-100}/10)}{2000} + \frac{\sqrt{x^2-100}}{200x^2} + C.$$

7.4.43 Let $x = 9 \sin \theta$ so that $dx = 9 \cos \theta \, d\theta$. Note that $81 - x^2 = 81 \cos^2 \theta$. Thus,

$$\int \frac{x^3}{(81 - x^2)^2} \, dx = \int \frac{9^3 \sin^3 \theta \cdot 9 \cos \theta}{9^4 \cos^4 \theta} \, d\theta = \int \tan^3 \theta \, d\theta$$

$$= \int (\tan \theta)(\sec^2 \theta - 1) \, d\theta = \int \sec^2 \theta \tan \theta \, d\theta - \int \tan \theta \, d\theta$$

$$= \frac{\sec^2 \theta}{2} + \ln|\cos \theta| + C = \frac{81}{2(81 - x^2)} + \ln \left| \frac{\sqrt{81 - x^2}}{9} \right| + C.$$

This can be written as $\frac{81}{2(81 - x^2)} + \ln \sqrt{81 - x^2} + C.$

7.4.44 Let $x = \sec \theta$ where $\theta \in (0, \pi/2)$. Then $dx = \sec \theta \tan \theta \, d\theta$ and $\sqrt{x^2 - 1} = \tan \theta$. Thus,

$$\int \frac{1}{x^3 \sqrt{x^2 - 1}} \, dx = \int \frac{\sec \theta \tan \theta}{\sec^3 \theta \tan \theta} \, d\theta = \int \cos^2 \theta \, d\theta = \frac{1}{2} \int 1 + \cos 2\theta \, d\theta = \frac{1}{2} \left(\theta + \frac{\sin 2\theta}{2} \right) + C$$

$$= \frac{1}{2} \left(\theta + \sin \theta \cos \theta \right) + C = \frac{1}{2} \left(\tan^{-1} \sqrt{x^2 - 1} + \frac{\sqrt{x^2 - 1}}{x^2} \right) + C.$$

7.4.45 Let $x = \sec \theta$ where $\theta \in (0, \pi/2)$. Then $dx = \sec \theta \tan \theta \, d\theta$ and $\sqrt{x^2 - 1} = \tan \theta$. Then

$$\int \frac{1}{x(x^2 - 1)^{3/2}} \, dx = \int \frac{\sec \theta \tan \theta}{\sec \theta \tan^3 \theta} \, d\theta = \int \cot^2 \theta \, d\theta$$

$$= \int \csc^2 \theta - 1 \, d\theta = -\cot \theta - \theta + C = -\frac{1}{\sqrt{x^2 - 1}} - \sec^{-1} x + C.$$

7.4.46 Let $x = 4 \sec \theta$ where $\theta \in (0, \pi/2)$. Then $dx = 4 \sec \theta \tan \theta \, d\theta$ and $\sqrt{x^2 - 16} = 4 \tan \theta$. Then

$$\int \frac{x^3}{(x^2 - 16)^{3/2}} \, dx = \int \frac{4^3 \sec^3 \theta \cdot 4 \sec \theta \tan \theta}{64 \tan^3 \theta} \, d\theta = 4 \int \frac{\sec^4 \theta}{\tan^2 \theta} \, d\theta$$

$$= 4 \int \frac{(\sec^2 \theta)(1 + \tan^2 \theta)}{\tan^2 \theta} \, d\theta.$$

Let $u = \tan \theta$ so that $du = \sec^2 \theta \, d\theta$. Then we have

$$4 \int \frac{1 + u^2}{u^2} \, du = 4 \int u^{-2} + 1 \, du = -\frac{4}{u} + 4u + C$$

$$= -4 \cot \theta + 4 \tan \theta + C = -\frac{16}{\sqrt{x^2 - 16}} + \sqrt{x^2 - 16} + C.$$

7.4.47 Let $x = 4 \tan \theta$ so that $dx = 4 \sec^2 \theta \, d\theta$. Note that $\sqrt{x^2 + 16} = 4 \sec \theta$. Thus, $\int_0^1 \frac{1}{\sqrt{x^2 + 16}} \, dx =$

$$\int_0^{\tan^{-1}(1/4)} \frac{4 \sec^2 \theta}{4 \sec \theta} \, d\theta = \int_0^{\tan^{-1}(1/4)} \sec \theta \, d\theta = \ln|\sec \theta + \tan \theta| \Big|_0^{\tan^{-1}(1/4)} = \ln \left(\frac{\sqrt{17} + 1}{4} \right).$$

7.4.48 Let $x = 8 \sec \theta$ so that $dx = 8 \sec \theta \tan \theta \, d\theta$ and $\sqrt{x^2 - 64} = 8 \tan \theta$. Then $\int_{8\sqrt{2}}^{16} \frac{dx}{\sqrt{x^2 - 64}} =$

$$\int_{\pi/4}^{\pi/3} \frac{8 \sec \theta \tan \theta}{8 \tan \theta} \, d\theta = \int_{\pi/4}^{\pi/3} \sec \theta \, d\theta = \ln|\sec \theta + \tan \theta| \Big|_{\pi/4}^{\pi/3} = \ln(2 + \sqrt{3}) - \ln(\sqrt{2} + 1) = \ln \left(\frac{2 + \sqrt{3}}{1 + \sqrt{2}} \right).$$

7.4.49 Let $x = \tan \theta$ so that $dx = \sec^2 \theta \, d\theta$ and $\sqrt{1 + x^2} = \sec \theta$. Substituting gives $\int_{\pi/6}^{\pi/4} \cot \theta \csc \theta \, d\theta =$

$$(-\csc \theta) \Big|_{\pi/6}^{\pi/4} = -(\sqrt{2} - 2) = 2 - \sqrt{2}.$$

7.4.50 Let $x = 2\sin\theta$, so that $dx = 2\cos\theta\,d\theta$. Note that when $x = 1$ we have $\theta = \frac{\pi}{6}$ and when $x = \sqrt{2}$ we have $\theta = \frac{\pi}{4}$. Also $\sqrt{4 - x^2} = 2\sqrt{\cos^2\theta} = 2\cos\theta$. Substituting gives $\frac{1}{4}\int_{\pi/6}^{\pi/4}\csc^2\theta\,d\theta = -\frac{1}{4}\left(\cot\theta\right)\Big|_{\pi/6}^{\pi/4} = -\frac{1}{4}\left(1 - \sqrt{3}\right) = \frac{\sqrt{3}-1}{4}$.

7.4.51 Let $x = \tan\theta$ so that $dx = \sec^2\theta\,d\theta$. Note that $\sqrt{x^2 + 1} = \sqrt{\tan^2\theta + 1} = \sqrt{\sec^2\theta} = \sec\theta$. Substituting gives $\int_0^{\pi/6}\sec^3\theta\,d\theta$. Recall from section 7.2 number 67 that $\int\sec^3\theta\,d\theta = \frac{1}{2}\sec\theta\tan\theta + \frac{1}{2}\ln|\sec\theta + \tan\theta|$. Thus the original integral is equal to $\left(\frac{1}{2}\sec\theta\tan\theta + \frac{1}{2}\ln|\sec\theta + \tan\theta|\right)\Big|_0^{\pi/6} = \frac{1\cdot 2\cdot 1}{2\cdot\sqrt{3}\cdot\sqrt{3}} + \frac{1}{2}\ln\left(\frac{2}{\sqrt{3}} + \frac{1}{\sqrt{3}}\right) = \frac{1}{3} + \frac{\ln 3}{4}$.

7.4.52 Let $x = \sec\theta$ so that $dx = \sec\theta\tan\theta\,d\theta$. Note that $\sqrt{x^2 - 1} = \sqrt{\tan^2\theta} = \tan\theta$. Substituting gives $\int_{\pi/4}^{\pi/3}\tan^2\theta\,d\theta = \int_{\pi/4}^{\pi/3}(\sec^2\theta - 1)\,d\theta = (\tan\theta - \theta)\Big|_{\pi/4}^{\pi/3} = \sqrt{3} - \pi/3 - (1 - \pi/4) = \sqrt{3} - 1 - \pi/12$.

7.4.53 Let $x = \frac{1}{3}\tan\theta$ so that $dx = \frac{1}{3}\sec^2\theta\,d\theta$. Note that $\sqrt{9x^2 + 1} = \sec\theta$. Thus $\int_0^{1/3}\frac{1}{(9x^2 + 1)^{3/2}}\,dx = \int_0^{\pi/4}\frac{\frac{1}{3}\sec^2\theta}{\sec^3\theta}\,d\theta = \frac{1}{3}\int_0^{\pi/4}\cos\theta\,d\theta = \frac{1}{3}\sin\theta\Big|_0^{\pi/4} = \frac{\sqrt{2}}{6}$.

7.4.54 Let $y = 5\sec\theta$ so that $dy = 5\sec\theta\tan\theta\,d\theta$. Then $\sqrt{y^2 - 25} = 5\tan\theta$. Then, $\int_{10/\sqrt{3}}^{10}\frac{1}{\sqrt{y^2 - 25}}\,dy = \int_{\pi/6}^{\pi/3}\frac{5\sec\theta\tan\theta}{5\tan\theta}\,d\theta = \int_{\pi/6}^{\pi/3}\sec\theta\,d\theta = \ln|\sec\theta + \tan\theta|\Big|_{\pi/6}^{\pi/3} = \ln(2 + \sqrt{3}) - \ln(\sqrt{3}) = \ln\left(\frac{2 + \sqrt{3}}{\sqrt{3}}\right)$.

7.4.55 Let $x = 2\sec\theta$ so that $dx = 2\sec\theta\tan\theta\,d\theta$ and $x^2 - 4 = 4\tan^2\theta$. Thus, $\int_{4/\sqrt{3}}^4\frac{1}{x^2(x^2 - 4)}\,dx = \int_{\pi/6}^{\pi/3}\frac{2\sec\theta\tan\theta}{4\sec^2\theta\cdot 4\tan^2\theta}\,d\theta = \frac{1}{8}\int_{\pi/6}^{\pi/3}\frac{\cos^2\theta}{\sin\theta}\,d\theta = \frac{1}{8}\int_{\pi/6}^{\pi/3}\frac{1 - \sin^2\theta}{\sin\theta}\,d\theta = \frac{1}{8}\int_{\pi/6}^{\pi/3}\csc\theta - \sin\theta\,d\theta = \frac{1}{8}\left(-\ln|\csc\theta + \cot\theta| + \cos\theta\right)\Big|_{\pi/6}^{\pi/3} = \frac{1}{8}\left(-\ln(\sqrt{3}(2 - \sqrt{3})) + \frac{1 - \sqrt{3}}{2}\right) = \frac{1}{16}[1 - \sqrt{3} - \ln(21 - 12\sqrt{3})]$.

7.4.56 Let $z = 6\tan\theta$ so that $dz = 6\sec^2\theta\,d\theta$. Note that $z^2 + 36 = 36\sec^2\theta$. Thus

$$\int_6^{6\sqrt{3}}\frac{z^2}{(z^2 + 36)^2}\,dz = \int_{\pi/4}^{\pi/3}\frac{36\tan^2\theta\cdot 6\sec^2\theta}{36^2\sec^4\theta}\,d\theta = \frac{1}{6}\int_{\pi/4}^{\pi/3}\frac{\tan^2\theta}{\sec^2\theta}\,d\theta$$

$$= \frac{1}{6}\int_{\pi/4}^{\pi/3}\frac{\sec^2\theta - 1}{\sec^2\theta}\,d\theta = \frac{1}{6}\int_{\pi/4}^{\pi/3}1 - \cos^2\theta\,d\theta = \frac{1}{6}\int_{\pi/4}^{\pi/3}\sin^2\theta\,d\theta$$

$$= \frac{1}{12}\int_{\pi/4}^{\pi/3}1 - \cos 2\theta\,d\theta = \frac{1}{12}\left(\theta - \frac{\sin 2\theta}{2}\right)\Big|_{\pi/4}^{\pi/3} = \frac{1}{12}\left(\theta - \sin\theta\cos\theta\right)\Big|_{\pi/4}^{\pi/3}$$

$$= \frac{1}{12}\left(\frac{\pi}{3} - \frac{\sqrt{3}}{4} - \frac{\pi}{4} + \frac{1}{2}\right) = \frac{\pi}{144} - \frac{\sqrt{3} - 2}{48}.$$

7.4.57

a. False. In fact, we would have $\csc\theta = \frac{\sqrt{x^2 + 16}}{x}$.

b. True. Almost every number in the interval $[1, 2]$ is not in the domain of $\sqrt{1 - x^2}$, so this integral isn't defined.

c. False. It does represent a finite real number, because $\sqrt{x^2 - 1}$ is continuous on the interval $[1, 2]$.

d. False. It can be so evaluated. The integral is equivalent to $\int \dfrac{1}{(x+2)^2 + 5} \, dx$, and this can be evaluated by the substitution $x + 2 = \sqrt{5} \tan \theta$.

7.4.58 Note that the given integral can be written $\int \dfrac{1}{(x-3)^2 + 25} \, dx = \int \dfrac{1}{u^2 + 25} \, du$ with $u = x - 3$. Now let $u = 5 \tan \theta$ so that $du = 5 \sec^2 \theta \, d\theta$ and $u^2 + 25 = 25 \sec^2 \theta$. Thus we have

$$\int \frac{5 \sec^2 \theta}{25 \sec^2 \theta} \, d\theta = \frac{\theta}{5} + C = \frac{\tan^{-1}((x-3)/5)}{5} + C.$$

7.4.59 Note that the given integral can be written $\int \dfrac{1}{(x+3)^2 + 9} \, dx = \int \dfrac{1}{u^2 + 9} \, du$ where $u = x + 3$. Now let $u = 3 \tan \theta$ so that $du = 3 \sec^2 \theta \, d\theta$ and $u^2 + 9 = 9 \sec^2 \theta$. Thus we have

$$\int \frac{3 \sec^2 \theta}{9 \sec^2 \theta} \, d\theta = \frac{\theta}{3} + C = \frac{\tan^{-1}((x+3)/3)}{3} + C.$$

7.4.60 Note that the given integral can be written $\dfrac{1}{2} \int \dfrac{1}{(u-3)^2 + 9} \, du = \dfrac{1}{2} \int \dfrac{1}{w^2 + 9} \, dw$ where $w = u - 3$. Now let $w = 3 \tan \theta$ so that $dw = 3 \sec^2 \theta \, d\theta$ and $w^2 + 9 = 9 \sec^2 \theta$. Thus we have

$$\frac{1}{2} \int \frac{3 \sec^2 \theta}{9 \sec^2 \theta} \, d\theta = \frac{\theta}{6} + C = \frac{\tan^{-1}((u-3)/3)}{6} + C.$$

7.4.61 Note that the given integral can be written as $\int \dfrac{(x-1)^2}{\sqrt{(x-1)^2 + 9}} \, dx = \int \dfrac{u^2}{\sqrt{u^2 + 9}} \, du$ where $u = x - 1$. Now let $u = 3 \tan \theta$ so that $du = 3 \sec^2 \theta \, d\theta$ and $u^2 + 9 = 9 \sec^2 \theta$. Thus we have

$$\int \frac{9 \tan^2 \theta \cdot 3 \sec^2 \theta}{3 \sec \theta} \, d\theta = 9 \int \tan^2 \theta \sec \theta \, d\theta = 9 \int (\sec^2 \theta - 1)(\sec \theta) \, d\theta$$

$$= 9 \int (\sec^3 \theta - \sec \theta) \, d\theta = 9 \left(\frac{1}{2} \sec \theta \tan \theta + \frac{1}{2} \int \sec \theta \, d\theta - \int \sec \theta \, d\theta \right)$$

$$= \frac{9}{2} \left(\sec \theta \tan \theta - \int \sec \theta \, d\theta \right)$$

$$= \frac{9}{2} \left(\sec \theta \tan \theta - \ln | \sec \theta + \tan \theta | \right) + C$$

$$= \frac{9}{2} \left(\frac{(x-1)\sqrt{(x-1)^2 + 9}}{9} - \ln \left| \frac{\sqrt{(x-1)^2 + 9}}{3} + \frac{x-1}{3} \right| \right) + C.$$

This can be written as $\frac{x-1}{2} \sqrt{x^2 - 2x + 10} - \frac{9}{2} \ln(x - 1 + \sqrt{x^2 - 2x + 10}) + C$. Note that in the middle of this derivation we used the reduction formula for $\int \sec^3 \theta \, d\theta$ given in problem 54 in the previous section.

7.4.62 Note that the given integral can be written $\int \dfrac{(x-2)^2 + 6(x-2) + 12}{\sqrt{(x-2)^2 - 4}} \, dx = \int \dfrac{u^2 + 6u + 12}{\sqrt{u^2 - 4}} \, du$ where $u = x - 2$. We can write this integral as $\int \dfrac{u^2}{\sqrt{u^2 - 4}} \, du + 6 \int \dfrac{u}{\sqrt{u^2 - 4}} \, du + 12 \int \dfrac{1}{\sqrt{u^2 - 4}} \, du$. Now for the first and last of these integrals, let $u = 2 \sec \theta$ so that $du = 2 \sec \theta \tan \theta \, d\theta$. Note also that $\sqrt{u^2 - 4} = 2 \tan \theta$. For the middle integral, let $v = u^2 - 4$ so that $dv = 2u \, du$. Then we have

$$\int \frac{4 \sec^2 \theta \cdot 2 \sec \theta \tan \theta}{2 \tan \theta} \, d\theta + 3 \int v^{-1/2} \, dv + 12 \int \frac{2 \sec \theta \tan \theta}{2 \tan \theta} \, d\theta = 4 \int \sec^3 \theta \, d\theta + 12 \int \sec \theta \, d\theta + 6 \sqrt{v}.$$

Using the reduction formula from number 66 in the previous section, we have

$$4\left(\frac{1}{2}\left(\sec\theta\tan\theta+\int\sec\theta\,d\theta\right)+3\int\sec\theta\,d\theta\right)+6\sqrt{v}$$

$$=2\sec\theta\tan\theta+14\int\sec\theta\,d\theta+6\sqrt{v}$$

$$=2\sec\theta\tan\theta+14\ln|\sec\theta+\tan\theta|+6\sqrt{u^2-4}+C$$

$$=\frac{(x-2)\sqrt{(x-2)^2-4}}{2}+14\ln\left(\frac{x-2}{2}+\frac{\sqrt{(x-2)^2-4}}{2}\right)+6\sqrt{(x-2)^2-4}+C.$$

This can be written as

$$\frac{1}{2}\left(\sqrt{(x-4)x}(x+10)+28\log\left(\frac{1}{2}\left(x+\sqrt{(x-4)x}-2\right)\right)\right)+C.$$

7.4.63 Note that the given integral can be written as $\displaystyle\int\frac{(x-4)^2}{(25-(x-4)^2)^{3/2}}\,dx$. Let $u=x-4$, and note that

we have $\displaystyle\int\frac{u^2}{(25-u^2)^{3/2}}\,du$. Now let $u=5\sin\theta$ so that $du=5\cos\theta\,d\theta$, and note that $\sqrt{25-u^2}=5\cos\theta$.

Thus we have $\displaystyle\int\frac{25\sin^2\theta\cdot5\cos\theta}{5^3\cos^3\theta}\,d\theta=\int\tan^2\theta\,d\theta=\int\sec^2\theta-1\,d\theta=\tan\theta-\theta+C=\frac{x-4}{\sqrt{25-(x-4)^2}}-$

$\sin^{-1}\left(\dfrac{x-4}{5}\right)+C.$

7.4.64 $\displaystyle\int_1^4\frac{1}{t^2-2t+10}\,dt=\int_1^4\frac{1}{(t-1)^2+9}\,dt$. Let $3\tan\theta=t-1$, so that $dt=3\sec^2\theta\,d\theta$. Note that

$(t-1)^2+9=9\sec^2\theta$. Then we have $\displaystyle\int_0^{\pi/4}\frac{3\sec^2\theta}{9\sec^2\theta}\,d\theta=\frac{1}{3}\theta\,\Big|_0^{\pi/4}=\frac{\pi}{12}.$

7.4.65 $\displaystyle\int_{1/2}^{(\sqrt{2}+3)/2\sqrt{2}}\frac{1}{8x^2-8x+11}\,dx=\int_{1/2}^{(\sqrt{2}+3)/2\sqrt{2}}\frac{1}{8(x-1/2)^2+9}\,dx$. Let $u=x-1/2$, so that our

integral becomes $\displaystyle\int_0^{3/2\sqrt{2}}\frac{1}{8u^2+9}\,du$. Now let $u=\frac{3}{\sqrt{8}}\tan\theta$ so that $du=\frac{3}{\sqrt{8}}\sec^2\theta\,d\theta$. Substituting gives

$\displaystyle\int_0^{\pi/4}\frac{\frac{3}{\sqrt{8}}\sec^2\theta}{9\sec^2\theta}\,d\theta=\frac{1}{6\sqrt{2}}\int d\theta=\frac{1}{6\sqrt{2}}\theta\,\Big|_0^{\pi/4}=\frac{\pi\sqrt{2}}{48}.$

7.4.66 Let A be the area of the ellipse. Using symmetry, we have $\dfrac{A}{4}=\displaystyle\int_0^b\frac{b}{a}\sqrt{a^2-x^2}\,dx$. Let $x=a\sin\theta$,

so that $dx=a\cos\theta\,d\theta$. Substituting yields $\dfrac{b}{a}\displaystyle\int_0^{\pi/2}a\cos\theta\cdot a\cos\theta\,d\theta=ab\int_0^{\pi/2}\cos^2\theta\,d\theta=\frac{ab}{2}\int_0^{\pi/2}(1+$

$\cos2\theta)\,d\theta=\dfrac{ab}{2}\left(\theta+\dfrac{\sin2\theta}{2}\right)\Big|_0^{\pi/2}=\dfrac{\pi ab}{4}$. So the total area of the ellipse is $A=\pi ab$.

7.4.67

a. Recall that the area of a circular sector subtended by an angle θ is given by $\frac{\theta r^2}{2}$. So the area of the cap is this area minus the area of the isosceles triangle with two sides of length r and angle between them θ. So $A_{\text{cap}}=A_{\text{sector}}-A_{\text{triangle}}=\frac{\theta r^2}{2}-\frac{r^2\sin\theta}{2}=\frac{r^2}{2}(\theta-\sin\theta)$.

b. For a cap we have $0\le\theta\le\pi$ so $0\le\theta/2\le\pi/2$. By symmetry, $\dfrac{A_{\text{cap}}}{2}=\displaystyle\int_{r\cos\theta/2}^r\sqrt{r^2-x^2}\,dx$. Let

$x=r\cos\alpha/2$ so that $dx=-\frac{r}{2}\sin\alpha/2\,d\alpha$. Then we have $\dfrac{A_{\text{cap}}}{2}=\displaystyle\int_\theta^0 r\sin(\alpha/2)\cdot-\frac{r}{2}\sin(\alpha/2)\,d\alpha=$

$$\frac{r^2}{2}\int_0^\theta \sin^2(\alpha/2)\,d\alpha = \frac{r^2}{4}\int_0^\theta (1-\cos\alpha)\,d\alpha = \frac{r^2}{4}\left(\alpha - \sin\alpha\right)\Big|_0^\theta = \frac{r^2}{4}(\theta - \sin\theta).$$

Thus $A_{\text{cap}} = \frac{r^2}{2}(\theta - \sin\theta)$.

7.4.68 The semicircles intersect where $16 - x^2 = 9 - (x-2)^2$, or $16 - x^2 = 9 - x^2 + 4x - 4$, which is when $11 = 4x$, or $x = \frac{11}{4}$. The area of the lune is the area of the larger circle minus the area of the smaller circle that is contained in the large circle. Let A_1 be the area of larger circle and A_2 the area of the smaller circle, and A the area of the smaller circle that is outside the bigger circle. Note that $A = A_{\text{cap}_2} - A_{\text{cap}_1}$ where the caps are as described in the previous problem. Thus the area of the lune is given by $A_1 - (A_2 - A) = A_1 - (A_2 - (A_{\text{cap}_2} - A_{\text{cap}_1})) = A_1 - A_2 + A_{\text{cap}_2} - A_{\text{cap}_1} = 16\pi - 9\pi + A_{\text{cap}_2} - A_{\text{cap}_1} = 7\pi + A_{\text{cap}_2} - A_{\text{cap}_1}$. Let θ_1 be the angle with vertex at the origin which subtends the cap associated with A_1 and let θ_2 be the angle with vertex at $(2,0)$ which subtends the cap associated with A_2. Using the right triangles with angle $\theta_1/2$ and $\theta_2/2$, we have $\tan(\theta_1/2) = \frac{3\sqrt{15}/4}{11/4}$, so $\theta_1 = 2\tan^{-1}\left(\frac{3\sqrt{15}}{11}\right)$, and $\tan(\theta_2/2) = \sqrt{15}$, so $\theta_2 = 2\tan^{-1}(\sqrt{15})$.

By the previous problem, we have $A_{\text{cap}_1} = \frac{r_1^2}{2}(\theta_1 - \sin\theta_1) = 8\left(2\tan^{-1}\left(\frac{3\sqrt{15}}{11}\right) - \frac{33\sqrt{15}}{128}\right)$ and $A_{\text{cap}_2} = \frac{r_2^2}{2}(\theta_2 - \sin\theta_2) = \frac{9}{2}\left(2\tan^{-1}(\sqrt{15}) - \frac{\sqrt{15}}{8}\right)$. Putting this all together yields

$$A_{\text{lune}} = 7\pi + 9\tan^{-1}(\sqrt{15}) - 16\tan^{-1}\left(\frac{3\sqrt{15}}{11}\right) + \frac{3\sqrt{15}}{2} \approx 26.660.$$

7.4.69

a. The area is given by $\int_0^4 \frac{1}{\sqrt{9+x^2}}\,dx$. Let $x = 3\tan\theta$, so that $dx = 3\sec^2\theta\,d\theta$. Substituting yields

$$\int_0^{\tan^{-1}(4/3)} \frac{3\sec^2\theta}{3\sec\theta}\,d\theta = \int_0^{\tan^{-1}(4/3)} \sec\theta\,d\theta = \ln|\sec\theta + \tan\theta|\,\Big|_0^{\tan^{-1}(4/3)} = \ln\left(\frac{5}{3} + \frac{4}{3}\right) = \ln 3.$$

b. Using disks, we have $\frac{V}{\pi} = \int_0^4 \frac{1}{9+x^2}\,dx$. Let $x = 3\tan\theta$ so that $dx = 3\sec^2\theta\,d\theta$. Substituting yields

$$\int_0^{\tan^{-1}(4/3)} \frac{3\sec^2\theta}{9\sec^2\theta}\,d\theta = \frac{1}{3}\int_0^{\tan^{-1}(4/3)} 1\,d\theta = \frac{1}{3}\theta\,\Big|_0^{\tan^{-1}(4/3)} = \frac{1}{3}\tan^{-1}(4/3).$$ Thus $V = \frac{\pi}{3}\tan^{-1}(4/3)$.

c. Using shells, we have $\frac{V}{2\pi} = \int_0^4 \frac{x}{(9+x^2)^{1/2}}\,dx$. Let $u = 9 + x^2$, so that $du = 2x\,dx$. Then we have

$$\frac{1}{2}\int_9^{25} u^{-1/2}\,du = \sqrt{u}\,\Big|_9^{25} = 5 - 3 = 2. \text{ So } V = 4\pi.$$

7.4.70

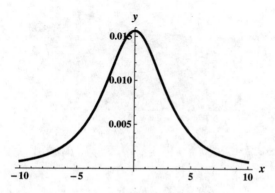

Note that $f'(x) = -\frac{3}{2}\cdot 2x(16+x^2)^{-5/2} = -\frac{3x}{\sqrt{(16+x^2)^5}}$. So f is increasing on $(-\infty, 0)$ and decreasing on $(0,\infty)$ and thus has a maximum at $x = 0$ of $\frac{1}{64}$. Also, $f''(x) = \frac{12(x^2-4)}{\sqrt{(16+x^2)^7}}$, so f is concave up on $(-\infty, -2)$ and on $(2,\infty)$ and is concave down on $(-2,2)$.

The area bounded by the curve and the axis on $[0, 3]$ is given by $\int_0^3 \dfrac{1}{(16 + x^2)^{3/2}}\, dx$.
Let $x = 4\tan\theta$ so that $dx = 4\sec^2\theta\, d\theta$. Substituting yields

$$\int_0^{\tan^{-1}(3/4)} \frac{4\sec^2\theta}{4^3\sec^3\theta}\, d\theta = \frac{1}{16}\int_0^{\tan^{-1}(3/4)} \cos\theta\, d\theta = \frac{\sin\theta}{16}\bigg|_0^{\tan^{-1}(3/4)} = \frac{3}{80}.$$

7.4.71 Because $y = ax^2$, we have $1 + \left(\dfrac{dy}{dx}\right)^2 = 1 + 4a^2x^2$, so the arc length is given by $\int_0^{10} \sqrt{1 + 4a^2x^2}\, dx$.
Let $x = \frac{1}{2a}\tan\theta$ so that $dx = \frac{1}{2a}\sec^2\theta\, d\theta$. Then we have

$$\frac{1}{2a}\int_0^{\tan^{-1}(20a)} \sec^2\theta\sec\theta\, d\theta = \frac{1}{2a}\int_0^{\tan^{-1}(20a)} \sec^3\theta\, d\theta = \frac{1}{4a}\left(\sec\theta\tan\theta + \ln|\sec\theta + \tan\theta|\right)\bigg|_0^{\tan^{-1}(20a)}$$

$$= \frac{1}{4a}\left(\sqrt{1 + 400a^2}(20a) + \ln(\sqrt{1 + 400a^2} + 20a)\right).$$

7.4.72

a. $\displaystyle\int_0^2 \frac{x^2}{3}\, dx = \frac{x^3}{9}\bigg|_0^2 = \frac{8}{9}$.

b. $\displaystyle\int_0^2 \frac{x^2}{\sqrt{9 - x^2}}\, dx$. Let $x = 3\sin\theta$ so that $dx = 3\cos\theta\, d\theta$. Then

$$\int_0^{\sin^{-1}(2/3)} \frac{9\sin^2\theta \cdot 3\cos\theta}{3\cos\theta}\, d\theta = 9\int_0^{\sin^{-1}(2/3)} \sin^2\theta\, d\theta = \frac{9}{2}\int_0^{\sin^{-1}(2/3)} 1 - \cos 2\theta\, d\theta$$

$$= \frac{9}{2}\left(\theta - \frac{\sin 2\theta}{2}\right)\bigg|_0^{\sin^{-1}(2/3)}$$

$$= \frac{9\sin^{-1}(2/3)}{2} - \frac{9}{2}\left(\frac{2\sqrt{5}}{3 \cdot 3}\right) = \frac{9}{2}\sin^{-1}(2/3) - \sqrt{5} \approx 1.05.$$

c. The area under g is bigger than the area under f.

7.4.73

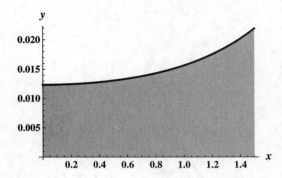

The area is given by $\displaystyle\int_0^{3/2} \frac{1}{(9 - x^2)^2}\, dx$. Let $x = 3\sin\theta$ so that $dx = 3\cos\theta\, d\theta$. Then we have

$$\int_0^{\pi/6} \frac{3\cos\theta}{9^2\cos^4\theta}\, d\theta = \frac{1}{27}\int_0^{\pi/6} \sec^3\theta\, d\theta = \frac{1}{54}\left(\sec\theta\tan\theta + \ln|\sec\theta + \tan\theta|\right)\bigg|_0^{\pi/6}$$

$$= \frac{1}{54}\left(\frac{2}{\sqrt{3}} \cdot \frac{1}{\sqrt{3}} + \ln\left(\frac{2}{\sqrt{3}} + \frac{1}{\sqrt{3}}\right)\right) = \frac{1}{81} + \frac{\ln(\sqrt{3})}{54}.$$

7.4.74

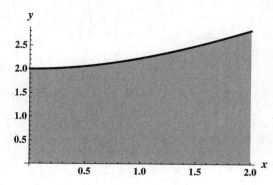

The area is given by $\int_0^2 \sqrt{4 + x^2}\, dx$. Let $x = 2\tan\theta$ so that $dx = 2\sec^2\theta\, d\theta$. Then we have

$$\int_0^{\pi/4} 2\sec^2\theta \cdot 2\sec\theta\, d\theta = 4\int_0^{\pi/4} \sec^3\theta\, d\theta = 2\left(\sec\theta\tan\theta + \ln|\sec\theta + \tan\theta|\right)\Big|_0^{\pi/4} = 2\left(\sqrt{2} + \ln(\sqrt{2} + 1)\right).$$

7.4.75

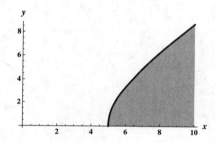

The area is given by $\int_5^{10} \sqrt{x^2 - 25}\, dx$. Let $x = 5\sec\theta$ so that $dx = 5\sec\theta\tan\theta\, d\theta$. Then we have

$$\int_0^{\pi/3} 5\sec\theta\tan\theta \cdot 5\tan\theta\, d\theta = 25\int_0^{\pi/3} \sec\theta\tan^2\theta\, d\theta = 25\int_0^{\pi/3} \sec\theta(\sec^2\theta - 1)\, d\theta$$

$$= 25\int_0^{\pi/3}(\sec^3\theta - \sec\theta)\, d\theta = \frac{25}{2}\left(\sec\theta\tan\theta - \ln|\sec\theta + \tan\theta|\right)\Big|_0^{\pi/3}$$

$$= \frac{25}{2}\left(2\sqrt{3} - \ln(2 + \sqrt{3})\right) = 25\sqrt{3} - \frac{25}{2}\cdot\ln(2 + \sqrt{3}).$$

7.4.76 $\int \dfrac{1}{\sqrt{(x-1)(3-x)}}\, dx = \int \dfrac{1}{\sqrt{1 - (x-2)^2}}\, dx = \int \dfrac{1}{\sqrt{1 - u^2}}\, du = \sin^{-1} u + C = \sin^{-1}(x - 2) + C.$

7.4.77 $\int_{2+\sqrt{2}}^{4} \dfrac{1}{\sqrt{(x-1)(x-3)}}\, dx = \int_{2+\sqrt{2}}^{4} \dfrac{1}{\sqrt{(x-2)^2 - 1}}\, dx = \int_{\sqrt{2}}^{2} \dfrac{1}{\sqrt{u^2 - 1}}\, du$, where $u = x - 2$. Now let

$u = \sec\theta$, so that $du = \sec\theta\tan\theta\, d\theta$. Then $\int_{\pi/4}^{\pi/3} \dfrac{\sec\theta\tan\theta}{\tan\theta}\, d\theta = \int_{\pi/4}^{\pi/3} \sec\theta\, d\theta = \ln(\sec\theta + \tan\theta)\Big|_{\pi/4}^{\pi/3} =$

$\ln(2 + \sqrt{3}) - \ln(\sqrt{2} + 1) = \ln\left(\dfrac{2 + \sqrt{3}}{\sqrt{2} + 1}\right) = \ln((2 + \sqrt{3})(\sqrt{2} - 1)).$

7.4.78 Let $x = 2\tan^{-1} u$ so that $u = \tan(x/2)$ and $\sec^2(x/2) = 1 + \tan^2(x/2) = 1 + u^2$. Also, $\cos^2(x/2) = 1/(1 + u^2)$. By the double angle identity, $\cos x = \cos^2(x/2) - \sin^2(x/2) = \cos^2(x/2) - u^2\cos^2(x/2) = (1 - u^2)\cos^2(x/2) = \frac{1 - u^2}{1 + u^2}.$

Also, $\sin x = 2\sin(x/2)\cos(x/2) = 2\tan(x/2)\cos^2(x/2) = \frac{2u}{1+u^2}$. Now

$$\int \frac{1}{1+\sin x + \cos x}\, dx = 2\int \frac{1}{1+u^2}\cdot\frac{1}{1+\frac{2u}{1+u^2}+\frac{1-u^2}{1+u^2}}\, du = 2\int \frac{1}{1+u^2+2u+1-u^2}\, du = 2\int \frac{1}{2+2u}\, du =$$

$$\int \frac{1}{1+u}\, du = \ln|1+u| + C = \ln|1+\tan(x/2)| + C.$$

7.4.79 Using washers, $V = \displaystyle\int_{-4}^{4} A(x)\, dx$. Now $A(x) = \pi((f(x))^2 - (g(x))^2) = \pi((6+\sqrt{16-x^2})^2 - (6-\sqrt{16-x^2})^2) = 24\pi\sqrt{16-x^2}$. Thus our integral is $\displaystyle\int_{-4}^{4} 24\pi\sqrt{16-x^2}\, dx = 48\pi\int_0^4 \sqrt{16-x^2}\, dx = 48\pi\left(\frac{\pi\cdot 4^2}{4}\right) = 192\pi^2.$

7.4.80 Consider a circle whose equation is $x^2 + \left(y - \frac{R+r}{2}\right)^2 = \left(\frac{R-r}{2}\right)^2$. We will imagine rotating this circle about the x-axis to generate the bagel. Here R stands for the outer radius and r for the inner radius. Let $f(x) = \sqrt{\left(\frac{R-r}{2}\right)^2 - x^2} + \frac{R+r}{2}$ and $g(x) = -\sqrt{\left(\frac{R-r}{2}\right)^2 - x^2} + \frac{R+r}{2}$. The cross sections are washers with

$$A(x) = \pi((f(x))^2 - (g(x))^2) = \pi\left(\left(\frac{R+r}{2}+\sqrt{\left(\frac{R-r}{2}\right)^2 - x^2}\right)^2 - \left(\frac{R+r}{2}-\sqrt{\left(\frac{R-r}{2}\right)^2 - x^2}\right)^2\right)$$

$$= 2\pi(R+r)\sqrt{\left(\frac{R-r}{2}\right)^2 - x^2}.$$

Thus, the volume V of the torus is

$$V = \int_{-(R+r)/2}^{(R+r)/2} 2\pi(R+r)\sqrt{\left(\frac{R-r}{2}\right)^2 - x^2}\, dx.$$

This is equal to

$$4\pi(R+r)\int_0^{(R+r)/2} \sqrt{\left(\frac{R-r}{2}\right)^2 - x^2}\, dx = 4\pi(R+r)\left(\frac{\pi\left(\frac{R-r}{2}\right)^2}{4}\right) = \frac{\pi^2}{4}(R+r)(R-r)^2.$$

Now suppose the inner radius r decreases to become $\frac{4}{5}r$. The resulting volume $V_1 = \frac{\pi^2}{4}(R+\frac{4}{5}r)(R-\frac{4}{5}r)^2 = \frac{\pi^2}{4\cdot 5^3}(5R+4r)(5R-4r)^2$. Likewise, an increase in R by 20 percent yields a new value for R of $\frac{6}{5}R$. Thus the resulting volume $V_2 = \frac{\pi^2}{4}(\frac{6}{5}R+r)(\frac{6}{5}R-r)^2 = \frac{\pi^2}{4\cdot 5^3}(6R+5r)(6R-5r)^2$. If we seek to find conditions for which $V_2 > V_1$, we see that this occurs when $R > r$, which is true by assumption. So the bagel which results from the 20 percent increase in the outer radius is bigger, independent of the size of the original bagels.

7.4.81

a. $E_x(a) = \dfrac{kQa}{2L}\displaystyle\int_{-L}^{L}\frac{dy}{(a^2+y^2)^{3/2}}$. Let $y = a\tan\theta$ so that $dy = a\sec^2\theta\, d\theta$. Then note that

$$\int_{-L}^{L}\frac{dy}{(a^2+y^2)^{3/2}} = 2\int_0^L \frac{dy}{(a^2+y^2)^{3/2}} = 2\int_0^{\tan^{-1}(L/a)} \frac{a\sec^2\theta}{a^3\sec^3\theta}\, d\theta = \frac{2}{a^2}\int_0^{\tan^{-1}(L/a)} \cos\theta\, d\theta$$

$$= \frac{2}{a^2}\sin\theta\,\Big|_0^{\tan^{-1}(L/a)} = \frac{2}{a^2}\cdot\frac{L}{\sqrt{a^2+L^2}} = \frac{2L}{a^2\sqrt{a^2+L^2}}.$$

Thus, $E_x(a) = \dfrac{kQ}{a\sqrt{a^2+L^2}}.$

b. Set $\rho = Q/(2L)$. Then because $\displaystyle\lim_{L\to\infty} \frac{2L}{a^2\sqrt{a^2 + L^2}} = \frac{2}{a^2}$, we have

$$E_x(a,0) \approx \frac{kQa}{2L} \lim_{L\to\infty} \int_{-L}^{L} \frac{dy}{(a^2 + y^2)^{3/2}} = \frac{kQa}{2L} \lim_{L\to\infty} \frac{2L}{a^2\sqrt{a^2 + L^2}} = \frac{kQa}{2L}\left(\frac{2}{a^2}\right) = \frac{2kQ}{2aL} = \frac{2k\rho}{a}.$$

7.4.82

a. Let β be the angle which forms a linear pair with θ, and let α be the angle in the pictured triangle with vertex at $(a,0)$. Note that $\theta + \beta = \pi$ and $\alpha + \beta = \frac{\pi}{2}$, so $\theta = \pi - \beta = \pi/2 + \alpha$. Thus, $\sin(\theta) = \sin(\pi/2 + \alpha) = \cos\alpha$. Now, because $r^2 = a^2 + y^2$ and $\cos\alpha = \frac{a}{r}$, we have that

$$\frac{\sin\theta}{r^2} = \frac{a}{r^3} = \frac{a}{(a^2 + y^2)^{3/2}}.$$

Thus

$$\int_{-L}^{L} \frac{\sin\theta}{r^2}\,dy = \int_{-L}^{L} \frac{a}{(a^2 + y^2)^{3/2}}\,dy = 2\int_{0}^{L} \frac{a}{(a^2 + y^2)^{3/2}}\,dy.$$

Let $y = a\tan u$ so that $dy = a\sec^2 u\,du$. Substituting, we have

$$2\int_{0}^{\tan^{-2}(L/a)} \frac{a^2\sec^2 u}{a^3\sec^3 u}\,du = \frac{2}{a}\int_{0}^{\tan^{-1}(L/a)} \cos u\,du = \frac{2}{a}\sin u\,\Big|_{0}^{\pi/2-\theta_0} = \frac{2}{a}\sin(\pi/2 - \theta_0) = \frac{2}{a}\cos\theta_0$$

where $\tan\theta_0 = \frac{a}{L}$. Thus,

$$B(a) = \frac{\mu_0 I}{4\pi}\cdot\frac{2}{a}\cos\theta_0 = \frac{\mu_0 I}{2\pi a}\cos\theta_0.$$

b. From part (a), $\cos\theta_0 = \frac{L}{\sqrt{a^2+L^2}}$, and thus $\displaystyle\lim_{L\to\infty}\cos\theta_0 = \lim_{L\to\infty}\frac{L}{\sqrt{a^2 + L^2}} = \lim_{L\to\infty}\frac{1}{\sqrt{(a^2/L^2) + 1}} = 1$. Therefore, $\displaystyle\lim_{L\to\infty} B(a) = \frac{\mu_0 I}{2\pi a}$.

7.4.83

a. Because $t \in [0, \pi]$ so that $\sin t \geq 0$, we have

$$\int_{a}^{b}\sqrt{\frac{1 - \cos t}{g(\cos a - \cos t)}}\,dt = \int_{a}^{b}\sqrt{\frac{(1 - \cos t)(1 + \cos t)}{g(1 + \cos t)(\cos a - \cos t)}}\,dt = \int_{a}^{b}\sin t\sqrt{\frac{1}{g(1 + \cos t)(\cos a - \cos t)}}\,dt.$$

Let $u = \cos t$ so that $du = -\sin t\,dt$. Then the given integral is equal to

$$-\frac{1}{\sqrt{g}}\int_{\cos a}^{\cos b}\sqrt{\frac{1}{(1 + u)(\cos a - u)}}\,du.$$

Now we complete the square:

$$(1 + u)(\cos a - u) = \cos a + (\cos a - 1)u - u^2$$

$$= -\left(u^2 - (\cos a - 1)u + \left(\frac{\cos a - 1}{2}\right)^2 - \left(\frac{\cos a - 1}{2}\right)^2\right) + \cos a$$

$$= \cos a + \left(\frac{\cos a - 1}{2}\right)^2 - \left(u - \frac{\cos a - 1}{2}\right)^2 = \left(\frac{\cos a + 1}{2}\right)^2 - \left(u - \frac{\cos a - 1}{2}\right)^2.$$

Thus, setting $v = u - \frac{\cos a - 1}{2}$ we have that the original integral is equal to

$$-\frac{1}{\sqrt{g}}\int_{(\cos a + 1)/2}^{\cos b - \frac{\cos a - 1}{2}}\frac{1}{\sqrt{k^2 - v^2}}\,dv \text{ where } k = \frac{(\cos a + 1)}{2}.$$

Now, $\int \dfrac{1}{\sqrt{k^2 - v^2}}\,dv = \int \dfrac{k\cos\theta}{k\cos\theta}\,d\theta = \theta + C = \sin^{-1}(v/k) + C$ where $v = k\sin\theta$.

Therefore, the original integral is equal to

$$-\frac{1}{\sqrt{g}}\sin^{-1}\left(\frac{2v}{\cos a + 1}\right)\Bigg|_{(\cos a + 1)/2}^{\cos b - (\cos a - 1)/2} = \frac{1}{\sqrt{g}}\left(\sin^{-1}\left(\frac{\cos a + 1}{\cos a + 1}\right) - \sin^{-1}\left(\frac{2\cos b - \cos a + 1}{\cos a + 1}\right)\right)$$

$$= \frac{1}{\sqrt{g}}\left(\frac{\pi}{2} - \sin^{-1}\left(\frac{2\cos b - \cos a + 1}{\cos a + 1}\right)\right).$$

b. Letting $b = \pi$, we have that the integral is equal to

$$\frac{1}{\sqrt{g}}\left(\frac{\pi}{2} - \sin^{-1}\left(\frac{-2 - \cos a + 1}{\cos a + 1}\right)\right)$$

$$= \frac{1}{\sqrt{g}}\left(\frac{\pi}{2} - \sin^{-1}(-1)\right) = \frac{1}{\sqrt{g}}\left(\frac{\pi}{2} - \left(-\frac{\pi}{2}\right)\right) = \frac{\pi}{\sqrt{g}}.$$

7.4.84

a. $0 = -\frac{1}{2}ka^2 + y_{\max}$ when $a = \sqrt{\dfrac{2y_{\max}}{k}}$.

b. $y'(x) = -kx$, so $1 + (y'(x))^2 = 1 + k^2 x^2$, so the arc length is given by $L = \displaystyle\int_{-a}^{a}\sqrt{1 + (y'(x))^2}\,dx =$ $\displaystyle\int_{-a}^{a}\sqrt{1 + k^2 x^2}\,dx = 2\int_{0}^{a}\sqrt{1 + k^2 x^2}\,dx$ because the function is an even function.

c. Let $x = \frac{1}{k}\tan\theta$ so that $dx = \frac{1}{k}\sec^2\theta\,d\theta$. Then the arc length integral is equal to

$$2\int_{0}^{\tan^{-1}(ak)}\frac{1}{k}\sec^2\theta\cdot\sec\theta\,d\theta = \frac{1}{k}\left(\sec\theta\tan\theta\Bigg|_{0}^{\tan^{-1}(ak)} + \ln|\sec\theta + \tan\theta|\right)\Bigg|_{0}^{\tan^{-1}(ak)}$$

$$= \frac{1}{k}\left(ak\sqrt{1 + a^2 k^2} + \ln(\sqrt{1 + a^2 k^2} + ak)\right).$$

Noting that $\tan(\theta) = ak$, $a = (V^2/g)\sin\theta\cos\theta$, and $k = \frac{g}{V^2\cos^2\theta}$, we can write L as a function of θ as $L(\theta) = (V^2/g)\sin\theta + (V^2/g)\cos^2\theta(\ln(\sqrt{1 + \tan^2\theta} + \tan\theta))$, and using an identity for the inverse hyperbolic sine function, this can be written as $L(\theta) = \frac{V^2}{g}\left(\sin\theta + \cos^2\theta\sinh^{-1}(\tan\theta)\right)$.

d. Using the expression for $L(\theta)$ above, we have
$L'(\theta) = (V^2/g)\left(\cos\theta - 2\cos\theta\sin\theta(\sinh^{-1}(\tan\theta)) - \cos^2\theta(1 + \tan^2\theta)^{-1/2}\sec^2\theta\right) =$
$\frac{2V^2\cos\theta}{g}\left(1 - \sin\theta\sinh^{-1}(\tan\theta)\right).$ This expression is 0 when $\sin\theta(\sinh^{-1}\tan\theta) = 1$, which is equivalent to $\sin\theta(\ln(\tan\theta + \sec\theta)) = 1$. Either the first or second derivative tests can be used to see that this critical number yields the maximum.

e. Some experimenting reveals that the maximum occurs for $\theta \approx 56.5$ degrees.

7.4.85 If $1 < x = \sec\theta$ then we need $\theta \in (0, \pi/2)$. Alternatively, if $-1 > x = \sec\theta$, then we need $\theta \in (\pi/2, \pi)$. So, in the former, $\displaystyle\int\frac{1}{x\sqrt{x^2 - 1}}\,dx = \int\frac{\sec\theta\tan\theta}{\sec\theta\tan\theta}\,d\theta = \theta + C = \sec^{-1}x + C = \tan^{-1}\sqrt{x^2 - 1} + C$. In the latter case, $\displaystyle\int\frac{1}{x\sqrt{x^2 - 1}}\,dx = \int\frac{\sec\theta}{\sec\theta(-\tan\theta)}\,d\theta = -\theta + C = -\sec^{-1}x + C = -\tan^{-1}\sqrt{x^2 - 1} + C$.

7.4.86 For $1 \le x = \sec\theta$ (where $\theta \in [0, \pi/2)$) we have $dx = \sec\theta\tan\theta\,d\theta$. Note that $|\tan\theta| = \tan\theta$ in this case. We have $\displaystyle\int\frac{\sqrt{x^2 - 1}}{x^3}\,dx = \int\frac{\sec\theta\tan\theta|\tan\theta|}{\sec^3\theta}\,d\theta = \int\frac{\tan^2\theta}{\sec^2\theta}\,d\theta = \int\sin^2\theta\,d\theta = \frac{1}{2}\int 1 - \cos 2\theta\,d\theta =$ $\frac{1}{2}\left(\theta - \frac{\sin 2\theta}{2}\right) + C = \frac{1}{2}\left(\sec^{-1}x - \frac{\sqrt{x^2 - 1}}{x^2}\right) + C.$

For the case $-1 \geq x = \sec\theta$, we have that $|\tan\theta| = -\tan\theta$. So in this case, $\displaystyle\int \frac{\sqrt{x^2 - 1}}{x^3}\,dx =$ $\displaystyle\int \frac{\sec\theta\tan\theta|\tan\theta|}{\sec^3\theta}\,d\theta = -\int \frac{\tan^2\theta}{\sec^2\theta}\,d\theta = -\int \sin^2\theta\,d\theta = -\frac{1}{2}\int 1 - \cos 2\theta\,d\theta = -\frac{1}{2}\left(\theta - \frac{\sin 2\theta}{2}\right) + C =$ $-\frac{1}{2}\left(\theta - \sin\theta\cos\theta\right) + C$. Now note that because $\theta \in (\pi/2, \pi]$, we must have that $\cos\theta < 0$. Thus we have $-\frac{1}{2}\left(\sec^{-1}x + \frac{\sqrt{x^2-1}}{x^2}\right) + C$.

7.4.87

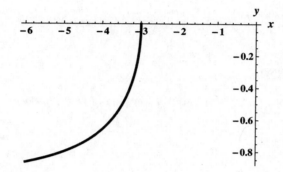

Let $x = 3\sec\theta$ for $x \in (\pi/2, \pi)$. Then $dx = 3\sec\theta\tan\theta\,d\theta$, and note that $|tan\theta| = -\tan\theta$. We have

$$\int_{-6}^{-3} \frac{\sqrt{x^2 - 9}}{x}\,dx = \int_{2\pi/3}^{\pi} \frac{3\sec\theta\tan\theta(-3\tan\theta)}{3\sec\theta}\,d\theta = -3\int_{2\pi/3}^{\pi} \tan^2\theta\,d\theta$$

$$= -3\left(\tan\theta - \theta\right)\Big|_{2\pi/3}^{\pi} = -3\left(-\pi - (-\sqrt{3} - 2\pi/3)\right) = \pi - 3\sqrt{3}.$$

Note that this number is less than zero, as suggested by the graph.

7.4.88

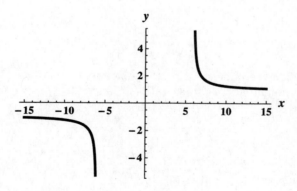

Let $x = 6\sec\theta$ so that $dx = 6\sec\theta\tan\theta\,d\theta$. Then

$$\int_{12/\sqrt{3}}^{12} \frac{1}{x\sqrt{x^2 - 36}}\,dx = \int_{\pi/6}^{\pi/3} \frac{6\sec\theta\tan\theta}{6\sec\theta \cdot 6\tan\theta}\,d\theta = \frac{1}{6}\int_{\pi/6}^{\pi/3} d\theta = \frac{\pi}{36}.$$

By making the substitution $u = -x$ we can see that the other integral has the opposite value of this integral, so

$$\int_{-12}^{-12/\sqrt{3}} \frac{1}{x\sqrt{x^2 - 36}}\,dx = -\frac{\pi}{36}.$$

7.4.89

a. The area of sector OAB is given by the formula $\frac{\theta}{2}a^2$ where $\sin\theta = x/a$. The area of triangle OBC is $\frac{x}{2}\sqrt{a^2-x^2}$. Thus,

$$F(x) = \frac{a^2\sin^{-1}(x/a)}{2} + \frac{x\sqrt{a^2-x^2}}{2}.$$

b. By the first fundamental theorem of calculus, $F(x)$ is an antiderivative of $\sqrt{a^2-x^2}$, because $F(x) = \int_0^x \sqrt{a^2-t^2}\,dt$. Thus, any other antiderivative differs from this by a constant, so

$$\int \sqrt{a^2-x^2}\,dx = \frac{a^2\sin^{-1}(x/a)}{2} + \frac{x\sqrt{a^2-x^2}}{2} + C.$$

7.5 Partial Fractions

7.5.1 Proper rational functions can be integrated using partial fraction decomposition.

7.5.2 Your answers may vary.

a. $x-1$.

b. $(x-1)^3$.

c. x^2+x+1.

d. $(x^2+x+1)^2$

7.5.3

a. $\dfrac{A}{x-3}$.

b. $\dfrac{A_1}{x-4}, \dfrac{A_2}{(x-4)^2}, \dfrac{A_3}{(x-4)^3}$.

c. $\dfrac{Ax+B}{x^2+2x+6}$.

7.5.4 The first step is to divide the numerator by the denominator via long division in order to write the quotient as the sum of a polynomial and a proper rational function. Thus we would write

$$\frac{x^2+2x-3}{x+1} = x+1 - \frac{4}{x+1}.$$

7.5.5 $\dfrac{2}{x^2-2x-8} = \dfrac{2}{(x-4)(x+2)} = \dfrac{A}{x-4} + \dfrac{B}{x+2}$. Thus, $2 = A(x+2) + B(x-4)$. Equating coefficients gives $A+B=0$ and $2A-4B=2$. Solving this system yields $A=1/3$ and $B=-1/3$. Thus,

$$\frac{2}{x^2-2x-8} = \frac{1/3}{x-4} - \frac{1/3}{x+2}.$$

7.5.6 $\dfrac{x-9}{x^2-3x-18} = \dfrac{x-9}{(x-6)(x+3)} = \dfrac{A}{x-6} + \dfrac{B}{x+3}$. Thus, $x-9 = A(x+3) + B(x-6)$. Equating coefficients gives $A+B=1$ and $3A-6B=-9$. Solving this system yields $A=-1/3$, $B=4/3$. Thus,

$$\frac{x-9}{x^2-3x-18} = -\frac{1/3}{x-6} + \frac{4/3}{x+3}.$$

7.5.7 $\dfrac{5x-7}{x^2-3x+2} = \dfrac{5x-7}{(x-1)(x-2)} = \dfrac{A}{x-1} + \dfrac{B}{x-2}$. Thus, $A(x-2) + B(x-1) = 5x-7$. Equating coefficients gives $A+B=5$ and $-2A-B=-7$. Solving this system yields $A=2$, $B=3$. Thus,

$$\frac{5x-7}{x^2-3x+2} = \frac{2}{x-1} + \frac{3}{x-2}.$$

7.5.8 $\dfrac{11x-10}{x(x-1)} = \dfrac{A}{x} + \dfrac{B}{x-1}$. Thus, $A(x-1) + Bx = 11x - 10$. Equating coefficients gives $A+B=11$, $-A = -10$. Solving this system yields $A=10$, $B=1$. Thus,

$$\frac{11x-10}{x^2-x} = \frac{10}{x} + \frac{1}{x-1}.$$

7.5.9 $\dfrac{x^2}{x^3-16x} = \dfrac{x}{(x-4)(x+4)} = \dfrac{A}{x-4} + \dfrac{B}{x+4}$. Thus, $x = A(x+4) + B(x-4)$. Equating coefficients gives $A+B=1$, $4A-4B=0$. Solving this system yields $A=B=1/2$. Thus,

$$\frac{x^2}{x^3-16x} = \frac{1/2}{x-4} + \frac{1/2}{x+4}.$$

7.5.10 $\dfrac{x^2-3x}{x^3-3x^2-4x} = \dfrac{x-3}{x^2-3x-4} = \dfrac{x-3}{(x-4)(x+1)} = \dfrac{A}{x-4} + \dfrac{B}{x+1}$. Thus, $x-3 = A(x+1) + B(x-4)$. Letting $x=-1$ yields $B=4/5$ and letting $x=4$ yields $A=1/5$. Thus,

$$\frac{x^2-3x}{x^3-3x^2-4x} = \frac{1/5}{x-4} + \frac{4/5}{x+1}.$$

7.5.11 $\dfrac{x+2}{x^3-3x^2+2x} = \dfrac{x+2}{(x-1)\cdot x \cdot (x-2)} = \dfrac{A}{x-1} + \dfrac{B}{x} + \dfrac{C}{x-2}$. Thus $x+2 = Ax(x-2) + B(x-1)(x-2) + Cx(x-1)$. Letting $x=1$ gives $A=-3$, letting $x=0$ gives $B=1$, and letting $x=2$ gives $C=2$. Therefore,

$$\frac{x+2}{x^3-3x^2+2x} = \frac{-3}{x-1} + \frac{1}{x} + \frac{2}{x-2}.$$

7.5.12 $\dfrac{x^2-4x+11}{(x-3)(x-1)(x+1)} = \dfrac{A}{x-3} + \dfrac{B}{x-1} + \dfrac{C}{x+1}$. Thus, $x^2-4x+11 = A(x-1)(x+1) + B(x-3)(x+1) + C(x-3)(x-1)$. Letting $x=1$ gives $B=-2$, letting $x=-1$ gives $C=2$, and letting $x=3$ gives $A=1$. Thus,

$$\frac{x^2-4x+11}{(x-3)(x-1)(x+1)} = \frac{1}{x-3} + \frac{-2}{x-1} + \frac{2}{x+1}.$$

7.5.13 If we write $\dfrac{3}{(x-1)(x+2)} = \dfrac{A}{x-1} + \dfrac{B}{x+2}$, we have $3 = A(x+2) + B(x-1)$. Letting $x=-2$ yields $B=-1$ and letting $x=1$ yields $A=1$. Thus, the original integral is equal to $\displaystyle\int \left(\dfrac{1}{x-1} - \dfrac{1}{x+2}\right) dx = \ln|x-1| - \ln|x+2| + C = \ln\left|\dfrac{x-1}{x+2}\right| + C$.

7.5.14 If we write $\dfrac{8}{(x-2)(x+6)} = \dfrac{A}{x-2} + \dfrac{B}{x+6}$, we have $8 = A(x+6) + B(x-2)$. Letting $x=-6$ yields $B=-1$ and letting $x=2$ yields $A=1$. Thus the original integral is equal to $\displaystyle\int \left(\dfrac{1}{x-2} - \dfrac{1}{x+6}\right) dx = \ln|x-2| - \ln|x+6| + C$.

7.5.15 If we write $\frac{6}{x^2-1} = \frac{6}{(x-1)(x+1)} = \frac{A}{x-1} + \frac{B}{x+1}$, then we have $6 = A(x+1) + B(x-1)$. Letting $x=-1$ yields $B=-3$ and letting $x=1$ yields $A=3$. Thus, the original integral is equal to $\displaystyle\int \left(\dfrac{3}{x-1} - \dfrac{3}{x+1}\right) dx = 3\left(\ln|x-1| - \ln|x+1|\right) + C = 3\ln\left|\dfrac{x-1}{x+1}\right| + C$.

7.5.16 If we write $\dfrac{1}{t^2 - 9} = \dfrac{A}{t-3} + \dfrac{B}{t+3}$, then we have $1 = A(t+3) + B(t-3)$. Letting $t = -3$ yields $B = -1/6$ and letting $t = 3$ yields $A = 1/6$. Thus the original integral is equal to $\displaystyle\int_0^1 \left(\dfrac{1/6}{t-3} - \dfrac{1/6}{t+3} \right) dt = \dfrac{1}{6} \left(\ln|t-3| - \ln|t+3| \right) \Big|_0^1 = -\dfrac{\ln 2}{6}$.

7.5.17 If we write $\dfrac{5x}{x^2 - x - 6} = \dfrac{A}{x-3} + \dfrac{B}{x+2}$, then we have $5x = A(x+2) + B(x-3)$. Letting $x = -2$ yields $B = 2$ and letting $x = 3$ yields $A = 3$. Thus the original integral is equal to $\displaystyle\int_{-1}^2 \left(\dfrac{3}{x-3} + \dfrac{2}{x+2} \right) dx = (3\ln|x-3| + 2\ln|x+2|) \Big|_{-1}^2 = \ln(16) - \ln(64) = -\ln 4$.

7.5.18 If we write $\dfrac{21x^2}{x^3 - x^2 - 12x} = \dfrac{21x^2}{x(x-4)(x+3)} = \dfrac{21x}{(x-4)(x+3)} = \dfrac{A}{x-4} + \dfrac{B}{x+3}$, then we have $21x = A(x+3) + B(x-4)$. Letting $x = 4$ yields $A = 12$. Letting $x = -3$ yields $B = 9$. Thus, the original integral is equal to $\displaystyle\int \left(\dfrac{12}{x-4} + \dfrac{9}{x+3} \right) dx = 12\ln|x-4| + 9\ln|x+3| + C$.

7.5.19 If we write $\dfrac{10x}{x^2 - 2x - 24} = \dfrac{10x}{(x-6)(x+4)} = \dfrac{A}{x-6} + \dfrac{B}{x+4}$, then we have $10x = A(x+4) + B(x-6)$. Letting $x = -4$ yields $B = 4$ and letting $x = 6$ yields $A = 6$. Thus the original integral is equal to $\displaystyle\int \left(\dfrac{6}{x-6} + \dfrac{4}{x+4} \right) dx = \ln|(x-6)^6 (x+4)^4| + C$.

7.5.20 If we write $\dfrac{y+1}{y^3 + 3y^2 - 18y} = \dfrac{y+1}{y(y+6)(y-3)} = \dfrac{A}{y} + \dfrac{B}{y+6} + \dfrac{C}{y-3}$, then $y + 1 = A(y+6)(y-3) + By(y-3) + Cy(y+6)$. Letting $y = -6$ yields $B = -5/54$. Letting $y = 3$ yields $C = 4/27$, and letting $y = 0$ yields $A = -1/18$. Thus, the original integral is equal to $\displaystyle\int \left(-\dfrac{1/18}{y} - \dfrac{5/54}{y+6} + \dfrac{4/27}{y-3} \right) dy = -\dfrac{1}{18}\ln|y| - \dfrac{5}{54}\ln|y+6| + \dfrac{4}{27}\ln|y-3| + C$.

7.5.21 Let $\dfrac{6x^2}{x^4 - 5x^2 + 4} = \dfrac{6x^2}{(x-2)(x+2)(x-1)(x+1)} = \dfrac{A}{x-2} + \dfrac{B}{x+2} + \dfrac{C}{x-1} + \dfrac{D}{x+1}$. Then $6x^2 = A(x+2)(x-1)(x+1) + B(x-2)(x-1)(x+1) + C(x-2)(x+2)(x+1) + D(x-2)(x+2)(x-1)$. Letting $x = 2$ gives $A = 2$, letting $x = -2$ gives $B = -2$, letting $x = 1$ gives $C = -1$, and letting $x = -1$ gives $D = 1$. Thus, the original integral is equal to $\displaystyle\int \left(\dfrac{2}{x-2} - \dfrac{2}{x+2} - \dfrac{1}{x-1} + \dfrac{1}{x+1} \right) dx = \ln\left| \dfrac{(x-2)^2(x+1)}{(x+2)^2(x-1)} \right| + C$

7.5.22 Let $\dfrac{4x-2}{x(x-1)(x+1)} = \dfrac{A}{x} + \dfrac{B}{x-1} + \dfrac{C}{x+1}$. Thus, $4x - 2 = A(x-1)(x+1) + Bx(x+1) + Cx(x-1)$. Letting $x = 0$ gives $A = 2$, letting $x = 1$ gives $B = 1$, and letting $x = -1$ gives $C = -3$. Thus, the original integral is equal to $\displaystyle\int \left(\dfrac{2}{x} + \dfrac{1}{x-1} - \dfrac{3}{x+1} \right) dx = \ln\left| \dfrac{x^2(x-1)}{(x+1)^3} \right| + C$.

7.5.23 Let $\dfrac{x^2 + 12x - 4}{x(x-2)(x+2)} = \dfrac{A}{x} + \dfrac{B}{x-2} + \dfrac{C}{x+2}$. Then $x^2 + 12x - 4 = A(x-2)(x+2) + Bx(x+2) + Cx(x-2)$. Letting $x = 0$ gives $A = 1$, letting $x = 2$ gives $B = 3$, and letting $x = -2$ gives $C = -3$. Thus, the original integral is equal to $\displaystyle\int \left(\dfrac{1}{x} + \dfrac{3}{x-2} - \dfrac{3}{x+2} \right) dx = \ln\left| \dfrac{x(x-2)^3}{(x+2)^3} \right| + C$.

7.5.24 Let $\dfrac{z^2 + 20z - 15}{z(z+5)(z-1)} = \dfrac{A}{z} + \dfrac{B}{z+5} + \dfrac{C}{z-1}$. Then $z^2 + 20z - 15 = A(z+5)(z-1) + Bz(z-1) + Cz(z+5)$. Letting $z = 0$ gives $A = 3$, letting $z = -5$ gives $B = -3$, and letting $z = 1$ gives $C = 1$. Thus, the original integral is equal to $\displaystyle\int \left(\dfrac{3}{z} - \dfrac{3}{z+5} + \dfrac{1}{z-1} \right) dz = \ln\left| \dfrac{z^3(z-1)}{(z+5)^3} \right| + C$.

7.5.25 If we write $\dfrac{1}{x^4 - 10x^2 + 9} = \dfrac{1}{(x-1)(x+1)(x-3)(x+3)} = \dfrac{A}{x-1} + \dfrac{B}{x+1} + \dfrac{C}{x-3} + \dfrac{D}{x+3}$ then
$1 = A(x+1)(x-3)(x+3) + B(x-1)(x-3)(x+3) + C(x-1)(x+1)(x+3) + D(x-1)(x+1)(x-3)$.
Letting $x = -1$ yields $B = 1/16$. Letting $x = 3$ yields $C = 1/48$. Letting $x = -3$ yields $D = -1/48$, and letting $x = 1$ yields $A = -1/16$. Thus the original integral is equal to

$$\int \left(-\frac{1/16}{x-1} + \frac{1/16}{x+1} + \frac{1/48}{x-3} - \frac{1/48}{x+3} \right) dx$$

$$= -\frac{1}{16} \ln|x-1| + \frac{1}{16} \ln|x+1| + \frac{1}{48} \ln|x-3| - \frac{1}{48} \ln|x+3| + C$$

$$= \ln \left| \frac{(x+1)^3(x-3)}{(x-1)^3(x+3)} \right|^{1/48} + C.$$

7.5.26 If we write $\dfrac{2}{x^2 - 4x - 32} = \dfrac{A}{x-8} + \dfrac{B}{x+4}$, then we have $2 = A(x+4) + B(x-8)$. Letting $x = -4$ yields $B = -1/6$ and letting $x = 8$ yields $A = 1/6$. Thus, the original integral is equal to

$$\int_0^5 \left(\frac{1/6}{x-8} - \frac{1/6}{x+4} \right) dx = \frac{1}{6} \left(\ln|x-8| - \ln|x+4| \right) \Big|_0^5 = \frac{1}{6}(\ln(1/3) - \ln 2) = -\frac{\ln 6}{6}.$$

7.5.27 If we write $\dfrac{81}{x^3 - 9x^2} = \dfrac{A}{x} + \dfrac{B}{x^2} + \dfrac{C}{x-9}$, then $81 = Ax(x-9) + B(x-9) + C(x^2)$. Letting $x = 0$ yields $B = -9$. Letting $x = 9$ yields $C = 1$. If we let $x = 10$, then we have $81 = 10A + B + 100C = 10A - 9 + 100$, so $A = -1$. Thus, the original integral is equal to $\displaystyle\int \left(-\frac{1}{x} - \frac{9}{x^2} + \frac{1}{x-9} \right) dx = \ln \left| \frac{(x-9)}{x} \right| + \frac{9}{x} + C.$

7.5.28 If we write $\dfrac{16x^2}{(x-6)(x+2)^2} = \dfrac{A}{x-6} + \dfrac{B}{x+2} + \dfrac{C}{(x+2)^2}$, then we have $16x^2 = A(x+2)^2 + B(x-6)(x+2) + C(x-6)$. Letting $x = 6$ yields $A = 9$. Letting $x = -2$ yields $C = -8$. Letting $x = 0$ gives $0 = 36 - 12B + 48$, so $B = 7$. Thus the original integral is equal to

$$\int \left(\frac{9}{x-6} + \frac{7}{x+2} - \frac{8}{(x+2)^2} \right) dx = \ln \left| (x+2)^7(x-6)^9 \right| + \frac{8}{x+2} + C.$$

7.5.29 If we write $\dfrac{x}{(x+3)^2} = \dfrac{A}{x+3} + \dfrac{B}{(x+3)^2}$, then we have $x = A(x+3) + B$. Letting $x = -3$ yields $B = -3$, and then letting $x = -2$ yields $A = 1$. Thus the original integral is equal to

$$\int_{-1}^1 \left(\frac{1}{x+3} - \frac{3}{(x+3)^2} \right) dx = \left(\ln|x+3| + \frac{3}{x+3} \right) \Big|_{-1}^1 = \ln 4 + \frac{3}{4} - \left(\ln 2 + \frac{3}{2} \right) = \ln 2 - \frac{3}{4}.$$

7.5.30 If we write $\dfrac{1}{x^3 - 2x^2 - 4x + 8} = \dfrac{1}{(x+2)(x-2)^2} = \dfrac{A}{x+2} + \dfrac{B}{x-2} + \dfrac{C}{(x-2)^2}$, then $1 = A(x-2)^2 + B(x+2)(x-2) + C(x+2)$. Letting $x = 2$ yields $C = 1/4$. Letting $x = -2$ yields $A = 1/16$. Letting $x = 3$ yields $1 = \frac{1}{16} + 5B + 5 \cdot \frac{1}{4}$, so $B = -\frac{1}{16}$. Thus the original integral is equal to

$$\int \left(\frac{1/16}{x+2} - \frac{1/16}{x-2} + \frac{1/4}{(x-2)^2} \right) dx = \frac{1}{16} \left(\ln|x+2| - \ln|x-2| \right) - \frac{1}{4(x-2)} + C.$$

7.5.31 If we write $\dfrac{2}{x^3 + x^2} = \dfrac{A}{x} + \dfrac{B}{x^2} + \dfrac{C}{x+1}$, then $2 = Ax(x+1) + B(x+1) + Cx^2$. Letting $x = 0$ yields $B = 2$, and letting $x = -1$ yields $C = 2$. Then letting $x = 1$ yields $A = -2$. So the original integral is equal to

$$\int \left(-\frac{2}{x} + \frac{2}{x^2} + \frac{2}{x+1} \right) dx = 2 \left(\ln|x+1| - \ln|x| \right) - \frac{2}{x} + C.$$

7.5.32 If we write $\dfrac{2}{t^3(t+1)} = \dfrac{A}{t} + \dfrac{B}{t^2} + \dfrac{C}{t^3} + \dfrac{D}{t+1}$ then we have $2 = At^2(t+1) + Bt(t+1) + C(t+1) + Dt^3$. Letting $t = 0$ yields $C = 2$, and letting $t = -1$ reveals that $D = -2$. Now if we let $t = 1$ we have that $2 = 2A + 2B + 4 - 2$, so $A = -B$. Letting $t = 2$ yields the equation $12 = 12A + 6B = 12A - 6A = 6A$, so $A = 2$ and $B = -2$. So the original integral is equal to

$$\int_1^2 \left(\frac{2}{t} - \frac{2}{t^2} + \frac{2}{t^3} - \frac{2}{t+1} \right) dt = \left(2 \left(\ln|t| - \ln|t+1| \right) + \frac{2}{t} - \frac{1}{t^2} \right) \Big|_1^2 = \ln(16/9) - 1/4.$$

7.5.33 If we write $\dfrac{x-5}{x^2(x+1)} = \dfrac{A}{x} + \dfrac{B}{x^2} + \dfrac{C}{x+1}$, then we have $x - 5 = Ax(x+1) + B(x+1) + Cx^2$. Letting $x = 0$ yields $B = -5$, and letting $x = -1$ yields $C = -6$. Then letting $x = 1$ yields $-4 = 2A - 10 - 6$, so $A = 6$. The original integral is thus equal to

$$\int \left(\frac{6}{x} - \frac{5}{x^2} - \frac{6}{x+1} \right) dx = 6 \left(\ln|x| - \ln|x+1| \right) + \frac{5}{x} + C.$$

7.5.34 Let $\dfrac{x^2}{(x-2)^3} = \dfrac{A}{x-2} + \dfrac{B}{(x-2)^2} + \dfrac{C}{(x-2)^3}$. Then $x^2 = A(x-2)^2 + B(x-2) + C$. Letting $x = 2$ gives $C = 4$. Letting $x = 0$ gives $0 = 4A - 2B + 4$, and letting $x = 1$ gives $1 = A - B + 4$. Solving the system of two linear equations results in $A = 1$ and $B = 4$. The original integral is therefore equal to

$$\int \left(\frac{1}{x-2} + \frac{4}{(x-2)^2} + \frac{4}{(x-2)^3} \right) dx = \ln|x-2| - \frac{4}{x-2} - \frac{2}{(x-2)^2} + C.$$

7.5.35 Let $\dfrac{x^2 - x}{(x-2)(x-3)^2} = \dfrac{A}{x-2} - \dfrac{B}{x-3} + \dfrac{C}{(x-3)^2}$. Then $x^2 - x = A(x-3)^2 + B(x-2)(x-3) + C(x-2)$. Letting $x = 2$ gives $A = 2$. Letting $x = 3$ gives $C = 6$. Letting $x = 0$ gives $0 = 18 + 6B - 12$, so $B = -1$. The original integral is thus

$$\int \left(\frac{2}{x-2} - \frac{1}{x-3} + \frac{6}{(x-3)^2} \right) dx = \ln \left| \frac{(x-2)^2}{x-3} \right| + \frac{-6}{x-3} + C.$$

7.5.36 Let $\dfrac{12y - 8}{y^4 - 2y^2 + 1} = \dfrac{A}{y+1} + \dfrac{B}{(y+1)^2} + \dfrac{C}{y-1} + \dfrac{D}{(y-1)^2}$. Then $12y - 8 = A(y+1)(y-1)^2 + B(y-1)^2 + C(y-1)(y+1)^2 + D(y+1)^2$. Letting $y = 1$ gives $D = 1$, and letting $y = -1$ gives $B = -5$. Then letting $y = 0$ gives $-8 = A - 5 - C + 1$ and letting $y = 2$ gives $16 = 3A - 5 + 9C + 9$, and solving this system of linear equations gives $A = -2$ and $C = 2$. The given integral is thus equal to

$$\int \left(-\frac{2}{y+1} - \frac{5}{(y+1)^2} + \frac{2}{y-1} + \frac{1}{(y-1)^2} \right) dy = \ln \left| \frac{(y-1)^2}{(y+1)^2} \right| + \frac{5}{y+1} - \frac{1}{y-1} + C.$$

7.5.37 Let $\dfrac{x^2 - 4}{x^3 - 2x^2 + x} = \dfrac{A}{x} + \dfrac{B}{x-1} + \dfrac{C}{(x-1)^2}$. Then $x^2 - 4 = A(x-1)^2 + Bx(x-1) + Cx$. Letting $x = 0$ gives $A = -4$. Letting $x = 1$ gives $C = -3$. Letting $x = 2$ gives $0 = -4 + 2B - 6$, so $B = 5$. The given integral is thus equal to

$$\int \left(-\frac{4}{x} + \frac{5}{x-1} - \frac{3}{(x-1)^2} \right) dx = \ln \left| \frac{(x-1)^5}{x^4} \right| + \frac{3}{x-1} + C.$$

7.5.38 $\dfrac{2}{x(x^2 - 6x + 9)} = \dfrac{2}{x(x-3)^2} = \dfrac{A}{x} + \dfrac{B}{x-3} + \dfrac{C}{(x-3)^2}$.

7.5.39 $\dfrac{20x}{(x-1)^2(x^2+1)} = \dfrac{A}{x-1} + \dfrac{B}{(x-1)^2} + \dfrac{Cx + D}{x^2 + 1}$.

7.5.40 $\dfrac{x^2}{x^3(x^2+1)} = \dfrac{A}{x} + \dfrac{B}{x^2} + \dfrac{C}{x^3} + \dfrac{Dx + E}{x^2 + 1}$.

7.5.41 $\dfrac{2x^2 + 3}{(x^2 - 8x + 16)(x^2 + 3x + 4)} = \dfrac{2x^2 + 3}{(x - 4)^2(x^2 + 3x + 4)} = \dfrac{A}{x - 4} + \dfrac{B}{(x - 4)^2} + \dfrac{Cx + D}{x^2 + 3x + 4}.$

7.5.42 Let $\dfrac{8(x^2 + 4)}{x(x^2 + 8)} = \dfrac{Ax + B}{x^2 + 8} + \dfrac{C}{x}$. Then $8(x^2 + 4) = Ax^2 + Bx + C(x^2 + 8)$. Letting $x = 0$ gives $C = 4$. Letting $x = 1$ gives $40 = A + B + 36$, so $A + B = 4$. Letting $x = -1$ gives $A - B = 4$, so $A = 4$ and $B = 0$. The original integral is thus equal to

$$\int \left(\frac{4x}{x^2 + 8} + \frac{4}{x} \right) dx = 2\ln(x^2 + 8) + 4\ln|x| + C = \ln((x^2 + 8)^2 x^4) + C.$$

7.5.43 Let $\dfrac{x^2 + x + 2}{(x + 1)(x^2 + 1)} = \dfrac{Ax + B}{x^2 + 1} + \dfrac{C}{x + 1}$. Then $x^2 + x + 2 = (Ax + B)(x + 1) + C(x^2 + 1)$. Letting $x = -1$ gives $C = 1$. Letting $x = 0$ gives $2 = B + 1$, so $B = 1$. Letting $x = 1$ gives $4 = 2A + 2 + 2$, so $A = 0$. The original integral is therefore equal to

$$\int \left(\frac{1}{x^2 + 1} + \frac{1}{x + 1} \right) dx = \tan^{-1}(x) + \ln|x + 1| + C.$$

7.5.44 Let $\dfrac{x^2 + 3x + 2}{x(x^2 + 2x + 2)} = \dfrac{Ax + B}{x^2 + 2x + 2} + \dfrac{C}{x}$. Then $x^2 + 3x + 2 = Ax^2 + Bx + C(x^2 + 2x + 2)$. Letting $x = 0$ gives $C = 1$. Letting $x = 1$ gives $6 = A + B + 5$, so $A + B = 1$. Letting $x = -1$ gives $0 = A - B + 1$. Solving the system of linear equations gives $A = 0$ and $B = 1$. The original integral is therefore equal to

$$\int \left(\frac{1}{x^2 + 2x + 2} + \frac{1}{x} \right) dx = \int \left(\frac{1}{(x^2 + 2x + 1) + 1} + \frac{1}{x} \right) dx$$

$$= \int \left(\frac{1}{(x + 1)^2 + 1} + \frac{1}{x} \right) dx = \tan^{-1}(x + 1) + \ln|x| + C.$$

7.5.45 Let $\dfrac{2x^2 + 5x + 5}{(x + 1)(x^2 + 2x + 2)} = \dfrac{Ax + B}{x^2 + 2x + 2} + \dfrac{C}{x + 1}$. Then $2x^2 + 5x + 5 = (Ax + B)(x + 1) + C(x^2 + 2x + 2)$. Letting $x = -1$ gives $C = 2$. Letting $x = 0$ gives $5 = B + 4$, so $B = 1$. Letting $x = 1$ gives $12 = 2A + 2 + 2(5)$, so $A = 0$. The original integral is therefore equal to

$$\int \left(\frac{1}{x^2 + 2x + 2} + \frac{2}{x + 1} \right) dx = \int \left(\frac{1}{(x + 1)^2 + 1} + \frac{2}{x + 1} \right) dx = \tan^{-1}(x + 1) + \ln((x + 1)^2) + C.$$

7.5.46 If we write $\dfrac{z + 1}{z(z^2 + 4)} = \dfrac{A}{z} + \dfrac{Bz + C}{z^2 + 4}$, then we have that $z + 1 = A(z^2 + 4) + (Bz + C)z$. Letting $z = 0$ yields $A = 1/4$, and we have $z + 1 = (1/4 + B)z^2 + Cz + 1$, so equating coefficients gives $B = -1/4$ and $C = 1$. So the original integral is equal to $\displaystyle\int \left(\dfrac{1}{4z} - \dfrac{z}{4(z^2 + 4)} + \dfrac{1}{z^2 + 4} \right) dz$. The middle term can be handled via the substitution $u = z^2 + 4$, and the last term is recognizable as the derivative of $\frac{1}{2}\tan^{-1}(z/2)$. Thus the original integral is equal to $\frac{1}{4}\ln|z| - \frac{1}{8}\ln(z^2 + 4) + \frac{1}{2}\tan^{-1}(z/2) + C$.

7.5.47 If we write $\dfrac{20x}{(x - 1)(x^2 + 4x + 5)} = \dfrac{A}{x - 1} + \dfrac{Bx + C}{x^2 + 4x + 5}$, then $20x = A(x^2 + 4x + 5) + (Bx + C)(x - 1)$. Letting $x = 1$ yields $A = 2$. Letting $x = 0$ yields $0 = 10 - C$, so $C = 10$. Letting $x = 2$ yields $40 = 34 + 2B + 10$, so $B = -2$. The original integral is thus $\displaystyle\int \left(\dfrac{2}{x - 1} - \dfrac{2x - 10}{x^2 + 4x + 5} \right) dx = \int \left(\dfrac{2}{x - 1} - \dfrac{(2x + 4) - 14}{x^2 + 4x + 5} \right) dx = $ $\displaystyle\int \left(\dfrac{2}{x - 1} - \dfrac{(2x + 4)}{x^2 + 4x + 5} + \dfrac{14}{(x + 2)^2 + 1} \right) dx = \ln\left| \dfrac{(x - 1)^2}{x^2 + 4x + 5} \right| + 14\tan^{-1}(x + 2) + C$

7.5.48 Note that this rational function is already in decomposition form, so any attempt to decompose it further will be futile. Instead we write the given integral as the sum $\displaystyle\int \dfrac{2x}{x^2 + 4}\, dx + \int \dfrac{1}{x^2 + 4}\, dx$. For the first integral, let $u = x^2 + 4$ so that $du = 2x\,dx$. It is then equal to $\int \dfrac{1}{u}\,du = \ln|x^2 + 4| + C$. The second integral can be written as $\dfrac{1}{4}\int \dfrac{1}{(x/2)^2 + 1}\,dx = \dfrac{1}{2}\tan^{-1}(x/2) + D$. So the original integral is equal to $\ln|x^2 + 4| + \frac{1}{2}\tan^{-1}(x/2) + E$.

7.5.49 If we write $\dfrac{x^2}{x^3 - x^2 + 4x - 4} = \dfrac{x^2}{(x-1)(x^2+4)} = \dfrac{A}{x-1} + \dfrac{Bx+C}{x^2+4}$, then $x^2 = A(x^2+4) + (Bx + C)(x-1)$. Letting $x = 1$ yields $A = 1/5$. Letting $x = 0$ yields $C = 4/5$, and then letting $x = 2$ and solving for B yields $B = 4/5$. Thus the original integral is equal to $\displaystyle\int \dfrac{1/5}{x-1}\,dx + \dfrac{4}{5}\int \dfrac{x}{x^2+4}\,dx + \dfrac{4}{5}\int \dfrac{1}{x^2+4}\,dx$. Thus, the original integral is equal to $\frac{1}{5}\ln|x-1| + \frac{2}{5}\ln(x^2+4) + \frac{2}{5}\tan^{-1}(x/2) + C$.

7.5.50 If we write $\dfrac{1}{(y^2+1)(y^2+2)} = \dfrac{Ay+B}{y^2+1} + \dfrac{Cy+D}{y^2+2}$ then $1 = (Ay+B)(y^2+2) + (Cy+D)(y^2+1) = (A+C)y^3 + (B+D)y^2 + (2A+C)y + 2B+D$. Equating coefficients gives us the equations $A + C = 0$, $B + D = 0$, $2A + C = 0$, and $2B + D = 1$. Solving this system yields $A = C = 0$, $B = 1$ and $D = -1$. Thus the original integral is equal to $\displaystyle\int \left(\dfrac{1}{y^2+1} - \dfrac{1}{y^2+2}\right)dy = \tan^{-1}y - \dfrac{1}{\sqrt{2}}\tan^{-1}\left(\dfrac{y}{\sqrt{2}}\right) + C$.

7.5.51

   a. False. Because the given integrand is improper, the first step would be to use long division to write the integrand as the sum of a polynomial and a proper rational function.

   b. False. This is easy to evaluate via the substitution $u = 3x^2 + x$.

   c. False. The discriminant of the denominator is $b^2 - 4ac = 169 - 168 = 1 > 0$, so the denominator factors into linear factors of the real numbers.

   d. True. The discriminant of the denominator is $b^2 - 4ac = 169 - 172 = -3 < 0$, so the given quadratic expression is irreducible.

7.5.52

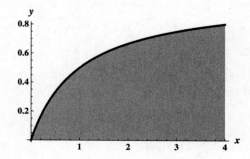

Note that we can write $\dfrac{x}{1+x} = 1 - \dfrac{1}{x+1}$. Thus the area is given by

$$\int_0^4 \left(1 - \dfrac{1}{x+1}\right)dx = x - \ln(x+1)\,\bigg|_0^4 = 4 - \ln 5.$$

7.5.53

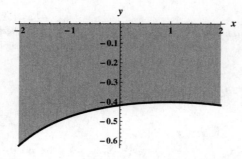

If we write $\dfrac{10}{x^2 - 2x - 24} = \dfrac{10}{(x-6)(x+4)} = \dfrac{A}{x-6} + \dfrac{B}{x+4}$, then $10 = A(x+4) + B(x-6)$. Letting $x = -4$ gives $B = -1$ and letting $x = 6$ gives $A = 1$. Thus the area in question is given by

$$-\int_{-2}^{2} \left(-\frac{1}{x+4} + \frac{1}{x-6} \right) dx = \left. \left(\ln(x+4) - \ln|x-6| \right) \right|_{-2}^{2} = \ln 6 - \ln 4 - (\ln 2 - \ln 8) = \ln 6.$$

7.5.54

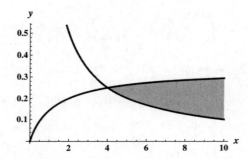

Note that the curves intersect when $x^2 = 3x + 4$, or at $x = 4$ and $x = -1$. However, because of the vertical asymptotes at $x = 0$ and $x = -4/3$, the only region which is truly bounded by this functions is the area between $x = 4$ and $x = 10$ which has $1/x$ on the bottom and $x/(3x+4)$ on the top. Thus the area is given by $\displaystyle\int_{4}^{10} \left(\dfrac{x}{3x+4} - \dfrac{1}{x} \right) dx$. Rewriting the first term after performing long division

yields $\displaystyle\int_{4}^{10} \left(\frac{1}{3} - \frac{4}{9} \cdot \frac{1}{x + (4/3)} - \frac{1}{x} \right) dx = \left. \frac{x}{3} - \frac{4}{9} \ln|x + (4/3)| - \ln|x| \, \right|_{4}^{10} = \frac{10}{3} - \frac{4}{9} \ln(34/3) - \ln(10) - \left(\frac{4}{3} - \frac{4}{9} \ln(16/3) - \ln(4) \right) = 2 - \frac{4}{9} \ln(17/8) + \ln(2/5)$.

7.5.55

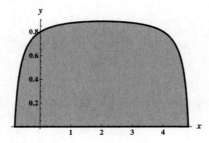

The curve intersects the x-axis at $x = 2 \pm 2\sqrt{2}$. We can write the integrand as $1 + \frac{1}{x^2 - 4x - 5} = 1 + \frac{1}{(x-5)(x+1)}$. If we write this second term in the form $\dfrac{A}{x-5} + \dfrac{B}{x+1}$, then $1 = A(x+1) + B(x-5)$. Letting $x = -1$ yields

$B = -1/6$ and letting $x = 5$ yields $A = 1/6$. Thus the area in question is given by

$$\int_{2-2\sqrt{2}}^{2+2\sqrt{2}} \left(1 + \frac{1/6}{x-5} - \frac{1/6}{x+1}\right) dx = x + \frac{1}{6}\ln|x-5| - \frac{1}{6}\ln|x+1| \Bigg|_{2-2\sqrt{2}}^{2+2\sqrt{2}} = 4\sqrt{2} + \frac{1}{6}\ln\left(\frac{3-2\sqrt{2}}{3+2\sqrt{2}}\right)^2.$$

7.5.56 Using shells, we have $\dfrac{V}{2\pi} = \displaystyle\int_0^2 \dfrac{x}{x+1}\, dx = \int_0^2 \left(1 - \dfrac{1}{x+1}\right) dx = x - \ln(x+1) \Big|_0^2 = 2 - \ln(3)$. Thus $V = 2\pi(2 - \ln(3))$.

7.5.57 Using disks, we have $\dfrac{V}{\pi} = \displaystyle\int_0^4 \dfrac{x^2}{(x+1)^2}\, dx$. Now we can perform long division to rewrite this integral as $\displaystyle\int_0^4 \left(1 - \dfrac{2x+2}{x^2+2x+1} + \dfrac{1}{(x+1)^2}\right) dx$. Thus we have $V = \pi \left(x - \ln|x^2 + 2x + 1| - \dfrac{1}{x+1} \Big|_0^4\right) = \pi\left(4 - \ln(25) - \dfrac{1}{5} - (-1)\right) = \pi\left(\dfrac{24}{5} - \ln(25)\right)$.

7.5.58 First note that $\dfrac{1}{\sqrt{1-x^2}} = 4$ when $x = \pm\sqrt{15}/4$. Using disks and symmetry we have , $V = 2\pi \displaystyle\int_0^{\sqrt{15}/4} \left(4 - \sqrt{\dfrac{1}{1-x^2}}\right)^2 dx = 2\pi \int_0^{\sqrt{15}/4} \left(16 - \dfrac{8}{\sqrt{1-x^2}} + \dfrac{1}{1-x^2}\right) dx$. Breaking this into three integrals, the first evaluates as $8\pi\sqrt{15}$, the second as $2\pi\left(-8\sin^{-1}(x)\right)\Big|_0^{\sqrt{15}/4} = -16\pi\sin^{-1}(\sqrt{15}/4)$.

If we write $\dfrac{1}{1-x^2} = \dfrac{A}{1-x} + \dfrac{B}{1+x}$, then we have $1 = A(1+x) + B(1-x)$, and letting $x = 1$ yields $A = 1/2$ and letting $x = -1$ yields $B = 1/2$. So the last inegral is $2\pi\int_0^{\sqrt{15}/4} \left(\dfrac{1/2}{1-x} + \dfrac{1/2}{1+x}\right) dx = \pi\left(-\ln|1-x| + \ln(1+x)\Big|_0^{\sqrt{15}/4}\right) = \pi\ln\left|\dfrac{1+x}{1-x}\right|\Big|_0^{\sqrt{15}/4} = \pi\ln\left(\dfrac{4+\sqrt{15}}{4-\sqrt{15}}\right)$.

Thus $V = 8\pi\sqrt{15} - 16\pi\sin^{-1}(\sqrt{15}/4) + \pi\ln\left(\dfrac{4+\sqrt{15}}{4-\sqrt{15}}\right)$.

7.5.59 Using disks, we have $\dfrac{V}{\pi} = \displaystyle\int_1^2 \dfrac{1}{x(3-x)}\, ,dx$. Now if we write $\dfrac{1}{x(3-x)} = \dfrac{A}{x} + \dfrac{B}{3-x}$, then we have $1 = A(3-x) + Bx$. Letting $x = 0$ yields $A = 1/3$ and letting $x = 3$ yields $B = 1/3$. Thus we have $V = \dfrac{\pi}{3}\displaystyle\int_1^2 \left(\dfrac{1}{x} - \dfrac{1}{x-3}\right) dx = \dfrac{\pi}{3}\left(\ln x - \ln|x-3|\Big|_1^2\right) = \dfrac{\pi}{3}\cdot 2\ln 2$.

7.5.60 Using disks, we have $\dfrac{V}{\pi} = \displaystyle\int_{-1}^1 \dfrac{1}{4-x^2}\, dx = 2\int_0^1 \dfrac{1}{4-x^2}\, dx$. If we write $\dfrac{1}{4-x^2} = \dfrac{A}{2-x} + \dfrac{B}{2+x}$, then we have $1 = A(2+x) + B(2-x)$. Letting $x = 2$ yields $A = 1/4$, and letting $x = -2$ yields $B = 1/4$. Thus we have $V = \dfrac{\pi}{2}\displaystyle\int_0^1 \left(\dfrac{1}{x+2} - \dfrac{1}{x-2}\right) dx = \dfrac{\pi}{2}\left(\ln|x+2| - \ln|x-2|\Big|_0^1\right) = \dfrac{\pi}{2}(\ln 3)$.

7.5.61 Using shells, we have $\dfrac{V}{2\pi} = \displaystyle\int_0^3 \dfrac{x+1}{x+2}\, dx = \int_0^3 \left(1 - \dfrac{1}{x+2}\right) dx = x - \ln|x+2| \Big|_0^3 = 3 + \ln(2/5)$. Thus, $V = 2\pi(3 + \ln(2/5))$.

7.5.62 Because $\dfrac{x^2}{(x-4)(x+5)}$ is not proper, it is not of the proper form to be decomposed via partial fractions.

7.5.63 Let $u = e^x$, so that $du = e^x \, dx$. Then $\int \dfrac{1}{1+e^x} \cdot \dfrac{e^x}{e^x} \, dx = \int \dfrac{1}{u(1+u)} \, du$. If we write $\dfrac{1}{u(1+u)} = \dfrac{A}{u} + \dfrac{B}{1+u}$, then $1 = A(1+u) + Bu$. Letting $u = 0$ yields $A = 1$ and letting $u = -1$ yields $B = -1$, so the original integral is equal to $\int \left(\dfrac{1}{u} - \dfrac{1}{1+u} \right) du = \ln|u| - \ln|1+u| + C = x - \ln(1+e^x) + C$.

7.5.64 After performing long division, we have that the original integrand is equal to $x - \dfrac{9x^2 - 1}{x(x^2+9)}$. If we write $\dfrac{9x^2 - 1}{x(x^2+9)} = \dfrac{A}{x} + \dfrac{Bx+C}{x^2+9}$, we have $9x^2 - 1 = A(x^2+9) + (Bx+C)x$. Letting $x = 0$ yields $A = -1/9$, and letting $x = 1$ yields $8 = 10(-1/9) + B + C$. Letting $x = -1$ yields $8 = 10(-1/9) + B - C$. Thus $C = 0$ and therefore $B = 82/9$. Therefore the original integral is equal to $\dfrac{x^2}{2} + \dfrac{1}{9} \ln|x| - \dfrac{82}{9} \int \dfrac{x}{x^2+9} \, dx = \dfrac{x^2}{2} + \dfrac{1}{9} \ln|x| - \dfrac{41}{9} \ln|x^2 + 9| + C$.

7.5.65 After performing long division, we have that the original integrand is equal to $3 + \dfrac{13x - 12}{(x-1)(x-2)}$, and if we write $\dfrac{13x - 12}{(x-1)(x-2)} = \dfrac{A}{x-1} + \dfrac{B}{x-2}$, then $13x - 12 = A(x-2) + B(x-1)$. Letting $x = 1$ yields $A = -1$ and letting $x = 2$ yields $B = 14$. Thus the original integral is equal to $3x - \int \dfrac{1}{x-1} \, dx + 14 \int \dfrac{1}{x-2} \, dx = 3x - \ln|x-1| + 14\ln|x-2| + C$.

7.5.66 After performing long division, we have that the original integrand is equal to $2z - 1 + \dfrac{7z+1}{(z+3)(z-2)}$. If we write $\dfrac{7z+1}{(z+3)(z-2)} = \dfrac{A}{z+3} + \dfrac{B}{z-2}$, then $7z + 1 = A(z-2) + B(z+3)$. Letting $z = 2$ yields $B = 3$ and letting $z = -3$ yields $A = 4$. Thus, the original integral is equal to $\int \left(2z - 1 + \dfrac{4}{z+3} + \dfrac{3}{z-2} \right) dz = z^2 - z + 4\ln|z+3| + 3\ln|z-2| + C$.

7.5.67 $\int \dfrac{1}{2+e^t} \, dt = \int \dfrac{e^t}{(e^t+2)e^t} \, dt$. Let $u = e^t$, so that $du = e^t \, dt$. Then we have $\int \dfrac{1}{(u+2)u} \, du$. If we write $\dfrac{1}{(u+2)u} = \dfrac{A}{u} + \dfrac{B}{u+2}$, then $A(u+2) + Bu = 1$, and we find that $A = 1/2$ and $B = -1/2$. Then we integrate $\int \left(\dfrac{1/2}{u} - \dfrac{1/2}{u+2} \right) du = \dfrac{1}{2} \left(\ln|u| - \ln|u+2| \right) + C = \dfrac{1}{2} \left(t - \ln(2+e^t) \right) + C$.

7.5.68 $\int \dfrac{1}{e^x + e^{2x}} \cdot \dfrac{e^x}{e^x} \, dx = \int \dfrac{e^x}{(e^x)^2(1+e^x)} \, dx$. Let $u = e^x$, so that $du = e^x \, dx$, yielding $\int \dfrac{1}{u^2(1+u)} \, du$. If we write $\dfrac{1}{u^2(1+u)} = \dfrac{A}{u} + \dfrac{B}{u^2} + \dfrac{C}{u+1}$, then we have $1 = Au(u+1) + B(u+1) + Cu^2$. Letting $u = 0$ yields $B = 1$. Letting $u = -1$ yields $C = 1$. Letting $u = 1$ then yields $1 = 2A + 2 + 1$, so $A = -1$. Thus, $\int \left(-\dfrac{1}{u} + \dfrac{1}{u^2} + \dfrac{1}{u+1} \right) du = -\ln|u| - \dfrac{1}{u} + \ln|u+1| + C = \ln(e^x + 1) - x - \dfrac{1}{e^x} + C$.

7.5.69 This can be written as

$$\int \dfrac{dt}{\cos t(1+\sin t)} = \int \dfrac{\cos t}{\cos^2 t(1+\sin t)} \, dt = \int \dfrac{\cos t}{(1-\sin^2 t)(1+\sin t)} \, dt.$$

Now let $u = \sin t$ so that $du = \cos t \, dt$. Substituting gives $\int \dfrac{du}{(1-u^2)(1+u)} = \int \dfrac{du}{(1+u)^2(1-u)}$. If we write $\dfrac{1}{(1+u)^2(1-u)} = \dfrac{A}{1+u} + \dfrac{B}{(1+u)^2} + \dfrac{C}{1-u}$ then $1 = A(1+u)(1-u) + B(1-u) + C(1+u)^2$. Letting

$u = -1$ yields $B = 1/2$. Letting $u = 1$ yields $C = 1/4$. Letting $u = 0$ then yields $A = 1/4$. Then our integral is equal to

$$\int \left(\frac{1/4}{1+u} + \frac{1/2}{(1+u)^2} + \frac{1/4}{1-u} \right) du = \frac{1}{4} \left(\frac{-2}{1+u} + \ln \left| \frac{1+u}{1-u} \right| \right) + C = \frac{1}{4} \left(\frac{-2}{1+\sin t} + \ln \left(\frac{1+\sin t}{1-\sin t} \right) \right) + C.$$

7.5.70 Let $u = \sqrt{e^x + 1}$, so that $u^2 = e^x + 1$ and $2u\,du = e^x\,dx = (u^2 - 1)\,dx$. Then the original integral is equal to $\int \frac{2u^2}{u^2 - 1}\,du = \int 2 + \frac{2}{u^2 - 1}\,du$. If we write $\frac{2}{u^2 - 1} = \frac{A}{u+1} + \frac{B}{u-1}$, then $2 = A(u-1) + B(u+1)$. Letting $u = 1$ yields $B = 1$ and letting $u = -1$ yields $A = -1$. Thus we have $\int \left(2 - \frac{1}{u+1} + \frac{1}{u-1} \right) du = 2u + \ln|u-1| - \ln|u+1| + C = 2\sqrt{e^x + 1} + \ln|\sqrt{e^x + 1} - 1| - \ln|\sqrt{e^x + 1} + 1| + C$.

7.5.71 Let $u = e^x$ so that $du = e^x\,dx$. Then the original integral is equal to $\int \frac{1}{(u-1)(u+2)}\,du$. If we write $\frac{1}{(u-1)(u+2)} = \frac{A}{u-1} + \frac{B}{u+2}$, then $1 = A(u+2) + B(u-1)$. Letting $u = -2$ yields $B = -1/3$ and letting $u = 1$ yields $A = 1/3$. Thus we have $\int \left(\frac{1/3}{u-1} - \frac{1/3}{u+2} \right) du = \frac{1}{3} \left(\ln|u-1| - \ln|u+2| \right) + C = \frac{1}{3} \ln \left| \frac{e^x - 1}{e^x + 2} \right| + C$.

7.5.72 Let $u = \sin x$ so that $du = \cos x\,dx$. Then we have $\int \frac{1}{u(u-2)(u+2)}\,du$. If we write $\frac{1}{u(u-2)(u+2)} = \frac{A}{u} + \frac{B}{u-2} + \frac{C}{u+2}$, then we have $1 = A(u-2)(u+2) + Bu(u+2) + Cu(u-2)$. Letting $u = 2$ yields $B = 1/8$ and letting $u = -2$ yields $C = 1/8$. Letting $u = 0$ yields $A = -1/4$. Thus we have

$$\int \left(-\frac{1}{4u} + \frac{1/8}{u-2} + \frac{1/8}{u+2} \right) du = -\frac{1}{4} \ln|u| + \frac{1}{8} \left(\ln|u-2| + \ln|u+2| \right) + C$$

$$= -\frac{1}{4} \ln|\sin x| + \frac{1}{8} \ln \left| (\sin x - 2)(\sin x + 2) \right| + C$$

$$= -\frac{1}{4} \ln|\sin x| + \frac{1}{8} \ln(4 - \sin^2 x) + C.$$

7.5.73 $\int \frac{1}{(e^x + e^{-x})^2} \cdot \frac{(e^x)^2}{(e^x)^2}\,dx = \int \frac{e^{2x}}{(e^{2x} + 1)^2}\,dx$. Let $u = e^x$ so that $du = e^x\,dx$. Then we have $\int \frac{u}{(u^2 + 1)^2}\,du$. If we let $w = u^2 + 1$, then $dw = 2u\,du$, so we have $\frac{1}{2} \int w^{-2}\,dw = -\frac{1}{2w} + C = -\frac{1}{2u^2 + 2} + C = -\frac{1}{2e^{2x} + 2} + C$.

7.5.74 Let $u = \sqrt{y}$, so that $du = \frac{1}{2\sqrt{y}}\,dy$. So $dy = 2u\,du$. Substituting gives $\int \frac{2u}{u^2(\sqrt{a} - u)}\,du = \int \frac{2}{u(\sqrt{a} - u)}\,du$. Write $\frac{2}{u(\sqrt{a} - u)} = \frac{A}{u} + \frac{B}{\sqrt{a} - u}$. Then $2 = A(\sqrt{a} - u) + Bu$. Letting $u = 0$ gives $A = \frac{2}{\sqrt{a}}$, and letting $u = \sqrt{a}$ gives $B = \frac{2}{\sqrt{a}}$. Our integral is therefore equal to

$$\int \left(\frac{2/\sqrt{a}}{u} - \frac{2/\sqrt{a}}{u - \sqrt{a}} \right) du = \frac{2}{\sqrt{a}} \ln \left| \frac{u}{u - \sqrt{a}} \right| + C = \frac{2}{\sqrt{a}} \ln \left| \frac{\sqrt{y}}{\sqrt{y} - \sqrt{a}} \right| + C.$$

7.5.75

    a. $\sec x = \frac{1}{\cos x} \cdot \frac{\cos x}{\cos x} = \frac{\cos x}{\cos^2 x} = \frac{\cos x}{1 - \sin^2 x}$.

b. $\int \sec x\,dx = \int \dfrac{\cos x}{1-\sin^2 x}\,dx$. Let $u=\sin x$ so that $du=\cos x\,dx$. Then our integral becomes $\int \dfrac{du}{1-u^2}$. If we write $\dfrac{1}{1-u^2}=\dfrac{1}{(1-u)(1+u)}=\dfrac{A}{1-u}+\dfrac{B}{1+u}$, we have $1=A(1+u)+B(1-u)$, so $A=\frac{1}{2}$ and $B=\frac{1}{2}$. We have

$$\int \frac{du}{1-u^2}=\frac{1}{2}\int\left(\frac{1}{1-u}+\frac{1}{1+u}\right)du=\frac{1}{2}\left(\ln|1+u|-\ln|1-u|\right)+C=\frac{1}{2}\ln\left|\frac{1+\sin x}{1-\sin x}\right|+C.$$

7.5.76 If we let $u^3=x$, then $3u^2\,du=dx$. Substituting yileds $\int \dfrac{3u^2}{u^3-u}\,du=3\int \dfrac{u}{(u-1)(u+1)}\,du$. If we write $\dfrac{u}{(u-1)(u+1)}=\dfrac{A}{u-1}+\dfrac{B}{u+1}$, then $u=A(u+1)+B(u-1)$. Letting $u=1$ yields $A=1/2$ and letting $u=-1$ yields $B=1/2$. Thus we have $3\int\left(\dfrac{1/2}{u-1}+\dfrac{1/2}{u+1}\right)du=\dfrac{3}{2}\left(\ln|u-1|+\ln|u+1|\right)+C=\dfrac{3}{2}\left(\ln|\sqrt[3]{x}-1|+\ln|\sqrt[3]{x}+1|\right)+C=\dfrac{3}{2}\ln|\sqrt[3]{x^2}-1|+C.$

7.5.77 If we let $u^4=x+2$, then $4u^3\,du=dx$. Substituting yields

$$\int \frac{4u^3}{u+1}\,du=\int\left(4u^2-4u+4-\frac{4}{u+1}\right)du=\frac{4}{3}u^3-2u^2+4u-4\ln|u+1|+C$$
$$=\frac{4}{3}(x+2)^{3/4}-2(x+2)^{1/2}+4(x+2)^{1/4}-4\ln((x+2)^{1/4}+1)+C.$$

7.5.78 If we let $u^2=2x+1$, then $2u\,du=2\,dx$. Substituting yields

$$\int \frac{2u}{u(u-1)(u+1)}\,du=2\int \frac{1}{(u-1)(u+1)}\,du=\int\frac{1}{u-1}-\frac{1}{u+1}\,du$$
$$=\ln|u-1|-\ln|u+1|+C=\ln\left|\frac{\sqrt{1+2x}-1}{\sqrt{1+2x}+1}\right|+C.$$

7.5.79 If we let $u^6=x$, then $6u^5\,du=dx$. Substituting yields

$$\int \frac{6u^5}{u^3+u^2}\,du=6\int \frac{u^3}{u+1}\,du=6\int\left(u^2-u+1-\frac{1}{u+1}\right)du$$
$$=2u^3-3u^2+6u-6\ln|u+1|+C=2\sqrt{x}-3\sqrt[3]{x}+6\sqrt[6]{x}-6\ln(\sqrt[6]{x}+1)+C.$$

7.5.80 If we let $u^4=x$, then $4u^3\,du=dx$. Substituting yields

$$\int \frac{4u^3}{u^4-u}\,du=4\int \frac{u^2}{u^3-1}\,du=4\int \frac{u^2}{(u-1)(u^2+u+1)}\,du.$$

If we write $\dfrac{u^2}{(u-1)(u^2+u+1)}=\dfrac{A}{u-1}+\dfrac{Bu+C}{u^2+u+1}$, then $u^2=A(u^2+u+1)+(Bu+C)(u-1)$. Letting $u=1$ yields $A=1/3$. Letting $u=0$ yields $C=1/3$. If we let $u=-1$, we can solve for B yielding $B=2/3$. Thus we have $4\int\left(\dfrac{1/3}{u-1}+\dfrac{1}{3}\left(\dfrac{2u+1}{u^2+u+1}\right)\right)du=\dfrac{4}{3}\left(\ln|u-1|+\ln|u^2+u+1|\right)+C=\dfrac{4}{3}\ln|u^3-1|+C=\dfrac{4}{3}\ln|x^{3/4}-1|+C.$

7.5.81 If we let $(u^2-1)^2=x$, then $2(u^2-1)\cdot 2u\,du=dx$. Substituting yields $\int \dfrac{4u(u^2-1)}{u}\,du=4\int(u^2-1)\,du=\dfrac{4u^3}{3}-4u+C=\dfrac{4}{3}u(u^2-3)+C=\dfrac{4}{3}\sqrt{1+\sqrt{x}}(\sqrt{x}-2)+C.$

7.5.82

a. If $y = \ln x$ then $\frac{dy}{dx} = \frac{1}{x}$, so $\sqrt{1 + \left(\frac{dy}{dx}\right)^2} = \frac{\sqrt{x^2+1}}{x}$. Thus the arc length is $L(a) = \int_1^a \frac{\sqrt{x^2+1}}{x}\, dx$. If we let $u^2 = x^2 + 1$, then $2u\, du = 2x\, dx$. Substituting gives $\int_{\sqrt{2}}^{\sqrt{a^2+1}} \frac{u}{\sqrt{u^2-1}} \cdot \frac{u}{\sqrt{u^2-1}}\, du = \int_{\sqrt{2}}^{\sqrt{a^2+1}} \frac{u^2}{u^2-1}\, du =$

$\int_{\sqrt{2}}^{\sqrt{a^2+1}} \left(1 + \frac{1}{u^2-1}\right) du = \int_{\sqrt{2}}^{\sqrt{a^2+1}} \left(1 + \frac{1}{2}\left(\frac{1}{u-1} - \frac{1}{u+1}\right)\right) du = u + \frac{1}{2}\ln\left|\frac{u-1}{u+1}\right| \Big|_{\sqrt{2}}^{\sqrt{a^2+1}} = \sqrt{a^2+1} - \sqrt{2} +$

$\frac{1}{2}\ln\left(\frac{\sqrt{a^2+1}-1}{\sqrt{a^2+1}+1}\right) + \frac{1}{2}\ln\left(\frac{\sqrt{2}+1}{\sqrt{2}-1}\right)$.

b.

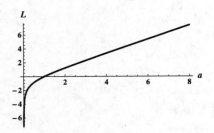

c. Because the only term in $L(a)$ which increases as $a \to \infty$ is $\sqrt{a^2+1}$, and this term increases like a (because $\lim_{x\to\infty} \frac{\sqrt{a^2+1}}{a} = 1$), this function increases like a.

7.5.83 If we write $\frac{2}{x(x^2+1)^2} = \frac{A}{x} + \frac{Bx+C}{x^2+1} + \frac{Dx+E}{(x^2+1)^2}$, then $2 = A(x^2+1)^2 + (Bx+C)x(x^2+1) + (Dx+E)x$. Letting $x = 0$ yields $A = 2$. Expanding the right-hand side yields $2 = (2+B)x^4 + Cx^3 + (4+B+D)x^2 + (C+E)x + 2$. Equating coefficients gives us the equations $2 + B = 0$, $C = 0$, $4 + B + D = 0$, and $C + E = 0$, from which we can deduce that $B = -2$, $C = 0$, $D = -2$ and $E = 0$. The original integral is thus equal to $\int\left(\frac{2}{x} - \frac{2x}{x^2+1} - \frac{2x}{(x^2+1)^2}\right) dx = 2\ln|x| - \ln|x^2+1| + \frac{1}{x^2+1} + C$.

7.5.84 If we write $\frac{1}{(x+1)(x^2+2x+2)^2} = \frac{A}{x+1} + \frac{Bx+C}{x^2+2x+2} + \frac{Dx+E}{(x^2+2x+2)^2}$, then $1 = A(x^2+2x+2)^2 + (Bx+C)(x+1)(x^2+2x+2) + (Dx+E)(x+1)$. Letting $x = -1$ yields $A = 1$. Then expanding the polynomial on the right-hand side gives $1 = (1+B)x^4 + (4+3B+C)x^3 + (8+4B+3C+D)x^2 + (8+2B+4C+D+E)x + (4+E+2C)$. Equating coefficients and then solving for the unknowns yields $B = -1$, $C = -1$, $D = -1$, and $E = -1$. The original integral is thus equal to $\int\left(\frac{1}{x+1} - \frac{x+1}{x^2+2x+2} - \frac{x+1}{(x^2+2x+2)^2}\right) dx =$

$\ln|x+1| - \frac{1}{2}\ln|x^2+2x+2| + \frac{1}{2(x^2+2x+2)} + C$.

7.5.85 If we write $\frac{x}{(x-1)(x^2+2x+2)^2} = \frac{A}{x-1} + \frac{Bx+C}{x^2+2x+2} + \frac{Dx+E}{(x^2+2x+2)^2}$, then $x = A(x^2+2x+2)^2 + (Bx+C)(x-1)(x^2+2x+2) + (Dx+E)(x-1)$. Letting $x = 1$ yields $A = 1/25$. Then expanding the polynomial on the right-hand side gives $25x = (1+25B)x^4 + (4+25(B+C))x^3 + (8+25D+25C)x^2 + (8+25E-25D-50B)x + (4-25E-50C)$. Equating coefficients and then solving for the unknowns yields $B = -1/25$, $C = -3/25$, $D = -5/25$, and $E = 10/25$. The original integral is thus equal to

$$\frac{1}{25}\int\left(\frac{1}{x-1} - \frac{x+3}{x^2+2x+2} - \frac{5x-10}{(x^2+2x+2)^2}\right) dx$$

$$= \frac{1}{25}\int\left(\frac{1}{x-1} - \frac{x+1}{x^2+2x+2} - 5\frac{x+1}{(x^2+2x+2)^2} - 2\frac{1}{(x+1)^2+1} + 15\frac{1}{((x+1)^2+1)^2}\right) dx$$

$$= \frac{1}{25}\left(\ln|x-1| - \frac{1}{2}\ln|x^2+2x+2| + \frac{5}{2}\cdot\frac{1}{x^2+2x+2} - 2\tan^{-1}(x+1)\right) + \frac{3}{5}\int\frac{1}{(v^2+1)^2}\, dv,$$

where $v = x + 1$. To compute this last term, we let $v = \tan\theta$ so that $dv = \sec^2\theta\, d\theta$. Then the last term is equal to

$$\frac{3}{5}\int \frac{\sec^2\theta}{\sec^4\theta}\, d\theta = \frac{3}{5}\int \cos^2\theta\, d\theta = \frac{3}{10}\int (1 + \cos 2\theta)\, d\theta$$

$$= \frac{3}{10}\left(\theta + \frac{\sin 2\theta}{2}\right) + C = \frac{3}{10}\left(\tan^{-1}(x+1) + \frac{x+1}{(x+1)^2 + 1}\right) + C.$$

Putting this all together yields

$$\frac{1}{25}\left(\ln|x-1| - \frac{1}{2}\ln|x^2 + 2x + 2|\right) + \frac{11}{50}\tan^{-1}(x+1) + \frac{1}{10}\left(\frac{3x+4}{(x+1)^2 + 1}\right) + C.$$

7.5.86 If we write $\dfrac{x^3 + 1}{(x)(x^2 + x + 1)^2} = \dfrac{A}{x} + \dfrac{Bx + C}{x^2 + x + 1} + \dfrac{Dx + E}{(x^2 + x + 1)^2}$, then $x^3 + 1 = A(x^2 + x + 1)^2 + (Bx + C)(x)(x^2 + x + 1) + (Dx + E)(x)$. Letting $x = 0$ yields $A = 1$. Then expanding the polynomial on the right-hand side gives $x^3 + 1 = (1 + B)x^4 + (2 + B + C)x^3 + (3 + D + B + C)x^2 + (2 + E + C)x + 1$. Equating coefficients and then solving for the unknowns yields $B = -1$, $C = 0$, $D = -2$, and $E = -2$. The original integral is thus equal to

$$\int \left(\frac{1}{x} - \frac{x}{x^2 + x + 1} - 2\frac{x+1}{(x^2 + x + 1)^2}\right) dx$$

$$= \int \left(\frac{1}{x} - \frac{2x+1}{2(x^2 + x + 1)} + \frac{1}{2(x^2 + x + 1)} - \frac{2x+1}{(x^2 + x + 1)^2} - \frac{1}{(x^2 + x + 1)^2}\right) dx$$

$$= \int \left(\frac{1}{x} - \frac{2x+1}{2(x^2 + x + 1)} + \frac{1}{2((x + 1/2)^2 + 3/4)} - \frac{2x+1}{(x^2 + x + 1)^2} - \frac{1}{((x + 1/2)^2 + 3/4)^2}\right) dx$$

$$= \ln|x| - \frac{1}{2}\ln|x^2 + x + 1| + \frac{1}{x^2 + x + 1} + \frac{1}{\sqrt{3}}\tan^{-1}((2x+1)/\sqrt{3}) - \int \frac{1}{((x + 1/2)^2 + 3/4)^2}\, dx.$$

This last integral can be computed via the substitution $x + 1/2 = (\sqrt{3}/2)\tan\theta$. The final result is $\ln|x| - \frac{1}{2}\ln|x^2 + x + 1| + \frac{1}{3}\frac{2 - 2x}{x^2 + x + 1} - \frac{\sqrt{3}}{9}\tan^{-1}((2x+1)/\sqrt{3}) + C$.

7.5.87 If we write $\dfrac{1}{x^2 - 1} = \dfrac{A}{x-1} + \dfrac{B}{x+1}$, then $1 = A(x+1) + B(x-1)$, so $A = 1/2$ and $B = -1/2$. Thus we have $\dfrac{1}{2}\int \dfrac{1}{x-1} - \dfrac{1}{x+1}\, dx = \dfrac{1}{2}\left(\ln|x-1| - \ln|x+1|\right) + C$.

Now let $x = \sec\theta$, so that $dx = \sec\theta\tan\theta\, d\theta$. Then the original integral is equal to $\displaystyle\int \csc\theta\, d\theta =$

$-\ln|\csc\theta + \cot\theta| + C = -\ln\left|\dfrac{x}{\sqrt{x^2 - 1}} + \dfrac{1}{\sqrt{x^2 - 1}}\right| + C = -\ln\left(\dfrac{|x+1|}{\sqrt{x^2 - 1}}\right) + C = -\ln\left(\sqrt{\left|\dfrac{x+1}{x-1}\right|}\right) + C =$

$\ln\left(\sqrt{\left|\dfrac{x-1}{x+1}\right|}\right) + C$. The two answers are equivalent.

7.5.88 If $x = 2\tan^{-1} u$, then $dx = \frac{2}{1+u^2}\, du$.

If $u = \tan(x/2)$, then $u^2 + 1 = \tan^2(x/2) + 1 = \sec^2(x/2) = \frac{1}{\cos^2(x/2)}$. Thus, $\frac{1}{u^2 + 1} = \cos^2(x/2) = \frac{1 + \cos x}{2}$, so $\cos x = \frac{2}{u^2 + 1} - 1 = \frac{1 - u^2}{u^2 + 1} = \frac{1 - u^2}{1 + u^2}$.

Also, $\sin x = 2\sin(x/2)\cos(x/2) = 2\tan(x/2)\cos^2(x/2) = \frac{2u}{1 + u^2}$.

7.5.89 Using the substitution $x = 2\tan^{-1} u$ yields

$$\int \frac{1}{1 + \sin x}\, dx = \int \frac{2}{1 + u^2} \cdot \frac{1}{1 + \frac{2u}{1 + u^2}}\, du = \int \frac{2}{u^2 + 2u + 1}\, du$$

$$= 2\int \frac{1}{(u+1)^2}\, du = -\frac{2}{u+1} + C = -\frac{2}{\tan(x/2) + 1} + C.$$

7.5.90 Using the substitution $x = 2\tan^{-1} u$ yields

$$\int \frac{1}{2 + \cos x}\, dx = \int \frac{2}{1 + u^2} \cdot \frac{1}{2 + \frac{1 - u^2}{1 + u^2}}\, du = 2 \int \frac{1}{3 + u^2}\, du = \frac{2\tan^{-1}\left(\frac{u}{\sqrt{3}}\right)}{\sqrt{3}} + C$$

$$= \frac{2\tan^{-1}\left(\frac{\tan\left(\frac{x}{2}\right)}{\sqrt{3}}\right)}{\sqrt{3}} + C.$$

7.5.91 Using the substitution $x = 2\tan^{-1} u$ yields $\displaystyle\int \frac{1}{1 - \frac{1 - u^2}{1 + u^2}} \cdot \frac{2}{1 + u^2}\, du = \int u^{-2}\, du = -\frac{1}{u} + C = -\cot(x/2) + C.$

7.5.92 Using the substitution $x = 2\tan^{-1} u$ yields

$$\int \frac{1}{1 + \frac{2u}{1 + u^2} + \frac{1 - u^2}{1 + u^2}} \cdot \frac{2}{1 + u^2}\, du$$

$$= \int \frac{2}{2 + 2u}\, du = \int \frac{1}{1 + u}\, du = \ln|1 + u| + C = \ln|1 + \tan(x/2)| + C.$$

7.5.93 Using the substitution $\theta = 2\tan^{-1} u$ yields $\displaystyle\int_0^1 \frac{1}{\frac{1 - u^2}{1 + u^2} + \frac{2u}{1 + u^2}} \cdot \frac{2}{1 + u^2}\, du = \int_0^1 \frac{2}{1 + 2u - u^2}\, du =$

$-2\displaystyle\int_0^1 \frac{1}{u^2 - 2u + 1 - 2}\, du = -2\int_0^1 \frac{1}{(u - 1)^2 - 2}\, du.$ If we factor the denominator as the difference of squares we have $(u - 1)^2 - 2 = (u - 1 - \sqrt{2})(u - 1 + \sqrt{2})$, and using a partial fractions decomposition yields

$\dfrac{1}{\sqrt{2}}\displaystyle\int_0^1 \left(\frac{1}{u + \sqrt{2} - 1} - \frac{1}{u - \sqrt{2} - 1} \right) du = \frac{1}{\sqrt{2}} \ln\left| \frac{u + \sqrt{2} - 1}{u - \sqrt{2} - 1} \right| \Big|_0^1 = \frac{1}{\sqrt{2}} \ln\left(\frac{\sqrt{2} + 1}{\sqrt{2} - 1} \right).$

7.5.94 Using the substitution $\theta = 2\tan^{-1} u$ yields

$$\int_0^{1/\sqrt{3}} \frac{\frac{2u}{1 + u^2}}{1 - \frac{2u}{1 + u^2}} \cdot \frac{2}{1 + u^2}\, du = \int_0^{1/\sqrt{3}} \frac{4u}{(1 + u^2)(u^2 - 2u + 1)}\, du = \int_0^{1/\sqrt{3}} \frac{4u}{(u^2 + 1)(u - 1)^2}\, du.$$

Decomposing this integral via partial fractions yields

$$\int_0^{1/\sqrt{3}} \left(\frac{2}{(u - 1)^2} - \frac{2}{u^2 + 1} \right) du = \left(\frac{-2}{u - 1} - 2\tan^{-1} u \right) \Big|_0^{1/\sqrt{3}} = \frac{-2}{\frac{1}{\sqrt{3}} - 1} - \frac{\pi}{3} - 2 = 1 + \sqrt{3} - \frac{\pi}{3}.$$

7.5.95 $s_A(t) = \int v_A(t)\, dt = 88 \int \frac{t}{t + 1}\, dt = 88 \int \left(1 - \frac{1}{1 + t} \right) dt = 88t - 88\ln(t + 1) + C.$ Because $s_A(0) = 0$, we see that $C = 0$, so $s_A(t) = 88t - 88\ln(1 + t)$.

$s_B(t) = \int v_B(t)\, dt = 88 \int \frac{t^2}{(t + 1)^2}\, dt = 88 \int \left(1 - \frac{2t + 2}{t^2 + 2t + 1} + \frac{1}{(t + 1)^2} \right) dt = 88(t - \ln(t^2 + 2t + 1) - \frac{1}{t + 1}) + D.$ Because $s_B(0) = 0$, we see that $D = 88$, so $s_B(t) = 88(t - \ln(t^2 + 2t + 1) - \frac{1}{t + 1} + 1).$

$s_C(t) = \int v_C(t)\, dt = 88 \int \frac{t^2}{t^2 + 1}\, dt = 88 \int \left(1 - \frac{1}{t^2 + 1} \right) dt = 88(t - \tan^{-1}(t)) + E.$ Because $s_C(0) = 0$, we have that $E = 0$. Thus $s_C(t) = 88t - 88\tan^{-1}(t)$.

a. $s_A(1) = 88(1 - \ln(2)) \approx 27.$ $s_B(1) = 88(1 - \ln 4 - (1/2) + 1) \approx 88(3/2 - \ln 4) \approx 10.$ $s_C(1) = 88(1 - \tan^{-1}(1)) \approx 18.9.$ So car A travels farthest.

b. $s_A(5) = 88(5 - \ln 6) \approx 282.$ $s_B(5) = 88(5 - \ln 36 - (1/6) + 1) \approx 198.$ $s_C(5) = 88(5 - \tan^{-1}(5)) \approx 319.$ So car C travels farthest.

c. See the development above.

d. Ultimately car C gains the lead. This can be seen by the fact that car C's velocity function is greater than that of the other cars.

7.5.96

a. $v(0) = V \cdot \frac{1-1}{1+1} = 0.$ $\lim_{t \to \infty} \frac{1 - (1/e^{kt})}{1 + (1/e^{kt})} = 1$, when $k = 2g/V > 0$ (which it is.) Thus $\lim_{t \to \infty} v(t) = V \cdot 1 = V.$

b.

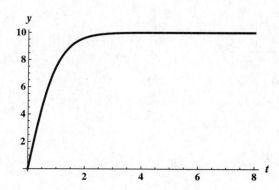

c. $s(t) = \int v(t)\, dt = V \int \frac{e^{kt} - 1}{e^{kt} + 1}\, dt = V \int \left(\frac{e^{kt}}{e^{kt} + 1} - \frac{1}{e^{kt} + 1} \right) dt.$ Let $u = e^{kt} + 1$ and $w = e^{kt}.$ Then we have $V \left(\frac{1}{k} \int \frac{1}{u}\, du - \frac{1}{k} \int \frac{1}{w(w+1)}\, dw \right) = \frac{V}{k} \ln |e^{kt} + 1| - \frac{V}{k} \int \left(\frac{1}{w} - \frac{1}{w+1} \right) dw = \frac{V}{k} \ln |e^{kt} +$
$1| - \frac{V}{k} \ln \left(\frac{e^{kt}}{e^{kt} + 1} \right) + C = \frac{V}{k} \left(2 \ln(e^{kt} + 1) - kt \right) + C.$ Now because $s(0) = 0$, we must have $C =$
$-\frac{V}{k} \ln 4.$ Thus, $s(t) = \frac{V}{k} (\ln(e^{kt} + 1)^2 - kt - \ln 4) = \frac{V}{k} \left(\ln \left(\frac{e^{kt}+1}{2} \right)^2 - kt \right) = \frac{V}{k} 2 \ln \left(\frac{e^{kt}+1}{2} \right) - Vt =$
$\frac{V^2}{g} \left(\ln \frac{1 + e^{-kt}}{2} + \ln e^{kt} \right) - Vt = \frac{V^2}{g} \ln \frac{1 + e^{-kt}}{2} + \frac{V^2}{g} kt - Vt = \frac{V^2}{g} \ln \frac{1 + e^{-kt}}{2} + Vt.$

d.

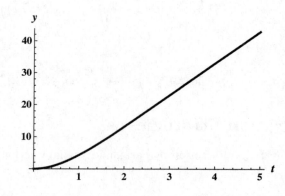

7.5.97 First note that the numerator of the given integrand can be written as $x^8 - 4x^7 + 6x^6 - 4x^5 + x^4$, and this quantity when divided by $x^2 + 1$ yields $x^6 - 4x^5 + 5x^4 - 4x^2 + 4 - \frac{4}{1+x^2}$. Thus the given integral is equal to $\left(\frac{x^7}{7} - \frac{2x^6}{3} + x^5 - \frac{4x^3}{3} + 4x \right) \Big|_0^1 - \left(4 \tan^{-1}(x) \right) \Big|_0^1 = \frac{1}{7} - \frac{2}{3} + 1 - \frac{4}{3} + 4 - \pi = \frac{22}{7} - \pi.$ Because the given integrand is positive on the interval $(0, 1)$, we know that this integral is positive. Thus,

$$0 < \int_0^1 \frac{x^4 (1 - x)^4}{1 + x^2}\, dx = \frac{22}{7} - \pi.$$

Adding π to both sides of this inequality yields $\pi < \frac{22}{7}$.

7.5.98 Let $u^2 = \tan x$ so that $2u\,du = \sec^2 x\,dx = 1 + u^4\,dx$. Then we can write

$$\int \sqrt{\tan x}\,dx = \int \frac{2u^2}{1+u^4}\,du = \int \frac{u^2}{(u^2 - \sqrt{2}u + 1)(u^2 + \sqrt{2}u + 1)}\,du.$$

If we write $\dfrac{u^2}{(u^2 - \sqrt{2}u + 1)(u^2 + \sqrt{2}u + 1)} = \dfrac{Au + B}{u^2 - \sqrt{2}u + 1} + \dfrac{Cu + D}{u^2 + \sqrt{2}u + 1}$ then we have $u^2 = (Au + B)(u^2 + \sqrt{2}u + 1) + (Cu + D)(u^2 - \sqrt{2}u + 1)$. Multiplying out the right-hand side, equating coefficients, and solving for the unknowns yields $A = \frac{\sqrt{2}}{4}$, $B = 0$, $C = -\frac{\sqrt{2}}{4}$, and $D = 0$. Now

$$\frac{u^2}{1+u^4} = \frac{\sqrt{2}}{4}\left(\frac{u}{u^2 - \sqrt{2}u + 1} - \frac{u}{u^2 + \sqrt{2}u + 1}\right) = \frac{\sqrt{2}}{8}\left(\frac{2u}{u^2 - \sqrt{2}u + 1} - \frac{2u}{u^2 + \sqrt{2}u + 1}\right)$$

$$= \frac{\sqrt{2}}{8}\left(\frac{2u - \sqrt{2}}{u^2 - \sqrt{2}u + 1} + \frac{\sqrt{2}}{u^2 - \sqrt{2}u + 1} - \frac{2u + \sqrt{2}}{u^2 + \sqrt{2}u + 1} + \frac{\sqrt{2}}{u^2 + \sqrt{2}u + 1}\right).$$

Then

$$2\int \frac{u^2}{1+u^4}\,du = \frac{\sqrt{2}}{4}\left(\ln|u^2 - \sqrt{2}u + 1| - \ln|u^2 + \sqrt{2}u + 1|\right)$$
$$+ \frac{1}{2}\int\left(\frac{1}{(u^2 - \sqrt{2}u + 1)} + \frac{1}{(u^2 + \sqrt{2}u + 1)}\right)\,du.$$

This last integral can be written as

$$\int\left(\frac{1}{(\sqrt{2}u + 1)^2 + 1} + \frac{1}{(1 - \sqrt{2}u)^2 + 1}\right)\,du = \frac{1}{\sqrt{2}}\left(\tan^{-1}(\sqrt{2}u + 1) - \tan^{-1}(1 - \sqrt{2}u)\right) + C.$$

Putting this all together and replacing u by $\sqrt{\tan x}$ yields

$$\frac{\sqrt{2}}{4}\left(\ln|\tan x - \sqrt{2\tan x} + 1| - \ln|\tan x + \sqrt{2\tan x} + 1|\right)$$
$$+ \frac{1}{\sqrt{2}}\left(\tan^{-1}(1 + \sqrt{2\tan x}) - \tan^{-1}(1 - \sqrt{2\tan x})\right) + C.$$

Thus,

$$\int_0^{\pi/4} \sqrt{\tan x}\,dx = \frac{\sqrt{2}}{4}\left(\ln(2 - \sqrt{2}) - \ln(2 + \sqrt{2}) + \frac{1}{\sqrt{2}}\left(\tan^{-1}(1 + \sqrt{2}) - \tan^{-1}(1 - \sqrt{2})\right)\right) \approx .4875.$$

7.6   Other Integration Strategies

7.6.1 The power rule, substitution, integration by parts, and partial fraction decomposition are examples of analytical methods.

7.6.2 Many computer algebra systems can give exact answers, although sometimes they don't express the answers in elementary terms, and many don't add the arbitrary constant.

7.6.3 The computer algebra system may use a different algorithm than whoever prepared the table, so the results may look different – however, they should differ by a constant.

7.6.4 Using a reduction formula is an analytical method, however, when reduced, the final integral may need to be attacked by a numerical method.

7.6.5 Using table entry 17, we have $\int \cos^{-1}(x)\,dx = x\cos^{-1} x - \sqrt{1 - x^2} + C$.

7.6.6 Using table entry 48, we have $\int \sin(3x) \cos(2x)\, dx = -\dfrac{\cos 5x}{10} - \dfrac{\cos x}{2} + C$.

7.6.7 Using table entry 77 for $\int \dfrac{1}{\sqrt{x^2 + a^2}}\, dx$, we see that $\int \dfrac{1}{\sqrt{x^2 + 16}}\, dx = \ln(x + \sqrt{x^2 + 16}) + C$.

7.6.8 Using table entry 69 for $\int \dfrac{1}{\sqrt{x^2 - a^2}}\, dx$, we see that $\int \dfrac{1}{\sqrt{x^2 - 25}}\, dx = \ln|x + \sqrt{x^2 - 25}| + C$.

7.6.9 Using table entry 90 for $\int \dfrac{x}{ax + b}\, dx$, we see that $\int \dfrac{3u}{2u + 7}\, du = \dfrac{3u}{2} - \dfrac{21}{4} \ln|2u + 7| + C$.

7.6.10 Using table entry 96 for $\int \dfrac{1}{x(ax + b)}\, dx$, we have $\int \dfrac{1}{y(2y + 9)}\, dy = \dfrac{1}{9} \ln\left|\dfrac{y}{2y + 9}\right| + C$.

7.6.11 Using table entry 47, we have $\int \dfrac{dx}{1 - \cos 4x} = -\dfrac{1}{4} \cot(2x) + C$.

7.6.12 Using table entry 62 for $\int \dfrac{1}{x\sqrt{a^2 - x^2}}\, dx$ we have that $\int \dfrac{1}{x\sqrt{81 - x^2}}\, dx = \dfrac{-1}{9} \ln\left|\dfrac{9 + \sqrt{81 - x^2}}{x}\right| + C$.

7.6.13 Using table entry 94 for $\int \dfrac{x}{\sqrt{ax + b}}\, dx$, we have that $\int \dfrac{x\, dx}{\sqrt{4x + 1}} = \dfrac{1}{24}(4x - 2)\sqrt{4x + 1} + C = \dfrac{1}{12}(2x - 1)\sqrt{4x + 1} + C$.

7.6.14 Using table entry 93 for $\int x\sqrt{ax + b}\, dx$ we have that $\int t\sqrt{4t + 12}\, dt = \dfrac{2}{240}(12t - 24)(4t + 12)^{3/2} + C = \dfrac{1}{10}(t - 2)(4t + 12)^{3/2} + C = \dfrac{4}{5}(t - 2)(t + 3)^{3/2} + C$.

7.6.15 Using table entry 69 for $\int \dfrac{1}{\sqrt{x^2 - a^2}}\, dx$ we have $\int \dfrac{1}{\sqrt{9x^2 - 100}}\, du = \dfrac{1}{3} \int \dfrac{1}{\sqrt{u^2 - 100}}\, du$ where $u = 3x$. This is then equal to $\frac{1}{3} \ln|u + \sqrt{u^2 - 100}| + C = \frac{1}{3} \ln|3x + \sqrt{9x^2 - 100}| + C$. This can be written as $\frac{1}{3} \ln|x + \sqrt{x^2 - (100/9)}| + C$.

7.6.16 $\int \dfrac{1}{225 - 16x^2}\, dx = \dfrac{1}{16} \int \dfrac{1}{(225/16) - x^2}\, dx$. Using table entry 67 for $\int \dfrac{1}{a^2 - x^2}\, dx$ we have

$$\dfrac{1}{16} \int \dfrac{1}{(15/4)^2 - x^2}\, dx = \dfrac{1}{16} \cdot \dfrac{2}{15} \ln\left|\dfrac{x + (15/4)}{x - (15/4)}\right| + C$$

$$= \dfrac{1}{120} \ln\left|\dfrac{4x + 15}{4x - 15}\right| + C.$$

7.6.17 Using table entry 84 for $\int \dfrac{1}{(a^2 + x^2)^{3/2}}\, dx$, we have $\int \dfrac{1}{(16 + 9x^2)^{3/2}}\, dx = \dfrac{1}{3} \int \dfrac{1}{(16 + u^2)^{3/2}}\, du = \dfrac{1}{3} \cdot \dfrac{3x}{16\sqrt{16 + 9x^2}} + C = \dfrac{x}{16\sqrt{16 + 9x^2}} + C$.

7.6.18 Using table entry 68 for $\int \sqrt{x^2 - a^2}\, dx$, we have $\int \sqrt{4x^2 - 9}\, dx = \dfrac{1}{2} \int \sqrt{u^2 - 9}\, du = \dfrac{x}{2}\sqrt{4x^2 - 9} - \dfrac{9}{4} \ln|2x + \sqrt{4x^2 - 9}| + C$.

7.6.19 Using table entry 62 for $\int \dfrac{1}{x\sqrt{a^2 - x^2}}\, dx$, we have $\int \dfrac{1}{x\sqrt{(12)^2 - x^2}}\, dx = \dfrac{-1}{12} \ln\left|\dfrac{12 + \sqrt{144 - x^2}}{x}\right| + C$.

7.6.20 Using table entry 85 for $\frac{dx}{x(x^2+a^2)}$, we have $\int \frac{dv}{v(v^2+8)} = \frac{1}{16} \ln\left(\frac{v^2}{v^2+8}\right) + C$.

7.6.21 Using table entry 103 for $\int \ln^n x \, dx$ we have that $\int \ln^2 x \, dx = x \ln^2 x - 2 \int \ln x \, dx = x \ln^2 x - 2(x \ln x - x) + C = 2x + x \ln^2 x - 2x \ln x + C$.

7.6.22 Using table entry 102 (twice) for $\int x^n e^{ax} \, dx$ we have that $\int x^2 e^{5x} \, dx = \frac{1}{5} x^2 e^{5x} - \frac{2}{5} \int x e^{ax} \, dx = \frac{1}{5} x^2 e^{5x} - \frac{2}{25} \left(x e^{5x} - \frac{1}{5} e^{5x} \right) + C$.

7.6.23 Note that $\sqrt{x^2 + 10x} = \sqrt{x^2 + 10x + 25 - 25} = \sqrt{(x+5)^2 - 5^2}$. Thus, the given integral is equal to $\int \sqrt{u^2 - 5^2} \, du$ where $u = x + 5$. Using table entry 68 we have that this is equal to $\frac{u}{2}\sqrt{u^2 - 25} - \frac{25}{2} \ln |u + \sqrt{u^2 - 25}| + C = \frac{x+5}{2}\sqrt{(x+5)^2 - 25} - \frac{25}{2} \ln |x + 5 + \sqrt{(x+5)^2 - 25}| + C$.

7.6.24 Note that $\sqrt{x^2 - 8x} = \sqrt{x^2 - 8x + 16 - 16} = \sqrt{(x-4)^2 - 4^2}$. Thus, the given integral is equal to $\int \sqrt{u^2 - 4^2} \, du$ where $u = x - 4$. Using table entry 68 we have that this is equal to $\frac{u}{2}\sqrt{u^2 - 16} - 8 \ln |u + \sqrt{u^2 - 16}| + C = \frac{x-4}{2}\sqrt{(x-4)^2 - 16} - 8 \ln |x - 4 + \sqrt{(x-4)^2 - 16}| + C$.

7.6.25 $\int \frac{1}{x^2 + 2x + 10} \, dx = \int \frac{1}{(x+1)^2 + 9} \, dx$. Using table entry 14 this is equal to $\frac{1}{3} \tan^{-1}\left(\frac{x+1}{3}\right) + C$.

7.6.26 $\int \sqrt{x^2 - 4x + 8} \, dx = \int \sqrt{(x-2)^2 + 4} \, dx$. Using table entry 76, this is equal to $\frac{x-2}{2}\sqrt{(x-2)^2 + 4} + 2 \ln(x - 2 + \sqrt{(x-2)^2 + 4}) + C$.

7.6.27 $\int \frac{1}{x(x^{10} + 1)} \, dx = \int \frac{10x^9}{10x^{10}(x^{10} + 1)} \, dx$. Let $u = x^{10} + 1$ so that $du = 10x^9 \, dx$. Substituting yields $\int \frac{1}{10} \cdot \frac{1}{(u-1)u} \, du$. Using table entry 96 for $\int \frac{dx}{x(ax+b)}$ we have $\frac{1}{10} \ln \left| \frac{u-1}{u} \right| + C = \frac{1}{10} \ln \left| \frac{x^{10}}{x^{10} + 1} \right| + C$.

7.6.28 $\int \frac{1}{t(t^8 - 256)} \, dt = \int \frac{8t^7}{8t^8(t^8 - 256)} \, dt$. Let $u = t^8 - 256$ so that $du = 8t^7 \, dt$. Substituting yields $\frac{1}{8} \int \frac{1}{u(u + 256)} \, du$. Using table entry 96 for $\int \frac{dt}{t(at+b)}$ we have $\frac{1}{2048} \ln \left| \frac{u}{u + 256} \right| + C = \frac{1}{2048} \ln \left| \frac{t^8 - 256}{t^8} \right| + C$.

7.6.29 $\int \frac{1}{\sqrt{x^2 - 6x}} \, dx = \int \frac{1}{\sqrt{(x-3)^2 - 9}} \, dx$. Using table entry 69, this is equal to $\ln |x - 3 + \sqrt{(x-3)^2 - 9}| + C$. This can also be written as $2 \ln(\sqrt{x-6} + \sqrt{x}) + C$.

7.6.30 $\int \frac{1}{\sqrt{x^2 + 10x}} \, dx = \int \frac{1}{\sqrt{(x+5)^2 - 25}} \, dx$. Using table entry 69, this is equal to $\ln |x + 5 + \sqrt{(x+5)^2 - 25}| + C$.

7.6.31 $\int \frac{e^x}{\sqrt{e^{2x} + 4}} \, dx = \int \frac{1}{\sqrt{u^2 + 4}} \, du$ where $u = e^x$. Then using table entry 77, we have $\ln(u + \sqrt{u^2 + 4}) + C = \ln(e^x + \sqrt{e^{2x} + 4}) + C$.

7.6.32 $\int \frac{\sqrt{\ln^2 x + 4}}{x} \, dx = \int \sqrt{u^2 + 4} \, du$ where $u = \ln x$. Then using table entry 76 we have $\frac{u}{2}\sqrt{u^2 + 4} + \frac{4}{2} \ln(u + \sqrt{u^2 + 4}) + C = \frac{\ln x}{2}\sqrt{\ln^2 x + 4} + 2 \ln(\ln x + \sqrt{\ln^2 x + 4}) + C$.

7.6.33 $\displaystyle\int \frac{\cos x}{\sin^2 x + 2\sin x}\,dx = \int \frac{1}{u^2 + 2u}\,du = \int \frac{1}{(u+1)^2 - 1}\,du$ where $u = \sin x$. Then using table entry 74, we have

$$-\frac{1}{2}\ln\left|\frac{u+2}{u}\right| + C = -\frac{1}{2}\ln\left|\frac{\sin x + 2}{\sin x}\right| + C.$$

7.6.34 Let $u = \sqrt{x}$, so that $du = \frac{1}{2\sqrt{x}}\,dx$. Substituting yields $2\displaystyle\int \cos^{-1} u\,du$. Then using table entry 17, we have $2\displaystyle\int \cos^{-1}(u)\,du = 2(u\cos^{-1}(u) - \sqrt{1-u^2}) + C = 2\sqrt{x}\cos^{-1}\sqrt{x} - 2\sqrt{1-x} + C.$

7.6.35 Let $u = x^3$, so that $du = 3x^2\,dx$. Substituting yields

$$\frac{1}{3}\int \frac{\tan^{-1}(u)}{u^2}\,du = -\frac{1}{3}\left(\frac{1}{u}\tan^{-1}(u) - \int \frac{1}{u(1+u^2)}\,du\right) = -\frac{1}{3}\left(\frac{\tan^{-1}(x^3)}{x^3}\right) + \frac{1}{3}\int \frac{1}{u(1+u^2)}\,du,$$

where we used table entry 18. Now let $w = u^2 + 1$ so that $dw = 2u\,du$. This last integral is thus equal to $\dfrac{1}{3}\displaystyle\int \frac{2u\,du}{2u^2(1+u^2)} = \frac{1}{6}\int \frac{dw}{(w-1)w} = -\frac{1}{6}\ln\left|\frac{w}{w-1}\right| + C = -\frac{1}{6}\ln\left|\frac{u^2+1}{u^2}\right| + C = -\frac{1}{6}\ln\left|\frac{x^6+1}{x^6}\right| + C,$

where we used table entry 96. Thus the original integral is equal to $-\dfrac{1}{3}\left(\dfrac{\tan^{-1}(x^3)}{x^3}\right) - \dfrac{1}{6}\ln\left|\dfrac{x^6+1}{x^6}\right| + C.$

This can be written as $-\dfrac{\tan^{-1}(x^3)}{3x^3} + \ln\left|\dfrac{x}{(x^6+1)^{1/6}}\right| + C.$

7.6.36 Let $u = e^t$ so that $du = e^t\,dt$. Substituting yields $\displaystyle\int \frac{u^2}{\sqrt{4+u^2}}\,du$. Using table entry 82, this yields

$-2\ln(u + \sqrt{4+u^2}) + \dfrac{u\sqrt{4+u^2}}{2} + C$, so the value of the integral is $-2\ln(e^t + \sqrt{4+e^{2t}}) + \dfrac{e^t\sqrt{4+e^{2t}}}{2} + C$

7.6.37 Let $u = \ln x$, so that $du = \frac{1}{x}\,dx$. Substituting yields $\displaystyle\int u\sin^{-1}(u)\,du = \frac{2u^2 - 1}{4}\sin^{-1}(u) + \frac{u\sqrt{1-u^2}}{4} +$

$C = \dfrac{2\ln^2 x - 1}{4}\sin^{-1}(\ln x) + \dfrac{\ln x\sqrt{1-\ln^2 x}}{4} + C$, where we used table entry 105.

7.6.38 Let $u = 1 + 4e^t$, so that $du = 4e^t\,dt$. Substituting yields $\displaystyle\int \frac{4e^t}{4e^t\sqrt{1+4e^t}}\,dt = \int \frac{1}{(u-1)\sqrt{u}}\,du$. Now

let $v = \sqrt{u}$, so that $dv = \frac{1}{2\sqrt{u}}\,du$. Then we have $\displaystyle\int \frac{2}{v^2 - 1}\,dv = \ln\left|\frac{v-1}{v+1}\right| + C = \ln\left|\frac{v^2-1}{(v+1)^2}\right| + C =$

$\ln\left|\dfrac{4e^t}{(\sqrt{1+4e^t}+1)^2}\right| + C$, where we used table entry 74.

7.6.39 The integral which gives the length of the curve is $\dfrac{1}{2}\displaystyle\int_0^8 \sqrt{4+x^2}\,dx$. Using table entry 76, we have

$\dfrac{1}{2}\left(\frac{x}{2}\sqrt{4+x^2} + \frac{4}{2}\ln(x+\sqrt{4+x^2})\right)\Big|_0^8 = 4\sqrt{17} + \ln(8+2\sqrt{17}) - \ln 2 = 4\sqrt{17} + \ln(4+\sqrt{17}) \approx 18.59.$

7.6.40 The integral which gives the length of the curve is $\dfrac{1}{2}\displaystyle\int_0^2 \sqrt{4+9x}\,dx = \dfrac{1}{18}\left(\frac{2}{3}\cdot(4+9x)^{3/2}\right)\Big|_0^2 =$

$\dfrac{1}{27}\left(\sqrt{22}^3 - 8\right) \approx 3.53.$ We used table entry 86.

7.6.41 The integral which gives the length of the curve is $\displaystyle\int_0^{\ln 2} \sqrt{1+e^{2x}}\,dx = \int_1^2 \frac{\sqrt{1+u^2}}{u}\,du$ where $u = e^x$.

This is equal to $\left(\sqrt{1+u^2} - \ln\left|\dfrac{1+\sqrt{1+u^2}}{u}\right|\right)\Big|_1^2 = \sqrt{5} - \sqrt{2} + \ln(1+\sqrt{2}) - \ln\left(\dfrac{1+\sqrt{5}}{2}\right) \approx 1.22.$ Note

that we used table entry 83.

7.6.42 The volume is given by $\pi \int_1^e x^4 \ln x \, dx$. We use table entry 100. This gives

$$\pi \left(\left(\frac{x^5 \ln x}{5} \right) - \frac{x^5}{25} \right) \Big|_1^e = \frac{\pi(4e^5 + 1)}{25}.$$

7.6.43 Using the method of shells, we have $\dfrac{V}{2\pi} = \displaystyle\int_0^{12} \dfrac{x}{\sqrt{x+4}} \, dx = \dfrac{2}{3}(x-8)\sqrt{x+4} \Big|_0^{12} = \dfrac{32}{3} + \dfrac{32}{3} = \dfrac{64}{3}$.
Thus $V = \frac{128\pi}{3}$. We used table entry 94 to compute the integral.

7.6.44 The area is given by

$$\int_0^3 \frac{1}{\sqrt{x^2 - 2x + 2}} \, dx = \int_0^3 \frac{1}{\sqrt{(x-1)^2 + 1}} \, dx = \int_{-1}^2 \frac{1}{\sqrt{u^2 + 1}} \, du = \ln(u + \sqrt{u^2 + 1}) \Big|_{-1}^2 = \ln \frac{2 + \sqrt{5}}{\sqrt{2} - 1}.$$

We used table entry 77 to compute the integral.

7.6.45 Using the method of disks, we have $\dfrac{V}{\pi} = \displaystyle\int_0^{\pi/2} \sin^2 y \, dy = \dfrac{y}{2} - \dfrac{\sin 2y}{4} \Big|_0^{\pi/2} = \dfrac{\pi}{4}$. Thus $V = \frac{\pi^2}{4}$. We used table entry 31 to compute the antiderivative.

7.6.46 The average value of f is

$$\frac{1}{2} \int_{-1}^1 \frac{2}{x^2 + 1} \, dx = \tan^{-1}(x) \Big|_{-1}^1 = \frac{\pi}{2} \approx 1.57.$$

The average value of g is

$$\frac{1}{2} \int_{-1}^1 \frac{7}{4\sqrt{x^2 + 1}} \, dx = \frac{7}{8} \int_{-1}^1 \frac{1}{\sqrt{x^2 + 1}} \, dx = \frac{7}{8} \left(\ln(x + \sqrt{x^2 + 1}) \Big|_{-1}^1 \right) = \frac{7}{8} \ln \left(\frac{\sqrt{2} + 1}{\sqrt{2} - 1} \right) \approx 1.542.$$

Thus, the average value of f is greater than the average value of g. We used table entries 14 and 77.

7.6.47 $\displaystyle\int \frac{x}{\sqrt{2x + 3}} \, dx = \frac{1}{3}(x-3)\sqrt{3 + 2x} + C.$

7.6.48 $\displaystyle\int \sqrt{4x^2 + 36} \, dx = 2 \left(\frac{1}{2} x \sqrt{x^2 + 9} + \frac{9}{2} \sinh^{-1} \left(\frac{x}{3} \right) \right) + C = \left(x\sqrt{x^2 + 9} + 9 \sinh^{-1} \left(\frac{x}{3} \right) \right) + C$

7.6.49 $\displaystyle\int \tan^2 3x \, dx = \frac{1}{3} \tan 3x - x + C.$

7.6.50 $\displaystyle\int (a^2 - t^2)^{-2} \, dt = \frac{1}{4} \frac{\ln(a+t)}{a^3} - \frac{1}{4} \frac{\ln(t-a)}{a^3} - \frac{1}{4a^2(t-a)} - \frac{1}{4a^2(t+a)} + C.$

7.6.51 $\displaystyle\int \frac{(x^2 - a^2)^{3/2}}{x} \, dx = \frac{1}{3}(x^2 - a^2)^{3/2} - a^2 \sqrt{x^2 - a^2} + a^3 \cos^{-1}(a/x) + C.$

7.6.52 $\displaystyle\int \frac{1}{x(a^2 - x^2)^2} \, dx = \frac{\frac{a^2}{a^2 - x^2} + 2\ln(x) - \ln(x^2 - a^2)}{2a^4} + C.$

7.6.53 $\displaystyle\int (a^2 - x^2)^{3/2} \, dx = \frac{-x}{8}(2x^2 - 5a^2)\sqrt{a^2 - x^2} + \frac{3a^4}{8} \sin^{-1}(x/a) + C.$

7.6.54 $\displaystyle\int (y^2 + a^2)^{-5/2} \, dy = \frac{y(3a^2 + 2y^2)}{3(a^2 + y^2)^{3/2} a^4} + C.$

7.6.55 $\displaystyle\int_{2/3}^{4/5} x^8 \, dx = \frac{(4/5)^9 - (2/3)^9}{9} \approx 0.012.$

7.6.56 $\displaystyle\int_{0}^{\pi/2} \cos^6 x \, dx = \frac{5\pi}{32} \approx 0.491.$

7.6.57 $\displaystyle\int_{0}^{4} (9 + x^2)^{3/2} \, dx = \frac{1540 + 243 \ln 3}{8} \approx 225.870.$

7.6.58 $\displaystyle\int_{1/2}^{1} \frac{\sin^{-1} x}{x} \, dx \approx 0.581.$

7.6.59 $\displaystyle\int_{0}^{\pi/2} \frac{1}{1 + \tan^2 t} \, dt = \frac{\pi}{4} \approx 0.785.$

7.6.60 $\displaystyle\int_{0}^{2\pi} \frac{1}{(4 + 2\sin t)^2} \, dt = \frac{\pi\sqrt{3}}{9} \approx 0.605.$

7.6.61 $\displaystyle\int_{0}^{1} \ln x \ln(1 + x) \, dx = 2 - \frac{\pi^2}{12} - \ln 4 \approx -0.209.$

7.6.62 $\displaystyle\int_{0}^{\pi/4} \ln(1 + \tan x) \, dx \approx 0.272.$

7.6.63

    a. Yes, it is possible, because these are equal for $x > 1$.

    b. Yes, because $\frac{1}{9} = 0.\overline{11}$.

7.6.64 Note that $\dfrac{d}{dx}\left(\dfrac{1}{2}\cos^{-1}\sqrt{x^{-4}}\right) = \dfrac{1}{2}\cdot\dfrac{-1}{\sqrt{1 - x^{-4}}}\cdot\dfrac{-2}{x^3} = \dfrac{1}{x^3}\cdot\dfrac{1}{\sqrt{1 - (1/x^4)}} = \dfrac{1}{x\sqrt{x^4 - 1}}.$

    Also, $\dfrac{d}{dx}\left(\dfrac{1}{2}\cos^{-1} x^{-2}\right) = \dfrac{1}{2}\cdot\dfrac{-1}{\sqrt{1 - x^{-4}}}\cdot\dfrac{-2}{x^3} = \dfrac{1}{x\sqrt{x^4 - 1}}.$

    And finally, $\dfrac{d}{dx}\left(\dfrac{1}{2}\tan^{-1}\sqrt{x^4 - 1}\right) = \dfrac{1}{2}\cdot\dfrac{1}{1 + x^4 - 1}\cdot\dfrac{4x^3}{2\sqrt{x^4 - 1}} = \dfrac{1}{x\sqrt{x^4 - 1}}.$

Thus all three answers are correct in the sense that they are all antiderivatives of the original integrand, and thus must differ by a constant.

7.6.65 The two answers differ by a constant, namely the constant one. This can be seen as follows:

$$\frac{2\sin(x/2)}{\cos(x/2) + \sin(x/2)} = \frac{2\tan(x/2)}{1 + \tan(x/2)} = 2\frac{\sin x}{1 + \cos x}\cdot\frac{1}{1 + \frac{\sin x}{1+\cos x}}$$

$$= \frac{2\sin x}{1 + \cos x + \sin x} = \frac{2\sin x}{1 + \cos x + \sin x}\cdot\frac{1 - \cos x - \sin x}{1 - \cos x - \sin x}$$

$$= \frac{2\sin x(1 - \cos x - \sin x)}{-2\sin x\cos x} = \frac{\sin x + \cos x - 1}{\cos x} = \frac{\sin x - 1}{\cos x} + 1.$$

7.6.66 Note that $\dfrac{\ln|x - 1|}{3} + \dfrac{\ln|x + 2|}{6} - \dfrac{\ln|x|}{2} + C = \dfrac{1}{6}\left(2\ln|x - 1| + \ln|x + 2| - 3\ln|x|\right) + C =$
$\dfrac{1}{6}\left(\ln(x - 1)^2 + \ln|x + 2| - \ln|x|^3\right) + C = \dfrac{1}{6}\ln\left(\dfrac{(x - 1)^2|x + 2|}{|x|^3}\right) + C.$

7.6.67 $\displaystyle\int x^3 e^{2x}\, dx = \frac{1}{2}x^3 e^{2x} - \frac{3}{2}\int x^2 e^{2x}\, dx = \frac{1}{2}x^3 e^{2x} - \frac{3}{2}\left(\frac{1}{2}x^2 e^{2x} - \int x e^{2x}\, dx\right) = \frac{1}{2}x^3 e^{2x} - \frac{3}{4}x^2 e^{2x} +$
$\dfrac{3}{2}\left(\dfrac{1}{2}x e^{2x} - \dfrac{1}{2}\int e^{2x}\, dx\right) = \dfrac{1}{2}x^3 e^{2x} - \dfrac{3}{4}x^2 e^{2x} + \dfrac{3}{4}x e^{2x} - \dfrac{3}{8}e^{2x} + C.$

7.6.68

$$\int p^2 e^{-3p}\, dp = \frac{-1}{3} p^2 e^{-3p} + \frac{2}{3} \int p e^{-3p}\, dp = -\frac{1}{3} p^2 e^{-3p} + \frac{2}{3}\left(-\frac{1}{3} p e^{-3p} + \frac{1}{3}\int e^{-3p}\, dp\right)$$

$$= -\frac{1}{3} p^2 e^{-3p} - \frac{2}{9} p e^{-3p} - \frac{2}{27} e^{-3p} + C.$$

7.6.69 Let $u = 3y$. Then $\displaystyle\int \tan^4 3y\, dy = \frac{1}{3}\int \tan^4 u\, du = \frac{1}{3}\left(\frac{1}{3}\tan^3 u - \int \tan^2 u\, du\right) = \frac{1}{9}\tan^3 u - $
$\displaystyle\frac{1}{3}\left(\tan u - \int du\right) = \frac{1}{9}\tan^3 3y - \frac{1}{3}\tan 3y + y + C.$

7.6.70 Let $u = 4t$. Then

$$\int \sec^4 4t\, dt = \frac{1}{4}\int \sec^4 u\, du = \frac{1}{4}\left(\frac{1}{3}\tan u \sec^2 u + \frac{2}{3}\int \sec^2 u\, du\right) = \frac{1}{12}\tan 4t \sec^2 4t + \frac{1}{6}\tan 4t + C.$$

7.6.71 Let $u = 2x$. Then $\displaystyle\int x\sin^{-1} 2x\, dx = \frac{1}{4}\int u\sin^{-1} u\, du = \frac{2u^2 - 1}{16}\sin^{-1} u + \frac{u\sqrt{1 - u^2}}{16} + C =$
$\displaystyle\frac{8x^2 - 1}{16}\sin^{-1} 2x + \frac{x\sqrt{1 - 4x^2}}{8} + C.$

7.6.72 Let $u = 10x$. Then

$$\frac{1}{25}\int u\cos^{-1} u\, du = \frac{1}{25}\left(\frac{2u^2 - 1}{4}\cos^{-1} u - \frac{u\sqrt{1 - u^2}}{4}\right) + C$$

$$= \frac{1}{25}\left(\frac{200x^2 - 1}{4}\cos^{-1} 10x - \frac{5x\sqrt{1 - 100x^2}}{2}\right) + C.$$

7.6.73 $\displaystyle\int x^{-2}\tan^{-1} x\, dx = -(1/x)\tan^{-1} x + \int \frac{1}{x(1 + x^2)}\, dx = \frac{-\tan^{-1} x}{x} + \ln\left(\frac{|x|}{\sqrt{1 + x^2}}\right) + C.$

7.6.74 $\displaystyle\int \frac{\sin^{-1} ax}{x^2}\, dx = -a\left(\frac{\sin^{-1} u}{u} - \int \frac{1}{u\sqrt{1 - u^2}}\, du\right)$, where $u = ax$. Then we have

$$\frac{-a\sin^{-1} u}{u} - a\ln\left|\frac{1 + \sqrt{1 - u^2}}{u}\right| + C = \frac{-\sin^{-1} ax}{x} - a\ln\left|\frac{1 + \sqrt{1 - (ax)^2}}{ax}\right| + C.$$

7.6.75

a. Note that $\displaystyle\int_0^b f(x)\, dx = \int_0^{b/2} f(x)\, dx + \int_{b/2}^b f(x)\, dx$. For the second integral, let $u = b - x$. Then $du = -dx$. The second integral is equal to $-\displaystyle\int_{b - (b/2)}^0 f(b - u)\, du = \int_0^{b/2} f(b - u)\, du$. Because this can be written as $\displaystyle\int_0^{b/2} f(b - x)\, dx$, we have $\displaystyle\int_0^b f(x)\, dx = \int_0^{b/2}(f(x) + f(b - x))\, dx$.

b.

$$\int_0^{\pi/4}\ln(1 + \tan x)\, dx = \int_0^{\pi/8}\left(\ln(1 + \tan x) + \ln(1 + \tan(\pi/4 - x))\right) dx$$

$$= \int_0^{\pi/8}\left(\ln(1 + \tan x) + \ln\left(1 + \frac{\tan \pi/4 - \tan x}{1 + \tan \pi/4 \tan x}\right)\right) dx$$

$$= \int_0^{\pi/8}\left(\ln(1 + \tan x) + \ln\left(1 + \frac{1 - \tan x}{1 + \tan x}\right)\right) dx$$

$$= \int_0^{\pi/8}\left(\ln(1 + \tan x) + \ln\left(\frac{2}{1 + \tan x}\right)\right) = \int_0^{\pi/8}\ln(2)\, dx = \frac{\pi \ln 2}{8}.$$

7.6.76

a. Let $u = \ln x$. Then $du = \frac{dx}{x}$, so $dx = x\,du = e^u\,du$. Substituting gives $\int \cos(u)e^u\,du$. Table entry 98 gives $\frac{e^u(\cos u + \sin u)}{2} + C = \frac{x(\cos \ln x + \sin \ln x)}{2} + C.$

b. Let $u = \cos \ln x$ and $dv = dx$. Then $du = \frac{-\sin \ln x}{x}\,dx$ and $v = x$. Then we have $\int \cos \ln x\,dx = x \cos \ln x + \int \sin \ln x\,dx$. Now, focusing on the last integral, let $u = \sin \ln x$ and $dv = dx$. Then $du = \frac{\cos \ln x}{x}\,dx$ and $v = x$. Now we have $\int \cos \ln x\,dx = x \cos \ln x + \int \sin \ln x\,dx = x \cos \ln x + x \sin \ln x - \int \cos \ln x\,dx$ Adding $\int \cos \ln x\,dx$ to both sides of this equation and dividing by 2 gives

$$\int \cos \ln x\,dx = \frac{x \cos \ln x + x \sin \ln x}{2} + C.$$

7.6.77

a. Using a computer algebra system, we have

θ_0	T	Relative Error
0.1	6.27927	0.000623603
0.2	6.26762	0.0024778
0.3	6.24854	0.0051388
0.4	6.22253	0.00965413
0.5	6.19021	0.0147967
0.6	6.15236	0.0208215
0.7	6.10979	0.0275963
0.8	6.06338	0.0349831
0.9	6.01399	0.0428433
1.0	5.96247	0.0510427

b. All of these values are within 10 percent of 2π.

7.6.78

a. $L(c) = \displaystyle\int_0^c \sqrt{1 + 4x^2}\,dx$. Note that $L'(c) = \sqrt{1 + 4c^2} > 0$, so L is increasing.

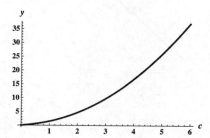

b. Note that $L''(c) = \frac{4c}{\sqrt{1+4c^2}} \geq 0$ on $[0, \infty)$, so L is concave up on that interval.

c. We have $\displaystyle\lim_{c \to \infty} \frac{L(c)}{c^2} = \lim_{c \to \infty} \frac{L'(c)}{2c} = \lim_{c \to \infty} \frac{\sqrt{1 + 4c^2}}{2c} = 1$. Thus $L(c)$ increases as c^2 increases.

7.6.79 Let $u = ax + b$, so that $du = a\,dx$. Then we have $\dfrac{1}{a}\displaystyle\int \dfrac{ax+b-b}{ax+b}\,dx = \dfrac{1}{a}\displaystyle\int \left(1 - \dfrac{b}{ax+b}\right)dx =$
$\dfrac{1}{a}\left(x - \dfrac{b}{a}\displaystyle\int \dfrac{1}{u}\,du\right) = \dfrac{1}{a}\left(x - \dfrac{b}{a}\ln|u|\right) + C = \dfrac{1}{a}\left(x - \dfrac{b}{a}\ln|ax+b|\right) + C.$

7.6.80 Let $u = \sqrt{ax + b}$, so that $du = \dfrac{a}{2\sqrt{ax+b}}\,dx$. Then we have $\dfrac{2}{a}\displaystyle\int x \cdot \dfrac{a}{2\sqrt{ax+b}}\,dx = \dfrac{2}{a}\displaystyle\int \dfrac{u^2-b}{a}\,du =$
$\dfrac{2}{a^2}\displaystyle\int (u^2 - b)\,du = \dfrac{2}{a^2}\left(\dfrac{u^3}{3} - bu\right) + C = \dfrac{2}{a^2}\left(\dfrac{(ax+b)^{3/2}}{3} - b\sqrt{ax+b}\right) + C.$

7.6.81 Let $u = ax + b$, so that $du = a\,dx$. Then we have $\dfrac{1}{a}\displaystyle\int \dfrac{u-b}{a}u^n\,du = \dfrac{1}{a^2}\displaystyle\int (u^{n+1} - bu^n)\,du =$
$\dfrac{1}{a^2}\left(\dfrac{u^{n+2}}{n+2} - \dfrac{bu^{n+1}}{n+1}\right) + C = \dfrac{1}{a^2}\left(\dfrac{(ax+b)^{n+2}}{n+2} - \dfrac{b(ax+b)^{n+1}}{n+1}\right) + C.$

7.6.82 Let $u = \sin^{-1} x$ and $dv = x^n\,dx$. Then $du = \dfrac{1}{\sqrt{1-x^2}}\,dx$ and $v = \dfrac{x^{n+1}}{n+1}$. Then the original integral is
equal to $\dfrac{x^{n+1}}{n+1}\sin^{-1} x - \displaystyle\int \dfrac{x^{n+1}}{n+1}\cdot\dfrac{1}{\sqrt{1-x^2}}\,dx = \dfrac{1}{n+1}\left(x^{n+1}\sin^{-1} x - \displaystyle\int \dfrac{x^{n+1}}{\sqrt{1-x^2}}\,dx\right).$

7.6.83

a. The result holds.

b. First note that $\displaystyle\int_0^{\pi/2} \cos^n x\,dx = -\int_{\pi/2}^0 \cos^n(\pi/2 - \theta)\,d\theta = \int_0^{\pi/2} \sin^n \theta\,d\theta$. So we only need to show

the result for $\displaystyle\int_0^{\pi/2} \sin^{10} x\,dx$. Repeatedly using the reduction formula we have $\displaystyle\int_0^{\pi/2} \sin^{10} x\,dx =$

$\dfrac{9}{10}\displaystyle\int_0^{\pi/2} \sin^8 x\,dx = \dfrac{9\cdot 7}{10\cdot 8}\displaystyle\int_0^{\pi/2} \sin^6 x\,dx = \dfrac{9\cdot 7\cdot 5}{10\cdot 8\cdot 6}\displaystyle\int_0^{\pi/2} \sin^4 x\,dx = \dfrac{9\cdot 7\cdot 5\cdot 3}{10\cdot 8\cdot 6\cdot 4}\displaystyle\int_0^{\pi/2} \sin^2 x\,dx =$

$\dfrac{9\cdot 7\cdot 5\cdot 3}{10\cdot 8\cdot 6\cdot 4\cdot 2}\displaystyle\int_0^{\pi/2} dx = \dfrac{63\pi}{2^9}.$

c. The values decrease as n increases.

7.6.84   The graphs change shape, but the area under the curve remains constant.

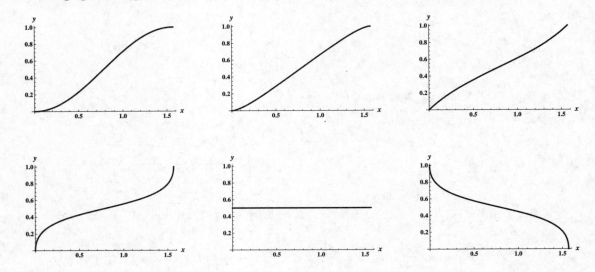

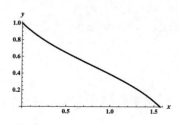 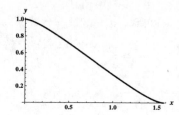 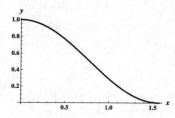

7.7 Numerical Integration

7.7.1 $\Delta x = \frac{18-4}{28} = \frac{1}{2}$.

7.7.2 The Midpoint Rule uses the value of the function evaluated at the midpoint of each subinterval to determine the height of the approximating rectangle over each subinterval. The areas of these rectangles are added up to yield an approximation to the definite integral.

7.7.3 The Trapezoidal Rule approximates the definite integral by using a trapezoid over each subinterval rather than a rectangle.

7.7.4 It is evaluated at 1, 5, and 9, which are the midpoints of the 3 subinterval of length 4.

7.7.5 The endpoints of the subintervals are -1, 1, 3, 5, 7, and 9. The trapezoidal rule uses the value of f at each of these endpoints.

7.7.6 $S(2n) = \frac{4T(2n) - T(n)}{3}$.

7.7.7 The absolute error is $|\pi - 3.14| \approx 0.0015926536$. The relative error is $\frac{|\pi - 3.14|}{\pi} \approx 5 \times 10^{-4}$.

7.7.8 The absolute error is $|\sqrt{2} - 1.414| \approx 2.14 \times 10^{-4}$. The relative error is $\frac{|\sqrt{2} - 1.414|}{\sqrt{2}} \approx 1.51 \times 10^{-4}$.

7.7.9 The absolute error is $|e - 2.72| \approx 0.0017181715$. The relative error is $\frac{|e - 2.72|}{e} \approx 6.32 \times 10^{-4}$.

7.7.10 The absolute error is $|e - 2.718| \approx 2.81 \times 10^{-4}$ and the relative error is $\frac{|e - 2.718|}{e} \approx 1.04 \times 10^{-4}$.

7.7.11

    For $n = 1$, we have $f(6) \cdot 8 = 72 \cdot 8 = 576$.
    For $n = 2$ we have $f(4) \cdot 4 + f(8) \cdot 4 = 32 \cdot 4 + 128 \cdot 4 = 640$.
    For $n = 4$, we have $f(3) \cdot 2 + f(5) \cdot 2 + f(7) \cdot 2 + f(9) \cdot 2 = 18 \cdot 2 + 50 \cdot 2 + 98 \cdot 2 + 162 \cdot 2 = 656$.

7.7.12

    For $n = 1$, we have $f(5) \cdot 8 = 125 \cdot 8 = 1000$.
    For $n = 2$ we have $f(3) \cdot 4 + f(7) \cdot 4 = 27 \cdot 4 + 343 \cdot 4 = 1480$.
    For $n = 4$, we have $f(2) \cdot 2 + f(4) \cdot 2 + f(6) \cdot 2 + f(8) \cdot 2 = 8 \cdot 2 + 64 \cdot 2 + 216 \cdot 2 + 512 \cdot 2 = 1600$.

7.7.13 We have

$$\frac{1}{6}\left(\sin(\pi/12) + \sin(\pi/4) + \sin(5\pi/12) + \sin(7\pi/12) + \sin(3\pi/4) + \sin(11\pi/12)\right) \approx 0.6439505509.$$

7.7.14 We have

$$\frac{1}{8}\left(e^{-1/16} + e^{-3/16} + e^{-5/16} + e^{-7/16} + e^{-9/16} + e^{-11/16} + e^{-13/16} + e^{-15/16}\right) \approx 0.6317092095.$$

7.7.15   For $n = 2$ we have $T(2) = \frac{4}{2}(f(2) + 2f(6) + f(10)) = 2(8 + 2(72) + 200) = 704$.

Using the results of number 11: For $n = 4$, note that $T(4) = \frac{T(2)+M(2)}{2} = \frac{704+640}{2} = 672$.

Using the results of number 11: For $n = 8$ we have that $T(8) = \frac{T(4)+M(4)}{2} = \frac{672+656}{2} = 664$.

7.7.16

Note that we can find $T(2) = \frac{T(1)+M(1)}{2}$ using problem 12 if we compute $T(1)$. We have $T(1) = \left(\frac{1}{2} + \frac{729}{2}\right) \cdot 8 = 2920$. Thus, $T(2) = \frac{2920+1000}{2} = 1960$.

For $n = 4$, we have $T(4) = \frac{T(2)+M(2)}{2} = \frac{1960+1480}{2} = 1720$.

For $n = 8$ we have $T(8) = \frac{T(4)+M(4)}{2} = \frac{1720+1600}{2} = 1660$.

7.7.17 We have $T(6) = \frac{1}{12}(\sin 0 + 2\sin \pi/6 + 2\sin \pi/3 + 2\sin \pi/2 + 2\sin 2\pi/3 + 2\sin 5\pi/6 + \sin \pi) = \frac{1}{6}(\frac{1}{2} + \frac{\sqrt{3}}{2} + 1 + \frac{\sqrt{3}}{2} + \frac{1}{2}) = \frac{1}{6}(2 + \sqrt{3})$.

7.7.18 $T(8) = \frac{1}{16}(e^{-0} + 2e^{-1/8} + 2e^{-1/4} + 2e^{-3/8} + 2e^{-1/2} + 2e^{-5/8} + 2e^{-3/4} + 2e^{-7/8} + e^{-1}) \approx .6329434182$.

7.7.19 The width of each subinterval is $1/25$, so $M(25) = \frac{1}{25}(\sin \pi/50 + \sin 3\pi/50 + \sin 5\pi/50 + \cdots + \sin 49\pi/50) \approx .6370388444$. Since $\int_0^1 \sin \pi x \; dx = \frac{2}{\pi}$, the absolute error is $|2/\pi - M(25)| \approx 4.19 \times 10^{-4}$ and the relative error is this number divided by $2/\pi$ which is approximately 6.58×10^{-4}. The Trapezoidal Rule yields approximately $.6357817937$, with a relative error of ≈ 0.001316.

7.7.20 The width of each subinterval is $1/50$, so $M(50) = \frac{1}{50}(e^{-1/100} + (e^{-1/100})^3 + (e^{-1/100})^5 + \cdots + (e^{-1/100})^{99}) \approx 0.6321100236$. $T(50) = \frac{1}{100}(e^0 + 2e^{-1/50} + 2e^{-2/50} + \cdots + 2e^{-49/50} + e^{-1}) \approx 0.6321416294$. The actual value of the integral is $1 - \frac{1}{e}$. The absolute error for $M(50)$ is $|1 - \frac{1}{e} - .63211002236| \approx 1 \times 10^{-5}$, and the relative error is that number divided by $1 - \frac{1}{e}$ which is about 1.66×10^{-5}. The absolute error for $T(50)$ is $|1 - \frac{1}{e} - .6321416294| \approx 2.1 \times 10^{-5}$ and the relative error is that number divided by $1 - \frac{1}{e}$ which is about 3.33×10^{-5}.

7.7.21

n	$M(n)$	Absolute Error	$T(n)$	Absolute Error
4	99	1	102	2
8	99.75	0.250	100.5	0.5
16	99.9375	0.0625	100.125	0.125
32	99.984375	0.0156	100.03125	0.03125

7.7.22

n	$T(n)$	Absolute Error	$M(n)$	Absolute Error
4	6	2	3	1
8	4.5	0.5	3.75	.25
16	4.125	.125	3.9375	0.0625
32	4.03125	.03125	3.984375	0.015625

7.7.23

n	$M(n)$	Absolute Error	$T(n)$	Absolute Error
4	1.50968181	9.7×10^{-3}	1.48067370	1.9×10^{-2}
8	1.50241228	2.4×10^{-3}	1.49517776	4.8×10^{-3}
16	1.50060256	6.0×10^{-4}	1.49879502	1.2×10^{-3}
32	1.50015061	1.5×10^{-4}	1.49969879	3.0×10^{-4}

n	$M(n)$	Absolute Error	$T(n)$	Absolute Error
4	1.004785839	4.8×10^{-3}	0.99036501	9.6×10^{-3}
8	1.001210217	1.2×10^{-3}	0.99757542	2.4×10^{-3}
16	1.000303459	3.03×10^{-4}	0.99939282	6.07×10^{-4}
32	1.000075922	7.59×10^{-5}	0.99984814	1.52×10^{-4}

7.7.24 is shown to the left of the table above.

7.7.25 Because the given function has odd symmetry about the midpoint of the interval $[0, \pi]$, the midpoint rule calculates to be zero for all even values of n, as does the trapezoidal rule.

n	$M(n)$	Absolute Error	$T(n)$	Absolute Error
4	0.27572053	.224	1.0373146	.54
8	0.425459016	.075	.65651757	.15
16	0.47975863	.02	.54098829	.041
32	.49482934	0.0052	0.51037346	.01

7.7.26 is shown to the left of the table above.

7.7.27 Answers may vary.

$$\overline{T} = \frac{1}{12} \int_0^{12} T(t)\, dt \approx \frac{1}{12} \text{Trapezoid}(12) \approx \frac{1}{24}(47+2(50+46+45+48+52+54+61+62+63+63+59)+55) = $$
54.5.

7.7.28 Answers may vary.

$$\overline{T} = \frac{1}{12} \int_0^{12} T(t)\, dt \approx \frac{1}{12} \text{Trapezoid}(12) \approx \frac{1}{24}(41+2(44+46+48+52+53+53+53+51+51+49+47)+47) = $$
49.25.

7.7.29 Answers may vary.

$$\overline{T} = \frac{1}{12} \int_0^{12} T(t)\, dt \approx \frac{1}{12} \text{Trapezoid}(12) \approx \frac{1}{24}(35 + 2(34 + 34 + 36 + 36 + 37 + 37 + 36 + 35 + 35 + 34 + $$
$33) + 32)) \approx 35.0$.

7.7.30 Answers may vary.

$$\overline{T} = \frac{1}{12} \int_0^{12} T(t)\, dt \approx \frac{1}{12} \text{Trapezoid}(12) \approx \frac{1}{24}(9+2(11+11+12+14+15+17+19+20+22+24+24)+25) \approx $$
17.1667.

7.7.31

a. Left Riemann sum: $\frac{1}{120}(70 \cdot 20 + 130 \cdot 25 + 200 \cdot 15 + 239 \cdot 30 + 311 \cdot 20 + 355 \cdot 10) = 204.917$.
   Right Riemann sum: $\frac{1}{120}(130 \cdot 20 + 200 \cdot 25 + 239 \cdot 15 + 311 \cdot 30 + 355 \cdot 20 + 375 \cdot 10) = 261.375$.
   Trapezoidal rule:

$$\frac{(70 + 130) \cdot 20}{2 \cdot 120} + \frac{(130 + 200) \cdot 25}{2 \cdot 120} + \frac{(200 + 239) \cdot 15}{2 \cdot 120} + \frac{(239 + 311) \cdot 30}{2 \cdot 120}$$
$$+ \frac{(311 + 355) \cdot 20}{2 \cdot 120} + \frac{(355 + 375) \cdot 10}{2 \cdot 120} = 233.146$$

These are approximations to the average temperature of the curling iron on the interval $[0, 120]$.

b. Because the function is increasing, the left Riemann sum is an underestimate and the right Riemann sum is an overestimate. The Trapezoidal rule appears to be a slight underestimate. The followings is a plot of the points with straight line segments connecting them. The shape suggests that the actual function is concave down on the interval, so the trapezoidal rule will be an underestimate.

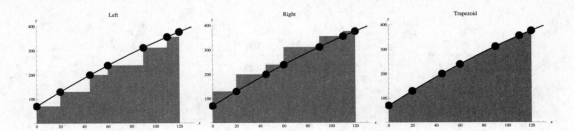

c. The change in temperature over the time interval is

$$\int_0^{120} T'(t)\,dt = T(120) - T(0) = 375 - 70 = 305\,\text{degrees}.$$

7.7.32

a. Left Riemann sum: $(3 \cdot 4 + 0 \cdot 3 + -2 \cdot 5 + -1 \cdot 2 + 2 \cdot 4 + 4 \cdot 2) = 16.$
Right Riemann sum: $(0 \cdot 4 + -2 \cdot 3 + -1 \cdot 5 + 2 \cdot 2 + 4 \cdot 4 + 7 \cdot 2) = 23.$
Trapezoidal rule:

$$\frac{(3+0) \cdot 4}{2} + \frac{(0+-2) \cdot 3}{2} + \frac{(-2+-1) \cdot 5}{2} + \frac{(2+-1) \cdot 2}{2} + \frac{(2+4) \cdot 4}{2} + \frac{(4+7) \cdot 2}{2} = 19.5$$

b. Plots of all three approximations, together with the point themselves and a curve fitted through the points (a degree 4 curve, actually) are:

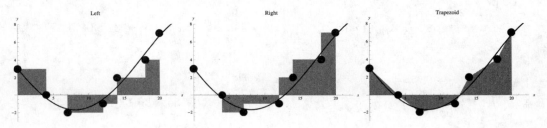

c. We have

$$\int_4^{12} (3f'(x) - 2)\,dx = 3\int_4^{12} f'(x)\,dx + \int_4^{12} 2\,dx = 3(f(12) - f(4)) + 2 \cdot (12 - 4) = 13.$$

7.7.33

a. The net change in elevation is $\int_0^5 v(t)\,dt$, which can be approximated by the trapezoidal rule to give

$$\frac{(0 + 100) \cdot 1}{2} + \frac{(100 + 120) \cdot 0.5}{2} + \frac{(120 + 150) \cdot 1.5}{2}$$

$$+ \frac{(150 + 110) \cdot 0.5}{2} + \frac{(110 + 90) \cdot 0.5}{2} + \frac{(90 + 80) \cdot 1}{2} = 507.5.$$

If we add the net change to the original elevation of 5400 feet, we have an elevation of approximately 5907.5 feet.

b. The right Riemann sum is

$$100 \cdot 1 + 120 \cdot 0.5 + 150 \cdot 1.5 + 110 \cdot 0.5 + 90 \cdot 0.5 + 80 \cdot 1 = 565.$$

If we add the net change to the original elevation of 5400 feet, we have an elevation of approximately 5965 feet.

c. The elevation can be estimated by

$$5400 + \int_0^5 g(t)\, dt = 5400 + \int_0^5 (3.49t^3 - 43.21t^2 + 142.43t - 1.75)\, dt \approx 5916.52,$$

so the elevation of the balloon is about 5917 feet.

7.7.34

a. The trapezoidal rule gives

$$\frac{(0 + 2.5) \cdot 1}{2} + \frac{(2.5 + 3.2) \cdot 1}{2} + \frac{(3.2 + 4) \cdot 1}{2} + \frac{(4 + 6) \cdot 1}{2}$$
$$+ \frac{(6 + 7) \cdot 2}{2} + \frac{(7 + 5.3) \cdot 1.5}{2} + \frac{(3 + 0) \cdot 0.5}{2} = 35.675.$$

b. The left Riemann sum gives

$$0 \cdot 1 + 2.5 \cdot 1 + 3.2 \cdot 1 + 4 \cdot 1 + 6 \cdot 2 + 7 \cdot 1.5 + 5.3 \cdot 0.5 = 34.85.$$

c. Although the surface area of the piece appears to be less than half of $81 = 9^2$ (the area of a 9×9 piece of wood), the shape prohibits the creation of two identical pieces.

7.7.35

n	$T(n)$	Absolute Error	$S(n)$	Absolute Error
25	3.19623162	—	—	—
50	3.19495398	4.3×10^{-4}	3.19452809	4.5×10^{-8}

7.7.36

n	$T(n)$	Absolute Error	$S(n)$	Absolute Error
30	6.411850535	—	—	—
60	6.402962881	.003	6.400000329	3.3×10^{-7}

7.7.37

n	$T(n)$	Absolute Error	$S(n)$	Absolute Error
50	1.00008509	—	—	—
100	1.00002127	2.1×10^{-5}	1.00000000	4.6×10^{-9}

7.7.38

n	$T(n)$	Absolute Error	$S(n)$	Absolute Error
64	0.6657662105	—	—	—
128	0.6657718648	1.9×10^{-6}	.665774	8.3×10^{-12}

7.7.39

n	$T(n)$	Absolute Error	$S(n)$	Absolute Error
4	1820	284	—	—
8	1607.75	71.8	1537	1
16	1553.9844	18	1536.0625	6.3×10^{-2}
32	1540.4990	4.5	1536.0039	3.9×10^{-3}

7.7.40

n	$T(n)$	Absolute Error	$S(n)$	Absolute Error
4	0.99036501	9.6×10^{-3}	—	—
8	0.99757542	2.4×10^{-3}	0.99997889	2.1×10^{-5}
16	0.99939282	6.1×10^{-4}	0.99999862	1.4×10^{-6}
32	0.99984814	1.5×10^{-4}	0.9999999	8.7×10^{-8}

n	$T(n)$	Absolute Error	$S(n)$	Absolute Error
4	0.46911538	5.3×10^{-2}	—	—
8	0.50826998	1.3×10^{-2}	0.52132152	2.9×10^{-4}
16	0.51825968	3.4×10^{-3}	0.52158957	1.7×10^{-5}
32	0.52076933	8.4×10^{-4}	0.52160588	1.1×10^{-6}

7.7.41

n	$T(n)$	Absolute Error	$S(n)$	Absolute Error
4	2.300552032	1.30	—	—
8	1.390088342	.39	1.086600445	8.7×10^{-2}
16	1.103308986	.1	1.007715867	7.7×10^{-3}
32	1.026229165	.026	1.000535892	5.4×10^{-4}

7.7.42

7.7.43

a. True. In the case of a linear function, the region under the curve and over each subinterval is a trapezoid, so the trapezoidal rule gives the exact area.

b. False. Since $E_M(n) \le \frac{k(b-a)^3}{24n^2}$, we have $E_M(3n) \le \frac{k(b-a)^3}{24(9n^2)}$, so the error decreases by a factor of about 9.

c. True. Since $E_T(n) \le \frac{k(b-a)^3}{12n^2}$, we have $E_T(4n) \le \frac{k(b-a)^3}{24(16n^2)}$, so the error decreases by a factor of about 16.

7.7.44 $\int_0^{\pi/2} \sin^6 x \, dx = \frac{5\pi}{32} \approx 0.4908738521.$

n	$M(n)$	Absolute Error	$T(n)$	Absolute Error
4	0.4908738521	2.341×10^{-11}	.4908738521	2.341×10^{-11}
8	0.4908738521	≈ 0	0.49087352	≈ 0
16	0.4908738521	≈ 0	0.49087352	≈ 0
32	0.4908738521	≈ 0	0.49087352	≈ 0

7.7.45 $\int_0^{\pi/2} \cos^9 x \, dx = \frac{128}{315}.$

n	$M(n)$	Absolute Error	$T(n)$	Absolute Error
4	0.40635058	1.4×10^{-6}	0.40634783	1.4×10^{-6}
8	0.40634921	7.6×10^{-10}	0.40634921	7.6×10^{-9}
16	0.40634921	6.6×10^{-13}	0.40634921	6.6×10^{-13}
32	0.40634921	8.9×10^{-16}	0.40634921	7.8×10^{-16}

n	$M(n)$	Absolute Error	$T(n)$	Absolute Error
4	.2192	2.2×10^{-3}	.2257	3.4×10^{-3}
8	.222	2.0×10^{-4}	.2224	2.2×10^{-4}
16	.2222	1.2×10^{-5}	.2222	1.4×10^{-5}
32	.2222	7.8×10^{-7}	.2222	3.9×10^{-7}

7.7.46

7.7.47 $\int_0^\pi \ln(5 + 3\cos x)x\,dx = \pi\ln(9/2)$.

n	$M(n)$	Absolute Error	$T(n)$	Absolute Error
4	4.72531820	1.2×10^{-4}	4.72507878	1.2×10^{-4}
8	4.72519851	9.1×10^{-9}	4.72519849	9.1×10^{-9}
16	4.72519850	0.	4.72519850	8.9×10^{-16}
32	4.72519850	0.	4.72519850	8.9×10^{-19}

7.7.48 $\int_0^{2\pi} \dfrac{1}{(5 + 3\sin x)^2}\,dx = \dfrac{5\pi}{32} \approx 0.4908738521$.

n	$S(n)$	Absolute Error
4	0.6400995032	0.149
8	0.475006	0.0159
16	0.49050507	3.7×10^{-4}

7.7.49 $\int_0^\pi \dfrac{\cos x}{(5/4) - \cos x}\,dx = \dfrac{2\pi}{3} \approx 2.094395102$.

n	$S(n)$	Absolute Error
4	1.916439963	0.178
8	2.080919302	0.0135
16	2.094341841	5.3×10^{-5}

7.7.50 $\int_0^\pi \ln(2 + \cos x)\,dx = \pi\ln\left(\dfrac{2 + \sqrt{3}}{2}\right) \approx 1.959759164$.

n	$S(n)$	Absolute Error
4	1.962437352	.0027
8	1.95976612	6.96×10^{-6}

7.7.51 $\int_0^\pi \sin 6x \cos 3x\,dx = \dfrac{4}{9} = 0.\overline{4}$.

n	$S(n)$	Absolute Error
8	0.0305049084	0.475
16	0.4540112289	0.0096
32	0.44487	0.00087

7.7.52 $T = \dfrac{4}{w}\int_0^{\pi/2} \dfrac{1}{\sqrt{1 - k^2\sin^2\phi}}\,d\phi$, $w = \sqrt{\dfrac{g}{L}}$, $g = 9.8$, and $k^2 = \sin^2(\theta_0/2)$.

n	$S(n)$
4	2.08732001
8	2.08732001

7.7.53 $\int_0^{2\pi} \sqrt{a^2\cos^2 t + b^2\sin^2 t}\,dt$, $a = 4$, $b = 8$.

n	$S(n)$
4	41.88790205
8	39.05860599

7.7.54 $Si(1) = \int_0^1 \dfrac{\sin t}{t}\, dt$. We have

n	$M(n)$
4	0.9468682055
8	0.9462791963
16	0.9461320920

For $Si(10) = \int_0^{10} \dfrac{\sin t}{t}\, dt$, we have

n	$M(n)$
4	1.682149231
8	1.663648208
16	1.659636470

7.7.55 We are computing $\dfrac{1}{3\sqrt{2\pi}} \int_{66}^{72} e^{-(x-69)^2/18}\, dx$. If we use Simpson's rule we obtain

n	$S(n)$
4	0.683
8	0.683

So about 68.3%.

7.7.56 We are computing $\dfrac{1}{22\sqrt{2\pi}} \int_{60}^{90} e^{-(x-110)^2/968}\, dx$. If we compute $S(8)$, we see that $S(8) \approx 0.17012657$.

7.7.57

a. For even n we have $S(n) = \frac{20}{n}(365)(f(a) + 4f(x_1) + 4f(x_2) + \ldots + 4f(x_{n-1}) + f(b))$. For $n = 6$ since there are 6 decades between 1940 and 2000, we have $S(6) \approx 160,000$ millions of barrels produced.

b. Following part (a) with $n = 6$ we have $S(n) \approx 68,000$ millions of barrels imported.

7.7.58

a. $T(50) = \frac{1}{100}(1 + 2\sum_{i=1}^{49} e^{i^2/50^2} + e) \approx 1.462832952$.

b. $f'(x) = 2xe^{x^2}$, so $f''(x) = 4x^2 e^{x^2} + 2e^{x^2} = 2e^{x^2}(2x + 1)$.

c. Since both e^{x^2} and $2x + 1$ are increasing and positive on $[0, 1]$, we have that $|e^{x^2}| \le e$ and $|2x + 1| \le 2 \cdot 1 + 1 = 3$. Thus $|f''(x)| = 2|e^{x^2}||2x + 1| \le 2e \cdot 3 < 2(3)^2 = 18$.

d. Since $E_T(n) \le k(b-a)^3/12n^2 = 18/12(50^2) = 6 \times 10^{-4}$, $T(50)$ is accurate to at least 3 decimal places.

7.7.59

a. $T(40) = \frac{1}{80}(\sin 1 + 2\sum_{i=1}^{39} \sin e^{i/40} + \sin e) \approx .8748$.

b. $f(x) = \sin e^x$, so $f'(x) = e^x \cos e^x$. $f''(x) = -e^{2x} \sin e^x + e^x \cos e^x = e^x(\cos e^x - e^x \sin e^x)$.

c. $|f''(x)| = |e^x| \cdot |\cos e^x - e^x \sin e^x| \le |e^x|(|\cos e^x| + |e^x \sin e^x|) \le e(1 + e) < 10.11$. However, the graph of the absolute value of $f''(x)$ reveals that is is actually bounded by 5.75 on the interval $[0, 1]$.

d. Since $E_T(n) \le k(b-a)^3/12n^2 = 6/(12(40^2)) = .0003125$, $T(40)$ is accurate to at least 3 decimal places.

7.7.60 $\int_a^b mx + k\, dx = \left[\dfrac{mx^2}{2} + kx\right]_a^b = \dfrac{mb^2}{2} + kb - \dfrac{ma^2}{2} - ka = \dfrac{m}{2}(b^2 - a^2) + k(b - a) = \left(\dfrac{m}{2}(b + a) + k\right)(b - a) = \dfrac{f(a) + f(b)}{2}(b - a) = T_{[a,b]}(1)$. Now for any n, the above argument shows that the trapezoidal rule gives the exact value of $\int_{x_{i-1}}^{x_i} mx + k\, dx$. Thus $\int_a^b mx + k\, dx = \sum_{i=1}^n \int_{x_{i-1}}^{x_i} mx + k\, dx = \sum_{i=1}^n T_{[x_{i-1},x_i]}(1) = T_{[a,b]}(n)$.

7.7.61

    a. The exact value is $\int_0^4 x^3 \, dx = \left.\frac{x^4}{4}\right|_0^4 = 64$. Simpson's rule gives $S(2) = (0 + 4 \cdot 8 + 64)\frac{2}{3} = 64$. The values match exactly.

    b. $S(4) = (0 + 4 \cdot 1 + 2 \cdot 8 + 4 \cdot 27 + 64)\frac{1}{3} = 64$. This also matches the exact value exactly.

    c. The 4th derivative of x^3 is 0, so the value of K in the theorem can be taken to be 0, so the error is 0.

    d. Any polynomial of degree 3 or less has 4th derivative equal to 0, so the value of K in the theorem can be taken to be 0, so the error is 0.

7.7.62 Let $x_j = a + j(b - a)/2n$ for $1 \le j \le 2n$ and let $x_i = a + i(b - a)/n$ and let $\overline{x_i}$ be the midpoint of the interval $[x_{i-1}, x_i]$. Then

$$T(2n) = \frac{b - a}{4n}\left(f(a) + 2\sum_{j=1}^{2n-1} f(x_j) + f(b)\right)$$

$$= \frac{1}{2} \cdot \frac{b - a}{2n}\left(f(a) + 2\sum_{1 \le j \le 2n-1, j \text{ even}} f(x_j) + f(b) + 2\sum_{1 \le j \le 2n-1, j \text{ odd}} f(x_j)\right)$$

$$= \frac{1}{2}\left(\frac{b - a}{2n}\left(f(a) + 2\sum_{i-1}^{n-1} f(x_i) + f(b)\right) + \frac{b - a}{n}\sum_{i=1}^{n} f(\overline{x_i})\right) = \frac{1}{2}(T(n) + M(n)).$$

7.7.63 The trapezoidal rule will be an overestimate in this case. This is because of the fact that if the function is above the axis and concave up on the given interval, then each trapezoid on each subinterval lies over the area under the curve for that corresponding subinterval.

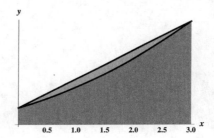

7.7.64 Let $x_i = a + i(b - a)/n$ for $1 \le i \le n$ and let $x_j = a + j(b - a)/2n$ for $1 \le j \le 2n$. We have
$4T(2n) - T(n)$
$= \frac{b-a}{2n}\left(2(f(a) + 2\sum_{j=1}^{2n-1} f(x_j) + f(b)) - (f(a) + 2\sum_{i=1}^{n-1} f(x_i) + f(b))\right)$
$= \frac{b-a}{2n}\left((f(a) + 4\sum_{1 \le j \le 2n-1, j \text{ odd}} f(x_j) + 4\sum_{2 \le j \le 2n-2, j \text{ even}} f(x_j) - 2\sum_{i=1}^{n-1} f(x_i) + f(b))\right)$
$= \frac{b-a}{2n}\left(f(a) + 4\sum_{1 \le j \le 2n-1, j \text{ odd}} f(x_j) + 4\sum_{2 \le j \le 2n-2} f(x_j) - 2\sum_{2 \le j \le 2n-1} f(x_j) + f(b)\right)$
$= \frac{b-a}{2n}\left(f(a) + 4\sum_{1 \le j \le 2n-1, j \text{ odd}} f(x_j) + 2\sum_{2 \le j \le 2n-2, j \text{ even}} f(x_j) + f(b)\right) = 3S(2n).$

7.7.65 Using the previous results, we have

$$S(2n) = \frac{4T(2n) - T(n)}{3} = \frac{2(T(n) + M(n)) - T(n)}{3} = \frac{2M(n) + T(n)}{3}.$$

So $S(50) = \frac{1}{3}(2M(25) + T(25)) \approx .8298251909$.

7.8 Improper Integrals

7.8.1 The interval of integration is infinite or the integrand is unbounded on the interval of integration.

7.8.2 Compute $\int_a^{\infty} f(x) \, dx = \lim_{b \to \infty} \int_a^b f(x) \, dx$.

7.8.3 Compute $\displaystyle\int_0^1 \frac{1}{\sqrt{x}}\, dx = \lim_{b\to 0^+}\int_b^1 \frac{1}{\sqrt{x}}\, dx.$

7.8.4 As shown in Example 2, this integral converges if and only if $p > 1$.

7.8.5 $\displaystyle\int_1^\infty x^{-2}\, dx = \lim_{b\to\infty}\int_1^b x^{-2}\, dx = \lim_{b\to\infty}\left(-\frac{1}{x}\right)\bigg|_1^b = \lim_{b\to\infty}\left(1 - \frac{1}{b}\right) = 1.$

7.8.6 $\displaystyle\int_0^\infty \frac{dx}{(x+1)^3} = \lim_{b\to\infty}\int_0^b \frac{dx}{(x+1)^3} = \lim_{b\to\infty}\left(-\frac{1}{2(x+1)^2}\bigg|_0^b\right) = \lim_{b\to\infty}\left(\frac{1}{2} - \frac{1}{2(b+1)^2}\right) = \frac{1}{2}.$

7.8.7 $\displaystyle\int_{-\infty}^0 e^x\, dx = \lim_{b\to-\infty}\int_b^0 e^x\, dx = \lim_{b\to-\infty} e^x\bigg|_b^0 = \lim_{b\to-\infty}\left(1 - e^b\right) = 1.$

7.8.8 $\displaystyle\int_1^\infty 2^{-x}\, dx = \lim_{b\to\infty}\int_1^b 2^{-x}\, dx = \lim_{b\to\infty}\left(\frac{-1}{\ln 2(2^x)}\right)\bigg|_1^b = \lim_{b\to\infty}\left(\frac{-1}{\ln 2(2^b)} + \frac{1}{2\ln 2}\right) = \frac{1}{2\ln 2}.$

7.8.9 $\displaystyle\int_2^\infty \frac{dx}{\sqrt{x}} = \lim_{b\to\infty}\int_2^b \frac{dx}{\sqrt{x}} = \lim_{b\to\infty} 2\sqrt{x}\big|_2^b = \lim_{b\to\infty} 2(\sqrt{b} - \sqrt{2}) = \infty,$ so the integral diverges.

7.8.10

$$\int_{-\infty}^0 \frac{dx}{\sqrt[3]{2-x}} = \lim_{b\to-\infty}\int_b^0 (2-x)^{-1/3}\, dx = \lim_{b\to-\infty}\left(-\frac{3}{2}(2-x)^{2/3}\right)\bigg|_b^0$$

$$= \lim_{b\to-\infty}\left(\frac{3}{2}\left(-2^{2/3} + (2-b)^{2/3}\right)\right) = \infty,$$

so the integral diverges.

7.8.11 $\displaystyle\int_0^\infty e^{-2x}\, dx = \lim_{b\to\infty}\int_0^b e^{-2x}\, dx = \lim_{b\to\infty}\left(-\frac{1}{2}e^{-2x}\right)\bigg|_0^b = \lim_{b\to\infty}\frac{1}{2}\left(1 - e^{-2b}\right) = \frac{1}{2}.$

7.8.12 $\displaystyle\int_{4/\pi}^\infty \frac{\sec^2(1/x)}{x^2}\, dx = \lim_{b\to\infty}\int_{4/\pi}^b \frac{\sec^2(1/x)}{x^2}\, dx.$ Let $u = 1/x$ so that $du = -1/x^2\, dx$. Then we have

$\displaystyle\lim_{b\to\infty}\int_{\pi/4}^{1/b} (-\sec^2 u)\, du = \lim_{b\to\infty} \tan u\bigg|_{1/b}^{\pi/4} = \lim_{b\to\infty}\left(1 - \tan(1/b)\right) = 1.$

7.8.13 $\displaystyle\int_0^\infty e^{-ax}\, dx = \lim_{b\to\infty}\int_0^b e^{-ax}\, dx = \lim_{b\to\infty}\left(-e^{-x}/a\right)\bigg|_0^b = \lim_{b\to\infty}\left(-\frac{1}{ae^b} + \frac{1}{a}\right) = \frac{1}{a}.$

7.8.14 $\displaystyle\int_2^\infty \frac{dy}{y\ln y} = \lim_{b\to\infty}\int_2^b \frac{dy}{y\ln y} = \lim_{b\to\infty}\left(\ln(\ln y)\right)\bigg|_2^b = \lim_{b\to\infty}\left(\ln(\ln b) - \ln(\ln 2)\right) = \infty,$ so the integral diverges.

7.8.15

$$\int_{e^2}^\infty \frac{dx}{x\ln^p x} = \lim_{b\to\infty}\int_{e^2}^b \frac{dx}{x\ln^p x} = \lim_{b\to\infty}\left(\frac{1}{1-p}\ln^{1-p} x\right)\bigg|_{e^2}^b = \lim_{b\to\infty}\frac{1}{p-1}\left(2^{1-p} - \ln^{1-p} b\right) = \frac{1}{(p-1)2^{p-1}}.$$

7.8.16 $\displaystyle\int_0^\infty \frac{p}{\sqrt[5]{p^2+1}}\, dp = \lim_{b\to\infty}\int_0^b \frac{p}{\sqrt[5]{p^2+1}}\, dp = \lim_{b\to\infty}\left(\frac{5}{8}(p^2+1)^{4/5}\right)\bigg|_0^b = \lim_{b\to\infty}\frac{5}{8}\left((b^2+1)^{4/5} - 1\right) = \infty,$
so the integral diverges.

7.8.17

$$\int_{-\infty}^{\infty} xe^{-x^2}\, dx = \lim_{b\to-\infty} \int_b^0 xe^{-x^2} + \lim_{b\to\infty} \int_0^b xe^{-x^2}$$

$$= \lim_{b\to-\infty} \left(-\frac{1}{2}e^{-x^2}\right)\Big|_b^0 + \lim_{b\to\infty} \left(-\frac{1}{2}e^{-x^2}\right)\Big|_0^b$$

$$= \lim_{b\to-\infty} \left(-\frac{1}{2}+\frac{1}{2}e^{-b^2}\right) + \lim_{b\to\infty} \left(-\frac{1}{2}e^{-b^2}+\frac{1}{2}\right) = -\frac{1}{2}+\frac{1}{2} = 0.$$

7.8.18 $\displaystyle\int_0^{\infty} \cos x\, dx = \lim_{b\to\infty} \int_0^b \cos x\, dx = \lim_{b\to\infty} \sin x\Big|_0^b = \lim_{b\to\infty} \sin b$, which does not exist so the integral diverges.

7.8.19 $\displaystyle\int_2^{\infty} \frac{\cos(\pi/x)}{x^2}\, dx = \lim_{b\to\infty} \int_2^b \frac{\cos(\pi/x)}{x^2}\, dx = \lim_{b\to\infty} \left(-\frac{1}{\pi}\sin(\pi/x)\right)\Big|_2^b = \lim_{b\to\infty} \frac{1}{\pi}(1-\sin(\pi/b)) = \frac{1}{\pi}.$

7.8.20 Note that $x^2 + 2x + 5 = (x^2 + 2x + 1) + 4 = (x+1)^2 + 4$. Also recall that $\int \frac{1}{(x+1)^2+4}\, dx = \frac{1}{2}\tan^{-1}\left(\frac{x+1}{2}\right) + C.$

$$\int_{-\infty}^{\infty} \frac{dx}{(x+1)^2+4} = \lim_{b\to-\infty} \int_b^0 \frac{dx}{(x+1)^2+4} + \lim_{b\to\infty} \int_0^b \frac{dx}{(x+1)^2+4}$$

$$= \lim_{b\to-\infty} \frac{1}{2}\tan^{-1}\left(\frac{x+1}{2}\right)\Big|_b^0 + \lim_{b\to\infty} \frac{1}{2}\tan^{-1}\left(\frac{x+1}{2}\right)\Big|_0^b$$

$$= \lim_{b\to-\infty} \frac{1}{2}\left(\tan^{-1}(1/2) - \tan^{-1}\left(\frac{b+1}{2}\right)\right) + \lim_{b\to\infty} \frac{1}{2}\left(\tan^{-1}\left(\frac{b+1}{2}\right) - \tan^{-1}(1/2)\right)$$

$$= \frac{1}{2}\left(\frac{\pi}{2}+\frac{\pi}{2}\right) = \frac{\pi}{2}.$$

7.8.21 $\displaystyle\int_0^{\infty} \frac{e^u}{e^{2u}+1}\, du = \lim_{b\to\infty} \int_0^b \frac{e^u}{e^{2u}+1}\, du.$ Let $u = e^u$ so that $du = e^u\, du.$ After substitution we have

$$\lim_{b\to\infty} \int_1^{e^b} \frac{1}{u^2+1}\, du = \lim_{b\to\infty} \left(\tan^{-1}(u)\right)\Big|_1^{e^b} = \lim_{b\to\infty} (\tan^{-1}(e^b) - \tan^{-1}(1)) = \pi/2 - \pi/4 = \pi/4.$$

7.8.22 $\displaystyle\int_{-\infty}^a \sqrt{e^x}\, dx = \lim_{b\to-\infty} \int_b^a e^{x/2}\, dx = \lim_{b\to-\infty} \left(2e^{x/2}\right)\Big|_b^a = \lim_{b\to-\infty} 2(e^{a/2} - e^{b/2}) = 2e^{a/2}.$

7.8.23 $\displaystyle\int_1^{\infty} \frac{1}{v(v+1)}\, dv = \lim_{b\to\infty} \int_1^b \left(\frac{1}{v} - \frac{1}{v+1}\right) dv = \lim_{b\to\infty} \ln\left|\frac{v}{v+1}\right|\,\Big|_1^b = \lim_{b\to\infty} \ln\left|\frac{b}{b+1}\right| - \ln(1/2) = 0 - \ln(1/2) = \ln 2.$

7.8.24 $\displaystyle\lim_{b\to\infty} \int_1^b \frac{1}{x^2(x+1)}\, dx = \lim_{b\to\infty} \int_1^b \left(\frac{1}{x^2} + \frac{1}{x+1} - \frac{1}{x}\right) dx = \lim_{b\to\infty} \left(\frac{-1}{x} + \ln\left|\frac{x+1}{x}\right|\right)\Big|_1^b =$

$\displaystyle\lim_{b\to\infty} \left(\frac{-1}{b} + \ln\left|\frac{b+1}{b}\right| - (-1+\ln 2)\right) = 1 - \ln 2.$

7.8.25 Let $u = x^3 + x$ so that $du = (3x^2 + 1)\, dx$ Substituting gives

$$\int_2^{\infty} \frac{1}{u}\, du = \lim_{b\to\infty} \int_2^b \frac{1}{u}\, du = \lim_{b\to\infty} \ln u\Big|_2^b = \lim_{b\to\infty} (\ln b - \ln 2) = \infty.$$

The given integral diverges.

7.8.26 Note that $\int \frac{1}{z^2} \sin(\pi/z)\, dz = -\frac{1}{\pi} \int \sin u\, du = \frac{1}{\pi} \cos u + C = \frac{1}{\pi} \cos(\pi/z) + C$. Thus,

$$\lim_{b \to \infty} \int_1^b \frac{1}{z^2} \sin(\pi/z)\, dz = \lim_{b \to \infty} \frac{1}{\pi} \cos(\pi/z) \Big|_1^b = \lim_{b \to \infty} \frac{1}{\pi} (\cos(\pi/b) - \cos(\pi)) = \frac{1}{\pi}(1 - (-1)) = \frac{2}{\pi}.$$

7.8.27 $\int_2^\infty \frac{dx}{(x+2)^2} = \lim_{b \to \infty} \int_2^b \frac{dx}{(x+2)^2} = \lim_{b \to \infty} -\frac{1}{x+2} \Big|_2^b = \lim_{b \to \infty} -\frac{1}{b+2} + \frac{1}{4} = \frac{1}{4}.$

7.8.28 $\int_1^\infty \frac{\tan^{-1} s}{s^2 + 1}\, ds = \lim_{b \to \infty} \int_1^b \frac{\tan^{-1} s}{s^2 + 1}\, ds = \lim_{b \to \infty} \left(\frac{1}{2}(\tan^{-1} s)^2 \right) \Big|_1^b = \lim_{b \to \infty} \frac{1}{2} \left((\tan^{-1} b)^2 - \left(\frac{\pi}{4} \right)^2 \right) = $
$\frac{1}{2} \left(\left(\frac{\pi}{2} \right)^2 - \left(\frac{\pi}{4} \right)^2 \right) = \frac{3\pi^2}{32}.$

7.8.29 Using the result from Example 2, we see that the volume is given by $V = \pi \int_1^\infty x^{-4}\, dx = \frac{\pi}{4-1} = \frac{\pi}{3}.$

7.8.30 $V = \pi \int_2^\infty \frac{dx}{x^2 + 1} = \pi \lim_{b \to \infty} \int_2^b \frac{dx}{x^2 + 1} = \pi \lim_{b \to \infty} (\tan^{-1} x) \Big|_2^b = \pi \left(\frac{\pi}{2} - \tan^{-1} 2 \right) \approx 1.457.$

7.8.31 Using the result from Example 2, we see that the volume is given by

$$V = \pi \int_1^\infty \left(\frac{1}{x^2} + \frac{1}{x^3} \right) dx = \frac{\pi}{2-1} + \frac{\pi}{3-1} = \frac{3\pi}{2}.$$

7.8.32 $V = 2\pi \int_0^\infty \frac{x}{(x+1)^3}\, dx$; using the method of partial fractions, we see that $\frac{x}{(x+1)^3} = \frac{1}{(x+1)^2} - \frac{1}{(x+1)^3}$, so

$$V = 2\pi \left(\int_0^\infty \frac{dx}{(x+1)^2} - \int_0^\infty \frac{dx}{(x+1)^3} \right).$$

Now make the substitution $u = x + 1$ and use the result from Example 2 to obtain

$$V = 2\pi \left(\int_1^\infty \frac{du}{u^2} - \int_1^\infty \frac{du}{u^3} \right) = 2\pi \left(\frac{1}{2-1} - \frac{1}{3-1} \right) = \pi.$$

7.8.33 $V = \pi \int_2^\infty \frac{dx}{x(\ln x)^2} = \pi \lim_{b \to \infty} \int_2^b \frac{dx}{x(\ln x)^2} = \pi \lim_{b \to \infty} \left(-\frac{1}{\ln x} \right) \Big|_2^b = \pi \lim_{b \to \infty} \left(\frac{1}{\ln 2} - \frac{1}{\ln b} \right) = \frac{\pi}{\ln 2}.$

7.8.34 The volume is given by

$$V = \pi \int_0^\infty \frac{x}{(x^2+1)^{2/3}}\, dx = \pi \lim_{b \to \infty} \int_0^b \frac{x}{(x^2+1)^{2/3}}\, dx$$

$$= \pi \lim_{b \to \infty} \left(\frac{3}{2}(x^2+1)^{1/3} \right) \Big|_0^b = \pi \lim_{b \to \infty} \frac{3}{2} \left((b^2+1)^{1/3} - 1 \right) = \infty,$$

so the volume is infinite.

7.8.35 $\int_0^8 \frac{dx}{\sqrt[3]{x}} = \lim_{c \to 0^+} \int_c^8 x^{-1/3}\, dx = \lim_{c \to 0^+} \left(\frac{3}{2} x^{2/3} \right) \Big|_c^8 = \frac{3}{2} \lim_{c \to 0^+} (4 - c^{2/3}) = 6.$

7.8.36 $\int_0^{\pi/2} \tan \theta\, d\theta = \lim_{c \to \pi/2^-} \int_0^c \tan \theta\, d\theta = \lim_{c \to \pi/2^-} (\ln \sec \theta) \Big|_0^c = \lim_{c \to \pi/2^-} \ln \sec c = \infty$, so the integral diverges.

7.8.37 $\displaystyle\lim_{c\to1^+}\int_c^2\frac{1}{\sqrt{x-1}}\,dx=\lim_{c\to1^+}\left(2\sqrt{x-1}\right)\Big|_c^2=\lim_{c\to1^+}\left(2-2\sqrt{c-1}\right)=2.$

7.8.38 $\displaystyle\lim_{c\to-3^+}\int_c^1(2x+6)^{-2/3}\,dx=\lim_{c\to-3^+}\left(\frac{3}{2}\sqrt[3]{2x+6}\right)\Big|_c^1=\lim_{c\to-3^+}\frac{3}{2}\left(2-\sqrt[3]{2c+6}\right)=3.$

7.8.39 $\displaystyle\lim_{b\to(\pi/2)^-}\int_0^b\sec x\tan x\,dx=\lim_{b\to(\pi/2)^-}(\sec x)\Big|_0^b=\lim_{b\to(\pi/2)^-}(\sec b-1)=\infty.$ The given integral diverges.

7.8.40 $\displaystyle\lim_{c\to3^+}\int_c^4(z-3)^{-3/2}\,dz=\lim_{c\to3^+}\left(-2(z-3)^{-1/2}\right)\Big|_c^4=\lim_{c\to3^+}\left(-2-(-2(c-3)^{-1/2})\right)=\infty.$ The given integral diverges.

7.8.41 Note that $\displaystyle\int\frac{e^{\sqrt{x}}}{\sqrt{x}}\,dx=2e^{\sqrt{x}}+C.$ Thus,

$$\lim_{c\to0^+}\int_c^1\frac{e^{\sqrt{x}}}{\sqrt{x}}\,dx=\lim_{c\to0^+}\left(2e^{\sqrt{x}}\right)\Big|_c^1=\lim_{c\to0^+}\left(2e-2e^{\sqrt{c}}\right)=2e-2.$$

7.8.42 Use the substitution $u=e^y-1$ so that $du=e^y\,dy$. Then $y=0$ corresponds to $u=0$ and $y=\ln3$ corresponds to $u=2$, so we have

$$\int_0^{\ln3}\frac{e^y}{(e^y-1)^{2/3}}\,dy=\int_0^2u^{-2/3}\,du=\lim_{b\to0^+}\int_b^2u^{-2/3}\,du=\lim_{b\to0^+}3u^{1/3}\Big|_b^2=\lim_{b\to0^+}(3\cdot2^{1/3}-3b^{1/3})=3\cdot2^{1/3}.$$

7.8.43 $\displaystyle\int_0^1\frac{x^3}{x^4-1}\,dx=\lim_{c\to1^-}\int_0^c\frac{x^3}{x^4-1}\,dx=\lim_{c\to1^-}\left(\frac{1}{4}\ln|x^4-1|\right)\Big|_0^c=\frac{1}{4}\lim_{c\to1^-}\ln|c^4-1|=-\infty,$ so the integral diverges.

7.8.44 This integral is improper at both limits, so we split it as $\displaystyle\int_1^\infty\frac{dx}{\sqrt[3]{x-1}}=\int_1^2\frac{dx}{\sqrt[3]{x-1}}+\int_2^\infty\frac{dx}{\sqrt[3]{x-1}}.$ If we let $u=x-1$ in the second integral on the right we obtain

$$\int_2^\infty\frac{dx}{\sqrt[3]{x-1}}=\int_1^\infty\frac{du}{u^{1/3}},$$

which diverges using the result in Example 2. Therefore the original integral diverges.

7.8.45

$$\int_0^{10}\frac{dx}{\sqrt[4]{10-x}}=\lim_{c\to10^-}\int_0^c(10-x)^{-1/4}\,dx=\lim_{c\to10^-}\left(-\frac{4}{3}(10-x)^{3/4}\right)\Big|_0^c$$
$$=\frac{4}{3}\lim_{c\to10^-}\left(10^{3/4}-(10-c)^{3/4}\right)=\frac{4}{3}10^{3/4}.$$

7.8.46 This integral is improper at the point $x=3$, so we split it as $\displaystyle\int_1^{11}\frac{dx}{(x-3)^{2/3}}=\int_1^3\frac{dx}{(x-3)^{2/3}}+\int_3^{11}\frac{dx}{(x-3)^{2/3}}$ and evaluate each integral separately:

$$\int_1^3\frac{dx}{(x-3)^{2/3}}=\lim_{c\to3^-}\int_1^c(x-3)^{-2/3}\,dx=\lim_{c\to3^-}\left(3(x-3)^{1/3}\right)\Big|_1^c=3\lim_{c\to3^-}\left(2^{1/3}-(3-c)^{1/3}\right)=3\cdot2^{1/3},$$

and

$$\int_3^{11} \frac{dx}{(x-3)^{2/3}} = \lim_{c \to 3^+} \int_c^{11} (x-3)^{-2/3} \, dx = \lim_{c \to 3^+} \left(3(x-3)^{1/3}\right)\Big|_c^{11} = 3 \lim_{c \to 3^+} \left(8^{1/3} - (c-3)^{1/3}\right) = 6,$$

so $\int_1^{11} \frac{dx}{(x-3)^{2/3}} = 6 + 3 \cdot 2^{1/3}.$

7.8.47 By the even symmetry of the integrand, this should be equal to $2\int_0^1 \ln y^2 \, dy$. Thus we have

$$2\int_0^1 \ln y^2 \, dy = 4 \lim_{c \to 0^+} \int_c^1 \ln y \, dx = 4 \lim_{c \to 0^+} (y \ln y - y)\Big|_c^1 = 4 \lim_{c \to 0^+} (-1 - c \ln c + c) = -4. \text{ (The fact that}$$
$\lim_{c \to 0^+} c \ln c = 0$ can be derived using L'Hôpital's rule, or from the result $\lim_{c \to 0^+} c^c = 1$).

7.8.48 We may write this integral as

$$\int_{-2}^2 \frac{1}{\sqrt{2-x}} \, dx + \int_2^6 \frac{1}{\sqrt{x-2}} \, dx = \lim_{b \to 2^-} \int_{-2}^b \frac{1}{\sqrt{2-x}} \, dx + \lim_{c \to 2^+} \int_c^6 \frac{1}{\sqrt{x-2}} \, dx.$$

Thus we have $\lim_{b \to 2^-} \left(-2\sqrt{2-x}\right)\Big|_{-2}^b + \lim_{c \to 2^+} \left(2\sqrt{x-2}\right)\Big|_c^6 = (0 - (-4)) + (4 - 0) = 8.$

7.8.49 By symmetry,

$$\int_{-2}^2 \frac{dp}{\sqrt{4-p^2}} = 2\int_0^2 \frac{dp}{\sqrt{4-p^2}} = 2 \lim_{c \to 2^-} \int_0^c \frac{dp}{\sqrt{4-p^2}}$$

$$= 2 \lim_{c \to 2^-} \left(\sin^{-1}(p/2)\right)\Big|_0^c = 2 \lim_{c \to 2^-} \left(\sin^{-1}(c/2) - \sin^{-1} 0\right)$$

$$= 2(\sin^{-1} 1 - 0) = \pi.$$

7.8.50 We can write this as

$$\int_0^1 \frac{1}{(x-1)^{1/3}} \, dx + \int_1^9 \frac{1}{(x-1)^{1/3}} \, dx = \lim_{b \to 1^-} \int_0^b \frac{1}{(x-1)^{1/3}} \, dx + \lim_{c \to 1^+} \int_c^9 \frac{1}{(x-1)^{1/3}} \, dx$$

$$= \lim_{b \to 1^-} \frac{3}{2}\left((x-1)^{2/3}\right)\Big|_0^b + \lim_{c \to 1^+} \frac{3}{2}\left((x-1)^{2/3}\right)\Big|_c^9 = -\frac{3}{2} + 6 = \frac{9}{2}.$$

7.8.51 Using disks, we have

$$V = \pi \int_1^2 (x-1)^{-1/2} \, dx = \pi \lim_{c \to 1^+} \int_c^2 (x-1)^{-1/2} \, dx = \pi \lim_{c \to 1^+} \left(2(x-1)^{1/2}\right)\Big|_c^2 = 2\pi \lim_{c \to 1^+} (1 - \sqrt{c-1}) = 2\pi.$$

7.8.52 Using shells, we have

$$V = 2\pi \int_1^2 x(x^2-1)^{-1/4} \, dx = 2\pi \lim_{c \to 1^+} \int_c^2 x(x^2-1)^{-1/4} \, dx$$

$$= \pi \lim_{c \to 1^+} \left(\frac{4}{3}(x^2-1)^{3/4}\right)\Big|_c^2 = \frac{4}{3}\pi \lim_{c \to 1^+} (3^{3/4} - (c^2-1)^{3/4}) = \frac{4\pi}{3^{1/4}}.$$

7.8.53 Using shells, we have

$$V = 2\pi \int_0^4 x(4-x)^{-1/3} \, dx = 2\pi \int_0^4 (4-u)u^{-1/3} \, du = 2\pi \int_0^4 (4u^{-1/3} - u^{2/3}) \, du$$

via the substitution $u = 4 - x$. Therefore

$$V = 2\pi \lim_{c \to 0^+} \int_c^4 (4u^{-1/3} - u^{2/3}) \, du = 2\pi \lim_{c \to 0^+} \left(6u^{2/3} - \frac{3}{5}u^{5/3}\right)\Big|_c^4 = \frac{72 \cdot 2^{1/3}\pi}{5}.$$

7.8.54 Using shells, we have

$$V = 2\pi \int_{-1}^{1} (x+1)(x+1)^{-3/2}\, dx = 2\pi \lim_{c \to -1^+} \int_{c}^{1} (x+1)^{-1/2}\, dx$$

$$= 2\pi \lim_{c \to -1^+} 2\sqrt{x+1}\,\Big|_{c}^{1} = 2\pi \lim_{c \to -1^+} (2\sqrt{2} - 2\sqrt{c+1}) = 4\sqrt{2}\pi.$$

7.8.55 $V = \pi \int_{0}^{\pi/2} \tan^2 x\, dx = \lim_{a \to \frac{\pi}{2}^-} \pi \int_{0}^{a} \tan^2 x\, dx = \lim_{a \to \frac{\pi}{2}^-} \pi \int_{0}^{a} (\sec^2 x - 1)\, dx = \lim_{a \to \frac{\pi}{2}^-} \pi (\tan x - x)\,\Big|_{0}^{a} = \lim_{a \to \frac{\pi}{2}^-} \pi (\tan a - a) = \infty$, so the volume doesn't exist.

7.8.56 First note that $\int \ln^2 x\, dx = 2x + x\ln^2 x - 2x\ln x$. This is obtained by integration by parts with $u = \ln x$ and $dv = \ln x\, dx$. This gives $du = \frac{1}{x}\, dx$ and $v = x\ln x - x$. Then we have $\int \ln^2 x\, dx = x\ln^2 x - x\ln x - \int (\ln x - 1)\, dx = x\ln^2 x - x\ln x - (x\ln x - x - x) + C = x\ln^2 x - 2x\ln x + 2x + C$.

Then the volume is $V = \pi \int_{0}^{1} (-\ln x)^2\, dx = \lim_{a \to 0^+} \pi \int_{a}^{1} \ln^2 x\, dx = \lim_{a \to 0^+} \pi \left(x\ln^2 x - 2x\ln x + 2x \right)\Big|_{a}^{1}$

$= \lim_{a \to 0^+} \pi \left(2 - (a\ln^2 a - 2a\ln a + 2a) \right) = 2\pi$. Note that

$$\lim_{a \to 0^+} a\ln a = \lim_{a \to 0^+} \frac{\ln a}{1/a} = \lim_{a \to 0^+} \frac{1/a}{-1/a^2} = \lim_{a \to 0^+} -a = 0,$$

by l'Hôpital's rule. Also

$$\lim_{a \to 0^+} a\ln^2 a = \lim_{a \to 0^+} \frac{\ln^2 a}{1/a} = \lim_{a \to 0^+} \frac{2\ln a/a}{-1/a^2} = \lim_{a \to 0^+} -2a\ln a = 0.$$

7.8.57 As in Example 7, we have

$$\text{AUC}_i = \int_{0}^{\infty} C_i(t)\, dt = 250 \int_{0}^{\infty} e^{-0.08t}\, dt = \frac{250}{0.08} = 3125$$

and

$$\text{AUC}_o = \int_{0}^{\infty} C_0(t)\, dt = 200 \int_{0}^{\infty} (e^{-0.08t} - e^{-1.8t})\, dt = 200 \left(\frac{1}{0.08} - \frac{1}{1.8} \right) = \frac{21{,}500}{9} \approx 2389,$$

(here we use the fact that $\int_{0}^{\infty} e^{-ax}\, dx = \frac{1}{a}$ for $a > 0$). Therefore the bioavailability of the drug is

$$F = \frac{\text{AUC}_o}{\text{AUC}_i} = \frac{21{,}500}{9 \cdot 3125} \approx 0.764.$$

7.8.58 The total amount of water drained is $W = 100 \int_{0}^{\infty} e^{-0.05t}\, dt = \frac{100}{0.05} = 2000\,\text{gal}$ (here we use the fact that $\int_{0}^{\infty} e^{-ax}\, dx = \frac{1}{a}$ for $a > 0$).

7.8.59 The maximum distance is

$$D = 10 \int_{0}^{\infty} (t+1)^{-2}\, dt = 10 \lim_{b \to \infty} \int_{0}^{b} (t+1)^{-2}\, dt = 10 \lim_{b \to \infty} \left(-(t+1)^{-1} \right)\Big|_{0}^{b} = 10\,\text{mi}.$$

7.8.60 If the extraction continues indefinitely, the total amount of oil extracted is

$$A = r_0 \int_{0}^{\infty} e^{-kt}\, dt = \frac{r_0}{k} = \frac{10^7}{0.005} = 2 \times 10^9\,\text{barrels},$$

which is the amount in the reserve; therefore the reserve is never exhausted, but the remaining amount of oil in the reserve goes to 0 as $t \to \infty$. (Note that here we used the fact that $\int_{0}^{\infty} e^{-ax}\, dx = \frac{1}{a}$ for $a > 0$.)

7.8.61

a. True. The area under the curve $y = f(x)$ from 0 to ∞ is less than the area under $y = g(x)$ on this interval, which by assumption is finite.

b. False. For example, take $f(x) = 1$; then $\int_0^\infty f(x)\, dx = \infty$.

c. False. For example, take $p = 1/2$ and $q = 1$.

d. True. The area under the curve $y = x^{-q}$ from 1 to ∞ is less than the area under $y = x^{-p}$ on this interval, which by assumption is finite.

e. True. Using the result in Example 2, we see that this integral exists if and only if $3p + 2 > 1$, which is equivalent to $p > -1/3$.

7.8.62 The fundamental theorem cannot be applied because the function $1/x$ is not continuous or bounded on $[-1, 1]$.

7.8.63

a. The function $e^{-|x|}$ is even, so $\int_{-\infty}^\infty e^{-|x|}\, dx = 2\int_0^\infty e^{-x}\, dx = 2$. (Note that here we used the fact that $\int_0^\infty e^{-ax}\, dx = \frac{1}{a}$ for $a > 0$).

b. The function $x^3/(1 + x^8)$ is odd, so $\int_{-\infty}^\infty \frac{x^3}{1+x^8}\, dx = \int_0^\infty \frac{x^3}{1+x^8}\, dx + \int_{-\infty}^0 \frac{x^3}{1+x^8}\, dx = \int_0^\infty \frac{x^3}{1+x^8}\, dx - \int_0^\infty \frac{x^3}{1+x^8}\, dx = 0$ assuming $\int_0^\infty \frac{x^3}{1 + x^8}\, dx$ exists, which is true because $0 < \frac{x^3}{1+x^8} < \frac{1}{x^5}$ on $[1, \infty)$ and $\int_1^\infty x^{-5}\, dx$ exists.

7.8.64 Let $u = \ln x$, so that $du = \frac{1}{x}\, dx$. Then we have $\int_{\ln 2}^\infty \frac{du}{u^p}$ which exists if and only if $p > 1$, from the result in Example 2.

7.8.65

n	$T_2(n)$	$T_4(n)$	$T_8(n)$
4	.880619	.886319	1.036632
8	.881704	.886227	.886319
16	.881986	.886227	.886227
32	.882058	.886227	.886227

Based on these results, we conclude that $\int_0^\infty e^{-x^2}\, dx \approx 0.886$.

7.8.66 Integration by parts gives $\int xe^{-x}\, dx = -(x+1)e^{-x} + C$, so $\int_0^\infty xe^{-x}\, dx = \lim_{b\to\infty}\int_0^b xe^{-x}\, dx = \lim_{b\to\infty}\left(-(x+1)e^{-x}\right)\big|_0^b = \lim_{b\to\infty}\left(1 - (b+1)e^{-b}\right) = 1$.

7.8.67 Integration by parts gives $\int x\ln x\, dx = \frac{x^2}{4}(2\ln x - 1) + C$, so $\int_0^1 x\ln x\, dx = \lim_{c\to 0^+}\int_c^1 x\ln x\, dx = \lim_{c\to 0^+}\left(\frac{x^2}{4}(2\ln x - 1)\right)\Big|_c^1 = \frac{1}{4}\lim_{c\to 0^+}\left(c^2(-2\ln c + 1) - 1\right) = -\frac{1}{4}$. (The fact that $\lim_{c\to 0^+} c^2\ln c = 0$ can be derived using L'Hôpital's rule, or from the result $\lim_{c\to 0^+} c^c = 1$).

7.8.68 Integration by parts gives $\int \frac{\ln x}{x^2}\, dx = -\frac{\ln x + 1}{x} + C$, so

$$\int_1^\infty \frac{\ln x}{x^2}\, dx = \lim_{b\to\infty}\int_1^b \frac{\ln x}{x^2}\, dx = \lim_{b\to\infty}\left(-\frac{\ln x + 1}{x}\right)\Big|_1^b = \lim_{b\to\infty}\left(1 - \frac{\ln b + 1}{b}\right) = 1,$$

since $\lim_{b\to\infty} \ln b/b = 0$.

7.8.69 Let $u = x^2$ so that $2x\,dx = du$. The first integral is then equal to $\frac{1}{2}\int_0^\infty e^{-u}\,du = \frac{1}{2}$, using the fact that $\int_0^\infty e^{-ax}\,dx = \frac{1}{a}$ for $a > 0$. The second integral cannot be evaluated by finding an antiderivative for $x^2 e^{-x^2}$; however using more advanced methods it can be shown that $\int_0^\infty x^2 e^{-x^2}\,dx = \frac{\sqrt{\pi}}{4} \approx 0.443$.

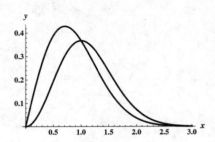

7.8.70 The region R has area $A = \int_1^\infty x^{-p}\,dx - \int_1^\infty x^{-q}\,dx = \dfrac{1}{p-1} - \dfrac{1}{q-1}$, where we use the result in Example 2.

7.8.71 The region R has area $A = \int_0^\infty e^{-bx}\,dx - \int_0^\infty e^{-ax}\,dx = \dfrac{1}{b} - \dfrac{1}{a}$.

7.8.72 We have $A(a) = \int_0^\infty e^{-ax}\,dx = \dfrac{1}{a}$, which is a decreasing function on $a > 0$.

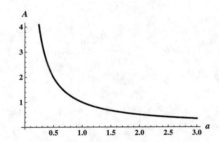

7.8.73

a. We have

$$A(a, b) = \int_b^\infty e^{-ax}\,dx = \lim_{c\to\infty}\int_b^c e^{-ax}\,dx = \lim_{c\to\infty}\left(-\frac{1}{a}e^{-ax}\right)\Big|_b^c = \frac{1}{a}\lim_{c\to\infty}\left(e^{-ab} - e^{-ac}\right) = \frac{e^{-ab}}{a}.$$

b. Solving $e^{-ab} = 2a$ for b gives $b = g(a) = -\frac{1}{a}\ln(2a)$.

c. The function g has $g'(x) = \frac{1}{x^2}\ln 2x - \frac{1}{x^2} = \frac{\ln 2x - 1}{x^2}$, so g has a critical point at $x = e/2$, and the first derivative test shows that g takes a minimum at this point. Hence $b^* = g(e/2) = -\frac{2}{e}$.

7.8.74 First, assume $p \neq 1$. Then

$$\int_0^1 x^{-p}\,dx = \lim_{c\to 0^+}\int_c^1 x^{-p}\,dx = \lim_{c\to 0^+}\left(\frac{x^{1-p}}{1-p}\right)\Big|_c^1$$

$$= \frac{1}{1-p}\lim_{c\to 0^+}\left(1 - c^{1-p}\right) = \frac{1}{1-p}$$

when $p < 1$ and is infinite otherwise. In the case $p = 1$ we have $\int_0^1 x^{-1}\,dx = \lim_{c\to 0^+}\int_c^1 x^{-1}\,dx = \lim_{c\to 0^+}(\ln x)\Big|_c^1 = \lim_{c\to 0^+}(-\ln c) = \infty$, so the integral exists if and only if $p < 1$.

7.8.75

a. The solid has volume $V = \pi\int_0^1 x^{-2p}\,dx$, which by the result in problem 74 is finite if and only if $2p < 1$, or $p < 1/2$.

b. The solid has volume $V = 2\pi \int_0^1 x^{1-p}\, dx$, which by the result in problem 74 is finite if and only if $p - 1 < 1$, or $p < 2$.

7.8.76

a. The solid has volume $V = \pi \int_1^\infty x^{-2p}\, dx$, which by the result in Example 2 is finite if and only if $2p > 1$, or $p > 1/2$.

b. The solid has volume $V = 2\pi \int_1^\infty x^{1-p}\, dx$, which by the result in Example 2 is finite if and only if $p - 1 > 1$, or $p > 2$.

7.8.77 These integrals cannot be evaluated by finding an antiderivative of their integrands. However, if we make the substitution $u = \pi/2 - x$ we find that $\int_0^{\pi/2} \ln\sin x\, dx = -\int_{\pi/2}^0 \ln\cos u\, du = \int_0^{\pi/2} \ln\cos x\, dx$. We also have

$$\int_{\pi/2}^\pi \ln\sin x\, dx = \int_0^{\pi/2} \ln\sin(x + \pi/2)\, dx = \int_0^{\pi/2} \ln\cos x\, dx,$$

and therefore

$$\int_0^{\pi/2} \ln\sin x\, dx = \frac{1}{2}\int_0^\pi \ln\sin x\, dx = \int_0^{\pi/2} \ln\sin 2y\, dy = \int_0^{\pi/2} (\ln\sin y + \ln\cos y + \ln 2)\, dy.$$

This implies $\int_0^{\pi/2} \ln\cos x\, dx = -\int_0^{\pi/2} \ln 2\, dx = -\frac{\pi\ln 2}{2}$.

7.8.78 This integral cannot be evaluated by finding an antiderivative of the integrand; however the result may be verified by numerical approximation.

7.8.79 This integral cannot be evaluated by finding an antiderivative of the integrand; however the result may be verified by numerical approximation.

7.8.80 This integral cannot be evaluated by finding an antiderivative of the integrand; however the result may be verified by numerical approximation.

7.8.81 We have the relation $B = I \int_0^\infty e^{-rt}\, dt = \frac{I}{r}$, using the result that $\int_0^\infty e^{-ax}\, dx = \frac{1}{a}$ for $a > 0$. Therefore $B = 5000/0.12 = \$41{,}666.67$.

7.8.82 The rate at which water is draining from the tank is given by $r(t) = 100(0.95)^t = 100e^{(\ln 0.95)t}$, so the total amount of water drained from the tank is $W = 100\int_0^\infty e^{(\ln 0.95)t}\, dt = \frac{100}{-\ln 0.95} \approx 1950\,\text{gal}$, using the result that $\int_0^\infty e^{-ax}\, dx = \frac{1}{a}$ for $a > 0$. Therefore the full $3{,}000$ gallon tank cannot be emptied at this rate.

7.8.83

a. We have $\int_0^\infty e^{-ax}\cos bx\, dx = \lim_{c\to\infty}\int_0^c e^{-ax}\cos bx\, dx = \lim_{c\to\infty}\left(\frac{e^{-ax}(b\sin bx - a\cos bx)}{a^2+b^2}\right)\Big|_0^c =$

$\lim_{c\to\infty}\frac{a + e^{-ac}(b\sin bc - a\cos bc)}{a^2+b^2} = \frac{a}{a^2+b^2}$.

b. We have $\int_0^\infty e^{-ax}\sin bx\, dx = \lim_{c\to\infty}\int_0^c e^{-ax}\sin bx\, dx = \lim_{c\to\infty}\left(-\frac{e^{-ax}(a\sin bx + b\cos bx)}{a^2+b^2}\right)\Big|_0^c =$

$\lim_{c\to\infty}\frac{b - e^{-ac}(a\sin bc + b\cos bc)}{a^2+b^2} = \frac{b}{a^2+b^2}$.

7.8.84

a. We will make use of the result $\int_b^\infty e^{-at}\, dt = \frac{e^{-ab}}{a}$ for $a > 0$ (this is derived in problem 73). The probability that a chip fails after $15{,}000$ hours of operation (or equivalently, lasts at least $15{,}000$ hours) is $p = 0.00005\int_{15{,}000}^\infty e^{-0.00005t}\, dt = e^{-0.00005\cdot 15{,}000} \approx 0.472$.

b. The probability that a chip fails after 30,000 hours of operation is $p = 0.00005 \int_{30,000}^{\infty} e^{-0.00005t} \, dt = e^{-0.00005 \cdot 30,000} \approx 0.223$. Of the chips that are still operating at 15,000 hours, the fraction that operate for at least another 15,000 hours is $\approx 0.223/0.472 = 0.472$.

c. From part a, we see that $0.00005 \int_0^{\infty} e^{-0.00005t} \, dt = 1$, which can be interpreted as meaning that all the chips are working initially.

7.8.85 Evaluate the improper integral $\int_0^{\infty} te^{-at} \, dt = \lim_{b \to \infty} \int_0^b te^{-at} \, dt = \lim_{b \to \infty} \left(-\frac{e^{-at}(at+1)}{a^2} \right) \Big|_0^b = \frac{1}{a^2} \lim_{b \to \infty} \left(1 - e^{-ab}(ab+1) \right) = \frac{1}{a^2}$, provided $a > 0$. Therefore $0.00005 \int_0^{\infty} te^{-0.00005t} \, dt = \frac{0.00005}{0.00005^2} = 20,000$ hrs.

7.8.86

a. Evaluate the improper integral
$$\int_0^{\infty} xe^{-cx} \, dx = \lim_{b \to \infty} \int_0^b xe^{-cx} \, dx$$
$$= \lim_{b \to \infty} \left(-\frac{e^{-cx}(cx+1)}{c^2} \right) \Big|_0^b$$
$$= \frac{1}{c^2} \lim_{b \to \infty} \left(1 - e^{-cb}(cb+1) \right)$$
$$= \frac{1}{c^2},$$
provided $c > 0$. We also have $\int_0^{\infty} e^{-cx} \, dx = \frac{1}{c}$ for $c > 0$. Hence $\bar{x} = 1/c = 1/2$ for the case $c = 2$.

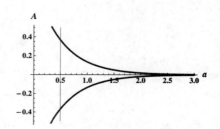

b. The curve $y = e^{-2x}$ has slope -2 at $x = 0$, so the equation of the tangent line at $(0, 1)$ is $y = 1 - 2x$. Similarly, the equation of the tangent line to $y = -e^{-2x}$ at $(0, -1)$ is $y = -1 + 2x$.

c. Both tangent lines intersect the x-axis at $x = 1/2$.

d. More generally, in the case $a = 0$ the center of mass is $\bar{x} = 1/c$ and the tangent lines at (0 ± 1) have equations $y = \pm(1 - cx)$, so both tangent lines meet the x-axis at the center of mass. The case for arbitrary a can be reduced to the case $a = 0$ by a horizontal shift.

7.8.87

a. We have $W = GMm \int_R^{\infty} x^{-2} \, dx = GMm \lim_{b \to \infty} \left(-\frac{1}{x} \right) \Big|_R^b = \frac{GMm}{R} \approx 6.279 \times 10^7 \, \text{m J}$.

b. Solve $\frac{1}{2} v_e^2 = 6.279 \times 10^7$ to obtain $v_e \approx 11.207$ km/s.

c. We need $\frac{GM}{R} \geq \frac{1}{2} c^2 \iff R \leq \frac{2GM}{c^2} \approx 9 \, \text{mm}$.

7.8.88 Let r_0 be the radius of the nucleus. The work required to bring a free proton to the edge of the nucleus is given by $W = kQq \int_{r_0}^{\infty} r^{-2} \, dr = kQq \lim_{b \to \infty} \left(-\frac{1}{r} \right) \Big|_{r_0}^b = \frac{kQq}{r_0} = \frac{50kq^2}{r_0} = 1.92 \times 10^{-16} \, \text{N m}$.

7.8.89

a.

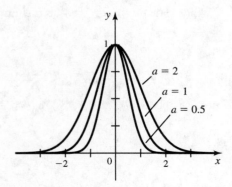

b. The areas are $\sqrt{2\pi}$, $\sqrt{\pi}$, $\sqrt{\pi/2}$ respectively.

c. Completing the square gives

$$ax^2 + bx + c = a\left(x + \frac{b}{2a}\right)^2 + \frac{4ac - b^2}{4a},$$

and therefore

$$\int_{-\infty}^{\infty} e^{-(ax^2+bx+c)} \, dx = e^{(b^2-4ac)/(4a)} \int_{-\infty}^{\infty} e^{-a(x+(b/2a))^2} \, dx.$$

Make the substitution $y = x + b/(2a)$ to obtain

$$\int_{-\infty}^{\infty} e^{-(ax^2+bx+c)} \, dx = e^{(b^2-4ac)/(4a)} \int_{-\infty}^{\infty} e^{-ay^2} \, dy = e^{(b^2-4ac)/(4a)} \sqrt{\frac{\pi}{a}}.$$

7.8.90 The Laplace transform of $f(t) = 1$ is given by $F(s) = \int_0^\infty e^{-st} \, dt = \frac{1}{s}$.

7.8.91 The Laplace transform of $f(t) = e^{at}$ is given by $F(s) = \int_0^\infty e^{-st}e^{at} \, dt = \int_0^\infty e^{-(s-a)t} \, dt = \frac{1}{s-a}$, using the formula $\int_0^\infty e^{-cx} \, dx = \frac{1}{c}$ for $c > 0$.

7.8.92 The Laplace transform of $f(t) = t$ is given by $F(s) = \int_0^\infty te^{-st} \, dt = \frac{1}{s^2}$ (this formula is derived in the solution to problem 86).

7.8.93 The Laplace transform of $f(t) = \sin at$ is given by $F(s) = \int_0^\infty e^{-st} \sin at \, dt = \frac{a}{s^2+a^2}$ (this formula is derived in the solution to problem 83 b).

7.8.94 The Laplace transform of $f(t) = \cos at$ is given by $F(s) = \int_0^\infty e^{-st} \cos at \, dt = \frac{s}{s^2+a^2}$ (this formula is derived in the solution to problem 83 a).

7.8.95

a. Make the substitution $x = y + 2$; then

$$\int_1^3 \frac{dx}{\sqrt{(x-1)(3-x)}} = \int_{-1}^1 \frac{dy}{\sqrt{1-y^2}} = 2\int_0^1 \frac{dy}{\sqrt{1-y^2}} = 2 \lim_{c \to 1^-} \left(\sin^{-1} x\right)\Big|_0^c = \pi.$$

b. The substitution $y = e^x$ gives

$$\int_1^\infty \frac{dx}{e^{x+1} + e^{3-x}} = \frac{1}{e} \int_1^\infty \frac{e^x dx}{e^{2x} + e^2} = \frac{1}{e} \int_e^\infty \frac{dy}{y^2 + e^2} = \frac{1}{e} \lim_{b \to \infty} \left(\frac{1}{e} \tan^{-1}\left(\frac{y}{e}\right)\right)\Big|_e^b = \frac{\pi}{4e^2}.$$

7.8.96 Using integration by parts, we have $\int_0^1 \ln x \, dx = \lim_{c \to 0+} (x \ln x - x) \Big|_c^1 = \lim_{c \to 0+} (-1 - c \ln c + c) =$ -1. The integral is the (signed) area of the region in the fourth quadrant between the y-axis and the curve $y = \ln x$; this region is identical to the region under the curve $y = e^{-x}$ in the first quadrant. Hence $\int_0^1 \ln x \, dx = -\int_0^\infty e^{-x} \, dx = -1$.

7.8.97 Because $p > 0$, the functions $1/(x^p + x^{-p})$ and $1/x^p$ have the same growth rate as $x \to \infty$; therefore by the result in Example 2, we have $\int_0^\infty \frac{dx}{x^p + x^{-p}} < \infty \iff p > 1$.

7.8.98

a. Repeatedly applying this reduction formula gives $\Gamma(p+1) = p(p-1) \cdots 2 \cdot 1 \cdot \int_0^\infty e^{-x} \, dx = p! \cdot 1 = p!$.

b. We have $\Gamma\left(\frac{1}{2}\right) = \int_0^\infty x^{-1/2} e^{-x} \, dx = 2 \int_0^\infty e^{-u^2} \, du = \sqrt{\pi}$.

7.8.99

a. Integrate by parts with $u = \sqrt{x} \ln x$ and $v = -1/(1+x)$: $\int_0^\infty \frac{\sqrt{x} \ln x}{(1+x)^2} \, dx = \frac{1}{2} \int_0^\infty \frac{\ln x + 2}{\sqrt{x}(x+1)} \, dx = \frac{1}{2} \int_0^\infty \frac{\ln x}{\sqrt{x}(x+1)} \, dx + \int_0^\infty \frac{dx}{\sqrt{x}(x+1)}$ (the integration by parts is legitimate for this improper integral because the product uv has limit 0 as $x \to \infty$ and as $x \to 0^+$).

b. Let $y = 1/x$. Then $dy = -\frac{1}{x^2} \, dx$.

c. We have $\int_0^1 \frac{\ln x}{\sqrt{x}(x+1)} \, dx = \int_\infty^1 \frac{-\ln y}{\frac{1}{\sqrt{y}}\left(\frac{1}{y}+1\right)} \left(-\frac{dy}{y^2}\right) = -\int_1^\infty \frac{\ln y}{\sqrt{y}(1+y)} \, dy$, and hence $\int_0^\infty \frac{\ln x}{\sqrt{x}(x+1)} \, dx = 0$.

d. The change of variables $z = \sqrt{x}$ gives $\int_0^\infty \frac{dx}{\sqrt{x}(x+1)} = 2 \int_0^\infty \frac{dz}{z^2+1} = \pi$.

7.8.100

a. We have $\frac{1}{n} \ln n! - \ln n = \left(\frac{1}{n} \sum_{k=1}^n \ln k\right) - \ln n = \frac{1}{n} \sum_{k=1}^n (\ln k - \ln n) = \frac{1}{n} \sum_{k=1}^n \ln\left(\frac{k}{n}\right)$.

b. This is the right-hand Riemann sum for the integral $\int_0^1 \ln x \, dx = -1$ (see the solution to problem 96). Therefore $L = \lim_{n \to \infty} \left(\frac{1}{n} \ln n! - \ln n\right) = -1$.

7.8.101 Recall that $\frac{d}{dx} x^x = x^x (1 + \ln x)$, which can be deduced from logarithmic differentiation. Thus we have $\int_0^a x^x (\ln x + 1) \, dx = \lim_{c \to 0+} x^x \Big|_c^a = \lim_{c \to 0+} (a^a - c^c) = (a^a - 1)$. This last limit is deduced as follows; let $z = c^c$, then $\ln z = c \ln c = \frac{\ln c}{1/c}$, and by L'hôpital's rule, we have $\lim_{c \to 0+} \frac{\ln c}{1/c} = \lim_{c \to 0+} \frac{1/c}{-1/c^2} = \lim_{c \to 0+} -c = 0$. Thus $\lim_{c \to 0+} z = e^0 = 1$.

7.8.102 We consider the integral as

$$\int_0^a x^{-x} (1 + \ln x) \, dx + \int_a^\infty x^{-x} (1 + \ln x) \, dx.$$

Recall that $\frac{d}{dx} x^{-x} = -x^{-x} (1 + \ln x)$ which can be deduced from logarithmic differentiation. Thus we have

$$\int_0^a x^{-x} (\ln x + 1) \, dx = \lim_{c \to 0+} -x^{-x} \Big|_0^a = 1 - \frac{1}{a^a}. \text{ Now}$$

$$\int_a^\infty x^{-x} (1 + \ln x) \, dx = \lim_{b \to \infty} -x^{-x} \Big|_a^b = \lim_{b \to \infty} \left(-\frac{1}{b^b} + \frac{1}{a^a}\right) = \frac{1}{a^a}.$$

Putting the two results together gives $\int_0^\infty x^{-x} (\ln x + 1) \, dx = 1$.

7.9 Introduction to Differential Equations

7.9.1 Second-order, because the highest-order derivative appearing in the equation is second order.

7.9.2 Linear, since the unknown function and its derivatives appear only to the first power.

7.9.3 The equation is second-order, so we expect two arbitrary constants in the general solution.

7.9.4 We have $y(0) = C + 10 = 5$, so $C = -5$.

7.9.5 A separable first-order differential equation is one that can be written in the form $g(y)y'(t) = h(t)$.

7.9.6 Yes, this equation is separable since it can be written in the form $y^{-2}y'(t) = t^{-2}(t+4)$.

7.9.7 Integrate both sides with respect to t and convert the integral on the left side to an integral with respect to y.

7.9.8 Choose a regular grid of points in the ty-plane, and at each point (t,y) make a small line segment with slope $F(t,y)$.

7.9.9 $y = Ce^{-5t}$ so $y' = -5Ce^{-5t}$. Then $y' + 5y = -5Ce^{-5t} + 5Ce^{-5t} = 0$.

7.9.10 $y = Ct^{-3}$ so $y' = -3Ct^{-4}$. Then $ty' + 3y = -3tCt^{-4} + 3Ct^{-3} = -3Ct^{-3} + 3Ct^{-3} = 0$.

7.9.11 $y = C_1 \sin 4t + C_2 \cos 4t$ so $y' = 4C_1 \cos 4t - 4C_2 \sin 4t$ and then $y'' = -16C_1 \sin 4t - 16C_2 \cos 4t$. Then $y'' + 16y = -16C_1 \sin 4t - 16C_2 \cos 4t + 16C_1 \sin 4t + 16C_2 \cos 4t = 0$.

7.9.12 $y = C_1 e^{-x} + C_2 e^x$ so $y' = -C_1 e^{-x} + C_2 e^x$ and $y'' = C_1 e^{-x} + C_2 e^x$. Then $y'' - y = C_1 e^{-x} + C_2 e^x - (C_1 e^{-x} + C_2 e^x) = 0$.

7.9.13 $y = 16e^{2t} - 10$, so $y' = 32e^{2t}$. So $y' - 2y = 32e^{2t} - 32e^{2t} + 20 = 20$. Also $y(0) = 16 - 10 = 6$.

7.9.14 $y = 8t^6 - 3$ so $y' = 48t^5$. Then $ty' - 6y = t \cdot 48t^5 - 6(8t^6 - 3) = 48t^6 - 48t^6 + 18 = 18$. Also $y(1) = 8 - 3 = 5$.

7.9.15 $y = -3\cos 3t$ so $y' = 9\sin 3t$ and $y'' = 27\cos 3t$. Then $y'' + 9y = 27\cos 3t - 27\cos 3t = 0$. Also $y(0) = -3\cos 0 = -3$ and $y'(0) = 9\sin 0 = 0$.

7.9.16 $y = \frac{1}{4}\left(e^{2x} - e^{-2x}\right)$ so $y' = \frac{1}{2}\left(e^{2x} + e^{-2x}\right)$ and $y'' = e^{2x} - e^{-2x}$. Then $y'' - 4y = e^{2x} - e^{-2x} - \left(e^{2x} - e^{-2x}\right) = 0$. Also, $y(0) = \frac{1}{4}(1 - 1) = 0$ and $y'(0) = \frac{1}{2}(1 + 1) = 1$.

7.9.17 Integrate both sides with respect to t: $\int y'(t)\, dt = \int (3t^2 - 4t + 10)\, dt$ $y(t) = t^3 - 2t^2 + 10t + C$; then substitute $y(0) = 20$ to obtain $y(0) = (t^3 - 2t^2 + 10t + C)\big|_{t=0} = C = 20$, so $y(t) = t^3 - 2t^2 + 10t + 20$.

7.9.18 Integrate both sides with respect to t: $\int y'(t)\, dt = \int (8e^{-4t} + 1)\, dt$ $y(t) = -2e^{-4t} + t + C$; then substitute $y(0) = 5$ to obtain $y(0) = (-2e^{-4t} + t + C)\big|_{t=0} = -2 + C = 5$, so $C = 7$ and thus $y(t) = -2e^{-4t} + t + 7$.

7.9.19 Integrate both sides with respect to t: $\int y'(t)\, dt = \int \frac{2t^2 + 4}{t}\, dt = \int \left(2t + \frac{4}{t}\right)\, dt$ $y(t) = t^2 + 4\ln t + C$; then substitute $y(1) = 2$ to obtain $y(1) = (t^2 + 4\ln t + C)\big|_{t=1} = 1 + C = 2$, so $C = 1$ and thus $y(t) = t^2 + 4\ln t + 1$.

7.9.20 Integrate both sides with respect to x: $\int y'(x)\, dx = \int (3\cos 2x + 2\sin 3x)\, dx$, so $y(x) = \frac{3}{2}\sin 2x - \frac{2}{3}\cos 3x + C$; then substitute $y(\pi/2) = 8$ to obtain $y(\pi/2) = \left(\frac{3}{2}\sin 2x - \frac{2}{3}\cos 3x + C\right)\big|_{x=\pi/2} = 0 + C = 8$, so $C = 8$ and thus $y(x) = \frac{3}{2}\sin 2x - \frac{2}{3}\cos 3x + 8$.

7.9.21 The general solution is $y(t) = Ce^{3t} + \frac{4}{3}$.

7.9.22 The general solution is $y(x) = Ce^{-x} + 2$.

7.9.23 The general solution is $y(x) = Ce^{-2x} - 2$.

7.9.24 The general solution is $y(t) = Ce^{2t} - 3$.

7.9.25 The general solution is $y(t) = Ce^{3t} + 2$; substitute $y(0) = 9$ to obtain $C + 2 = 9$, so $C = 7$; hence $y(t) = 7e^{3t} + 2$.

7.9.26 The general solution is $y(x) = Ce^{-x} + 2$; substitute $y(0) = -2$ to obtain $C + 2 = -2$, so $C = -4$; hence $y(x) = -4e^{-x} + 2$.

7.9.27 The general solution is $y(t) = Ce^{-2t} - 2$; substitute $y(0) = 0$ to obtain $C - 2 = 0$, so $C = 2$; hence $y(t) = 2e^{-2t} - 2$.

7.9.28 The general solution is $u(x) = Ce^{2x} - 3$; substitute $u(1) = 6$ to obtain $Ce^2 - 3 = 6$, so $C = 9e^{-2}$; hence $u(x) = 9e^{2x-2} - 3$.

7.9.29

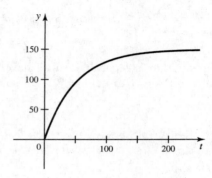

  a. The general solution is $y(t) = Ce^{-0.02t} + 150$; substitute $y(0) = 0$ to obtain $C + 150 = 0$, so $C = -150$; hence $y(t) = 150(1 - e^{-0.02t})$.

  b. The steady-state level is $\lim_{t \to \infty} 150(1 - e^{-0.02t}) = 150$ mg.

  c. We have $150(1 - e^{-0.02t}) = 0.9 \cdot 150$, so $e^{-0.02t} = 0.1$, and thus $t = \frac{\ln 10}{0.02} \approx 115$ hrs.

7.9.30

  a. The general solution is $y(t) = Ce^{0.1t} + 10b$; substitute $y(0) = 500$ to obtain $C + 10b = 500$, so $C = 500 - 10b$; hence $y(t) = (500 - 10b)e^{0.1t} + 10b$.

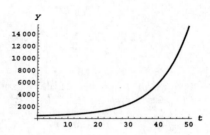

  b. In this case the solution is $y(t) = 100e^{0.1t} + 400$, which approaches ∞ as $t \to \infty$.

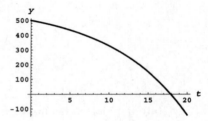

  c. In this case the solution is $y(t) = -100e^{0.1t} + 600$, which reaches 0 when $e^{0.1t} = 6$ or $t = 10 \ln 6 \approx 17.9$ yrs.

7.9.31 The equation is separable, so we have $\int y\,dy = \int 3t^2\,dt$. So $\frac{y^2}{2} = t^3 + C$, and thus $y = \pm\sqrt{2t^3 + C}$.

7.9.32 The equation is separable (and $y > 0$), so we have $\int \frac{dy}{y} = \int (x^2 + 1)\,dx$, and thus $\ln y = \frac{x^3}{3} + x + C$, so $y = e^{\left(\frac{x^3}{3} + x + C\right)}$.

7.9.33 The equation is separable, so we have $\int e^{-y/2}\,dy = \int \sin t\,dt$, and so $-2e^{-y/2} = -\cos t + C$. Thus, $y = -2\ln\left(\frac{1}{2}\cos t + C\right)$.

7.9.34 The equation is separable, so we have $\int w^{-1/2}\,dw = \int \frac{3x+1}{x^2}\,dx = \int \left(\frac{3}{x} + \frac{1}{x^2}\right)\,dx$, so $2w^{1/2} = 3\ln|x| - \frac{1}{x} + C$, and thus $w = \left(\frac{3}{2}\ln|x| - \frac{1}{2x} + C\right)^2$.

7.9.35 This equation is not separable.

7.9.36 This equation is separable, so we have $\int \frac{dy}{y} = \int (4t^3 + 1)\,dt$, and thus $\ln|y| = t^4 + t + C$. Therefore, $y = \pm e^{\left(t^4 + t + C\right)} = C'e^{t^4 + t}$. Substituting $y(0) = 4$ gives $C' = 4$, so the solution to this initial value problem is $y = 4e^{t^4 + t}$.

7.9.37 This equation is separable, so we have $\int 2y\,dy = \int e^t\,dt$, so $y^2 = e^t + C$, and thus $y = \pm\sqrt{e^t + C}$. Substituting $y(\ln 2) = 1$ gives $1 = 2 + C$ so $C = -1$, and the solution to this initial value problem is $y = \sqrt{e^t - 1}$.

7.9.38 This equation is separable, so we have $\int y^{-3}\,dy = \int \cos x\,dx$, so $-\frac{y^{-2}}{2} = \sin x + C$. Therefore, $y = \pm(-2\sin x + C)^{-1/2}$. Substituting $y(0) = 3$ gives $C = 1/9$, so the solution to this initial value problem is $y = \left(-2\sin x + \frac{1}{9}\right)^{-1/2}$.

7.9.39 This equation is separable, so we have $\int e^y\,dy = \int e^x\,dx$, and thus $e^y = e^x + C$. Therefore, $y = \ln(e^x + C)$. Substituting $y(0) = \ln 3$ gives $\ln 3 = \ln(1 + C)$, so $C = 2$ and the solution to this initial value problem is $y = \ln(e^x + 2)$.

7.9.40 This equation is separable, so we have $\int e^{-3y}\,dy = \int 2e^{-t}\,dt$, and thus $-\frac{1}{3}e^{-3y} = -2e^{-t} + C$. Therefore, $y = -\frac{1}{3}\ln(6e^{-t} + C)$. Substituting $y(0) = 0$ gives $0 = \ln(6 + C)$, so $C = -5$ and the solution to this initial value problem is $y = -\frac{1}{3}\ln(6e^{-t} - 5)$.

7.9.41

a. This equation is separable, so we have $\int \frac{200}{P(200-P)}\,dP = \int 0.08\,dt$, so $\int \left(\frac{1}{P} + \frac{1}{200-P}\right)\,dP = 0.08t + C$. Therefore, $\ln\left|\frac{P}{200-P}\right| = 0.08t + C$. Substituting $P(0) = 50$ gives $-\ln 3 = C$, and solving for P gives $P(t) = \frac{200}{3e^{-0.08t}+1}$.

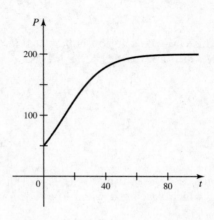

b. The steady-state population is $\lim_{t\to\infty} P(t) = 200$.

7.9.42

a. This equation is separable, so we have $\int \frac{A}{P(A-P)}\, dP = \int k\, dt$, so $\int \left(\frac{1}{P} + \frac{1}{A-P} \right) dP = kt + D$. Therefore, $\ln \left| \frac{P}{A-P} \right| = kt + D$, which is equivalent to $\frac{P}{A-P} = Ce^{kt}$. Substituting $P(0) = P_0$ gives $C = P_0/(A - P_0)$, and solving for P gives $P(t) = \frac{AP_0}{P_0 + (A-P_0)e^{-kt}}$.

b.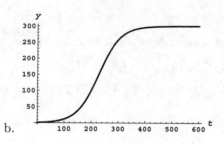

c. The denominator in $P(t)$ above is positive for all $t \geq 0$ when $0 < P_0 < A$, so $P(t)$ is defined for all $t \geq 0$; we have $\lim_{t \to \infty} P(t) = A$, which is the steady-state solution.

7.9.43

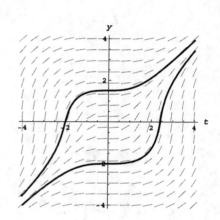

7.9.44

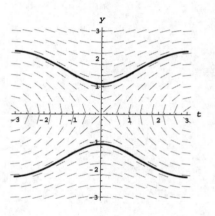

7.9.45

a. This matches with D.

b. This matches with B.

c. This matches with A.

d. This matches with C.

7.9.46

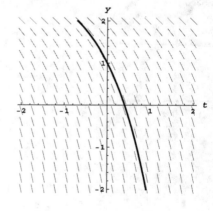

7.9.47

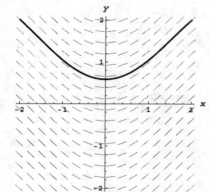

7.9.48

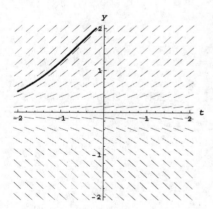

7.9.49

   a. False. The general solution is $y = Ce^{20t}$.

   b. False. They both do satisfy this differential equation.

   c. False. Rewrite the equation as $y'(t) = (t+2)(y+2)$.

   d. True. $y'(t) = 2(t+1) = 2\sqrt{(t+1)^2} = 2\sqrt{y}$.

7.9.50

   a. $y = -2$ is an equilibrium solution, since
      $2(-2) + 4 = 0$.

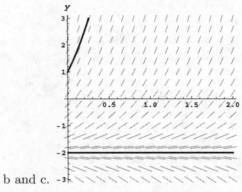

                                   b and c.

7.9.51

   a. $y = 0$ is an equilibrium solution.

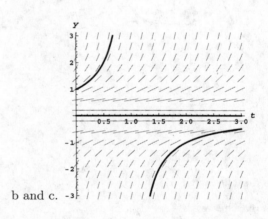

                                   b and c.

7.9.52

   a. Solve $y(2-y) = 0$ to get equilibrium solutions
      $y = 0$ and $y = 2$.

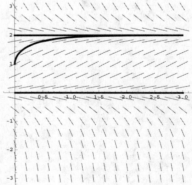

                                   b and c.

7.9.53

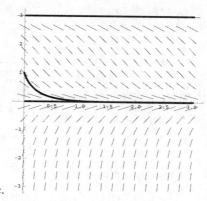

  a. Solve $y(y-3) = 0$ to get equilibrium solutions
    $y = 0$ and $y = 3$.

b and c.

7.9.54

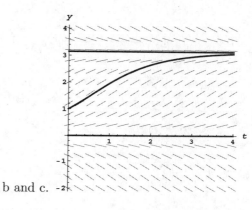

  a. Solve $\sin y = 0$ to get equilibrium solutions
    $y = k\pi$, where k is any integer.

b and c.

7.9.55

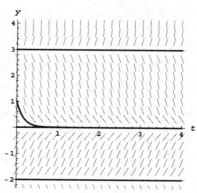

  a. The equilibrium solutions are $y = 0$, $y = -2$
    and $y = 3$.

b and c.

7.9.56 This is a first-order linear equation, so the general solution is $u(t) = Ce^{4t} + \frac{1}{2}$; the initial condition gives $C + 1/2 = 4$ so $C = 7/2$ and the solution to this initial value problem is $u(t) = \frac{7}{2}e^{4t} + \frac{1}{2}$.

7.9.57 This equation is separable, so we have $\int \frac{dp}{p+1} = \int \frac{dt}{t^2}$, so $\ln|p+1| = -\frac{1}{t} + D$, and thus $p = Ce^{-1/t} - 1$. Substituting $p(1) = 3$ gives $3 = Ce^{-1} - 1$, so $C = 4e$ and the solution to this initial value problem is $p = 4e^{1-1/t} - 1$.

7.9.58 This equation is separable, so we have $\int \frac{dz}{z^2} = \int \frac{dx}{1+x^2}$, and thus $-\frac{1}{z} = \tan^{-1} x + C$. Therefore, $z = \frac{1}{C-\tan^{-1}x}$. Substituting $z(0) = 1/6$ gives $1/6 = 1/C$, so $C = 6$ and the solution to this initial value problem is $z = \frac{1}{6-\tan^{-1}x}$.

7.9.59 This equation is separable, so we have $\int \sec^2 w \, dw = \int 2t \, dt$, so $\tan w = t^2 + C$. Thus, $w = \tan^{-1}(t^2 + C)$. Substituting $w(0) = \pi/4$ gives $\pi/4 = \tan^{-1} C$, so $C = \tan(\pi/4) = 1$ and the solution to this initial value problem is $w = \tan^{-1}(t^2 + 1)$.

7.9.60

a. The equation $y'(t) = 0.008y - h$ has steady-state solution $y = h/0.008 = 125h$, so we solve $y_0 = 2000 = 125h$ to obtain $h = 16$.

b. If $h = 200$, then the steady-state solution is $y = 125 \cdot 200 = 25{,}000$.

7.9.61

a. This equation is separable, so we have $\int \frac{1}{y(1-y)} \, dy = \int k \, dt$, so $\int \left(\frac{1}{y} + \frac{1}{1-y} \right) \, dy = kt + D$. Therefore, $\ln \left| \frac{y}{1-y} \right| = kt + D$, which is equivalent to $\frac{y}{1-y} = Ce^{kt}$. Substituting $y(0) = y_0$ gives $C = y_0/(1 - y_0)$, and thus $y = \frac{y_0}{(1-y_0)e^{-kt} + y_0}$.

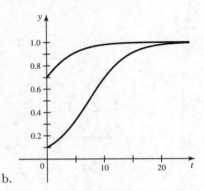

c. The denominator in $y(t)$ above is positive for all $t \geq 0$ when $0 < y_0 < 1$, so $y(t)$ is defined for all $t \geq 0$; we have $\lim_{t \to \infty} y(t) = 1$, which is the steady-state solution.

b.

7.9.62

a. We have $mv'(t) = mg - kv^2$, so $v'(t) = g - av^2$ with $a = k/m$.

b. We solve $av^2 = g$ to obtain the terminal velocity $\tilde{v} = \sqrt{g/a}$.

c. This equation is separable, so we have $\int \frac{1}{g - av^2} \, dv = \int dt$, so $-\frac{1}{a} \int \frac{1}{v^2 - \tilde{v}^2} \, dv = t + D$.

Thus, $-\frac{1}{2a\tilde{v}} \int \left(\frac{1}{v - \tilde{v}} - \frac{1}{v + \tilde{v}} \right) \, dv = t + D$, and $-\frac{1}{2a\tilde{v}} \ln \left| \frac{v - \tilde{v}}{v + \tilde{v}} \right| = t + D$, hence $\frac{v - \tilde{v}}{v + \tilde{v}} = Ce^{-2a\tilde{v}t}$ The initial condition $v(0) = 0$ gives $C = -1$, and solving for v gives $v = \frac{1 - e^{-2a\tilde{v}t}}{1 + e^{-2a\tilde{v}t}} \tilde{v}$.

d. We have $a = 0.1$, $\tilde{v} \approx 9.90$ m/s

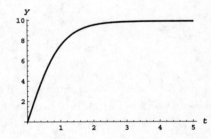

7.9.63

a. We have $mv'(t) = mg - Rv$, so $v'(t) = g - bv$ with $b = R/m$.

b. Solve $bv = g$ to obtain terminal velocity $\tilde{v} = g/b = mg/R$.

c. The equation $v' = g - bv$ is first-order linear, with general solution $v = Ce^{-bv} + \tilde{v}$. The initial condition $v(0) = 0$ gives $C = -\tilde{v}$, which gives $v = \tilde{v}(1 - e^{-bt})$.

d. We have $b = 0.1$, $\tilde{v} = 98$ m/s.

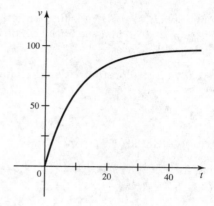

7.9.64

a. The equation $h' = 2k\sqrt{h}$ is separable, so we have $\int \frac{dh}{2\sqrt{h}} = \int k\,dt$, so $\sqrt{h} = kt + C$. The initial condition $h(0) = H$ gives $C = \sqrt{H}$, so the solution is $h = (\sqrt{H} + kt)^2$.

b. The solution for $k = 0.1$ and $H = 0.5$ is $h = (0.7071 + 0.1t)^2$.

c. The tank is drained when $h(t) = 0$, which gives $t = -\sqrt{H}/k$.

7.9.65

a. The general solution to $y' = -ky$ is $y = Ce^{-kt}$.

b. The equation $y' = -ky^2$ is separable, so we have $-\int \frac{dy}{y^2} = \int k\,dt$, so $\frac{1}{y} = kt + C$. The initial condition $y(0) = y_0$ gives $C = 1/y_0$, and solving for y gives $y = \frac{1}{kt + 1/y_0} = \frac{y_0}{1 + ky_0 t}$.

c.

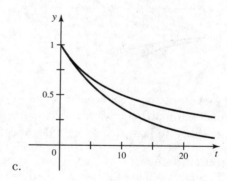

7.9.66

a. The growth rate is positive when $0 < M < K$. The function $R(M)$ has derivative $R'(M) = -a\left(\ln\left(\frac{M}{K}\right) + M \cdot \frac{K}{M} \cdot \frac{1}{K}\right) = -a\left(\ln\left(\frac{M}{K}\right) + 1\right)$ which is 0 when $M/K = 1/e$ or $M = K/e$. We also observe that $\lim_{M \to 0^+} R(M) = 0$ and $R(K) = 0$, so $R(M)$ takes its maximum at the critical point $M = K/e$.

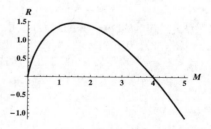

b. The equation is separable, so we have $\int \frac{dM}{M(\ln M - \ln K)} = -\int a\,dt$, so $\ln|\ln M - \ln K| = -at + D$, and thus $\ln\left(\frac{M}{K}\right) = Ce^{-at}$. Therefore $M = K\exp(Ce^{-at})$.

The conditions $a = 1$, $K = 4$ and $M_0 = 1$ give $C = -\ln 4$ and $M = 4\exp((-\ln 4)e^{-t})$. Observe that $\lim_{t \to \infty} M(t) = 4\exp(0) = 4$, so the limiting size of the tumor is 4.

c. In general, the limiting size of the tumor is $\lim_{t\to\infty} K\exp(Ce^{-at}) = K$, since $a > 0$.

7.9.67

a. The equation $B' = aB - m$ is first-order linear, with general solution $B = Ce^{at} + m/a$; in this case $a = 0.05$, $m/a = 20{,}000$, and the initial condition $B_0 = 15{,}000$ gives $C = -5000$, so $B = 20{,}000 - 5000e^{0.05t}$. The balance decreases.

b. The steady-state (constant balance) solution is $B = m/a = \$50{,}000$, which gives $m = 0.05 \cdot 50{,}000 = \$2500$.

7.9.68

a. We have $C = \ln(50/250) = \ln(1/5)$.

b. Solving for $P(t)$ gives $\frac{P}{300-P} = \frac{1}{5}e^{0.1t}$, so $P(t) = \frac{300}{1+5e^{-0.1t}}$.

7.9.69

a. Solving $y' = 0$ gives the equilibrium solution $y = -b/a$, which is a horizontal line.

b. 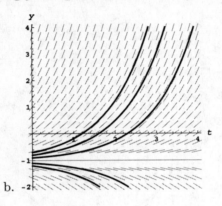   c.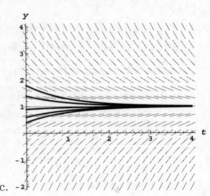

Note that the general solutions $y = (y_0 + \frac{b}{a})e^{at} - \frac{b}{a}$ increases without bound if $a > 0$ and $y_0 > \frac{-b}{a}$, and decreases without bound if $a > 0$ but $y_0 < \frac{-b}{a}$. But if $a < 0$, the general solutions have limit $\frac{-b}{a}$, but must increase to it if $y_0 < \frac{-b}{a}$ and decrease to it if $y_0 > \frac{-b}{a}$.

7.9.70 Note that an analysis of the sign of P' as a function of P shows that $P' > 0$ for $0 < P < 300$ and $P' < 0$ for $P > 300$. Differentiating the both sides of the differential equation with respect to t yields

$$P''(t) = 0.1P'(t)\left(1 - \frac{P}{300}\right) + 0.1P\left(\frac{-1}{300}\right)P'(t) = 0.1P'(t)\left(1 - \frac{P}{150}\right).$$

Then for $0 < P < 150$ we have that $P''(t) > 0$ because both $P'(t)$ and $1 - \frac{P}{150}$ are positive. For $150 < P < 300$ we have that $P''(t) < 0$ because $P'(t) > 0$ but $1 - \frac{P}{150} < 0$. Then for $P > 300$ we have that $P''(t) > 0$ because $P'(t) < 0$ and $1 - \frac{P}{150} < 0$. Thus P is concave up for $0 < P < 150$ and for $P > 300$ and is concave down for $150 < P < 300$.

Chapter Seven Review

1

a. True. Two applications of integration by parts are needed to reduce to $\int x^2 e^{2x}\, dx$.

b. False. This integral can be done using a trigonometric substitution.

c. False. Both are correct, since $-\cos^2 x = \sin^2 x - 1$, so $\sin^2 x$ and $-\cos^2 x$ differ by a constant.

d. True. Recall that $2\sin x \cos x = \sin 2x$.

e. False. Use long division to write the integrand as the sum of a polynomial and a proper rational function.

2 Let $u = x/2 + \pi/3$. Then $du = \frac{1}{2}\,dx$. Substituting gives

$$2\int \cos u\,du = 2\sin u + C = 2\sin(x/2 + \pi/3) + C.$$

3 Let $u = x + 4$ so that $du = dx$. Note that $x = u - 4$. Substituting gives

$$\int \frac{3(u-4)}{\sqrt{u}}\,du = 3\int \left(u^{1/2} - 4u^{-1/2}\right)du = 3\left((2/3)u^{3/2} - 8u^{1/2}\right) + C$$

$$= 2(x+4)^{3/2} - 24\sqrt{x+4} + C = 2\sqrt{x+4}(x+4-12) + C = 2\sqrt{x+4}(x-8) + C.$$

4 $\int \left(2\sec^2 2\theta - \tan 2\theta \sec 2\theta\right)d\theta = \tan 2\theta - \frac{1}{2}\sec 2\theta + C.$

5

$$\int_{-2}^{1} \frac{3}{(x+2)^2 + 9}\,dx = \left(\tan^{-1}((x+2)/3)\right)\Big|_{-2}^{1} = \pi/4 - 0 = \pi/4.$$

6 By long division, $\frac{x^3 + 3x^2 + 1}{x^3 + 1} = 1 + \frac{3x^2}{x^3 + 1}$. Thus $\int \frac{x^3 + 3x^2 + 1}{x^3 + 1}\,dx = \int \left(1 + \frac{3x^2}{x^3 + 1}\right)dx = x + \ln|x^3 + 1| + C.$

7 Let $u = \sqrt{t-1}$. Then $u^2 + 1 = t$, and $2u\,du = dt$. Substituting gives $\int \frac{u^2}{u^2 + 1}\,du = \int \left(1 - \frac{1}{u^2 + 1}\right)du = u - \tan^{-1} u + C = \sqrt{t-1} - \tan^{-1}\sqrt{t-1} + C.$

8 Let $u = 3t$ and $dv = e^{-t}\,dt$ Then $du = 3dt$ and $v = -e^{-t}$. Thus $\int_{-1}^{\ln 2} 3te^{-t}\,dt$ is equal to

$$-3te^{-t}\Big|_{-1}^{\ln 2} - \int_{-1}^{\ln 2}(-3e^{-t})\,dt = -3te^{-t}\Big|_{-1}^{\ln 2} - 3e^{-t}\Big|_{-1}^{\ln 2} = -\frac{3\ln 2}{2} - 3e - (3/2 - 3e) = -\frac{3}{2}(\ln 2 + 1).$$

9 Let $u = x$ and $dv = (1/2)(x+2)^{-1/2}\,dx$. Then $du = dx$ and $v = (x+2)^{1/2}$. We have

$$\int \frac{x}{2\sqrt{x+2}}\,dx = x\sqrt{x+2} - \int \sqrt{x+2}\,dx = x\sqrt{x+2} - \frac{2}{3}(x+2)^{3/2} + C$$

$$= \frac{1}{3}\sqrt{x+2}(3x - 2x - 4) + C = \frac{1}{3}\sqrt{x+2}(x-4) + C.$$

10 Let $u = \tan^{-1} x$ and $dv = x\,dx$. Then $du = \frac{dx}{x^2 + 1}$ and $v = x^2/2$. We have

$$\int x\tan^{-1} x\,dx = \frac{1}{2}x^2\tan^{-1} x - \int \frac{x^2}{2x^2 + 2}\,dx = \frac{1}{2}x^2\tan^{-1} x - \frac{1}{2}\int \left(1 - \frac{1}{x^2 + 1}\right)dx$$

$$= \frac{1}{2}x^2\tan^{-1} x - \frac{1}{2}\left(x - \tan^{-1}(x)\right) + C = \frac{1}{2}x^2\tan^{-1} x - \frac{x}{2} + \frac{\tan^{-1} x}{2} + C.$$

11 Let $u = x$ and $dv = \sinh x\,dx$. Then $du = dx$ and $v = \cosh x$. We have $\int x\sinh x\,dx = x\cosh x - \int \cosh x\,dx = x\cosh x - \sinh x + C.$

12

$$\int_{\pi}^{2\pi} \frac{\cos(x/3)}{\sin(x/3)}\,dx = 3\left(\ln|\sin(x/3)|\right)\Big|_{\pi}^{2\pi} = 3\ln\left|\frac{\sin(2\pi/3)}{\sin(\pi/3)}\right| = 3\ln 1 = 0.$$

13 $\int_0^{\pi/4} \cos^5 2x \sin^2 2x\, dx = \int_0^{\pi/4} \cos(2x)(1 - \sin^2 2x)^2 \sin^2 2x\, dx.$ Let $u = \sin 2x$ so that $du = 2\cos 2x\, dx.$ Substituting gives

$$\frac{1}{2}\int_0^1 (1 - u^2)^2 u^2\, du = \frac{1}{2}\int_0^1 (u^2 - 2u^4 + u^6)\, du = \frac{1}{2}\left(u^3/3 - 2u^5/5 + u^7/7\right)\Big|_0^1 = \frac{1}{2}(1/3 - 2/5 + 1/7) - 0 = \frac{4}{105}.$$

14 $\int \tan^3 \theta\, d\theta = \int \tan\theta(\sec^2\theta - 1)\, d\theta = \int \tan\theta \sec^2\theta\, d\theta - \int \tan\theta\, d\theta.$ For the first integral, let $u = \tan\theta$ and for the second, let $w = \cos\theta.$ Substituting gives

$$\int u\, du + \int \frac{1}{w}\, dw = u^2/2 + \ln|w| + C = \frac{\tan^2\theta}{2} + \ln|\cos\theta| + C.$$

15 $\int \tan^4 t \sec^2 t\, dt.$ Let $u = \tan t$ so that $du = \sec^2 t\, dt.$ Substituting gives

$$\int u^4\, du = u^5/5 + C = \frac{1}{5}\tan^5 t + C.$$

16 $\int \csc^2 x \cot x\, dx.$ Let $u = \cot x$ so that $du = -\csc^2 x\, dx.$ Substituting gives

$$-\int u\, du = -u^2/2 + C = \frac{-\cot^2 x}{2} + C.$$

17 $\int \tan^2\theta \sec^2\theta(\sec\theta\tan\theta)\, d\theta = \int (\sec^2\theta - 1)\sec^2\theta(\sec\theta\tan\theta)\, d\theta.$ Let $u = \sec\theta$ so that $du = \sec\theta\tan\theta\, d\theta.$ Substituting gives

$$\int (u^2 - 1)u^2\, du = \int (u^4 - u^2)\, du = u^5/5 - u^3/3 + C = \frac{1}{5}\sec^5\theta - \frac{1}{3}\sec^3\theta + C.$$

18 Let $x = \sin\theta$ so that $dx = \cos\theta\, d\theta$ and $\sqrt{1 - x^2} = \cos\theta.$ Substituting gives

$$\int \frac{\cos^2\theta}{\sin\theta}\, d\theta = \int \frac{1 - \sin^2\theta}{\sin\theta}\, d\theta$$
$$= \int (\csc\theta - \sin\theta)\, d\theta = -\ln|\csc\theta + \cot\theta| + \cos\theta + C$$
$$= -\ln|\csc \sin^{-1} x + \cot \sin^{-1} x| + \cos \sin^{-1} x + C$$
$$= -\ln|(1/x) + \sqrt{1 - x^2}/x| + \sqrt{1 - x^2} + C.$$

19 Let $x = \sec\theta$ so that $dx = \sec\theta\tan\theta\, d\theta$ and $\sqrt{x^2 - 1} = \tan\theta.$ Substituting gives

$$\int_{\pi/4}^{\pi/3} \tan^2\theta\, d\theta = \int_{\pi/4}^{\pi/3} (\sec^2\theta - 1)\, d\theta = (\tan\theta - \theta)\Big|_{\pi/4}^{\pi/3} = \sqrt{3} - \pi/3 - (1 - \pi/4) = \sqrt{3} - 1 - \frac{\pi}{12}.$$

20 Let $w = 2\sin\theta$ so that $dw = 2\cos\theta\, d\theta$ and $\sqrt{4 - w^2} = 2\cos\theta.$ Substituting gives

$$\int \frac{8\sin^3\theta}{2\cos\theta} 2\cos\theta\, d\theta = \int 8\sin\theta(1 - \cos^2\theta)\, d\theta.$$

Let $u = \cos\theta$ so that $du = -\sin\theta\, d\theta.$ Substituting again gives

$$8\int (u^2 - 1)\, du = 8u^3/3 - 8u + C = (8/3)\cos^3\theta - 8\cos\theta + C$$
$$= (8/3)(\cos(\sin^{-1}(w/2)))^3 - 8\cos(\sin^{-1}(w/2)) + C = (1/3)(\sqrt{4 - w^2})^3 - 4\sqrt{4 - w^2} + C$$
$$= (1/3)\sqrt{4 - w^2}(4 - w^2 - 12) = -\frac{1}{3}\sqrt{4 - w^2}(w^2 + 8) + C.$$

21 Let $x = 2\tan\theta$ so that $dx = 2\sec^2\theta\,d\theta$ and $\sqrt{x^2 + 4} = 2\sec\theta$. Substituting gives

$$\int \frac{8\tan^3\theta}{2\sec\theta} 2\sec^2\theta\,d\theta = 8\int \tan\theta\sec\theta(\sec^2\theta - 1)\,d\theta.$$

Let $u = \sec\theta$ so that $du = \sec\theta\tan\theta\,d\theta$. Substituting again gives

$$8\int (u^2 - 1)\,du = \frac{8}{3}u^3 - 8u + C = \frac{8}{3}\sec^3\theta - 8\sec\theta + C$$

$$= \frac{8}{3}(\sec(\tan^{-1}(x/2)))^3 - 8\sec\tan^{-1}(x/2) + C = \frac{1}{3}\sqrt{x^2 + 4}(x^2 + 4) - 4\sqrt{x^2 + 4} + C$$

$$= \frac{1}{3}\sqrt{x^2 + 4}(x^2 + 4 - 12) + C = \frac{1}{3}\sqrt{x^2 + 4}(x^2 - 8) + C.$$

22 Write $\frac{8x+5}{2x^2+3x+1} = \frac{A}{2x+1} + \frac{B}{x+1}$. Then $8x + 5 = A(x + 1) + B(2x + 1)$. Letting $x = -1$ gives $B = 3$ and letting $x = -1/2$ gives $A = 2$. Thus $\frac{8x+5}{2x^2+3x+1} = \frac{2}{2x+1} + \frac{3}{x+1}$. Our integral is therefore equal to

$$\int \left(\frac{2}{2x+1} + \frac{3}{x+1}\right) dx = \ln|(2x+1)(x+1)^3| + C.$$

23 Write $\frac{2x^2+7x+4}{x^3+2x^2+2x} = \frac{Ax+B}{x^2+2x+2} + \frac{C}{x}$. Then $2x^2 + 7x + 4 = Ax^2 + Bx + C(x^2 + 2x + 2)$. Letting $x = 0$ gives $C = 2$. Letting $x = 1$ gives $13 = A + B + 10$, so $A + B = 3$. Letting $x = -1$ gives $-1 = A - B + 2$, so $A - B = -3$. Solving this system of linear equations gives $A = 0$ and $B = 3$. Thus our integral is equal to

$$\int \left(\frac{3}{x^2+2x+2} + \frac{2}{x}\right) dx = \int \left(\frac{3}{(x+1)^2+1} + \frac{2}{x}\right) dx = 3\tan^{-1}(x+1) + 2\ln|x| + C.$$

24 Note that $\frac{u^2+1}{u^2-1} = 1 + \frac{2}{u^2-1} = 1 + \frac{1}{u-1} - \frac{1}{u+1}$. Our integral is therefore equal to

$$\int_{-1/2}^{1/2} \left(-\frac{1}{u+1} + \frac{1}{u-1} + 1\right) du = \left(\ln\left|\frac{u-1}{u+1}\right| + u\right)\Big|_{-1/2}^{1/2} = \ln(1/3) + 1/2 - (\ln 3 - 1/2) = 1 - 2\ln 3.$$

25 Write $\frac{3x^3+4x^2+6x}{(x+1)^2(x^2+4)} = \frac{Ax+B}{x^2+4} + \frac{C}{x+1} + \frac{D}{(x+1)^2}$. Then $3x^3 + 4x^2 + 6x = (Ax + B)(x + 1)^2 + C(x + 1)(x^2 + 4) + D(x^2 + 4)$. Letting $x = -1$ gives $D = -1$. Letting $x = 0$ gives $0 = B + 4C - 4$, so $B + 4C = 4$. Letting $x = 1$ gives $13 = 4A + 4B + 10C - 5$, so $9 = 2A + 2B + 5C$. Letting $x = 2$ gives $52 = 18A + 9B + 24C - 8$, so $60 = 18A + 9B + 24C$, so $20 = 6A + 3B + 8C$. Solving the system of linear equations gives $A = 2$, $B = 0$, and $C = 1$. Our integral is thus equal to

$$\int \left(\frac{2x}{x^2+4} + \frac{1}{x+1} - \frac{1}{(x+1)^2}\right) dx = \ln\left|(x^2+4)(x+1)\right| + \frac{1}{x+1} + C.$$

26 Using the table of integrals entry 84, we find that

$$\int x(ax+b)^n\,dx = \frac{(ax+b)^{n+1}(a(n+1)x - b)}{a^2(n+1)(n+2)} + C.$$

Therefore

$$\int x(2x+3)^5\,dx = \frac{(2x+3)^6(12x-3)}{168} + C.$$

27 Using the table of integrals entry 77, we find that

$$\int \frac{dx}{x\sqrt{ax-b}} = \frac{2}{\sqrt{b}}\tan^{-1}\left(\sqrt{\frac{ax-b}{b}}\right) + C.$$

Therefore

$$\int \frac{dx}{x\sqrt{4x-6}} = \frac{\sqrt{6}}{3}\tan^{-1}\left(\sqrt{\frac{2x-3}{3}}\right) + C.$$

28 Using the table of integrals entry 34, we find that

$$\int_0^{\pi/2} \frac{d\theta}{1 + \sin 2\theta} = \left(\frac{-1}{2} \tan\left(\pi/4 - \theta \right) \right) \Big|_0^{\pi/2} = \frac{-1}{2}(\tan(-\pi/4) - \tan(\pi/4)) = \frac{1}{2}(1 - (-1)) = 1.$$

29 Using the table of integrals reduction formula (number 45) twice, we have

$$\int \sec^5 x \, dx = \frac{\sec^3 x \tan x}{4} + \frac{3}{4} \int \sec^3 x \, dx$$

$$= \frac{\sec^3 x \tan x}{4} + \frac{3}{4} \left(\frac{\sec x \tan x}{2} + \frac{1}{2} \int \sec x \, dx \right)$$

$$= \frac{\sec^3 x \tan x}{4} + \frac{3}{4} \left(\frac{\sec x \tan x}{2} + \frac{1}{2} (\ln|\sec x + \tan x|) \right) + C$$

$$= \frac{\sec^3 x \tan x}{4} + \frac{3 \sec x \tan x}{8} + \frac{3}{8} (\ln|\sec x + \tan x| + C.$$

30 Using a CAS, we find that

$$\int_1^{\sqrt{e}} x^3 (\ln x)^3 \, dx \approx 0.081.$$

31 Using a CAS, we find that

$$\int_{-1}^{1} e^{-2x^2} \, dx \approx 1.196.$$

32

n	T_n	M_n	Abs error in T_n	Abs error in M_n
4	8.74127	−3.96138	8.74127	3.96138
8	2.38995	−1.16842	2.38995	1.16842
16	0.61076	−0.30371	0.61076	.30371
32	0.15353	−0.07666	0.15353	0.07666
64	0.03845	−0.01921	0.083843	0.01921

c. Each time n is doubled, the errors in T_n are reduced approximately by a factor of 4.

d. Each time n is doubled, the errors in M_n are reduced approximately by a factor of 4.

33

a. Using a calculator program for the trapezoid and midpoint rules, we find that $T_6 = 9.125$, $M_6 = 8.937$.

b. Similarly, $T_{12} = 9.031$, $M_{12} = 8.984$.

34 This can be written as

$$\lim_{b \to -\infty} \int_b^{-1} \frac{1}{(x-1)^4} \, dx = \lim_{b \to -\infty} \left(\frac{-1}{3(x-1)^3} \right) \Big|_b^{-1} = \lim_{b \to -\infty} \left(\frac{1}{24} + \frac{1}{3(b-1)^3} \right) = \frac{1}{24}.$$

35 First evaluate

$$\int_0^b x e^{-x} \, dx = -e^{-x}(x+1) \Big|_0^b = 1 - (b+1)e^{-b}.$$

Then

$$\int_0^\infty x e^{-x} \, dx = \lim_{b \to \infty} (1 - (b+1)e^{-b}) = 1.$$

36 First consider $\int_0^{\pi/2} \sec^2 x\, dx$. We have $\int_0^{\pi/2} \sec^2 x\, dx = \lim_{a \to \pi/2^-} \int_0^a \sec^2 x\, dx = \lim_{a \to \pi/2^-} \tan x \Big|_0^a = \lim_{a \to \pi/2^-} \tan a - 0 = \infty$. This integral diverges, and thus $\int_0^{\pi} \sec^2 x\, dx$ diveges.

37 First take $0 < c < 3$ and evaluate

$$\int_0^c \frac{dx}{\sqrt{9 - x^2}} = \sin^{-1}\left(\frac{x}{3}\right) \Big|_0^c = \sin^{-1}\left(\frac{c}{3}\right).$$

Then

$$\int_0^3 \frac{dx}{\sqrt{9 - x^2}} = \lim_{c \to 3^-} \sin^{-1}\left(\frac{c}{3}\right) = \frac{\pi}{2}.$$

38 Note that by long division $\frac{x^2 - 4}{x + 4} = x - 4 + \frac{12}{x + 4}$. The original integral is therefore equal to

$$\int \left(x - 4 + \frac{12}{x + 4} \right) dx = x^2/2 - 4x + 12 \ln|x + 4| + C.$$

39

$$\int \frac{1}{1 + \cos \theta} \cdot \frac{1 - \cos \theta}{1 - \cos \theta}\, d\theta = \int \frac{1 - \cos \theta}{\sin^2 \theta}\, d\theta = \int (\csc^2 \theta - \csc \theta \cot \theta)\, d\theta = -\cot \theta + \csc \theta + C.$$

40 Two applications of integration by parts gives

$$\int x^2 \cos x\, dx = x^2 \sin x - 2 \int x \sin x\, dx = x^2 \sin x - 2 \left(x(-\cos x) + \int \cos x\, dx \right) = (x^2 - 2) \sin x + 2x \cos x + C.$$

41 Two applications of integration by parts gives

$$\int e^x \sin x\, dx = e^x \sin x - \int e^x \cos x\, dx = e^x \sin x - e^x \cos x - \int e^x \sin x\, dx.$$

Thus,

$$2 \int e^x \sin x\, dx = e^x \sin x - e^x \cos x,$$

so

$$\int e^x \sin x\, dx = \frac{1}{2}(e^x \sin x - e^x \cos x) + C.$$

42 Integration by parts gives

$$\int x^2 \ln x\, dx = \frac{x^3}{3} \ln x - \int \frac{x^3}{3} \cdot \frac{1}{x}\, dx = \frac{x^3}{3} \left(\ln x - \frac{1}{3} \right) + C.$$

Thus,

$$\int_1^e x^2 \ln x\, dx = \frac{x^3}{3} \left(\ln x - \frac{1}{3} \right) \Big|_1^e = \frac{e^3}{3} \cdot \frac{2}{3} - \frac{1}{3} \left(-\frac{1}{3} \right) = \frac{2e^3 + 1}{9}.$$

43 Let $u = 4\theta$, Then

$$\int \cos^2 \theta\, d\theta = \frac{1}{4} \int \cos^2 u\, du = \frac{1}{4} \int \frac{1 + \cos 2u}{2}\, du = \frac{u}{8} + \frac{\sin 2u}{16} + C = \frac{\theta}{2} + \frac{\sin 8\theta}{16} + C.$$

44 Let $u = \cos 3x$. Then $du = -3 \sin 3x\, dx$ and

$$\int \sin 3x \cos^6 3x\, dx = -\frac{1}{3} \int u^6\, du = -\frac{u^7}{21} + C = -\frac{\cos^7 3x}{21} + C.$$

45 Let $u = \sec z$. Then $du = \sec z \tan z \, dz$ and

$$\int \sec^5 z \tan z \, dz = \int u^4 \, du = \frac{u^5}{5} + C = \frac{\sec^5 z}{5} + C.$$

46 Using the identity $\cos^2 x = \frac{1 + \cos 2x}{2}$, we obtain

$$\int_0^{\frac{\pi}{2}} \cos^4 x \, dx = \int_0^{\frac{\pi}{2}} \left(\frac{1 + \cos 2x}{2} \right)^2 dx = \frac{1}{4} \int_0^{\frac{\pi}{2}} (1 + 2\cos 2x + \cos^2 2x) \, dx$$

$$= \frac{1}{4} \int_0^{\frac{\pi}{2}} \left(1 + 2\cos 2x + \frac{1 + \cos 4x}{2} \right) dx = \frac{1}{4} \int_0^{\frac{\pi}{2}} \left(\frac{3}{2} + 2\cos 2x + \frac{1}{2} \cos 4x \right) dx$$

$$= \left(\frac{3x}{8} + \frac{1}{4} \sin 2x + \frac{1}{32} \sin 4x \right) \Bigg|_0^{\frac{\pi}{2}} = \frac{3\pi}{16}.$$

47 Let $u = \cos x$ so that $du = -\sin x \, dx$. Then

$$\int_0^{\pi/6} \sin^5 \theta \, d\theta = \int_0^{\pi/6} \sin^4 \theta \cdot \sin \theta \, d\theta = -\int_1^{\sqrt{3}/2} (1 - u^2)^2 \, du = \int_{\sqrt{3}/2}^1 (1 - u^2)^2 \, du$$

$$= \int_{\sqrt{3}/2}^1 (1 - 2u^2 + u^4) \, du = \left(u - \frac{2}{3} u^3 + \frac{1}{5} u^5 \right) \Big|_{\sqrt{3}/2}^1$$

$$= \frac{8}{15} - \frac{49\sqrt{3}}{160} = \frac{256 - 147\sqrt{3}}{480}.$$

48 Use the identity $\tan^2 u = \sec^2 u - 1$ and the substitution $v = \tan u$, we have

$$\int \tan^4 u \, du = \int \tan^2 u \sec^2 u \, du - \int \tan^2 u \, du = \int v^2 \, dv - \int (\sec^2 u - 1) \, du$$

$$= \frac{v^3}{3} - \tan u + u + C = \frac{1}{3} \tan^3 u - \tan u + u + C.$$

49 Let $x = 2\sin\theta$ so that $dx = 2\cos\theta \, d\theta$. Then

$$\int \frac{dx}{\sqrt{4 - x^2}} = \int \frac{2\cos\theta \, d\theta}{2\cos\theta} = \theta + C = \sin^{-1}(x/2) + C.$$

50 Let $x = (5/3)\sec\theta$ so that $dx = (5/3)\sec\theta \tan\theta \, d\theta$. Then

$$\int \frac{dx}{\sqrt{9x^2 - 25}} = \frac{5}{3} \int \frac{\sec\theta \tan\theta \, d\theta}{5\tan\theta} = \frac{1}{3} \int \sec\theta \, d\theta = \frac{1}{3} \ln|\sec\theta + \tan\theta| + C.$$

Now substitute $\sec\theta = (3/5)x$, $\tan\theta = (1/5)\sqrt{9x^2 - 25}$ to obtain

$$\int \frac{dx}{\sqrt{9x^2 - 25}} = \frac{1}{3} \ln(3x + \sqrt{9x^2 - 25}) + C$$

(note that we absorb the constant $-\ln 5$ into C, and we don't need absolute values because we were given $x > 5/3$).

51 Let $y = 3\sin\theta$ so that $dy = 3\cos\theta \, d\theta$. Then

$$\int \frac{dy}{y^2 \sqrt{9 - y^2}} = \int \frac{3\cos\theta \, d\theta}{9\sin^2\theta \cdot 3\cos\theta} = \frac{1}{9} \int \csc^2 \theta \, d\theta = -\frac{1}{9} \cot\theta + C.$$

Now use $\sin\theta = y/3$, $\cos\theta = (1/3)\sqrt{9 - y^2}$ to obtain

$$\int \frac{dy}{y^2 \sqrt{9 - y^2}} = -\frac{1}{9y} \sqrt{9 - y^2} + C.$$

52 Let $x = \sin\theta$ so that $dx = \cos\theta\,d\theta$. Then

$$\int_0^{\sqrt{3}/2} \frac{x^2}{(1-x^2)^{3/2}}\,dx = \int_0^{\pi/3} \frac{\sin^2\theta}{\cos^3\theta}\cos\theta\,d\theta = \int_0^{\pi/3} \tan^2\theta\,d\theta = \int_0^{\pi/3}(\sec^2\theta - 1)\,d\theta$$

$$= (\tan\theta - \theta)\Big|_0^{\pi/3} = \sqrt{3} - \frac{\pi}{3}.$$

53 Let $x = (3/2)\tan\theta$ so that $dx = (3/2)\sec^2\theta\,d\theta$, and note that $(3/2)\tan(\pi/6) = \sqrt{3}/2$. Then

$$\int_0^{\sqrt{3}/2} \frac{4}{9+4x^2}\,dx = \int_0^{\pi/6} \frac{4}{9\sec^2\theta}\cdot\frac{3}{2}\sec^2\theta\,d\theta = \frac{2}{3}\int_0^{\pi/6} d\theta = \frac{\pi}{9}.$$

54 Let $u = \sin\theta$ so that $du = \cos\theta\,d\theta$. Then

$$\int \frac{(1-u^2)^{5/2}}{u^8}\,du = \int \frac{\cos^5\theta}{\sin^8\theta}\cos\theta\,d\theta = \int \cot^6\theta\csc^2\theta\,d\theta.$$

Now make the substitution $v = \cot\theta$ so that $dv = -\csc^2\theta\,d\theta$ to obtain

$$\int \cot^6\theta\csc^2\theta\,d\theta = -\int v^6\,dv = -\frac{v^7}{7} + C,$$

so

$$\int \frac{(1-u^2)^{5/2}}{u^8}\,du = -\frac{1}{7}\left(\frac{\sqrt{1-u^2}}{u}\right)^7 + C.$$

55 Let $u = \cosh x$ so that $du = \sinh x\,dx$. Then

$$\int \frac{\sinh x}{\cosh^2 x}\,dx = \int u^{-2}\,du = \frac{-1}{u} + C = \frac{-1}{\cosh x} + C = -\operatorname{sech} x + C.$$

56 Let $u = x^2$ and $dv = \cosh x\,dx$. Then $du = 2x\,dx$ and $v = \sinh x$. The given integral is equal to $x^2\sinh x - \int 2x\sinh x\,dx$. Now let $u = x$ and $dv = \sinh x\,dx$, so that $du = dx$ and $v = \cosh x$. Then we have

$$x^2\sinh x - 2\left(x\cosh x - \int \cosh x\,dx\right) = x^2\sinh x - 2x\cosh x + 2\sinh x + C = (x^2+2)\sinh x - 2x\cosh x + C.$$

57 Let $u = \sinh x$ so that $du = \cosh x\,dx$. Substituting gives

$$\int_0^{\sqrt{3}} \frac{1}{\sqrt{4-u^2}}\,du = \left(\sin^{-1}(u/2)\right)\Big|_0^{\sqrt{3}} = \frac{\pi}{3}.$$

58 Let $u = \sinh^{-1}(x)$ and $dv = dx$, so that $du = \frac{1}{\sqrt{1+x^2}}\,dx$ and $v = x$. Then

$$\int \sinh^{-1} x\,dx = x\sinh^{-1}(x) - \int \frac{x}{\sqrt{1+x^2}}\,dx = x\sinh^{-1}(x) - \sqrt{1+x^2} + C.$$

59 Using the method of partial fractions, we express $\frac{1}{x^2-2x-15} = \frac{1}{(x-5)(x+3)} = \frac{A}{x-5} + \frac{B}{x+3}$. Clearing denominators gives $1 = A(x+3) + B(x-5)$ and comparing coefficients gives $A + B = 0$, $3A - 5B = 1$ which has solution $A = 1/8$, $B = -1/8$. Hence

$$\int \frac{dx}{x^2-2x-15} = \frac{1}{8}\int\left(\frac{1}{x-5} - \frac{1}{x+3}\right)dx = \frac{1}{8}\ln\left|\frac{x-5}{x+3}\right| + C.$$

60 Using the method of partial fractions, we express $\frac{1}{x^3-2x^2} = \frac{1}{x^2(x-2)} = \frac{A}{x} + \frac{B}{x^2} + \frac{C}{x-2}$. Clearing denominators gives $1 = Ax(x-2) + B(x-2) + Cx^2$ and comparing coefficients gives $A + C = 0$, $-2A + B = 0$ and $-2B = 1$, which has solution $A = -1/4$, $B = -1/2$, $C = 1/4$. Hence

$$\int \frac{dx}{x^2-2x-15} = \frac{1}{4}\int\left(-\frac{1}{x} - \frac{2}{x^2} + \frac{1}{x-2}\right)dx = \frac{1}{2x} + \frac{1}{4}\ln\left|\frac{x-2}{x}\right| + C.$$

61 Using the method of partial fractions, we express $\frac{1}{(y+1)(y^2+1)} = \frac{A}{y+1} + \frac{By+C}{y^2+1}$. Clearing denominators gives $1 = A(y^2+1) + (By+C)(y+1)$ and comparing coefficients gives $A + B = 0$, $B + C = 0$ and $A + C = 1$, which has solution $A = 1/2$, $B = -1/2$, $C = 1/2$. Hence

$$\int_0^1 \frac{dy}{(y+1)(y^2+1)} = \frac{1}{2}\int_0^1 \left(\frac{1}{y+1} + \frac{1-y}{y^2+1}\right) dy = \frac{1}{2}\left(\ln(y+1) + \tan^{-1} y - \frac{1}{2}\ln(y^2+1)\right)\Big|_0^1 = \frac{1}{4}\ln 2 + \frac{\pi}{8}.$$

62 First we consider $\int \frac{6x}{1+x^6}\, dx$. Let $u = x^2$, so that $du = 2x\, dx$. Then we have $3\int \frac{1}{1+u^3}\, du = \int\left(\frac{1}{1+u} + \frac{2-u}{u^2-u+1}\right) du$ where this is obtained through a partial fraction decomposition. The first term evaluates to $\ln|u+1|$ while the second can be written as

$$-\frac{1}{2}\int \frac{2u-4}{u^2-u+1}\, du = -\frac{1}{2}\int\left(\frac{2u-1}{u^2-u+1} - \frac{3}{u^2-u+1}\right) du = -\frac{1}{2}\ln|u^2-u+1| + \frac{3}{2}\int \frac{1}{u^2-u+1}\, du.$$

This last integral can be written as $\frac{3}{2}\int \frac{1}{(u-1/2)^2+3/4}\, du = \frac{3}{\sqrt{3}}\tan^{-1}\left(\frac{2u-1}{\sqrt{3}}\right) + C$. Putting this all together, we have $\int \frac{6x}{1+x^6}\, dx = \ln(x^2+1) - \frac{1}{2}\ln(x^4-x^2+1) + \frac{3}{\sqrt{3}}\tan^{-1}\left(\frac{2x^2-1}{\sqrt{3}}\right) + C$. If we let $G(x) = \ln(x^2+1) - \frac{1}{2}\ln(x^4-x^2+1) + \frac{3}{\sqrt{3}}\tan^{-1}\left(\frac{2x^2-1}{\sqrt{3}}\right)$, then $G(1) = \frac{\sqrt{3}\pi}{6} + \ln 2$, and $\lim_{b\to\infty} G(b) = \frac{\sqrt{3}\pi}{2}$. This limit is computed as follows:

$$\lim_{b\to\infty} G(b) = \lim_{b\to\infty}\left(\ln\left(\frac{b^2+1}{\sqrt{b^4-b^2+1}}\right) + \frac{3}{\sqrt{3}}\tan^{-1}\left(\frac{2b^2-1}{\sqrt{3}}\right)\right) = \ln 1 + \frac{3}{\sqrt{3}}\cdot\frac{\pi}{2} = \frac{\sqrt{3}}{2}.$$

Thus we have $\int_1^\infty \frac{6x}{1+x^6}\, dx = \frac{\sqrt{3}\pi}{3} - \ln 2$.

63 First consider $\int_0^1 \frac{dx}{\sqrt[3]{|x-1|}} = \lim_{a\to 1^-}\int \frac{dx}{\sqrt[3]{1-x}} = \lim_{a\to 1^-} -\frac{3}{2}(1-x)^{2/3}\Big|_0^a = \lim_{a\to 1^-} -\frac{3}{2}\left((1-a)^{2/3} - 1\right) = \frac{3}{2}$.

Now consider $\int_1^2 \frac{dx}{\sqrt[3]{|x-1|}} = \lim_{b\to 1^+}\int_b^2 \frac{dx}{\sqrt[3]{x-1}} = \lim_{b\to 1^+} \frac{3}{2}(x-1)^{2/3}\Big|_b^2 = \lim_{b\to 1^+} \frac{3}{2}\left(1 - (b-1)^{2/3}\right) = \frac{3}{2}$.

Thus, $\int_0^2 \frac{dx}{\sqrt[3]{|x-1|}} = \frac{3}{2} + \frac{3}{2} = 3$.

64 Let $u = x + 1$. Then we have

$$\int_{-1}^1 \frac{dx}{x^2+2x+5} = \int_0^2 \frac{du}{u^2+2^2} = \frac{1}{2}\tan^{-1}\left(\frac{u}{2}\right)\Big|_0^2 = \frac{\pi}{8}.$$

65 Factor $x^2 - x - 2 = (x-2)(x+1)$ and use the method of partial fractions: $\frac{1}{(x-2)(x+1)} = \frac{A}{x-2} + \frac{B}{x+1}$. Clearing denominators gives $1 = A(x+1) + B(x-2)$ and equating coefficients gives $A + B = 0$, $A - 2B = 1$, so $A = 1/3$, $B = -1/3$. Therefore

$$\int \frac{dx}{x^2-x-2} = \frac{1}{3}\int\left(\frac{1}{x-2} - \frac{1}{x+1}\right) dx = \frac{1}{3}\ln\left|\frac{x-2}{x+1}\right| + C.$$

66 As a preliminary step, express $\frac{3x^2+x-3}{x^2-1} = \frac{3(x^2-1+1)+x-3}{x^2-1} = 3 + \frac{x}{x^2-1}$; hence

$$\int \frac{3x^2+x-3}{x^2-1}\, dx = 3x + \int \frac{x}{x^2-1}\, dx = 3x + \frac{1}{2}\ln|x^2-1| + C,$$

where we make the substitution $u = x^2 - 1$ for the final integral above.

67 As a preliminary step, observe that

$$\frac{2x^2 - 4x}{x^2 - 4} = \frac{2x(x-2)}{(x-2)(x+2)} = \frac{2x}{x+2} = \frac{2(x+2-2)}{x+2} = 2 - \frac{4}{x+2}.$$

Hence

$$\int \frac{2x^2 - 4x}{x^2 - 4}\, dx = 2x - 4\ln|x+2| + C = 2(x - 2\ln|x+2|) + C.$$

68 Make the preliminary substitution $u = 2\sqrt{x}$; then $du = dx/\sqrt{x}$ and

$$\int_{1/12}^{1/4} \frac{dx}{\sqrt{x}(1+4x)} = \int_{1/\sqrt{3}}^{1} \frac{du}{1+u^2} = \tan^{-1} u \Big|_{1/\sqrt{3}}^{1} = \frac{\pi}{4} - \frac{\pi}{6} = \frac{\pi}{12}.$$

69 Make the preliminary substitution $x = e^{2t}$, $dx = 2e^{2t}$. Then we have

$$\int \frac{e^{2t}}{(1+e^{4t})^{3/2}}\, dt = \frac{1}{2}\int \frac{dx}{(1+x^2)^{3/2}}.$$

Now let $x = \tan\theta$, $dx = \sec^2\theta\, d\theta$ and

$$\frac{1}{2}\int \frac{dx}{(1+x^2)^{3/2}} = \frac{1}{2}\int \frac{\sec^2\theta}{\sec^3\theta}\, d\theta = \frac{1}{2}\int \cos\theta\, d\theta = \frac{1}{2}\sin\theta + C.$$

Now

$$\sin\theta = \frac{\tan\theta}{\sec\theta} = \frac{x}{\sqrt{1+x^2}} = \frac{e^{2t}}{\sqrt{1+e^{4t}}}.$$

Therefore

$$\int \frac{e^{2t}}{(1+e^{4t})^{3/2}}\, dt = \frac{1}{2}\frac{e^{2t}}{\sqrt{1+e^{4t}}} + C.$$

70

i. $\frac{1}{4-x^2} = \frac{A}{x-2} + \frac{B}{x+2}$. Clearing denominators gives $-1 = A(x+2) + B(x-2)$ so $A+B = 0$, $2(A-B) = -1$ which has solution $A = -1/4$, $B = 1/4$. Hence

$$\int \frac{dx}{4-x^2} = \frac{1}{4}\int \left(\frac{1}{x+2} - \frac{1}{x-2}\right) dx = \frac{1}{4}\ln\left|\frac{x+2}{x-2}\right| + C.$$

ii. We can also evaluate this integral via the trig substitution $x = 2\sin\theta$, $dx = 2\cos\theta\, d\theta$:

$$\int \frac{dx}{4-x^2} = \int \frac{2\cos\theta}{4\cos^2\theta}\, d\theta = \frac{1}{2}\int \sec\theta\, d\theta = \frac{1}{2}\ln|\sec\theta + \tan\theta| + C.$$

Observe that

$$\sin\theta = \frac{x}{2}, \quad \cos\theta = \sqrt{1 - \left(\frac{x}{2}\right)^2} = \frac{\sqrt{4-x^2}}{2}$$

so

$$\frac{1}{2}\ln|\sec\theta + \tan\theta| = \frac{1}{2}\ln\left|\frac{2}{\sqrt{4-x^2}} + \frac{x}{\sqrt{4-x^2}}\right| = \frac{1}{4}\ln\left|\frac{(x+2)^2}{4-x^2}\right| = \frac{1}{4}\ln\left|\frac{x+2}{x-2}\right|,$$

and we get the same result as from the first method.

iii. Assume $|x| < 2$. Then the theorem gives that the integral is equal to

$$\frac{1}{2}\tanh^{-1}(x/2) + C = \frac{1}{4}\ln\left(\frac{1 + (x/2)}{1 - (x/2)}\right) + C = \frac{1}{4}\ln\left(\frac{2+x}{2-x}\right) + C.$$

Now assume $|x| > 2$. Then the theorem gives that the integral is equal to

$$\frac{1}{2}\coth^{-1}(x/2) + C = \frac{1}{2}\tanh^{-1}(2/x) + C = \frac{1}{4}\ln\left(\frac{1 + (2/x)}{1 - (2/x)}\right) + C = \frac{1}{4}\ln\left(\frac{x+2}{x-2}\right) + C.$$

Combining these cases, we see that the integral is equal to $\frac{1}{4}\ln\left|\frac{x+2}{x-2}\right| + C$, the same result as the previous parts of this problem.

71 The volume is

$$V = \pi\int_1^e (\ln x)^2\, dx = \pi x((\ln x)^2 - 2\ln x + 2)\Big|_1^e = \pi(e - 2).$$

72 The volume is

$$V = 2\pi\int_1^e x\ln x\, dx = \frac{\pi}{2}x^2(2\ln x - 1)\Big|_1^e = \frac{\pi}{2}\left(e^2 + 1\right).$$

73 The volume is

$$V = 2\pi\int_1^e (x-1)\ln x\, dx = \frac{\pi}{2}x\left(2(x-2)\ln x - x + 4\right)\Big|_1^e = \frac{\pi}{2}\left(e^2 - 3\right).$$

74 The volume is

$$V = \pi\int_1^e \left(1 - (1 - \ln x)^2\right)dx = \pi\int_1^e \left(2\ln x - \ln^2 x\right)dx = \pi\left(-4x + 4x\ln x - x\ln^2 x\right)\Big|_1^e = \pi(4 - e).$$

75 The volume generated by revolving around the x-axis is

$$V_x = \pi\int_0^\pi \sin^2 x\, dx = \pi\left(\frac{x}{2} - \frac{\sin 2x}{4}\right)\Big|_0^\pi = \frac{\pi^2}{2},$$

and the volume generated by revolving around the y-axis is

$$V_y = 2\pi\int_0^\pi x\sin x\, dx = 2\pi(\sin x - x\cos x)\Big|_0^\pi = 2\pi^2,$$

so the greater volume is obtained by revolving around the y-axis.

76 The area is given by the improper integral

$$\int_0^\infty ae^{-ax}\, dx = \lim_{b\to\infty}\int_0^b ae^{-ax}\, dx = \lim_{b\to\infty}\left(-e^{-ax}\Big|_0^b\right) = \lim_{b\to\infty}(1 - e^{-ab}) = 1$$

as long as $a > 0$.

77

    a. Observe that

$$\int_{1/2}^b \ln x\, dx = (x\ln x - x)\Big|_{1/2}^b \approx b\ln b - b + 0.847;$$

    solve $b\ln b - b + 0.847 = 0$ numerically to obtain $b \approx 1.603$.

    b. Similarly, we have

$$\int_{1/3}^b \ln x\, dx = (x\ln x - x)\Big|_{1/3}^b \approx b\ln b - b + 0.700;$$

    solve $b\ln b - b + 0.700 = 0$ numerically to obtain $b \approx 1.870$.

c. In general, the pair (a, b) must satisfy the equation

$$\int_a^b \ln x \, dx = (b \ln b - b) - (a \ln a - a) = 0,$$

which gives $b \ln b - b = a \ln a - a$.

d. As a increases there is less negative area to the right of $x = 1$, so $b = g(a)$ is a decreasing function of a.

78 The arc length is given by the integral $\int_1^{e^2} \sqrt{1 + \frac{1}{x^2}} \, dx = \int_1^{e^2} \frac{\sqrt{1+x^2}}{x} \, dx$, which can be evaluated by the trigonometric substitution $x = \tan \theta$ or using a CAS. We obtain

$$\int_1^{e^2} \frac{\sqrt{1+x^2}}{x} \, dx = \left(\sqrt{x^2 + 1} - \ln \left(2 \left(\sqrt{x^2 + 1} + 1 \right) \right) + \ln x \right) \Big|_1^{e^2} \approx 6.789.$$

79 The average velocity is

$$\bar{v} = \frac{1}{\pi} \int_0^\pi 10 \sin 3t \, dt = -\frac{10}{3\pi} \cos 3t \Big|_0^\pi = \frac{20}{3\pi}.$$

80

a. The distance traveled by car A after 2 hrs is

$$\int_0^2 \frac{40}{t+1} \, dt = 40 \ln(t+1) \Big|_0^2 = 40 \ln 3 \approx 43.944 \text{ mi}$$

and the distance traveled by car B after 2 hrs is

$$\int_0^2 40 e^{-t/2} \, dt = -80 e^{-t/2} \Big|_0^2 = 80(1 - e^{-1}) \approx 50.570 \text{ mi},$$

so car B traveled farther.

b. The distance traveled by car A after 3 hrs is

$$\int_0^3 \frac{40}{t+1} \, dt = 40 \ln(t+1) \Big|_0^3 = 40 \ln 4 \approx 55.452 \text{ mi}$$

and the distance traveled by car B after 2 hrs is

$$\int_0^3 40 e^{-t/2} \, dt = -80 e^{-t/2} \Big|_0^3 = 80(1 - e^{-3/2}) \approx 62.150 \text{ mi},$$

so car B traveled farther.

c. The distance traveled by car A after t hrs is

$$\int_0^t \frac{40}{s+1} \, ds = 40 \ln(s+1) \Big|_0^t = 40 \ln(t+1)$$

and the distance traveled by car B after t hrs is

$$\int_0^t 40 e^{-s/2} \, ds = -80 e^{-s/2} \Big|_0^t = 80(1 - e^{-t/2}).$$

The distance traveled by car A increases without bound, whereas the distance traveled by car B approaches 80 mi as $t \to \infty$.

81 The number of cars is given by the integral

$$\int_0^4 800te^{-t/2}\,dt = -1600(t+2)e^{-t/2}\Big|_0^4 = 3200(1-3e^{-2}) \approx 1901.$$

82   Observe that both $g(x)$ and $h(x)$ lie between the functions $\pm 1/x^2$, which have finite area from 1 to ∞. Therefore the improper integrals of both $g(x)$ and $h(x)$ from 1 to ∞ are finite.

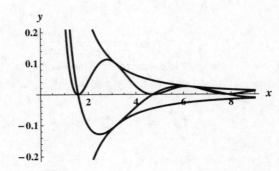

83

a. Using integration by parts, we find that

$$I(p) = \int_1^e \frac{\ln x}{x^p}\,dx = -\frac{x^{1-p}}{(p-1)^2}\left((p-1)\ln x + 1\right)\Big|_1^e = \frac{1}{(p-1)^2}(1 - pe^{1-p})$$

for $p \neq 1$, and using the substitution $u = \ln x$ gives

$$I(1) = \int_1^e \frac{\ln x}{x}\,dx = \frac{(\ln x)^2}{2}\Big|_1^e = \frac{1}{2}.$$

b. We have

$$\lim_{p\to\infty} I(p) = \lim_{p\to\infty}\frac{1}{(p-1)^2}(1 - pe^{1-p}) = \lim_{p\to\infty}\left(\frac{1}{(p-1)^2} - \frac{pe}{(p-1)^2}e^{-p}\right) = 0,$$

and

$$\lim_{p\to-\infty} I(p) = \lim_{p\to-\infty}\left(\frac{1}{(p-1)^2} - \frac{pe}{(p-1)^2}e^{-p}\right) = \infty,$$

since e^{-p} grows much faster than $(p-1)^2/p$ as $p \to -\infty$.

c. By inspection we see that $I(0) = 1$.

84 Note that

$$y' = \frac{1}{2}\sqrt{3-x^2} + \frac{x}{2}\frac{-2x}{2\sqrt{3-x^2}} + \frac{3}{2\sqrt{3}}\frac{1}{\sqrt{1-x^2/3}} = \frac{(6-2x^2)-2x^2+6}{4\sqrt{3-x^2}} = \frac{3-x^2}{\sqrt{3-x^2}} = \sqrt{3-x^2}.$$

$$L = \int_0^1 \sqrt{1+3-x^2}\,dx = \int_0^1 \sqrt{4-x^2}\,dx.$$

Using the table of integrals entry 51, we have

$$L = \left((x/2)\sqrt{4-x^2} + 2\sin^{-1}(x/2)\right)\Big|_0^1 = \frac{\sqrt{3}}{2} + \frac{\pi}{3}.$$

85 Use a calculator program for, say, Simpson's rule with $n = 100$, but replace the limits with 0.00000001 and 0.99999999 to avoid errors coming from trying to evaluate the function at $x = 0$ or $x = 1$; we obtain

$$\int_0^1 \frac{x^2-x}{\ln x}\,dx \approx 0.4054651.$$

86 Numerically approximate the integral to obtain

$$\int_0^{1/2} \frac{\ln(1 + 2x)}{x} \, dx \approx 0.8224;$$

therefore $n = \pi^2/0.8224 = 12$. (When approximating the integral, replace the lower limit 0 with a small positive number like 0.00001 to avoid an error from evaluating the integrand at $x = 0$.)

87 Numerically approximate the integral to obtain

$$\int_0^1 \frac{\sin^{-1} x}{x} \, dx \approx 1.0889;$$

therefore $n = \pi \ln 2/1.0889 = 2$. (When approximating the integral, replace the lower limit 0 with a small positive number like 0.00001 to avoid an error from evaluating the integrand at $x = 0$.)

88

a. Following the hint, write

$$I(a) = \int_0^1 \frac{dx}{(1 + x^a)(1 + x^2)} + \int_1^\infty \frac{dx}{(1 + x^a)(1 + x^2)}$$

and make the substitution $u = 1/x$ in the second integral to obtain

$$I(a) = \int_0^1 \frac{dx}{(1 + x^a)(1 + x^2)} - \int_1^0 \frac{du}{(1 + u^{-a})(1 + u^{-2})u^2}$$

$$= \int_0^1 \frac{dx}{(1 + x^a)(1 + x^2)} + \int_0^1 \frac{u^a \, du}{(1 + u^a)(1 + u^2)}$$

$$= \int_0^1 \frac{1 + x^a}{(1 + x^a)(1 + x^2)} \, dx = \int_0^1 \frac{dx}{1 + x^2} = \tan^{-1} x = \frac{\pi}{4}.$$

b. Let

$$I = \int_0^{\pi/2} \frac{f(\cos x)}{f(\cos x) + f(\sin x)} \, dx$$

and make the substitution $u = \pi/2 - x$ to obtain

$$I = -\int_{\pi/2}^0 \frac{f(\sin u)}{f(\sin u) + f(\cos u)} \, du = \int_0^{\pi/2} \frac{f(\sin u)}{f(\sin u) + f(\cos u)} \, du.$$

Therefore

$$2I = \int_0^{\pi/2} \frac{f(\cos x)}{f(\cos x) + f(\sin x)} \, dx + \int_0^{\pi/2} \frac{f(\sin x)}{f(\cos x) + f(\sin x)} \, dx = \int_0^{\pi/2} dx = \frac{\pi}{2},$$

so $I = \pi/4$.

89

a. Using integration by parts or a CAS, we find that the volume is $V_1(a) = \pi \int_1^a (\ln x)^2 \, dx = \pi x ((\ln x)^2 - 2 \ln x + 2) \Big|_1^a = \pi[(a \ln^2 a - 2a \ln a + 2(a - 1)].$

b. Using integration by parts or a CAS, we find that the volume is $V_2(a) = 2\pi \int_1^a x \ln x \, dx = \frac{\pi}{2} x^2 (2 \ln x - 1) \Big|_1^a = \frac{\pi}{2}(2a^2 \ln a - a^2 + 1).$

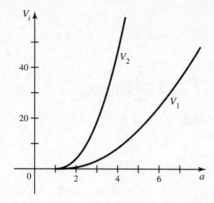

c.   As shown by the graph, $V_2(a) > V_1(a)$ for all $a > 1$.

90

a.   We have $V_1 = \pi \int_1^\infty x^{-2p}\, dx = \frac{\pi}{2p-1}$ for $p > \frac{1}{2}$, and $V_1 = \infty$ for $p \le 1/2$ (see Example 2 in Section 7.4 for the evaluation of this improper integral.)   Similarly $V_2 = 2\pi \int_1^\infty x^{1-p}\, dx = \frac{2\pi}{p-2}$ for $p > 2$, and $V_2 = \infty$ for $p \le 2$. Observe that $V_1 = \frac{2\pi}{4p-2} < \frac{2\pi}{p-2} = V_2$ for all $p > 2$. Therefore $V_1 = V_2$ only when both are infinite.

b.   We will use the fact that $\int_0^1 x^a\, dx = \frac{1}{a+1}$ for $a > -1$ and is infinite otherwise.   We have $V_1 = \pi \int_0^1 x^{-2p}\, dx = \frac{\pi}{1-2p}$ for $p < \frac{1}{2}$, and $V_1 = \infty$ for $p \ge 1/2$. Similarly $V_2 = 2\pi \int_0^1 x^{1-p}\, dx = \frac{2\pi}{2-p}$ for $p < 2$, and $V_2 = \infty$ for $p \ge 2$. As above, $V_1 = V_2$ only when both are infinite.

91 We have

$$V_1 = \pi \int_0^b e^{-2ax}\, dx = -\frac{\pi}{2a} e^{-2ax}\Big|_0^b = \frac{\pi}{2a}\left(1 - e^{-2ab}\right),$$

and

$$V_2 = \pi \int_b^\infty e^{-2ax}\, dx = \lim_{c\to\infty}\left(-\frac{\pi}{2a} e^{-2ax}\Big|_b^c\right) = \frac{\pi}{2a} e^{-2ab}.$$

Equating and solving gives $e^{-2ab} = 1/2$, which is equivalent to $ab = (1/2)\ln 2$.

92 This equation is separable.   We can write $dy = -3y\, dt$, or $\frac{1}{y} dy = -3\, dt$. Then $\int \frac{1}{y}\, dy = \int(-3)\, dt$, so $\ln|y| = -3t + C$ and $y = Ae^{-3t}$. Because $y(0) = 6$ we have $A = 6$, so $y = 6e^{-3t}$.

93 This first-order linear equation has general solution $y = Ce^{2t} - 2$; the initial condition gives $C - 2 = 8$, so $C = 10$ and hence $y = 10e^{2t} - 2$.

94 This equation is separable.   We have $\int \frac{\ln y}{y}\, dy = \int 2t\, dt$, so $\frac{1}{2}(\ln y)^2 = t^2 + C$. The initial condition gives $1/2 = 4 + C$, so $C = -7/2$ and solving for y gives $y = e^{\left(\sqrt{2t^2 - 7}\right)}$.

95 This equation is separable.   We have $\int 2y\, dy = \int\left(1 + \frac{1}{t}\right) dt$, so $y^2 = t + \ln t + C$. The initial condition gives $16 = 1 + C$, so $C = 15$ and solving for y gives $y = \sqrt{t + \ln t + 15}$.

96 This equation is separable.   We have $\int \frac{dy}{\sqrt{y}} = \int \sin t\, dt$, so $2\sqrt{y} = -\cos t + C$. The initial condition gives $4 = -1 + C$, so $C = 5$ and solving for y gives $y = (5 - \cos t)^2/4$.

97 This equation is separable.   We have $\int \cos y\, dy = \int \frac{dt}{t^2}$, so $\sin y = -\frac{1}{t} + C$. The initial condition gives $0 = -1 + C$, so $C = 1$ and solving for y gives $y = \sin^{-1}\left(1 - \frac{1}{t}\right)$. Therefore $\lim_{t\to\infty} y(t) = \lim_{t\to\infty} \sin^{-1}\left(1 - \frac{1}{t}\right) = \sin^{-1} 1 = \frac{\pi}{2}$.

98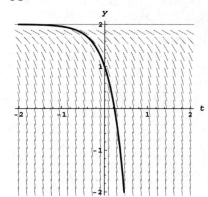

99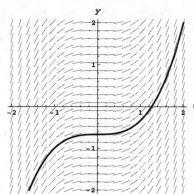

100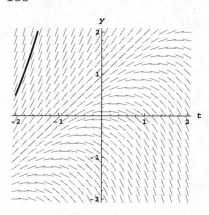

101 This equation is separable. We have

$$\int dt = -\frac{1}{10} \int \left(1 + \frac{5}{s}\right) ds \implies t = -\frac{s + 5\ln s}{10} + C.$$

The initial condition gives $s(0) = 50$ gives $C = (50 + 5\ln 50)/10$, so the solution is given implicitly by

$$t = \frac{-s - 5\ln s + 50 + 5\ln 50}{10}.$$

As $t \to \infty$ we must have $s + 5\ln s \to -\infty$, which implies that $\lim_{t\to\infty} s(t) = 0$.

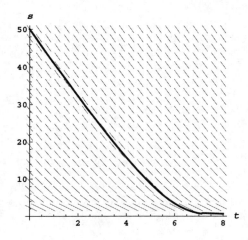

102 This first-order linear equation has general solution

$$B(t) = Ce^{0.005t} - \frac{100}{0.005} = Ce^{0.005t} - 20,000.$$

The initial condition gives $C - 20,000 = 100$, so $C = 20,100$ and hence

$$B(t) = 20,100e^{0.005t} - 20,000.$$

Solving $B(t) = 7500$ gives

$$e^{0.005t} = \frac{27,500}{20,100} \implies t = \frac{1}{0.005} \ln\left(\frac{27,500}{20,100}\right) \approx 62.69,$$

or about 63 months.

Chapter 8

Sequences and Infinite Series

8.1 An Overview

8.1.1 A *sequence* is an ordered list of numbers $a_1, a_2, a_3, \ldots$, often written $\{a_1, a_2, \ldots\}$ or $\{a_n\}$. For example, the natural numbers $\{1, 2, 3, \ldots\}$ are a sequence where $a_n = n$ for every n.

8.1.2 $a_1 = \frac{1}{1} = 1$; $a_2 = \frac{1}{2}$; $a_3 = \frac{1}{3}$; $a_4 = \frac{1}{4}$; $a_5 = \frac{1}{5}$.

8.1.3 $a_1 = 1$ (given); $a_2 = 1 \cdot a_1 = 1$; $a_3 = 2 \cdot a_2 = 2$; $a_4 = 3 \cdot a_3 = 6$; $a_5 = 4 \cdot a_4 = 24$.

8.1.4 A *finite sum* is the sum of a finite number of items, for example the sum of a finite number of terms of a sequence.

8.1.5 An *infinite series* is an infinite sum of numbers. Thus if $\{a_n\}$ is a sequence, then $a_1 + a_2 + \cdots = \sum_{k=1}^{\infty} a_k$ is an infinite series. For example, if $a_k = \frac{1}{k}$, then $\sum_{k=1}^{\infty} a_k = \sum_{k=1}^{\infty} \frac{1}{k}$ is an infinite series.

8.1.6 $S_1 = \sum_{k=1}^{1} k = 1$; $S_2 = \sum_{k=1}^{2} k = 1 + 2 = 3$; $S_3 = \sum_{k=1}^{3} k = 1 + 2 + 3 = 6$; $S_4 = \sum_{k=1}^{4} k = 1 + 2 + 3 + 4 = 10$.

8.1.7 $S_1 = \sum_{k=1}^{1} k^2 = 1$; $S_2 = \sum_{k=1}^{2} k^2 = 1 + 4 = 5$; $S_3 = \sum_{k=1}^{3} k^2 = 1 + 4 + 9 = 14$; $S_4 = \sum_{k=1}^{4} k^2 = 1 + 4 + 9 + 16 = 30$.

8.1.8 $S_1 = \sum_{k=1}^{1} \frac{1}{k} = \frac{1}{1} = 1$; $S_2 = \sum_{k=1}^{2} \frac{1}{k} = \frac{1}{1} + \frac{1}{2} = \frac{3}{2}$; $S_3 = \sum_{k=1}^{3} \frac{1}{k} = \frac{1}{1} + \frac{1}{2} + \frac{1}{3} = \frac{11}{6}$; $S_4 = \sum_{k=1}^{4} \frac{1}{k} = \frac{1}{1} + \frac{1}{2} + \frac{1}{3} + \frac{1}{4} = \frac{25}{12}$.

8.1.9 $a_1 = \dfrac{1}{10}$; $a_2 = \dfrac{1}{100}$; $a_3 = \dfrac{1}{1000}$; $a_4 = \dfrac{1}{10000}$.

8.1.10 $a_1 = 3(1) + 1 = 4$. $a_2 = 3(2) + 1 = 7$, $a_3 = 3(3) + 1 = 10$, $a_4 = 3(4) + 1 = 13$.

8.1.11 $a_1 = \frac{-1}{2}$, $a_2 = \frac{1}{2^2} = \frac{1}{4}$. $a_3 = \frac{-2}{2^3} = \frac{-1}{8}$, $a_4 = \frac{1}{2^4} = \frac{1}{16}$.

8.1.12 $a_1 = 2 - 1 = 1$. $a_2 = 2 + 1 = 3$, $a_3 = 2 - 1 = 1$, $a_4 = 2 + 1 = 3$.

8.1.13 $a_1 = \frac{2^2}{2+1} = \frac{4}{3}$. $a_2 = \frac{2^3}{2^2+1} = \frac{8}{5}$. $a_3 = \frac{2^4}{2^3+1} = \frac{16}{9}$. $a_4 = \frac{2^5}{2^4+1} = \frac{32}{17}$.

8.1.14 $a_1 = 1 + \frac{1}{1} = 2$; $a_2 = 2 + \frac{1}{2} = \frac{5}{2}$; $a_3 = 3 + \frac{1}{3} = \frac{10}{3}$; $a_4 = 4 + \frac{1}{4} = \frac{17}{4}$.

8.1.15 $a_1 = 1 + \sin(\pi/2) = 2$; $a_2 = 1 + \sin(2\pi/2) = 1 + \sin \pi = 1$; $a_3 = 1 + \sin(3\pi/2) = 0$; $a_4 = 1 + \sin(4\pi/2) = 1 + \sin 2\pi = 1$.

8.1.16 $a_1 = 2 \cdot 1^2 - 3 \cdot 1 + 1 = 0$; $a_2 = 2 \cdot 2^2 - 3 \cdot 2 + 1 = 3$; $a_3 = 2 \cdot 3^2 - 3 \cdot 3 + 1 = 10$; $a_4 = 2 \cdot 4^2 - 3 \cdot 4 + 1 = 21$.

8.1.17 $a_1 = 2$, $a_2 = 2 \cdot 2 = 4$, $a_3 = 2(4) = 8$, $a_4 = 2 \cdot 8 = 16$.

8.1.18 $a_1 = 32$, $a_2 = 32/2 = 16$, $a_3 = 16/2 = 8$, $a_4 = 8/2 = 4$.

8.1.19 $a_1 = 10$ (given); $a_2 = 3 \cdot a_1 - 12 = 30 - 12 = 18$; $a_3 = 3 \cdot a_2 - 12 = 54 - 12 = 42$; $a_4 = 3 \cdot a_3 - 12 = 126 - 12 = 114$.

8.1.20 $a_1 = 1$ (given); $a_2 = a_1^2 - 1 = 0$; $a_3 = a_2^2 - 1 = -1$; $a_4 = a_3^2 - 1 = 0$.

8.1.21 $a_1 = 0$ (given); $a_2 = 3 \cdot a_1^2 + 1 + 1 = 2$; $a_3 = 3 \cdot a_2^2 + 2 + 1 = 15$; $a_4 = 3 \cdot a_3^2 + 3 + 1 = 679$.

8.1.22 $a_0 = 1$ (given); $a_1 = 1$ (given); $a_2 = a_1 + a_0 = 2$; $a_3 = a_2 + a_1 = 3$; $a_4 = a_3 + a_2 = 5$.

8.1.23

   a. $\frac{1}{32}$, $\frac{1}{64}$.

   b. $a_1 = 1$; $a_{n+1} = \frac{a_n}{2}$.

   c. $a_n = \frac{1}{2^{n-1}}$.

8.1.24

   a. -6, 7.

   b. $a_1 = 1$; $a_{n+1} = (-1)^n(|a_n| + 1)$.

   c. $a_n = (-1)^{n+1}n$.

8.1.25

   a. -5, 5.

   b. $a_1 = -5$, $a_{n+1} = -a_n$.

   c. $a_n = (-1)^n \cdot 5$.

8.1.26

   a. 14, 17.

   b. $a_1 = 2$; $a_{n+1} = a_n + 3$.

   c. $a_n = -1 + 3n$.

8.1.27

   a. 32, 64.

   b. $a_1 = 1$; $a_{n+1} = 2a_n$.

   c. $a_n = 2^{n-1}$.

8.1.28

   a. 36, 49.

   b. $a_1 = 1$; $a_{n+1} = (\sqrt{a_n} + 1)^2$.

   c. $a_n = n^2$.

8.1.29

   a. 243, 729.

   b. $a_1 = 1$; $a_{n+1} = 3a_n$.

   c. $a_n = 3^{n-1}$.

8.1.30

   a. 2, 1.

   b. $a_1 = 64$; $a_{n+1} = \frac{a_n}{2}$.

   c. $a_n = \frac{64}{2^{n-1}} = 2^{7-n}$.

8.1.31 $a_1 = 9$, $a_2 = 99$, $a_3 = 999$, $a_4 = 9999$. This sequence diverges, because the terms get larger without bound.

8.1.32 $a_1 = 2$, $a_2 = 17$, $a_3 = 82$, $a_4 = 257$. This sequence diverges, because the terms get larger without bound.

8.1.33 $a_1 = \frac{1}{10}$, $a_2 = \frac{1}{100}$, $a_3 = \frac{1}{1000}$, $a_4 = \frac{1}{10,000}$. This sequence converges to zero.

8.1.34 $a_1 = \frac{1}{10}$, $a_2 = \frac{1}{100}$, $a_3 = \frac{1}{1000}$, $a_4 = \frac{1}{10,000}$. This sequence converges to zero.

8.1.35 $a_1 = -\frac{1}{2}$, $a_2 = \frac{1}{4}$, $a_3 = -\frac{1}{8}$, $a_4 = \frac{1}{16}$. This sequence converges to 0 because each term is smaller in absolute value than the preceding term and they get arbitrarily close to zero.

8.1.36 $a_1 = 0.9$, $a_2 = 0.99$, $a_3 = 0.999$, $a_4 = .9999$. This sequence converges to 1.

8.1.37 $a_1 = 1 + 1 = 2$, $a_2 = 1 + 1 = 2$, $a_3 = 2$, $a_4 = 2$. This constant sequence converges to 2.

8.1.38 $a_1 = 9 + \frac{9}{10} = 9.9$, $a_2 = 9 + \frac{9.9}{10} = 9.99$, $a_3 = 9 + \frac{9.99}{10} = 9.999$, $a_4 = 9 + \frac{9.999}{10} = 9.9999$. This sequence converges to 10.

8.1.39 $a_1 = \frac{50}{11} + 50 \approx 54.545$, $a_2 = \frac{54.545}{11} + 50 \approx 54.959$, $a_3 = \frac{54.959}{11} + 50 \approx 54.996$, $a_4 = \frac{54.996}{11} + 50 \approx 55.000$. This sequence converges to 55.

8.1.40 $a_1 = 0 - 1 = -1$. $a_2 = -10 - 1 = -11$, $a_3 = -110 - 1 = -111$, $a_4 = -1110 - 1 = -1111$. This sequence diverges.

8.1.41

n	1	2	3	4	4	6	7	8	9	10
a_n	0.4636	0.2450	0.1244	0.0624	0.0312	0.0156	0.0078	0.0039	0.0020	0.0010

This sequence appears to converge to 0.

8.1.42

n	1	2	3	4	5	6	7	8	9	10
a_n	3.1396	3.1406	3.1409	3.1411	3.1412	3.1413	3.1413	3.1413	3.1414	3.1414

This sequence appears to converge to π.

8.1.43

n	1	2	3	4	5	6	7	8	9	10
a_n	0	2	6	12	20	30	42	56	72	90

This sequence appears to diverge.

8.1.44

n	1	2	3	4	5	6	7	8	9	10
a_n	9.9	9.95	9.9667	9.975	9.98	9.9833	9.9857	9.9875	9.9889	9.99

This sequence appears to converge to 10.

8.1.45

n	1	2	3	4	5	6	7	8	9	10
a_n	0.83333	0.96154	0.99206	0.99840	0.99968	0.99994	0.99999	1.0000	1.0000	1.0000

This sequence appears to converge to 1.

8.1.46

n	1	2	3	4	5	6	7	8	9	10	11
a_n	0.9589	0.9896	0.9974	0.9993	0.9998	1.000	1.000	1.0000	1.000	1.000	1.000

This sequence converges to 1.

8.1.47

a. 2.5, 2.25, 2.125, 2.0625.

b. The limit is 2.

8.1.48

a. 1.33333, 1.125, 1.06667, 1.04167.

b. The limit is 1.

8.1.49

n	0	1	2	3	4	5	6	7	8	9	10
a_n	3	3.500	3.750	3.875	3.938	3.969	3.984	3.992	3.996	3.998	3.999

This sequence converges to 4.

8.1.50

n	0	1	2	3	4	5	6	7	8	9
a_n	1	-2.75	-3.688	-3.922	-3.981	-3.995	-3.999	-4.000	-4.000	-4.000

This sequence converges to -4.

8.1.51

n	0	1	2	3	4	5	6	7	8	9	10
a_n	0	1	3	7	15	31	63	127	255	511	1023

This sequence diverges.

8.1.52

n	0	1	2	3	4	5	6	7	8	9	10
a_n	10	4	3.4	3.34	3.334	3.333	3.333	3.333	3.333	3.333	3.333

This sequence converges to $\frac{10}{3}$.

8.1.53

n	0	1	2	3	4	5	6	7	8	9
a_n	1000	18.811	5.1686	4.1367	4.0169	4.0021	4.0003	4.0000	4.0000	4.0000

This sequence converges to 4.

8.1.54

n	0	1	2	3	4	5	6	7	8	9	10
a_n	1	1.4212	1.5538	1.5981	1.6119	1.6161	1.6174	1.6179	1.6180	1.6180	1.6180

This sequence converges to $\frac{1+\sqrt{5}}{2} \approx 1.618$.

8.1.55

a. 20, 10, 5, 2.5.

b. $h_n = 20(0.5)^n$.

8.1.56

a. 10, 9, 8.1, 7.29.

b. $h_n = 10(0.9)^n$.

8.1.57

a. 30, 7.5, 1.875, 0.46875.

b. $h_n = 30(0.25)^n$.

8.1.58

a. 20, 15, 11.25, 8.438

b. $h_n = 20(0.75)^n$.

8.1.59 $S_1 = 0.3$, $S_2 = 0.33$, $S_3 = 0.333$, $S_4 = 0.3333$. It appears that the infinite series has a value of $0.3333\ldots = \frac{1}{3}$.

8.1.60 $S_1 = 0.6$, $S_2 = 0.66$, $S_3 = 0.666$, $S_4 = 0.6666$. It appears that the infinite series has a value of $0.6666\ldots = \frac{2}{3}$.

8.1.61 $S_1 = 4$, $S_2 = 4.9$, $S_3 = 4.99$, $S_4 = 4.999$. The infinite series has a value of $4.999 \cdots = 5$.

8.1.62 $S_1 = 1$, $S_2 = \frac{3}{2} = 1.5$, $S_3 = \frac{7}{4} = 1.75$, $S_4 = \frac{15}{8} = 1.875$. The infinite series has a value of **2**.

8.1.63

    a. $S_1 = \frac{2}{3}$, $S_2 = \frac{4}{5}$, $S_3 = \frac{6}{7}$, $S_4 = \frac{8}{9}$.

    b. It appears that $S_n = \frac{2n}{2n+1}$.

    c. The series has a value of 1 (the partial sums converge to 1).

8.1.64

    a. $S_1 = \frac{1}{2}$, $S_2 = \frac{3}{4}$, $S_3 = \frac{7}{8}$, $S_4 = \frac{15}{16}$.

    b. $S_n = 1 - \frac{1}{2^n}$.

    c. The partial sums converge to 1, so that is the value of the series.

8.1.65

    a. $S_1 = \frac{1}{3}$, $S_2 = \frac{2}{5}$, $S_3 = \frac{3}{7}$, $S_4 = \frac{4}{9}$.

    b. $S_n = \frac{n}{2n+1}$.

    c. The partial sums converge to $\frac{1}{2}$, which is the value of the series.

8.1.66

    a. $S_1 = \frac{2}{3}$, $S_2 = \frac{8}{9}$, $S_3 = \frac{26}{27}$, $S_4 = \frac{80}{81}$.

    b. $S_n = 1 - \frac{1}{3^n}$.

    c. The partial sums converge to 1, which is the value of the series.

8.1.67

    a. True. For example, $S_2 = 1 + 2 = 3$, and $S_4 = a_1 + a_2 + a_3 + a_4 = 1 + 2 + 3 + 4 = 10$.

    b. False. For example, $\frac{1}{2}, \frac{3}{4}, \frac{7}{8}, \cdots$ where $a_n = 1 - \frac{1}{2^n}$ converges to 1, but each term is greater than the previous one.

    c. True. In order for the partial sums to converge, they must get closer and closer together. In order for this to happen, the difference between successive partial sums, which is just the value of a_n, must approach zero.

8.1.68 The height at the nth bounce is given by the recurrence $h_n = r \cdot h_{n-1}$; an explicit form for this sequence is $h_n = h_0 \cdot r^n$. The distance traveled by the ball between the nth and the $(n+1)^{\text{st}}$ bounce is thus $2h_n = 2h_0 \cdot r^n$, so that $S_{n+1} = \sum_{i=0}^{n} 2h_0 \cdot r^i$.

    a. Here $h_0 = 20$, $r = 0.5$, so $S_1 = 40$, $S_2 = 40 + 40 \cdot 0.5 = 60$, $S_3 = S_2 + 40 \cdot (0.5)^2 = 70$, $S_4 = S_3 + 40 \cdot (0.5)^3 = 75$, $S_5 = S_4 + 40 \cdot (0.5)^4 = 77.5$

    b.

n	1	2	3	4	5	6
a_n	40	60	70	75	77.5	78.75
n	7	8	9	10	11	12
a_n	79.375	79.688	79.844	79.922	79.961	79.980
n	13	14	15	16	17	18
a_n	79.990	79.995	79.998	79.999	79.999	80.000
n	19	20	21	22	23	24
a_n	80.000	80.000	80.000	80.000	80.000	80.000

The sequence converges to 80.

8.1.69   Using the work from the previous problem:

a. Here $h_0 = 20$, $r = 0.75$, so $S_1 = 40$, $S_2 = 40 + 40 \cdot 0.75 = 70$, $S_3 = S_2 + 40 \cdot (0.75)^2 = 92.5$, $S_4 = S_3 + 40 \cdot (0.75)^3 = 109.375$, $S_5 = S_4 + 40 \cdot (0.75)^4 = 122.03125$

b.

n	1	2	3	4	5	6
a_n	40	70	92.5	109.375	122.031	131.523
n	7	8	9	10	11	12
a_n	138.643	143.982	147.986	150.990	153.242	154.932
n	13	14	15	16	17	18
a_n	156.199	157.149	157.862	158.396	158.797	159.098
n	19	20	21	22	23	24
a_n	159.323	159.493	159.619	159.715	159.786	159.839

The sequence converges to 160.

8.1.70

a. $s_1 = -1$, $s_2 = 0$, $s_3 = -1$, $s_4 = 0$.

b. The limit does not exist.

8.1.71

a. 0.9, 0.99, 0.999, .9999.

b. The limit is 1.

8.1.72

a. 1.5, 3.75, 7.125, 12.1875.

b. The limit does not exist.

8.1.73

a. $\frac{1}{3}, \frac{4}{9}, \frac{13}{27}, \frac{40}{81}$.

b. The limit is 1/2.

8.1.74

a. 1, 3, 6, 10.

b. The limit does not exist.

8.1.75

a. -1, 0, -1, 0.

b. The limit does not exist.

8.1.76

a. -1, 1, -2, 2.

b. The limit does not exist.

8.1.77

a. $\frac{3}{10} = 0.3$, $\frac{33}{100} = 0.33$, $\frac{333}{1000} = 0.333$, $\frac{3333}{10000} = 0.3333$.

b. The limit is 1/3.

8.1.78

a. $p_0 = 250$, $p_1 = 250 \cdot 1.03 = 258$, $p_2 = 250 \cdot 1.03^2 = 265$, $p_3 = 250 \cdot 1.03^3 = 273$, $p_4 = 250 \cdot 1.03^4 = 281$.

b. The initial population is 250, so that $p_0 = 250$. Then $p_n = 250 \cdot (1.03)^n$, because the population increases by 3 percent each month.

c. $p_{n+1} = p_n \cdot 1.03$.

d. The population increases without bound.

8.1.79

 a. $M_0 = 20$, $M_1 = 20 \cdot 0.5 = 10$, $M_2 = 20 \cdot 0.5^2 = 5$, $M_3 = 20 \cdot 0.5^3 = 2.5$, $M_4 = 20 \cdot 0.5^4 = 1.25$

 b. $M_n = 20 \cdot 0.5^n$.

 c. The initial mass is $M_0 = 20$. We are given that 50% of the mass is gone after each decade, so that $M_{n+1} = 0.5 \cdot M_n$, $n \geq 0$.

 d. The amount of material goes to 0.

8.1.80

 a. $c_0 = 100$, $c_1 = 103$, $c_2 = 106.09$, $c_3 = 109.27$, $c_4 = 112.55$.

 b. $c_n = 100(1.03)^n$ for $n \geq 0$.

 c. We are given that $c_0 = 100$ (where year 0 is 1984); because it increases by 3% per year, $c_{n+1} = 1.03 \cdot c_n$.

 d. The sequence diverges.

8.1.81

 a. $d_0 = 200$, $d_1 = 200 \cdot .95 = 190$, $d_2 = 200 \cdot .95^2 = 180.5$, $d_3 = 200 \cdot .95^3 = 171.475$, $d_4 = 200 \cdot .95^4 = 162.90125$.

 b. $d_n = 200(0.95)^n$, $n \geq 0$.

 c. We are given $d_0 = 200$; because 5% of the drug is washed out every hour, that means that 95% of the preceding amount is left every hour, so that $d_{n+1} = 0.95 \cdot d_n$.

 d. The sequence converges to 0.

8.1.82

 a. Using the recurrence $a_{n+1} = \frac{1}{2}\left(a_n + \frac{10}{a_n}\right)$, we build a table:

n	0	1	2	3	4	5
a_n	10	5.5	3.659090909	3.196005081	3.162455622	3.162277665

The true value is $\sqrt{10} \approx 3.162277660$, so the sequence converges with an error of less than 0.01 after only 4 iterations, and is within 0.0001 after only 5 iterations.

 b. The recurrence is now $a_{n+1} = \frac{1}{2}\left(a_n + \frac{2}{a_n}\right)$

c	$\sqrt{c}$	0	1	2	3	4	5	6
2	1.414	2	1.5	1.417	1.414	1.414	1.414	1.414
3	1.732	3	2	1.750	1.732	1.732	1.732	1.732
4	2.000	4	2.5	2.050	2.001	2.000	2.000	2.000
5	2.236	5	3	2.333	2.238	2.236	2.236	2.236
6	2.449	6	3.6	2.607	2.454	2.449	2.449	2.449
7	2.646	7	4	2.875	2.655	2.646	2.646	2.646
8	2.828	8	4.5	3.139	2.844	2.828	2.828	2.828
9	3.000	9	5.0	3.400	3.024	3.000	3.000	3.000
10	3.162	10	5.5	3.659	3.196	3.162	3.162	3.162

For $c = 2$ the sequence converges to within 0.01 after two iterations.
For $c = 3, 4, 5, 6$, and 7 the sequence converges to within 0.01 after three iterations.
For $c = 8, 9$, and 10 it requires four iterations.

8.2 Sequences

8.2.1 There are many examples; one is $a_n = \frac{1}{n}$. This sequence is nonincreasing (in fact, it is decreasing) and has a limit of 0.

8.2.2 Again there are many examples; one is $a_n = \ln(n)$. It is increasing, and has no limit.

8.2.3 There are many examples; one is $a_n = \frac{1}{n}$. This sequence is nonincreasing (in fact, it is decreasing), is bounded above by 1 and below by 0, and has a limit of 0.

8.2.4 For example, $a_n = (-1)^n$. For all values of n we have $|a_n| = 1$, so it is bounded. All the odd terms are -1 and all the even terms are 1, so the sequence does not have a limit.

8.2.5 $\{r^n\}$ converges for $-1 < r \leq 1$. It diverges for all other values of r (see Theorem 8.3).

8.2.6 By Theorem 8.1, if we can find a function $f(x)$ such that $f(n) = a_n$ for all positive integers n, then if $\lim_{x \to \infty} f(x)$ exists and is equal to L, we then have $\lim_{n \to \infty} a_n$ exists and is also equal to L. This means that we can apply function-oriented limit methods such as L'Hôpital's rule to determine limits of sequences.

8.2.7 $\{e^{n/100}\}$ grows faster than $\{n^{100}\}$ as $n \to \infty$.

8.2.8 The definition of the limit of a sequence involves only the behavior of the nth term of a sequence as n gets large (see the Definition of Limit of a Sequence). Thus suppose a_n, b_n differ in only finitely many terms, and that M is large enough so that $a_n = b_n$ for $n > M$. Suppose a_n has limit L. Then for $\varepsilon > 0$, if N is such that $|a_n - L| < \varepsilon$ for $n > N$, first increase N if required so that $N > M$ as well. Then we also have $|b_n - L| < \varepsilon$ for $n > N$. Thus a_n and b_n have the same limit. A similar argument applies if a_n has no limit.

8.2.9 Divide numerator and denominator by n^4 to get $\lim_{n \to \infty} \frac{1/n}{1 + \frac{1}{n^4}} = 0$.

8.2.10 Divide numerator and denominator by n^{12} to get $\lim_{n \to \infty} \frac{1}{3 + \frac{4}{n^{12}}} = \frac{1}{3}$.

8.2.11 Divide numerator and denominator by n^3 to get $\lim_{n \to \infty} \frac{3 - n^{-3}}{2 + n^{-3}} = \frac{3}{2}$.

8.2.12 Divide numerator and denominator by e^n to get $\lim_{n \to \infty} \frac{2 + (1/e^n)}{1} = 2$.

8.2.13 Divide numerator and denominator by 3^n to get $\lim_{n \to \infty} \frac{3 + (1/3^{n-1})}{1} = 3$.

8.2.14 Divide numerator by k and denominator by $k = \sqrt{k^2}$ to get $\lim_{k \to \infty} \frac{1}{\sqrt{9 + (1/k^2)}} = \frac{1}{3}$.

8.2.15 $\lim_{n \to \infty} \tan^{-1} n = \frac{\pi}{2}$.

8.2.16 Multiply by $\dfrac{\sqrt{n^2 + 1} + n}{\sqrt{n^2 + 1} + n}$ to obtain

$$\lim_{n \to \infty} \left(\sqrt{n^2 + 1} - n \right) = \lim_{n \to \infty} \frac{\left(\sqrt{n^2 + 1} - n \right)\left(\sqrt{n^2 + 1} + n \right)}{\sqrt{n^2 + 1} + n} = \lim_{n \to \infty} \frac{1}{\sqrt{n^2 + 1} + n} = 0.$$

8.2.17 Because $\lim_{n \to \infty} \tan^{-1} n = \frac{\pi}{2}$, $\lim_{n \to \infty} \frac{\tan^{-1} n}{n} = 0$.

8.2.18 Let $y = n^{2/n}$. Then $\ln y = \frac{2 \ln n}{n}$. By L'Hôpital's rule we have $\lim_{x \to \infty} \frac{2 \ln x}{x} = \lim_{x \to \infty} \frac{2}{x} = 0$, so $\lim_{n \to \infty} n^{2/n} = e^0 = 1$.

8.2.19 Find the limit of the logarithm of the expression, which is $n \ln \left(1 + \frac{2}{n}\right)$. Using L'Hôpital's rule:

$$\lim_{n \to \infty} n \ln \left(1 + \frac{2}{n}\right) = \lim_{n \to \infty} \frac{\ln \left(1 + \frac{2}{n}\right)}{1/n} = \lim_{n \to \infty} \frac{\frac{1}{1+(2/n)} \left(\frac{-2}{n^2}\right)}{-1/n^2} = \lim_{n \to \infty} \frac{2}{1 + (2/n)} = 2.$$

Thus the limit of the original expression is e^2.

8.2.20 Take the logarithm of the expression and use L'Hôpital's rule:

$$\lim_{n \to \infty} n \ln \left(\frac{n}{n+5}\right) = \lim_{n \to \infty} \frac{\ln \left(\frac{n}{n+5}\right)}{1/n} = \lim_{n \to \infty} \frac{\frac{n+5}{n} \cdot \frac{5}{(n+5)^2}}{-1/n^2} = \lim_{n \to \infty} \frac{-5n}{n+5} = -5.$$

Thus the original limit is e^{-5}.

8.2.21 Take the logarithm of the expression and use L'Hôpital's rule:

$$\lim_{n \to \infty} \frac{n}{2} \ln \left(1 + \frac{1}{2n}\right) = \lim_{n \to \infty} \frac{\ln(1 + (1/2n))}{2/n} = \lim_{n \to \infty} \frac{\frac{1}{1+(1/2n)} \cdot \frac{-1}{2n^2}}{-2/n^2} = \lim_{n \to \infty} \frac{1}{4(1 + (1/2n))} = \frac{1}{4}.$$

Thus the original limit is $e^{1/4}$.

8.2.22 Find the limit of the logarithm of the expression, which is $3n \ln \left(1 + \frac{4}{n}\right)$. Using L'Hôpital's rule:

$$\lim_{n \to \infty} 3n \ln \left(1 + \frac{4}{n}\right) = \lim_{n \to \infty} \frac{3 \ln \left(1 + \frac{4}{n}\right)}{1/n} = \lim_{n \to \infty} \frac{\frac{1}{1+(4/n)} \left(\frac{-12}{n^2}\right)}{-1/n^2} = \lim_{n \to \infty} \frac{12}{1 + (4/n)} = 12.$$

Thus the limit of the original expression is e^{12}.

8.2.23 Using L'Hôpital's rule: $\lim_{n \to \infty} \frac{n}{e^n + 3n} = \lim_{n \to \infty} \frac{1}{e^n + 3} = 0$.

8.2.24 $\ln \frac{1}{n} = -\ln n$, so this is $-\lim_{n \to \infty} \frac{\ln n}{n}$. By L'Hôpital's rule, we have $-\lim_{n \to \infty} \frac{\ln n}{n} = -\lim_{n \to \infty} \frac{1}{n} = 0$.

8.2.25 Taking logs, we have $\lim_{n \to \infty} \frac{1}{n} \ln(1/n) = \lim_{n \to \infty} -\frac{\ln n}{n} = \lim_{n \to \infty} \frac{-1}{n} = 0$ by L'Hôpital's rule. Thus the original sequence has limit $e^0 = 1$.

8.2.26 Find the limit of the logarithm of the expression, which is $n \ln \left(1 - \frac{4}{n}\right)$, using L'Hôpital's rule: $\lim_{n \to \infty} n \ln \left(1 - \frac{4}{n}\right) = \lim_{n \to \infty} \frac{\ln \left(1 - \frac{4}{n}\right)}{1/n} = \lim_{n \to \infty} \frac{\frac{1}{1-(4/n)} \left(\frac{4}{n^2}\right)}{-1/n^2} = \lim_{n \to \infty} \frac{-4}{1-(4/n)} = -4$. Thus the limit of the original expression is e^{-4}.

8.2.27 Except for a finite number of terms, this sequence is just $a_n = ne^{-n}$, so it has the same limit as this sequence. Note that $\lim_{n \to \infty} \frac{n}{e^n} = \lim_{n \to \infty} \frac{1}{e^n} = 0$, by L'Hôpital's rule.

8.2.28 $\ln(n^3 + 1) - \ln(3n^3 + 10n) = \ln \left(\frac{n^3+1}{3n^3+10n}\right) = \ln \left(\frac{1+n^{-3}}{3+10n^{-2}}\right)$, so the limit is $\ln(1/3) = -\ln 3$.

8.2.29 $\ln(\sin(1/n)) + \ln n = \ln(n \sin(1/n)) = \ln \left(\frac{\sin(1/n)}{1/n}\right)$. As $n \to \infty$, $\sin(1/n)/(1/n) \to 1$, so the limit of the original sequence is $\ln 1 = 0$.

8.2.30 Using L'Hôpital's rule:

$$\lim_{n \to \infty} n(1 - \cos(1/n)) = \lim_{n \to \infty} \frac{1 - \cos(1/n)}{1/n} = \lim_{n \to \infty} \frac{-\sin(1/n)(-1/n^2)}{-1/n^2} = -\sin(0) = 0.$$

8.2.31 $\lim_{n \to \infty} n \sin(6/n) = \lim_{n \to \infty} \frac{\sin(6/n)}{1/n} = \lim_{n \to \infty} \frac{\frac{-6\cos(6/n)}{n^2}}{(-1/n^2)} = \lim_{n \to \infty} 6 \cos(6/n) = 6 \cdot \cos 0 = 6.$

8.2.32 Because $-\frac{1}{n} \le \frac{(-1)^n}{n} \le \frac{1}{n}$, and because both $-\frac{1}{n}$ and $\frac{1}{n}$ have limit 0 as $n \to \infty$, the limit of the given sequence is also 0 by the Squeeze Theorem.

8.2.33 The terms with odd-numbered subscripts have the form $-\frac{n}{n+1}$, so they approach -1, while the terms with even-numbered subscripts have the form $\frac{n}{n+1}$ so they approach 1. Thus, the sequence has no limit.

8.2.34 Because $\frac{-n^2}{2n^3+n} \le \frac{(-1)^{n+1}n^2}{2n^3+n} \le \frac{n^2}{2n^3+n}$, and because both $\frac{-n^2}{2n^3+n}$ and $\frac{n^2}{2n^3+n}$ have limit 0 as $n \to \infty$, the limit of the given sequence is also 0 by the Squeeze Theorem. Note that $\lim\limits_{n\to\infty} \frac{n^2}{2n^3+n} = \lim\limits_{n\to\infty} \frac{1/n}{2+1/n^2} = \frac{0}{2} = 0$.

8.2.35 When n is an integer, $\sin\left(\frac{n\pi}{2}\right)$ oscillates between the values ± 1 and 0, so this sequence does not converge.

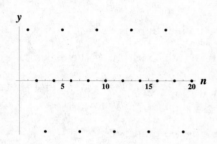

8.2.36 The even terms form a sequence $b_{2n} = \frac{2n}{2n+1}$, which converges to 1 (e.g. by L'Hôpital's rule); the odd terms form the sequence $b_{2n+1} = -\frac{n}{n+1}$, which converges to -1. Thus the sequence as a whole does not converge.

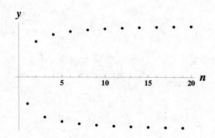

8.2.37 The numerator is bounded in absolute value by 1, while the denominator goes to ∞, so the limit of this sequence is 0.

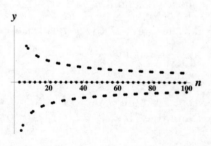

8.2.38 The reciprocal of this sequence is $b_n = \frac{1}{a_n} = 1 + \left(\frac{4}{3}\right)^n$, which increases without bound as $n \to \infty$. Thus a_n converges to zero.

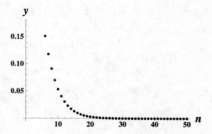

8.2.39 $\lim_{n \to \infty} (1 + \cos(1/n)) = 1 + \cos(0) = 2.$

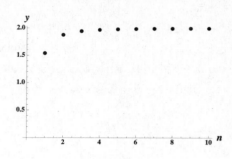

8.2.40 By L'Hôpital's rule we have: $\lim_{n \to \infty} \frac{e^{-n}}{2\sin(e^{-n})} = \lim_{n \to \infty} \frac{-e^{-n}}{2\cos(e^{-n})(-e^{-n})} = \frac{1}{2\cos 0} = \frac{1}{2}.$

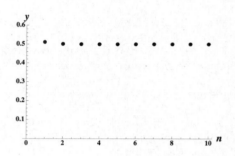

8.2.41 This is the sequence $\frac{\cos n}{e^n}$; the numerator is bounded in absolute value by 1 and the denominator increases without bound, so the limit is zero.

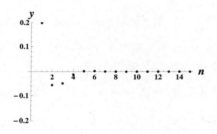

8.2.42 Using L'Hôpital's rule, we have $\lim_{n \to \infty} \frac{\ln n}{n^{1.1}} = \lim_{n \to \infty} \frac{1/n}{(1.1)n^{.1}} = \lim_{n \to \infty} \frac{1}{(1.1)n^{1.1}} = 0.$

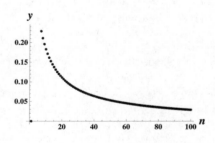

8.2.43 Ignoring the factor of $(-1)^n$ for the moment, we see, taking logs, that $\lim_{n \to \infty} \frac{\ln n}{n} = 0$, so that $\lim_{n \to \infty} \sqrt[n]{n} = e^0 = 1$. Taking the sign into account, the odd terms converge to -1 while the even terms converge to 1. Thus the sequence does not converge.

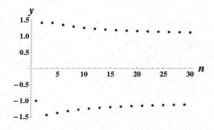

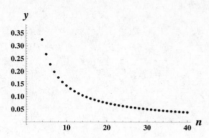

8.2.44 $\lim_{n \to \infty} \frac{n\pi}{2n+2} = \frac{\pi}{2}$, using L'Hôpital's rule. Thus the sequence converges to $\cot(\pi/2) = 0$.

8.2.45 Because $0.2 < 1$, this sequence converges to 0. Because $0.2 > 0$, the convergence is monotone.

8.2.46 Because $1.2 > 1$, this sequence diverges monotonically to ∞.

8.2.47 Because $|-0.7| < 1$, the sequence converges to 0; because $-0.7 < 0$, it does not do so monotonically. The sequence converges by oscillation.

8.2.48 Because $|-1.01| > 1$, the sequence diverges; because $-1.01 < 0$, the divergence is not monotone.

8.2.49 Because $1.00001 > 1$, the sequence diverges; because $1.00001 > 0$, the divergence is monotone.

8.2.50 This is the sequence

$$\frac{2^{n+1}}{3^n} = 2 \cdot \left(\frac{2}{3}\right)^n;$$

because $0 < \frac{2}{3} < 1$, the sequence converges monotonically to zero.

8.2.51 Because $|-2.5| > 1$, the sequence diverges; because $-2.5 < 0$, the divergence is not monotone. The sequence diverges by oscillation.

8.2.52 $|-0.003| < 1$, so the sequence converges to zero; because $-.003 < 0$, the convergence is not monotone.

8.2.53 Because $-1 \le \cos n \le 1$, we have $\frac{-1}{n} \le \frac{\cos n}{n} \le \frac{1}{n}$. Because both $\frac{-1}{n}$ and $\frac{1}{n}$ have limit 0 as $n \to \infty$, the given sequence does as well.

8.2.54 Because $-1 \le \sin 6n \le 1$, we have $-\frac{1}{5n} \le \frac{\sin 6n}{5n} \le \frac{1}{5n}$. Because both $-\frac{1}{5n}$ and $\frac{1}{5n}$ have limit 0 as $n \to \infty$, the given sequence does as well.

8.2.55 Because $-1 \le \sin n \le 1$ for all n, the given sequence satisfies $-\frac{1}{2^n} \le \frac{\sin n}{2^n} \le \frac{1}{2^n}$, and because both $\pm\frac{1}{2^n} \to 0$ as $n \to \infty$, the given sequence converges to zero as well by the Squeeze Theorem.

8.2.56 Because $-1 \le \cos(n\pi/2) \le 1$ for all n, we have $\frac{-1}{\sqrt{n}} \le \frac{\cos(n\pi/2)}{\sqrt{n}} \le \frac{1}{\sqrt{n}}$ and because both $\pm\frac{1}{\sqrt{n}} \to 0$ as $n \to \infty$, the given sequence converges to 0 as well by the Squeeze Theorem.

8.2.57 The inverse tangent function takes values between $-\pi/2$ and $\pi/2$, so the numerator is always between $-\pi$ and π. Thus $\frac{-\pi}{n^3+4} \le \frac{2\tan^{-1} n}{n^3+4} \le \frac{\pi}{n^3+4}$, and by the Squeeze Theorem, the given sequence converges to zero.

8.2.58 This sequence diverges. To see this, call the given sequence a_n, and assume it converges to limit L. Then because the sequence $b_n = \frac{n}{n+1}$ converges to 1, the sequence $c_n = \frac{a_n}{b_n}$ would converge to L as well. But $c_n = \sin^3 \frac{\pi n}{2}$ doesn't converge (because it is $1, -1, 1, -1 \cdots$), so the given sequence doesn't converge either.

8.2.59

a. After the nth dose is given, the amount of drug in the bloodstream is $d_n = 0.5 \cdot d_{n-1} + 80$, because the half-life is one day. The initial condition is $d_1 = 80$.

b. The limit of this sequence is 160 mg.

c. Let $L = \lim\limits_{n \to \infty} d_n$. Then from the recurrence relation, we have $d_n = 0.5 \cdot d_{n-1} + 80$, and thus $\lim\limits_{n \to \infty} d_n = 0.5 \cdot \lim\limits_{n \to \infty} d_{n-1} + 80$, so $L = 0.5 \cdot L + 80$, and therefore $L = 160$.

8.2.60

a.

$$B_0 = \$20,000$$
$$B_1 = 1.005 \cdot B_0 - \$200 = \$19,900$$
$$B_2 = 1.005 \cdot B_1 - \$200 = \$19,799.50$$
$$B_3 = 1.005 \cdot B_2 - \$200 = \$19,698.50$$
$$B_4 = 1.005 \cdot B_3 - \$200 = \$19,596.99$$
$$B_5 = 1.005 \cdot B_4 - \$200 = \$19,494.97$$

b. $B_n = 1.005 \cdot B_{n-1} - \$200$

c. Using a calculator or computer program, B_n becomes negative after the 139th payment, so 139 months or almost 11 years.

8.2.61

a.

$$B_0 = 0$$
$$B_1 = 1.0075 \cdot B_0 + \$100 = \$100$$
$$B_2 = 1.0075 \cdot B_1 + \$100 = \$200.75$$
$$B_3 = 1.0075 \cdot B_2 + \$100 = \$302.26$$
$$B_4 = 1.0075 \cdot B_3 + \$100 = \$404.52$$
$$B_5 = 1.0075 \cdot B_4 + \$100 = \$507.56$$

b. $B_n = 1.0075 \cdot B_{n-1} + \$100.$

c. Using a calculator or computer program, $B_n > \$5,000$ during the 43rd month.

8.2.62

a. Let D_n be the *total number* of liters of alcohol in the mixture after the nth replacement. At the next step, 2 liters of the 100 liters is removed, thus leaving $0.98 \cdot D_n$ liters of alcohol, and then $0.1 \cdot 2 = 0.2$ liters of alcohol are added. Thus $D_n = 0.98 \cdot D_{n-1} + 0.2$. Now, $C_n = D_n/100$, so we obtain a recurrence relation for C_n by dividing this equation by 100: $C_n = 0.98 \cdot C_{n-1} + 0.002$.

$$C_0 = 0.4$$
$$C_1 = 0.98 \cdot 0.4 + 0.002 = 0.394$$
$$C_2 = 0.98 \cdot C_1 + 0.002 = 0.38812$$
$$C_3 = 0.98 \cdot C_2 + 0.002 = 0.38236$$
$$C_4 = 0.98 \cdot C_3 + 0.002 = 0.37671$$
$$C_5 = 0.98 \cdot C_4 + 0.002 = 0.37118$$

The rounding is done to five decimal places.

b. Using a calculator or a computer program, $C_n < 0.15$ after the 89th replacement.

c. If the limit of C_n is L, then taking the limit of both sides of the recurrence equation yields $L = 0.98L + 0.002$, so $.02L = .002$, and $L = .1 = 10\%$.

8.2.63 Because $n! \ll n^n$ by Theorem 8.6, we have $\lim\limits_{n\to\infty} \frac{n!}{n^n} = 0$.

8.2.64 $\{3^n\} \ll \{n!\}$ because $\{b^n\} \ll \{n!\}$ in Theorem 8.6. Thus, $\lim\limits_{n\to\infty} \frac{3^n}{n!} = 0$.

8.2.65 Theorem 8.6 indicates that $\ln^q n \ll n^p$, so $\ln^{20} n \ll n^{10}$, so $\lim\limits_{n\to\infty} \frac{n^{10}}{\ln^{20} n} = \infty$.

8.2.66 Theorem 8.6 indicates that $\ln^q n \ll n^p$, so $\ln^{1000} n \ll n^{10}$, so $\lim\limits_{n\to\infty} \frac{n^{10}}{\ln^{1000} n} = \infty$.

8.2.67 By Theorem 8.6, $n^p \ll b^n$, so $n^{1000} \ll 2^n$, and thus $\lim\limits_{n\to\infty} \frac{n^{1000}}{2^n} = 0$.

8.2.68 Note that $e^{1/10} = \sqrt[10]{e} \approx 1.1$. Let $r = \frac{e^{1/10}}{2}$ and note that $0 < r < 1$. Thus $\lim\limits_{n\to\infty} \frac{e^{n/10}}{2^n} = \lim\limits_{n\to\infty} r^n = 0$.

8.2.69 Let $\varepsilon > 0$ be given and let N be an integer with $N > \frac{1}{\varepsilon}$. Then if $n > N$, we have $\left|\frac{1}{n} - 0\right| = \frac{1}{n} < \frac{1}{N} < \varepsilon$.

8.2.70 Let $\varepsilon > 0$ be given. We wish to find N such that $|(1/n^2) - 0| < \varepsilon$ if $n > N$. This means that $\left|\frac{1}{n^2} - 0\right| = \frac{1}{n^2} < \varepsilon$. So choose N such that $\frac{1}{N^2} < \varepsilon$, so that $N^2 > \frac{1}{\varepsilon}$, and then $N > \frac{1}{\sqrt{\varepsilon}}$. This shows that such an N always exists for each ε and thus that the limit is zero.

8.2.71 Let $\varepsilon > 0$ be given. We wish to find N such that for $n > N$, $\left|\frac{3n^2}{4n^2+1} - \frac{3}{4}\right| = \left|\frac{-3}{4(4n^2+1)}\right| = \frac{3}{4(4n^2+1)} < \varepsilon$. But this means that $3 < 4\varepsilon(4n^2 + 1)$, or $16\varepsilon n^2 + (4\varepsilon - 3) > 0$. Solving the quadratic, we get $n > \frac{1}{4}\sqrt{\frac{3}{\varepsilon} - 4}$, provided $\varepsilon < 3/4$. So let $N = \frac{1}{4}\sqrt{\frac{3}{\varepsilon}}$ if $\epsilon < 3/4$ and let $N = 1$ otherwise.

8.2.72 Let $\varepsilon > 0$ be given. We wish to find N such that for $n > N$, $|b^{-n} - 0| = b^{-n} < \varepsilon$, so that $-n \ln b < \ln \varepsilon$. So choose N to be any integer greater than $-\frac{\ln \varepsilon}{\ln b}$.

8.2.73 Let $\varepsilon > 0$ be given. We wish to find N such that for $n > N$, $\left|\frac{cn}{bn+1} - \frac{c}{b}\right| = \left|\frac{-c}{b(bn+1)}\right| = \frac{c}{b(bn+1)} < \varepsilon$. But this means that $\varepsilon b^2 n + (b\varepsilon - c) > 0$, so that $N > \frac{c}{b^2 \varepsilon}$ will work.

8.2.74 Let $\varepsilon > 0$ be given. We wish to find N such that for $n > N$, $\left|\frac{n}{n^2+1} - 0\right| = \frac{n}{n^2+1} < \varepsilon$. Thus we want $n < \varepsilon(n^2 + 1)$, or $\varepsilon n^2 - n + \varepsilon > 0$. Whenever n is larger than the larger of the two roots of this quadratic, the desired inequality will hold. The roots of the quadratic are $\frac{1 \pm \sqrt{1 - 4\varepsilon^2}}{2\varepsilon}$, so we choose N to be any integer greater than $\frac{1 + \sqrt{1 - 4\varepsilon^2}}{2\varepsilon}$.

8.2.75

a. True. See Theorem 8.2 part 4.

b. False. For example, if $a_n = 1/n$ and $b_n = e^n$, then $\lim\limits_{n\to\infty} a_n b_n = \infty$.

c. True. The definition of the limit of a sequence involves only the behavior of the nth term of a sequence as n gets large (see the Definition of Limit of a Sequence). Thus suppose a_n, b_n differ in only finitely many terms, and that M is large enough so that $a_n = b_n$ for $n > M$. Suppose a_n has limit L. Then for $\varepsilon > 0$, if N is such that $|a_n - L| < \varepsilon$ for $n > N$, first increase N if required so that $N > M$ as well. Then we also have $|b_n - L| < \varepsilon$ for $n > N$. Thus a_n and b_n have the same limit. A similar argument applies if a_n has no limit.

d. True. Note that a_n converges to zero. Intuitively, the nonzero terms of b_n are those of a_n, which converge to zero. More formally, given ϵ, choose N_1 such that for $n > N_1$, $a_n < \epsilon$. Let $N = 2N_1 + 1$. Then for $n > N$, consider b_n. If n is even, then $b_n = 0$ so certainly $b_n < \epsilon$. If n is odd, then $b_n = a_{(n-1)/2}$, and $(n-1)/2 > ((2N_1 + 1) - 1)/2 = N_1$ so that $a_{(n-1)/2} < \epsilon$. Thus b_n converges to zero as well.

e. False. If $\{a_n\}$ happens to converge to zero, the statement is true. But consider for example $a_n = 2 + \frac{1}{n}$. Then $\lim_{n \to \infty} a_n = 2$, but $(-1)^n a_n$ does not converge (it oscillates between positive and negative values increasingly close to ± 2).

f. True. Suppose $\{0.000001 a_n\}$ converged to L, and let $\epsilon > 0$ be given. Choose N such that for $n > N$, $|0.000001 a_n - L| < \epsilon \cdot 0.000001$. Dividing through by 0.000001, we get that for $n > N$, $|a_n - 1000000L| < \epsilon$, so that a_n converges as well (to $1000000L$).

8.2.76 $\{2n - 3\}_{n=3}^{\infty}$.

8.2.77 $\{(n - 2)^2 + 6(n - 2) - 9\}_{n=3}^{\infty} = \{n^2 + 2n - 17\}_{n=3}^{\infty}$.

8.2.78 If $f(t) = \int_1^t x^{-2} dx$, then $\lim_{t \to \infty} f(t) = \lim_{n \to \infty} a_n$. But

$$\lim_{t \to \infty} f(t) = \int_1^{\infty} x^{-2} dx = \lim_{b \to \infty} \left[-\frac{1}{x} \Big|_1^b \right] = \lim_{b \to \infty} \left(-\frac{1}{b} + 1 \right) = 1.$$

8.2.79 Evaluate the limit of each term separately: $\lim_{n \to \infty} \frac{75^{n-1}}{99^n} = \frac{1}{99} \lim_{n \to \infty} \left(\frac{75}{99} \right)^{n-1} = 0$, while $\frac{-5^n}{8^n} \le \frac{5^n \sin n}{8^n} \le \frac{5^n}{8^n}$, so by the Squeeze Theorem, this second term converges to 0 as well. Thus the sum of the terms converges to zero.

8.2.80 Because $\lim_{n \to \infty} \frac{10n}{10n+4} = 1$, and because the inverse tangent function is continuous, the given sequence has limit $\tan^{-1} 1 = \pi/4$.

8.2.81 Because $\lim_{n \to \infty} 0.99^n = 0$, and because cosine is continuous, the first term converges to $\cos 0 = 1$. The limit of the second term is $\lim_{n \to \infty} \frac{7^n + 9^n}{63^n} = \lim_{n \to \infty} \left(\frac{7}{63} \right)^n + \lim_{n \to \infty} \left(\frac{9}{63} \right)^n = 0$. Thus the sum converges to 1.

8.2.82 Dividing the numerator and denominator by $n!$ gives $a_n = \frac{(4^n/n!) + 5}{1 + (2^n/n!)}$. By Theorem 8.6, we have $4^n \ll n!$ and $2^n \ll n!$. Thus, $\lim_{n \to \infty} a_n = \frac{0+5}{1+0} = 5$.

8.2.83 Dividing the numerator and denominator by 6^n gives $a_n = \frac{1 + (1/2)^n}{1 + (n^{100}/6^n)}$. By Theorem 8.6, $n^{100} \ll 6^n$. Thus $\lim_{n \to \infty} a_n = \frac{1+0}{1+0} = 1$.

8.2.84 Dividing the numerator and denominator by n^8 gives $a_n = \frac{1 + (1/n)}{(1/n) + \ln n}$. Because $1 + (1/n) \to 1$ as $n \to \infty$ and $(1/n) + \ln n \to \infty$ as $n \to \infty$, we have $\lim_{n \to \infty} a_n = 0$.

8.2.85 We can write $a_n = \frac{(7/5)^n}{n^7}$. Theorem 8.6 indicates that $n^7 \ll b^n$ for $b > 1$, so $\lim_{n \to \infty} a_n = \infty$.

8.2.86 A graph shows that the sequence appears to converge. Assuming that it does, let its limit be L. Then $\lim_{n \to \infty} a_{n+1} = \frac{1}{2} \lim_{n \to \infty} a_n + 2$, so $L = \frac{1}{2}L + 2$, and thus $\frac{1}{2}L = 2$, so $L = 4$.

8.2.87 A graph shows that the sequence appears to converge. Let its supposed limit be L, then $\lim_{n \to \infty} a_{n+1} = \lim_{n \to \infty} (2a_n(1 - a_n)) = 2(\lim_{n \to \infty} a_n)(1 - \lim_{n \to \infty} a_n)$, so $L = 2L(1 - L) = 2L - 2L^2$, and thus $2L^2 - L = 0$, so $L = 0, \frac{1}{2}$. Thus the limit appears to be either 0 or 1/2; with the given initial condition, doing a few iterations by hand confirms that the sequence converges to 1/2: $a_0 = 0.3$; $a_1 = 2 \cdot 0.3 \cdot 0.7 = .42$; $a_2 = 2 \cdot 0.42 \cdot 0.58 = 0.4872$.

8.2.88 A graph shows that the sequence appears to converge, and to a value other than zero; let its limit be L. Then $\lim\limits_{n\to\infty} a_{n+1} = \lim\limits_{n\to\infty} \frac{1}{2}(a_n + \frac{2}{a_n}) = \frac{1}{2}\lim\limits_{n\to\infty} a_n + \frac{1}{\lim\limits_{n\to\infty} a_n}$, so $L = \frac{1}{2}L + \frac{1}{L}$, and therefore $L^2 = \frac{1}{2}L^2 + 1$. So $L^2 = 2$, and thus $L = \sqrt{2}$.

8.2.89 Computing three terms gives $a_0 = 0.5, a_1 = 4 \cdot 0.5 \cdot 0.5 = 1, a_2 = 4 \cdot 1 \cdot (1-1) = 0$. All successive terms are obviously zero, so the sequence converges to 0.

8.2.90 A graph shows that the sequence appears to converge. Let its limit be L. Then $\lim\limits_{n\to\infty} a_{n+1} = \sqrt{2 + \lim\limits_{n\to\infty} a_n}$, so $L = \sqrt{2 + L}$. Thus we have $L^2 = 2 + L$, so $L^2 - L - 2 = 0$, and thus $L = -1, 2$. A square root can never be negative, so this sequence must converge to 2.

8.2.91 For $b = 2$, $2^3 > 3!$ but $16 = 2^4 < 4! = 24$, so the crossover point is $n = 4$. For e, $e^5 \approx 148.41 > 5! = 120$ while $e^6 \approx 403.4 < 6! = 720$, so the crossover point is $n = 6$. For 10, $24! \approx 6.2 \times 10^{23} < 10^{24}$, while $25! \approx 1.55 \times 10^{25} > 10^{25}$, so the crossover point is $n = 25$.

8.2.92

a. Rounded to the nearest fish, the populations are

$$F_0 = 4000$$
$$F_1 = 1.015F_0 - 80 = 3980$$
$$F_2 = 1.015F_1 - 80 \approx 3960$$
$$F_3 = 1.015F_2 - 80 \approx 3939$$
$$F_4 = 1.015F_3 - 80 \approx 3918$$
$$F_5 = 1.015F_4 - 80 \approx 3897$$

b. $F_n = 1.015F_{n-1} - 80$

c. The population decreases and eventually reaches zero.

d. With an initial population of 5500 fish, the population increases without bound.

e. If the initial population is less than 5333 fish, the population will decline to zero. This is essentially because for a population of less than 5333, the natural increase of 1.5% does not make up for the loss of 80 fish.

8.2.93

a. The profits for each of the first ten days, in dollars are:

n	0	1	2	3	4	5	6	7	8	9	10
h_n	130.00	130.75	131.40	131.95	132.40	132.75	133.00	133.15	133.20	133.15	133.00

b. The profit on an item is revenue minus cost. The total cost of keeping the heifer for n days is $.45n$, and the revenue for selling the heifer on the nth day is $(200 + 5n) \cdot (.65 - .01n)$, because the heifer gains 5 pounds per day but is worth a penny less per pound each day. Thus the total profit on the nth day is $h_n = (200 + 5n) \cdot (.65 - .01n) - .45n = 130 + 0.8n - 0.05n^2$. The maximum profit occurs when $-.1n + .8 = 0$, which occurs when $n = 8$. The maximum profit is achieved by selling the heifer on the 8th day.

8.2.94

a. $x_0 = 7$, $x_1 = 6$, $x_2 = 6.5 = \frac{13}{2}$, $x_3 = 6.25$, $x_4 = 6.375 = \frac{51}{8}$, $x_5 = 6.3125 = \frac{101}{16}$, $x_6 = 6.34375 = \frac{203}{32}$.

b. For the formula given in the problem, we have $x_0 = \frac{19}{3} + \frac{2}{3}\left(-\frac{1}{2}\right)^0 = 7$, $x_1 = \frac{19}{3} + \frac{2}{3}\cdot\frac{-1}{2} = \frac{19}{3} - \frac{1}{3} = 6$, so that the formula holds for $n = 0, 1$. Now assume the formula holds for all integers $\leq k$; then

$$x_{k+1} = \frac{1}{2}(x_k + x_{k-1}) = \frac{1}{2}\left(\frac{19}{3} + \frac{2}{3}\left(-\frac{1}{2}\right)^k + \frac{19}{3} + \frac{2}{3}\left(-\frac{1}{2}\right)^{k-1}\right)$$

$$= \frac{1}{2}\left(\frac{38}{3} + \frac{2}{3}\left(-\frac{1}{2}\right)^{k-1}\left(-\frac{1}{2} + 1\right)\right)$$

$$= \frac{1}{2}\left(\frac{38}{3} + 4\cdot\frac{2}{3}\left(-\frac{1}{2}\right)^{k+1}\cdot\frac{1}{2}\right)$$

$$= \frac{1}{2}\left(\frac{38}{3} + 2\cdot\frac{2}{3}\left(-\frac{1}{2}\right)^{k+1}\right)$$

$$= \frac{19}{3} + \frac{2}{3}\left(-\frac{1}{2}\right)^{k+1}.$$

c. As $n \to \infty$, $(-1/2)^n \to 0$, so that the limit is $19/3$, or $6\ 1/3$.

8.2.95 The approximate first few values of this sequence are:

n	0	1	2	3	4	5	6
c_n	.7071	.6325	.6136	.6088	.6076	.6074	.6073

The value of the constant appears to be around 0.607.

8.2.96 We first prove that d_n is bounded by 200. If $d_n \leq 200$, then $d_{n+1} = 0.5\cdot d_n + 100 \leq 0.5\cdot 200 + 100 \leq 200$. Because $d_0 = 100 < 200$, all d_n are at most 200. Thus the sequence is bounded. To see that it is monotone, look at

$$d_n - d_{n-1} = 0.5 \cdot d_{n-1} + 100 - d_{n-1} = 100 - 0.5d_{n-1}.$$

But we know that $d_{n-1} \leq 200$, so that $100 - 0.5d_{n-1} \geq 0$. Thus $d_n \geq d_{n-1}$ and the sequence is nondecreasing.

8.2.97

a. If we "cut off" the expression after n square roots, we get a_n from the recurrence given. We can thus *define* the infinite expression to be the limit of a_n as $n \to \infty$.

b. $a_0 = 1$, $a_1 = \sqrt{2}$, $a_2 = \sqrt{1 + \sqrt{2}} \approx 1.5538$, $a_3 \approx 1.5981$, $a_4 \approx 1.6118$, and $a_5 \approx 1.6161$.

c. $a_{10} \approx 1.618$, which differs from $\frac{1+\sqrt{5}}{2} \approx 1.61803394$ by less than .001.

d. Assume $\lim_{n\to\infty} a_n = L$. Then $\lim_{n\to\infty} a_{n+1} = \lim_{n\to\infty} \sqrt{1 + a_n} = \sqrt{1 + \lim_{n\to\infty} a_n}$, so $L = \sqrt{1 + L}$, and thus $L^2 = 1 + L$. Therefore we have $L^2 - L - 1 = 0$, so $L = \frac{1\pm\sqrt{5}}{2}$.
   Because clearly the limit is positive, it must be the positive square root.

e. Letting $a_{n+1} = \sqrt{p + \sqrt{a_n}}$ with $a_0 = p$ and assuming a limit exists we have $\lim_{n\to\infty} a_{n+1} = \lim_{n\to\infty} \sqrt{p + a_n}$ $= \sqrt{p + \lim_{n\to\infty} a_n}$, so $L = \sqrt{p + L}$, and thus $L^2 = p + L$. Therefore, $L^2 - L - p = 0$, so $L = \frac{1\pm\sqrt{1+4p}}{2}$, and because we know that L is positive, we have $L = \frac{1+\sqrt{4p+1}}{2}$. The limit exists for all positive p.

8.2.98 Note that $1 - \frac{1}{i} = \frac{i-1}{i}$, so that the product is $\frac{1}{2}\cdot\frac{2}{3}\cdot\frac{3}{4}\cdot\frac{4}{5}\cdots$, so that $a_n = \frac{1}{n}$ for $n \geq 2$. The sequence $\{\frac{1}{2}, \frac{1}{3}, \frac{1}{4}, \ldots\}$ has limit zero.

8.2.99

a. Define a_n as given in the problem statement. Then we can *define* the value of the continued fraction to be $\lim_{n\to\infty} a_n$.

b. $a_0 = 1$, $a_1 = 1 + \frac{1}{a_0} = 2$, $a_2 = 1 + \frac{1}{a_1} = \frac{3}{2} = 1.5$, $a_3 = 1 + \frac{1}{a_2} = \frac{5}{3} \approx 1.667$, $a_4 = 1 + \frac{1}{a_3} = \frac{8}{5} = 1.6$, $a_5 = 1 + \frac{1}{a_4} = \frac{13}{8} = 1.625$.

c. From the list above, the values of the sequence alternately decrease and increase, so we would expect that the limit is somewhere between 1.6 and 1.625.

d. Assume that the limit is equal to L. Then from $a_{n+1} = 1 + \frac{1}{a_n}$, we have $\lim_{n\to\infty} a_{n+1} = 1 + \frac{1}{\lim_{n\to\infty} a_n}$, so $L = 1 + \frac{1}{L}$, and thus $L^2 - L - 1 = 0$. Therefore, $L = \frac{1\pm\sqrt{5}}{2}$, and because L is clearly positive, it must be equal to $\frac{1+\sqrt{5}}{2} \approx 1.618$.

e. Here $a_0 = a$ and $a_{n+1} = a + \frac{b}{a_n}$. Assuming that $\lim_{n\to\infty} a_n = L$ we have $L = a + \frac{b}{L}$, so $L^2 = aL + b$, and thus $L^2 - aL - b = 0$. Therefore, $L = \frac{a\pm\sqrt{a^2+4b}}{2}$, and because $L > 0$ we have $L = \frac{a+\sqrt{a^2+4b}}{2}$.

8.2.100

a. With $p = 0.5$ we have for $a_{n+1} = a_n^p$:

n	1	2	3	4	5	6	7
a_n	0.707	0.841	0.971	0.958	0.979	0.989	0.995

Experimenting with recurrence (1) one sees that for $0 < p \le 1$ the sequence converges to 1, while for $p > 1$ the sequence diverges to ∞.

b. With $p = 1.2$ and $a_n = p^{a_{n-1}}$ we obtain

n	1	2	3	4	5	6	7	8	9	10
a_n	1.2	1.2446	1.2547	1.2570	1.2577	1.2577	1.2577	1.2577	1.2577	1.2577

With recurrence (2), in addition to converging for $p < 1$ it also converges for values of p less than approximately 1.444. Here is a table of approximate values for different values of p:

p	1.1	1.2	1.3	1.4	1.44	1.444	1.445
$\lim_{n\to\infty} a_n$	1.1118	1.25776	1.471	1.887	2.39385	2.587	Diverges

It appears that the upper limit of convergence is about 1.444.

8.2.101

a. $f_0 = f_1 = 1$, $f_2 = 2$, $f_3 = 3$, $f_4 = 5$, $f_5 = 8$, $f_6 = 13$, $f_7 = 21$, $f_8 = 34$, $f_9 = 55$, $f_{10} = 89$.

b. The sequence is clearly not bounded.

c. $\frac{f_{10}}{f_9} \approx 1.61818$

d. We use induction. Note that $\frac{1}{\sqrt{5}}\left(\varphi + \frac{1}{\varphi}\right) = \frac{1}{\sqrt{5}}\left(\frac{1+\sqrt{5}}{2} + \frac{2}{1+\sqrt{5}}\right) = \frac{1}{\sqrt{5}}\left(\frac{1+2\sqrt{5}+5+4}{2(1+\sqrt{5})}\right) = 1 = f_1$. Also note that $\frac{1}{\sqrt{5}}\left(\varphi^2 - \frac{1}{\varphi^2}\right) = \frac{1}{\sqrt{5}}\left(\frac{3+\sqrt{5}}{2} - \frac{2}{3+\sqrt{5}}\right) = \frac{1}{\sqrt{5}}\left(\frac{9+6\sqrt{5}+5-4}{2(3+\sqrt{5})}\right) = 1 = f_2$. Now note that

$$f_{n-1} + f_{n-2} = \frac{1}{\sqrt{5}}(\varphi^{n-1} - (-1)^{n-1}\varphi^{1-n} + \varphi^{n-2} - (-1)^{n-2}\varphi^{2-n})$$

$$= \frac{1}{\sqrt{5}}((\varphi^{n-1} + \varphi^{n-2}) - (-1)^n(\varphi^{2-n} - \varphi^{1-n})).$$

Now, note that $\varphi - 1 = \frac{1}{\varphi}$, so that

$$\varphi^{n-1} + \varphi^{n-2} = \varphi^{n-1}\left(1 + \frac{1}{\varphi}\right) = \varphi^{n-1} \cdot \varphi = \varphi^n$$

and

$$\varphi^{2-n} - \varphi^{1-n} = \varphi^{-n}(\varphi^2 - \varphi) = \varphi^{-n}(\varphi(\varphi - 1)) = \varphi^{-n}.$$

Making these substitutions, we get

$$f_n = f_{n-1} + f_{n-2} = \frac{1}{\sqrt{5}}(\varphi^n - (-1)^n\varphi^{-n})$$

8.2.102

a. We show that the arithmetic mean of any two positive numbers exceeds their geometric mean. Let a, $b > 0$; then $\frac{a+b}{2} - \sqrt{ab} = \frac{1}{2}(a - 2\sqrt{ab} + b) = \frac{1}{2}(\sqrt{a} - \sqrt{b})^2 \geq 0$. Because in addition $a_0 > b_0$, we have $a_n > b_n$ for all n.

b. To see that $\{a_n\}$ is decreasing, note that

$$a_{n+1} = \frac{a_n + b_n}{2} < \frac{a_n + a_n}{2} = a_n.$$

Similarly,

$$b_{n+1} = \sqrt{a_n b_n} > \sqrt{b_n b_n} = b_n,$$

so that $\{b_n\}$ is increasing.

c. $\{a_n\}$ is monotone and nonincreasing by part (b), and bounded below by part (a) (it is bounded below by any of the b_n), so it converges by the monotone convergence theorem. Similarly, $\{b_n\}$ is monotone and nondecreasing by part (b) and bounded above by part (a), so it too converges.

d.

$$a_{n+1} - b_{n+1} = \frac{a_n + b_n}{2} - \sqrt{a_n b_n} = \frac{1}{2}(a_n - 2\sqrt{a_n b_n} + b_n) < \frac{1}{2}(a_n - 2\sqrt{b_n^2} + b_n) = \frac{1}{2}(a_n - b_n).$$

Thus the difference between a_{n+1} and b_{n+1} is less than half the difference between a_n and b_n, so that difference goes to zero and the two limits are the same.

e. The AGM of 12 and 20 is approximately 15.745; Gauss' constant is $\frac{1}{\text{AGM}(1,\sqrt{2})} \approx 0.8346$.

8.2.103

a.

$$
\begin{array}{rl}
2: & 1 \\
3: & 10,\ 5,\ 16,\ 8,\ 4,\ 2,\ 1 \\
4: & 2,\ 1 \\
5: & 16,\ 8,\ 4,\ 2,\ 1 \\
6: & 3,\ 10,\ 5,\ 16,\ 8,\ 4,\ 2,\ 1 \\
7: & 22,\ 11,\ 34,\ 17,\ 52,\ 26,\ 13,\ 40,\ 20,\ 10,\ 5,\ 16,\ 8,\ 4,\ 2,\ 1 \\
8: & 4,\ 2,\ 1 \\
9: & 28,\ 14,\ 7,\ 22,\ 11,\ 34,\ 17,\ 52,\ 26,\ 13,\ 40,\ 20,\ 10,\ 5,\ 16,\ 8,\ 4,\ 2,\ 1 \\
10: & 5,\ 16,\ 8,\ 4,\ 2,\ 1
\end{array}
$$

b. From the above, $H_2 = 1, H_3 = 7$, and $H_4 = 2$.

c. This plot is for $1 \le n \le 100$. Like hailstones, the numbers in the sequence a_n rise and fall but eventually crash to the earth. The conjecture appears to be true.

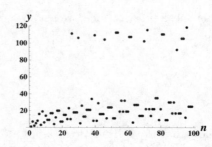

8.2.104 $\{a_n\} \ll \{b_n\}$ means that $\lim\limits_{n \to \infty} \frac{a_n}{b_n} = 0$. But $\lim\limits_{n \to \infty} \frac{ca_n}{db_n} = \frac{c}{d} \lim\limits_{n \to \infty} \frac{a_n}{b_n} = 0$, so that $\{ca_n\} \ll \{db_n\}$.

8.2.105

a. Note that $a_2 = \sqrt{3a_1} = \sqrt{3\sqrt{3}} > \sqrt{3} = a_1$. Now assume that $\sqrt{3} = a_1 < a_2 < \ldots a_{k-1} < a_k$. Then

$$a_{k+1} = \sqrt{3a_k} > \sqrt{3a_{k-1}} = a_k.$$

Thus $\{a_n\}$ is increasing.

b. Clearly because $a_1 = \sqrt{3} > 0$ and $\{a_n\}$ is increasing, the sequence is bounded below by $\sqrt{3} > 0$. Further, $a_1 = \sqrt{3} < 3$; assume that $a_k < 3$. Then $a_{k+1} = \sqrt{3a_k} < \sqrt{3 \cdot 3} = 3$, so that $a_{k+1} < 3$. So by induction, $\{a_k\}$ is bounded above by 3.

c. Because $\{a_n\}$ is bounded and monotonically increasing, $\lim\limits_{n \to \infty} a_n$ exists by Theorem 8.5.

d. Because the limit exists, we have

$$\lim_{n \to \infty} a_{n+1} = \lim_{n \to \infty} \sqrt{3a_n} = \sqrt{3} \lim_{n \to \infty} \sqrt{a_n} = \sqrt{3}\sqrt{\lim_{n \to \infty} a_n}.$$

Let $L = \lim\limits_{n \to \infty} a_{n+1} = \lim\limits_{n \to \infty} a_n$; then $L = \sqrt{3}\sqrt{L}$, so that $L = 3$.

8.2.106 By Theorem 8.6,

$$\lim_{n \to \infty} \frac{2 \ln n}{\sqrt{n}} = 2 \lim_{n \to \infty} \frac{\ln n}{n^{1/2}} = 0,$$

so that $\sqrt{n}$ has the larger growth rate. Using computational software, we see that $\sqrt{74} \approx 8.60233 < 2 \ln 74 \approx 8.60813$, while $\sqrt{75} \approx 8.66025 > 2 \ln 75 \approx 8.63493$.

8.2.107 By Theorem 8.6,

$$\lim_{n\to\infty}\frac{n^5}{e^{n/2}}=2^5\lim_{n\to\infty}\frac{(n/2)^5}{e^{n/2}}=0,$$

so that $e^{n/2}$ has the larger growth rate. Using computational software we see that $e^{35/2}\approx 3.982\times 10^7<35^5\approx 5.252\times 10^7$, while $e^{36/2}\approx 6.566\times 10^7>36^5\approx 6.047\times 10^7$.

8.2.108 By Theorem 8.6, $\ln n^{10}\ll n^{1.001}$, so that $n^{1.001}$ has the larger growth rate. Using computational software we see that $35^{1.001}\approx 35.1247<\ln 35^{10}\approx 35.5535$ while $36^{1.001}\approx 36.1292>\ln 36^{10}\approx 35.8352$.

8.2.109 Experiment with a few widely separated values of n:

n	$n!$	$n^{0.7n}$
1	1	1
10	3.63×10^6	10^7
100	9.33×10^{157}	10^{140}
1000	4.02×10^{2567}	10^{2100}

It appears that $n^{0.7n}$ starts out larger, but is overtaken by the factorial somewhere between $n=10$ and $n=100$, and that the gap grows wider as n increases. Looking between $n=10$ and $n=100$ revels that for $n=18$, we have $n!\approx 6.402\times 10^{15}<n^{0.7n}\approx 6.553\times 10^{15}$ while for $n=19$ we have $n!\approx 1.216\times 10^{17}>n^{0.7n}\approx 1.017\times 10^{17}$.

8.2.110 By Theorem 8.6,

$$\lim_{n\to\infty}\frac{n^9\ln^3 n}{n^{10}}=\lim_{n\to\infty}\frac{\ln^3 n}{n}=0,$$

so that n^{10} has a larger growth rate. Using computational software we see that $93^{10}\approx 4.840\times 10^{19}<93^9\ln^3 93\approx 4.846\times 10^{19}$ while $94^{10}\approx 5.386\times 10^{19}>94^9\ln^3 94\approx 5.374\times 10^{19}$.

8.2.111 First note that for $a=1$ we already know that $\{n^n\}$ grows fast than $\{n!\}$. So if $a>1$, then $n^{an}\geq n^n$, so that $\{n^{an}\}$ grows faster than $\{n!\}$ for $a>1$ as well. To settle the case $a<1$, recall Stirling's formula which states that for large values of n,

$$n!\sim\sqrt{2\pi n}\,n^n e^{-n}.$$

Thus

$$
\begin{aligned}
\lim_{n\to\infty}\frac{n!}{n^{an}}&=\lim_{n\to\infty}\frac{\sqrt{2\pi n}\,n^n e^{-n}}{n^{an}}\\
&=\sqrt{2\pi}\lim_{n\to\infty}n^{\frac12+(1-a)n}e^{-n}\\
&\geq\sqrt{2\pi}\lim_{n\to\infty}n^{(1-a)n}e^{-n}\\
&=\sqrt{2\pi}\lim_{n\to\infty}e^{(1-a)n\ln n}e^{-n}\\
&=\sqrt{2\pi}\lim_{n\to\infty}e^{((1-a)\ln n-1)n}.
\end{aligned}
$$

If $a<1$ then $(1-a)\ln n-1>0$ for large values of n because $1-a>0$, so that this limit is infinite. Hence $\{n!\}$ grows faster than $\{n^{an}\}$ exactly when $a<1$.

8.3 Infinite Series

8.3.1 A geometric series is a series in which the ratio of successive terms in the underlying sequence is a constant. Thus a geometric series has the form $\sum ar^k$ where r is the constant. One example is $3+6+12+24+48+\cdots$ in which $a=3$ and $r=2$.

8.3.2 A geometric sum is the sum of a finite number of terms which have a constant ratio; a geometric series is the sum of an infinite number of such terms.

8.3.3 The ratio is the common ratio between successive terms in the sum.

8.3.4 Yes, because there are only a finite number of terms.

8.3.5 No. For example, the geometric series with $a_n = 3 \cdot 2^n$ does not have a finite sum.

8.3.6 The series converges if and only if $|r| < 1$.

8.3.7 $S = 1 \cdot \dfrac{1 - 3^9}{1 - 3} = \dfrac{19682}{2} = 9841.$

8.3.8 $S = 1 \cdot \dfrac{1 - (1/4)^{11}}{1 - (1/4)} = \dfrac{4^{11} - 1}{3 \cdot 4^{10}} = \dfrac{4194303}{3 \cdot 1048576} = \dfrac{1398101}{1048576} \approx 1.333.$

8.3.9 $S = 1 \cdot \dfrac{1 - (4/25)^{21}}{1 - 4/25} = \dfrac{25^{21} - 4^{21}}{25^{21} - 4 \cdot 25^{20}} \approx 1.1905.$

8.3.10 $S = 16 \cdot \dfrac{1 - 2^9}{1 - 2} = 511 \cdot 16 = 8176.$

8.3.11 $S = 1 \cdot \dfrac{1 - (-3/4)^{10}}{1 + 3/4} = \dfrac{4^{10} - 3^{10}}{4^{10} + 3 \cdot 4^9} = \dfrac{141361}{262144} \approx 0.5392.$

8.3.12 $S = (-2.5) \cdot \dfrac{1 - (-2.5)^5}{1 + 2.5} = -70.46875.$

8.3.13 $S = 1 \cdot \dfrac{1 - \pi^7}{1 - \pi} = \dfrac{\pi^7 - 1}{\pi - 1} \approx 1409.84.$

8.3.14 $S = \dfrac{4}{7} \cdot \dfrac{1 - (4/7)^{10}}{3/7} = \dfrac{375235564}{282475249} \approx 1.328.$

8.3.15 $S = 1 \cdot \dfrac{1 - (-1)^{21}}{2} = 1.$

8.3.16 $\dfrac{65}{27}.$

8.3.17 $\dfrac{1093}{2916}.$

8.3.18 $\dfrac{1}{5}\left(\dfrac{1 - (3/5)^6}{1 - 3/5}\right) = \dfrac{7448}{15625}.$

8.3.19 $\dfrac{1}{1 - 1/4} = \dfrac{4}{3}.$

8.3.20 $\dfrac{1}{1 - 3/5} = \dfrac{5}{2}.$

8.3.21 $\dfrac{1}{1 - 0.9} = 10.$

8.3.22 $\dfrac{1}{1 - 2/7} = \dfrac{7}{5}.$

8.3.23 Divergent, because $r > 1$.

8.3.24 $\dfrac{1}{1 - 1/\pi} = \dfrac{\pi}{\pi - 1}.$

8.3.25 $\dfrac{e^{-2}}{1 - e^{-2}} = \dfrac{1}{e^2 - 1}.$

8.3.26 $\dfrac{5/4}{1 - 1/2} = \dfrac{5}{2}.$

8.3.27 $\dfrac{2^{-3}}{1 - 2^{-3}} = \dfrac{1}{7}.$

8.3.28 $\dfrac{3 \cdot 4^3/7^3}{1 - 4/7} = \dfrac{64}{49}.$

8.3.29 $\dfrac{1/625}{1 - 1/5} = \dfrac{1}{500}.$

8.3.30 Note that this is the same as $\sum_{i=0}^{\infty} \left(\frac{3}{4}\right)^k$. Then $S = \dfrac{1}{1 - 3/4} = 4.$

8.3.31 $\dfrac{1}{1 - e/\pi} = \dfrac{\pi}{\pi - e}.$ (Note that $e < \pi$, so $r < 1$ for this series.)

8.3.32 $\dfrac{1/16}{1 - 3/4} = \dfrac{1}{4}.$

8.3.33 $\displaystyle\sum_{k=0}^{\infty} \left(\frac{1}{4}\right)^k 5^{3-k} = 5^3 \sum_{k=0}^{\infty} \left(\frac{1}{20}\right)^k = 5^3 \cdot \dfrac{1}{1 - 1/20} = \dfrac{5^3 \cdot 20}{19} = \dfrac{2500}{19}.$

8.3.34 $\dfrac{3^6/8^6}{1 - (3/8)^3} = \dfrac{729}{248320}$

8.3.35 $\dfrac{1}{1 + 9/10} = \dfrac{10}{19}.$

8.3.36 $-\dfrac{2/3}{1 + 2/3} = -\dfrac{2}{5}.$

8.3.37 $3 \cdot \dfrac{1}{1 + 1/\pi} = \dfrac{3\pi}{\pi + 1}.$

8.3.38 $\displaystyle\sum_{k=1}^{\infty} \left(-\frac{1}{e}\right)^k = -\dfrac{1/e}{1 + 1/e} = -\dfrac{1}{e+1}.$

8.3.39 $\dfrac{0.15^2}{1.15} = \dfrac{9}{460} \approx 0.0196.$

8.3.40 $-\dfrac{3/8^3}{1 + 1/8^3} = -\dfrac{1}{171}.$

8.3.41

  a. $0.\overline{3} = 0.333\ldots = \sum_{k=1}^{\infty} 3(0.1)^k.$

  b. The limit of the sequence of partial sums is $1/3$.

8.3.42

  a. $0.\overline{6} = 0.666\ldots = \sum_{k=1}^{\infty} 6(0.1)^k.$

  b. The limit of the sequence of partial sums is $2/3$.

8.3.43

  a. $0.\overline{1} = 0.111\ldots = \sum_{k=1}^{\infty} (0.1)^k.$

  b. The limit of the sequence of partial sums is $1/9$.

8.3.44

  a. $0.\overline{5} = 0.555\ldots = \sum_{k=1}^{\infty} 5(0.1)^k.$

  b. The limit of the sequence of partial sums is $5/9$.

8.3.45

  a. $0.\overline{09} = 0.0909\ldots = \sum_{k=1}^{\infty} 9(0.01)^k.$

  b. The limit of the sequence of partial sums is $1/11$.

8.3.46

  a. $0.\overline{27} = 0.272727\ldots = \sum_{k=1}^{\infty} 27(0.01)^k.$

  b. The limit of the sequence of partial sums is $3/11$.

8.3.47

  a. $0.\overline{037} = 0.037037037\ldots = \sum_{k=1}^{\infty} 37(0.001)^k.$

  b. The limit of the sequence of partial sums is $37/999 = 1/27$.

8.3.48

  a. $0.\overline{027} = 0.027027027\ldots = \sum_{k=1}^{\infty} 27(0.001)^k$

  b. The limit of the sequence of partial sums is $27/999 = 1/37$.

8.3.49 $0.\overline{12} = 0.121212\ldots = \displaystyle\sum_{k=0}^{\infty} .12 \cdot 10^{-2k} = \dfrac{.12}{1 - 1/100} = \dfrac{12}{99} = \dfrac{4}{33}.$

8.3.50 $1.\overline{25} = 1.252525\ldots = 1 + \displaystyle\sum_{k=0}^{\infty} .25 \cdot 10^{-2k} = 1 + \dfrac{.25}{1 - 1/100} = 1 + \dfrac{25}{99} = \dfrac{124}{99}.$

8.3.51 $0.\overline{456} = 0.456456456\ldots = \sum_{k=0}^{\infty} .456 \cdot 10^{-3k} = \dfrac{.456}{1 - 1/1000} = \dfrac{456}{999} = \dfrac{152}{333}.$

8.3.52 $1.00\overline{39} = 1.00393939\ldots = 1 + \sum_{k=0}^{\infty} .0039 \cdot 10^{-2k} = 1 + \dfrac{.0039}{1 - 1/100} = 1 + \dfrac{.39}{99} = 1 + \dfrac{39}{9900} = \dfrac{9939}{9900} = \dfrac{3313}{3300}.$

8.3.53 $0.00\overline{952} = 0.00952952\ldots = \sum_{k=0}^{\infty} .00952 \cdot 10^{-3k} = \dfrac{.00952}{1 - 1/1000} = \dfrac{9.52}{999} = \dfrac{952}{99900} = \dfrac{238}{24975}.$

8.3.54 $5.12\overline{83} = 5.12838383\ldots = 5.12 + \sum_{k=0}^{\infty} .0083 \cdot 10^{-2k} = 5.12 + \dfrac{.0083}{1 - 1/100} = \dfrac{512}{100} + \dfrac{.83}{99} = \dfrac{128}{25} + \dfrac{83}{9900} = \dfrac{50771}{9900}.$

8.3.55 The second part of each term cancels with the first part of the succeeding term, so $S_n = \frac{1}{1+1} - \frac{1}{n+2} = \frac{n}{2n+4}$, and $\lim_{n\to\infty} \frac{n}{2n+4} = \frac{1}{2}$.

8.3.56 The second part of each term cancels with the first part of the succeeding term, so $S_n = \frac{1}{1+2} - \frac{1}{n+3} = \frac{n}{3n+6}$, and $\lim_{n\to\infty} \frac{n}{3n+9} = \frac{1}{3}$.

8.3.57 $\dfrac{1}{(k+6)(k+7)} = \dfrac{1}{k+6} - \dfrac{1}{k+7}$, so the series given is the same as $\sum_{k=1}^{\infty} \left(\frac{1}{k+6} - \frac{1}{k+7} \right)$. In that series, the second part of each term cancels with the first part of the succeeding term, so $S_n = \frac{1}{1+6} - \frac{1}{n+7}$. Thus $\lim_{n\to\infty} S_n = \frac{1}{7}$.

8.3.58 $\dfrac{1}{(3k+1)(3k+4)} = \dfrac{1}{3}\left(\dfrac{1}{3k+1} - \dfrac{1}{3k+4} \right)$, so the series given can be written $\dfrac{1}{3} \sum_{k=0}^{\infty} \left(\dfrac{1}{3k+1} - \dfrac{1}{3k+4} \right)$. In that series, the second part of each term cancels with the first part of the succeeding term (because $3(k+1)+1 = 3k+4$), so we are left with $S_n = \frac{1}{3}\left(\frac{1}{1} - \frac{1}{3n+4} \right) = \frac{n+1}{3n+4}$ and $\lim_{n\to\infty} \frac{n+1}{3n+4} = \frac{1}{3}$.

8.3.59 Note that $\frac{4}{(4k-3)(4k+1)} = \frac{1}{4k-3} - \frac{1}{4k+1}$. Thus the given series is the same as $\sum_{k=3}^{\infty} \left(\dfrac{1}{4k-3} - \dfrac{1}{4k+1} \right)$. In that series, the second part of each term cancels with the first part of the succeeding term (because $4(k+1)-3 = 4k+1$), so we have $S_n = \frac{1}{9} - \frac{1}{4n+1}$, and thus $\lim_{n\to\infty} S_n = \dfrac{1}{9}$.

8.3.60 Note that $\frac{2}{(2k-1)(2k+1)} = \frac{1}{2k-1} - \frac{1}{2k+1}$. Thus the given series is the same as $\sum_{k=3}^{\infty} \left(\dfrac{1}{2k-1} - \dfrac{1}{2k+1} \right)$. In that series, the second part of each term cancels with the first part of the succeeding term (because $2(k+1)-1 = 2k+1$), so we have $S_n = \frac{1}{5} - \frac{1}{2n+1}$. Thus, $\lim_{n\to\infty} S_n = \dfrac{1}{5}$.

8.3.61 $\ln\left(\dfrac{k+1}{k} \right) = \ln(k+1) - \ln k$, so the series given is the same as $\sum_{k=1}^{\infty} (\ln(k+1) - \ln k)$, in which the first part of each term cancels with the second part of the next term, so we have $S_n = \ln(n+1) - \ln 1 = \ln(n+1)$, and thus the series diverges.

8.3.62 Note that $S_n = (\sqrt{2} - \sqrt{1}) + (\sqrt{3} - \sqrt{2}) + \cdots + (\sqrt{n+1} - \sqrt{n})$. The second part of each term cancels with the first part of the previous term. Thus, $S_n = \sqrt{n+1} - 1$. and because $\lim_{n\to\infty} \sqrt{n+1} - 1 = \infty$, the series diverges.

8.3.63 $\frac{1}{(k+p)(k+p+1)} = \frac{1}{k+p} - \frac{1}{k+p+1}$, so that $\sum_{k=1}^{\infty} \frac{1}{(k+p)(k+p+1)} = \sum_{k=1}^{\infty} \left(\frac{1}{k+p} - \frac{1}{k+p+1} \right)$ and this series telescopes to give $S_n = \frac{1}{p+1} - \frac{1}{n+p+1} = \frac{n}{n(p+1)+(p+1)^2}$ so that $\lim_{n\to\infty} S_n = \frac{1}{p+1}$.

8.3.64 $\frac{1}{(ak+1)(ak+a+1)} = \frac{1}{a} \left(\frac{1}{ak+1} - \frac{1}{ak+a+1} \right)$, so that $\sum_{k=1}^{\infty} \frac{1}{(ak+1)(ak+a+1)} =$
$\frac{1}{a} \sum_{k=1}^{\infty} \left(\frac{1}{ak+1} - \frac{1}{ak+a+1} \right)$. This series telescopes - the second term of each summand cancels with the first term of the succeeding summage – so that $S_n = \frac{1}{a} \left(\frac{1}{a+1} - \frac{1}{an+a+1} \right)$, and thus the limit of the sequence is $\frac{1}{a(a+1)}$.

8.3.65 Let $a_n = \frac{1}{\sqrt{n+1}} - \frac{1}{\sqrt{n+3}}$. Then the second term of a_n cancels with the first term of a_{n+2}, so the series telescopes and $S_n = \frac{1}{\sqrt{2}} + \frac{1}{\sqrt{3}} - \frac{1}{\sqrt{n-1+3}} - \frac{1}{\sqrt{n+3}}$ and thus the sum of the series is the limit of S_n, which is $\frac{1}{\sqrt{2}} + \frac{1}{\sqrt{3}}$.

8.3.66 The first term of the kth summand is $\sin(\frac{(k+1)\pi}{2k+1})$; the second term of the $(k+1)^{\text{st}}$ summand is $-\sin(\frac{(k+1)\pi}{2(k+1)-1})$; these two are equal except for sign, so they cancel. Thus $S_n = -\sin 0 + \sin(\frac{(n+1)\pi}{2n+1}) = \sin(\frac{(n+1)\pi}{2n+1})$. Because $\frac{(n+1)\pi}{2n+1}$ has limit $\pi/2$ as $n \to \infty$, and because the sine function is continuous, it follows that $\lim_{n\to\infty} S_n$ is $\sin(\frac{\pi}{2}) = 1$.

8.3.67 $16k^2 + 8k - 3 = (4k+3)(4k-1)$, so $\frac{1}{16k^2+8k-3} = \frac{1}{(4k+3)(4k-1)} = \frac{1}{4} \left(\frac{1}{4k-1} - \frac{1}{4k+3} \right)$. Thus the series given is equal to $\frac{1}{4} \sum_{k=0}^{\infty} \left(\frac{1}{4k-1} - \frac{1}{4k+3} \right)$. This series telescopes, so $S_n = \frac{1}{4} \left(-1 - \frac{1}{4n+3} \right)$, so the sum of the series is equal to $\lim_{n\to\infty} S_n = -\frac{1}{4}$.

8.3.68 This series clearly telescopes to give $S_n = -\tan^{-1}(1) + \tan^{-1}(n) = \tan^{-1}(n) - \frac{\pi}{4}$. Then because $\lim_{n\to\infty} \tan^{-1}(n) = \frac{\pi}{2}$, the sum of the series is equal to $\lim_{n\to\infty} S_n = \frac{\pi}{4}$.

8.3.69

a. True. $\left(\frac{\pi}{e}\right)^{-k} = \left(\frac{e}{\pi}\right)^k$; because $e < \pi$, this is a geometric series with ratio less than 1.

b. True. If $\sum_{k=12}^{\infty} a^k = L$, then $\sum_{k=0}^{\infty} a^k = \left(\sum_{k=0}^{11} a^k \right) + L$.

c. False. For example, let $0 < a < 1$ and $b > 1$.

d. True. Suppose $a > \frac{1}{2}$. Then we want $a = \sum_{k=0}^{\infty} r^k = \frac{1}{1-r}$. Solving for r gives $r = 1 - \frac{1}{a}$. Because $a > 0$ we have $r < 1$; because $a > \frac{1}{2}$ we have $r > 1 - \frac{1}{1/2} = -1$. Thus $|r| < 1$ so that $\sum_{k=0}^{\infty} r^k$ converges, and it converges to a.

e. True. Suppose $a > -\frac{1}{2}$. Then we want $a = \sum_{k=1}^{\infty} r^k = \frac{r}{1-r}$. Solving for r gives $r = \frac{a}{a+1}$. For $a \geq 0$, clearly $0 \leq r < 1$ so that $\sum_{k=1}^{\infty} r^k$ converges to a. For $-\frac{1}{2} < a < 0$, clearly $r < 0$, but $|a| < |a+1|$, so that $|r| < 1$. Thus in this case $\sum_{k=1}^{\infty} r^k$ also converges to a.

8.3.70 We have

$$S_n = \left(\sin^{-1} 1 - \sin^{-1} \frac{1}{2} \right) + \left(\sin^{-1} \frac{1}{2} - \sin^{-1} \frac{1}{3} \right) + \cdots + \left(\sin^{-1} \frac{1}{n} - \sin^{-1} \frac{1}{n+1} \right).$$

Note that the first part of each term cancels the second part of the previous term, so the nth partial sum telescopes to be $\sin^{-1} 1 - \sin^{-1} \frac{1}{n+1}$. Because $\sin^{-1} 1 = \frac{\pi}{2}$ and $\lim\limits_{n\to\infty} \sin^{-1} \frac{1}{n+1} = \sin^{-1} 0 = 0$, we have $\lim\limits_{n\to\infty} S_n = \frac{\pi}{2}$.

8.3.71 This can be written as $\frac{1}{3} \sum\limits_{k=1}^{\infty} \left(-\frac{2}{3}\right)^k$. This is a geometric series with ratio $r = -\frac{2}{3}$ so the sum is $\frac{1}{3} \cdot \frac{-2/3}{1-(-2/3)} = \frac{1}{3} \cdot \left(-\frac{2}{5}\right) = -\frac{2}{15}$.

8.3.72 This can be written as $\frac{1}{e} \sum\limits_{k=1}^{\infty} \left(\frac{\pi}{e}\right)^k$. This is a geometric series with $r = \frac{\pi}{e} > 1$, so the series diverges.

8.3.73 Note that

$$\frac{\ln((k+1)k^{-1})}{(\ln k)\ln(k+1)} = \frac{\ln(k+1)}{(\ln k)\ln(k+1)} - \frac{\ln k}{(\ln k)\ln(k+1)} = \frac{1}{\ln k} - \frac{1}{\ln(k+1)}.$$

In the partial sum S_n, the first part of each term cancels the second part of the preceding term, so we have $S_n = \frac{1}{\ln 2} - \frac{1}{\ln(n+1)}$. Thus we have $\lim\limits_{n\to\infty} S_n = \frac{1}{\ln 2}$.

8.3.74

a. Because the first part of each term cancels the second part of the previous term, the nth partial sum telescopes to be $S_n = \frac{1}{2} - \frac{1}{2^{n+1}}$. Thus, the sum of the series is $\lim\limits_{n\to\infty} S_n = \frac{1}{2}$.

b. Note that $\frac{1}{2^k} - \frac{1}{2^{k+1}} = \frac{2^{k+1}-2^k}{2^k 2^{k+1}} = \frac{1}{2^{k+1}}$. Thus, the original series can be written as $\sum\limits_{k=1}^{\infty} \frac{1}{2^{k+1}}$ which is geometric with $r = 1/2$ and $a = 1/4$, so the sum is $\frac{1/4}{1-1/2} = \frac{1}{2}$.

8.3.75

a. Because the first part of each term cancels the second part of the previous term, the nth partial sum telescopes to be $S_n = \frac{4}{3} - \frac{4}{3^{n+1}}$. Thus, the sum of the series is $\lim\limits_{n\to\infty} S_n = \frac{4}{3}$.

b. Note that $\frac{4}{3^k} - \frac{4}{3^{k+1}} = \frac{4\cdot 3^{k+1}-4\cdot 3^k}{3^k 3^{k+1}} = \frac{8}{3^{k+1}}$. Thus, the original series can be written as $\sum\limits_{k=1}^{\infty} \frac{8}{3^{k+1}}$ which is geometric with $r = 1/3$ and $a = 8/9$, so the sum is $\frac{8/9}{1-1/3} = \frac{8}{9} \cdot \frac{3}{2} = \frac{4}{3}$.

8.3.76 It will take Achilles $1/5$ hour to cover the first mile. At this time, the tortoise has gone $1/5$ mile more, and it will take Achilles $1/25$ hour to reach this new point. At that time, the tortoise has gone another $1/25$ of a mile, and it will take Achilles $1/125$ hour to reach this point. Adding the times up, we have

$$\frac{1}{5} + \frac{1}{25} + \frac{1}{125} + \cdots = \frac{1/5}{1-1/5} = \frac{1}{4},$$

so it will take Achilles $1/4$ of an hour (15 minutes) to catch the tortoise.

8.3.77 At the nth stage, there are 2^{n-1} triangles of area $A_n = \frac{1}{8} A_{n-1} = \frac{1}{8^{n-1}} A_1$, so the total area of the triangles formed at the nth stage is $\frac{2^{n-1}}{8^{n-1}} A_1 = \left(\frac{1}{4}\right)^{n-1} A_1$. Thus the total area under the parabola is

$$\sum_{n=1}^{\infty} \left(\frac{1}{4}\right)^{n-1} A_1 = A_1 \sum_{n=1}^{\infty} \left(\frac{1}{4}\right)^{n-1} = A_1 \frac{1}{1-1/4} = \frac{4}{3} A_1.$$

8.3.78

a. Note that $\frac{3^k}{(3^{k+1}-1)(3^k-1)} = \frac{1}{2} \cdot \left(\frac{1}{3^k-1} - \frac{1}{3^{k+1}-1}\right)$. Then

$$\sum_{k=1}^{\infty} \frac{3^k}{(3^{k+1}-1)(3^k-1)} = \frac{1}{2} \sum_{k=1}^{\infty} \left(\frac{1}{3^k-1} - \frac{1}{3^{k+1}-1}\right).$$

This series telescopes to give $S_n = \frac{1}{2}\left(\frac{1}{3-1} - \frac{1}{3^{n+1}-1}\right)$, so that the sum of the series is $\lim_{n\to\infty} S_n = \frac{1}{4}$.

b. We mimic the above computations. First, $\frac{a^k}{(a^{k+1}-1)(a^k-1)} = \frac{1}{a-1} \cdot \left(\frac{1}{a^k-1} - \frac{1}{a^{k+1}-1}\right)$, so we see that we cannot have $a = 1$, because the fraction would then be undefined. Continuing, we obtain $S_n = \frac{1}{a-1}\left(\frac{1}{a-1} - \frac{1}{a^{n+1}-1}\right)$. Now, $\lim_{n\to\infty} \frac{1}{a^{n+1}-1}$ converges if and only if the denominator grows without bound; this happens if and only if $|a| > 1$. Thus, the original series converges for $|a| > 1$, when it converges to $\frac{1}{(a-1)^2}$. Note that this is valid even for a negative.

8.3.79 It appears that the loan is paid off after about 470 months. Let B_n be the loan balance after n months. Then $B_0 = 180000$ and $B_n = 1.005 \cdot B_{n-1} - 1000$. Then $B_n = 1.005 \cdot B_{n-1} - 1000 = 1.005(1.005 \cdot B_{n-2} - 1000) - 1000 = (1.005)^2 \cdot B_{n-2} - 1000(1 + 1.005) = (1.005)^2 \cdot (1.005 \cdot B_{n-3} - 1000) - 1000(1 + 1.005) = (1.005)^3 \cdot B_{n-3} - 1000(1 + 1.005 + (1.005)^2) = \cdots = (1.005)^n B_0 - 1000(1 + 1.005 + (1.005)^2 + \cdots + (1.005)^{n-1}) = (1.005)^n \cdot 180000 - 1000 \left(\frac{(1.005)^n - 1}{1.005 - 1}\right)$. Solving this equation for $B_n = 0$ gives $n \approx 461.667$ months, so the loan is paid off after 462 months.

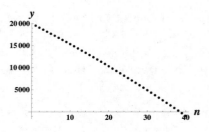

8.3.80 It appears that the loan is paid off after about 38 months. Let B_n be the loan balance after n months. Then $B_0 = 20000$ and $B_n = 1.0075 \cdot B_{n-1} - 60$. Then $B_n = 1.0075 \cdot B_{n-1} - 600 = 1.0075(1.0075 \cdot B_{n-2} - 600) - 600 = (1.0075)^2 \cdot B_{n-2} - 600(1 + 1.0075) = (1.0075)^2(1.0075 \cdot B_{n-3} - 600) - 600(1 + 1.0075) = (1.0075)^3 \cdot B_{n-3} - 600(1 + 1.0075 + (1.0075)^2) = \cdots = (1.0075)^n B_0 - 600(1 + 1.0075 + (1.0075)^2 + \cdots + (1.0075)^{n-1}) = (1.0075)^n \cdot 20000 - 600\left(\frac{(1.0075)^n - 1}{1.0075 - 1}\right)$. Solving this equation for $B_n = 0$ gives $n \approx 38.501$ months, so the loan is paid off after 39 months.

8.3.81 $F_n = (1.015)F_{n-1} - 120 = (1.015)((1.015)F_{n-2} - 120) - 120 = (1.015)((1.015)((1.015)F_{n-3} - 120) - 120) - 120 = \cdots = (1.015)^n(4000) - 120(1 + (1.015) + (1.015)^2 + \cdots + (1.015)^{n-1})$. This is equal to

$$(1.015)^n(4000) - 120\left(\frac{(1.015)^n - 1}{1.015 - 1}\right) = (-4000)(1.015)^n + 8000.$$

The long term population of the fish is 0.

8.3.82 Let A_n be the amount of antibiotic in your blood after n 6-hour periods. Then $A_0 = 200, A_n = 0.5A_{n-1} + 200$. We have $A_n = .5A_{n-1} + 200 = .5(.5A_{n-2} + 200) + 200 = .5(.5(.5A_{n-3} + 200) + 200) + 200 = \cdots = .5^n(200) + 200(1 + .5 + .5^2 + \cdots + .5^{n-1})$. This is equal to

$$.5^n(200) + 200\left(\frac{.5^n - 1}{.5 - 1}\right) = (.5^n)(200 - 400) + 400 = (-200)(.5^n) + 400.$$

The limit of this expression as $n \to \infty$ is 400, so the steady-state amount of antibiotic in your blood is 400 mg.

8.3.83 Under the one-child policy, each couple will have one child. Under the one-son policy, we compute the expected number of children as follows: with probability $1/2$ the first child will be a son; with probability $(1/2)^2$, the first child will be a daughter and the second child will be a son; in general, with probability $(1/2)^n$, the first $n - 1$ children will be girls and the nth a boy. Thus the expected number of children is the sum $\sum_{i=1}^{\infty} i \cdot \left(\frac{1}{2}\right)^i$. To evaluate this series, use the following "trick": Let $f(x) = \sum_{i=1}^{\infty} ix^i$. Then $f(x) + \sum_{i=1}^{\infty} x^i = \sum_{i=1}^{\infty}(i+1)x^i$. Now, let

$$g(x) = \sum_{i=1}^{\infty} x^{i+1} = -1 - x + \sum_{i=0}^{\infty} x^i = -1 - x + \frac{1}{1 - x}$$

and

$$g'(x) = f(x) + \sum_{i=1}^{\infty} x^i = f(x) - 1 + \sum_{i=0}^{\infty} x^i = f(x) - 1 + \frac{1}{1 - x}.$$

Evaluate $g'(x) = -1 - \frac{1}{(1-x)^2}$; then

$$f(x) = 1 - \frac{1}{1 - x} - 1 - \frac{1}{(1 - x)^2} = \frac{-1 + x + 1}{(1 - x)^2} = \frac{x}{(1 - x)^2}$$

Finally, evaluate at $x = \frac{1}{2}$ to get $f\left(\frac{1}{2}\right) = \sum_{i=1}^{\infty} i \cdot \left(\frac{1}{2}\right)^i = \frac{1/2}{(1-1/2)^2} = 2$. There will thus be twice as many children under the one-son policy as under the one-child policy.

8.3.84 Let L_n be the amount of light transmitted through the window the nth time the beam hits the second pane. Then the amount of light that was available before the beam went through the pane was $\frac{L_n}{1-p}$, so $\frac{pL_n}{1-p}$ is reflected back to the first pane, and $\frac{p^2 L_n}{1-p}$ is then reflected back to the second pane. Of that, a fraction equal to $1 - p$ is transmitted through the window. Thus

$$L_{n+1} = (1 - p)\frac{p^2 L_n}{1 - p} = p^2 L_n.$$

The amount of light transmitted through the window the first time is $(1 - p)^2$. Thus the total amount is

$$\sum_{i=0}^{\infty} p^{2n}(1 - p)^2 = \frac{(1 - p)^2}{1 - p^2} = \frac{1 - p}{1 + p}.$$

8.3.85 Ignoring the initial drop for the moment, the height after the nth bounce is $10p^n$, so the total time spent in that bounce is $2 \cdot \sqrt{2 \cdot 10p^n/g}$ seconds. The total time before the ball comes to rest (now including the time for the initial drop) is then $\sqrt{20/g} + \sum_{i=1}^{\infty} 2 \cdot \sqrt{2 \cdot 10p^n/g} = \sqrt{\frac{20}{g}} + 2\sqrt{\frac{20}{g}} \sum_{i=1}^{\infty} (\sqrt{p})^n = \sqrt{\frac{20}{g}} + 2\sqrt{\frac{20}{g}} \frac{\sqrt{p}}{1 - \sqrt{p}} = \sqrt{\frac{20}{g}}\left(1 + \frac{2\sqrt{p}}{1 - \sqrt{p}}\right) = \sqrt{\frac{20}{g}}\left(\frac{1 + \sqrt{p}}{1 - \sqrt{p}}\right)$ seconds.

8.3.86

a. The fraction of available wealth spent each month is $1 - p$, so the amount spent in the nth month is $W(1-p)^n$. The total amount spent is then $\sum_{n=1}^{\infty} W(1-p)^n = \frac{W(1-p)}{1-(1-p)} = W\left(\frac{1-p}{p}\right)$ dollars.

b. As $p \to 1$, the total amount spent approaches 0. This makes sense, because in the limit, if everyone saves all of the money, none will be spent. As $p \to 0$, the total amount spent gets larger and larger. This also makes sense, because almost all of the available money is being respent each month.

8.3.87

a. I_{n+1} is obtained by I_n by dividing each edge into three equal parts, removing the middle part, and adding two parts equal to it. Thus 3 equal parts turn into 4, so $L_{n+1} = \frac{4}{3}L_n$. This is a geometric sequence with a ratio greater than 1, so the nth term grows without bound.

b. As the result of part (a), I_n has $3 \cdot 4^n$ sides of length $\frac{1}{3^n}$; each of those sides turns into an added triangle in I_{n+1} of side length 3^{-n-1}. Thus the added area in I_{n+1} consists of $3 \cdot 4^n$ equilateral triangles with side 3^{-n-1}. The area of an equilateral triangle with side x is $\frac{x^2\sqrt{3}}{4}$. Thus $A_{n+1} = A_n + 3 \cdot 4^n \cdot \frac{3^{-2n-2}\sqrt{3}}{4} = A_n + \frac{\sqrt{3}}{12} \cdot \left(\frac{4}{9}\right)^n$, and $A_0 = \frac{\sqrt{3}}{4}$. Thus $A_{n+1} = A_0 + \sum_{i=0}^{n} \frac{\sqrt{3}}{12} \cdot \left(\frac{4}{9}\right)^i$, so that

$$A_\infty = A_0 + \frac{\sqrt{3}}{12}\sum_{i=0}^{\infty}\left(\frac{4}{9}\right)^i = \frac{\sqrt{3}}{4} + \frac{\sqrt{3}}{12}\frac{1}{1-4/9} = \frac{\sqrt{3}}{4}(1+\frac{3}{5}) = \frac{2}{5}\sqrt{3}.$$

8.3.88

a. $5\sum_{i=1}^{\infty} 10^{-k} = 5\sum_{i=1}^{\infty}\left(\frac{1}{10}\right)^k = 5\left(\frac{1/10}{9/10}\right) = \frac{5}{9}$.

b. $54\sum_{i=1}^{\infty} 10^{-2k} = 54\sum_{i=1}^{\infty}\left(\frac{1}{100}\right)^k = 54\left(\frac{1/100}{99/100}\right) = \frac{54}{99}$.

c. Suppose $x = 0.n_1 n_2 \ldots n_p n_1 n_2 \ldots$. Then we can write this decimal as $n_1 n_2 \ldots n_p \sum_{i=1}^{\infty} 10^{-ip} = n_1 n_2 \ldots n_p \sum_{i=1}^{\infty}\left(\frac{1}{10^p}\right)^i = n_1 n_2 \ldots n_p \frac{1/10^p}{(10^p-1)/10^p} = \frac{n_1 n_2 \ldots n_p}{999 \ldots 9}$, where here $n_1 n_2 \ldots n_p$ does not mean multiplication but rather the digits in a decimal number, and where there are p 9's in the denominator.

d. According to part (c), $0.123456789123456789123 \ldots = \frac{123456789}{999999999}$

e. Again using part (c), $0.\bar{9} = \frac{9}{9} = 1$.

8.3.89 $|S - S_n| = \left|\sum_{i=n}^{\infty} r^k\right| = \left|\frac{r^n}{1-r}\right|$ because the latter sum is simply a geometric series with first term r^n and ratio r.

8.3.90

a. Solve $\frac{0.6^n}{0.4} < 10^{-6}$ for n to get $n = 29$.

b. Solve $\frac{0.15^n}{0.85} < 10^{-6}$ for n to get $n = 8$.

8.3.91

a. Solve $\left|\frac{(-0.8)^n}{1.8}\right| = \frac{0.8^n}{1.8} < 10^{-6}$ for n to get $n = 60$.

b. Solve $\frac{0.2^n}{0.8} < 10^{-6}$ for n to get $n = 9$.

8.3.92

   a. Solve $\frac{0.72^n}{0.28} < 10^{-6}$ for n to get $n = 46$.

   b. Solve $\left|\frac{(-0.25)^n}{1.25}\right| = \frac{0.25^n}{1.25} < 10^{-6}$ for n to get $n = 10$.

8.3.93

   a. Solve $\frac{1/\pi^n}{1 - 1/\pi} < 10^{-6}$ for n to get $n = 13$.

   b. Solve $\frac{1/e^n}{1 - 1/e} < 10^{-6}$ for n to get $n = 15$.

8.3.94

   a. $f(x) = \sum_{k=0}^{\infty} x^k = \frac{1}{1-x}$; because f is represented by a geometric series, $f(x)$ exists only for $|x| < 1$. Then $f(0) = 1$, $f(0.2) = \frac{1}{0.8} = 1.25$, $f(0.5) = \frac{1}{1-0.5} = 2$. Neither $f(1)$ nor $f(1.5)$ exists.

   b. The domain of f is $\{x : |x| < 1\}$.

8.3.95

   a. $f(x) = \sum_{k=0}^{\infty} (-1)^k x^k = \frac{1}{1+x}$; because f is a geometric series, $f(x)$ exists only when the ratio, $-x$, is such that $|-x| = |x| < 1$. Then $f(0) = 1$, $f(0.2) = \frac{1}{1.2} = \frac{5}{6}$, $f(0.5) = \frac{1}{1+.05} = \frac{2}{3}$. Neither $f(1)$ nor $f(1.5)$ exists.

   b. The domain of f is $\{x : |x| < 1\}$.

8.3.96

   a. $f(x) = \sum_{k=0}^{\infty} x^{2k} = \frac{1}{1-x^2}$. f is a geometric series, so $f(x)$ is defined only when the ratio, x^2, is less than 1, which means $|x| < 1$. Then $f(0) = 1$, $f(0.2) = \frac{1}{1-.04} = \frac{25}{24}$, $f(0.5) = \frac{1}{1-0.25} = \frac{4}{3}$. Neither $f(1)$ nor $f(1.5)$ exists.

   b. The domain of f is $\{x : |x| < 1\}$.

8.3.97 $f(x)$ is a geometric series with ratio $\frac{1}{1+x}$; thus $f(x)$ converges when $\left|\frac{1}{1+x}\right| < 1$. For $x > -1$, $\left|\frac{1}{1+x}\right| = \frac{1}{1+x}$ and $\frac{1}{1+x} < 1$ when $1 < 1 + x$, $x > 0$. For $x < -1$, $\left|\frac{1}{1+x}\right| = \frac{1}{-1-x}$, and this is less than 1 when $1 < -1 - x$, i.e. $x < -2$. So $f(x)$ converges for $x > 0$ and for $x < -2$. When $f(x)$ converges, its value is $\frac{1}{1 - \frac{1}{1+x}} = \frac{1+x}{x}$, so $f(x) = 3$ when $1 + x = 3x$, $x = \frac{1}{2}$.

8.3.98

   a. Clearly for $k < n$, h_k is a leg of a right triangle whose hypotenuse is r_k and whose other leg is formed where the vertical line (in the picture) meets a diameter of the next smaller sphere; thus the other leg of the triangle is r_{k+1}. The Pythagorean theorem then implies that $h_k^2 = r_k^2 - r_{k+1}^2$.

   b. The height is $H_n = \sum_{i=1}^{n} h_i = r_n + \sum_{i=1}^{n-1} \sqrt{r_i^2 - r_{i+1}^2}$ by part (a).

   c. From part (b), because $r_i = a^{i-1}$,

$$H_n = r_n + \sum_{i=1}^{n-1} \sqrt{r_i^2 - r_{i+1}^2} = a^{n-1} + \sum_{i=1}^{n-1} \sqrt{a^{2i-2} - a^{2i}}$$

$$= a^{n-1} + \sum_{i=1}^{n-1} a^{i-1} \sqrt{1 - a^2} = a^{n-1} + \sqrt{1 - a^2} \sum_{i=1}^{n-1} a^{i-1}$$

$$= a^{n-1} + \sqrt{1 - a^2} \left(\frac{1 - a^{n-1}}{1 - a}\right)$$

d. $\lim\limits_{n\to\infty} H_n = \lim\limits_{n\to\infty} a^{n-1} + \sqrt{1-a^2}\,\lim\limits_{n\to\infty}\frac{1-a^{n-1}}{1-a} = 0 + \sqrt{1-a^2}\left(\frac{1}{1-a}\right) = \sqrt{\frac{1-a^2}{(1-a)(1-a)}} = \sqrt{\frac{1+a}{1-a}}.$

8.3.99

a. Using Theorem 8.7 in each case except for $r = 0$ gives

r	$f(r)$
-0.9	0.526
-0.7	0.588
-0.5	0.667
-0.2	0.833
0	1
0.2	1.250
0.5	2
0.7	3.333
0.9	10

b. A plot of f is

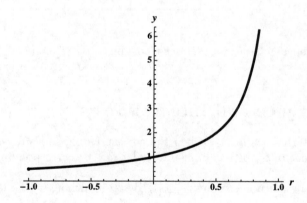

c. For $-1 < r < 1$ we have $f(r) = \frac{1}{1-r}$, so that

$$\lim_{r\to-1^+} f(r) = \lim_{r\to-1^+}\frac{1}{1-r} = \frac{1}{2}, \qquad \lim_{r\to1^-} f(r) = \lim_{r\to1^-}\frac{1}{1-r} = \infty.$$

8.3.100

a. In each case (except for $r = 0$ where $N(r)$ is clearly 0), compute $|S - S_n|$ for various values of n gives the following results:

r	$N(r)$	$\lvert S - S_{N(r)-1}\rvert$	$\lvert S - S_{N(r)}\rvert$
-0.9	81	1.0×10^{-4}	9.3×10^{-5}
-0.7	24	1.1×10^{-4}	7.9×10^{-5}
-0.5	12	1.6×10^{-4}	8.1×10^{-5}
-0.2	5	2.7×10^{-4}	5.3×10^{-5}
0	0	—	0
0.2	5	4.0×10^{-4}	8.0×10^{-5}
0.5	14	1.2×10^{-4}	6.1×10^{-5}
0.7	29	1.1×10^{-4}	7.5×10^{-5}
0.9	109	1.0×10^{-4}	9.3×10^{-5}

b. A plot of r versus $N(r)$ for these values of r is

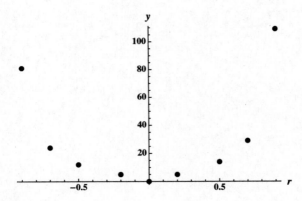

c. The rate of convergence is faster for r closer to 0, since $N(r)$ is smaller. The reason for this is that r^k gets smaller faster as k increases when $\lvert r\rvert$ is closer to zero than when it is closer to 1.

8.4   The Divergence and Integral Tests

8.4.1 If the sequence of terms has limit 1, then the corresponding series diverges. It is necessary (but not sufficient) that the sequence of terms has limit 0 in order for the corresponding series to be convergent.

8.4.2 No. For example, the harmonic serkes $\sum_{k=1}^{\infty} \frac{1}{k}$ diverges although $\frac{1}{k} \to 0$ as $k \to \infty$.

8.4.3 Yes. Either the series and the integral both converge, or both diverge, if the terms are positive and decreasing.

8.4.4 It converges for $p > 1$, and diverges for all other values of p.

8.4.5 For the same values of p as in the previous problem – it converges for $p > 1$, and diverges for all other values of p.

8.4.6 Let S_n be the partial sums. Then $S_{n+1} - S_n = a_{n+1} > 0$ because $a_{n+1} > 0$. Thus the sequence of partial sums is increasing.

8.4.7 The remainder of an infinite series is the error in approximating a convergent infinite series by a finite number of terms.

8.4.8 Yes. Suppose $\sum a_k$ converges to S, and let the sequence of partial sums be $\{S_n\}$. Then for any $\epsilon > 0$ there is some N such that for any $n > N$, $|S - S_n| < \epsilon$. But $|S - S_n|$ is simply the remainder R_n when the series is approximated to n terms. Thus $R_n \to 0$ as $n \to \infty$.

8.4.9 $a_k = \frac{k}{2k+1}$ and $\lim\limits_{k \to \infty} a_k = \frac{1}{2}$, so the series diverges.

8.4.10 $a_k = \frac{k}{k^2+1}$ and $\lim\limits_{k \to \infty} a_k = 0$, so the divergence test is inconclusive.

8.4.11 $a_k = \frac{k}{\ln k}$ and $\lim\limits_{k \to \infty} a_k = \infty$, so the series diverges.

8.4.12 $a_k = \frac{k^2}{2^k}$ and $\lim\limits_{k \to \infty} a_k = 0$, so the divergence test is inconclusive.

8.4.13 $a_k = \frac{1}{1000+k}$ and $\lim\limits_{k \to \infty} a_k = 0$, so the divergence test is inconclusive.

8.4.14 $a_k = \frac{k^3}{k^3+1}$ and $\lim\limits_{k \to \infty} a_k = 1$, so the series diverges.

8.4.15 $a_k = \frac{\sqrt{k}}{\ln^{10} k}$ and $\lim\limits_{k \to \infty} a_k = \infty$, so the series diverges.

8.4.16 $a_k = \frac{\sqrt{k^2+1}}{k}$ and $\lim\limits_{k \to \infty} a_k = 1$, so the series diverges.

8.4.17 $a_k = k^{1/k}$. In order to compute $\lim_{k \to \infty} a_k$, we let $y_k = \ln a_k = \frac{\ln k}{k}$. By Theorem 9.6, (or by L'Hôpital's rule), $\lim_{k \to \infty} y_k = 0$, so $\lim_{k \to \infty} a_k = e^0 = 1$. The given series thus diverges.

8.4.18 By Theorem 9.6 $k^3 \ll k!$, so $\lim_{k \to \infty} \frac{k^3}{k!} = 0$. The divergence test is inconclusive.

8.4.19 Clearly $\frac{1}{e^x} = e^{-x}$ is continuous, positive, and decreasing for $x \geq 2$ (in fact, for all x), so the integral test applies. Because

$$\int_2^\infty e^{-x} \, dx = \lim_{c \to \infty} \int_2^c e^{-x} \, dx = \lim_{c \to \infty} \left. (-e^{-x}) \right|_2^c = \lim_{c \to \infty} (e^{-2} - e^{-c}) = e^{-2},$$

the Integral Test tells us that the original series converges as well.

8.4.20 Let $f(x) = \frac{x}{\sqrt{x^2+4}}$. $f(x)$ is continuous for $x \geq 1$. Note that $f'(x) = \frac{4}{(\sqrt{x^2+4})^3} > 0$. Thus f is increasing, and the conditions of the Integral Test aren't satisfied. The given series diverges by the Divergence Test.

8.4.21 Let $f(x) = x \cdot e^{-2x^2}$. This function is continuous for $x \geq 1$. Its derivative is $e^{-2x^2}(1 - 4x^2) < 0$ for $x \geq 1$, so $f(x)$ is decreasing. Because $\int_1^\infty x \cdot e^{-2x^2} \, dx = \frac{1}{4e^2}$, the series converges.

8.4.22 Let $f(x) = \frac{1}{\sqrt[3]{x+10}}$. $f(x)$ is obviously continuous and decreasing for $x \geq 1$. Because $\int_1^\infty \frac{1}{\sqrt[3]{x+10}} \, dx = \infty$, the series diverges.

8.4.23 Let $f(x) = \frac{1}{\sqrt{x+8}}$. $f(x)$ is obviously continuous and decreasing for $x \geq 1$. Because $\int_1^\infty \frac{1}{\sqrt{x+8}} \, dx = \infty$, the series diverges.

8.4.24 Let $f(x) = \frac{1}{x(\ln x)^2}$. $f(x)$ is continuous and decreasing for $x \geq 2$. Because $\int_2^\infty f(x) \, dx = \frac{1}{\ln 2}$ the series converges.

8.4.25 Let $f(x) = \frac{x}{e^x}$. $f(x)$ is clearly continuous for $x > 1$, and its derivative, $f'(x) = \frac{e^x - xe^x}{e^{2x}} = (1 - x)\frac{e^x}{e^{2x}}$, is negative for $x > 1$ so that $f(x)$ is decreasing. Because $\int_1^\infty f(x) \, dx = 2e^{-1}$, the series converges.

8.4.26 Let $f(x) = \frac{1}{x \cdot \ln x \cdot \ln \ln x}$. $f(x)$ is continuous and decreasing for $x > 3$, and $\int_3^\infty \frac{1}{x \cdot \ln x \cdot \ln \ln x} \, dx = \infty$. The given series therefore diverges.

8.4.27 The integral test does not apply, because the sequence of terms is not decreasing.

8.4.28 $f(x) = \frac{x}{(x^2+1)^3}$ is decreasing and continuous, and $\int_1^\infty \frac{x}{(x^2+1)^3}\, dx = \frac{1}{16}$. Thus, the given series converges.

8.4.29 This is a p-series with $p = 10$, so this series converges.

8.4.30 $\sum_{k=2}^\infty \frac{k^e}{k^\pi} = \sum_{k=2}^\infty \frac{1}{k^{\pi-e}}$. Note that $\pi - e \approx 3.1416 - 2.71828 < 1$, so this series diverges.

8.4.31 $\sum_{k=3}^\infty \frac{1}{(k-2)^4} = \sum_{k=1}^\infty \frac{1}{k^4}$, which is a p-series with $p = 4$, thus convergent.

8.4.32 $\sum_{k=1}^\infty 2k^{-3/2} = 2\sum_{k=1}^\infty \frac{1}{k^{3/2}}$ is a p-series with $p = 3/2$, thus convergent.

8.4.33 $\sum_{k=1}^\infty \frac{1}{\sqrt[3]{k}} = \sum_{k=1}^\infty \frac{1}{k^{1/3}}$ is a p-series with $p = 1/3$, thus divergent.

8.4.34 $\sum_{k=1}^\infty \frac{1}{\sqrt[3]{27k^2}} = \frac{1}{3}\sum_{k=1}^\infty \frac{1}{k^{2/3}}$ is a p-series with $p = 2/3$, thus divergent.

8.4.35

   a. The remainder R_n is bounded by $\int_n^\infty \frac{1}{x^6}\, dx = \frac{1}{5n^5}$.

   b. We solve $\frac{1}{5n^5} < 10^{-3}$ to get $n = 3$.

   c. $L_n = S_n + \int_{n+1}^\infty \frac{1}{x^6}\, dx = S_n + \frac{1}{5(n+1)^5}$, and $U_n = S_n + \int_n^\infty \frac{1}{x^6}\, dx = S_n + \frac{1}{5n^5}$.

   d. $S_{10} \approx 1.017341512$, so $L_{10} \approx 1.017341512 + \frac{1}{5\cdot 11^5} \approx 1.017342754$, and $U_{10} \approx 1.017341512 + \frac{1}{5\cdot 10^5} \approx 1.017343512$.

8.4.36

   a. The remainder R_n is bounded by $\int_n^\infty \frac{1}{x^8}\, dx = \frac{1}{7n^7}$.

   b. We solve $\frac{1}{7n^7} < 10^{-3}$ to obtain $n = 3$.

   c. $L_n = S_n + \int_{n+1}^\infty \frac{1}{x^8}\, dx = S_n + \frac{1}{7(n+1)^7}$, and $U_n = S_n + \int_n^\infty \frac{1}{x^8}\, dx = S_n + \frac{1}{7n^7}$.

   d. $S_{10} \approx 1.004077346$, so $L_{10} \approx 1.004077346 + \frac{1}{7\cdot 11^7} \approx 1.004077353$, and $U_{10} \approx 1.004077346 + \frac{1}{7\cdot 10^7} \approx 1.004077360$.

8.4.37

   a. The remainder R_n is bounded by $\int_n^\infty \frac{1}{3^x}\, dx = \frac{1}{3^n \ln 3}$.

   b. We solve $\frac{1}{3^n \ln 3} < 10^{-3}$ to obtain $n = 7$.

   c. $L_n = S_n + \int_{n+1}^\infty \frac{1}{3^x}\, dx = S_n + \frac{1}{3^{n+1} \ln 3}$, and $U_n = S_n + \int_n^\infty \frac{1}{3^x}\, dx = S_n + \frac{1}{3^n \ln 3}$.

   d. $S_{10} \approx 0.4999915325$, so $L_{10} \approx 0.4999915325 + \frac{1}{3^{11} \ln 3} \approx 0.4999966708$, and $U_{10} \approx 0.4999915325 + \frac{1}{3^{10} \ln 3} \approx 0.5000069475$.

8.4.38

   a. The remainder R_n is bounded by $\int_n^\infty \frac{1}{x \ln^2 x}\, dx = \frac{1}{\ln n}$.

   b. We solve $\frac{1}{\ln n} < 10^{-3}$ to get $n = e^{1000} \approx 10^{434}$.

   c. $L_n = S_n + \int_{n+1}^\infty \frac{1}{x \ln^2 x}\, dx = S_n + \frac{1}{\ln(n+1)}$, and $U_n = S_n + \int_n^\infty \frac{1}{x \ln^2 x}\, dx = S_n + \frac{1}{\ln n}$.

   d. $S_{11} = \sum_{k=2}^{11} \frac{1}{k \ln^2 k} \approx 1.700396385$, so $L_{11} \approx 1.700396385 + \frac{1}{\ln 12} \approx 2.102825989$, and $U_{11} \approx 1.700396385 + \frac{1}{\ln 11} \approx 2.117428776$.

8.4.39

a. The remainder R_n is bounded by $\int_n^\infty \frac{1}{x^{3/2}}\,dx = 2n^{-1/2}$.

b. We solve $2n^{-1/2} < 10^{-3}$ to get $n > 4 \times 10^6$, so let $n = 4 \times 10^6 + 1$.

c. $L_n = S_n + \int_{n+1}^\infty \frac{1}{x^{3/2}}\,dx = S_n + 2(n+1)^{-1/2}$, and $U_n = S_n + \int_n^\infty \frac{1}{x^{3/2}}\,dx = S_n + 2n^{-1/2}$.

d. $S_{10} = \sum_{k=1}^{10} \frac{1}{k^{3/2}} \approx 1.995336493$, so $L_{10} \approx 1.995336493 + 2 \cdot 11^{-1/2} \approx 2.598359182$, and $U_{10} \approx 1.995336493 + 2 \cdot 10^{-1/2} \approx 2.627792025$.

8.4.40

a. The remainder R_n is bounded by $\int_n^\infty e^{-x}\,dx = e^{-n}$.

b. We solve $e^{-n} < 10^{-3}$ to get $n = 7$.

c. $L_n = S_n + \int_{n+1}^\infty e^{-x}\,dx = S_n + e^{-(n+1)}$, and $U_n = S_n + \int_n^\infty e^{-x}\,dx = S_n + e^{-n}$.

d. $S_{10} = \sum_{k=1}^{10} e^{-k} \approx 0.5819502852$, so $L_{10} \approx 0.5819502852 + e^{-11} \approx 0.5819669869$, and $U_{10} \approx 0.5819502852 + e^{-10} \approx 0.5819956851$.

8.4.41

a. The remainder R_n is bounded by $\int_n^\infty \frac{1}{x^3}\,dx = \frac{1}{2n^2}$.

b. We solve $\frac{1}{2n^2} < 10^{-3}$ to get $n = 23$.

c. $L_n = S_n + \int_{n+1}^\infty \frac{1}{x^3}\,dx = S_n + \frac{1}{2(n+1)^2}$, and $U_n = S_n + \int_n^\infty \frac{1}{x^3}\,dx = S_n + \frac{1}{2n^2}$.

d. $S_{10} \approx 1.197531986$, so $L_{10} \approx 1.197531986 + \frac{1}{2 \cdot 11^2} \approx 1.201664217$, and $U_{10} \approx 1.197531986 + \frac{1}{2 \cdot 10^2} \approx 1.202531986$.

8.4.42

a. The remainder R_n is bounded by $\int_n^\infty xe^{-x^2}\,dx = \frac{1}{2e^{n^2}}$.

b. We solve $\frac{1}{2e^{n^2}} < 10^{-3}$ to get $n = 3$.

c. $L_n = S_n + \int_{n+1}^\infty xe^{-x^2}\,dx = S_n + \frac{1}{2e^{(n+1)^2}}$, and $U_n = S_n + \int_n^\infty xe^{-x^2}\,dx = S_n + \frac{1}{2e^{n^2}}$.

d. $S_{10} \approx 0.4048813986$, so $L_{10} \approx 0.4048813986 + \frac{1}{2e^{11^2}} \approx 0.4048813986$, and $U_{10} \approx 0.4048813986 + \frac{1}{2e^{10^2}} \approx 0.4048813986$.

8.4.43 This is a geometric series with $a = \frac{1}{3}$ and $r = \frac{1}{12}$, so $\sum_{k=1}^\infty \frac{4}{12^k} = \frac{1/3}{1-1/12} = \frac{1/3}{11/12} = \frac{4}{11}$.

8.4.44 This is a geometric series with $a = 3/e^2$ and $r = 1/e$, so $\sum_{k=2}^\infty 3e^{-k} = \frac{3/e^2}{1-(1/e)} = \frac{3/e^2}{(e-1)/e} = \frac{3}{e(e-1)}$.

8.4.45 $\sum_{k=0}^\infty \left(3\left(\frac{2}{5}\right)^k - 2\left(\frac{5}{7}\right)^k \right) = 3\sum_{k=0}^\infty \left(\frac{2}{5}\right)^k - 2\sum_{k=0}^\infty \left(\frac{5}{7}\right)^k = 3\left(\frac{1}{3/5}\right) - 2\left(\frac{1}{2/7}\right) = 5 - 7 = -2$.

8.4.46 $\sum_{k=1}^\infty \left(2\left(\frac{3}{5}\right)^k + 3\left(\frac{4}{9}\right)^k \right) = 2\sum_{k=1}^\infty \left(\frac{3}{5}\right)^k + 3\sum_{k=1}^\infty \left(\frac{4}{9}\right)^k = 2\left(\frac{3/5}{2/5}\right) + 3\left(\frac{4/9}{5/9}\right) = 3 + \frac{12}{5} = \frac{27}{5}$.

8.4.47 $\sum_{k=1}^\infty \left(\frac{1}{3}\left(\frac{5}{6}\right)^k + \frac{3}{5}\left(\frac{7}{9}\right)^k \right) = \frac{1}{3}\sum_{k=1}^\infty \left(\frac{5}{6}\right)^k + \frac{3}{5}\sum_{k=1}^\infty \left(\frac{7}{9}\right)^k = \frac{1}{3}\left(\frac{5/6}{1/6}\right) + \frac{3}{5}\left(\frac{7/9}{2/9}\right) = \frac{5}{3} + \frac{21}{10} = \frac{113}{30}$.

8.4.48 $\sum_{k=0}^{\infty}\left(\frac{1}{2}(0.2)^k + \frac{3}{2}(0.8)^k\right) = \frac{1}{2}\sum_{k=0}^{\infty}(0.2)^k + \frac{3}{2}\sum_{k=0}^{\infty}(0.8)^k = \frac{1}{2}\left(\frac{1}{0.8}\right) + \frac{3}{2}\left(\frac{1}{0.2}\right) = \frac{5}{8} + \frac{15}{2} = \frac{65}{8}.$

8.4.49 $\sum_{k=1}^{\infty}\left(\left(\frac{1}{6}\right)^k + \left(\frac{1}{3}\right)^{k-1}\right) = \sum_{k=1}^{\infty}\left(\frac{1}{6}\right)^k + \sum_{k=1}^{\infty}\left(\frac{1}{3}\right)^{k-1} = \frac{1/6}{5/6} + \frac{1}{2/3} = \frac{17}{10}.$

8.4.50 $\sum_{k=0}^{\infty}\frac{2-3^k}{6^k} = \sum_{k=0}^{\infty}\left(\frac{2}{6^k} - \frac{3^k}{6^k}\right) = 2\sum_{k=0}^{\infty}\left(\frac{1}{6}\right)^k - \sum_{k=0}^{\infty}\left(\frac{1}{2}\right)^k = 2\left(\frac{1}{5/6}\right) - \frac{1}{1/2} = \frac{2}{5}.$

8.4.51

a. True. The two series differ by a finite amount ($\sum_{k=1}^{9} a_k$), so if one converges, so does the other.

b. True. The same argument applies as in part (a).

c. False. If $\sum a_k$ converges, then $a_k \to 0$ as $k \to \infty$, so that $a_k + 0.0001 \to 0.0001$ as $k \to \infty$, so that $\sum(a_k + 0.0001)$ cannot converge.

d. False. Suppose $p = -1.0001$. Then $\sum p^k$ diverges but $p + 0.001 = -0.9991$ so that $\sum(p + .0001)^k$ converges.

e. False. Let $p = 1.0005$; then $-p + .001 = -(p - .001) = -.9995$, so that $\sum k^{-p}$ converges (p-series) but $\sum k^{-p+.001}$ diverges.

f. False. Let $a_k = \frac{1}{k}$, the harmonic series.

8.4.52 Diverges by the Divergence Test because $\lim_{k\to\infty} a_k = \lim_{k\to\infty}\sqrt{\frac{k+1}{k}} = 1 \neq 0$.

8.4.53 Converges by the Integral Test because $\int_1^{\infty}\frac{1}{(3x+1)(3x+4)}\,dx = \int_1^{\infty}\frac{1}{3(3x+1)} - \frac{1}{3(3x+4)}\,dx =$
$\lim_{b\to\infty}\int_1^b\left(\frac{1}{3(3x+1)} - \frac{1}{3(3x+4)}\right)dx = \lim_{b\to\infty}\frac{1}{9}\left(\ln\left(\frac{3x+1}{3x+4}\right)\right)\Big|_1^b = \lim_{b\to\infty} = -\frac{1}{9}\cdot\ln(4/7) \approx 0.06217 < \infty.$

Alternatively, this is a telescoping series with nth partial sum equal to $S_n = \frac{1}{3}\left(\frac{1}{4} - \frac{1}{3n+4}\right)$ which converges to $\frac{1}{12}$.

8.4.54 Converges by the Integral Test because $\int_0^{\infty}\frac{10}{x^2+9}\,dx = \frac{10}{3}\lim_{b\to\infty}\left(\tan^{-1}(x/3)\Big|_0^b\right) = \frac{10}{3}\frac{\pi}{2} \approx 5.236 < \infty.$

8.4.55 Diverges by the Divergence Test because $\lim_{k\to\infty} a_k = \lim_{k\to\infty}\frac{k}{\sqrt{k^2+1}} = 1 \neq 0$.

8.4.56 Converges because it is the sum of two geometric series. In fact, $\sum_{k=1}^{\infty}\frac{2^k+3^k}{4^k} = \sum_{k=1}^{\infty}(2/4)^k + \sum_{k=1}^{\infty}(3/4)^k = \frac{1/2}{1-(1/2)} + \frac{3/4}{1-(3/4)} = 1 + 3 = 4.$

8.4.57 Converges by the Integral Test because $\int_2^{\infty}\frac{4}{x\ln^2 x}\,dx = \lim_{b\to\infty}\left(\frac{-4}{\ln x}\Big|_2^b\right) = \frac{4}{\ln 2} < \infty.$

8.4.58

a. In order for the series to converge, the integral $\int_2^{\infty}\frac{1}{x(\ln x)^p}\,dx$ must exist. But

$$\int\frac{1}{x(\ln x)^p}\,dx = \frac{1}{1-p}(\ln x)^{1-p},$$

so in order for this improper integral to exist, we must have that $1 - p < 0$ or $p > 1$.

b. The series converges faster for $p = 3$ because the terms of the series get smaller faster.

8.4.59

a. Note that $\int \frac{1}{x \ln x (\ln \ln x)^p} \, dx = \frac{1}{1-p}(\ln \ln x)^{1-p}$, and thus the improper integral with bounds n and ∞ exists only if $p > 1$ because $\ln \ln x > 0$ for $x > e$. So this series converges for $p > 1$.

b. For large values of z, clearly $\sqrt{z} > \ln z$, so that $z > (\ln z)^2$. Write $z = \ln x$; then for large x, $\ln x > (\ln \ln x)^2$; multiplying both sides by $x \ln x$ we have that $x \ln^2 x > x \ln x (\ln \ln x)^2$, so that the first series converges faster because the terms get smaller faster.

8.4.60

a. $\sum \frac{1}{k^{2.5}}$.

b. $\sum \frac{1}{k^{0.75}}$.

c. $\sum \frac{1}{k^{3/2}}$.

8.4.61 Let $S_n = \sum_{k=1}^{n} \frac{1}{\sqrt{k}}$. Then this looks like a left Riemann sum for the function $y = \frac{1}{\sqrt{x}}$ on $[1, n+1]$. Because each rectangle lies above the curve itself, we see that S_n is bounded below by the integral of $\frac{1}{\sqrt{x}}$ on $[1, n+1]$. Now,

$$\int_1^{n+1} \frac{1}{\sqrt{x}} \, dx = \int_1^{n+1} x^{-1/2} \, dx = 2\sqrt{x} \Big|_1^{n+1} = 2\sqrt{n+1} - 2.$$

This integral diverges as $n \to \infty$, so the series does as well by the bound above.

8.4.62 $\sum_{k=1}^{\infty} (a_k \pm b_k) = \lim_{n \to \infty} \sum_{k=1}^{n} (a_k \pm b_k) = \lim_{n \to \infty} \left(\sum_{k=1}^{n} a_k \pm \sum_{k=1}^{n} b_k \right) = \lim_{n \to \infty} \sum_{k=1}^{n} a_k \pm \lim_{n \to \infty} \sum_{k=1}^{n} b_k = A \pm B$.

8.4.63 $\sum_{k=1}^{\infty} c a_k = \lim_{n \to \infty} \sum_{k=1}^{n} c a_k = \lim_{n \to \infty} c \sum_{k=1}^{n} a_k = c \lim_{n \to \infty} \sum_{k=1}^{n} a_k$, so that one sum diverges if and only if the other one does.

8.4.64 $\displaystyle\sum_{k=2}^{\infty} \frac{1}{k \ln k}$ diverges by the Integral Test, because $\int_2^{\infty} \frac{1}{x \ln x} = \lim_{b \to \infty} \left(\ln \ln x \Big|_2^b \right) = \infty$.

8.4.65 To approximate the sequence for $\zeta(m)$, note that the remainder R_n after n terms is bounded by

$$\int_n^{\infty} \frac{1}{x^m} \, dx = \frac{1}{m-1} n^{1-m}.$$

For $m = 3$, if we wish to approximate the value to within 10^{-3}, we must solve $\frac{1}{2} n^{-2} < 10^{-3}$, so that $n = 23$, and $\displaystyle\sum_{k=1}^{23} \frac{1}{k^3} \approx 1.201151926$. The true value is ≈ 1.202056903.

For $m = 5$, if we wish to approximate the value to within 10^{-3}, we must solve $\frac{1}{4} n^{-4} < 10^{-3}$, so that $n = 4$, and $\displaystyle\sum_{k=1}^{4} \frac{1}{k^5} \approx 1.036341789$. The true value is ≈ 1.036927755.

8.4.66

a. Starting with $\cot^2 x < \dfrac{1}{x^2} < 1 + \cot^2 x$, substitute $k\theta$ for x:

$$\cot^2(k\theta) < \frac{1}{k^2\theta^2} < 1 + \cot^2(k\theta),$$

$$\sum_{k=1}^{n} \cot^2(k\theta) < \sum_{k=1}^{n} \frac{1}{k^2\theta^2} < \sum_{k=1}^{n}(1 + \cot^2(k\theta)),$$

$$\sum_{k=1}^{n} \cot^2(k\theta) < \frac{1}{\theta^2}\sum_{k=1}^{n} \frac{1}{k^2} < n + \sum_{k=1}^{n} \cot^2(k\theta).$$

Note that the identity is valid because we are only summing for k up to n, so that $k\theta < \frac{\pi}{2}$.

b. Substitute $\dfrac{n(2n-1)}{3}$ for the sum, using the identity:

$$\frac{n(2n-1)}{3} < \frac{1}{\theta^2}\sum_{k=1}^{n} \frac{1}{k^2} < n + \frac{n(2n-1)}{3},$$

$$\theta^2 \frac{n(2n-1)}{3} < \sum_{k=1}^{n} \frac{1}{k^2} < \theta^2 \frac{n(2n+2)}{3},$$

$$\frac{n(2n-1)\pi^2}{3(2n+1)^2} < \sum_{k=1}^{n} \frac{1}{k^2} < \frac{n(2n+2)\pi^2}{3(2n+1)^2}.$$

c. By the Squeeze Theorem, if the expressions on either end have equal limits as $n \to \infty$, the expression in the middle does as well, and its limit is the same. The expression on the left is

$$\pi^2 \frac{2n^2 - n}{12n^2 + 12n + 3} = \pi^2 \frac{2 - n^{-1}}{12 + 12n^{-1} + 3n^{-2}},$$

which has a limit of $\dfrac{\pi^2}{6}$ as $n \to \infty$. The expression on the right is

$$\pi^2 \frac{2n^2 + 2n}{12n^2 + 12n + 3} = \pi^2 \frac{2 + 2n^{-1}}{12 + 12n^{-1} + 3n^{-3}},$$

which has the same limit. Thus $\displaystyle\lim_{n\to\infty} \sum_{k=1}^{n} \frac{1}{k^2} = \sum_{k=1}^{\infty} \frac{1}{k^2} = \frac{\pi^2}{6}$.

8.4.67 $\displaystyle\sum_{k=1}^{\infty} \frac{1}{k^2} = \sum_{k=1}^{\infty} \frac{1}{(2k)^2} + \sum_{k=1}^{\infty} \frac{1}{(2k-1)^2}$, splitting the series into even and odd terms. But $\sum_{k=1}^{\infty} \frac{1}{(2k)^2} = \frac{1}{4}\sum_{k=1}^{\infty} \frac{1}{k^2}$. Thus $\frac{\pi^2}{6} = \frac{1}{4}\frac{\pi^2}{6} + \sum_{k=1}^{\infty} \frac{1}{(2k-1)^2}$, so that the sum in question is $\frac{3\pi^2}{24} = \frac{\pi^2}{8}$.

8.4.68

a. $\{F_n\}$ is a decreasing sequence because each term in F_n is smaller than the corresponding term in F_{n-1} and thus the sum of terms in F_n is smaller than the sum of terms in F_{n-1}.

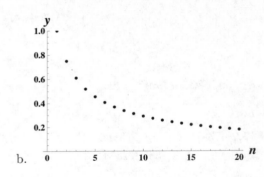

c. It appears that $\lim\limits_{n\to\infty} F_n = 0$.

8.4.69

a. $x_1 = \sum_{k=2}^{2} \frac{1}{k} = \frac{1}{2}$, $x_2 = \sum_{k=3}^{4} \frac{1}{k} = \frac{1}{3} + \frac{1}{4} = \frac{7}{12}$, $x_3 = \sum_{k=4}^{6} \frac{1}{k} = \frac{1}{4} + \frac{1}{5} + \frac{1}{6} = \frac{37}{60}$.

b. x_n has n terms. Each term is bounded below by $\frac{1}{2n}$ and bounded above by $\frac{1}{n+1}$. Thus $x_n \geq n \cdot \frac{1}{2n} = \frac{1}{2}$, and $x_n \leq n \cdot \frac{1}{n+1} < n \cdot \frac{1}{n} = 1$.

c. The right Riemann sum for $\int_1^2 \frac{dx}{x}$ using n subintervals has n rectangles of width $\frac{1}{n}$; the right edges of those rectangles are at $1 + \frac{i}{n} = \frac{n+i}{n}$ for $i = 1, 2, \ldots, n$. The height of such a rectangle is the value of $\frac{1}{x}$ at the right endpoint, which is $\frac{n}{n+i}$. Thus the area of the rectangle is $\frac{1}{n} \cdot \frac{n}{n+i} = \frac{1}{n+i}$. Adding up over all the rectangles gives x_n.

d. The limit $\lim\limits_{n\to\infty} x_n$ is the limit of the right Riemann sum as the width of the rectangles approaches zero. This is precisely $\int_1^2 \frac{dx}{x} = \ln x \Big|_1^2 = \ln 2$.

8.4.70

The first diagram is a left Riemann sum for $f(x) = \frac{1}{x}$ on the interval $[1, 11]$ (we assume $n = 10$ for purposes of drawing a graph). The area under the curve is $\int_1^{n+1} \frac{1}{x}\,dx = \ln(n+1)$, and the sum of the areas of the rectangles is obviously $1 + \frac{1}{2} + \frac{1}{3} + \cdots + \frac{1}{n}$. Thus

$$\ln(n+1) < 1 + \frac{1}{2} + \frac{1}{3} + \cdots + \frac{1}{n}.$$

a. The second diagram is a right Riemann sum for the same function on the same interval. Considering only $[1, n]$, we see that, comparing the area under the curve and the sum of the areas of the rectangles, that

$$\frac{1}{2} + \frac{1}{3} + \cdots + \frac{1}{n} < \ln n.$$

Adding 1 to both sides gives the desired inequality.

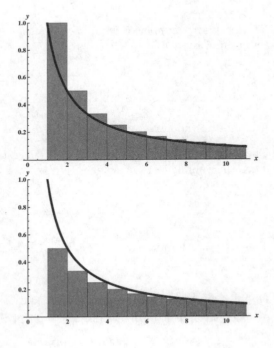

b. According to part (a), $\ln(n+1) < S_n$ for $n = 1, 2, 3, \ldots,$, so that $E_n = S_n - \ln(n+1) > 0$.

c. Using the second figure above and assuming $n = 9$, the final rectangle corresponds to $\frac{1}{n+1}$, and the area under the curve between $n+1$ and $n+2$ is clearly $\ln(n+2) - \ln(n+1)$.

d. $E_{n+1} - E_n = S_{n+1} - \ln(n+2) - (S_n - \ln(n+1)) = \frac{1}{n+1} - (\ln(n+2) - \ln(n+1))$. But this is positive because of the bound established in part (c).

e. Using part (a), $E_n = S_n - \ln(n+1) < 1 + \ln n - \ln(n+1) < 1$.

f. E_n is a monotone (increasing) sequence that is bounded, so it has a limit.

g. The first ten values (E_1 through E_{10}) are

$$.3068528194, .401387711, .447038972, .473895421, .491573864,$$
$$.504089851, .513415601, .520632566, .526383161, .531072981.$$

$E_{1000} \approx 0.576716082.$

h. For $S_n > 10$ we need $10 - 0.5772 = 9.4228 > \ln(n+1)$. Solving for n gives $n \approx 12366.16$, so $n = 12367$.

8.4.71

a. Note that the center of gravity of any stack of dominoes is the average of the locations of their centers. Define the midpoint of the zeroth (top) domino to be $x = 0$, and stack additional dominoes down and to its right (to increasingly positive x-coordinates). Let $m(n)$ be the x-coordinate of the midpoint of the nth domino. Then in order for the stack not to fall over, the left edge of the nth domino must be placed directly under the center of gravity of dominos 0 through $n - 1$, which is $\frac{1}{n} \sum_{i=0}^{n-1} m(i)$, so that $m(n) = 1 + \frac{1}{n} \sum_{i=0}^{n-1} m(i)$. We claim that in fact $m(n) = \sum_{k=1}^{n} \frac{1}{k}$. Use induction. This is certainly true for $n = 1$. Note first that $m(0) = 0$, so we can start the sum at 1 rather than at 0. Now, $m(n) = 1 + \frac{1}{n} \sum_{i=1}^{n-1} m(i) = 1 + \frac{1}{n} \sum_{i=1}^{n-1} \sum_{j=1}^{i} \frac{1}{j}$. Now, 1 appears $n - 1$ times in the double sum, 2 appears $n - 2$ times, and so forth, so we can rewrite this sum as $m(n) = 1 + \frac{1}{n} \sum_{i=1}^{n-1} \frac{n-i}{i} = 1 + \frac{1}{n} \sum_{i=1}^{n-1} \left(\frac{n}{i} - 1\right) = 1 + \frac{1}{n} \left(n \sum_{i=1}^{n-1} \frac{1}{i} - (n-1)\right) = \sum_{i=1}^{n-1} \frac{1}{i} + 1 - \frac{n-1}{n} = \sum_{i=1}^{n} \frac{1}{i}$, and we are done by induction (noting that the statement is clearly true for $n = 0$, $n = 1$). Thus the maximum overhang is $\sum_{k=2}^{n} \frac{1}{k}$.

b. For an infinite number of dominos, because the overhang is the harmonic series, the distance is potentially infinite.

8.4.72

a. The circumference of the kth layer is $2\pi \cdot \frac{1}{k}$, so its area is $2\pi \cdot \frac{1}{k}$ and thus the total vertical surface area $\sum_{k=1}^{\infty} 2\pi \cdot \frac{1}{k} = 2\pi \sum_{k=1}^{\infty} \frac{1}{k} = \infty$. The horizontal surface area, however, is π, since looking at the cake from above, the horizontal surface covers the circle of radius 1, which has area $\pi \cdot 1^2 = \pi$.

b. The volume of a cylinder of radius r and height h is $\pi r^2 h$, so the volume of the kth layer is $\pi \cdot \frac{1}{k^2} \cdot 1 = \frac{\pi}{k^2}$. Thus the volume of the cake is

$$\sum_{k=1}^{\infty} \frac{\pi}{k^2} = \pi \sum_{k=1}^{\infty} \frac{1}{k^2} = \frac{\pi^3}{6} \approx 5.168.$$

c. This cake has infinite surface area, yet it has finite volume!

8.4.73

a. Dividing both sides of the recurrence equation by f_n gives $\frac{f_{n+1}}{f_n} = 1 + \frac{f_{n-1}}{f_n}$. Let the limit of the ratio of successive terms be L. Taking the limit of the previous equation gives $L = 1 + \frac{1}{L}$. Thus $L^2 = L + 1$, so $L^2 - L - 1 = 0$. The quadratic formula gives $L = \frac{1 \pm \sqrt{1 - 4 \cdot (-1)}}{2}$, but we know that all the terms are positive, so we must have $L = \frac{1 + \sqrt{5}}{2} = \phi \approx 1.618$.

b. Write the recurrence in the form $f_{n-1} = f_{n+1} - f_n$ and divide both sides by f_{n+1}. Then we have $\frac{f_{n-1}}{f_{n+1}} = 1 - \frac{f_n}{f_{n+1}}$. Taking the limit gives $1 - \frac{1}{\phi}$ on the right-hand side.

c. Consider the harmonic series with the given groupings, and compare it with the sum of $\frac{f_{k-1}}{f_{k+1}}$ as shown. The first three terms match exactly. The sum of the next two are $\frac{1}{4} + \frac{1}{5} > \frac{1}{5} + \frac{1}{5} = \frac{2}{5}$. The sum of the next three are $\frac{1}{6} + \frac{1}{7} + \frac{1}{8} > \frac{1}{8} + \frac{1}{8} + \frac{1}{8} = \frac{3}{8}$. The sum of the next five are $\frac{1}{9} + \cdots + \frac{1}{13} > 5 \cdot \frac{1}{13} = \frac{5}{13}$. Thus the harmonic series is bounded below by the series $\sum_{k=1}^{\infty} \frac{f_{k-1}}{f_{k+1}}$.

d. The result above implies that the harmonic series diverges, because the series $\sum_{k=1}^{\infty} \frac{f_{k-1}}{f_{k+1}}$ diverges, since its general term has limit $1 - \frac{1}{\phi} \neq 0$.

8.5   The Ratio, Root, and Comparison Tests

8.5.1 Given a series $\sum a_k$ of positive terms, compute $\lim_{k\to\infty} \frac{a_{k+1}}{a_k}$ and call it r. If $0 \leq r < 1$, the given series converges. If $r > 1$ (including $r = \infty$), the given series diverges. If $r = 1$, the test is inconclusive.

8.5.2 Given a series $\sum a_k$ of positive terms, compute $\lim_{k\to\infty} \sqrt[k]{a_k}$ and call it r. If $0 \leq r < 1$, the given series converges. If $r > 1$ (including $r = \infty$), the given series diverges. If $r = 1$, the test is inconclusive.

8.5.3 Given a series of positive terms $\sum a_k$ that you suspect converges, find a series $\sum b_k$ that you know converges, for which $\lim_{k\to\infty} \frac{a_k}{b_k} = L$ where $L \geq 0$ is a finite number. If you are successful, you will have shown that the series $\sum a_k$ converges.

Given a series of positive terms $\sum a_k$ that you suspect diverges, find a series $\sum b_k$ that you know diverges, for which $\lim_{k\to\infty} \frac{a_k}{b_k} = L$ where $L > 0$ (including the case $L = \infty$). If you are successful, you will have shown that $\sum a_k$ diverges.

8.5.4 The Divergence Test.

8.5.5 The Ratio Test.

8.5.6 The Comparison Test or the Limit Comparison Test.

8.5.7 The difference between successive partial sums is a term in the sequence. Because the terms are positive, differences between successive partial sums are as well, so the sequence of partial sums is increasing.

8.5.8 No. They all determine convergence or divergence by approximating or bounding the series by some other series known to converge or diverge; thus, the actual value of the series cannot be determined.

8.5.9 The ratio between successive terms is $\frac{a_{k+1}}{a_k} = \frac{1}{(k+1)!} \cdot \frac{(k)!}{1} = \frac{1}{k+1}$, which goes to zero as $k \to \infty$, so the given series converges by the Ratio Test.

8.5.10 The ratio between successive terms is $\frac{a_{k+1}}{a_k} = \frac{2^{k+1}}{(k+1)!} \cdot \frac{(k)!}{2^k} = \frac{2}{k+1}$; the limit of this ratio is zero, so the given series converges by the Ratio Test.

8.5.11 The ratio between successive terms is $\frac{a_{k+1}}{a_k} = \frac{(k+1)^2}{4^{(k+1)}} \cdot \frac{4^k}{(k)^2} = \frac{1}{4}\left(\frac{k+1}{k}\right)^2$. The limit is $1/4$ as $k \to \infty$, so the given series converges by the Ratio Test.

8.5.12 The ratio between successive terms is

$$\frac{a_{k+1}}{a_k} = \frac{(k+1)^{(k+1)}}{2^{(k+1)}} \cdot \frac{2^k}{k^k} = \frac{k+1}{2}\left(\frac{k+1}{k}\right)^k.$$

Note that $\lim_{k\to\infty}\left(\frac{k+1}{k}\right)^k = e$, but $\lim_{k\to\infty} \frac{k+1}{2} = \infty$, so the given series diverges by the Ratio Test.

8.5.13 The ratio between successive terms is $\frac{a_{k+1}}{a_k} = \frac{(k+1)e^{-(k+1)}}{(k)e^{-(k)}} = \frac{k+1}{(k)e}$. The limit of this ratio as $k \to \infty$ is $1/e < 1$, so the given series converges by the Ratio Test.

8.5.14 The ratio between successive terms is $\frac{a_{k+1}}{a_k} = \frac{(k+1)^{k+1}}{(k+1)!} \cdot \frac{k!}{k^k} = \left(\frac{k+1}{k}\right)^k$. This has limit e as $k \to \infty$, so the limit of the ratio of successive terms is $e > 1$, so the given series diverges by the Ratio Test.

8.5.15 The ratio between successive terms is $\frac{2^{k+1}}{(k+1)^{99}} \cdot \frac{(k)^{99}}{2^k} = 2\left(\frac{k}{k+1}\right)^{99}$; the limit as $k \to \infty$ is 2, so the given series diverges by the Ratio Test.

8.5.16 The ratio between successive terms is $\frac{(k+1)^6}{(k+1)!} \cdot \frac{(k)!}{(k)^6} = \frac{1}{k+1}\left(\frac{k+1}{k}\right)^6$; the limit as $k \to \infty$ is zero, so the given series converges by the Ratio Test.

8.5.17 The ratio between successive terms is $\frac{((k+1)!)^2}{(2(k+1))!} \cdot \frac{(2k)!}{((k)!)^2} = \frac{(k+1)^2}{(2k+2)(2k+1)}$; the limit as $k \to \infty$ is $1/4$, so the given series converges by the Ratio Test.

8.5.18 Note that this series is $\sum_{k=1}^{\infty} \frac{2^k}{k^4}$. The ratio between successive terms is $\frac{2^{k+1}k^4}{2^k(k+1)^4} = 2\left(\frac{k}{k+1}\right)^4 \to 2$ as $k \to \infty$. So the given series diverges by the ratio test.

8.5.19 The kth root of the kth term is $\frac{10k^3+3}{9k^3+k+1}$. The limit of this as $k \to \infty$ is $\frac{10}{9} > 1$, so the given series diverges by the Root Test.

8.5.20 The kth root of the kth term is $\frac{2k}{k+1}$. The limit of this as $k \to \infty$ is $2 > 1$, so the given series diverges by the Root Test.

8.5.21 The kth root of the kth term is $\frac{k^{2/k}}{2}$. The limit of this as $k \to \infty$ is $\frac{1}{2} < 1$, so the given series converges by the Root Test.

8.5.22 The kth root of the kth term is $\left(1 + \frac{3}{k}\right)^k$. The limit of this as $k \to \infty$ is $= e^3 > 1$, so the given series diverges by the Root Test.

8.5.23 The kth root of the kth term is $\left(\frac{k}{k+1}\right)^{2k}$. The limit of this as $k \to \infty$ is $e^{-2} < 1$, so the given series converges by the Root Test.

8.5.24 The kth root of the kth term is $\frac{1}{\ln(k+1)}$. The limit of this as $k \to \infty$ is 0, so the given series converges by the Root Test.

8.5.25 The kth root of the kth term is $\left(\frac{1}{k^k}\right)$. The limit of this as $k \to \infty$ is 0, so the given series converges by the Root Test.

8.5.26 The kth root of the kth term is $\frac{k^{1/k}}{e}$. The limit of this as $k \to \infty$ is $\frac{1}{e} < 1$, so the given series converges by the Root Test.

8.5.27 $\frac{1}{k^2+4} < \frac{1}{k^2}$, and $\sum_{k=1}^{\infty} \frac{1}{k^2}$ converges, so $\sum_{k=1}^{\infty} \frac{1}{k^2+4}$ converges as well, by the Comparison Test.

8.5.28 Use the Limit Comparison Test with $\left\{\frac{1}{k^2}\right\}$. The ratio of the terms of the two series is $\frac{k^4+k^3-k^2}{k^4+4k^2-3}$ which has limit 1 as $k \to \infty$. Because the comparison series converges, the given series does as well.

8.5.29 Use the Limit Comparison Test with $\left\{\frac{1}{k}\right\}$. The ratio of the terms of the two series is $\frac{k^3-k}{k^3+4}$ which has limit 1 as $k \to \infty$. Because the comparison series diverges, the given series does as well.

8.5.30 Use the Limit Comparison Test with $\left\{\frac{1}{k}\right\}$. The ratio of the terms of the two series is $\frac{0.0001k}{k+4}$ which has limit 0.0001 as $k \to \infty$. Because the comparison series diverges, the given series does as well.

8.5.31 For all k, $\frac{1}{k^{3/2}+1} < \frac{1}{k^{3/2}}$. The series whose terms are $\frac{1}{k^{3/2}}$ is a p-series which converges, so the given series converges as well by the Comparison Test.

8.5.32 Use the Limit Comparison Test with $\{1/k\}$. The ratio of the terms of the two series is $k\sqrt{\frac{k}{k^3+1}} = \sqrt{\frac{k^3}{k^3+1}}$, which has limit 1 as $k \to \infty$. Because the comparison series diverges, the given series does as well.

8.5.33 $\sin(1/k) > 0$ for $k \geq 1$, so we can apply the Comparison Test with $1/k^2$. $\sin(1/k) < 1$, so $\frac{\sin(1/k)}{k^2} < \frac{1}{k^2}$. Because the comparison series converges, the given series converges as well.

8.5.34 Use the Limit Comparison Test with $\{1/3^k\}$. The ratio of the terms of the two series is $\frac{3^k}{3^k - 2^k} = \frac{1}{1 - \left(\frac{2^k}{3^k}\right)}$, which has limit 1 as $k \to \infty$. Because the comparison series converges, the given series does as well.

8.5.35 Use the Limit Comparison Test with $\{1/k\}$. The ratio of the terms of the two series is $\frac{k}{2k - \sqrt{k}} = \frac{1}{2 - 1/\sqrt{k}}$, which has limit $1/2$ as $k \to \infty$. Because the comparison series diverges, the given series does as well.

8.5.36 $\frac{1}{k\sqrt{k+2}} < \frac{1}{k\sqrt{k}} = \frac{1}{k^{3/2}}$. Because the series whose terms are $\frac{1}{k^{3/2}}$ is a p−series with $p > 1$, it converges. Because the comparison series converges, the given series converges as well.

8.5.37 Use the Limit Comparison Test with $\frac{k^{2/3}}{k^{3/2}}$. The ratio of corresponding terms of the two series is $\frac{\sqrt[3]{k^2+1}}{\sqrt{k^3+1}} \cdot \frac{k^{3/2}}{k^{2/3}} = \frac{\sqrt[3]{k^2+1}}{\sqrt[3]{k^2}} \cdot \frac{\sqrt{k^3}}{\sqrt{k^3+1}}$, which has limit 1 as $k \to \infty$. The comparison series is the series whose terms are $k^{2/3 - 3/2} = k^{-5/6}$, which is a p-series with $p < 1$, so it, and the given series, both diverge.

8.5.38 For all k, $\frac{1}{(k \ln k)^2} < \frac{1}{k^2}$. Because the series whose terms are $\frac{1}{k^2}$ converges, the given series converges as well.

8.5.39

    a. False. For example, let $\{a_k\}$ be all zeros, and $\{b_k\}$ be all 1's.

    b. True. This is a result of the Comparison Test.

    c. True. Both of these statements follow from the Comparison Test.

    d. True. The limit of the ratio is always 1 in the case, so the test is inconclusive.

8.5.40 Use the Divergence Test: $\lim_{k \to \infty} a_k = \lim_{k \to \infty} \left(1 - \frac{1}{k}\right)^k = \frac{1}{e} \neq 0$, so the given series diverges.

8.5.41 Use the Divergence Test: $\lim_{k \to \infty} a_k = \lim_{k \to \infty} \left(1 + \frac{2}{k}\right)^k = e^2 \neq 0$, so the given series diverges.

8.5.42 Use the Root Test: The kth root of the kth term is $\frac{k^2}{2k^2+1}$. The limit of this as $k \to \infty$ is $\frac{1}{2} < 1$, so the given series converges by the Root Test.

8.5.43 Use the Ratio Test: the ratio of successive terms is $\frac{(k+1)^{100}}{(k+2)!} \cdot \frac{(k+1)!}{k^{100}} = \left(\frac{k+1}{k}\right)^{100} \cdot \frac{1}{k+2}$. This has limit $1^{100} \cdot 0 = 0$ as $k \to \infty$, so the given series converges by the Ratio Test.

8.5.44 Use the Comparison Test. Note that $\sin^2 k \leq 1$ for all k, so $\frac{\sin^2 k}{k^2} \leq \frac{1}{k^2}$ for all k. Because $\sum_{k=1}^{\infty} \frac{1}{k^2}$ converges, so does the given series.

8.5.45 Use the Root Test. The kth root of the kth term is $(k^{1/k} - 1)^2$, which has limit 0 as $k \to \infty$, so the given series converges by the Root Test.

8.5.46 Use the Limit Comparison Test with the series whose kth term is $\left(\frac{2}{e}\right)^k$. Note that $\lim_{k \to \infty} \frac{2^k}{e^k - 1} \cdot \frac{e^k}{2^k} = \lim_{k \to \infty} \frac{e^k}{e^k - 1} = 1$. The given series thus converges because $\sum_{k=1}^{\infty} \left(\frac{2}{e}\right)^k$ converges (because it is a geometric series with $r = \frac{2}{e} < 1$). Note that it is also possible to show convergence with the Ratio Test.

8.5.47 Use the Divergence Test: $\lim_{k \to \infty} \frac{k^2 + 2k + 1}{3k^2 + 1} = \frac{1}{3} \neq 0$, so the given series diverges.

8.5.48 Use the Limit Comparison Test with the series whose kth term is $\frac{1}{5^k}$. Note that $\lim_{k\to\infty} \frac{1}{5^k-1} \cdot \frac{5^k}{1} = 1$, and the series $\sum_{k=1}^{\infty} \frac{1}{5^k}$ converges because it is a geometric series with $r = \frac{1}{5}$. Thus, the given series also converges.

8.5.49 Use the Limit Comparison Test with the harmonic series. Note that $\lim_{k\to\infty} \frac{\frac{\ln k}{k}}{\frac{1}{k}} = \lim_{k\to\infty} \frac{k}{\ln k} = \infty$, and because the harmonic series diverges, the given series does as well.

8.5.50 Use the Limit Comparison Test with the series whose kth term is $\frac{1}{5^k}$. Note that $\lim_{k\to\infty} \frac{1}{5^k-3^k} \cdot \frac{5^k}{1} = \lim_{k\to\infty} \frac{1}{1-(3/5)^k} = 1$, and the series $\sum_{k=3}^{\infty} \frac{1}{5^k}$ converges because it is a geometric series with $r = \frac{1}{5}$. Thus, the given series also converges.

8.5.51 Use the Limit Comparison Test with the series whose kth term is $\frac{1}{k^{3/2}}$. Note that $\lim_{k\to\infty} \frac{1}{\sqrt{k^3-k+1}} \cdot \frac{\sqrt{k^3}}{1} = \lim_{k\to\infty} \sqrt{\frac{k^3}{k^3-k+1}} = \sqrt{1} = 1$, and the series $\sum_{k=1}^{\infty} \frac{1}{k^{3/2}}$ converges because it is a p-series with $p = \frac{3}{2}$. Thus, the given series also converges.

8.5.52 Use the Ratio Test: $\frac{a_{k+1}}{a_k} = \frac{((k+1)!)^3}{(3k+3)!} \cdot \frac{(3k)!}{(k!)^3} = \frac{(k+1)^3}{(3k+1)(3k+2)(3k+3)}$, which has limit $1/27$ as $k \to \infty$. Thus the given series converges.

8.5.53 Use the Comparison Test. Each term $\frac{1}{k} + 2^{-k} > \frac{1}{k}$. Because the harmonic series diverges, so does this series.

8.5.54 Use the Comparison Test with $\{5/k\}$. Note that $\frac{5\ln k}{k} > \frac{5}{k}$ for $k > 1$. Because the series whose terms are $5/k$ diverges, the given series diverges as well.

8.5.55 Use the Ratio Test. $\frac{a_{k+1}}{a_k} = \frac{2^{k+1}(k+1)!}{(k+1)^{k+1}} \cdot \frac{(k)^k}{2^k (k)!} = 2\left(\frac{k}{k+1}\right)^k$, which has limit $\frac{2}{e}$ as $k \to \infty$, so the given series converges.

8.5.56 Use the Root Test. $\lim_{k\to\infty} \left(1 - \frac{1}{k}\right)^k = e^{-1} < 1$, so the given series converges.

8.5.57 Use the Limit Comparison Test with $\{1/k^3\}$. The ratio of corresponding terms is $\frac{k^{11}}{k^{11}+3}$, which has limit 1 as $k \to \infty$. Because the comparison series converges, so does the given series.

8.5.58 Use the Root Test. $\lim_{k\to\infty} \frac{1}{1+p} = \frac{1}{1+p} < 1$ because $p > 0$, so the given series converges.

8.5.59 This is a p-series with exponent greater than 1, so it converges.

8.5.60 Use the Comparison Test: $\frac{1}{k^2 \ln k} < \frac{1}{k^2}$. Because the series whose terms are $\frac{1}{k^2}$ is a convergent p–series, the given series converges as well.

8.5.61 $\ln\left(\frac{k+2}{k+1}\right) = \ln(k+2) - \ln(k+1)$, so this series telescopes. We get $\sum_{k=1}^{n} \ln\left(\frac{k+2}{k+1}\right) = \ln(n+2) - \ln 2$. Because $\lim_{n\to\infty} \ln(n+2) - \ln 2 = \infty$, the sequence of partial sums diverges, so the given series is divergent.

8.5.62 Use the Divergence Test. Note that $\lim_{k\to\infty} k^{-1/k} = \lim_{k\to\infty} \frac{1}{\sqrt[k]{k}} = 1 \neq 0$, so the given series diverges.

8.5.63 For $k > 7$, $\ln k > 2$ so note that $\frac{1}{k^{\ln k}} < \frac{1}{k^2}$. Because $\sum_{k=1}^{\infty} \frac{1}{k^2}$ converges, the given series converges as well.

8.5.64 Use the Limit Comparison Test with $\{1/k^2\}$. Note that $\frac{\sin^2(1/k)}{1/k^2} = \left(\frac{\sin(1/k)}{1/k}\right)^2$. Because $\lim_{x\to 0} \frac{\sin x}{x} = 1$, the limit of this expression is $1^2 = 1$ as $k \to \infty$. Because $\sum_{k=1}^{\infty} \frac{1}{k^2}$ converges, the given series does as well.

8.5.65 Use the Limit Comparison Test with the harmonic series. $\frac{\tan(1/k)}{1/k}$ has limit 1 as $k \to \infty$ because $\lim_{x\to 0} \frac{\tan x}{x} = 1$. Thus the original series diverges.

8.5.66 Use the Root Test. $\lim_{k \to \infty} \sqrt[k]{a_k} = \lim_{k \to \infty} \sqrt[k]{100} \cdot \frac{1}{k} = 0$, so the given series converges.

8.5.67 Note that $\dfrac{1}{(2k+1) \cdot (2k+3)} = \dfrac{1}{2}\left(\dfrac{1}{2k+1} - \dfrac{1}{2k+3}\right)$. Thus this series telescopes.

$$\sum_{k=0}^{n} \frac{1}{(2k+1)(2k+3)} = \frac{1}{2} \sum_{k=0}^{n} \left(\frac{1}{2k+1} - \frac{1}{2k+3}\right) = \frac{1}{2}\left(-\frac{1}{2n+3} + 1\right),$$

so the given series converges to $1/2$, because that is the limit of the sequence of partial sums.

8.5.68 This series is $\sum_{k=1}^{\infty} \frac{k-1}{k^2} = \sum_{k=1}^{\infty} \left(\frac{1}{k} - \frac{1}{k^2}\right)$. Because $\sum_{k=1}^{\infty} \frac{1}{k^2}$ converges, if the original series also converged, we would have that $\sum_{k=1}^{\infty} \frac{1}{k}$ converged, which is false. Thus the original series diverges.

8.5.69 This series is $\sum_{k=1}^{\infty} \frac{k^2}{k!}$. By the Ratio Test, $\frac{a_{k+1}}{a_k} = \frac{(k+1)^2}{(k+1)!} \cdot \frac{k!}{k^2} = \frac{1}{k+1}\left(\frac{k+1}{k}\right)^2$, which has limit 0 as $k \to \infty$, so the given series converges.

8.5.70 For any p, if k is sufficently large then $k^{1/p} > \ln k$ because powers grow faster than logs, so that $k > (\ln k)^p$ and thus $1/k < 1/(\ln k)^p$. Because $\sum 1/k$ diverges, we see that the original series diverges for all p.

8.5.71 For $p \le 1$ and $k > e$, $\frac{\ln k}{k^p} > \frac{1}{k^p}$. The series $\sum_{k=1}^{\infty} \frac{1}{k^p}$ diverges, so the given series diverges. For $p > 1$, let $q < p - 1$; then for sufficiently large k, $\ln k < k^q$, so that by the Comparison Test, $\frac{\ln k}{k^p} < \frac{k^q}{k^p} = \frac{1}{k^{p-q}}$. But $p - q > 1$, so that $\sum_{k=1}^{\infty} \frac{1}{k^{p-q}}$ is a convergent p-series. Thus the original series is convergent precisely when $p > 1$.

8.5.72 For $p \ne 1$,

$$\int_2^{\infty} \frac{dx}{x \ln x (\ln \ln x)^p} = \lim_{b \to \infty} \left(\frac{(\ln \ln x)^{1-p}}{1-p}\bigg|_2^b\right).$$

This improper integral converges if and only $p > 1$. If $p = 1$, we have

$$\int_2^{\infty} \frac{dx}{x(\ln x) \ln \ln x} = \lim_{b \to \infty} \ln \ln \ln x \bigg|_2^b = \infty.$$

Thus the original series converges for $p > 1$.

8.5.73 For $p \le 1$, $\frac{(\ln k)^p}{k^p} > \frac{1}{k^p}$ for $k \ge 3$, and $\sum_{k=1}^{\infty} \frac{1}{k^p}$ diverges for $p \le 1$, so the original series diverges. For $p > 1$, let $q < p - 1$; then for sufficiently large k, $(\ln k)^p < k^q$. Note that $\frac{(\ln k)^p}{k^p} < \frac{k^q}{k^p} = \frac{1}{k^{p-q}}$. But $p - q > 1$, so $\sum_{k=1}^{\infty} \frac{1}{k^{p-q}}$ converges, so the given series converges. Thus, the given series converges exactly for $p > 1$.

8.5.74 Using the Ratio Test, $\frac{a_{k+1}}{a_k} = \frac{(k+1)! p^{k+1}}{(k+2)^{k+1}} \cdot \frac{(k+1)^k}{(k)! p^k} = \frac{(k+1) p (k+1)^k}{(k+2)^{k+1}} = p\left(\frac{k+1}{k+2}\right)^{k+1} = p \cdot \left(\frac{1}{1+\frac{1}{k+1}}\right)^{k+1}$, which has limit pe^{-1}. The series converges if the ratio limit is less than 1, so if $p < e$. If $p > e$, the given series diverges by the Ratio Test. If $p = e$, the given series diverges by the Divergence Test.

8.5.75 Use the Ratio Test:

$$\lim_{k \to \infty} \frac{a_{k+1}}{a_k} = \lim_{k \to \infty} \frac{(k+1) p^{k+1}}{k+2} \cdot \frac{k+1}{k p^k} = p,$$

so the given series converges for $p < 1$ and diverges for $p > 1$. For $p = 1$ the given series diverges by limit comparison with the harmonic series.

8.5.76 $\ln\left(\frac{k}{k+1}\right)^p = p(\ln(k) - \ln(k+1))$, so

$$\sum_{k=1}^{\infty} \ln\left(\frac{k}{k+1}\right)^p = p \sum_{k=1}^{\infty} (\ln(k) - \ln(k+1))$$

which telescopes, and the nth partial sum is $-p \ln(n+1)$, and $\lim_{n \to \infty} -p \ln(n+1)$ is not a finite number for any value of p other than 0. The given series diverges for all values of p other than $p = 0$.

8.5.77 $\lim\limits_{k\to\infty} a_k = \lim\limits_{k\to\infty}\left(1-\frac{p}{k}\right)^k = e^{-p} \neq 0$, so this sequence diverges for all p by the Divergence Test.

8.5.78 Use the Limit Comparison Test: $\lim\limits_{k\to\infty}\frac{a_k^2}{a_k} = \lim\limits_{k\to\infty} a_k = 0$, because $\sum a_k$ converges. By the Limit Comparison Test, the series $\sum a_k^2$ must converge as well.

8.5.79 These tests apply only for series with positive terms, so assume $r > 0$. Clearly the series do not converge for $r = 1$, so we assume $r \neq 1$ in what follows. Using the Integral Test, $\sum r^k$ converges if and only if $\int_1^\infty r^x\,dx$ converges. This improper integral has value $\lim\limits_{b\to\infty}\frac{r^x}{\ln r}\Big|_1^b$, which converges only when $\lim\limits_{b\to\infty} r^b$ exists, which occurs only for $r < 1$. Using the Ratio Test, $\frac{a_{k+1}}{a_k} = \frac{r^{k+1}}{r^k} = r$, so by the Ratio Test, the series converges if and only if $r < 1$. Using the Root Test, $\lim\limits_{k\to\infty}\sqrt[k]{a_k} = \lim\limits_{k\to\infty}\sqrt[k]{r^k} = \lim\limits_{k\to\infty} r = r$, so again we have convergence if and only if $r < 1$. By the Divergence Test, we know that a geometric series diverges if $|r| \geq 1$.

8.5.80

  a. Use the Limit Comparison Test with the divergent harmonic series. Note that $\lim\limits_{k\to\infty}\frac{\sin(1/k)}{1/k} = 1$, because $\lim\limits_{x\to 0}\frac{\sin x}{x} = 1$. Because the comparison series diverges, the given series does as well.

  b. We use the Limit Comparison Test with the convergent series $\sum\frac{1}{k^2}$. Note that $\lim\limits_{k\to\infty}\frac{(1/k)\sin(1/k)}{1/k^2} = \lim\limits_{k\to\infty}\frac{\sin(1/k)}{1/k} = 1$, so the given series converges.

8.5.81 To prove case (2), assume $L = 0$ and that $\sum b_k$ converges. Because $L = 0$, for every $\varepsilon > 0$, there is some N such that for all $n > N$, $\left|\frac{a_k}{b_k}\right| < \varepsilon$. Take $\varepsilon = 1$; this then says that there is some N such that for all $n > N$, $0 < a_k < b_k$. By the Comparison Test, because $\sum b_k$ converges, so does $\sum a_k$. To prove case (3), because $L = \infty$, then $\lim\limits_{k\to\infty}\frac{b_k}{a_k} = 0$, so by the argument above, we have $0 < b_k < a_k$ for sufficient large k. But $\sum b_k$ diverges, so by the Comparison Test, $\sum a_k$ does as well.

8.5.82 The series clearly converges for $x = 0$. For $x \neq 0$, we have $\frac{a_{k+1}}{a_k} = \frac{x^{k+1}}{(k+1)!}\cdot\frac{k!}{x^k} = \frac{x}{k+1}$. This has limit 0 as $k \to \infty$ for any value of x, so the series converges for all $x \geq 0$.

8.5.83 The series clearly converges for $x = 0$. For $x \neq 0$, we have $\frac{a_{k+1}}{a_k} = \frac{x^{k+1}}{x^k} = x$. This has limit x as $k \to \infty$, so the series converges for $x < 1$. It clearly does not converge for $x = 1$. So the series converges for $x \in [0,1)$.

8.5.84 The series clearly converges for $x = 0$. For $x \neq 0$, we have $\frac{a_{k+1}}{a_k} = \frac{x^{k+1}}{k+1}\cdot\frac{k}{x^k} = x\cdot\frac{k}{k+1}$, which has limit x as $k \to \infty$. Thus this series converges for $x < 1$; additionally, for $x = 1$ (where the Ratio Test is inconclusive), the series is the harmonic series which diverges. So the series converges for $x \in [0,1)$.

8.5.85 The series clearly converges for $x = 0$. For $x \neq 0$, we have $\frac{a_{k+1}}{a_k} = \frac{x^{k+1}}{(k+1)^2}\cdot\frac{k^2}{x^k} = x\left(\frac{k}{k+1}\right)^2$, which has limit x as $k \to \infty$. Thus the series converges for $x < 1$. When $x = 1$, the series is $\frac{1}{k^2}$, which converges. Thus the original series converges for $0 \leq x \leq 1$.

8.5.86 The series clearly converges for $x = 0$. For $x \neq 0$, we have $\frac{a_{k+1}}{a_k} = \frac{x^{2k+2}}{(k+1)^2}\cdot\frac{k^2}{x^{2k}} = x^2\left(\frac{k}{k+1}\right)^2$, which has limit x^2 as $k \to \infty$, so the series converges for $x < 1$. When $x = 1$, the series is $\frac{1}{k^2}$, which converges. Thus this series converges for $0 \leq x \leq 1$.

8.5.87 The series clearly converges for $x = 0$. For $x \neq 0$, we have $\dfrac{a_{k+1}}{a_k} = \dfrac{x^{k+1}}{2^{k+1}} \cdot \dfrac{2^k}{x^k} = \dfrac{x}{2}$, which has limit $x/2$ as $k \to \infty$. Thus the series converges for $0 \leq x < 2$. For $x = 2$, it is obviously divergent.

8.5.88

a. Let P_n be the nth partial product of the a_k: $P_n = \prod_{k=1}^{n} a_k$. Then $\sum_{k=1}^{n} \ln a_k = \ln \prod_{k=1}^{n} a_k = \ln P_n$. If $\sum \ln a_k$ is a convergent series, then $\sum_{k=1}^{\infty} \ln a_k = \lim_{n \to \infty} \ln P_n = L < \infty$. But then $e^L = \lim_{n \to \infty} e^{\ln P_n} = \lim_{n \to \infty} P_n$, so that the infinite product converges.

b.

n	2	3	4	5	6	7	8
P_n	3/4	2/3	5/8	3/5	7/12	4/7	9/16

It appears that $P_n = \frac{n+1}{2n}$, so that $\lim_{n \to \infty} P_n = \frac{1}{2}$.

c. Because $\lim_{n \to \infty} \prod_{k=2}^{n} \left(1 - \frac{1}{k^2}\right) = \frac{1}{2}$, taking logs and using part (a) we see that $\lim_{n \to \infty} \sum_{k=1}^{n} \ln \left(1 - \frac{1}{k^2}\right) = \ln \frac{1}{2} = -\ln 2$.

8.5.89

a. $\ln \prod_{k=0}^{\infty} e^{1/2^k} = \sum_{k=0}^{\infty} \frac{1}{2^k} = 2$, so that the original product converges to e^2.

b. $\ln \prod_{k=2}^{\infty} \left(1 - \frac{1}{k}\right) = \ln \prod_{k=2}^{\infty} \frac{k-1}{k} = \sum_{k=2}^{\infty} \ln \frac{k-1}{k} = \sum_{k=2}^{\infty} (\ln(k-1) - \ln(k))$. This series telescopes to give $S_n = -\ln(n)$, so the original series has limit $\lim_{n \to \infty} P_n = \lim_{n \to \infty} e^{-\ln(n)} = 0$.

8.5.90 The sum on the left is simply the left Riemann sum over n equal intervals between 0 and 1 for $f(x) = x^p$. The limit of the sum is thus $\int_0^1 x^p dx = \frac{1}{p+1} x^{p+1} \Big|_0^1 = \frac{1}{p+1}$, because p is positive.

8.5.91

a. Use the Ratio Test:

$$\frac{a_{k+1}}{a_k} = \frac{1 \cdot 3 \cdot 5 \cdots (2k+1)}{p^{k+1}(k+1)!} \cdot \frac{p^k(k)!}{1 \cdot 3 \cdot 5 \cdots (2k-1)} = \frac{(2k+1)}{(k+1)p}$$

and this expression has limit $\frac{2}{p}$ as $k \to \infty$. Thus the series converges for $p > 2$.

b. Following the hint, when $p = 2$ we have $\displaystyle\sum_{k=1}^{\infty} \frac{(2k)!}{2^k k! (2 \cdot 4 \cdot 6 \cdots 2k)} = \sum_{k=1}^{\infty} \frac{(2k)!}{(2^k)^2 (k!)^2}$. Using Stirling's formula, the numerator is asymptotic to $2\sqrt{\pi}\sqrt{k}(2k)^{2k} e^{-2k} = 2\sqrt{\pi}\sqrt{k}(2^k)^2 (k^k)^2 e^{-2k}$ while the denominator is asymptotic to $(2^k)^2 2\pi k (k^k)^2 e^{-2k}$, so the quotient is asymptotic to $\frac{1}{\sqrt{\pi}\sqrt{k}}$. Thus the original series diverges for $p = 2$ by the Limit Comparison Test with the divergent p-series $\sum_{k=1}^{\infty} \frac{1}{k^{1/2}}$.

8.6 Alternating Series

8.6.1 Because $S_{n+1} - S_n = (-1)^n a_{n+1}$ alternates signs.

8.6.2 Check that the terms of the series are nonincreasing in magnitude after some finite number of terms, and that $\lim_{k \to \infty} a_k = 0$.

8.6.3 We have
$$S = S_{2n+1} + (a_{2n} - a_{2n+1}) + (a_{2n+2} - a_{2n+3}) + \cdots$$
and each term of the form $a_{2k} - a_{2k+1} > 0$, so that $S_{2n+1} < S$. Also
$$S = S_{2n} + (-a_{2n+1} + a_{2n+2}) + (-a_{2n+3} + a_{2n+4}) + \cdots$$
and each term of the form $-a_{2k+1} + a_{2k+2} < 0$, so that $S < S_{2n}$. Thus the sum of the series is trapped between the odd partial sums and the even partial sums.

8.6.4 The difference between L and S_n is bounded in magnitude by a_{n+1}.

8.6.5 The remainder is less than the first neglected term because
$$S - S_n = (-1)^{n+1}(a_{n+1} + (-a_{n+2} + a_{n+3}) + \cdots)$$
so that the sum of the series *after* the first disregarded term has the opposite sign from the first disregarded term.

8.6.6 The alternating harmonic series $\sum(-1)^k \frac{1}{k}$ converges, but not absolutely.

8.6.7 No. If the terms are positive, then the absolute value of each term is the term itself, so convergence and absolute convergence would mean the same thing in this context.

8.6.8 The idea of the proof is to note that $0 \leq |a_k| + a_k \leq 2|a_k|$ and apply the Comparison Test to conclude that if $\sum |a_k|$ converges, then so does $\sum 2|a_k|$, and thus so must $\sum(|a_k| + a_k)$, and then conclude that $\sum a_k$ must converge as well.

8.6.9 Yes. For example, $\sum \frac{(-1)^k}{k^3}$ converges absolutely and thus not conditionally (see the definition).

8.6.10 The alternating harmonic series $\sum(-1)^k \frac{1}{k}$ converges conditionally, but not absolutely.

8.6.11 The terms of the series decrease in magnitude, and $\lim_{k\to\infty} \frac{1}{2k+1} = 0$, so the given series converges.

8.6.12 The terms of the series decrease in magnitude, and $\lim_{k\to\infty} \frac{1}{\sqrt{k}} = 0$, so the given series converges.

8.6.13 $\lim_{k\to\infty} \frac{k}{3k+2} = \frac{1}{3} \neq 0$, so the given series diverges.

8.6.14 $\lim_{k\to\infty} \left(1 + \frac{1}{k}\right)^k = e \neq 0$, so the given series diverges.

8.6.15 The terms of the series decrease in magnitude, and $\lim_{k\to\infty} \frac{1}{k^3} = 0$, so the given series converges.

8.6.16 The terms of the series decrease in magnitude, and $\lim_{k\to\infty} \frac{1}{k^2+10} = 0$, so the given series converges.

8.6.17 The terms of the series decrease in magnitude, and $\lim_{k\to\infty} \frac{k^2}{k^3+1} = \lim_{k\to\infty} \frac{1/k}{1+1/k^3} = 0$, so the given series converges.

8.6.18 The terms of the series eventually decrease in magnitude, because if $f(x) = \frac{\ln x}{x^2}$, then $f'(x) = \frac{x(1-2\ln x)}{x^4} = \frac{1-2\ln x}{x^3}$, which is negative for large enough x. Further, $\lim_{k\to\infty} \frac{\ln k}{k^2} = \lim_{k\to\infty} \frac{1/k}{2k} = \lim_{k\to\infty} \frac{1}{2k^2} = 0$. Thus the given series converges.

8.6.19 $\lim_{k\to\infty} \frac{k^2-1}{k^2+3} = 1$, so the terms of the series do not tend to zero and thus the given series diverges.

8.6.20 $\sum_{k=0}^{\infty} \left(-\frac{1}{5}\right)^k = \sum_{k=0}^{\infty}(-1)^k \left(\frac{1}{5}\right)^k$. $(1/5)^k$ is decreasing, and tends to zero as $k \to \infty$, so the given series converges.

8.6.21 $\lim\limits_{k\to\infty}\left(1+\frac{1}{k}\right)=1$, so the given series diverges.

8.6.22 Note that $\cos(\pi k)=(-1)^k$, and so the given series is alternating. Because $\lim\limits_{k\to\infty}\frac{1}{k^2}=0$ and $\frac{1}{k^2}$ is decreasing, the given series is convergent.

8.6.23 The derivative of $f(k)=\frac{k^{10}+2k^5+1}{k(k^{10}+1)}$ is $f'(k)=\frac{-(k^{20}+2k^{10}+12k^{15}-8k^5+1)}{k^2(k^{10}+1)^2}$. The numerator is negative for large enough values of k, and the denominator is always positive, so the derivative is negative for large enough k. Also, $\lim\limits_{k\to\infty}\frac{k^{10}+2k^5+1}{k(k^{10}+1)}=\lim\limits_{k\to\infty}\frac{1+2k^{-5}+k^{-10}}{k+k^{-9}}=0$. Thus the given series converges.

8.6.24 Clearly $\frac{1}{k\ln^2 k}$ is nonincreasing, and $\lim\limits_{k\to\infty}\frac{1}{k\ln^2 k}=0$, so the given series converges.

8.6.25 $\lim\limits_{k\to\infty}k^{1/k}=1$ (for example, take logs and apply L'Hôpital's rule), so the given series diverges by the Divergence Test.

8.6.26 $a_{k+1}<a_k$ because $\frac{a_{k+1}}{a_k}=\frac{(k+1)!}{(k+1)^{k+1}}\cdot\frac{k^k}{k!}=\left(\frac{k}{k+1}\right)^k<1$. Additionally, $\frac{k!}{k^k}\to 0$ as $k\to\infty$, so the given series converges.

8.6.27 $\frac{1}{\sqrt{k^2+4}}$ is decreasing and tends to zero as $k\to\infty$, so the given series converges.

8.6.28 $\lim\limits_{k\to\infty}k\sin(1/k)=\lim\limits_{k\to\infty}\frac{\sin(1/k)}{1/k}=1$, so the given series diverges.

8.6.29 We want $\frac{1}{n+1}<10^{-4}$, or $n+1>10^4$, so $n=10^4$.

8.6.30 The series starts with $k=0$, so we want $\frac{1}{n!}<10^{-4}$, or $n!>10^4=10000$. This happens for $n=8$.

8.6.31 The series starts with $k=0$, so we want $\frac{1}{2n+1}<10^{-4}$, or $2n+1>10^4$, $n=5000$.

8.6.32 We want $\frac{1}{(n+1)^2}<10^{-4}$, or $(n+1)^2>10^4$, so $n=100$.

8.6.33 We want $\frac{1}{(n+1)^4}<10^{-4}$, or $(n+1)^4>10^4$, so $n=10$.

8.6.34 The series starts with $k=0$, so we want $\frac{1}{(2n+1)^3}<10^{-4}$, or $2n+1>10^{4/3}$, so $n=11$.

8.6.35 The series starts with $k=0$, so we want $\frac{1}{3n+1}<10^{-4}$, or $3n+1>10^4$, $n=3334$.

8.6.36 We want $\frac{1}{(n+1)^6}<10^{-4}$, or $(n+1)^6>10^4=10000$, so $n=4$.

8.6.37 The series starts with $k=0$, so we want $\frac{1}{4^n}\left(\frac{2}{4n+1}+\frac{2}{4n+2}+\frac{1}{4n+3}\right)<10^{-4}$, or $\frac{4^n(4n+1)(4n+2)(4n+3)}{4(20n^2+21n+5)}>10000$, which occurs first for $n=6$.

8.6.38 The series starts with $k=0$, so we want $\frac{1}{3n+2}<10^{-4}$, so $3n+2>10000$, $n=3333$.

8.6.39 To figure out how many terms we need to sum, we must find n such that $\frac{1}{(n+1)^5}<10^{-3}$, so that $(n+1)^5>1000$; this occurs first for $n=3$. Thus $\frac{-1}{1}+\frac{1}{2^5}-\frac{1}{3^5}\approx-0.973$.

8.6.40 To figure out how many terms we need to sum, we must find n such that $\frac{1}{(2(n+1)+1)^3}<10^{-3}$, or $(2n+3)^3>10^3$, so $2n+3>10$ and $n=4$. Thus the approximation is $\sum_{k=1}^{4}\frac{(-1)^n}{(2n+1)^3}\approx-0.306$.

8.6.41 To figure out how many terms we need to sum, we must find n so that $\frac{n+1}{(n+1)^2+1}<10^{-3}$, so that $\frac{(n+1)^2+1}{n+1}=n+1+\frac{1}{n+1}>1000$. This occurs first for $n=999$. We have $\sum_{k=1}^{999}\frac{(-1)^k k}{k^2+1}\approx-0.269$.

8.6.42 To figure out how many terms we need to sum, we must find n such that $\frac{n+1}{(n+1)^4+1} < 10^{-3}$, so that $\frac{(n+1)^4+1}{n+1} = (n+1)^3 + \frac{1}{n+1} > 1000$, which occurs for $n = 9$. We have $\sum_{k=1}^{9} \frac{(-1)^k k}{k^4+1} \approx -0.409$.

8.6.43 To figure how many terms we need to sum, we must find n such that $\frac{1}{(n+1)^{n+1}} < 10^{-3}$, or $(n+1)^{n+1} > 1000$, so $n = 4$ ($5^5 = 3125$). Thus the approximation is $\sum_{k=1}^{4} \frac{(-1)^n}{n^n} \approx -.783$.

8.6.44 To figure how many terms we need to sum, we must find n such that $\frac{1}{(2(n+1)+1)!} < 10^{-3}$, or $(2n+3)! > 1000$, so $2n+3 \geq 7$ and $n = 2$. The approximation is $\sum_{k=1}^{2} \frac{(-1)^{n+1}}{(2n+1)!} \approx 0.158$

8.6.45 The series of absolute values is a p-series with $p = 2/3$, so it diverges. The given alternating series does converge, though, by the Alternating Series Test. Thus, the given series is conditionally convergent.

8.6.46 The series of absolute values is a p-series with $p = 1/2$, so it diverges. The given alternating series does converge, though, by the Alternating Series Test. Thus, the given series is conditionally convergent.

8.6.47 The series of absolute values is a p-series with $p = 3/2$, so it converges absolutely.

8.6.48 The series of absolute values is $\sum \frac{1}{3^k}$, which converges, so the series converges absolutely.

8.6.49 The series of absolute values is $\sum \frac{|\cos(k)|}{k^3}$, which converges by the Comparison Test because $\frac{|\cos(k)|}{k^3} \leq \frac{1}{k^3}$. Thus the series converges absolutely.

8.6.50 The series of absolute values is $\sum \frac{k^2}{\sqrt{k^6+1}}$. The limit comparison test with $\frac{1}{k}$ gives $\lim_{k\to\infty} \frac{k^3}{\sqrt{k^6+1}} = \lim_{k\to\infty} \sqrt{\frac{k^6}{k^6+1}} = 1$. Because the comparison series diverges, so does the series of absolute values. The original series converges conditionally, however, because the terms are nonincreasing and $\lim_{k\to\infty} \frac{k^2}{\sqrt{k^6+1}} = \lim_{k\to\infty} \sqrt{\frac{k^4}{k^6+1}} = 0$.

8.6.51 The absolute value of the kth term of this series has limit $\pi/2$ as $k \to \infty$, so the given series is divergent by the Divergence Test.

8.6.52 The series of absolute values is a geometric series with $r = \frac{1}{e}$ and $|r| < 1$, so the given series converges absolutely

8.6.53 The series of absolute values is $\sum \frac{k}{2k+1}$, but $\lim_{k\to\infty} \frac{k}{2k+1} = \frac{1}{2}$, so by the Divergence Test, this series diverges. The original series does not converge conditionally, either, because $\lim_{k\to\infty} a_k = \frac{1}{2} \neq 0$.

8.6.54 The series of absolute values is $\sum \frac{1}{\ln k}$, which diverges, so the series does not converge absolutely. However, because $\lim_{k\to\infty} \frac{1}{\ln k} \to 0$ and the terms are nonincreasing, the series does converge conditionally.

8.6.55 The series of absolute values is $\sum \frac{\tan^{-1}(k)}{k^3}$, which converges by the Comparison Test because $\frac{\tan^{-1}(k)}{k^3} < \frac{\pi}{2} \frac{1}{k^3}$, and $\sum \frac{\pi}{2} \frac{1}{k^3}$ converges because it is a constant multiple of a convergent $p-$series. So the original series converges absolutely.

8.6.56 The series of absolute values is $\sum \frac{e^k}{(k+1)!}$. Using the ratio test, $\frac{a_{k+1}}{a_k} = \frac{e^{k+1}}{(k+2)!} \cdot \frac{(k+1)!}{e^k} = \frac{e}{k+2}$, which tends to zero as $k \to \infty$, so the original series converges absolutely.

8.6.57

a. False. For example, consider the alternating harmonic series.

b. True. This is part of Theorem 8.21.

c. True. This statement is simply saying that a convergent series converges.

d. True. This is part of Theorem 8.21.

e. False. Let $a_k = \frac{1}{k}$.

f. True. Use the Comparison Test: $\lim\limits_{k\to\infty} \frac{a_k^2}{a_k} = \lim\limits_{k\to\infty} a_k = 0$ because $\sum a_k$ converges, so $\sum a_k^2$ and $\sum a_k$ converge or diverge together. Because the latter converges, so does the former.

g. True, by definition. If $\sum |a_k|$ converged, the original series would converge absolutely, not conditionally.

8.6.58 Neither condition is satisfied. $\frac{a_{k+1}}{a_k} = \frac{(k+1)(2k+1)}{(2k+3)k} = \frac{2k^2+3k+1}{2k^2+3k} > 1$, and $\lim\limits_{k\to\infty} a_k = \frac{1}{2}$.

8.6.59 $\sum_{k=1}^{\infty} \frac{1}{k^2} - \sum_{k=1}^{\infty} \frac{(-1)^{k+1}}{k^2} = 2\sum_{k=1}^{\infty} \frac{1}{(2k)^2} = 2 \cdot \frac{1}{4} \sum_{k=1}^{\infty} \frac{1}{k^2}$, and thus $\sum_{k=1}^{\infty} \frac{(-1)^{k+1}}{k^2} = \frac{\pi^2}{6} - \frac{1}{2} \cdot \frac{\pi^2}{6} = \frac{\pi^2}{12}$.

8.6.60 $\sum_{k=1}^{\infty} \frac{1}{k^4} - \sum_{k=1}^{\infty} \frac{(-1)^{k+1}}{k^4} = 2\sum_{k=1}^{\infty} \frac{1}{(2k)^4} = 2 \cdot \frac{1}{16} \sum_{k=1}^{\infty} \frac{1}{k^4}$, and thus $\sum_{k=1}^{\infty} \frac{(-1)^{k+1}}{k^4} = \frac{\pi^4}{90} - \frac{1}{8} \cdot \frac{\pi^4}{90} = \frac{7\pi^4}{720}$.

8.6.61 Write $r = -s$; then $0 < s < 1$ and $\sum r^k = \sum (-1)^k s^k$. Because $|s| < 1$, the terms s^k are nonincreasing and tend to zero, so by the Alternating Series Test, the series $\sum (-1)^k s^k = \sum r^k$ converges.

8.6.62

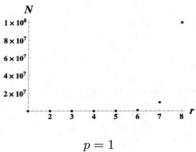

$p = 1$

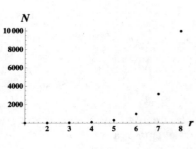

$p = 2$

a. As p gets larger, fewer terms are needed to achieve a particular level of accuracy; this means that for larger p, the series converge faster.

$p = 3$

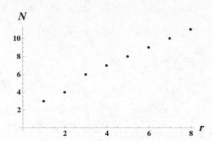

b.   This graph shows that $\sum \frac{1}{k!}$ converges much faster than any of the powers of k.

8.6.63 Let $S = 1 - \frac{1}{2} + \frac{1}{3} - \cdots$. Then

$$S \;=\; \left(1 - \tfrac{1}{2}\right) \;+\; \left(\tfrac{1}{3} - \tfrac{1}{4}\right) \;+\; \left(\tfrac{1}{5} - \tfrac{1}{6}\right) \;+\; \left(\tfrac{1}{7} - \tfrac{1}{8}\right) \;+\; \cdots$$

$$\tfrac{1}{2}S \;=\; \qquad \tfrac{1}{2} \qquad - \qquad \tfrac{1}{4} \qquad + \qquad \tfrac{1}{6} \qquad - \qquad \tfrac{1}{8} \qquad + \cdots$$

Add these two series together to get

$$\frac{3}{2}S = \frac{3}{2}\ln 2 = 1 + \frac{1}{3} - \frac{1}{2} + \frac{1}{5} + \cdots$$

To see that the results are as desired, consider a collection of four terms:

$$\cdots + \;\left(\tfrac{1}{4k+1} - \tfrac{1}{4k+2}\right) \;+\; \left(\tfrac{1}{4k+3} - \tfrac{1}{4k+4}\right) \;+\; \cdots$$

$$\cdots \qquad + \qquad \tfrac{1}{4k+2} \qquad - \qquad \tfrac{1}{4k+4} \;+\; \cdots$$

Adding these results in the desired sign pattern. This repeats for each group of four elements.

8.6.64

a. Note that we can write

$$S_n = -\frac{a_1}{2} + \frac{1}{2}\left(\sum_{k=1}^{n-1}(-1)^k(a_i - a_{i+1})\right) + \frac{(-1)^n a_n}{2},$$

so that

$$S_n + \frac{(-1)^{n+1}a_{n+1}}{2} = -\frac{a_1}{2} + \frac{1}{2}\left(\sum_{k=1}^{n}(-1)^k d_i\right)$$

where $d_i = a_i - a_{i+1}$. Now consider the expression on the right-hand side of this last equation as the nth partial sum of a series which converges to S. Because the d_i's are decreasing and positive, the error made by stopping the sum after n terms is less than the absolute value of the first omitted term, which would be $\frac{1}{2}|d_{n+1}| = \frac{1}{2}|a_{n+1} - a_{n+2}|$. The method in the text for approximating the error simply takes the absolute value of the first unused term as an approximation of $|S - S_n|$. Here, S_n is modified by adding half the next term. Because the terms are decreasing in magnitude, this should be a better approximation to S than just S_n itself; the right side shows that this intuition is correct, because $\frac{1}{2}|a_{n+1} - a_{n+2}|$ is at most a_{n+1} and is generally less than that (because generally $a_{n+2} < a_{n+1}$).

b.   i. Using the method from the text, we need n such that $\frac{1}{n+1} < 10^{-6}$, i.e. $n > 10^6 - 1$. Using the modified method from this problem, we want $\frac{1}{2}|a_{n+1} - a_{n+2}| < 10^{-6}$, so

$$\frac{1}{2}\left(\frac{1}{n+1} - \frac{1}{n+2}\right) = \frac{1}{2(n+1)(n+2)} < 10^{-6}$$

This is true when $10^6 < 2(n+1)(n+2)$, which requires $n > 705.6$, so $n \geq 706$.

ii. Using the method from the book, we need n such that $k \ln k > 10^6$, which means $k \geq 87848$. Using the method of this problem, we want

$$\frac{1}{2}\left|\left(\frac{1}{k \ln k} - \frac{1}{(k+1)\ln(k+1)}\right)\right| = \left|\frac{(k+1)\ln(k+1) - k \ln k}{2k(k+1)\ln k \ln(k+1)}\right| < 10^{-6},$$

so that $|2k(k+1)\ln k \ln(k+1)| > |10^6(k \ln k - (k+1)\ln(k+1))|$, which means $k \geq 319$.

iii. Using the method from the book, we need k such that $\sqrt{k} > 10^6$, so $k > 10^{12}$. Using the method of this problem, we want

$$\frac{1}{2}\left(\frac{1}{\sqrt{k}} - \frac{1}{\sqrt{k+1}}\right) = \frac{\sqrt{k+1} - \sqrt{k}}{2\sqrt{k(k+1)}} < 10^{-6}$$

which means that $k > 3968.002$ so that $k \geq 3969$.

8.6.65 Both series diverge, so comparisons of their values are not meaningful.

8.6.66

a. The first ten terms are

$$(2 - 1) + \left(1 - \frac{1}{2}\right) + \left(\frac{2}{3} - \frac{1}{3}\right) + \left(\frac{1}{2} - \frac{1}{4}\right) + \left(\frac{2}{5} - \frac{1}{5}\right)$$

Suppose that $k = 2i$ is even (and so $k - 1 = 2i - 1$ is odd). Then the sum of the $(k-1)$st term and the kth term is $\frac{4}{k} - \frac{2}{k} = \frac{2}{k} = \frac{1}{i}$. Then the sum of the first $2n$ terms of the given series is $\sum_{i=1}^{n} \frac{1}{i}$.

b. Note that $\lim_{k \to \infty} \frac{4}{k+1} = \lim_{k \to \infty} \frac{2}{k} = 0$. Thus given $\epsilon > 0$ there exists N_1 so that for $k > N_1$, we have $\frac{4}{k+1} < \epsilon$. Also, there exist N_2 so that for $k > N_2$, $\frac{2}{k} < \epsilon$. Let N be the larger of N_1 or N_2. Then for $k > N$, we have $a_k < \epsilon$, as desired.

c. The series can be seen to diverge because the even partial sums have limit ∞. This does not contradict the alternating series test because the terms a_k are not nonincreasing.

Chapter Eight Review

1

a. False. Let $a_n = 1 - \frac{1}{n}$. This sequence has limit 1.

b. False. The terms of a sequence tending to zero is necessary but not sufficient for convergence of the series.

c. True. This is the definition of convergence of a series.

d. False. If a series converges absolutely, the definition says that it does not converge conditionally.

e. True. It has limit 1 as $n \to \infty$.

f. False. The subsequence of the even terms has limit 1 and the subsequence of odd terms has limit -1, so the sequence does not have a limit.

g. False. It diverges by the Divergence Test because $\lim_{k \to \infty} \frac{k^2}{k^2+1} = 1 \neq 0$.

h. True. The given series converges by the Limit Comparison Test with the series $\sum_{k=1}^{\infty} \frac{1}{k^2}$, and thus its sequence of partial sums converges.

2 $\lim\limits_{n\to\infty} \dfrac{n^2+4}{\sqrt{4n^4+1}} = \lim\limits_{n\to\infty} \dfrac{1+4n^{-2}}{\sqrt{4+n^{-4}}} = \dfrac{1}{2}.$

3 $\lim\limits_{n\to\infty} \dfrac{8^n}{n!} = 0$ because exponentials grow more slowly than factorials.

4 After taking logs, we want to compute

$$\lim_{n\to\infty} 2n\ln(1+3/n) = \lim_{n\to\infty} \frac{\ln(1+3/n)}{1/(2n)}.$$

By L'Hôpital's rule, this is $\lim\limits_{n\to\infty} \frac{6n}{n+3}$ (after some algebraic manipulations), which is 6. Thus the original limit is e^6.

5 Take logs and compute $\lim\limits_{n\to\infty} (1/n)\ln n = \lim\limits_{n\to\infty} (\ln n)/n = \lim\limits_{n\to\infty} \frac{1}{n} = 0$ by L'Hôpital's rule. Thus the original limit is $e^0 = 1$.

6 $\lim\limits_{n\to\infty} (n - \sqrt{n^2-1}) = \lim\limits_{n\to\infty} \frac{n-\sqrt{n^2-1}}{1}\cdot\frac{n+\sqrt{n^2-1}}{n+\sqrt{n^2-1}} = \lim\limits_{n\to\infty} \frac{1}{n+\sqrt{n^2+1}} = 0.$

7 Take logs, and then evaluate $\lim\limits_{n\to\infty} \frac{1}{\ln n}\ln(1/n) = \lim\limits_{n\to\infty} (-1) = -1$, so the original limit is e^{-1}.

8 This series oscillates among the values $\pm1/2, \pm\sqrt{3}/2, \pm1$, and 0, so it has no limit.

9 $a_n = (-1/0.9)^n = (-10/9)^n$. The terms grow without bound so the sequence does not converge.

10 $\lim\limits_{n\to\infty} \tan^{-1} n = \lim\limits_{x\to\infty} \tan^{-1} x = \dfrac{\pi}{2}.$

11

    a. $S_1 = \frac{1}{3}$, $S_2 = \frac{11}{24}$, $S_3 = \frac{21}{40}$, $S_4 = \frac{17}{30}$.

    b. $S_n = \dfrac{1}{2}\left(\dfrac{1}{1} + \dfrac{1}{2} - \dfrac{1}{n+1} - \dfrac{1}{n+2}\right)$, because the series telescopes.

    c. From part (b), $\lim\limits_{n\to\infty} S_n = \frac{3}{4}$, which is the sum of the series.

12 This is a geometric series with ratio 9/10, so the sum is $\frac{9/10}{1-9/10} = 9$.

13 $\sum_{k=1}^{\infty} 3(1.001)^k = 3\sum_{k=1}^{\infty} (1.001)^k$. This is a geometric series with ratio greater than 1, so it diverges.

14 This is a geometric series with ratio $-1/5$, so the sum is $\frac{1}{1+1/5} = \frac{5}{6}$

15 $\frac{1}{k(k+1)} = \frac{1}{k} - \frac{1}{k+1}$, so the series telescopes, and $S_n = 1 - \frac{1}{n+1}$. Thus $\lim\limits_{n\to\infty} S_n = 1$, which is the value of the series.

16 This series clearly telescopes, and $S_n = \frac{1}{\sqrt{n}} - 1$, so $\lim\limits_{n\to\infty} S_n = -1$.

17 This series telescopes. $S_n = 3 - \frac{3}{3n+1}$, so that $\lim\limits_{n\to\infty} S_n = 3$, which is the value of the series.

18 $\sum_{k=1}^{\infty} 4^{-3k} = \sum_{k=1}^{\infty} (1/64)^k$. This is a geometric series with ratio 1/64, so its sum is $\frac{1/64}{1-1/64} = \frac{1}{63}$.

19 $\sum\limits_{k=1}^{\infty} \dfrac{2^k}{3^{k+2}} = \dfrac{1}{9}\sum\limits_{k=1}^{\infty}\left(\dfrac{2}{3}\right)^k = \dfrac{1}{9}\cdot\dfrac{2/3}{1-2/3} = \dfrac{2}{9}.$

20 This is the difference of two convergent geometric series (because both have ratios less than 1). Thus the sum of the series is equal to

$$\sum_{k=0}^{\infty} \left(\frac{1}{3}\right)^k - \sum_{k=0}^{\infty} \left(\frac{2}{3}\right)^{k+1} = \frac{1}{1-1/3} - \frac{2/3}{1-2/3} = \frac{3}{2} - 2 = -\frac{1}{2}.$$

21

    a. It appears that the series converges, because the sequence of partial sums appears to converge to 1.5.

    b. The convergence is uncertain.

    c. This series clearly appears to diverge, because the partial sums seem to be growing without bound.

22 This is p-series with $p = 3/2 > 1$, so this series is convergent.

23 The series can be written $\sum \frac{1}{k^{2/3}}$, which is a p-series with $p = 2/3 < 1$, so this series diverges.

24 $a_k = \frac{2k^2+1}{\sqrt{k^3+2}} = \sqrt{\frac{4k^4+4k^2+1}{k^3+2}}$, so the sequence of terms diverges. By the Divergence Test, the given series diverges as well.

25 This is a geometric series with ratio $2/e < 1$, so the series converges.

26 Note that $\frac{1}{a_k} = \left(\left(1 + \frac{3}{k}\right)^k\right)^2$, so $\lim_{k \to \infty} \frac{1}{a_k} = \lim_{k \to \infty} \left(\left(1 + \frac{3}{k}\right)^k\right)^2 = (e^3)^2$, so $\lim_{k \to \infty} a_k = \frac{1}{e^6} \neq 0$, so the given series diverges by the Divergence Test.

27 Applying the Ratio Test:

$$\lim_{k \to \infty} \frac{a_{k+1}}{a_k} = \lim_{k \to \infty} \frac{2^{k+1}(k+1)!}{(k+1)^{k+1}} \cdot \frac{k^k}{2^k k!} = \lim_{k \to \infty} 2\left(\frac{k}{k+1}\right)^k = \frac{2}{e} < 1,$$

so the given series converges.

28 Use the Limit Comparison Test with $\frac{1}{k}$:

$$\frac{1}{\sqrt{k^2+k}} \Bigg/ \frac{1}{k} = \frac{k}{\sqrt{k^2+k}} = \sqrt{\frac{k^2}{k^2+k}},$$

which has limit 1 as $k \to \infty$. Because $\sum 1/k$ diverges, the original series does as well.

29 Use the Comparison Test: $\frac{3}{2+e^k} < \frac{3}{e^k}$, but $\sum \frac{3}{e^k}$ converges because it is a geometric series with ratio $\frac{1}{e} < 1$. Thus the original series converges as well.

30 $\lim_{k \to \infty} a_k = \lim_{k \to \infty} k \sin(1/k) = \lim_{k \to \infty} \frac{\sin(1/k)}{1/k} = 1$, so the given series diverges by the Divergence Test.

31 $a_k = \frac{k^{1/k}}{k^3} = \frac{1}{k^{3-1/k}}$. For $k \geq 2$, then, $a_k < \frac{1}{k^2}$. Because $\sum \frac{1}{k^2}$ converges, the given series also converges, by the Comparison Test.

32 Use the Comparison Test: $\frac{1}{1+\ln k} > \frac{1}{k}$ for $k > 1$. Because $\sum \frac{1}{k}$ diverges, the given series does as well.

33 Use the Ratio Test: $\frac{a_{k+1}}{a_k} = \frac{(k+1)^5}{e^{k+1}} \cdot \frac{e^k}{k^5} = \frac{1}{e} \cdot \left(\frac{k+1}{k}\right)^5$, which has limit $1/e < 1$ as $k \to \infty$. Thus the given series converges.

34 For $k > 5$, we have $k^2 - 10 > (k-1)^2$, so that $a_k = \frac{2}{k^2-10} < \frac{2}{(k-1)^2}$. Because $\sum \frac{2}{(k-1)^2}$ converges, the original series does as well.

35 Use the Comparison Test. Because $\lim\limits_{k\to\infty}\dfrac{\ln k}{k^{1/2}}=0$, we have that for sufficiently large k, $\ln k < k^{1/2}$, so that $a_k=\dfrac{2\ln k}{k^2}<\dfrac{2k^{1/2}}{k^2}=\dfrac{2}{k^{3/2}}$. Now $\sum\dfrac{2}{k^{3/2}}$ is convergent, because it is a p-series with $p=3/2>1$. Thus the original series is convergent.

36 By the Ratio Test: $\lim\limits_{k\to\infty}\dfrac{a_{k+1}}{a_k}=\lim\limits_{k\to\infty}\dfrac{k+1}{e^{k+1}}\cdot\dfrac{e^k}{k}=\lim\limits_{k\to\infty}\dfrac{1}{e}\cdot\dfrac{k+1}{k}=\dfrac{1}{e}<1$. Thus the given series converges.

37 Use the Ratio Test. The ratio of successive terms is $\dfrac{2\cdot 4^{k+1}}{(2k+3)!}\cdot\dfrac{(2k+1)!}{2\cdot 4^k}=\dfrac{4}{(2k+3)(2k+2)}$. This has limit 0 as $k\to\infty$, so the given series converges.

38 Use the Ratio Test. The ratio of successive term is $\dfrac{9^{k+1}}{(2k+2)!}\cdot\dfrac{(2k)!}{9^k}=\dfrac{9}{(2k+2)(2k+1)}$. This has limit 0 as $k\to\infty$, so the given series converges.

39 Use the Limit Comparison Test with the harmonic series. Note that $\lim\limits_{k\to\infty}\dfrac{\coth k}{k}\cdot\dfrac{k}{1}=\lim\limits_{k\to\infty}\coth k=1$. Because the harmonic series diverges, the given series does as well.

40 Use the Limit Comparison Test with the convergent geometric series whose kth term is $\dfrac{1}{e^k}$. We have $\lim_{k\to\infty}\dfrac{1}{\sinh k}\cdot\dfrac{e^k}{1}=\lim_{k\to\infty}\dfrac{2e^k}{e^k-e^{-k}}=2\lim_{k\to\infty}\dfrac{1}{1-e^{-2k}}=2$. The given series is therefore convergent.

41 Use the Divergence Test. $\lim_{k\to\infty}\tanh k=\lim_{k\to\infty}\dfrac{e^k+e^{-k}}{e^k-e^{-k}}=1\neq 0$, so the given series diverges.

42 Use the Limit Comparison Test with the convergent geometric series whose kth term is $\dfrac{1}{e^k}$. We have $\lim_{k\to\infty}\dfrac{1}{\cosh k}\cdot\dfrac{e^k}{1}=\lim_{k\to\infty}\dfrac{2e^k}{e^k+e^{-k}}=2\lim_{k\to\infty}\dfrac{1}{1+e^{-2k}}=2$. The given series is therefore convergent.

43 $|a_k|=\dfrac{1}{k^2-1}$. Use the Limit Comparison Test with the convergent series $\sum\dfrac{1}{k^2}$. Because $\lim\limits_{k\to\infty}\dfrac{\frac{1}{k^2-1}}{\frac{1}{k^2}}=\lim\limits_{k\to\infty}\dfrac{k^2}{k^2-1}=1$, the given series converges absolutely.

44 This series does not converge, because $\lim\limits_{k\to\infty}|a_k|=\lim\limits_{k\to\infty}\dfrac{k^2+4}{2k^2+1}=\dfrac{1}{2}$.

45 Use the Ratio Test on the absolute values of the sequence of terms: $\lim\limits_{k\to\infty}\left|\dfrac{a_{k+1}}{a_k}\right|=\lim\limits_{k\to\infty}\dfrac{k+1}{e^{k+1}}\cdot\dfrac{e^k}{k}=\lim\limits_{k\to\infty}\dfrac{1}{e}\cdot\dfrac{k+1}{k}=\dfrac{1}{e}<1$. Thus, the original series is absolutely convergent.

46 Using the Limit Comparison Test with the harmonic series, we consider $\lim\limits_{k\to\infty}a_k/(1/k)=\lim\limits_{k\to\infty}\dfrac{k}{\sqrt{k^2+1}}$ $=\lim\limits_{k\to\infty}\sqrt{\dfrac{k^2}{k^2+1}}=1$; because the comparison series diverges, so does the original series. Thus the series is not absolutely convergent. However, the terms are clearly decreasing to zero, so it is conditionally convergent.

47 Use the Ratio Test on the absolute values of the sequence of terms: $\lim\limits_{k\to\infty}\left|\dfrac{a_{k+1}}{a_k}\right|=\lim\limits_{k\to\infty}\dfrac{10}{k+1}=0$, so the series converges absolutely.

48 $\sum\dfrac{1}{k\ln k}$ does not converge because $\int_2^\infty\dfrac{1}{x\ln x}\,dx=\lim\limits_{b\to\infty}\ln(\ln x)\Big|_2^\infty=\infty$, so the improper integral diverges. Thus the given series does not converge absolutely. However, it does converge conditionally because the terms are decreasing and approach zero.

49 Because $k^2\ll 2^k$, $\lim\limits_{k\to\infty}\dfrac{-2\cdot(-2)^k}{k^2}\neq 0$. The given series thus diverges by the Divergence Test.

50 The series of absolute values converges, by the Limit Comparison Test with the convergent geometric series whose kth term is $\dfrac{1}{e^k}$. This follows because $\lim_{k\to\infty}\dfrac{1}{e^k+e^{-k}}\cdot\dfrac{e^k}{1}=\lim_{k\to\infty}\dfrac{1}{1+e^{-2k}}=1$.

51

    a. For $|x| < 1$, $\lim\limits_{k \to \infty} x^k = 0$, so this limit is zero.

    b. This is a geometric series with ratio $-4/5$, so the sum is $\frac{1}{1+4/5} = \frac{5}{9}$.

52

    a. $\lim\limits_{k \to \infty} \left(\frac{1}{k} - \frac{1}{k+1} \right) = \lim\limits_{k \to \infty} \frac{1}{k(k+1)} = 0$.

    b. This series telescopes, and $S_n = 1 - \frac{1}{n+1}$, so $\lim\limits_{n \to \infty} S_n = 1$, which is the sum of the series.

53 Consider the constant sequence with $a_k = 1$ for all k. The sequence $\{a_k\}$ converges to 1, but the corresponding series $\sum a_k$ diverges by the divergence test.

54 This is not possible. If the series $\sum_{k=1}^{\infty} a_k$ converges, then we must have $\lim_{k \to \infty} a_k = 0$.

55

    a. This sequence converges because $\lim_{k \to \infty} \frac{k}{k+1} = \lim_{k \to \infty} \frac{1}{1+\frac{1}{k}} = \frac{1}{1+0} = 1$.

    b. Because the sequence of terms has limit 1 (which means its limit isn't zero) this series diverges by the divergence test.

56 No. The geometric sequence converges for $-1 < r \leq 1$, while the geometric series converges for $-1 < r < 1$. So the geometric sequence converges for $r = 1$ but the geometric series does not.

57 Because the series converges, we must have $\lim\limits_{k \to \infty} a_k = 0$. Because it converges to 8, the partial sums converge to 8, so that $\lim\limits_{k \to \infty} S_k = 8$.

58 R_n is given by

$$R_n \leq \int_n^\infty \frac{1}{x^5}\, dx = \lim_{b \to \infty} \left(-\frac{1}{4x^4} \Big|_n^b \right) = \frac{1}{4n^4}.$$

Thus to approximate the sum to within 10^{-4}, we need $\frac{1}{4n^4} < 10^{-4}$, so $4n^4 > 10^4$ and $n = 8$.

59 The series converges absolutely for $p > 1$, conditionally for $0 < p \leq 1$ in which case $\{k^{-p}\}$ is decreasing to zero.

60 By the Integral Test, the series converges if and only if the following integral converges:

$$\int_2^\infty \frac{1}{x \ln^p(x)}\, dx = \lim_{b \to \infty} \left(\frac{1}{1-p} \ln^{(1-p)}(x) \Big|_2^b \right) = \lim_{b \to \infty} \frac{1}{1-p} \ln^{(1-p)}(b) - \left(\frac{1}{1-p} \right) \cdot \ln^{(1-p)}(2).$$

This limit exists only if $1 - p < 0$, i.e. $p > 1$. Note that the above calculation is for the case $p \neq 1$. In the case $p = 1$, the integral also diverges.

61 The sum is 0.2500000000 to ten decimal places. The maximum error is

$$\int_{20}^\infty \frac{1}{5^x}\, dx = \lim_{b \to \infty} \left(-\frac{1}{5^x \ln 5} \Big|_{20}^b \right) = \frac{1}{5^{20} \ln 5} \approx 6.5 \times 10^{-15}.$$

62 The sum is 1.037. The maximum error is

$$\int_{20}^\infty \frac{1}{x^5}\, dx = \lim_{b \to \infty} \left(-\frac{1}{4x^4} \Big|_{20}^b \right) = \frac{1}{4 \cdot 20^4} \approx 1.6 \times 10^{-6}.$$

63 The maximum error is a_{n+1}, so we want $a_{n+1} = \frac{1}{(k+1)^4} < 10^{-8}$, or $(k+1)^4 > 10^8$, so $k = 100$.

64

a. $\sum_{k=0}^{\infty} e^{kx} = \sum_{k=0}^{\infty} (e^x)^k = \frac{1}{1-e^x} = 2$, so $1 - e^x = 1/2$. Thus $e^x = 1/2$ and $x = -\ln(2)$.

b. $\sum_{k=0}^{\infty} (3x)^k = \frac{1}{1-3x} = 4$, so that $1 - 3x = \frac{1}{4}$, $x = \frac{1}{4}$.

c. The x's cancel, so the equation reads $\sum_{k=0}^{\infty} \left(\frac{1}{k-1/2} - \frac{1}{k+1/2} \right) = 6$. The series telescopes, so that the left side, up to n, is

$$\sum_{k=0}^{n} \left(\frac{1}{k-1/2} - \frac{1}{k+1/2} \right) = \frac{1}{-1/2} - \frac{1}{n+1/2} = -2 - \frac{1}{n+1/2}$$

and in the limit the equation then reads $-2 = 6$, so that there is no solution.

65

a. Let T_n be the amount of additional tunnel dug during week n. Then $T_0 = 100$ and $T_n = .95 \cdot T_{n-1} = (.95)^n T_0 = 100(0.95)^n$, so the total distance dug in N weeks is

$$S_N = 100 \sum_{k=0}^{N-1} (0.95)^k = 100 \left(\frac{1 - (0.95)^N}{1 - 0.95} \right) = 2000(1 - 0.95^N).$$

Then $S_{10} \approx 802.5$ meters and $S_{20} \approx 1283.03$ meters.

b. The longest possible tunnel is $S_\infty = 100 \sum_{k=0}^{\infty} (0.95)^k = \frac{100}{1 - .95} = 2000$ meters.

66 Let t_n be the time required to dig meters $(n-1) \cdot 100$ through $n \cdot 100$, so that $t_1 = 1$ week. Then $t_n = 1.1 \cdot t_{n-1} = (1.1)^{n-1} t_1 = (1.1)^{n-1}$ weeks. The time required to dig 1500 meters is then

$$\sum_{k=1}^{15} t_k = \sum_{k=1}^{15} (1.1)^{k-1} \approx 31.77 \text{ weeks.}$$

So it is not possible.

67

a. The area of a circle of radius r is πr^2. For $r = 2^{1-n}$, this is $2^{2-2n}\pi$. There are 2^{n-1} circles on the nth page, so the total area of circles on the nth page is $2^{n-1} \cdot \pi 2^{2-2n} = 2^{1-n}\pi$.

b. The sum of the areas on all pages is $\sum_{k=1}^{\infty} 2^{1-k}\pi = 2\pi \sum_{k=1}^{\infty} 2^{-k} = 2\pi \cdot \frac{1/2}{1/2} = 2\pi$.

68 $x_0 = 1$, $x_1 \approx 1.540302$, $x_2 \approx 1.57079$, $x_3 \approx 1.570796327$, which is $\frac{\pi}{2}$ to nine decimal places. Thus $p = 2$.

69

a. $B_n = 1.0025 B_{n-1} + 100$ and $B_0 = 100$.

b. $B_n = 100 \cdot 1.0025^n + 100 \cdot \frac{1 - 1.0025^n}{1 - 1.0025} = 100 \cdot 1.0025^n - 40000(1 - 1.0025^n) = 40000(1.0025^{n+1} - 1)$.

70

a. $a_n = \int_0^1 x^n \, dx = \frac{1}{n+1} x^{n+1} \Big|_0^1 = \frac{1}{n+1}$, so $\lim_{n \to \infty} a_n = 0$.

b. $b_n = \int_1^n \frac{1}{x^p} \, dx = \frac{1}{1-p} x^{1-p} \Big|_1^n = \frac{1}{1-p}(n^{1-p} - 1)$. Because $p > 1$, $n^{1-p} \to 0$ as $n \to \infty$, so that $\lim_{n \to \infty} b_n = \frac{1}{p-1}$.

71

a. $T_1 = \frac{\sqrt{3}}{16}$ and $T_2 = \frac{7\sqrt{3}}{64}$.

b. At stage n, 3^{n-1} triangles of side length $1/2^n$ are removed. Each of those triangles has an area of $\frac{\sqrt{3}}{4 \cdot 4^n} = \frac{\sqrt{3}}{4^{n+1}}$, so a total of

$$3^{n-1} \cdot \frac{\sqrt{3}}{4^{n+1}} = \frac{\sqrt{3}}{16} \cdot \left(\frac{3}{4}\right)^{n-1}$$

is removed at each stage. Thus

$$T_n = \frac{\sqrt{3}}{16} \sum_{k=1}^{n} \left(\frac{3}{4}\right)^{k-1} = \frac{\sqrt{3}}{16} \sum_{k=0}^{n-1} \left(\frac{3}{4}\right)^{k} = \frac{\sqrt{3}}{4} \left(1 - \left(\frac{3}{4}\right)^n\right).$$

c. $\lim\limits_{n \to \infty} T_n = \frac{\sqrt{3}}{4}$ because $\left(\frac{3}{4}\right)^n \to 0$ as $n \to \infty$.

d. The area of the triangle was originally $\frac{\sqrt{3}}{4}$, so none of the original area is left.

72 Because the given sequence is non-decreasing and bounded above by 1, it must have a limit. A reasonable conjecture is that the limit is 1.

Chapter 9

Power Series

9.1 Approximating Functions With Polynomials

9.1.1 Let the polynomial be $p(x)$. Then $p(0) = f(0)$, $p'(0) = f'(0)$, and $p''(0) = f''(0)$.

9.1.2 It generally increases, because the more derivatives of f are taken into consideration, the better "fit" the polynomial will provide to f.

9.1.3 The approximations are $p_0(0.1) = 1$, $p_1(0.1) = 1 + \frac{0.1}{2} = 1.05$, and $p_2(0.1) = 1 + \frac{0.1}{2} - \frac{.01}{8} = 1.04875$.

9.1.4 The first three terms: $f(a) + f'(a)(x - a) + \frac{1}{2}f''(a)(x - a)^2$.

9.1.5 The remainder is the difference between the value of the Taylor polynomial at a point and the true value of the function at that point, $R_n(x) = f(x) - p_n(x)$.

9.1.6 This is explained in Theorem 9.2. The idea is that the error when using an nth order Taylor polynomial centered at a is $|R_n(x)| \leq M \cdot \frac{|x-a|^{n+1}}{(n+1)!}$ where M is an upper bound for the $(n+1)$st derivative of f for values between a and x.

9.1.7

    a. Note that $f(1) = 8$, and $f'(x) = 12\sqrt{x}$, so $f'(1) = 12$. Thus, $p_1(x) = 8 + 12(x - 1)$.

    b. $f''(x) = 6/\sqrt{x}$, so $f''(1) = 6$. Thus $p_2(x) = 8 + 12(x - 2) + 3(x - 1)^2$.

    c. $p_1(1.1) = 12 \cdot 0.1 + 8 = 9.2$. $p_2(1.1) = 3(.1)^2 + 12 \cdot 0.1 + 8 = 9.23$.

9.1.8

    a. Note that $f(1) = 1$, and that $f'(x) = -1/x^2$, so $f'(1) = -1$. Thus, $p_1(x) = 1 - (x - 1) = -x + 2$.

    b. $f''(x) = 2/x^3$, so $f''(1) = 2$. Thus, $p_2(x) = 2 - x + (x - 1)^2$.

    c. $p_1(1.05) = 0.95$. $p_2(1.05) = (0.05)^2 - 0.05 + 2 = .953$.

9.1.9

    a. $f'(x) = -e^{-x}$, so $p_1(x) = f(0) + f'(0)x = 1 - x$.

    b. $f''(x) = e^{-x}$, so $p_2(x) = f(0) + f'(0)x + \frac{1}{2}f''(0)x^2 = 1 - x + \frac{1}{2}x^2$.

    c. $p_1(0.2) = 0.8$, and $p_2(0.2) = 1 - 0.2 + \frac{1}{2}(0.04) = 0.82$.

9.1.10

   a. $f'(x) = \frac{1}{2}x^{-1/2}$, so $p_1(x) = f(4) + f'(4)(x-4) = 2 + \frac{1}{4}(x-4)$.

   b. $f''(x) = -\frac{1}{4}x^{-3/2}$, so $p_2(x) = f(4) + f'(4)(x-4) + \frac{1}{2}f''(4)(x-4)^2 = 2 + \frac{1}{4}(x-4) - \frac{1}{64}(x-4)^2$.

   c. $p_1(3.9) = 2 + \frac{1}{4}(-0.1) = 2 - 0.025 = 1.975$, and $p_2(3.9) = 2 - 0.025 - \frac{1}{64}(0.001) = 1.975$.

9.1.11

   a. $f'(x) = -\frac{1}{(x+1)^2}$, so $p_1(x) = f(0) + f'(0)x = 1 - x$.

   b. $f''(x) = \frac{2}{(x+1)^3}$, so $p_2(x) = f(0) + f'(0)x + \frac{1}{2}f''(0)x^2 = 1 - x + x^2$.

   c. $p_1(0.05) = 0.95$, and $p_2(0.05) = 1 - 0.05 + 0.0025 = 0.953$.

9.1.12

   a. $f'(x) = -\sin x$, so $p_1(x) = \cos(\pi/4) - \sin(\pi/4)(x - \pi/4) = \frac{\sqrt{2}}{2}(1 - (x - \pi/4))$.

   b. $f''(x) = -\cos x$, so

$$p_2(x) = \cos(\pi/4) - \sin(\pi/4)(x - \pi/4) - \frac{1}{2}\cos(\pi/4)(x - \pi/4)^2$$
$$= \frac{\sqrt{2}}{2}\left(1 - (x - \pi/4) - \frac{1}{2}(x - \pi/4)^2\right).$$

   c. $p_1(0.24\pi) \approx 0.729$, $p_2(0.24\pi) \approx 0.729$.

9.1.13

   a. $f'(x) = (1/3)x^{-2/3}$, so $p_1(x) = f(8) + f'(8)(x-8) = 2 + \frac{1}{12}(x-8)$.

   b. $f''(x) = (-2/9)x^{-5/3}$, so $p_2(x) = f(8) + f'(8)(x-8) + \frac{1}{2}f''(8)(x-8)^2 = 2 + \frac{1}{12}(x-8) - \frac{1}{288}(x-8)^2$.

   c. $p_1(7.5) \approx 1.958$, $p_2(7.5) \approx 1.957$.

9.1.14

   a. $f'(x) = \frac{1}{1+x^2}$, so $p_1(x) = f(0) + f'(0)x = x$.

   b. $f''(x) = -\frac{2x}{(1+x^2)^2}$, so $p_2(x) = f(0) + f'(0)x + \frac{1}{2}f''(0)x^2 = x$.

   c. $p_1(0.1) = p_2(0.1) = 0.1$.

9.1.15 $f(0) = 1, f'(0) = -\sin 0 = 0, f''(0) = -\cos 0 = -1$, so that $p_0(x) = 1, p_1(x) = 1, p_2(x) = 1 - \frac{1}{2}x^2$.

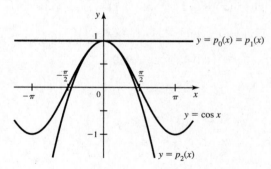

9.1.16 $f(0) = 1, f'(0) = -e^0 = -1, f''(0) = e^0 = 1$, so that $p_0(x) = 1, p_1(x) = 1 - x, p_2(x) = 1 - x + \frac{x^2}{2}$.

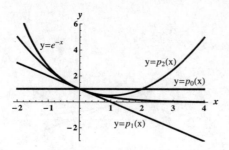

9.1.17 $f(0) = 0$, $f'(0) = -\frac{1}{1-0} = -1$, $f''(0) = -\frac{1}{(1-0)^2} = -1$, so that $p_0(x) = 0$, $p_1(x) = -x$, $p_2(x) = -x - \frac{1}{2}x^2$.

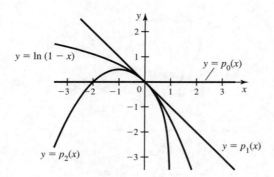

9.1.18 $f(0) = 1$, $f'(0) = (-1/2)(0+1)^{-3/2} = -1/2$, $f''(0) = (3/4)(0+1)^{-5/2} = 3/4$, so that $p_0(x) = 1$, $p_1(x) = 1 - \frac{x}{2}$, $p_2(x) = 1 - \frac{x}{2} + \frac{3}{8}x^2$.

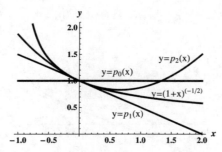

9.1.19 $f(0) = 0$. $f'(x) = \sec^2 x$, $f''(x) = 2\tan x \sec^2 x$, so that $f'(0) = 1$, $f''(0) = 0$. Thus $p_0(x) = 0$, $p_1(x) = x$, $p_2(x) = x$.

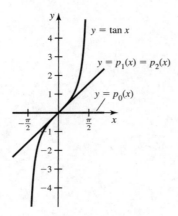

9.1.20 $f(0) = 1$, $f'(0) = (-2)(1+0)^{-3} = -2$, $f''(0) = 6(1+0)^{-4} = 6$. Thus $p_0(x) = 1$, $p_1(x) = 1 - 2x$, $p_2(x) = 1 - 2x + 3x^2$.

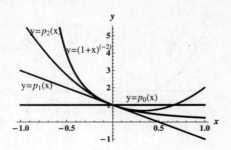

9.1.21 $f(0) = 1$, $f'(0) = -3(1 + 0)^{-4} = -3$, $f''(0) = 12(1 + 0)^{-5} = 12$, so that $p_0(x) = 1$, $p_1(x) = 1 - 3x$, $p_2(x) = 1 - 3x + 6x^2$.

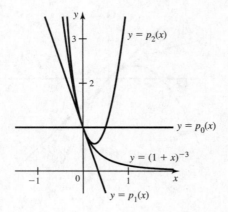

9.1.22 $f(0) = 0$, $f'(x) = \frac{1}{\sqrt{1-x^2}}$, $f''(x) = \frac{x}{(1-x^2)^{3/2}}$, so that $f'(0) = 1$, $f''(0) = 0$. Thus $p_0(x) = 0$, $p_1(x) = x$, $p_2(x) = x$.

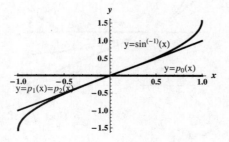

9.1.23

   a. $p_2(0.05) \approx 1.025$.

   b. The absolute error is $\sqrt{1.05} - p_2(0.05) \approx 7.68 \times 10^{-6}$.

9.1.24

   a. $p_2(0.1) \approx 1.032$.

   b. The absolute error is $1.1^{1/3} - p_2(0.1) \approx 5.8 \times 10^{-5}$.

9.1.25

   a. $p_2(0.08) \approx 0.962$.

   b. The absolute error is $p_2(0.08) - \frac{1}{\sqrt{1.08}} \approx 1.5 \times 10^{-4}$.

9.1.26

a. $p_2(0.06) = 0.058$.

b. The absolute error is $\ln 1.06 - p_2(0.06) \approx 6.9 \times 10^{-5}$.

9.1.27

a. $p_2(0.15) \approx 0.861$.

b. The absolute error is $p_2(0.15) - e^{-0.15} \approx 5.4 \times 10^{-4}$.

9.1.28

a. $p_2(0.12) \approx 0.726$.

b. The absolute error is $p_2(0.12) = \frac{1}{1.12^3} \approx 1.5 \times 10^{-2}$.

9.1.29

a. Note that $f(1) = 1$, $f'(1) = 3$, and $f''(1) = 6$. Thus, $p_0(x) = 1$, $p_1(x) = 1 + 3(x-1)$, and $p_2(x) = 1 + 3(x-1) + 3(x-1)^2$.

b.

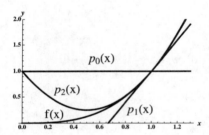

9.1.30

a. Note that $f(1) = 8$, $f'(1) = \frac{4}{\sqrt{1}} = 4$, and $f''(1) = \frac{-2}{(1)^{3/2}} = -2$ Thus, $p_0(x) = 8$, $p_1(x) = 8 + 4(x-1)$, $p_2(x) = 8 + 4(x-1) - (x-1)^2$.

b.

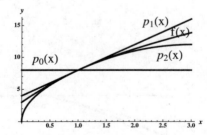

9.1.31

a. $p_0(x) = \frac{\sqrt{2}}{2}$, $p_1(x) = \frac{\sqrt{2}}{2} + \frac{\sqrt{2}}{2}(x - \frac{\pi}{4})$, $p_2(x) = \frac{\sqrt{2}}{2} + \frac{\sqrt{2}}{2}(x - \frac{\pi}{4}) - \frac{\sqrt{2}}{4}(x - \frac{\pi}{4})^2$.

b.

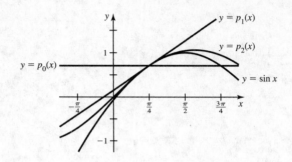

9.1.32

a. $p_0(x) = \frac{\sqrt{3}}{2}$, $p_1(x) = \frac{\sqrt{3}}{2} - \frac{1}{2}\left(x - \frac{\pi}{6}\right)$, $p_2(x) = \frac{\sqrt{3}}{2} - \frac{1}{2}\left(x - \frac{\pi}{6}\right) - \frac{\sqrt{3}}{4}\left(x - \frac{\pi}{6}\right)^2$.

b.

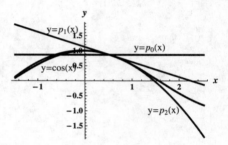

9.1.33

a. $p_0(x) = 3$, $p_1(x) = 3 + \frac{1}{6}(x - 9)$, $p_2(x) = 3 + \frac{1}{6}(x - 9) - \frac{1}{216}(x - 9)^2$.

b.

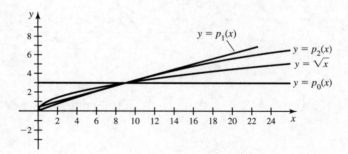

9.1.34

a. $p_0(x) = 2$, $p_1(x) = 2 + \frac{1}{12}(x - 8)$, $p_2(x) = x + \frac{1}{12}(x - 8) - \frac{1}{288}(x - 8)^2$.

b.

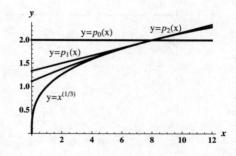

9.1.35

a. $p_0(x) = 1$, $p_1(x) = 1 + \frac{1}{e}(x - e)$, $p_2(x) = 1 + \frac{1}{e}(x - e) - \frac{1}{2e^2}(x - e)^2$.

b.

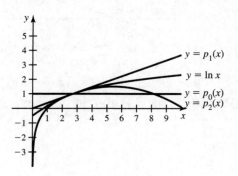

9.1.36

a. $p_0(x) = 2$, $p_1(x) = 2 + \frac{1}{32}(x - 16)$, $p_2(x) = 2 + \frac{1}{32}(x - 16) - \frac{3}{4096}(x - 16)^2$.

b.

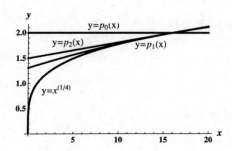

9.1.37

a. $f(1) = \frac{\pi}{4} + 2$, $f'(1) = \frac{1}{2} + 2 = \frac{5}{2}$. $f''(1) = -\frac{1}{2} + 2 = \frac{3}{2}$. $p_0(x) = 2 + \frac{\pi}{4}$, $p_1(x) = 2 + \frac{\pi}{4} + \frac{5}{2}(x - 1)$, $p_2(x) = 2 + \frac{\pi}{4} + \frac{5}{2}(x - 1) + \frac{3}{4}(x - 1)^2$.

b.

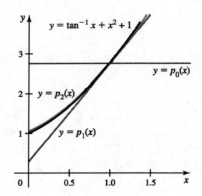

9.1.38

a. $f(\ln 2) = 2$, $f'(\ln 2) = 2$, $f''(\ln 2) = 2$. So $p_0(x) = 2$, $p_1(x) = 2 + 2(x - \ln 2)$, $p_2(x) = 2 + 2(x - \ln 2) + (x - \ln 2)^2$.

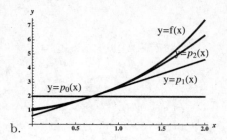

b.

9.1.39

a. Ue the Taylor polynomial centered at 0 with $f(x) = e^x$. We have $p_3(x) = 1 + x + \frac{1}{2}x^2 + \frac{1}{6}x^3$. $p_3(0.12) \approx 1.127$.

b. $|f(0.12) - p_3(0.12)| \approx 8.9 \times 10^{-6}$.

9.1.40

a. Use the Taylor polynomial centered at 0 with $f(x) = \cos(x)$. We have $p_3(x) = 1 - \frac{1}{2}x^2$. $p_3(-0.2) = 0.98$.

b. $|f(0.12) - p_3(0.12)| \approx 6.7 \times 10^{-5}$.

9.1.41

a. Use the Taylor polynomial centered at 0 with $f(x) = \tan(x)$. We have $p_3(x) = x + \frac{1}{3}x^3$. $p_3(-0.1) \approx -0.100$.

b. $|p_3(-0.1) - f(-0.1)| \approx 1.3 \times 10^{-6}$.

9.1.42

a. Use the Taylor polynomial centered at 0 with $f(x) = \ln(1 + x)$. We have $p_3(x) = x - \frac{1}{2}x^2 + \frac{1}{3}x^3$. $p_3(0.05) \approx 0.0488$.

b. $|p_3(0.05) - f(0.05)| \approx 1.5 \times 10^{-6}$.

9.1.43

a. Use the Taylor polynomial centered at 0 with $f(x) = \sqrt{1 + x}$. We have $p_3(x) = 1 + \frac{1}{2}x - \frac{1}{8}x^2 + \frac{1}{16}x^3$. $p_3(0.06) \approx 1.030$.

b. $|f(0.06) - p_3(0.06)| \approx 4.9 \times 10^{-7}$.

9.1.44

a. Use the Taylor polynomial centered at 81 with $f(x) = \sqrt[4]{x}$. We have $p_3(x) = 3 + \frac{1}{108}(x - 81) - \frac{1}{23328}(x - 81)^2 + \frac{7}{22674816}(x - 81)^3$. $p_3(79) \approx 2.981$.

b. $|p_3(79) - f(79)| \approx 4.3 \times 10^{-8}$.

9.1.45

a. Use the Taylor polynomial centered at 100 with $f(x) = \sqrt{x}$. We have $p_3(x) = 10 + \frac{1}{20}(x - 100) - \frac{1}{8000}(x - 100)^2 + \frac{1}{1600000}(x - 100)^3$. $p_3(101) \approx 10.050$.

b. $|p_3(101) - f(101)| \approx 3.9 \times 10^{-9}$.

9.1.46

a. Use the Taylor polynomial centered at 125 with $f(x) = \sqrt[3]{x}$. We have $p_3(x) = 5 + \frac{1}{75}(x - 125) - \frac{1}{28125}(x - 125)^2 + \frac{1}{6328125}(x - 125)^3$. $p_3(125) \approx 5.013$.

b. $|p_3(126) - f(126)| \approx 8.4 \times 10^{-10}$.

9.1.47

a. Use the Taylor polynomial centered at 0 with $f(x) = \sinh(x)$. Note that $f(0) = 0$, $f'(0) = 1$, $f''(0) = 0$ and $f'''(0) = 1$. Then we have $p_3(x) = x + x^3/6$, so $\sinh(.5) \approx (.5)^3/6 + .5 \approx 0.521$.

b. $|p_3(.5) - \sinh(.5)| \approx 2.6 \times 10^{-4}$.

9.1.48

a. Use the Taylor polynomial centered at 0 with $f(x) = \tanh(x)$, Note that $f(0) = 0$, $f'(0) = 1$, $f''(0) = 0$, $f'''(0) = -2$. Then we have $p_3(x) = -x^3/3 + x$, so $\tanh(.5) \approx -(.5)^2/3 + .5 \approx 0.449$.

b. $|p_3(x) - \tanh(.5)| \approx 3.8 \times 10^{-3}$.

9.1.49 With $f(x) = \sin x$ we have $R_n(x) = \dfrac{f^{(n+1)}(c)}{(n+1)!} x^{n+1}$ for c between 0 and x.

9.1.50 With $f(x) = \cos 2x$ we have $R_n(x) = \dfrac{f^{(n+1)}(c)}{(n+1)!} x^{n+1}$ for c between 0 and x.

9.1.51 With $f(x) = e^{-x}$ we have $f^{(n+1)}(x) = (-1)^{n+1}e^{-x}$, so that $R_n(x) = \dfrac{(-1)^{n+1}e^{-c}}{(n+1)!} x^{n+1}$ for c between 0 and x.

9.1.52 With $f(x) = \cos x$ we have $R_n(x) = \dfrac{f^{(n+1)}(c)}{(n+1)!} \left(x - \dfrac{\pi}{2}\right)^{n+1}$ for c between $\frac{\pi}{2}$ and x.

9.1.53 With $f(x) = \sin x$ we have $R_n(x) = \dfrac{f^{(n+1)}(c)}{(n+1)!} \left(x - \dfrac{\pi}{2}\right)^{n+1}$ for c between $\frac{\pi}{2}$ and x.

9.1.54 With $f(x) = \frac{1}{1-x}$ we have $f^{(n+1)}(x) = (-1)^{n+1}\frac{1}{(1-x)^{n+2}}$ so that $R_n(x) = \dfrac{(-1)^{n+1}}{(1-c)^{n+2}} \left(x^{n+1}\right)$ for c between 0 and x.

9.1.55 $f(x) = \sin x$, so $f^{(5)}(x) = \cos x$. Because $\cos x$ is bounded in magnitude by 1, the remainder is bounded by $|R_4(x)| \leq \frac{0.3^5}{5!} \approx 2.0 \times 10^{-5}$.

9.1.56 $f(x) = \cos x$, so $f^{(4)}(x) = \cos x$. Because $\cos x$ is bounded in magnitude by 1, the remainder is bounded by $|R_3(x)| \leq \frac{0.45^4}{4!} \approx 1.7 \times 10^{-3}$.

9.1.57 $f(x) = e^x$, so $f^{(5)}(x) = e^x$. Because $e^{0.25}$ is bounded by 2, $|R_4(x)| \leq 2 \cdot \frac{0.25^5}{5!} \approx 1.63 \times 10^{-5}$.

9.1.58 $f(x) = \tan x$, so $f^{(3)}(x) = 2\sec^2 x(\sec^2 x + 2\tan^2 x)$. Now, since both $\tan x$ and $\sec x$ are increasing on $[0, \pi/2]$, and $0.3 < \frac{\pi}{6} \approx 0.524$, we can get an upper bound on $f^{(3)}(x)$ on $[0, 0.3]$ by evaluating at $\frac{\pi}{6}$; this gives $f^{(3)}(x) < \frac{16}{3}$ on $[0, 0.3]$. Thus $|R_2(x)| \leq \frac{16}{3} \cdot \frac{0.3^3}{3!} = 2.4 \times 10^{-2}$.

9.1.59 $f(x) = e^{-x}$, so $f^{(5)}(x) = -e^{-x}$. Because $f^{(5)}$ achieves its maximum magnitude in the range at $x = 0$, which has absolute value 1, $|R_4(x)| \leq 1 \cdot \frac{0.5^5}{5!} \approx 2.6 \times 10^{-4}$.

9.1.60 $f(x) = \ln(1+x)$, so $f^{(4)}(x) = -\frac{6}{(x+1)^4}$. On $[0, 0.4]$, the maximum magnitude is 6, so $|R_3(x)| \leq 6 \cdot \frac{0.4^4}{4!} = 6.4 \times 10^{-3}$.

9.1.61 Here $n = 3$ or 4, so use $n = 4$, and $M = 1$ because $f^{(5)}(x) = \cos x$, so that $R_4(x) \leq \frac{(\pi/4)^5}{5!} \approx 2.49 \times 10^{-3}$.

9.1.62 $n = 2$ or 3, so use $n = 3$, and $M = 1$ because $f^{(4)}(x) = \cos x$, so that $|R_3(x)| \leq \frac{(\pi/4)^4}{4!} \approx 1.6 \times 10^{-2}$.

9.1.63 $n = 2$ and $M = e^{1/2} < 2$, so $|R_2(x)| \leq 2 \cdot \frac{(1/2)^3}{3!} \approx 4.2 \times 10^{-2}$.

9.1.64 $n = 1$ or 2, so use 2, and $f^{(3)}(x) = 2\sec^2 x(\sec^2 x + 2\tan^2 x)$. On $\left[\frac{-\pi}{6}, \frac{\pi}{6}\right]$ this achieves its maximum value at $\pm\frac{\pi}{6}$; that value is $\frac{16}{3}$. Thus $|R_2(x)| \leq \frac{16}{3} \cdot \frac{(\pi/6)^3}{3!} \approx 1.28 \times 10^{-1}$.

9.1.65 $n = 2$; $f^{(3)}(x) = \frac{2}{(1+x)^3}$, which achieves its maximum at $x = -0.2$: $|f^{(3)}(x)| = \frac{2}{0.8^3} < 4$. Then $|R_2(x)| \leq 4 \cdot \frac{0.2^3}{3!} \approx 5.4 \times 10^{-3}$.

9.1.66 $n = 1$, $f''(x) = -\frac{1}{4}(1+x)^{-3/2}$, which achieves its maximum magnitude at $x = -0.1$, where it is less than $1/3$. Thus $R_1(x) \leq \frac{1}{3} \cdot \frac{0.1^2}{2!} \approx 1.7 \times 10^{-3}$.

9.1.67 Use the Taylor series for e^x at $x = 0$. The derivatives of e^x are e^x. On $[-0.5, 0]$, the maximum magnitude of any derivative is thus 1 at $x = 0$, so $|R_n(-0.5)| \leq \frac{0.5^{n+1}}{(n+1)!}$, so for $R_n(-0.5) < 10^{-3}$ we need $n = 4$.

9.1.68 Use the Taylor series at $x = 0$ for $\sin x$. The magnitude of any derivative of $\sin x$ is bounded by 1, so $|R_n(0.2)| \leq \frac{0.2^{n+1}}{(n+1)!}$, so for $R_n(0.2) < 10^{-3}$ we need $n = 3$.

9.1.69 Use the Taylor series for $\cos x$ at $x = 0$. The magnitude of any derivative of $\cos x$ is bounded by 1, so $|R_n(-0.25)| \leq \frac{0.25^{n+1}}{(n+1)!}$, so for $|R_n(-0.25)| < 10^{-3}$ we need $n = 3$.

9.1.70 Use the Taylor series for $f(x) = \ln(1+x)$ at $x = 0$. Then $|f^{(n+1)}(x)| = \frac{n!}{(1+x)^{n+1}}$, which for $x \in [-0.15, 0]$ achieves its maximum at $x = -.15$. This maximum is less than $(1.2)^{n+1} \cdot n!$. Thus $|R_n(-0.15)| \leq (1.2)^{n+1} \cdot n! \cdot \frac{.18^{n+1}}{(n+1)!} = \frac{1.2 \cdot (0.15)^{n+1}}{n}$, so for $|R_n(-0.15)| < 10^{-3}$ we need $n = 3$.

9.1.71 Use the Taylor series for $f(x) = \sqrt{x}$ at $x = 1$. Then $|f^{(n+1)}(x)| = \frac{1 \cdot 3 \cdots \cdot (2n-1)}{2^{n+1}} x^{-(2n+1)/2}$, which achieves its maximum on $[1, 1.06]$ at $x = 1$. Then

$$|R_n(1.06)| \leq \frac{1 \cdot 3 \cdots \cdot (2n-1)}{2^{n+1}} \cdot \frac{(1.06-1)^{n+1}}{(n+1)!},$$

and for $|R_n(0.06)| < 10^{-3}$ we need $n = 1$.

9.1.72 Use the Taylor series for $f(x) = \sqrt{1/(1-x)}$ at $x = 0$. Then $|f^{(n+1)}(x)| = \frac{1 \cdot 3 \cdots \cdot (2n+1)}{2^{n+1}}(1-x)^{(-3-2n)/2}$, which achieves its maximum on $[0, 0.15]$ at $x = 0.15$. Thus

$$\begin{aligned}
|R_n(0.15)| &\leq \frac{1 \cdot 3 \cdots \cdot (2n+1)}{2^{n+1}} \cdot \left(\frac{1}{1-0.15}\right)^{(2n+3)/2} \cdot \frac{0.15^{n+1}}{(n+1)!} \\
&= \frac{1 \cdot 3 \cdots \cdot (2n+1)}{2^{n+1}(n+1)!} \cdot \left(\frac{0.15^{n+1}}{0.85^{(2n+3)/2}}\right),
\end{aligned}$$

and for $|R_n(0.15)| < 10^{-3}$ we need $n = 3$.

9.1.73

a. False. If $f(x) = e^{-2x}$, then $f^{(n)}(x) = (-1)^n 2^n e^{-2x}$, so that $f^{(n)}(0) \neq 0$ and all powers of x are present in the Taylor series.

b. True. The constant term of the Taylor series is $f(0) = 1$. Higher-order terms all involve derivatives of $f(x) = x^5 - 1$ evaluated at $x = 0$; clearly for $n < 5$, $f^{(n)}(0) = 0$, and for $n > 5$, the derivative itself vanishes. Only for $n = 5$, where $f^{(5)}(x) = 5!$, is the derivative nonzero, so the coefficient of x^5 in the Taylor series is $f^{(5)}(0)/5! = 1$ and the Taylor polynomial of order 10 is in fact $x^5 - 1$. Note that this statement is true of any polynomial of degree at most 10.

c. True. The odd derivatives of $\sqrt{1+x^2}$ vanish at $x = 0$, while the even ones do not.

d. True. Clearly the second-order Taylor polynomial for f at a has degree at most 2. However, the coefficient of $(x-a)^2$ is $\frac{1}{2}f''(a)$, which is zero because f has an inflection point at a.

9.1.74 Let $p(x) = \sum_{k=0}^{n} c_k(x-a)^k$ be the nth polynomial for $f(x)$ at a. Because $f(a) = p(a)$, it follows that $c_0 = f(0)$. Now, the kth derivative of $p(x)$, $1 \le k \le n$, is $p^{(k)}(x) = k!c_k + $ terms involving $(x-a)^i$, $i > 0$, so that $f^{(k)}(a) = p^{(k)}(a) = k! \cdot c_k$ so that $c_k = \frac{f^{(k)}(a)}{k!}$.

9.1.75

a. This matches (C) because for $f(x) = (1+2x)^{1/2}$, $f''(x) = -(1+2x)^{-3/2}$ so $\frac{f''(0)}{2!} = -\frac{1}{2}$.

b. This matches (E) because for $f(x) = (1+2x)^{-1/2}$, $f''(x) = 3(1+2x)^{-5/2}$, so $\frac{f''(0)}{2!} = \frac{3}{2}$.

c. This matches (A) because $f^{(n)}(x) = 2^n e^{2x}$, so that $f^{(n)}(0) = 2^n$, which is (A)'s pattern.

d. This matches (D) because $f''(x) = 8(1+2x)^{-3}$ and $f''(0) = 8$, so that $f''(0)/2! = 4$

e. This matches (B) because $f'(x) = -6(1+2x)^{-4}$ so that $f'(0) = -6$.

f. This matches (F) because $f^{(n)}(x) = (-2)^n e^{-2x}$, so $f^{(n)}(0) = (-2)^n$, which is (F)'s pattern.

9.1.76

a.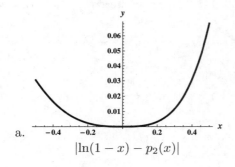
$$|\ln(1-x) - p_2(x)|$$

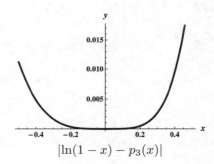
$$|\ln(1-x) - p_3(x)|$$

b. The error seems to be largest at $x = \frac{1}{2}$ and smallest at $x = 0$.

c. The error bound found in Example 7 for $|\ln(1-x) - p_3(x)|$ was 0.25. The actual error seems much less than that, about 0.02.

9.1.77

a. $p_2(0.1) = 0.1$. The maximum error in the approximation is $1 \cdot \frac{0.1^3}{3!} \approx 1.67 \times 10^{-4}$.

b. $p_2(0.2) = 0.2$. The maximum error in the approximation is $1 \cdot \frac{0.2^3}{3!} \approx 1.33 \times 10^{-3}$.

9.1.78

a. $p_1(0.1) = 0.1$. $f''(x) = 2\tan x(1 + \tan^2 x)$. Because $\tan(0.1) < 0.2$, $|f''(c)| \le 2(.2)(1 + .2^2) = 0.416$. Thus the maximum error is $\frac{0.416}{2!} \cdot 0.1^2 \approx 2.1 \times 10^{-3}$.

b. $p_1(0.2) = 0.2$. The maximum error is $\frac{0.416}{2} \cdot 0.2^2 \approx 8.3 \times 10^{-3}$.

9.1.79

a. $p_3(0.1) = 1 - .01/2 = 0.995$. The maximum error is $1 \cdot \frac{0.1^4}{4!} \approx 4.2 \times 10^{-6}$.

b. $p_3(0.2) = 1 - .04/2 = 0.98$. The maximum error is $1 \cdot \frac{0.2^4}{4!} \approx 6.7 \times 10^{-5}$.

9.1.80

a. $p_2(0.1) = 0.1$ (we can take $n = 2$ because the coefficient of x^2 in $p_2(x)$ is 0). $f^{(3)}(x) = \frac{6x^2-2}{(x^2+1)^3}$ has a maximum magnitude value of 2, the maximum error is $2 \cdot \frac{0.1^3}{3!} \approx 3.3 \times 10^{-4}$.

b. $p_2(0.2) = 0.2$. The maximum error is $2 \cdot \frac{0.2^3}{3!} \approx 2.7 \times 10^{-3}$.

9.1.81

a. $p_1(0.1) = 1.05$. Because $|f''(x)| = \frac{1}{4}(1+x)^{-3/2}$ has a maximum value of $1/4$ at $x = 0$, the maximum error is $\frac{1}{4} \cdot \frac{0.1^2}{2} \approx 1.3 \times 10^{-3}$.

b. $p_1(0.2) = 1.1$. The maximum error is $\frac{1}{4} \cdot \frac{0.2^2}{2} = 5 \times 10^{-3}$.

9.1.82

a. $p_2(0.1) = 0.1 - 0.01/2 = 0.095$. Because $|f^{(3)}(x)| = \frac{2}{(x+1)^3}$ achieves a maximum of 2 at $x = 0$, the maximum error is $2 \cdot \frac{0.1^3}{3!} \approx 3.3 \times 10^{-4}$.

b. $p_2(0.2) = 0.2 - 0.04/2 = 0.18$. The maximum error is $2 \cdot \frac{0.2^3}{3!} \approx 2.7 \times 10^{-3}$.

9.1.83

a. $p_1(0.1) = 1.1$. Because $f''(x) = e^x$ is less than 2 on $[0, 0.1]$, the maximum error is less than $2 \cdot \frac{0.1^2}{2!} = 10^{-2}$.

b. $p_1(0.2) = 1.2$. The maximum error is less than $2 \cdot \frac{0.2^2}{2!} = .04 = 4 \times 10^{-2}$.

9.1.84

a. $p_1(0.1) = 0.1$. Because $f''(x) = \frac{x}{(1-x^2)^{3/2}}$ is less than 1 on $[0, 0.2]$, the maximum error is $1 \cdot \frac{0.1^3}{3!} \approx 1.7 \times 10^{-4}$.

b. $p_1(0.2) = 0.2$. The maximum error is $1 \cdot \frac{0.2^3}{3!} \approx 1.3 \times 10^{-3}$.

9.1.85

a.

	$|\sec x - p_2(x)|$	$|\sec x - p_4(x)|$
-0.2	3.4×10^{-4}	5.5×10^{-6}
-0.1	2.1×10^{-5}	8.5×10^{-8}
0.0	0	0
0.1	2.1×10^{-5}	8.5×10^{-8}
0.2	3.4×10^{-4}	5.5×10^{-6}

b. The errors are equal for positive and negative x. This makes sense, because $\sec(-x) = \sec x$ and $p_n(-x) = p_n(x)$ for $n = 2, 4$. The errors appear to get larger as x gets farther from zero.

9.1.86

a.

	$|\cos x - p_2(x)|$	$|\cos x - p_4(x)|$
-0.2	6.66×10^{-5}	8.88×10^{-8}
-0.1	4.17×10^{-6}	1.39×10^{-9}
0.0	0	0
0.1	4.17×10^{-6}	1.39×10^{-9}
0.2	6.66×10^{-5}	8.88×10^{-8}

b. The errors are equal for positive and negative x. This makes sense, because $\cos(-x) = \cos x$ and $p_n(-x) = p_n(x)$ for $n = 2, 4$. The errors appear to get larger as x gets farther from zero.

9.1.87

a.

	$\lvert e^{-x} - p_1(x) \rvert$	$\lvert e^{-x} - p_2(x) \rvert$
-0.2	2.14×10^{-2}	1.40×10^{-3}
-0.1	5.17×10^{-3}	1.71×10^{-4}
0.0	0	0
0.1	4.84×10^{-3}	1.63×10^{-4}
0.2	1.87×10^{-2}	1.27×10^{-3}

b. The errors are different for positive and negative displacements from zero, and appear to get larger as x gets farther from zero.

9.1.88

a.

	$\lvert f(x) - p_1(x) \rvert$	$\lvert f(x) - p_2(x) \rvert$
-0.2	2.31×10^{-2}	3.14×10^{-4}
-0.1	5.36×10^{-3}	3.61×10^{-4}
0.0	0	0
0.1	4.69×10^{-3}	3.10×10^{-4}
0.2	1.77×10^{-2}	2.32×10^{-3}

b. The errors are different for positive and negative displacements from zero, and appear to get larger as x gets farther from zero.

9.1.89

a.

	$\lvert \tan x - p_1(x) \rvert$	$\lvert \tan x - p_3(x) \rvert$
-0.2	2.71×10^{-3}	4.34×10^{-5}
-0.1	3.35×10^{-4}	1.34×10^{-6}
0.0	0	0
0.1	3.35×10^{-4}	1.34×10^{-6}
0.2	2.71×10^{-3}	4.34×10^{-5}

b. The errors are equal for positive and negative x. This makes sense, because $\tan(-x) = -\tan x$ and $p_n(-x) = -p_n(x)$ for $n = 1, 3$. The errors appear to get larger as x gets farther from zero.

9.1.90 The true value of $\cos \dfrac{\pi}{12} = \dfrac{1 + \sqrt{3}}{2\sqrt{2}} \approx 0.966$. The 6th-order Taylor polynomial for $\cos x$ centered at $x = 0$ is

$$p_6(x) = 1 - \frac{x^2}{2} + \frac{x^4}{24} - \frac{x^6}{720}.$$

Evaluating the polynomials at $x = \pi/12$ produces the following table:

n	$p_n\left(\frac{\pi}{12}\right)$	$\left\lvert p_n\left(\frac{\pi}{12}\right) - \cos\frac{\pi}{12} \right\rvert$
1	1.0000000000	3.41×10^{-2}
2	0.9657305403	1.95×10^{-4}
3	0.9657305403	1.95×10^{-4}
4	0.9659262729	4.47×10^{-7}
5	0.9659262729	4.47×10^{-7}
6	0.9659258257	5.47×10^{-10}

The 6th-order Taylor polynomial for $\cos x$ centered at $x = \pi/6$ is

$$p_6(x) = \frac{\sqrt{3}}{2} - \frac{1}{2}\left(x - \frac{\pi}{6}\right) - \frac{\sqrt{3}}{4}\left(x - \frac{\pi}{6}\right)^2 + \frac{1}{12}\left(x - \frac{\pi}{6}\right)^3$$
$$+ \frac{\sqrt{3}}{48}\left(x - \frac{\pi}{6}\right)^4 - \frac{1}{240}\left(x - \frac{\pi}{6}\right)^5 - \frac{\sqrt{3}}{1440}\left(x - \frac{\pi}{6}\right)^6.$$

Evaluating the polynomials at $x = \pi/12$ produces the following table:

n	$p_n\left(\frac{\pi}{12}\right)$	$\left|p_n\left(\frac{\pi}{12}\right) - \cos\frac{\pi}{12}\right|$
1	0.9969250977	3.10×10^{-2}
2	0.9672468750	1.32×10^{-3}
3	0.9657515877	1.74×10^{-4}
4	0.9659210972	4.73×10^{-6}
5	0.9659262214	3.95×10^{-7}
6	0.9659258342	7.88×10^{-9}

Comparing the tables shows that using the polynomial centered at $x = 0$ is more accurate when n is even while using the polynomial centered at $x = \pi/6$ is more accurate when n is odd. To see why, consider the remainder. Let $f(x) = \cos x$. By Theorem 9.2, the magnitude of the remainder when approximating $f(\pi/12)$ by the polynomial p_n centered at 0 is:

$$\left|R_n\left(\frac{\pi}{12}\right)\right| = \frac{|f^{(n+1)}(c)|}{(n+1)!}\left(\frac{\pi}{12}\right)^{n+1}$$

for some c with $0 < c < \frac{\pi}{12}$, while the magnitude of the remainder when approximating $f(\pi/12)$ by the polynomial p_n centered at $\pi/6$ is:

$$\left|R_n\left(\frac{\pi}{12}\right)\right| = \frac{|f^{(n+1)}(c)|}{(n+1)!}\left(\frac{\pi}{12}\right)^{n+1}$$

for some c with $\frac{\pi}{12} < c < \frac{\pi}{6}$. When n is odd, $|f^{(n+1)}(c)| = |\cos c|$. Because $\cos x$ is a positive and decreasing function over $[0, \pi/6]$, the magnitude of the remainder in using the polynomial centered at $\pi/6$ will be less than the remainder in using the polynomial centered at 0, and the former polynomial will be more accurate. When n is even, $|f^{(n+1)}(c)| = |\sin c|$. Because $\sin x$ is a positive and increasing function over $[0, \pi/6]$, the remainder in using the polynomial centered at 0 will be less than the remainder in using the polynomial centered at $\pi/6$, and the former polynomial will be more accurate.

9.1.91 The true value of $e^{0.35} \approx 1.419067549$. The 6th-order Taylor polynomial for e^x centered at $x = 0$ is

$$p_6(x) \;=\; 1 + x + \frac{x^2}{2} + \frac{x^3}{6} + \frac{x^4}{24} + \frac{x^5}{120} + \frac{x^6}{720}.$$

Evaluating the polynomials at $x = 0.35$ produces the following table:

n	$p_n(0.35)$	$\left|p_n(0.35) - e^{0.35}\right|$
1	1.350000000	6.91×10^{-2}
2	1.411250000	7.82×10^{-3}
3	1.418395833	6.72×10^{-4}
4	1.419021094	4.65×10^{-5}
5	1.419064862	2.69×10^{-6}
6	1.419067415	1.33×10^{-7}

The 6th-order Taylor polynomial for e^x centered at $x = \ln 2$ is

$$p_6(x) = 2 + 2(x - \ln 2) + (x - \ln 2)^2 + \frac{1}{3}(x - \ln 2)^3 + \frac{1}{12}(x - \ln 2)^4$$
$$+ \frac{1}{60}(x - \ln 2)^5 + \frac{1}{360}(x - \ln 2)^6.$$

Evaluating the polynomials at $x = 0.35$ produces the following table:

n	$p_n(0.35)$	$\lvert p_n(0.35) - e^{0.35}\rvert$
1	1.313705639	1.05×10^{-1}
2	1.431455626	1.24×10^{-2}
3	1.417987101	1.08×10^{-3}
4	1.419142523	7.50×10^{-5}
5	1.419063227	4.32×10^{-6}
6	1.419067762	2.13×10^{-7}

Comparing the tables shows that using the polynomial centered at $x = 0$ is more accurate for all n. To see why, consider the remainder. Let $f(x) = e^x$. By Theorem 9.2, the magnitude of the remainder when approximating $f(0.35)$ by the polynomial p_n centered at 0 is:

$$|R_n(0.35)| = \frac{|f^{(n+1)}(c)|}{(n+1)!}(0.35)^{n+1} = \frac{e^c}{(n+1)!}(0.35)^{n+1}$$

for some c with $0 < c < 0.35$ while the magnitude of the remainder when approximating $f(0.35)$ by the polynomial p_n centered at $\ln 2$ is:

$$|R_n(0.35)| = \frac{|f^{(n+1)}(c)|}{(n+1)!}|0.35 - \ln 2|^{n+1} = \frac{e^c}{(n+1)!}(\ln 2 - 0.35)^{n+1}$$

for some c with $0.35 < c < \ln 2$. Because $\ln 2 - 0.35 \approx 0.35$, the relative size of the magnitudes of the remainders is determined by e^c in each remainder. Because e^x is an increasing function, the remainder in using the polynomial centered at 0 will be less than the remainder in using the polynomial centered at $\ln 2$, and the former polynomial will be more accurate.

9.1.92

a. Let x be a point in the interval on which the derivatives of f are assumed continuous. Then f' is continuous on $[a, x]$, and the Fundamental Theorem of Calculus implies that because f is an antiderivative of f', then $\int_a^x f'(t)\,dt = f(x) - f(a)$, or $f(x) = f(a) + \int_a^x f'(t)\,dt$.

b. Using integration by parts with $u = f'(t)$ and $dv = dt$, note that we may choose any antiderivative of dv; we choose $t - x = -(x - t)$. Then

$$f(x) = f(a) - f'(t)(x - t)\Big|_{t=a}^{x} + \int_a^x (x - t)f''(t)\,dt$$

$$= f(a) - f'(a)(x - a) + \int_a^x (x - t)f''(t)\,dt.$$

c. Integrate by parts again, using $u = f''(t)$, $dv = (x - t)\,dt$, so that $v = -\frac{(x-t)^2}{2}$:

$$f(x) = f(a) + f'(a)(x - a) + \int_a^x (x - t)f''(t)\,dt$$

$$= f(a) + f'(a)(x - a) - \frac{(x - t)^2}{2}f''(t)\Big|_a^x + \frac{1}{2}\int_a^x (x - t)^2 f'''(t)\,dt$$

$$= f(a) + f'(a)(x - a) + \frac{f''(t)}{2}(x - a)^2 + \frac{1}{2}\int_a^x (x - t)^2 f'''(t)\,dt.$$

It is clear that continuing this process will give the desired result, because successive integral of $x - t$ give $-\frac{1}{k!}(x - t)^k$.

d. **Lemma:** Let g and h be continuous functions on the interval $[a, b]$ with $g(t) \geq 0$. Then there is a number c in $[a, b]$ with

$$\int_a^b h(t)g(t)\, dt = h(c)\int_a^b g(t)\, dt.$$

Proof: We note first that if $g(t) = 0$ for all t in $[a, b]$, then the result is clearly true. We can thus assume that there is some t in $[a, b]$ for which $g(t) > 0$. Because g is continuous, there must be an interval about this t on which g is strictly positive, so we may assume that

$$\int_a^b g(t)\, dt > 0.$$

Because h is continuous on $[a, b]$, the Extreme Value Theorem shows that h has an absolute minimum value m and an absolute maximum value M on the interval $[a, b]$. Thus

$$m \leq h(t) \leq M$$

for all t in $[a, b]$, so

$$m \int_a^b g(t)\, dt \leq \int_a^b h(t)g(t)\, dt \leq M \int_a^b g(t)\, dt.$$

Because $\int_a^b g(t)\, dt > 0$, we have

$$m \leq \frac{\int_a^b h(t)g(t)\, dt}{\int_a^b g(t)\, dt} \leq M.$$

Now there are points in $[a, b]$ at which $h(t)$ equals m and M, so the Intermediate Value Theorem shows that there is a point c in $[a, b]$ at which

$$h(c) = \frac{\int_a^b h(t)g(t)\, dt}{\int_a^b g(t)\, dt}$$

or

$$\int_a^b h(t)g(t)\, dt = h(c)\int_a^b g(t)\, dt.$$

Applying the lemma with $h(t) = \frac{f^{(n+1)}(t)}{n!}$, $g(t) = (x-t)^n$, we see that $R_n(x) = \frac{f^{(n+1)}(c)}{n!}\int_a^x (x-t)^n\, dt = \frac{f^{(n+1)}(c)}{n!}\cdot\frac{1}{n+1}(x-a)^{n+1} = \frac{f^{(n+1)}(c)}{(n+1)!}(x-a)^{n+1}$ for some $c \in [a, b]$.

9.1.93

a. The slope of the tangent line to $f(x)$ at $x = a$ is by definition $f'(a)$; by the point-slope form for the equation of a line, we have $y - f(a) = f'(a)(x - a)$, or $y = f(a) + f'(a)(x - a)$.

b. The Taylor polynomial centered at a is $p_1(x) = f(a) + f'(a)(x - a)$, which is the tangent line at a.

9.1.94

a. $p_2(x) = f(a) + f'(a)(x - a) + \frac{f''(a)}{2}(x - a)^2$, so that $p_2'(x) = f'(a) + f''(a)(x - a)$ and $p_2''(x) = f''(a)$. If f has a local maximum at a, then $f'(a) = 0, f''(a) \leq 0$, but then $p_2'(a) = 0$ and $p_2''(a) \leq 0$ by the above, so that $p_2(x)$ also has a local maximum at a.

b. Similarly, if f has a local minimum at a, then $f'(a) = 0, f''(a) \geq 0$, but then $p_2'(a) = 0$ and $p_2''(a) \geq 0$ by the above, so that $p_2(x)$ also has a local minimum at a.

c. Recall that f has an inflection point at a if the second derivative of f changes sign at a. But $p_2''(x)$ is a constant, so p_2 does not have an inflection point at a (or anywhere else).

d. No. For example, let $f(x) = x^3$. Then $p_2(x) = 0$, so that the second-order Taylor polynomial has a local maximum at $x = 0$, but $f(x)$ does not. It also has a local minimum at $x = 0$, but $f(x)$ does not.

9.1.95

a. We have

$$f(0) = f^{(4)}(0) = \sin 0 = 0 \qquad f(\pi) = f^{(4)}(\pi) = \sin \pi = 0$$
$$f'(0) = f^{(5)}(0) = \cos 0 = 1 \qquad f'(\pi) = f^{(5)}(0) = \cos \pi = -1$$
$$f''(0) = -\sin 0 = 0 \qquad f''(\pi) = -\sin \pi = 0$$
$$f'''(0) = -\cos 0 = -1 \qquad f'''(\pi) = -\cos \pi = 1.$$

Thus

$$p_5(x) = x - \frac{x^3}{3!} + \frac{x^5}{5!}$$

$$q_5(x) = -(x - \pi) + \frac{1}{3!}(x - \pi)^3 - \frac{1}{5!}(x - \pi)^5.$$

b. A plot of the three functions, with $\sin x$ the black solid line, $p_5(x)$ the dashed line, and $q_5(x)$ the dotted line is below.

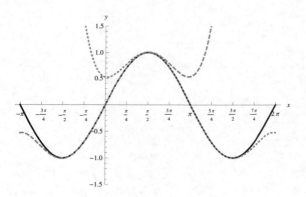

$p_5(x)$ and $\sin x$ are almost indistinguishable on $[-\pi/2, \pi/2]$, after which $p_5(x)$ diverges pretty quickly from $\sin x$. $q_5(x)$ is reasonably close to $\sin x$ over the entire range, but the two are almost indistinguishable on $[\pi/2, 3\pi/2]$. $p_5(x)$ is a better approximation than $q_5(x)$ on about $[-\pi, \pi/2)$, while $q_5(x)$ is better on about $(\pi/2, 2\pi]$.

c. Evaluating the errors gives

x	$|\sin x - p_5(x)|$	$|\sin x - q_5(x)|$
$\frac{\pi}{4}$	3.6×10^{-5}	7.4×10^{-2}
$\frac{\pi}{2}$	4.5×10^{-3}	4.5×10^{-3}
$\frac{3\pi}{4}$	7.4×10^{-2}	3.6×10^{-5}
$\frac{5\pi}{4}$	2.3	3.6×10^{-5}
$\frac{7\pi}{4}$	20.4	7.4×10^{-2}

d. $p_5(x)$ is a better approximation than $q_5(x)$ only at $x = \frac{\pi}{4}$, in accordance with part (b). The two are equal at $x = \frac{\pi}{2}$, after which $q_5(x)$ is a substantially better approximation than $p_5(x)$.

9.1.96

a. We have

$$f(1) = \ln 1 = 0 \qquad\qquad f(e) = \ln e = 1$$

$$f'(1) = 1 \qquad\qquad f'(e) = \frac{1}{3}$$

$$f''(1) = -1 \qquad\qquad f''(e) = -\frac{1}{e^2}$$

$$f'''(1) = 2 \qquad\qquad f'''(e) = \frac{2}{e^3}.$$

Thus

$$p_3(x) = (x-1) - \frac{1}{2!}(x-1)^2 + \frac{2}{3!}(x-1)^3 = (x-1) - \frac{1}{2}(x-1)^2 + \frac{1}{3}(x-1)^3$$

$$q_3(x) = 1 + \frac{1}{e}(x-e) - \frac{1}{2e^2}(x-e)^2 + \frac{1}{3e^3}(x-e)^3.$$

b. A plot of the three functions, with $\ln x$ the black solid line, $p_3(x)$ the dashed line, and $q_3(x)$ the dotted line is below.

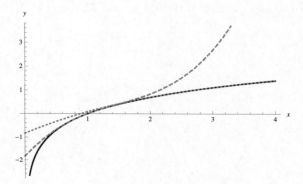

c. Evaluating the errors gives

x	$|\ln x - p_3(x)|$	$|\ln x - q_3(x)|$
0.5	2.6×10^{-2}	3.6×10^{-1}
1.0	0	8.4×10^{-2}
1.5	1.1×10^{-2}	1.6×10^{-2}
2.0	1.4×10^{-1}	1.5×10^{-3}
2.5	5.8×10^{-1}	1.1×10^{-5}
3.0	1.6	2.7×10^{-5}
3.5	3.3	1.4×10^{-3}

d. $p_3(x)$ is a better approximation than $q_3(x)$ for $x = 0.5$, 1.0, and 1.5, and $q_3(x)$ is a better approximation for the other points. To see why this is true, note that on $[0.5, 4]$ that $f^{(4)}(x) = -\frac{6}{x^4}$ is bounded in magnitude by $\frac{6}{0.5^4} = 96$, so that (using P_3 for the error term for p_3 and Q_3 as the error term for q_3)

$$P_3(x) \le 96 \cdot \frac{|x-1|^4}{4!} = 4\,|x-1|^4, \qquad\qquad Q_3(x) \le 96 \cdot \frac{|x-e|^4}{4!} = 4\,|x-e|^4.$$

Thus the relative sizes of $P_3(x)$ and $Q_3(x)$ are governed by the distance of x from 1 and e. Looking at the different possibilities for x reveals why the results in part (c) hold.

9.1.97

a. We have

$$f(36) = \sqrt{36} = 6 \qquad\qquad f(49) = \sqrt{49} = 7$$

$$f'(36) = \frac{1}{2} \cdot \frac{1}{\sqrt{36}} = \frac{1}{12} \qquad\qquad f'(49) = \frac{1}{2} \cdot \frac{1}{\sqrt{49}} = \frac{1}{14}.$$

Thus

$$p_1(x) = 6 + \frac{1}{12}(x - 36) \qquad\qquad q_1(x) = 7 + \frac{1}{14}(x - 49).$$

b. Evaluating the errors gives

x	$\left|\sqrt{x} - p_1(x)\right|$	$\left|\sqrt{x} - q_1(x)\right|$
37	5.7×10^{-4}	6.0×10^{-2}
39	5.0×10^{-3}	4.1×10^{-2}
41	1.4×10^{-2}	2.5×10^{-2}
43	2.6×10^{-2}	1.4×10^{-2}
45	4.2×10^{-2}	6.1×10^{-3}
47	6.1×10^{-2}	1.5×10^{-3}

c. $p_1(x)$ is a better approximation than $q_1(x)$ for $x \leq 41$, and $q_1(x)$ is a better approximation for $x \geq 43$. To see why this is true, note that $f''(x) = -\frac{1}{4}x^{-3/2}$, so that on $[36, 49]$ it is bounded in magnitude by $\frac{1}{4} \cdot 36^{-3/2} = \frac{1}{864}$. . Thus (using P_1 for the error term for p_1 and Q_1 for the error term for q_1)

$$P_1(x) \leq \frac{1}{864} \cdot \frac{|x - 36|^2}{2!} = \frac{1}{1728}(x - 36)^2, \qquad Q_1(x) \leq \frac{1}{864} \cdot \frac{|x - 49|^2}{2!} = \frac{1}{1728}(x - 49)^2.$$

It follows that the relative sizes of $P_1(x)$ and $Q_1(x)$ are governed by the distance of x from 36 and 49. Looking at the different possibilities for x reveals why the results in part (b) hold.

9.1.98

a. The quadratic Taylor polynomial for $\sin x$ centered at $\frac{\pi}{2}$ is

$$p_2(x) = \sin\frac{\pi}{2} + \cos\frac{\pi}{2} \cdot \left(x - \frac{\pi}{2}\right) - \frac{1}{2}\sin\frac{\pi}{2} \cdot \left(x - \frac{\pi}{2}\right)^2$$

$$= 1 - \frac{1}{2}\left(x - \frac{\pi}{2}\right)^2$$

$$= -\frac{1}{2}x^2 + \frac{\pi}{2}x + 1 - \frac{\pi^2}{8}.$$

b. Let $q(x) = ax^2 + bx + c$. Because $q(0) = \sin 0 = 0$, we must have $c = 0$, so that $q(x) = ax^2 + bx$. Then the other two conditions give us a pair of linear equation in a and b:

$$\frac{\pi^2}{4}a + \frac{\pi}{2}b = 1$$

$$\pi^2 a + \pi b = 0$$

where the first equation comes from the fact that $q(\pi/2) = \sin(\pi/2) = 1$ and the second from the fact that $q(\pi) = \sin \pi = 0$. Solving the linear system of equations gives $b = \frac{4}{\pi}$ and $a = -\frac{4}{\pi^2}$, so that

$$q(x) = -\frac{4}{\pi^2}x^2 + \frac{4}{\pi}x.$$

c. A plot of the three function, with $\sin x$ the black solid line, $p_2(x)$ the dashed line, and $q(x)$ the dotted line is below.

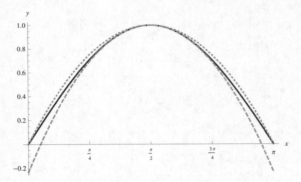

d. Evaluating the errors gives

x	$\lvert \sin x - p_2(x) \rvert$	$\lvert \sin x - q(x) \rvert$
$\frac{\pi}{4}$	1.6×10^{-2}	4.3×10^{-2}
$\frac{\pi}{2}$	0	0
$\frac{3\pi}{4}$	1.6×10^{-2}	4.3×10^{-2}
π	2.3×10^{-1}	0

e. q is a better approximation than p at $x = \pi$, and the two are equal at $x = \frac{\pi}{2}$. At the other two points, however, $p_2(x)$ is a better approximation than $q(x)$. Clearly $q(x)$ will be exact at $x = 0$, $x = \frac{\pi}{2}$, and $x = \pi$, because it was chosen that way. Also clearly $p_2(x)$ will be exact at $x = \frac{\pi}{2}$ since it is the Taylor polynomial centered at $\frac{\pi}{2}$. The fact that $p_2(x)$ is a better approximation than $q(x)$ at the two intermediate points is a result of the way the polynomials were constructed: the goal of $p_2(x)$ was to be as good an approximation as possible near $x = \frac{\pi}{2}$, while the goal of $q(x)$ was to match $\sin x$ at three given points. Overall, it appears that $q(x)$ does a better job over the full range (the total area between $q(x)$ and $\sin x$ is certainly smaller than the total area between $p_2(x)$ and $\sin x$).

9.2　Properties of Power Series

9.2.1 $c_0 + c_1 x + c_2 x^2 + c_3 x^3$.

9.2.2 $c_0 + c_1(x - 3) + c_2(x - 3)^2 + c_3(x - 3)^3$.

9.2.3 Generally the Ratio Test or Root Test is used.

9.2.4 Theorem 9.3 says that on the interior of the interval of convergence, a power series centered at a converges absolutely, and that the interval of convergence is symmetric about a. So it makes sense to try to find this interval using the Ratio Test, and check the endpoints individually.

9.2.5 The radius of convergence does not change, but the interval of convergence may change at the endpoints.

9.2.6 $2R$, because for $\lvert x \rvert < 2R$ we have $\lvert x/2 \rvert < R$ so that $\sum c_k (x/2)^k$ converges.

9.2.7 $\lvert x \rvert < \frac{1}{4}$.

9.2.8 $(-1)^k c_k x^k = c_k(-x)^k$, so the two series have the same radius of convergence, because $\lvert -x \rvert = \lvert x \rvert$.

9.2.9 Using the Root Test: $\lim_{k\to\infty} \sqrt[k]{|a_k|} = \lim_{k\to\infty} |2x| = |2x|$. So the radius of convergence is $\frac{1}{2}$. At $x = 1/2$ the series is $\sum 1$ which diverges, and at $x = -1/2$ the series is $\sum (-1)^k$ which also diverges. So the interval of convergence is $(-1/2, 1/2)$.

9.2.10 Using the Ratio Test: $\lim_{k\to\infty} \left| \frac{a_{k+1}}{a_k} \right| = \lim_{k\to\infty} \left| \frac{(2x)^{k+1}}{(k+1)!} \cdot \frac{k!}{(2x)^k} \right| = \lim_{k\to\infty} \left| \frac{2x}{k+1} \right| = 0$. So the radius of convergence is ∞ and the interval of convergence is $(-\infty, \infty)$.

9.2.11 Using the Root Test, $\lim_{k\to\infty} \sqrt[k]{|a_k|} = \lim_{k\to\infty} \frac{|x-1|}{k^{1/k}} = |x-1|$. So the radius of convergence is 1. At $x = 2$, we have the harmonic series (which diverges) and at $x = 0$ we have the alternating harmonic series (which converges). Thus the interval of convergence is $[0, 2)$.

9.2.12 Using the Ratio Test: $\lim_{k\to\infty} \left| \frac{a_{k+1}}{a_k} \right| = \lim_{k\to\infty} \left| \frac{(x-1)^{k+1}}{(k+1)!} \cdot \frac{k!}{(x-1)^k} \right| = \lim_{k\to\infty} \left| \frac{x-1}{k+1} \right| = 0$. Thus the radius of convergence is ∞ and the interval of convergence is $(-\infty, \infty)$.

9.2.13 Using the Ratio Test: $\lim_{k\to\infty} \left| \frac{a_{k+1}}{a_k} \right| = \lim_{k\to\infty} \left| \frac{(k+1)^{k+1} x^{k+1}}{k^k x^k} \right| = \lim_{k\to\infty} (k+1) \left(\frac{k+1}{k} \right)^k |x| = \infty$ (for $x \neq 0$) because $\lim_{k\to\infty} \left(\frac{k+1}{k} \right)^k = e$. Thus, the radius of convergence is 0, the series only converges at $x = 0$.

9.2.14 Using the Ratio Test: $\lim_{k\to\infty} \left| \frac{a_{k+1}}{a_k} \right| = \lim_{k\to\infty} \left| \frac{(k+1)!(x-10)^{k+1}}{k!(x-10)^k} \right| = \lim_{k\to\infty} (k+1)|x-10| = \infty$ (for $x \neq 10$). Thus, the radius of convergence is 0, the series only converges at $x = 10$.

9.2.15 Using the Root Test: $\lim_{k\to\infty} \sqrt[k]{|a_k|} = \lim_{k\to\infty} \sin(1/k)|x| = \sin(0)|x| = 0$. Thus, the radius of convergence is ∞ and the interval of convergence is $(-\infty, \infty)$.

9.2.16 Using the Root Test: $\lim_{k\to\infty} \sqrt[k]{|a_k|} = \lim_{k\to\infty} \frac{2|x-3|}{k^{1/k}} = 2|x-3|$. Thus, the radius of convergence is $1/2$. When $x = 7/2$, we have the harmonic series (which diverges), and when $x = 5/2$, we have the alternating harmonic series which converges. The interval of convergence is thus $[5/2, 7/2)$.

9.2.17 Using the Root Test: $\lim_{k\to\infty} \sqrt[k]{|a_k|} = \lim_{k\to\infty} \frac{|x|}{3} = \frac{|x|}{3}$, so the radius of convergence is 3. At -3, the series is $\sum (-1)^k$, which diverges. At 3, the series is $\sum 1$, which diverges. So the interval of convergence is $(-3, 3)$.

9.2.18 Using the Root Test: $\lim_{k\to\infty} \sqrt[k]{|a_k|} = \lim_{k\to\infty} \frac{|x|}{5} = \frac{|x|}{5}$, so the radius of convergence is 5. At 5, we obtain $\sum (-1)^k$ which diverges. At -5, we have $\sum 1$, which also diverges. So the interval of convergence is $(-5, 5)$.

9.2.19 Using the Root Test: $\lim_{k\to\infty} \sqrt[k]{|a_k|} = \lim_{k\to\infty} \frac{|x|}{k} = 0$, so the radius of convergence is infinite and the interval of convergence is $(-\infty, \infty)$.

9.2.20 Using the Ratio Test: $\lim_{k\to\infty} \left| \frac{a_{k+1}}{a_k} \right| = \lim_{k\to\infty} \left| \left(\frac{(k+1)(x-4)^{k+1}}{2^{k+1}} \cdot \frac{2^k}{k(x-4)^k} \right) \right| = \lim_{k\to\infty} \left(\frac{k+1}{k} \cdot \frac{|x-4|}{2} \right) = \frac{|x-4|}{2}$, so that the radius of convergence is 2. The interval is $(2, 6)$, because at the left endpoint, the series becomes $\sum k$ (which diverges) and at the right endpoint, it becomes $\sum (-1)^k k$ (which diverges).

9.2.21 Using the Ratio Test: $\lim_{k\to\infty} \left| \frac{(k+1)^2 x^{2k+2}}{(k+1)!} \cdot \frac{k!}{k^2 x^{2k}} \right| = \lim_{k\to\infty} \frac{k+1}{k^2} x^2 = 0$, so the radius of convergence is infinite, and the interval of convergence is $(-\infty, \infty)$.

9.2.22 Using the Root Test: $\lim_{k\to\infty} \sqrt[k]{|a_k|} = \lim_{k\to\infty} k^{1/k} |x-1| = |x-1|$. The radius of convergence is therefore 1. At both $x = 2$ and $x = 0$ the series diverges by the Divergence Test. The interval of convergence is therefore $(0, 2)$.

9.2.23 Using the Ratio Test: $\lim_{k\to\infty} \left| \frac{a_{k+1}}{a_k} \right| = \left| \frac{x^{2k+3}}{3^k} \cdot \frac{3^{k-1}}{x^{2k+1}} \right| = \frac{x^2}{3}$ so that the radius of convergence is $\sqrt{3}$. At $x = \sqrt{3}$, the series is $\sum 3\sqrt{3}$, which diverges. At $x = -\sqrt{3}$, the series is $\sum (-3\sqrt{3})$, which also diverges, so the interval of convergence is $(-\sqrt{3}, \sqrt{3})$.

9.2.24 $\sum \left(\frac{-x}{10}\right)^{2k} = \sum \left(\frac{x^2}{100}\right)^k$. Using the Root Test: $\lim\limits_{k\to\infty} \sqrt[k]{|a_k|} = \lim\limits_{k\to\infty} \frac{x^2}{100} = \frac{x^2}{100}$, so that the radius of convergence is 10. At $x = \pm 10$, the series is then $\sum 1$, which diverges, so the interval of convergence is $(-10, 10)$.

9.2.25 Using the Root Test: $\lim\limits_{k\to\infty} \sqrt[k]{|a_k|} = \lim\limits_{k\to\infty} \frac{(|x-1|)k}{k+1} = |x - 1|$, so the series converges when $|x - 1| < 1$, so for $0 < x < 2$. The radius of convergence is 1. At $x = 2$, the series diverges by the Divergence Test. At $x = 0$, the series diverges as well by the Divergence Test. Thus the interval of convergence is $(0, 2)$.

9.2.26 Using the Ratio Test:

$$\lim_{k\to\infty} \frac{|a_{k+1}|}{|a_k|} = \left| \frac{(-2)^{k+1}(x+3)^{k+1}}{3^{k+2}} \cdot \frac{3^{k+1}}{(-2)^k(x+3)^k} \right| = \frac{2}{3}|x+3|.$$

Thus the series converges when $\frac{2}{3}|x + 3| < 1$, or $-\frac{9}{2} < x < -\frac{3}{2}$. At $x = -\frac{9}{2}$, the series diverges by the Divergence Test. At $x = -\frac{3}{2}$, the series diverges by the Divergence Test. Thus the interval of convergence is $\left(-\frac{9}{2}, -\frac{3}{2}\right)$.

9.2.27 Using the Ratio Test: $\lim\limits_{k\to\infty} \left| \frac{a_{k+1}}{a_k} \right| = \left| \frac{(k+1)^{20}x^{k+1}}{(2k+3)!} \cdot \frac{(2k+1)!}{x^k k^{20}} \right| = \lim\limits_{k\to\infty} \left(\frac{k+1}{k}\right)^{20} \frac{|x|}{(2k+2)(2k+3)} = 0$, so the radius of convergence is infinite, and the interval of convergence is $(-\infty, \infty)$.

9.2.28 Using the Root Test: $\lim\limits_{k\to\infty} \sqrt[k]{|a_k|} = \lim\limits_{k\to\infty} \frac{|x^3|}{27} = \frac{|x^3|}{27}$, so the radius of convergence is 3. The series is divergent by the Divergence Test for $x = \pm 3$, so the interval of convergence is $(-3, 3)$.

9.2.29 $f(3x) = \frac{1}{1-3x} = \sum_{k=0}^{\infty} 3^k x^k$, which converges for $|x| < 1/3$, and diverges at the endpoints.

9.2.30 $g(x) = \frac{x^3}{1-x} = \sum_{k=0}^{\infty} x^{k+3}$, which converges for $|x| < 1$ and is divergent at the endpoints.

9.2.31 $h(x) = \frac{2x^3}{1-x} = \sum_{k=0}^{\infty} 2x^{k+3}$, which converges for $|x| < 1$ and is divergent at the endpoints.

9.2.32 $f(x^3) = \frac{1}{1-x^3} = \sum_{k=0}^{\infty} x^{3k}$. By the Root Test, $\lim\limits_{k\to\infty} \sqrt[k]{|a_k|} = |x^3|$, so this series also converges for $|x| < 1$. It is divergent at the endpoints.

9.2.33 $p(x) = \frac{4x^{12}}{1-x} = \sum_{k=0}^{\infty} 4x^{k+12} = 4\sum_{k=0}^{\infty} x^{k+12}$, which converges for $|x| < 1$. It is divergent at the endpoints.

9.2.34 $f(-4x) = \frac{1}{1+4x} = \sum_{k=0}^{\infty}(-4x)^k = \sum_{k=0}^{\infty}(-1)^k 4^k x^k$, which converges for $|x| < 1/4$ and is divergent at the endpoints.

9.2.35 $f(3x) = \ln(1 - 3x) = -\sum_{k=1}^{\infty} \frac{(3x)^k}{k} = -\sum_{k=1}^{\infty} \frac{3^k}{k} x^k$. Using the Ratio Test:

$$\lim_{k\to\infty} \left| \frac{a_{k+1}}{a_k} \right| = \lim_{k\to\infty} \frac{3k}{k+1}|x| = 3|x|,$$

so the radius of convergence is 1/3. The series diverges at 1/3 (harmonic series), and converges at $-1/3$ (alternating harmonic series).

9.2.36 $g(x) = x^3 \ln(1 - x) = -\sum_{k=1}^{\infty} \frac{x^{k+3}}{k}$. Using the Ratio Test: $\lim\limits_{k\to\infty} \left| \frac{a_{k+1}}{a_k} \right| = \lim\limits_{k\to\infty} \frac{k}{k+1}|x| = |x|$, so the radius of convergence is 1. The series diverges at 1 and converges at -1.

9.2.37 $h(x) = x \ln(1 - x) = -\sum_{k=1}^{\infty} \frac{x^{k+1}}{k}$. Using the Ratio Test: $\lim\limits_{k\to\infty} \left| \frac{a_{k+1}}{a_k} \right| = \lim\limits_{k\to\infty} \frac{k}{k+1}|x| = |x|$, so the radius of convergence is 1, and the series diverges at 1 (harmonic series) but converges at -1 (alternating harmonic series).

9.2.38 $f(x^3) = \ln(1-x^3) = -\sum_{k=1}^{\infty} \frac{x^{3k}}{k}$. Using the Ratio Test: $\lim\limits_{k\to\infty} \left|\frac{a_{k+1}}{a_k}\right| = \lim\limits_{k\to\infty} \frac{k}{k+1}\left|x^3\right| = \left|x^3\right|$, so the radius of convergence is 1. The series diverges at 1 (harmonic series) but converges at -1 (alternating harmonic series).

9.2.39 $p(x) = 2x^6 \ln(1-x) = -2\sum_{k=1}^{\infty} \frac{x^{k+6}}{k}$. Using the Ratio Test: $\lim\limits_{k\to\infty} \left|\frac{a_{k+1}}{a_k}\right| = \lim\limits_{k\to\infty} \frac{k}{k+1}\left|x\right| = \left|x\right|$, so the radius of convergence is 1. The series diverges at 1 (harmonic series) but converges at -1 (alternating harmonic series).

9.2.40 $f(-4x) = \ln(1+4x) = -\sum_{k=1}^{\infty} \frac{(-4x)^k}{k}$. Using the Ratio Test: $\lim\limits_{k\to\infty} \left|\frac{a_{k+1}}{a_k}\right| = \lim\limits_{k\to\infty} \frac{k}{k+1}4\left|x\right| = 4\left|x\right|$, so the radius of convergence is $1/4$. The series converges at $1/4$ (alternating harmonic series) but diverges at $-1/4$ (harmonic series).

9.2.41 The power series for $f(x)$ is $\sum_{k=0}^{\infty}(2x)k$, convergent for $-1 < 2x < 1$, so for $-1/2 < x < 1/2$. The power series for $g(x) = f'(x)$ is $\sum_{k=1}^{\infty} k(2x)^{k-1}\cdot 2 = 2\sum_{k=1}^{\infty} k(2x)^{k-1}$, also convergent on $|x| < 1/2$.

9.2.42 The power series for $f(x)$ is $\sum_{k=0}^{\infty} x^k$, convergent for $-1 < x < 1$, so the power series for $g(x) = \frac{1}{2}f''(x)$ is $\frac{1}{2}\sum_{k=2}^{\infty} k(k-1)x^{k-2} = \frac{1}{2}\sum_{k=0}^{\infty}(k+1)(k+2)x^k$, also convergent on $|x| < 1$.

9.2.43 The power series for $f(x)$ is $\sum_{k=0}^{\infty} x^k$, convergent for $-1 < x < 1$, so the power series for $g(x) = \frac{1}{6}f'''(x)$ is $\frac{1}{6}\sum_{k=3}^{\infty} k(k-1)(k-2)x^{k-3} = \frac{1}{6}\sum_{k=0}^{\infty}(k+1)(k+2)(k+3)x^k$, also convergent on $|x| < 1$.

9.2.44 The power series for $f(x)$ is $\sum_{k=0}^{\infty}(-1)^k x^{2k}$, convergent on $|x| < 1$. Because $g(x) = -\frac{1}{2}f'(x)$, the power series for g is $-\frac{1}{2}\sum_{k=1}^{\infty}(-1)^k 2kx^{2k-1} = \sum_{k=1}^{\infty}(-1)^{k+1}kx^{2k-1}$, also convergent on $|x| < 1$.

9.2.45 The power series for $\frac{1}{1-3x}$ is $\sum_{k=0}^{\infty}(3x)^k$, convergent on $|x| < 1/3$. Because $g(x) = \ln(1-3x) = -3\int \frac{1}{1-3x}\,dx$ and because $g(0) = 0$, the power series for $g(x)$ is $-3\sum_{k=0}^{\infty} 3^k\frac{1}{k+1}x^{k+1} = -\sum_{k=1}^{\infty}\frac{3^k}{k}x^k$, also convergent on $[-1/3, 1/3)$.

9.2.46 The power series for $\frac{x}{1+x^2}$ is $x\sum_{k=0}^{\infty}(-1)^k x^{2k} = \sum_{k=0}^{\infty}(-1)^k x^{2k+1}$, convergent on $|x| < 1$. Because $g(x) = 2\int f(x)\,dx$, and because $g(0) = 0$, the power series for $g(x)$ is $2\sum_{k=0}^{\infty}(-1)^k\frac{1}{2k+2}x^{2k+2} = \sum_{k=0}^{\infty}(-1)^k\frac{1}{k+1}x^{2k+2}$. This can be written as $\sum_{k=1}^{\infty}(-1)^{k+1}\frac{1}{k}x^{2k}$, which is convergent on $[-1, 1]$.

9.2.47 Start with $g(x) = \frac{1}{1+x}$. The power series for $g(x)$ is $\sum_{k=0}^{\infty}(-1)^k x^k$. Because $f(x) = g(x^2)$, its power series is $\sum_{k=0}^{\infty}(-1)^k x^{2k}$. The radius of convergence is still 1, and the series is divergent at both endpoints. The interval of convergence is $(-1, 1)$.

9.2.48 Start with $g(x) = \frac{1}{1-x}$. The power series for $g(x)$ is $\sum_{k=0}^{\infty} x^k$. Because $f(x) = g(x^4)$, its power series is $\sum_{k=0}^{\infty} x^{4k}$. The radius of convergence is still 1, and the series is divergent at both endpoints. The interval of convergence is $(-1, 1)$.

9.2.49 Note that $f(x) = \frac{3}{3+x} = \frac{1}{1+(1/3)x}$. Let $g(x) = \frac{1}{1+x}$. The power series for $g(x)$ is $\sum_{k=0}^{\infty}(-1)^k x^k$, so the power series for $f(x) = g((1/3)x)$ is $\sum_{k=0}^{\infty}(-1)^k 3^{-k}x^k = \sum_{k=0}^{\infty}\left(\frac{-x}{3}\right)^k$. Using the Ratio Test: $\lim\limits_{k\to\infty}\left|\frac{a_{k+1}}{a_k}\right| = \lim\limits_{k\to\infty}\left|\frac{3^{-(k+1)}x^{k+1}}{3^{-k}x^k}\right| = \frac{|x|}{3}$, so the radius of convergence is 3. The series diverges at both endpoints. The interval of convergence is $(-3, 3)$.

9.2.50 Note that $f(x) = \frac{1}{2}\ln(1-x^2)$. The power series for $g(x) = \ln(1-x)$ is $-\sum_{k=1}^{\infty}\frac{1}{k}x^k$, so the power series for $f(x) = \frac{1}{2}g(x^2)$ is $\frac{-1}{2}\sum_{k=1}^{\infty}\frac{1}{k}x^{2k}$. The radius of convergence is still 1. The series diverges at both 1 and -1, its interval of convergence is $(-1, 1)$.

9.2.51 Note that $f(x) = \ln\sqrt{4-x^2} = \frac{1}{2}\ln(4-x^2) = \frac{1}{2}\left(\ln 4 + \ln\left(1 - \frac{x^2}{4}\right)\right) = \ln 2 + \frac{1}{2}\ln\left(1 - \frac{x^2}{4}\right)$. Now, the power series for $g(x) = \ln(1-x)$ is $-\sum_{k=1}^{\infty}\frac{1}{k}x^k$, so the power series for $f(x)$ is $\ln 2 - \frac{1}{2}\sum_{k=1}^{\infty}\frac{1}{k}\frac{x^{2k}}{4^k} = \ln 2 - \sum_{k=1}^{\infty}\frac{x^{2k}}{k2^{2k+1}}$. Now, $\lim\limits_{k\to\infty}\left|\frac{a_{k+1}}{a_k}\right| = \lim\limits_{k\to\infty}\left|\frac{x^{2k+2}}{(k+1)2^{2k+3}}\cdot\frac{k2^{2k+1}}{x^{2k}}\right| = \lim\limits_{k\to\infty}\frac{k}{4(k+1)}x^2 = \frac{x^2}{4}$, so that the radius of convergence is 2. The series diverges at both endpoints, so its interval of convergence is $(-2, 2)$.

9.2.52 By Example 5, the Taylor series for $g(x) = \tan^{-1} x$ is $\sum_{k=0}^{\infty} \frac{(-1)^k x^{2k+1}}{2k+1}$, so that $f(x) = g((2x)^2)$ has Taylor series $\sum_{k=0}^{\infty} \frac{(-1)^k (2x)^{4k+2}}{2k+1} = \sum_{k=0}^{\infty} \frac{(-1)^k 4^{2k+1}}{2k+1} x^{4k+2}$. Using the Ratio Test: $\lim\limits_{k\to\infty} \left| \frac{a_{k+1}}{a_k} \right| =$ $\lim\limits_{k\to\infty} \left| \frac{4^{2k+3} x^{4k+6}}{2k+3} \cdot \frac{2k+1}{4^{2k+1} x^{4k+2}} \right| = \lim\limits_{k\to\infty} \frac{16(2k+1)}{2k+3} x^4 = 16 x^4$, so that the radius of convergence is $1/2$. The interval of convergence is $(-1/2, 1/2)$.

9.2.53

   a. True. This power series is centered at $x = 3$, so its interval of convergence will be symmetric about 3.

   b. True. Use the Root Test.

   c. True. Substitute x^2 for x in the series.

   d. True. Because the power series is zero on the interval, all its derivatives are as well, which implies (differentiating the power series) that all the c_k are zero.

9.2.54 Using the Root Test: $\lim\limits_{k\to\infty} \sqrt[k]{|a_k|} = \lim\limits_{k\to\infty} \left(1 + \frac{1}{k}\right)^k |x| = ex$. Thus, the radius of convergence is $\frac{1}{e}$.

9.2.55 Using the Ratio Test: $\lim\limits_{k\to\infty} \left| \frac{a_{k+1}}{a_k} \right| = \lim\limits_{k\to\infty} \left| \frac{(k+1)! x^{k+1}}{(k+1)^{k+1}} \cdot \frac{k^k}{k! x^k} \right| = \lim\limits_{k\to\infty} \left(\frac{k}{k+1} \right)^k |x| = \frac{1}{e}|x|$. The radius of convergence is therefore e.

9.2.56 $1 + \sum_{k=1}^{\infty} \frac{1}{2k} x^k$

9.2.57 $\sum_{k=0}^{\infty} (-1)^k \frac{1}{k+1} x^k$

9.2.58 $\sum_{k=0}^{\infty} (-1)^k \frac{x^{2k+1}}{(k+1)^2}$

9.2.59 $\sum_{k=1}^{\infty} (-1)^k \frac{x^{2k}}{k!}$

9.2.60 The power series for $f(ax)$ is $\sum c_k (ax)^k$. Then $\sum c_k (ax)^k$ converges if and only if $|ax| < R$ (because $\sum c_k x^k$ converges for $|x| < R$), which happens if and only if $|x| < \frac{R}{|a|}$.

9.2.61 The power series for $f(x-a)$ is $\sum c_k (x-a)^k$. Then $\sum c_k (x-a)^k$ converges if and only if $|x - a| < R$, which happens if and only if $a - R < x < a + R$, so the radius of convergence is the same.

9.2.62 Let's first consider where this series converges. By the Root Test, $\lim\limits_{k\to\infty} \sqrt[k]{|a_k|} = \lim\limits_{k\to\infty} (x^2 + 1)^2 = (x^2 + 1)^2$, which is always greater than 1 for $x \neq 0$. This series also diverges when $x = 0$, because there we have the divergent series $\sum 1$. Because this series diverges everywhere, it doesn't represent any function, except perhaps the empty function.

9.2.63 This is a geometric series with ratio $\sqrt{x} - 2$, so its sum is $\frac{1}{1 - (\sqrt{x} - 2)} = \frac{1}{3 - \sqrt{x}}$. Again using the Root Test, $\lim\limits_{k\to\infty} \sqrt[k]{|a_k|} = |\sqrt{x} - 2|$, so the interval of convergence is given by $|\sqrt{x} - 2| < 1$, so $1 < \sqrt{x} < 3$ and $1 < x < 9$. The series diverges at both endpoints.

9.2.64 This series is $\frac{1}{4} \sum_{k=1}^{\infty} \frac{x^{2k}}{k}$. Because $\sum_{k=1}^{\infty} \frac{x^k}{k}$ is the power series for $-\ln(1-x)$, the power series given is $-\frac{1}{4} \ln(1 - x^2)$. Using the Ratio Test: $\lim\limits_{k\to\infty} \left| \frac{a_{k+1}}{a_k} \right| = \left| \lim\limits_{k\to\infty} \frac{x^{2k+2}}{4k+4} \cdot \frac{4k}{x^{2k}} \right| = \lim\limits_{k\to\infty} \frac{k}{k+1} x^2 = x^2$, so the radius of convergence is 1. The series diverges at both endpoints (it is a multiple of the harmonic series). The interval of convergence is $(-1, 1)$.

9.2.65 This is a geometric series with ratio e^{-x}, so its sum is $\frac{1}{1 - e^{-x}}$. By the Root Test, $\lim\limits_{k\to\infty} \sqrt[k]{|a_k|} = e^{-x}$, so the power series converges for $x > 0$.

9.2.66 This is a geometric series with ratio $\frac{x-2}{9}$, so its sum is $\frac{(x-2)/9}{1-(x-2)/9} = \frac{x-2}{9-(x-2)} = \frac{x-2}{11-x}$. Using the Root Test: $\lim\limits_{k\to\infty} \sqrt[k]{|a_k|} = \lim\limits_{k\to\infty} \left|\frac{x-2}{9}\right| = \left|\frac{x-2}{9}\right|$, so the series converges for $|x-2| < 9$, or $-7 < x < 11$. It diverges at both endpoints.

9.2.67 This is a geometric series with ratio $(x^2-1)/3$, so its sum is $\frac{1}{1-\frac{x^2-1}{3}} = \frac{3}{3-(x^2-1)} = \frac{3}{4-x^2}$. Using the Root Test, the series converges for $|x^2-1| < 3$, so that $-2 < x^2 < 4$ or $-2 < x < 2$. It diverges at both endpoints.

9.2.68 Replacing x by $x-1$ gives $\ln x = \sum_{k=1}^{\infty} \frac{(-1)^{k+1}(x-1)^k}{k}$. Using the Ratio Test: $\lim\limits_{k\to\infty} \left|\frac{a_{k+1}}{a_k}\right| = \lim\limits_{k\to\infty} \left|\frac{(x-1)^{k+1}}{k+1} \cdot \frac{k}{(x-1)^k}\right| = \lim\limits_{k\to\infty} \frac{k}{k+1}|x-1| = |x-1|$, so that the series converges for $|x-1| < 1$. Checking the endpoints, the interval of convergence is $(0, 2]$.

9.2.69 The power series for e^x is $\sum_{k=0}^{\infty} \frac{x^k}{k!}$. Substitute $-x$ for x to get $e^{-x} = \sum_{k=0}^{\infty}(-1)^k \frac{x^k}{k!}$. The series converges for all x.

9.2.70 Substitute $2x$ for x in the power series for e^x to get $e^{2x} = \sum_{k=0}^{\infty} \frac{(2x)^k}{k!} = \sum_{k=0}^{\infty} \frac{2^k}{k!}x^k$. The series converges for all x.

9.2.71 Substitute $-3x$ for x in the power series for e^x to get $e^{-3x} = \sum_{k=0}^{\infty} \frac{(-3x)^k}{k!} = \sum_{k=0}^{\infty}(-1)^k \frac{3^k}{k!}x^k$. The series converges for all x.

9.2.72 Multiply the power series for e^x by x^2 to get $x^2 e^x = \sum_{k=0}^{\infty} \frac{x^{k+2}}{k!}$, which converges for all x.

9.2.73 The power series for $x^m f(x)$ is $\sum c_k x^{k+m}$. The radius of convergence of this power series is determined by the limit

$$\lim_{k\to\infty} \left|\frac{c_{k+1}x^{k+1+m}}{c_k x^{k+m}}\right| = \lim_{k\to\infty} \left|\frac{c_{k+1}x^{k+1}}{c_k x^k}\right|,$$

and the right-hand side is the limit used to determine the radius of convergence for the power series for $f(x)$. Thus the two have the same radius of convergence.

9.2.74

a. $R_n = f(x) - S_n(x) = \sum_{k=n}^{\infty} x^k$. This is a geometric series with ratio x. Its sum is then $R_n = \frac{x^n}{1-x}$ as desired.

b. $R_n(x)$ increases without bound as x approaches 1, and its absolute value smallest at $x = 0$ (where it is zero). In general, for $x > 0$, $R_n(x) < R_{n-1}(x)$, so the approximations get better the more terms of the series are included.

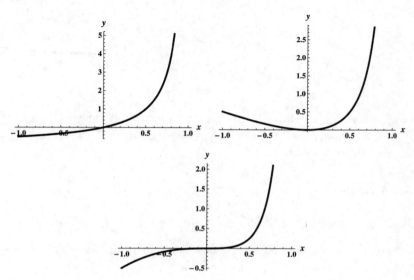

c. To minimize $|R_n(x)|$, set its derivative to zero. Assuming $n > 1$, we have $R_n'(x) = \frac{n(1-x)x^{n-1}+x^n}{(1-x)^2}$, which is zero for $x = 0$. There is a minimum at this critical point.

d. The following is a plot that shows, for each $x \in (0,1)$, the n required so that $R_n(x) < 10^{-6}$. The closer x gets to 1, the more terms are required in order for the estimate given by the power series to be accurate. The number of terms increases rapidly as $x \to 1$.

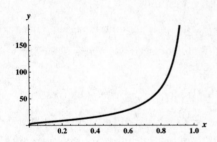

9.2.75

a. $f(x)g(x) = c_0 d_0 + (c_0 d_1 + c_1 d_0)x + (c_0 d_2 + c_1 d_1 + c_2 d_0)x^2 + \dots$

b. The coefficient of x^n in $f(x)g(x)$ is $\sum_{i=0}^{n} c_i d_{n-i}$.

9.2.76 The function $\frac{1}{\sqrt{1-x^2}}$ is the derivative of the inverse sine function, and $\sin^{-1}(0) = 0$, so the power series for $\sin^{-1} x$ is the integral of the given power series, or $x + \frac{1}{6}x^3 + \frac{1\cdot3}{2\cdot4\cdot5}x^5 + \frac{1\cdot3\cdot5}{2\cdot4\cdot6\cdot7}x^7 + \dots$. This can also be written $x + \sum_{k=1}^{\infty} \frac{1\cdot3\cdots(2k-1)}{2\cdot4\cdots2k\cdot(2k+1)}x^{2k+1}$.

9.2.77

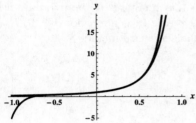

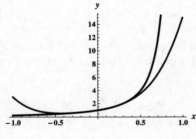

a. For both graphs, the difference between the true value and the estimate is greatest at the two ends of the range; the difference at 0.9 is greater than that at -0.9.

b. The difference between $f(x)$ and $S_n(x)$ is greatest for $x = 0.9$; at that point, $f(x) = \frac{1}{(1-0.9)^2} = 100$, so we want to find n such that $S_n(x)$ is within 0.01 of 100. We find that $S_{111} \approx 99.98991435$ and $S_{112} \approx 99.99084790$, so $n = 112$.

9.3   Taylor Series

9.3.1 The nth Taylor Polynomial is the nth sum of the corresponding Taylor Series.

9.3.2 In order to have a Taylor series centered at a, a function f must have derivatives of all orders on some interval containing a.

9.3.3 The nth coefficient is $\frac{f^{(n)}(a)}{n!}$.

9.3.4 The interval of convergence is found in the same manner that it is found for a more general power series.

9.3.5 Substitute x^2 for x in the Taylor series. By theorems proved in the previous section about power series, the interval of convergence does not change except perhaps at the endpoints of the interval.

9.3.6 The Taylor series terminates if $f^{(n)}(0) = 0$ for $n > N$ for some N. For $(1+x)^p$, this occurs if and only if p is an integer ≥ 0.

9.3.7 It means that the limit of the remainder term is zero.

9.3.8 The Maclaurin series is $e^{2x} = \sum_{k=0}^{\infty} \frac{(2x)^k}{k!}$. This is determined by substituting $2x$ for x in the Maclaurin series for e^x.

9.3.9

   a. Note that $f(0) = 1$, $f'(0) = -1$, $f''(0) = 1$, and $f'''(0) = -1$. So the Maclaurin series is $1 - x + x^2/2 - x^3/6 + \cdots$.

   b. $\sum_{k=0}^{\infty} (-1)^k \frac{x^k}{k!}$.

   c. The series converges on $(-\infty, \infty)$, as can be seen from the Ratio Test.

9.3.10

   a. Note that $f(0) = 1$, $f'(0) = 0$, $f''(0) = -4$, $f'''(0) = 0$, $f^{(4)}(0) = 16, \ldots$. Thus the Maclaurin series is $1 - 2x^2 + \frac{2x^4}{3} - \frac{4x^6}{45} + \cdots$.

   b. $\sum_{k=0}^{\infty} (-1)^k \frac{(2x)^{2k}}{(2k)!}$

   c. The series converges on $(-\infty, \infty)$, as can be seen from the Ratio Test.

9.3.11

   a. Because the series for $\frac{1}{1+x}$ is $1 - x + x^2 - x^3 + \cdots$, the series for $\frac{1}{1+x^2}$ is $1 - x^2 + x^4 - x^6 + \cdots$.

   b. $\sum_{k=0}^{\infty} (-1)^k x^{2k}$.

   c. The absolute value of the ratio of consecutive terms is x^2, so by the Ratio Test, the radius of convergence is 1. The series diverges at the endpoints by the Divergence Test, so the interval of convergence is $(-1, 1)$.

9.3.12

   a. Note that $f(0) = 0$, $f'(0) = 4$, $f''(0) = -16$, $f'''(0) = 128$, and $f''''(0) = -1526$. Thus, the series is given by $4x - \frac{16x^2}{2} + \frac{128x^3}{6} - \frac{1536x^4}{24} + \cdots$.

   b. $\sum_{k=1}^{\infty} (-1)^{k+1} \frac{(k-1)!(4x)^k}{k!} = \sum_{k=1}^{\infty} (-1)^{k+1} \frac{(4x)^k}{k}$.

   c. The absolute value of the ratio of consecutive terms is $\frac{4|x|k}{k+1}$, which has limit $4|x|$ as $k \to \infty$, so the interval of convergence is $(-1/4, 1/4]$. Note that for $x = 1/4$ we have the alternating harmonic series, while for $x = -1/4$ we have negative 1 times the harmonic series, which diverges.

9.3.13

   a. Note that $f(0) = 1$, and that $f^{(n)}(0) = 2^n$. Thus, the series is given by $1 + 2x + \frac{4x^2}{2} + \frac{8x^3}{6} + \cdots$.

b. $\sum_{k=0}^{\infty} \frac{(2x)^k}{k!}$.

c. The absolute value of the ratio of consecutive terms is $\frac{2|x|}{n}$, which has limit 0 as $n \to \infty$. So by the Ratio Test, the interval of convergence is $(-\infty, \infty)$.

9.3.14

a. Substitute $2x$ for x in the Taylor series for $(1 + x)^{-1}$, to obtain the series $1 - 2x + 4x^2 - 8x^3 + \cdots$.

b. $\sum_{k=0}^{\infty} (-1)^k (2x)^k$.

c. The Root Test shows that the series converges absolutely for $|2x| < 1$, or $|x| < 1/2$. The interval of convergence is $(-1/2, 1/2)$, because the series at both endpoints diverge by the Divergence Test.

9.3.15

a. By integrating the Taylor series for $\frac{1}{1+x^2}$ (which is the derivative of $\tan^{-1}(x)$), we obtain the series $x - \frac{x^3}{3} + \frac{x^5}{5} - \frac{x^7}{7} + \cdots$. Then by replacing x by $x/2$ we have $\frac{x}{2} - \frac{x^3}{3 \cdot 2^3} + \frac{x^5}{5 \cdot 2^5} - \frac{x^7}{7 \cdot 2^7} + \cdots$.

b. $\sum_{k=0}^{\infty} (-1)^k \frac{1}{(2k+1) \cdot 2^{2k+1}} x^{2k+1}$.

c. By the Ratio Test (the ratio of consecutive terms has limit $\frac{x^2}{4}$), the radius of convergence is $|x| < 2$. Also, at the endpoints we have convergence by the Alternating Series Test, so the interval of convergence is $[-2, 2]$.

9.3.16

a. Substitute $3x$ for x in the Taylor series for $\sin x$, to obtain the series $3x - \frac{9x^3}{2} + \frac{81x^5}{40} - \frac{243x^7}{560} + \cdots$.

b. $\sum_{k=0}^{\infty} (-1)^k \frac{3^{2k+1}}{(2k+1)!} x^{2k+1}$.

c. The ratio of successive terms is $\frac{9}{2n(2n+1)} x^2$, which has limit zero as $n \to \infty$, so the interval of convergence is $(-\infty, \infty)$.

9.3.17

a. Note that $f(0) = 1$, $f'(0) = \ln 3$, $f''(0) = \ln^2 3$, $f''(0) = \ln^3 3$. So the first four terms of the desired series are $1 + (\ln 3)x + \frac{\ln^2 3}{2} x^2 + \frac{\ln^3 3}{6} x^3 + \cdots$.

b. $\sum_{k=0}^{\infty} \frac{(\ln^k 3) x^k}{k!}$.

c. The ratio of successive terms is $\frac{(\ln^{k+1} 3) x^{k+1}}{(k+1)!} \cdot \frac{k!}{(\ln^k 3) x^k} = \frac{\ln 3}{k+1} x$, and the limit as $k \to \infty$ of this quantity is 0, so the interval of convergence is $(-\infty, \infty)$.

9.3.18

a. Note that $f(0) = 0$, $f'(0) = \frac{1}{\ln 3}$, $f''(0) = -\frac{1}{\ln 3}$, $f'''(0) = \frac{2}{\ln 3}$, $f''''(0) = -\frac{6}{\ln 3}$. So the first terms of the desired series are $0 + \frac{x}{\ln 3} - \frac{x^2}{2 \ln 3} + \frac{x^3}{3 \ln 3} - \frac{x^4}{4 \ln 3} + \cdots$.

b. $\sum_{k=1}^{\infty} \frac{(-1)^{k+1} x^k}{k \ln 3}$.

c. The absolute value of the ratio of successive terms is $\left| \frac{x^{k+1}}{(k+1) \ln 3} \cdot \frac{k \ln 3}{x^k} \right| = \frac{k}{k+1} |x|$, which has limit $|x|$ as $k \to \infty$. Thus the radius of convergence is 1. At $x = -1$ we have a multiple of the harmonic series (which diverges) and at $x = 1$ we have a multiple of the alternating harmonic series (which converges) so the interval of convergence is $(-1, 1]$.

9.3.19

a. Note that $f(0) = 1$, $f'(0) = 0$, $f''(0) = 9$, $f'''(0) = 0$, etc. The first terms of the series are $1 + 9x^2/2 + 81x^4/4! + 3^6 x^6/6! + \cdots$.

b. $\sum_{k=0}^{\infty} \frac{(3x)^{2k}}{(2k)!}$.

c. The absolute value of the ratio of successive terms is $\left| \frac{(3x)^{2k+2}}{(2k+2)!} \cdot \frac{(2k)!}{(3x)^{2k}} \right| = \frac{1}{(2k+2)(2k+1)} \cdot 9x^2$, which has limit 0 as $x \to \infty$. The interval of convergence is therefore $(-\infty, \infty)$.

9.3.20

a. Note that $f(0) = 0$, $f'(0) = 2$, $f''(0) = 0$, $f'''(0) = 8$, etc. The first terms of the series are $2x + 8x^3/6 + 32x^5/5! + 128x^7/7! + \cdots$, or $2x + \frac{4x^3}{3} + \frac{4x^5}{15} + \frac{8x^7}{315} + \cdots$.

b. $\sum_{k=0}^{\infty} \frac{2^{2k+1} x^{2k+1}}{(2k+1)!}$.

c. The absolute value of the ratio of successive terms is $\left| \frac{2^{2k+3} x^{2k+3}}{(2k+3)!} \cdot \frac{(2k+1)!}{2^{2k+1} x^{2k+1}} \right| = \frac{4}{(2k+3)(2k+2)} x^2$, which has limit 0 as $x \to \infty$. The interval of convergence is therefore $(-\infty, \infty)$.

9.3.21

a. Note that $f(\pi/2) = 1$, $f'(\pi/2) = \cos(\pi/2) = 0$, $f''(\pi/2) = -\sin(\pi/2) = -1$, $f'''(\pi/2) = -\cos(\pi/2) = 0$, and so on. Thus the series is given by $1 - \frac{1}{2}\left(x - \frac{\pi}{2}\right)^2 + \frac{1}{24}\left(x - \frac{\pi}{2}\right)^4 - \frac{1}{720}\left(x - \frac{\pi}{2}\right)^6 + \cdots$.

b. $\sum_{k=0}^{\infty} (-1)^k \frac{1}{(2k)!} \left(x - \frac{\pi}{2}\right)^{2k}$.

9.3.22

a. Note that $f(\pi) = -1$, $f'(\pi) = -\sin\pi = 0$, $f''(\pi) = -\cos\pi = 1$, $f'''(\pi) = -\sin\pi = 0$, and so on. Thus the series is given by $-1 + \frac{1}{2}(x - \pi)^2 - \frac{1}{24}(x - \pi)^4 + \frac{1}{720}(x - \pi)^6 + \cdots$.

b. $\sum_{k=0}^{\infty} (-1)^{k+1} \frac{1}{(2k)!} (x - \pi)^{2k}$.

9.3.23

a. Note that $f^{(k)}(1) = (-1)^k \frac{k!}{1^{k+1}} = (-1)^k \cdot k!$. Thus the series is given by $1 - (x-1) + (x-1)^2 - (x-1)^3 + \cdots$.

b. $\sum_{k=0}^{\infty} (-1)^k (x - 1)^k$.

9.3.24

a. Note that $f^{(k)}(2) = (-1)^k \frac{k!}{2^{k+1}}$. Thus the series is given by $\frac{1}{2} - \frac{x-2}{4} + \frac{1}{8}(x-2)^2 - \frac{1}{16}(x-2)^3 + \frac{1}{32}(x-2)^4 + \cdots$.

b. $\sum_{k=0}^{\infty} (-1)^k \frac{1}{2^{k+1}} (x - 2)^k$.

9.3.25

a. Note that $f^{(k)}(3) = (-1)^{k-1} \frac{(k-1)!}{3^k}$. Thus the series is given by $\ln(3) + \frac{x-3}{3} - \frac{1}{18}(x-3)^2 + \frac{1}{81}(x-3)^3 + \cdots$.

b. $\ln 3 + \sum_{k=1}^{\infty} (-1)^{k+1} \frac{1}{k \cdot 3^k} (x - 3)^k$.

9.3.26

a. Note that $f^{(k)}(\ln 2) = 2$. Thus the series is given by $2 + 2(x - \ln(2)) + (x - \ln(2))^2 + \frac{1}{3}(x - \ln(2))^3 + \frac{1}{12}(x - \ln(2))^4 + \cdots$.

b. $\sum_{k=0}^{\infty} \frac{2}{k!} (x - \ln(2))^k$.

9.3.27

a. Note that $f(1) = 2$, $f'(1) = 2\ln 2$, $f''(1) = 2\ln^2 2$, $f'''(1) = 2\ln^3 2$. The first terms of the series are $2 + (2\ln 2)(x-1) + (\ln^2 2)(x-1)^2 + \frac{(\ln^3 2)(x-1)^3}{3} + \cdots$.

b. $\sum_{k=0}^{\infty} \frac{2(x-1)^k \ln^k 2}{k!}$.

9.3.28

a. Note that $f(2) = 100$, $f'(2) = 100\ln 10$, $f''(2) = 100\ln^2 10$, $f'''(2) = 100\ln^3 10$. The first terms of the series are $100 + 100(\ln 10)(x-2) + 50(\ln^2 10)(x-2)^2 + \frac{50}{3}(\ln^3 10)(x-2)^3 + \cdots$.

b. $\sum_{k=0}^{\infty} \frac{100(x-2)^k \ln^k 10}{k!}$.

9.3.29 Because the Taylor series for $\ln(1+x)$ is $x - \frac{x^2}{2} + \frac{x^3}{3} - \frac{x^4}{4} + \cdots$, the first four terms of the Taylor series for $\ln(1+x^2)$ are $x^2 - \frac{x^4}{2} + \frac{x^6}{3} - \frac{x^8}{4} + \cdots$, obtained by substituting x^2 for x.

9.3.30 Because the Taylor series for $\sin x$ is $x - \frac{x^3}{3!} + \frac{x^5}{5!} - \frac{x^7}{7!} + \cdots$, the first four terms of the Taylor series for $\sin x^2$ are $x^2 - \frac{x^6}{3!} + \frac{x^{10}}{5!} - \frac{x^{14}}{7!} + \cdots$, obtained by substituting x^2 for x.

9.3.31 Because the Taylor series for $\frac{1}{1-x} = 1 + x + x^2 + x^3 + \cdots$, the first four terms of the Taylor series for $\frac{1}{1-2x}$ are $1 + 2x + 4x^2 + 8x^3 + \cdots$ obtained by substituting $2x$ for x.

9.3.32 Because the Taylor series for $\ln(1+x)$ is $x - x^2/2 + x^3/3 - x^4/4 + \cdots$, the first four terms of the Taylor series for $2x - 2x^2 + 8x^3/3 - 4x^4 + \cdots$ obtained by substituting $2x$ for x.

9.3.33 The Taylor series for $e^x - 1$ is the Taylor series for e^x, less the constant term of 1, so it is $x + \frac{x^2}{2} + \frac{x^3}{3!} + \frac{x^4}{4!} + \cdots$. Thus, the first four terms of the Taylor series for $\frac{e^x - 1}{x}$ are $1 + \frac{x}{2!} + \frac{x^2}{3!} + \frac{x^3}{4!} + \cdots$, obtained by dividing the terms of the first series by x.

9.3.34 Because the Taylor series for $\cos x$ is $1 - \frac{x^2}{2} + \frac{x^4}{4!} - \frac{x^6}{6!} + \cdots$, the first four terms of the Taylor series for $\cos x^3$ are $1 - \frac{x^6}{2!} + \frac{x^{12}}{4!} - \frac{x^{18}}{6!} + \cdots$, obtained by substituting x^3 for x.

9.3.35 Because the Taylor series for $(1+x)^{-1}$ is $1 - x + x^2 - x^3 + \cdots$, if we substitute x^4 for x, we obtain $1 - x^4 + x^8 - x^{12} + \cdots$.

9.3.36 The Taylor series for $\tan^{-1} x$ is $x - \frac{x^3}{3} + \frac{x^5}{5} - \frac{x^7}{7} - \cdots$. Thus, the Taylor series for $\tan^{-1} x^2$ is $x^2 - \frac{x^6}{3} + \frac{x^{10}}{5} - \frac{x^{14}}{7} - \cdots$ and, multiplying by x, the Taylor series for $x\tan^{-1} x^2$ is $x^3 - \frac{x^7}{3} + \frac{x^{11}}{5} - \frac{x^{15}}{7} - \cdots$.

9.3.37 The Taylor series for $\sinh x$ is $x + \frac{x^3}{6} + \frac{x^5}{120} + \frac{x^7}{5040} + \cdots$. Thus, the Taylor series for $\sinh x^2$ is $x^2 + \frac{x^6}{6} + \frac{x^{10}}{120} + \frac{x^{14}}{5040} + \cdots$ obtained by substituting x^2 for x.

9.3.38 The Taylor series for $\cosh x$ is $1 + \frac{x^2}{2} + \frac{x^4}{24} + \frac{x^6}{720} + \cdots$. Thus, the Taylor series for $\cosh 3x$ is $1 + \frac{9x^2}{2} + \frac{81x^4}{24} + \frac{729x^6}{720} + \cdots$, obtained by substituting $3x$ for x.

9.3.39

a. The binomial coefficients are $\binom{-2}{0} = 1$, $\binom{-2}{1} = \frac{-2}{1!} = -2$, $\binom{-2}{2} = \frac{(-2)(-3)}{2!} = 3$, $\binom{-2}{3} = \frac{(-2)(-3)(-4)}{3!} = -4$.

Thus the first four terms of the series are $1 - 2x + 3x^2 - 4x^3 + \cdots$.

b. $1 - 2 \cdot 0.1 + 3 \cdot 0.01 - 4 \cdot 0.001 = 0.826$

9.3.40

a. The binomial coefficients are $\binom{1/2}{0} = 1$, $\binom{1/2}{1} = \frac{1/2}{1!} = \frac{1}{2}$, $\binom{1/2}{2} = \frac{(1/2)(-1/2)}{2!} = -\frac{1}{8}$, $\binom{1/2}{3} = \frac{(1/2)(-1/2)(-3/2)}{3!} = \frac{1}{16}$, so the first four terms of the series are $1 + \frac{1}{2}x - \frac{1}{8}x^2 + \frac{1}{16}x^3 + \cdots$.

b. $1 + \frac{1}{2} \cdot .06 - \frac{1}{8} \cdot .06^2 + \frac{1}{16} \cdot .06^3 \approx 1.030$

9.3.41

a. The binomial coefficients are $\binom{1/4}{0} = 1$, $\binom{1/4}{1} = \frac{1/4}{1} = \frac{1}{4}$, $\binom{1/4}{2} = \frac{(1/4)(-3/4)}{2!} = -\frac{3}{32}$, $\binom{1/4}{3} = \frac{(1/4)(-3/4)(-7/4)}{3!} = \frac{7}{128}$, so the first four terms of the series are $1 + \frac{1}{4}x - \frac{3}{32}x^2 + \frac{7}{128}x^3 + \cdots$.

b. Substitute $x = 0.12$ to get approximately 1.029.

9.3.42

a. The binomial coefficients are $\binom{-3}{0} = 1$, $\binom{-3}{1} = -3$, $\binom{-3}{2} = \frac{(-3)(-4)}{2!} = 6$, $\binom{-3}{3} = \frac{(-3)(-4)(-5)}{3!} = -10$, so the first four terms of the series are $1 - 3x + 6x^2 - 10x^3 + \cdots$.

b. Substitute $x = 0.1$ to get 0.750.

9.3.43

a. The binomial coefficients are $\binom{-2/3}{0} = 1$, $\binom{-2/3}{1} = -\frac{2}{3}$, $\binom{-2/3}{2} = \frac{(-2/3)(-5/3)}{2!} = \frac{5}{9}$, $\binom{-2/3}{3} = \frac{(-2/3)(-5/3)(-8/3)}{3!} = -\frac{40}{81}$, so the first four terms of the series are $1 - \frac{2}{3}x + \frac{5}{9}x^2 - \frac{40}{81}x^3 + \cdots$.

b. Substitute $x = 0.18$ to get 0.89512.

9.3.44

a. The binomial coefficients are $\binom{2/3}{0} = 1$, $\binom{2/3}{1} = \frac{2}{3}$, $\binom{2/3}{2} = \frac{(2/3)(-1/3)}{2!} = -\frac{1}{9}$, $\binom{2/3}{3} = \frac{(2/3)(-1/3)(-4/3)}{3!} = \frac{4}{81}$, so the first four terms of the series are $1 + \frac{2}{3}x - \frac{1}{9}x^2 + \frac{4}{81}x^3 + \cdots$.

b. Substitute $x = 0.02$ to get ≈ 1.013289284.

9.3.45 $\sqrt{1 + x^2} = 1 + \frac{x^2}{2} - \frac{x^4}{8} + \frac{x^6}{16} - \cdots$. By the Ratio Test, the radius of convergence is 1. At the endpoints, the series obtained are convergent by the Alternating Series Test. Thus, the interval of convergence is $[-1, 1]$.

9.3.46 $\sqrt{4 + x} = 2\sqrt{1 + x/4} = 2 + \frac{x}{4} - \frac{x^2}{64} + \frac{x^3}{512} + \cdots$. The interval of convergence is $(-4, 4]$.

9.3.47 $\sqrt{9 - 9x} = 3\sqrt{1 - x} = 3 - \frac{3}{2}x - \frac{3}{8}x^2 - \frac{3}{16}x^3 - \cdots$. The interval of convergence is $[-1, 1]$.

9.3.48 $\sqrt{1 - 4x} = 1 - 2x - 2x^2 - 4x^3 - \cdots$, obtained by substituting $-4x$ for x in the original series. The interval of convergence of $[-1/4, 1/4)$.

9.3.49 $\sqrt{a^2 + x^2} = a\sqrt{1 + \frac{x^2}{a^2}} = a + \frac{x^2}{2a} - \frac{x^4}{8a^3} + \frac{x^6}{16a^5} - \cdots$. The series converges when $\frac{x^2}{a^2}$ is less than 1 in magnitude, so the radius of convergence is a. The series given by the endpoints is convergent by the Alternating Series Test, so the interval of convergence is $[-a, a]$.

9.3.50 $\sqrt{4 - 16x^2} = 2\sqrt{1 - (2x)^2} = 2 - 4x^2 - 4x^4 - 8x^6 - \cdots$. Because $2x$ was substituted for x to produce this series, this series converges when $-1 < 2x < 1$, or $-\frac{1}{2} < x < \frac{1}{2}$. Because only even powers of x appear in the series, the series at $x = -\frac{1}{2}$ and $x = \frac{1}{2}$ are identical, and are convergent. Thus the interval of convergence is $\left[-\frac{1}{2}, \frac{1}{2}\right]$.

9.3.51 $(1 + 4x)^{-2} = 1 - 2(4x) + 3(4x)^2 - 4(4x)^3 + \cdots = 1 - 8x + 48x^2 - 256x^3 + \cdots$.

9.3.52 $\frac{1}{(1-4x)^2} = (1 - 4x)^{-2} = 1 - 2(-4x) + 3(-4x)^2 - 4(-4x)^3 + \cdots = 1 + 8x + 48x^2 + 256x^3$.

9.3.53 $\frac{1}{(4+x^2)^2} = (4+x^2)^{-2} = \frac{1}{16}(1+(x^2/4))^{-2} = \frac{1}{16}\left(1-2\cdot\frac{x^2}{4}+3\cdot\frac{x^4}{16}-4\cdot\frac{x^6}{64}+\cdots\right) = \frac{1}{16}-\frac{1}{32}x^2 + \frac{3}{256}x^4 - \frac{1}{256}x^6 + \cdots$

9.3.54 Note that $x^2 - 4x + 5 = 1 + (x-2)^2$, so $(1+(x-2)^2)^{-2} = 1 - 2(x-2)^2 + 3(x-2)^4 - 4(x-2)^6 + \cdots$.

9.3.55 $(3+4x)^{-2} = \frac{1}{9}\left(1+\frac{4x}{3}\right)^{-2} = \frac{1}{9} - \frac{2}{9}\left(\frac{4x}{3}\right) + \frac{3}{9}\left(\frac{4x}{3}\right)^2 - \frac{4}{9}\left(\frac{4x}{3}\right)^3 + \cdots$.

9.3.56 $(1+4x^2)^{-2} = (1+(2x)^2)^{-2} = 1 - 2(2x)^2 + 3(2x)^4 - 4(2x)^6 + \cdots = 1 - 8x^2 + 48x^4 - 256x^6 + \cdots$.

9.3.57 The interval of convergence for the Taylor series for $f(x) = \sin x$ is $(-\infty, \infty)$. The remainder is $R_n(x) = \frac{f^{(n+1)}(c)}{(n+1)!}x^{n+1}$ for some c. Because $f^{(n+1)}(x)$ is $\pm\sin x$ or $\pm\cos x$, we have

$$\lim_{n\to\infty}|R_n(x)| \leq \lim_{n\to\infty}\frac{1}{(n+1)!}\left|x^{n+1}\right| = 0$$

for any x.

9.3.58 The interval of convergence for the Taylor series for $f(x) = \cos 2x$ is $(-\infty, \infty)$. The remainder is $R_n(x) = \frac{f^{(n+1)}(c)}{(n+1)!}x^{n+1}$ for some c. The nth derivative of $\cos 2x$ is 2^n times either $\pm\sin x$ or $\pm\cos x$, so that $f^{(n+1)}$ is bounded by 2^{n+1} in magnitude. Thus $\lim_{n\to\infty}|R_n(x)| \leq \lim_{n\to\infty}\frac{2^{n+1}}{(n+1)!}\left|x^{n+1}\right| = \lim_{n\to\infty}\frac{(2|x|)^{n+1}}{(n+1)!} = 0$ for any x.

9.3.59 The interval of convergence for the Taylor series for e^{-x} is $(-\infty, \infty)$. The remainder is $R_n(x) = \frac{(-1)^{n+1}e^{-c}}{(n+1)!}x^{n+1}$ for some c. Thus $\lim_{n\to\infty}|R_n(x)| = 0$ for any x.

9.3.60 The interval of convergence for the Taylor series for $f(x) = \cos x$ is $(-\infty, \infty)$. The remainder is $R_n(x) = \frac{f^{(n+1)}(c)}{(n+1)!}(x-\pi/2)^{n+1}$ for some c. Because $f^{n+1}(x)$ is $\pm\cos x$ or $\pm\sin x$, we have

$$\lim_{n\to\infty}|R_n(x)| \leq \lim_{n\to\infty}\frac{1}{(n+1)!}\left|(x-\pi/2)^{n+1}\right| = 0$$

for any x.

9.3.61

a. False. Not all of its derivatives are defined at zero - in fact, none of them are.

b. True. The derivatives of $\csc x$ involve positive powers of $\csc x$ and $\cot x$, both of which are defined at $\pi/2$, so that $\csc x$ has continuous derivatives at $\pi/2$.

c. False. For example, the Taylor series for $f(x^2)$ doesn't converge at $x = 1.9$, because the Taylor series for $f(x)$ doesn't converge at $1.9^2 = 3.61$.

d. False. The Taylor series centered at 1 involves derivatives of f evaluated at 1, not at 0.

e. True. The follows because the Taylor series must itself be an even function.

9.3.62

a. The relevant Taylor series are: $\cos 2x = 1 - 2x^2 + \frac{2}{3}x^4 - \frac{4}{45}x^6 + \cdots$, and $2\sin x = 2x - \frac{1}{3}x^3 + \frac{1}{60}x^5 - \cdots$. Thus, the first four terms of the resulting series are $\cos 2x + 2\sin x = 1 + 2x - 2x^2 - \frac{1}{3}x^3 + \frac{2}{3}x^4 + \cdots$.

b. Because each series converges (absolutely) on $(-\infty, \infty)$, so does their sum. The radius of convergence is ∞.

9.3.63

a. The relevant Taylor series are: $e^x = 1 + x + \frac{x^2}{2!} + \frac{x^3}{3!} + \frac{x^4}{4!} + \frac{x^5}{5!} + \frac{x^6}{6!} + \cdots$ and $e^{-x} = 1 - x + \frac{x^2}{2!} - \frac{x^3}{3!} + \frac{x^4}{4!} - \frac{x^5}{5!} + \frac{x^6}{6!} + \cdots$. Thus the first four terms of the resulting series are $\frac{1}{2}(e^x + e^{-x}) = 1 + \frac{x^2}{2!} + \frac{x^4}{4!} + \frac{x^6}{6!} + \cdots$.

b. Because each series converges (absolutely) on $(-\infty, \infty)$, so does their sum. The radius of convergence is ∞.

9.3.64

a. The first four terms of the Taylor series for $\sin x$ are $x - \frac{x^3}{6} + \frac{x^5}{120} - \frac{x^7}{5040}$, so the first four terms for $\frac{\sin x}{x}$ are $1 - \frac{x^2}{6} + \frac{x^4}{120} - \frac{x^6}{5040}$.

b. The radius of convergence is the same as that for $\sin x$, namely ∞.

9.3.65

a. Use the binomial theorem. The binomial coefficients are $\binom{-2/3}{0} = 1$, $\binom{-2/3}{1} = -\frac{2}{3}$, $\binom{-2/3}{2} = \frac{(-2/3)(-5/3)}{2!} = \frac{5}{9}$, $\binom{-2/3}{3} = \frac{(-2/3)(-5/3)(-8/3)}{3!} = -\frac{40}{81}$ and then, substituting x^2 for x, we obtain $1 - \frac{2}{3}x^2 + \frac{5}{9}x^4 - \frac{40}{81}x^6 + \cdots$.

b. From Theorem 9.6 the radius of convergence is determined from $\left|x^2\right| < 1$, so it is 1.

9.3.66

a. The first four terms of $\cos x$ are $1 - \frac{x^2}{2} + \frac{x^4}{24} - \frac{x^6}{720}$, so the first four terms of $\cos x^2$ are $1 - \frac{x^4}{2} + \frac{x^8}{24} - \frac{x^{12}}{720}$, and thus the first four terms of $x^2 \cos x^2$ are $x^2 - \frac{x^6}{2} + \frac{x^{10}}{24} - \frac{x^{14}}{720}$.

b. The radius of convergence is ∞.

9.3.67

a. From the binomial formula, the Taylor series for $(1 - x)^p$ is $\sum \binom{p}{k}(-1)^k x^k$, so the Taylor series for $(1 - x^2)^p$ is $\sum \binom{p}{k}(-1)^k x^{2k}$. Here $p = 1/2$, and the binomial coefficients are $\binom{1/2}{0} = 1$, $\binom{1/2}{1} = \frac{1/2}{1!} = \frac{1}{2}$, $\binom{1/2}{2} = \frac{(1/2)(-1/2)}{2!} = -\frac{1}{8}$, $\binom{1/2}{3} = \frac{(1/2)(-1/2)(-3/2)}{3!} = \frac{1}{16}$ so that $(1 - x^2)^{1/2} = 1 - \frac{1}{2}x^2 - \frac{1}{8}x^4 - \frac{1}{16}x^6 + \cdots$.

b. From Theorem 9.6 the radius of convergence is determined from $\left|x^2\right| < 1$, so it is 1.

9.3.68

a. Because $b^x = e^{x \ln b}$, the Taylor series is $1 + x \ln b + \frac{1}{2!}(x \ln b)^2 + \frac{1}{3!}(x \ln b)^3 + \cdots$

b. Because the series for e^x converges on $(-\infty, \infty)$, the radius of convergence for the series in part a is ∞.

9.3.69

a. $f(x) = (1 + x^2)^{-2}$; using the binomial series and substituting x^2 for x we obtain $1 - 2x^2 + 3x^4 - 4x^6 + \cdots$.

b. From Theorem 9.6 the radius of convergence is determined from $\left|x^2\right| < 1$, so it is 1.

9.3.70 Because $f(36) = 6$, and $f'(x) = \frac{1}{2}x^{-1/2}$, $f'(36) = \frac{1}{12}$, $f''(x) = -\frac{1}{4}x^{-3/2}$, $f''(36) = -\frac{1}{864}$, $f'''(x) = \frac{3}{8}x^{-5/2}$, and $f'''(36) = \frac{3}{62208}$, the first four terms of the Taylor series are $6 + \frac{1}{12}(x - 36) - \frac{1}{864 \cdot 2!}(x - 36)^2 + \frac{3}{62208 \cdot 3!}(x - 36)^3$. Evaluating at $x = 39$ we get 6.245008681.

9.3.71 Because $f(64) = 4$, and $f'(x) = \frac{1}{3}x^{-2/3}$, $f'(64) = \frac{1}{48}$, $f''(x) = -\frac{2}{9}x^{-5/3}$, $f''(64) = -\frac{1}{4608}$, $f'''(x) = \frac{10}{27}x^{-8/3}$, and $f'''(64) = \frac{10}{1769472} = \frac{5}{884736}$, the first four terms of the Taylor series are $4 + \frac{1}{48}(x - 64) - \frac{1}{4608 \cdot 2!}(x - 64)^2 + \frac{5}{884736 \cdot 3!}(x - 64)^3$. Evaluating at $x = 60$, we get 3.914870274.

9.3.72 Because $f(4) = \frac{1}{2}$, and $f'(x) = -\frac{1}{2}x^{-3/2}$, $f'(4) = -\frac{1}{16}$, $f''(x) = \frac{3}{4}x^{-5/2}$, $f''(4) = \frac{3}{128}$, $f'''(x) = -\frac{15}{8}x^{-7/2}$, and $f'''(4) = -\frac{15}{1024}$, the first four terms of the Taylor series are $\frac{1}{2} - \frac{1}{16}(x-4) + \frac{3}{128 \cdot 2!}(x-4)^2 - \frac{15}{1024 \cdot 3!}(x-4)^3$. Evaluating at $x = 3$, we get 0.5766601563.

9.3.73 Because $f(16) = 2$, and $f'(x) = \frac{1}{4}x^{-3/4}$, $f'(16) = \frac{1}{32}$, $f''(x) = -\frac{3}{16}x^{-7/4}$, $f''(16) = -\frac{3}{2048}$, $f'''(x) = \frac{21}{64}x^{-11/4}$, and $f'''(16) = \frac{21}{131072}$, the first four terms of the Taylor series are $2 + \frac{1}{32}(x-16) - \frac{3}{2048 \cdot 2!}(x-16)^2 + \frac{21}{131072 \cdot 3!}(x-16)^3$. Evaluating at $x = 13$, we get 1.898937225.

9.3.74 Evaluate the binomial coefficient $\binom{-1}{k} = \frac{(-1)(-2)\cdots(-1-k+1)}{k!} = (-1)^k$, so that the binomial expansion for $(1+x)^{-1}$ is $\sum_{k=0}^{\infty}(-1)^k x^k$. Substituting $-x$ for x, we obtain $(1-x)^{-1} = \sum_{k=0}^{\infty}(-1)^k(-x)^k = \sum_{k=0}^{\infty}x^k$.

9.3.75 Evaluate the binomial coefficient $\binom{1/2}{k} = \frac{(1/2)(-1/2)(-3/2)\cdots(1/2-k+1)}{k!} = \frac{(1/2)(-1/2)\cdots((3-2k)/2)}{k!} = (-1)^{k-1}2^{-k}\frac{1 \cdot 3 \cdots (2k-3)}{k!} = (-1)^{k-1}2^{-k}\frac{(2k-2)!}{2^{k-1}\cdot(k-1)!\cdot k!} = (-1)^{k-1}2^{1-2k} \cdot \frac{1}{k}\binom{2k-2}{k-1}$. This is the coefficient of x^k in the Taylor series for $\sqrt{1+x}$. Substituting $4x$ for x, the Taylor series becomes $\sum_{k=0}^{\infty}(-1)^{k-1}2^{1-2k} \cdot \frac{1}{k}\binom{2k-2}{k-1}(4x)^k = \sum_{k=0}^{\infty}(-1)^{k-1}\frac{2}{k}\binom{2k-2}{k-1}x^k$. If we can show that k divides $\binom{2k-2}{k-1}$, we will be done, for then the coefficient of x^k will be an integer. But $\binom{2k-2}{k-1} - \binom{2k-2}{k-2} = \frac{(2k-2)!}{(k-1)!(k-1)!} - \frac{(2k-2)!}{(k-2)!k!} = \frac{(2k-2)!}{(k-1)!(k-1)!} - \frac{(2k-2)!(k-1)}{(k-1)!(k-1)!k} = \frac{k(2k-2)!-(k-1)(2k-2)!}{k(k-1)!(k-1)!} = \frac{1}{k}\frac{(2k-2)!}{(k-1)!(k-1)!} = \frac{1}{k}\binom{2k-2}{k-1}$ and thus we have shown that k divides $\binom{2k-2}{k-1}$.

9.3.76 The two Taylor series are:

$$8 + \frac{1}{16}(x-64) - \frac{1}{4096}(x-64)^2 + \frac{1}{524288}(x-64)^3 - \frac{5}{268435456}(x-64)^4 + \cdots$$

$$9 + \frac{1}{18}(x-81) - \frac{1}{5832}(x-81)^2 + \frac{1}{944784}(x-81)^3 - \frac{5}{612220032}(x-81)^4 + \cdots.$$

Evaluating these Taylor series at $n = 2, 3, 4$ (after the quadratic, cubic, and quartic terms) we obtain the errors:

n	64	81
2	9.064×10^{-4}	-8.297×10^{-4}
3	-7.019×10^{-5}	-5.813×10^{-5}
4	6.106×10^{-6}	-4.550×10^{-6}

The errors using the Taylor series centered at 81 are consistently smaller.

9.3.77

a. The Maclaurin series for $\sin x$ is $x - \frac{1}{3!}x^3 + \frac{1}{5!}x^5 - \frac{1}{7!}x^7 + \cdots$. Squaring the first four terms yields

$$\left(x - \frac{1}{3!}x^3 + \frac{1}{5!}x^5 - \frac{1}{7!}x^7\right)^2$$

$$= x^2 - \frac{2}{3!}x^4 + \left(\frac{2}{5!} + \frac{1}{3!3!}\right)x^6 + \left(-2 \cdot \frac{1}{7!} - 2 \cdot \frac{1}{3!5!}\right)x^8$$

$$= x^2 - \frac{1}{3}x^4 + \frac{2}{45}x^6 - \frac{1}{315}x^8.$$

b. The Maclaurin series for $\cos x$ is $1 - \frac{1}{2}x^2 + \frac{1}{4!}x^4 - \frac{1}{6!}x^6 + \frac{1}{8!}x^8 - \cdots$. Substituting $2x$ for x in the Maclaurin series for $\cos x$ and then computing $(1 - \cos 2x)/2$, we obtain

$$(1 - (1 - \frac{1}{2}(2x)^2 + \frac{1}{4!}(2x)^4 - \frac{1}{6!}(2x)^6) + \frac{1}{8!}(2x)^8)/2$$

$$= (2x^2 - \frac{2}{3}x^4 + \frac{4}{45}x^6 - \frac{2}{315}x^8)/2$$

$$= x^2 - \frac{1}{3}x^4 + \frac{2}{45}x^6 - \frac{1}{315}x^8,$$

and the two are the same.

c. If $f(x) = \sin^2 x$, then $f(0) = 0$, $f'(x) = \sin 2x$, so $f'(0) = 0$. $f''(x) = 2\cos 2x$, so $f''(x) = 2$, $f'''(x) = -4\sin 2x$, so $f'''(0) = 0$. Note that from this point $f^{(n)}(0) = 0$ if n is odd and $f^{(n)}(0) = \pm 2^{n-1}$ if n is even, with the signs alternating for every other even n. Thus, the series for $\sin^2 x$ is

$$2x^2/2 - 8x^4/4! + 32x^6/6! - 128x^8/8! + \cdots = x^2 - \frac{1}{3}x^4 + \frac{2}{45}x^6 - \frac{1}{315}x^8 + \cdots.$$

9.3.78

a. The Maclaurin series for $\cos x$ is $1 - \frac{1}{2}x^2 + \frac{1}{4!}x^4 - \frac{1}{6!}x^6 + \frac{1}{8!}x^8 - \cdots$. Squaring the first four terms yields

$$(1 - \frac{1}{2}x^2 + \frac{1}{4!}x^4 - \frac{1}{6!}x^6)^2$$
$$= 1 - (\frac{1}{2} + \frac{1}{2})x^2 + (\frac{1}{4!} + \frac{1}{4!} + \frac{1}{4})x^4 + (-\frac{1}{6!} - \frac{1}{6!} - \frac{1}{2 \cdot 4!} - \frac{1}{2 \cdot 4!})x^6$$
$$= 1 - x^2 + \frac{1}{3}x^4 - \frac{2}{45}x^6.$$

b. Substituting $2x$ for x in the Maclaurin series for $\cos x$ and then computing $(1 + \cos 2x)/2$, we obtain

$$(1 + 1 - \frac{1}{2}(2x)^2 + \frac{1}{4!}(2x)^4 - \frac{1}{6!}(2x)^6)/2$$
$$= (2 - 2x^2 + \frac{2}{3}x^4 - \frac{4}{45}x^6)/2$$
$$= 1 - x^2 + \frac{1}{3}x^4 - \frac{2}{45}x^6,$$

and the two are the same.

c. If $f(x) = \cos^2 x$, then $f(0) = 1$. Also, $f'(x) = -2\cos x \sin x = -\sin 2x$. So $f'(0) = 0$. $f''(x) = -2\cos 2x$, so $f''(0) = -2$. $f'''(x) = 8\sin 2x$, so $f'''(0) = 0$. Note that from this point on, $f^{(n)}(0) = 0$ if n is odd, and $f^{(n)}(0) = \pm 2^{n-1}$ if n is even, with the signs alternating for every other even n. Thus, the series for $\cos^2 x$ is

$$1 - 2x^2/2 + 8x^4/4! - 32x^6/6! + \cdots = 1 - x^2 + \frac{1}{3}x^4 - \frac{2}{45}x^6 + \cdots.$$

9.3.79 There are many solutions. For example, first find a series that has $(-1, 1)$ as an interval of convergence, say $\frac{1}{1-x} = \sum_{k=0}^{\infty} x^k$. Then the series $\frac{1}{1-x/2} = \sum_{k=0}^{\infty} \left(\frac{x}{2}\right)^k$ has $(-2, 2)$ as its interval of convergence. Now shift the series up so that it is centered at 4. We have $\sum_{k=0}^{\infty} \left(\frac{x-4}{2}\right)^k$, which has interval of convergence $(2, 6)$.

9.3.80 $-\frac{1 \cdot 3 \cdot 5}{2 \cdot 4 \cdot 6 \cdot 8}x^4 + \frac{1 \cdot 3 \cdot 5 \cdot 7}{2 \cdot 4 \cdot 6 \cdot 8 \cdot 10}x^5$.

9.3.81 $\frac{1 \cdot 3 \cdot 5 \cdot 7}{2 \cdot 4 \cdot 6 \cdot 8}x^4 - \frac{1 \cdot 3 \cdot 5 \cdot 7 \cdot 9}{2 \cdot 4 \cdot 6 \cdot 8 \cdot 10}x^5$.

9.3.82

a. The Maclaurin series in question are

$$\sin x = x - \frac{1}{3!}x^3 + \frac{1}{5!}x^5 - \cdots$$
$$e^x = 1 + x + \frac{1}{2!}x^2 + \frac{1}{3!}x^3 + \cdots,$$

so substituting the series for $\sin x$ for x in the series for e^x (and considering only those terms that will give us an exponent at most 3), we obtain $e^{\sin x} = 1 + (x - \frac{1}{3!}x^3) + \frac{1}{2!}x^2 + \frac{1}{3!}x^3 + \cdots = 1 + x + \frac{1}{2}x^2 + \cdots$.

b. The Maclaurin series in question are

$$\tan x = x + \frac{1}{3}x^3 + \frac{2}{15}x^5 + \cdots$$

$$e^x = 1 + x + \frac{1}{2!}x^2 + \frac{1}{3!}x^3 + \cdots,$$

so substituting the series for $\tan x$ for x in the series for e^x (and considering only those terms that will give us an exponent at most 3), we obtain $e^{\tan x} = 1 + (x + \frac{1}{3}x^3) + \frac{1}{2!}x^2 + \frac{1}{3!}x^3 + \cdots = 1 + x + \frac{1}{2}x^2 + \cdots$.

c. The Maclaurin series in question are

$$\sin x = x - \frac{1}{3!}x^3 + \frac{1}{5!}x^5 - \cdots$$

$$\sqrt{1+x^2} = 1 + \frac{1}{2}x^2 - \frac{1}{8}x^4 + \cdots,$$

so substituting the series for $\sin x$ for x in the series for $\sqrt{1+x^2}$ (and considering only those terms that will give us an exponent at most 4), we obtain $\sqrt{1+\sin^2 x} = 1 + \frac{1}{2}(x - \frac{1}{3!}x^3)^2 - \frac{1}{8}x^4 + \cdots = 1 + \frac{1}{2}x^2 - \frac{7}{24}x^4 + \cdots$.

9.3.83 Use the Taylor series for $\cos x$ centered at $\pi/4$: $\frac{\sqrt{2}}{2}(1 - (x - \pi/4) - \frac{1}{2}(x - \pi/4)^2 + \frac{1}{6}(x - \pi/4)^3 + \cdots)$. The remainder after n terms (because the derivatives of $\cos x$ are bounded by 1 in magnitude) is $|R_n(x)| \le \frac{1}{(n+1)!} \cdot \left(\frac{\pi}{4} - \frac{2\pi}{9}\right)^{n+1}$.

Solving for $|R_n(x)| < 10^{-4}$, we obtain $n = 3$. Evaluating the first four terms (through $n = 3$) of the series we get 0.7660427050. The true value is ≈ 0.7660444431.

9.3.84 Use the Taylor series for $\sin x$ centered at π: $-(x - \pi) + \frac{1}{6}(x - \pi)^3 - \frac{1}{120}(x - \pi)^5 + \cdots$. The remainder after n terms (because the derivatives of $\sin x$ are bounded by 1 in magnitude) is $|R_n(x)| \le \frac{1}{(n+1)!} \cdot (\pi - 0.98\pi)^{n+1}$.

Solving for $|R_n(x)| < 10^{-4}$, we obtain $n = 2$. Evaluating the first term of the series gives 0.06283185307. The true value is ≈ 0.06279051953.

9.3.85 Use the Taylor series for $f(x) = x^{1/3}$ centered at 64: $4 + \frac{1}{48}(x - 64) - \frac{1}{9216}(x - 64)^2 + \cdots$. Because we wish to evaluate this series at $x = 83$, $|R_n(x)| = \frac{|f^{(n+1)}(c)|}{(n+1)!}(83 - 64)^{n+1}$. We compute that $|f^{(n+1)}(c)| = \frac{2 \cdot 5 \cdots (3n-1)}{3^{n+1}c^{(3n+2)/3}}$, which is maximized at $c = 64$. Thus

$$|R_n(x)| \le \frac{2 \cdot 5 \cdots (3n-1)}{3^{n+1}64^{(3n+2)/3}(n+1)!}19^{n+1}$$

Solving for $|R_n(x)| < 10^{-4}$, we obtain $n = 5$. Evaluating the terms of the series through $n = 5$ gives 4.362122553. The true value is ≈ 4.362070671.

9.3.86 Use the Taylor series for $f(x) = x^{-1/4}$ centered at 16: $\frac{1}{2} - \frac{1}{128}(x - 16) + \frac{5}{16384}(x - 16)^2 + \cdots$. Because we wish to evaluate this series at $x = 17$, $|R_n(x)| = \frac{|f^{(n+1)}(c)|}{(n+1)!}(17 - 16)^{n+1}$. We compute that $|f^{(n+1)}(c)| = \frac{1 \cdot 5 \cdots (4n+1)}{4^{n+1}c^{(4n+5)/4}}$ which is maximized at $c = 16$. Thus

$$|R_n(x)| \le \frac{1 \cdot 5 \cdots (4n+1)}{4^{n+1}16^{(4n+5)/4}(n+1)!}1^{n+1}$$

Solving for $|R_n(x)| < 10^{-4}$, we obtain $n = 2$. Evaluating the terms of the series through $n = 2$ gives 0.4924926758. The true value is ≈ 0.4924790605.

9.3.87

   a. Use the Taylor series for $(125 + x)^{1/3}$ centered at $x = 0$. Using the first four terms and evaluating at $x = 3$ gives a result (5.03968) accurate to within 10^{-4}.

   b. Use the Taylor series for $x^{1/3}$ centered at $x = 125$. Note that this gives the identical Taylor series except that the exponential terms are $(x - 125)^n$ rather than x^n. Thus we need terms up through $(x - 125)^3$, just as before, evaluated at $x = 128$, and we obtain the identical result.

   c. Because the two Taylor series are the same except for the shifting, the results are equivalent.

9.3.88 Suppose that f is differentiable.

Consider the remainder after the zeroth term of the Taylor series. Taylor's Theorem says that

$$R_0(x) = \frac{f'(c)}{1!}(x - a)^1 \quad \text{for some } c \text{ between } x \text{ and } a,$$

but $f(x) = f(a) + R_0(x)$, which gives $f(x) = f(a) + f'(c)(x - a)$. Rearranging, we obtain $f'(c) = \frac{f(x) - f(a)}{x - a}$ for some c between x and a, which is the conclusion of the Mean Value Theorem.

9.3.89 Consider the remainder after the first term of the Taylor series. Taylor's Theorem indicates that $R_1(x) = \frac{f''(c)}{2}(x - a)^2$ for some c between x and a, so that $f(x) = f(a) + f'(a)(x - a) + \frac{f''(c)}{2}(x - a)^2$. But $f'(a) = 0$, so that for every x in an interval containing a, there is a c between x and a such that $f(x) = f(a) + \frac{f''(c)}{2}(x - a)^2$.

   a. If $f''(x) > 0$ on the interval containing a, then for every x in that interval, we have $f(x) = f(a) + \frac{f''(c)}{2}(x - a)^2$ for some c between x and a. But $f''(c) > 0$ and $(x - a)^2 > 0$, so that $f(x) > f(a)$ and a is a local minimum.

   b. If $f''(x) < 0$ on the interval containing a, then for every x in that interval, we have $f(x) = f(a) + \frac{f''(c)}{2}(x - a)^2$ for some c between x and a. But $f''(c) < 0$ and $(x - a)^2 > 0$, so that $f(x) < f(a)$ and a is a local maximum.

9.3.90

   a. To show that $f'(0) = 0$, we compute the limits of the left and right difference quotients and show that they are both zero:

$$\lim_{x \to 0^+} \frac{e^{-1/x^2} - 0}{x} = \lim_{x \to 0^+} \frac{e^{-1/x^2}}{x} \quad \text{and} \quad \lim_{x \to 0^-} \frac{e^{-1/x^2} - 0}{x} = \lim_{x \to 0^-} \frac{e^{-1/x^2}}{x}.$$

For the limit from the right, use the substitution $x = \frac{1}{\sqrt{y}}$; then $y = x^2$ and the limit becomes

$$\lim_{y \to \infty} e^{-y} \sqrt{y} = \lim_{y \to \infty} \frac{\sqrt{y}}{e^y} = 0,$$

because exponentials dominate power functions. Similarly, for the limit from the left, use the substitution $x = -\frac{1}{\sqrt{y}}$; then again $y = x^2$ and the limit becomes

$$\lim_{y \to \infty} (-e^{-y} \sqrt{y}) = -\lim_{y \to \infty} \frac{\sqrt{y}}{e^y} = 0.$$

Since the left and right limits are both zero, it follows that f is differentiable at $x = 0$, and its derivative is zero.

   b. Because $f^{(k)}(0) = 0$, the Taylor series centered at 0 has only one term: $f(x) = f(0) = 0$, so the Taylor series is zero.

   c. It does not converge to $f(x)$ because $f(x) \neq 0$ for all $x \neq 0$.

9.4   Working with Taylor Series

9.4.1 Replace f and g by their Taylor series centered at a, and evaluate the limit.

9.4.2 Integrate the Taylor series for $f(x)$ centered at a, and evaluate it at the endpoints.

9.4.3 Substitute -0.6 for x in the Taylor series for e^x centered at 0. Note that this series is an alternating series, so the error can easily be estimated by looking at the magnitude of the first neglected term.

9.4.4 Take the Taylor series for $\sin^{-1}(x)$ centered at 0 and evaluate it at $x = 1$, then multiply the result by 2.

9.4.5 The series is $f'(x) = \sum_{k=1}^{\infty} kc_k x^{k-1}$, which converges for $|x| < b$.

9.4.6 It must have derivatives of all orders on some interval containing a.

9.4.7 Because $e^x = 1 + x + x^2/2! + x^3/3! + \cdots$, we have $\frac{e^x - 1}{x} = 1 + x/2! + \cdots$, so $\lim_{x \to 0} \frac{e^x - 1}{x} = 1$.

9.4.8 Because $\tan^{-1} x = x - \frac{x^3}{3} + \frac{x^5}{5} - \frac{x^7}{7} + \cdots$, we have $\frac{\tan^{-1} x - x}{x^3} = \frac{-1}{3} + \frac{x^2}{5} - \cdots$.
 So $\lim_{x \to 0} \frac{\tan^{-1} x - x}{3} = \frac{-1}{3}$.

9.4.9 Because $-\ln(1 - x) = x + \frac{x^2}{2} + \frac{x^3}{3} + \frac{x^4}{4} + \frac{x^5}{5} + \cdots$, we have $\frac{-x - \ln(1-x)}{x^2} = \frac{1}{2} + \frac{x}{3} + \frac{x^2}{4} + \cdots$, so $\lim_{x \to 0} \frac{-x - \ln(1-x)}{x^2} = \frac{1}{2}$.

9.4.10 Because $\sin 2x = 2x - \frac{4x^3}{3} + \frac{4x^5}{15} + \cdots$, we have $\frac{\sin 2x}{x} = 2 - \frac{4x^2}{3} + \frac{4x^4}{15} + \cdots$, so $\lim_{x \to 0} \frac{\sin 2x}{x} = 2$.

9.4.11 We compute that

$$
\begin{aligned}
\frac{e^x - e^{-x}}{x} &= \frac{1}{x}\left(\left(1 + x + \frac{x^2}{2} + \frac{x^3}{6} + \cdots\right) - \left(1 - x + \frac{x^2}{2} - \frac{x^3}{6} + \cdots\right)\right) \\
&= \frac{1}{x}\left(2x + \frac{x^3}{3} + \cdots\right) = 2 + \frac{x^2}{3} + \cdots
\end{aligned}
$$

so the limit of $\frac{e^x - e^{-x}}{x}$ as $x \to 0$ is 2.

9.4.12 Because $-e^x = -1 - x - x^2/2 - x^3/6 + \cdots$, we have $\frac{1 + x - e^x}{4x^2} = -\frac{1}{8} - \frac{x}{24} + \cdots$, so $\lim_{x \to 0} \frac{1 + x - e^x}{4x^2} = -\frac{1}{8}$.

9.4.13 We compute that

$$
\begin{aligned}
\frac{2\cos 2x - 2 + 4x^2}{2x^4} &= \frac{1}{2x^4}\left(2\left(1 - \frac{(2x)^2}{2} + \frac{(2x)^4}{24} - \frac{(2x)^6}{720} + \cdots\right) - 2 + 4x^2\right) \\
&= \frac{1}{2x^4}\left(\frac{(2x)^4}{12} - \frac{(2x)^6}{360} + \cdots\right) = \frac{2}{3} - \frac{4x^2}{45} + \cdots
\end{aligned}
$$

so the limit of $\frac{2\cos 2x - 2 + 4x^2}{2x^4}$ as $x \to 0$ is $\frac{2}{3}$.

9.4.14 We substitute $t = \frac{1}{x}$ and find $\lim_{t \to 0} \frac{\sin t}{t}$. We compute that

$$
\frac{\sin t}{t} = \frac{1}{t}\left(t - \frac{t^3}{6} + \cdots\right) = 1 - \frac{t^2}{6} + \cdots
$$

so the limit of $x \sin\left(\frac{1}{x}\right)$ as $x \to \infty$ is 1.

9.4.15 We have $\ln(1 + x) = x - \frac{1}{2}x^2 + \frac{1}{3}x^3 - \frac{1}{4}x^4 + \cdots$, so that

$$\frac{\ln(1 + x) - x + x^2/2}{x^3} = \frac{x^3/3 - x^4/4 + \cdots}{x^3} = \frac{1}{3} - \frac{x}{4} + \cdots$$

so that $\lim\limits_{x \to 0} \dfrac{\ln(1 + x) - x + x^2/2}{x^3} = \dfrac{1}{3}$.

9.4.16 The Taylor series for $\ln(x - 3)$ centered at $x = 4$ is

$$(x - 4) - \frac{1}{2}(x - 4)^2 + \cdots.$$

We compute that

$$\frac{x^2 - 16}{\ln(x - 3)} = \frac{x^2 - 16}{(x - 4) - \frac{1}{2}(x - 4)^2 + \cdots} = \frac{(x - 4)(x + 4)}{(x - 4) - \frac{1}{2}(x - 4)^2 + \cdots}$$

$$= \frac{x + 4}{1 - \frac{1}{2}(x - 4) + \cdots}$$

so the limit of $\dfrac{x^2 - 16}{\ln(x - 3)}$ as $x \to 4$ is 8.

9.4.17 We compute that

$$\frac{3\tan^{-1} x - 3x + x^3}{x^5} = \frac{1}{x^5}\left(3\left(x - \frac{x^3}{3} + \frac{x^5}{5} - \frac{x^7}{7} + \cdots\right) - 3x + x^3\right)$$

$$= \frac{1}{x^5}\left(\frac{3x^5}{5} - \frac{3x^7}{7} + \cdots\right) = \frac{3}{5} - \frac{3x^2}{7} + \cdots$$

so the limit of $\dfrac{3\tan^{-1} x - 3x + x^3}{x^5}$ as $x \to 0$ is $\dfrac{3}{5}$.

9.4.18 The Taylor series for $\sqrt{1 + x}$ centered at 0 is

$$\sqrt{1 + x} = 1 + \frac{1}{2}x - \frac{1}{8}x^2 + \frac{1}{16}x^3 + \cdots.$$

We compute that

$$\frac{\sqrt{1 + x} - 1 - (x/2)}{4x^2} = \frac{1}{4x^2}\left(\left(1 + \frac{x}{2} - \frac{x^2}{8} + \frac{x^3}{16} + \cdots\right) - 1 - \frac{x}{2}\right)$$

$$= \frac{1}{4x^2}\left(-\frac{x^2}{8} + \frac{x^3}{16} + \cdots\right) = -\frac{1}{32} + \frac{x}{64} + \cdots$$

so the limit of $\dfrac{\sqrt{1 + x} - 1 - (x/2)}{4x^2}$ as $x \to 0$ is $-\dfrac{1}{32}$.

9.4.19 The Taylor series for $\sin 2x$ centered at 0 is

$$\sin 2x = 2x - \frac{1}{3!}(2x)^3 + \frac{1}{5!}(2x)^5 - \frac{1}{7!}(2x)^7 + \cdots = 2x - \frac{4}{3}x^3 + \frac{4}{15}x^5 - \frac{8}{315}x^7 + \cdots.$$

Thus

$$\frac{12x - 8x^3 - 6\sin 2x}{x^5} = \frac{12 - 8x^3 - \left(12x - 8x^3 + \frac{8}{5}x^5 - \frac{16}{105}x^7 + \cdots\right)}{x^5}$$

$$= -\frac{8}{5} + \frac{16}{105}x^2 - \cdots,$$

so $\lim\limits_{x \to 0} \dfrac{12x - 8x^3 - 6\sin 2x}{x^5} = -\dfrac{8}{5}$.

9.4.20 The Taylor series for $\ln x$ centered at 1 is

$$\ln x = (x-1) - \frac{1}{2}(x-1)^2 + \cdots.$$

We compute that

$$\frac{x-1}{\ln x} = \frac{x-1}{(x-1) - \frac{1}{2}(x-1)^2 + \cdots} = \frac{1}{1 - \frac{1}{2}(x-1) + \cdots}$$

so the limit of $\dfrac{x-1}{\ln x}$ as $x \to 1$ is 1.

9.4.21 The Taylor series for $\ln(x-1)$ centered at 2 is

$$\ln(x-1) = (x-2) - \frac{1}{2}(x-2)^2 + \cdots.$$

We compute that

$$\frac{x-2}{\ln(x-1)} = \frac{x-2}{(x-2) - \frac{1}{2}(x-2)^2 + \cdots} = \frac{1}{1 - \frac{1}{2}(x-2) + \cdots}$$

so the limit of $\dfrac{x-2}{\ln(x-1)}$ as $x \to 2$ is 1.

9.4.22 Because $e^{1/x} = 1 + (1/x) + 1/(2x^2) + \cdots$, we have

$$x(e^{1/x} - 1) = 1 + 1/(2x) + \cdots.$$

Thus, $\lim_{x \to \infty} x(e^{1/x} - 1) = 1$.

9.4.23 Computing Taylor series centers at 0 gives

$$e^{-2x} = 1 - 2x + \frac{1}{2!}(-2x)^2 + \frac{1}{3!}(-2x)^3 + \cdots = 1 - 2x + 2x^2 - \frac{4}{3}x^3 + \cdots$$

$$e^{-x/2} = 1 - \frac{x}{2} + \frac{1}{2!}\left(-\frac{x}{2}\right)^2 + \frac{1}{3!}\left(-\frac{x}{2}\right)^3 + \cdots = 1 - \frac{x}{2} + \frac{1}{8}x^2 - \frac{1}{48}x^3 + \cdots.$$

Thus

$$\frac{e^{-2x} - 4e^{-x/2} + 3}{2x^2} = \frac{1 - 2x + 2x^2 - \frac{4}{3}x^3 + \cdots - (4 - 2x + \frac{1}{2}x^2 - \frac{1}{12}x^3 + \cdots) + 3}{2x^2}$$

$$= \frac{\frac{3}{2}x^2 - \frac{5}{4}x^3 + \cdots}{2x^2}$$

$$= \frac{3}{4} - \frac{5}{8}x + \cdots$$

so $\lim\limits_{x \to 0} \dfrac{e^{-2x} - 4e^{-x/2} + 3}{2x^2} = \dfrac{3}{4}$.

9.4.24 The Taylor series for $(1 - 2x)^{-1/2}$ centered at 0 is

$$(1 - 2x)^{-1/2} = 1 + x + \frac{3x^2}{2} + \frac{5x^3}{2} + \cdots.$$

We compute that

$$\frac{(1-2x)^{-1/2} - e^x}{8x^2} = \frac{1}{8x^2}\left(\left(1 + x + \frac{3x^2}{2} + \frac{5x^3}{2} + \cdots\right) - \left(1 + x + \frac{x^2}{2} + \frac{x^3}{6} + \cdots\right)\right)$$

$$= \frac{1}{8x^2}\left(x^2 + \frac{7x^3}{3} + \cdots\right) = \frac{1}{8} + \frac{7x}{24} + \cdots$$

so the limit of $\dfrac{(1-2x)^{-1/2} - e^x}{8x^2}$ as $x \to 0$ is $\dfrac{1}{8}$.

9.4.25

a. $f'(x) = \frac{d}{dx}(\sum_{k=0}^{\infty} \frac{x^k}{k!}) = \sum_{k=1}^{\infty} k\frac{x^{k-1}}{k!} = \sum_{k=0}^{\infty} \frac{x^k}{k!} = f(x)$.

b. $f'(x) = e^x$ as well.

c. The series converges on $(-\infty, \infty)$.

9.4.26

a. $f'(x) = \frac{d}{dx}(\sum_{k=0}^{\infty}(-1)^k \frac{x^{2k}}{(2k)!}) = \sum_{k=1}^{\infty}(-1)^k(2k)\frac{x^{2k-1}}{(2k)!} = \sum_{k=1}^{\infty}(-1)^k\frac{x^{2k-1}}{(2k-1)!} = -\sum_{k=0}^{\infty}(-1)^k\frac{x^{2k+1}}{(2k+1)!}$.

b. $f'(x) = -\sin x$.

c. The series converges on $(-\infty, \infty)$, because the series for $\cos x$ does.

9.4.27

a. $f'(x) = \frac{d}{dx}(\ln(1+x)) = \frac{d}{dx}(\sum_{k=1}^{\infty}(-1)^{k+1}\frac{1}{k}x^k) = \sum_{k=1}^{\infty}(-1)^{k+1}x^{k-1} = \sum_{k=0}^{\infty}(-1)^k x^k$.

b. This is the power series for $\frac{1}{1+x}$.

c. The Taylor series for $\ln(1+x)$ converges on $(-1, 1)$, as does the Taylor series for $\frac{1}{1+x}$.

9.4.28

a. $f'(x) = \frac{d}{dx}(\sin x^2) = \frac{d}{dx}(\sum_{k=0}^{\infty}(-1)^k \frac{x^{4k+2}}{(2k+1)!}) = \sum_{k=0}^{\infty}(-1)^k \cdot 2(2k+1)\frac{x^{4k+1}}{(2k+1)!} = 2\sum_{k=0}^{\infty}(-1)^k \frac{x^{4k+1}}{(2k)!} = 2x\sum_{k=0}^{\infty}(-1)^k \frac{x^{4k}}{(2k)!}$.

b. This is the power series for $2x\cos x^2$.

c. Because the Taylor series for $\sin x^2$ converges everywhere, the Taylor series for $2x\cos x^2$ does as well.

9.4.29

a.

$$f'(x) = \frac{d}{dx}(e^{-2x}) = \frac{d}{dx}(\sum_{k=0}^{\infty} \frac{(-2x)^k}{k!}) = \frac{d}{dx}(\sum_{k=0}^{\infty}(-2)^k \frac{x^k}{k!}) = -2\sum_{k=1}^{\infty}(-2)^{k-1}\frac{x^{k-1}}{(k-1)!} = -2\sum_{k=0}^{\infty}\frac{(-2x)^k}{k!}.$$

b. This is the Taylor series for $-2e^{-2x}$.

c. Because the Taylor series for e^{-2x} converges on $(-\infty, \infty)$, so does this one.

9.4.30

a. We have

$$f'(x) = \frac{d}{dx}\left(\frac{1}{1-x}\right) = \frac{d}{dx}\left(\sum_{k=0}^{\infty} x^k\right) = \frac{d}{dx}\left(1 + \sum_{k=1}^{\infty} x^k\right) = \sum_{k=1}^{\infty} kx^{k-1} = \sum_{k=0}^{\infty}(k+1)x^k.$$

b. From the formula for $(1+x)^p$ in Table 9.5, we see that the Taylor series for $\frac{1}{(1-x)^2}$ is

$$\sum_{k=0}^{\infty} \frac{(-2)(-3)\cdots(-2-k+1)}{k!}(-x)^k = \sum_{k=0}^{\infty}(-1)^k(-1)^k \frac{(k+1)!}{k!}x^k = \sum_{k=0}^{\infty}(k+1)x^k,$$

so that $f'(x)$ is simply $\frac{1}{(1-x)^2}$ as expected.

c. Since the Taylor series for $\frac{1}{1-x}$ converges on $(-1,1)$, so does the series for $\frac{1}{(1-x)^2}$. Checking the endpoints, we see that the series diverges at both endpoints by the Divergence test, so that the interval of convergence for $f'(x)$ is also $(-1,1)$.

9.4.31

a. $\tan^{-1} x = x - \frac{x^3}{3} + \frac{x^5}{5} - \cdots$, so $\frac{d}{dx} \tan^{-1} x^2 = 1 - x^2 + x^4 - x^6 + \cdots$.

b. This is the series for $\frac{1}{1+x^2}$.

c. Because the series for $\tan^{-1} x$ has a radius of convergence of 1, this series does too. Checking the endpoints shows that the interval of convergence is $(-1,1)$.

9.4.32

a. $-\ln(1-x) = x + \frac{x^2}{2} + \frac{x^3}{3} + \frac{x^4}{4} + \frac{x^5}{5} + \cdots$, so $\frac{d}{dx}[-\ln(1-x)] = 1 + x + x^2 + x^3 + \cdots$.

b. This is the series for $\frac{1}{1-x}$.

c. The interval of convergence for $\frac{1}{1-x}$ is $(-1,1)$.

9.4.33

a. Because $y(0) = 2$, we have $0 = y'(0) - y(0) = y'(0) - 2$ so that $y'(0) = 2$. Differentiating the equation gives $y''(0) = y'(0)$, so that $y''(0) = 2$. Successive derivatives also have the value 2 at 0, so the Taylor series is $2 \sum_{k=0}^{\infty} \frac{t^k}{k!}$.

b. $2 \sum_{k=0}^{\infty} \frac{t^k}{k!} = 2e^t$.

9.4.34

a. Because $y(0) = 0$, we see that $y'(0) = 8$. Differentiating the equation gives $y''(0) + 4y'(0) = 0$, so $y''(0) + 4 \cdot 8 = 0$, $y''(0) = -4 \cdot 8$. Continuing, $y'''(0) + 4 \cdot (-4 \cdot 8) = 0$, so $y'''(0) = 4 \cdot 4 \cdot 8$, and in general $y^{(k)}(0) = (-1)^{k+1} 2 \cdot 4^k$ for $k \geq 1$, so the Taylor series is $2 \sum_{k=1}^{\infty} (-1)^{k+1} \frac{(4t)^k}{k!}$.

b. $2 \sum_{k=1}^{\infty} (-1)^{k+1} \frac{(4t)^k}{k!} = 2(1 - e^{-4t})$.

9.4.35

a. $y(0) = 2$, so that $y'(0) = 16$. Differentiating, $y''(t) - 3y'(t) = 0$, so that $y''(0) = 48$, and in general $y^{(k)}(0) = 3y^{(k-1)}(0) = 3^{k-1} \cdot 16$. Thus the power series is $2 + \frac{16}{3} \sum_{k=1}^{\infty} \frac{(3t)^k}{k!} = 2 + \sum_{k=1}^{\infty} \frac{3^{k-1} 16}{k!} t^k$.

b. $2 + \frac{16}{3} \sum_{k=1}^{\infty} \frac{(3t)^k}{k!} = 2 + \frac{16}{3}(e^{3t} - 1) = \frac{16}{3} e^{3t} - \frac{10}{3}$.

9.4.36

a. $y(0) = 2$, so $y'(0) = 12 + 9 = 21$. Differentiating, $y^{(n)}(0) = 6y^{(n-1)}(0)$ for $n > 1$, so that $y^{(n)}(0) = 6^{n-1} \cdot 21$ for $n \geq 1$. Thus the power series is $2 + \sum_{k=1}^{\infty} 21 \cdot 6^{k-1} \frac{t^k}{k!} = 2 + \frac{7}{2} \sum_{k=1}^{\infty} \frac{(6t)^k}{k!}$.

b. $2 + \frac{7}{2} \sum_{k=1}^{\infty} \frac{(6t)^k}{k!} = 2 + \frac{7}{2}(e^{6t} - 1) = \frac{7}{2} e^{6t} - \frac{3}{2}$.

9.4.37 The Taylor series for e^{-x^2} is $\sum_{k=0}^{\infty} (-1)^k \frac{x^{2k}}{k!}$. Thus, the desired integral is $\int_0^{0.25} \sum_{k=0}^{\infty} (-1)^k \frac{x^{2k}}{k!} \, dx = \sum_{k=0}^{\infty} (-1)^k \frac{x^{2k+1}}{(2k+1)k!} \Big|_0^{0.25} = \sum_{k=0}^{\infty} (-1)^k \frac{1}{(2k+1)k! 4^{2k+1}}$. Because this is an alternating series, to approximate it to within 10^{-4}, we must find n such that $a_{n+1} < 10^{-4}$, or $\frac{1}{(2n+3)(n+1)! \cdot 4^{2n+3}} < 10^{-4}$. This occurs for $n = 1$, so $\sum_{k=0}^{1} (-1)^k \frac{1}{(2k+1) \cdot k! \cdot 4^{2k+1}} = \frac{1}{4} - \frac{1}{192} \approx 0.245$.

9.4.38 The Taylor series for $\sin x^2$ is $\sum_{k=0}^{\infty}(-1)^k \frac{x^{4k+2}}{(2k+1)!}$. Thus the desired integral is

$$\int_0^{0.2} \sum_{k=0}^{\infty}(-1)^k \frac{x^{4k+2}}{(2k+1)!}\,dx = \sum_{k=0}^{\infty}(-1)^k \frac{x^{4k+3}}{(4k+3)(2k+1)!}\bigg|_0^{0.2} = \sum_{k=0}^{\infty}(-1)^k \frac{0.2^{4k+3}}{(4k+3)(2k+1)!}.$$

Because this is an alternating series, to approximate it to within 10^{-4}, we must find n such that $a_{n+1} < 10^{-4}$, or $\frac{0.2^{4n+7}}{(4n+7)(2n+3)!} < 10^{-4}$. This occurs first for $n = 0$, so we obtain $\frac{0.2^3}{3\cdot 1!} \approx 2.67 \times 10^{-3}$.

9.4.39 The Taylor series for $\cos 2x^2$ is $\sum_{k=0}^{\infty}(-1)^k \frac{(2x^2)^{2k}}{(2k)!} = \sum_{k=0}^{\infty}(-1)^k \frac{4^k x^{4k}}{(2k)!}$. Note that $\cos x$ is an even function, so we compute the integral from 0 to 0.35 and double it:

$$2\int_0^{0.35} \sum_{k=0}^{\infty}(-1)^k \frac{4^k x^{4k}}{(2k)!}\,dx = 2\left(\sum_{k=0}^{\infty}(-1)^k \frac{4^k x^{4k+1}}{(4k+1)(2k)!}\right)\bigg|_0^{0.35} = 2\left(\sum_{k=0}^{\infty}(-1)^k \frac{4^k (0.35)^{4k+1}}{(4k+1)(2k)!}\right).$$

Because this is an alternating series, to approximate it to within $\frac{1}{2}\cdot 10^{-4}$, we must find n such that $a_{n+1} < \frac{1}{2}\cdot 10^{-4}$, or $\frac{4^{n+1}(0.35)^{4n+5}}{(4n+3)(2n+2)!} < \frac{1}{2}\cdot 10^{-4}$. This occurs first for $n = 1$, and we have $2\left(.35 - \frac{4\cdot(0.35)^5}{5\cdot 2!}\right) \approx 0.696$.

9.4.40 The Taylor series for $(1+x^4)^{1/2}$ is $\sum_{k=0}^{\infty}\binom{1/2}{k}x^{4k}$, so the desired integral is

$$\int_0^{0.2} \sum_{k=0}^{\infty}\binom{1/2}{k}x^{4k}\,dx = \sum_{k=0}^{\infty}\frac{1}{4k+1}\binom{1/2}{k}x^{4k+1}\bigg|_0^{0.2} = \sum_{k=0}^{\infty}\frac{1}{4k+1}\binom{1/2}{k}(0.2)^{4k+1}.$$

This is an alternating series because the binomial coefficients alternate in sign, so to approximate it to within 10^{-4}, we must find n such that $a_{n+1} < 10^{-4}$, or $\left|\frac{1}{4n+5}\binom{1/2}{n+1}(0.2)^{4n+5}\right| < 10^{-4}$. This happens first for $n = 0$, so the approximation is $\binom{1/2}{0}\cdot 0.2 = 0.2$.

9.4.41 $\tan^{-1}x = x - x^3/3 + x^5/5 - x^7/7 + x^9/9 - \cdots$, so $\int \tan^{-1}x\,dx = \int(x - x^3/3 + x^5/5 - x^7/7 + x^9/9 - \cdots)\,dx = C + \frac{x^2}{2} - \frac{x^4}{12} + \frac{x^6}{30} - \frac{x^8}{56} + \cdots$. Thus, $\int_0^{0.35}\tan^{-1}x\,dx = \frac{(0.35)^2}{2} - \frac{(0.35)^4}{12} + \frac{(0.35)^6}{30} - \frac{(0.35)^8}{56} + \cdots$. Note that this series is alternating, and $\frac{(0.35)^6}{30} < 10^{-4}$, so we add the first two terms to approximate the integral to the desired accuracy. Calculating gives approximately 0.060.

9.4.42 $\ln(1+x^2) = x^2 - \frac{x^4}{2} + \frac{x^6}{3} - \frac{x^8}{4} + \cdots$, so $\int \ln(1+x^2)\,dx = \int(x^2 - \frac{x^4}{2} + \frac{x^6}{3} - \frac{x^8}{4} + \cdots)\,dx = C + \frac{x^3}{3} - \frac{x^5}{10} + \frac{x^7}{21} - \frac{x^9}{36} + \frac{x^{11}}{55} + \cdots$. Thus, $\int_0^{0.4}\ln(1+x^2)\,dx = \frac{(0.4)^3}{3} - \frac{(0.4)^5}{10} + \frac{(0.4)^7}{21} - \frac{(0.4)^9}{36} + \cdots$. Because $\frac{(0.4)^7}{21} < 10^{-4}$, we add the first two terms to approximate the integral to the desired accuracy. Calculating gives approximately 0.020.

9.4.43 The Taylor series for $(1+x^6)^{-1/2}$ is $\sum_{k=0}^{\infty}\binom{-1/2}{k}x^{6k}$, so the desired integral is $\int_0^{0.5}\sum_{k=0}^{\infty}\binom{-1/2}{k}x^{6k}\,dx = \sum_{k=0}^{\infty}\frac{1}{6k+1}\binom{-1/2}{k}x^{6k+1}\bigg|_0^{0.5} = \sum_{k=0}^{\infty}\frac{1}{6k+1}\binom{-1/2}{k}(0.5)^{6k+1}$. This is an alternating series because the binomial coefficients alternate in sign, so to approximate it to within 10^{-4}, we must find n such that $a_{n+1} < 10^{-4}$, or $\left|\frac{1}{6n+7}\binom{-1/2}{n+1}(0.5)^{6n+7}\right| < 10^{-4}$. This occurs first for $n = 1$, so we have $\binom{-1/2}{0}0.5 + \frac{1}{7}\binom{-1/2}{1}(0.5)^7 \approx 0.499$.

9.4.44 The Taylor series for $\frac{\ln(1+t)}{t}$ centered at 0 is $\sum_{k=0}^{\infty}(-1)^k \frac{t^k}{k+1}$. The desired integral is thus

$\int_0^{0.2}\sum_{k=0}^{\infty}(-1)^k \frac{t^k}{k+1}\,dt = \sum_{k=0}^{\infty}(-1)^k \frac{t^{k+1}}{(k+1)^2}\bigg|_0^{0.2} = \sum_{k=0}^{\infty}(-1)^k \frac{(0.2)^{k+1}}{(k+1)^2}$. This is an alternating series, so to approximate it to within 10^{-4}, we must find n such that $a_{n+1} < 10^{-4}$, or $\frac{(0.2)^{n+2}}{(n+2)^2} < 10^{-4}$. This occurs first for $n = 3$, so we have $\sum_{k=0}^{3}(-1)^k \frac{(0.2)^{k+1}}{(k+1)^2} \approx 0.191$.

9.4.45 Use the Taylor series for e^x at 0: $1 + \frac{2}{1!} + \frac{2^2}{2!} + \frac{2^3}{3!}$.

9.4.46 Use the Taylor series for e^x at 0: $1 + \frac{1/2}{1!} + \frac{(1/2)^2}{2!} + \frac{(1/2)^3}{3!} = 1 + \frac{1}{2} + \frac{1}{8} + \frac{1}{8 \cdot 3!}$.

9.4.47 Use the Taylor series for $\cos x$ at 0: $1 - \frac{2^2}{2!} + \frac{2^4}{4!} - \frac{2^6}{6!}$

9.4.48 Use the Taylor series for $\sin x$ at 0: $1 - \frac{1^3}{3!} + \frac{1^5}{5!} - \frac{1^7}{7!} = 1 - \frac{1}{3!} + \frac{1}{5!} - \frac{1}{7!}$.

9.4.49 Use the Taylor series for $\ln(1+x)$ evaluated at $x = 1/2$: $\frac{1}{2} - \frac{1}{2} \cdot \frac{1}{4} + \frac{1}{3} \cdot \frac{1}{8} - \frac{1}{4} \cdot \frac{1}{16}$.

9.4.50 Use the Taylor series for $\tan^{-1} x$ evaluated at $1/2$: $\frac{1}{2} - \frac{1}{3} \cdot \frac{1}{8} + \frac{1}{5} \cdot \frac{1}{32} - \frac{1}{7} \cdot \frac{1}{128}$.

9.4.51 The Taylor series for f centered at 0 is $\frac{-1 + \sum_{k=0}^{\infty} \frac{x^k}{k!}}{x} = \frac{\sum_{k=1}^{\infty} \frac{x^k}{k!}}{x} = \sum_{k=1}^{\infty} \frac{x^{k-1}}{k!} = \sum_{k=0}^{\infty} \frac{x^k}{(k+1)!}$. Evaluating both sides at $x = 1$, we have $e - 1 = \sum_{k=0}^{\infty} \frac{1}{(k+1)!}$.

9.4.52 The Taylor series for f centered at 0 is $\frac{-1 + \sum_{k=0}^{\infty} \frac{x^k}{k!}}{x} = \frac{\sum_{k=1}^{\infty} \frac{x^k}{k!}}{x} = \sum_{k=1}^{\infty} \frac{x^{k-1}}{k!} = \sum_{k=0}^{\infty} \frac{x^k}{(k+1)!}$. Differentiating, the Taylor series for $f'(x)$ is $f'(x) = \frac{(x-1)e^x + 1}{x^2} = \sum_{k=1}^{\infty} \frac{kx^{k-1}}{(k+1)!}$. Evaluating both sides at 2 gives $\frac{e^2 + 1}{4} = \sum_{k=1}^{\infty} \frac{k \cdot 2^{k-1}}{(k+1)!}$.

9.4.53 The Maclaurin series for $\ln(1+x)$ is $x - \frac{1}{2}x^2 + \frac{1}{3}x^3 - \frac{1}{4}x^4 + \cdots = \sum_{k=1}^{\infty} (-1)^{k+1} \frac{x^k}{k}$. By the Ratio Test, $\lim_{k \to \infty} \left| \frac{a_{k+1}}{a_k} \right| = \lim_{k \to \infty} \left| \frac{x^{k+1}k}{x^k(k+1)} \right| = |x|$, so the radius of convergence is 1. The series diverges at -1 and converges at 1, so the interval of convergence is $(-1, 1]$. Evaluating at 1 gives $\ln 2 = \sum_{k=1}^{\infty} (-1)^{k+1} \frac{1}{k} = 1 - \frac{1}{2} + \frac{1}{3} - \frac{1}{4} + \cdots$.

9.4.54 The Taylor series for $\ln(1+x)$ at 0 is $x - \frac{1}{2}x^2 + \frac{1}{3}x^3 - \frac{1}{4}x^4 + \cdots = \sum_{k=1}^{\infty} (-1)^{k+1} \frac{x^k}{k}$. By the Ratio Test, $\lim_{k \to \infty} \left| \frac{a_{k+1}}{a_k} \right| = \lim_{k \to \infty} \left| \frac{x^{k+1}k}{x^k(k+1)} \right| = |x|$, so the radius of convergence is 1. The series diverges at -1 and converges at 1, so the interval of convergence is $(-1, 1]$. Evaluate both sides at $-1/2$ to get $f(\frac{-1}{2}) = \ln(1/2) = -\ln 2 = \sum_{k=1}^{\infty} (-1)^{k+1} \frac{(-1/2)^k}{k} = -\sum_{k=1}^{\infty} \frac{1}{k \cdot 2^k}$, so that $\ln 2 = \sum_{k=1}^{\infty} \frac{1}{k \cdot 2^k}$.

9.4.55 $\sum_{k=0}^{\infty} \frac{x^k}{2^k} = \sum_{k=0}^{\infty} \left(\frac{x}{2} \right)^k = \frac{1}{1 - \frac{x}{2}} = \frac{2}{2-x}$.

9.4.56 $\sum_{k=0}^{\infty} (-1)^k \frac{x^k}{3^k} = \sum_{k=0}^{\infty} \left(\frac{-x}{3} \right)^k = \frac{1}{1 + \frac{x}{3}} = \frac{3}{3+x}$.

9.4.57 $\sum_{k=0}^{\infty} (-1)^k \frac{x^{2k}}{4^k} = \sum_{k=0}^{\infty} \left(\frac{-x^2}{4} \right)^k = \frac{1}{1 + \frac{x^2}{4}} = \frac{4}{4+x^2}$.

9.4.58 $\sum_{k=0}^{\infty} 2^k x^{2k+1} = x \sum_{k=0}^{\infty} (2x^2)^k = \frac{x}{1 - 2x^2}$.

9.4.59 $\ln(1+x) = -\sum_{k=1}^{\infty} (-1)^k \frac{x^k}{k}$, so $\ln(1-x) = -\sum_{k=1}^{\infty} \frac{x^k}{k}$, and finally $-\ln(1-x) = \sum_{k=1}^{\infty} \frac{x^k}{k}$.

9.4.60 $\sum_{k=0}^{\infty} \frac{(-1)^k x^{k+1}}{4^k} = -4 \sum_{k=0}^{\infty} \left(\frac{-x}{4} \right)^{k+1} = -4 \left(-1 + \sum_{k=0}^{\infty} \left(\frac{-x}{4} \right)^k \right) = 4 - \frac{4}{1 + \frac{x}{4}} = 4 - \frac{16}{4+x} = \frac{4x}{4+x}$

9.4.61

$$
\begin{aligned}
\sum_{k=1}^{\infty} (-1)^k \frac{kx^{k+1}}{3^k} &= \sum_{k=1}^{\infty} (-1)^k \frac{k}{3^k} x^{k+1} = \sum_{k=1}^{\infty} k \left(-\frac{1}{3} \right)^k x^{k+1} \\
&= x^2 \sum_{k=1}^{\infty} \left(-\frac{1}{3} \right)^k k x^{k-1} = x^2 \sum_{k=1}^{\infty} \left(-\frac{1}{3} \right)^k \frac{d}{dx}(x^k) \\
&= x^2 \frac{d}{dx} \left(\sum_{k=1}^{\infty} \left(-\frac{x}{3} \right)^k \right) = x^2 \frac{d}{dx} \left(\frac{1}{1 + \frac{x}{3}} \right) = -\frac{3x^2}{(x+3)^2}.
\end{aligned}
$$

9.4.62 By Exercise 53, $\sum_{k=1}^{\infty} \frac{x^k}{k} = -\ln(1-x)$, so $\sum_{k=1}^{\infty} \frac{x^{2k}}{k} = \sum_{k=1}^{\infty} \frac{(x^2)^k}{k} = -\ln(1-x^2)$.

9.4.63 $\sum_{k=2}^{\infty} \frac{k(k-1)x^k}{3^k} = x^2 \sum_{k=2}^{\infty} \frac{k(k-1)x^{k-2}}{3^k} = x^2 \frac{d^2}{dx^2}\left(\sum_{k=2}^{\infty} \frac{x^k}{3^k}\right)$

$= x^2 \frac{d^2}{dx^2}\left(\sum_{k=2}^{\infty} \left(\frac{x}{3}\right)^k\right) = x^2 \frac{d^2}{dx^2}\left(\frac{x^2}{9} \cdot \frac{1}{1-\frac{x}{3}}\right) = x^2 \frac{d^2}{dx^2}\left(\frac{x^2}{9-3x}\right) = x^2 \frac{-6}{(x-3)^3} = \frac{-6x^2}{(x-3)^3}.$

9.4.64 $\sum_{k=2}^{\infty} \frac{x^k}{k(k-1)} = \sum_{k=2}^{\infty} \frac{x^k}{k-1} - \sum_{k=2}^{\infty} \frac{x^k}{k} = x \sum_{k=1}^{\infty} \frac{x^k}{k} - \sum_{k=1}^{\infty} \frac{x^k}{k} + x, = -x\ln(1-x) + \ln(1-x) + x =$
$x + (1-x)\ln(1-x).$

9.4.65

a. False. This is because $\frac{1}{1-x}$ is not continuous at 1, which is in the interval of integration.

b. False. The Ratio Test shows that the radius of convergence for the Taylor series for $\tan^{-1} x$ centered at 0 is 1.

c. True. $\sum_{k=0}^{\infty} \frac{x^k}{k!} = e^x$. Substitute $x = \ln 2$.

9.4.66 The Taylor series for e^{ax} centered at 0 is

$$e^{ax} = 1 + ax + \frac{(ax)^2}{2} + \frac{(ax)^3}{6} + \cdots .$$

We compute that

$$\frac{e^{ax} - 1}{x} = \frac{1}{x}\left(\left(1 + ax + \frac{(ax)^2}{2} + \frac{(ax)^3}{6} + \cdots\right) - 1\right)$$

$$= \frac{1}{x}\left(ax + \frac{(ax)^2}{2} + \frac{(ax)^3}{6} + \cdots\right) = a + \frac{a^2 x}{2} + \frac{a^3 x^2}{6} + \cdots$$

so the limit of $\frac{e^{ax} - 1}{x}$ as $x \to 0$ is a.

9.4.67 The Taylor series for $\sin x$ centered at 0 is

$$\sin x = x - \frac{x^3}{6} + \frac{x^5}{120} - \cdots .$$

We compute that

$$\frac{\sin ax}{\sin bx} = \frac{ax - \frac{(ax)^3}{6} + \frac{(ax)^5}{120} - \cdots}{bx - \frac{(bx)^3}{6} + \frac{(bx)^5}{120} - \cdots}$$

$$= \frac{a - \frac{a^3 x^2}{6} + \frac{a^5 x^4}{120} - \cdots}{b - \frac{b^3 x^2}{6} + \frac{b^5 x^4}{120} - \cdots}$$

so the limit of $\frac{\sin ax}{\sin bx}$ as $x \to 0$ is $\frac{a}{b}$.

9.4.68 The Taylor series for $\sin ax$ centered at 0 is

$$\sin ax = ax - \frac{(ax)^3}{6} + \frac{(ax)^5}{120} - \cdots$$

and the Taylor series for $\tan^{-1} ax$ centered at 0 is

$$\tan^{-1} ax = ax - \frac{(ax)^3}{3} + \frac{(ax)^5}{5} - \cdots .$$

We compute that

$$\frac{\sin ax - \tan^{-1} ax}{bx^3} = \frac{1}{bx^3}\left(\left(ax - \frac{(ax)^3}{6} + \frac{(ax)^5}{120} - \cdots\right) - \left(ax - \frac{(ax)^3}{3} + \frac{(ax)^5}{5} - \cdots\right)\right)$$

$$= \frac{1}{bx^3}\left(\frac{(ax)^3}{6} - \frac{23(ax)^5}{120} + \cdots\right) = \frac{a^3}{6b} - \frac{23a^5}{120b}x^2 + \cdots$$

so the limit of $\frac{\sin ax - \tan^{-1} ax}{bx^3}$ as $x \to 0$ is $\frac{a^3}{6b}$.

9.4.69 Compute instead the limit of the log of this expression, $\lim_{x\to 0} \frac{\ln(\sin x/x)}{x^2}$. If the Taylor expansion of $\ln(\sin x/x)$ is $\sum_{k=0}^{\infty} c_k x^k$, then $\lim_{x\to 0} \frac{\ln(\sin x/x)}{x^2} = \lim_{x\to 0} \sum_{k=0}^{\infty} c_k x^{k-2} = \lim_{x\to 0} c_0 x^{-2} + c_1 x^{-1} + c_2$, because the higher-order terms have positive powers of x and thus approach zero as x does. So compute the terms of the Taylor series of $\ln\left(\frac{\sin x}{x}\right)$ up through the quadratic term. The relevant Taylor series are: $\frac{\sin x}{x} = 1 - \frac{1}{6}x^2 + \frac{1}{120}x^4 - \cdots$, $\ln(1+x) = x - \frac{1}{2}x^2 + \frac{1}{3}x^3 - \cdots$ and we substitute the Taylor series for $\frac{\sin x}{x} - 1$ for x in the Taylor series for $\ln(1+x)$. Because the lowest power of x in the first Taylor series is 2, it follows that only the linear term in the series for $\ln(1+x)$ will give any powers of x that are at most quadratic. The only term that results is $-\frac{1}{6}x^2$. Thus $c_0 = c_1 = 0$ in the above, and $c_2 = -\frac{1}{6}$, so that $\lim_{x\to 0} \frac{\ln(\sin x/x)}{x^2} = -\frac{1}{6}$ and thus $\lim_{x\to 0} \left(\frac{\sin x}{x}\right)^{1/x^2} = e^{-1/6}$.

9.4.70 We can find the Taylor series for $\ln(x + \sqrt{1+x^2})$ by substituting into $\ln(1+t)$ the Taylor series for $x + \sqrt{x^2+1} - 1$. The Taylor series in question are: $x + \sqrt{x^2+1} - 1 = x + \frac{1}{2}x^2 - \frac{1}{8}x^4 + \frac{1}{16}x^6 - \cdots$, $\ln(1+t) = t - \frac{1}{2}t^2 + \frac{1}{3}t^3 - \frac{1}{4}t^4 + \frac{1}{5}t^5 - \frac{1}{6}t^6 + \frac{1}{7}t^7 - \cdots$. Substituting the former into the latter and simplifying (not a simple task!), we obtain $\ln(x + \sqrt{x^2+1}) = x - \frac{1}{6}x^3 + \frac{3}{40}x^5 - \frac{5}{112}x^7 + \cdots$. Using the second definition, start with the Taylor series for $(1+t^2)^{-1/2}$, which is $1 - \frac{1}{2}t^2 + \frac{3}{8}t^4 - \frac{5}{16}t^6 + \cdots$, and integrate it:
$$\int_0^x \left(1 - \tfrac{1}{2}t^2 + \tfrac{3}{8}t^4 - \tfrac{5}{16}t^6 + \ldots\right) dt = \left(t - \tfrac{1}{6}t^3 + \tfrac{3}{40}t^5 - \tfrac{5}{112}t^7 + \ldots\right)\Big|_0^x = x - \tfrac{1}{6}x^3 + \tfrac{3}{40}x^5 - \tfrac{5}{112}x^7 + \cdots.$$

9.4.71 The Taylor series we need are $\cos x = 1 - \frac{1}{2}x^2 + \frac{1}{24}x^4 + \ldots$, $e^t = 1 + t + \frac{1}{2!}t^2 + \frac{1}{3!}t^3 + \frac{1}{4!}t^4 + \ldots$. We are looking for powers of x^3 and x^4 that occur when the first series is substituted for t in the second series. Clearly there will be no odd powers of x, because $\cos x$ has only even powers. Thus the coefficient of x^3 is zero, so that $f^{(3)}(0) = 0$. The coefficient of x^4 comes from the expansion of $1 - \frac{1}{2}x^2 + \frac{1}{24}x^4$ in each term of e^t. Higher powers of x clearly cannot contribute to the coefficient of x^4. Thus consider $\left(1 - \frac{1}{2}x^2 + \frac{1}{24}x^4\right)^k$. The term $-\frac{1}{2}x^2$ generates $\binom{k}{2}$ terms of value $\frac{1}{4}x^4$ for $k \geq 2$, while the other term generates k terms of value $\frac{1}{24}x^4$ for $k \geq 1$. These terms all have to be divided by the $k!$ appearing in the series for e^t. So the total coefficient of x^4 is $\frac{1}{24}\sum_{k=1}^{\infty} \frac{k}{k!} + \frac{1}{4}\sum_{k=2}^{\infty} \binom{k}{2}\frac{1}{k!}$, $= \frac{1}{24}\sum_{k=1}^{\infty} \frac{1}{(k-1)!} + \frac{1}{4}\sum_{k=2}^{\infty} \frac{1}{2\cdot(k-2)!}$, $= \frac{1}{24}\sum_{k=0}^{\infty} \frac{1}{k!} + \frac{1}{8}\sum_{k=0}^{\infty} \frac{1}{k!}$, $= \frac{1}{24}e + \frac{1}{8}e = \frac{e}{6}$. Thus $f^{(4)}(0) = \frac{e}{6}\cdot 4! = 4e$.

9.4.72 The Taylor series for $(1+x)^{-1/3}$ is $(1+x)^{-1/3} = 1 - \frac{1}{3}x + \frac{2}{9}x^2 - \frac{14}{81}x^3 + \frac{35}{243}x^4 - \ldots$, so we want the coefficients of x^3 and x^4 in $(x^2+1)\left(1 - \frac{1}{3}x + \frac{2}{9}x^2 - \frac{14}{81}x^3 + \frac{35}{243}x^4\right)$. The coefficient of x^3 is $-\frac{1}{3} - \frac{14}{81} = -\frac{41}{81}$, and the coefficient of x^4 is $\frac{2}{9} + \frac{35}{243} = \frac{89}{243}$. Thus $f^{(3)}(0) = 6\cdot \frac{-41}{81} = \frac{-82}{27}$, and $f^{(4)}(0) = 24\cdot \frac{89}{243} = \frac{712}{81}$.

9.4.73 The Taylor series for $\sin t^2$ is $\sin t^2 = t^2 - \frac{1}{3!}t^6 + \frac{1}{5!}t^{10} - \ldots$, so that $\int_0^x \sin t^2\, dt = \frac{1}{3}t^3 - \frac{1}{7\cdot 3!}t^7 + \ldots\Big|_0^x = \frac{1}{3}x^3 - \frac{1}{7\cdot 3!}x^7 + \cdots$. Thus $f^{(3)}(0) = \frac{3!}{3} = 2$ and $f^{(4)}(0) = 0$.

9.4.74 $\frac{1}{1+t^4} = 1 - t^4 + t^8 + \ldots$, so that $\int_0^x \frac{1}{1+t^4} dt = t - \frac{1}{5}t^5 + \frac{1}{9}t^9 + \ldots\Big|_0^x = x - \frac{1}{5}x^5 + \cdots$. so that both $f^{(3)}(0)$ and $f^{(4)}(0)$ are zero.

9.4.75 Consider the series $\sum_{k=1}^{\infty} x^k = \frac{x}{1-x}$. Differentiating both sides gives $\frac{1}{(1-x)^2} = \sum_{k=0}^{\infty} kx^{k-1} = \frac{1}{x}\sum_{k=0}^{\infty} kx^k$ so that $\frac{x}{(1-x)^2} = \sum_{k=0}^{\infty} kx^k$. Evaluate both sides at $x = 1/2$ to see that the sum of the series is $\frac{1/2}{(1-1/2)^2} = 2$. Thus the expected number of tosses is 2.

9.4.76

a. $\sum_{k=0}^{\infty} \frac{1}{6}\left(\frac{5}{6}\right)^{2k} = \frac{1}{6}\sum_{k=0}^{\infty} \left(\frac{25}{36}\right)^k = \frac{1}{6}\cdot \frac{1}{1-25/36} = \frac{6}{11}$.

b. Consider the series $\sum_{k=1}^{\infty} x^k = \frac{x}{1-x}$. Differentiating both sides gives $\frac{1}{(1-x)^2} = \sum_{k=1}^{\infty} kx^{k-1}$ Evaluating at $x = 5/6$ and multiplying the result by $1/6$, we get $\frac{1}{6}\cdot \frac{1}{(1-5/6)^2} = 6$.

9.4.77

a. We look first for a Taylor series for $(1 - k^2 \sin^2 \theta)^{-1/2}$. Because $(1 - k^2 x^2)^{-1/2} = (1 - (kx)^2)^{-1/2} = \sum_{i=0}^{\infty} \binom{-1/2}{i} (kx)^{2i}$, and $\sin \theta = \theta - \frac{1}{3!}\theta^3 + \frac{1}{5!}\theta^5 - \dots$, substituting the second series into the first gives
$$\frac{1}{\sqrt{1 - k^2 \sin^2 \theta}} = 1 + \frac{1}{2}k^2 \theta^2 + \left(-\frac{1}{6}k^2 + \frac{3}{8}k^4\right)\theta^4 + \left(\frac{1}{45}k^2 - \frac{1}{4}k^4 + \frac{5}{16}k^6\right)\theta^6 + \left(\frac{-1}{630}k^2 + \frac{3}{40}k^4 - \frac{5}{16}k^6 + \frac{35}{128}k^8\right)\theta^8 + \dots.$$
Integrating with respect to θ and evaluating at $\pi/2$ (the value of the antiderivative is 0 at 0) gives $\frac{1}{2}\pi + \frac{1}{48}k^2 \pi^3 + \frac{1}{160}\left(-\frac{1}{6}k^2 + \frac{3}{8}k^4\right)\pi^5 + \frac{1}{896}\left(\frac{1}{45}k^2 - \frac{1}{4}k^4 + \frac{5}{16}k^6\right)\pi^7 + \frac{1}{4608}\left(-\frac{1}{630}k^2 + \frac{3}{40}k^4 - \frac{5}{16}k^6 + \frac{35}{128}k^8\right)\pi^9$. Evaluating these terms for $k = 0.1$ gives $F(0.1) \approx 1.574749680$. (The true value is approximately 1.574745562.)

b. The terms above, with coefficients of k^n converted to decimal approximations, is $1.5707 + .3918 \cdot k^2 + .3597 \cdot k^4 - .9682 \cdot k^6 + 1.7689 \cdot k^8$. The coefficients are all less than 2 and do not appear to be increasing very much if at all, so if we want the result to be accurate to within 10^{-3} we should probably take n such that $k^n < \frac{1}{2} \times 10^{-3} = .0005$, so $n = 4$ for this value of k.

c. By the above analysis, we would need a larger n because $0.2^n > 0.1^n$ for a given value of n.

9.4.78

a. $\frac{\sin t}{t} = \sum_{k=0}^{\infty} (-1)^k \frac{x^{2k}}{(2k+1)!} = 1 - \frac{x^2}{3!} + \frac{x^4}{5!} - \dots$.

b. $\int_0^x \frac{\sin t}{t} \, dt = \sum_{k=0}^{\infty} \int_0^x (-1)^k \frac{t^{2k}}{(2k+1)!} \, dt = \sum_{k=0}^{\infty} (-1)^k \frac{x^{2k+1}}{(2k+1)(2k+1)!}$.

c. This is an alternating series, so we want n such that $a_{n+1} < 10^{-3}$, or $\frac{0.5^{2n+3}}{(2n+3)(2n+3)!} < 10^{-3}$ (resp. $\frac{1^{2n+3}}{(2n+3)(2n+3)!} < 10^{-3}$), which gives $n = 1$ (resp. $n = 2$). Thus $\mathrm{Si}(0.5) \approx \frac{0.5}{1} - \frac{0.5^3}{3 \cdot 3!} \approx 0.4930555556$, $\mathrm{Si}(1.0) \approx 1 - \frac{1}{3 \cdot 3!} + \frac{1}{5 \cdot 5!} \approx 0.9461111111$.

9.4.79

a. By the Fundamental Theorem, $S'(x) = \sin x^2$, $C'(x) = \cos x^2$.

b. The relevant Taylor series are $\sin t^2 = t^2 - \frac{1}{3!}t^6 + \frac{1}{5!}t^{10} - \frac{1}{7!}t^{14} + \dots$, and $\cos t^2 = 1 - \frac{1}{2!}t^4 + \frac{1}{4!}t^8 - \frac{1}{6!}t^{12} + \dots$. Integrating, we have $S(x) = \frac{1}{3}x^3 - \frac{1}{7 \cdot 3!}x^7 + \frac{1}{11 \cdot 5!}x^{11} - \frac{1}{15 \cdot 7!}x^{15} + \dots$, and $C(x) = x - \frac{1}{5 \cdot 2!}x^5 + \frac{1}{9 \cdot 4!}x^9 - \frac{1}{13 \cdot 6!}x^{13} + \dots$.

c. $S(0.05) \approx \frac{1}{3}(0.05)^3 - \frac{1}{42}(0.05)^7 + \frac{1}{1320}(0.05)^{11} - \frac{1}{75600}(0.05)^{15} \approx 4.166664807 \times 10^{-5}$. $C(-0.25) \approx (-0.25) - \frac{1}{10}(-0.25)^5 + \frac{1}{216}(-0.25)^9 - \frac{1}{9360}(-0.25)^{13} \approx -.2499023616$.

d. The series is alternating. Because $a_{n+1} = \frac{1}{(4n+7)(2n+3)!}(0.05)^{4n+7}$, and this is less than 10^{-4} for $n = 0$, only one term is required.

e. The series is alternating. Because $a_{n+1} = \frac{1}{(4n+5)(2n+2)!}(0.25)^{4n+5}$, and this is less than 10^{-6} for $n = 1$, two terms are required.

9.4.80

a. $\frac{d}{dx}\mathrm{erf}(x) = \frac{2}{\sqrt{\pi}}(e^{-x^2})$.

b. $e^{-t^2} = 1 - t^2 + \frac{t^4}{2!} - \frac{t^6}{3!} + \dots = \sum_{k=0}^{\infty} (-1)^k \frac{t^{2k}}{k!}$, so that the Maclaurin series for the error function is $\mathrm{erf}(x) = \frac{2}{\sqrt{\pi}}\left(x - \frac{x^3}{3} + \frac{x^5}{5 \cdot 2!} - \frac{x^7}{7 \cdot 3!} + \dots\right)$.

c. $\mathrm{erf}(0.15) \approx \frac{2}{\sqrt{\pi}}\left(0.15 - \frac{0.15^3}{3} + \frac{0.15^5}{10} - \frac{0.15^7}{42}\right) \approx 0.1679959712$.

$\mathrm{erf}(-0.09) \approx \frac{2}{\sqrt{\pi}}\left(-0.09 + \frac{0.09^3}{3} - \frac{0.09^5}{10} + \frac{0.09^7}{42}\right) \approx -.1012805939$.

d. The first omitted term in each case is $\frac{x^9}{9 \cdot 5!} = \frac{x^9}{1080}$. For $x = 0.15$, this is $\approx 3.56 \times 10^{-11}$. For $x = -0.09$, this is (in absolute value) $\approx 3.59 \times 10^{-13}$.

9.4.81

a. $J_0(x) = 1 - \frac{1}{4}x^2 + \frac{1}{16 \cdot 2!^2}x^4 - \frac{1}{2^6 \cdot 3!^2}x^6 + \dots$.

b. Using the Ratio Test: $\left| \frac{a_{k+1}}{a_k} \right| = \frac{x^{2k+2}}{2^{2k+2}((k+1)!)^2} \cdot \frac{2^{2k}(k!)^2}{x^{2k}} = \frac{x^2}{4(k+1)^2}$, which has limit 0 as $k \to \infty$ for any x. Thus the radius of convergence is infinite and the interval of convergence is $(-\infty, \infty)$.

c. Starting only with terms up through x^8, we have $J_0(x) = 1 - \frac{1}{4}x^2 + \frac{1}{64}x^4 - \frac{1}{2304}x^6 + \frac{1}{147456}x^8 + \dots$, $J_0'(x) = -\frac{1}{2}x + \frac{1}{16}x^3 - \frac{1}{384}x^5 + \frac{1}{18432}x^7 + \dots$, $J_0''(x) = -\frac{1}{2} + \frac{3}{16}x^2 - \frac{5}{384}x^4 + \frac{7}{18432}x^6 + \dots$ so that $x^2 J_0(x) = x^2 - \frac{1}{4}x^4 + \frac{1}{64}x^6 - \frac{1}{2304}x^8 + \frac{1}{147456}x^{10} + \dots$, $x J_0'(x) = -\frac{1}{2}x^2 + \frac{1}{16}x^4 - \frac{1}{384}x^6 + \frac{1}{18432}x^8 + \dots$, $x^2 J_0''(x) = -\frac{1}{2}x^2 + \frac{3}{16}x^4 - \frac{5}{384}x^6 + \frac{7}{18432}x^8 + \dots$, and $x^2 J_0''(x) + x J_0'(x) + x^2 J_0(x) = 0$.

9.4.82 $\sec x = \frac{1}{\cos x} = \frac{1}{1 - \frac{x^2}{2} + \frac{x^4}{24} + \dots} = 1 + \frac{1}{2}x^2 + \frac{5}{24}x^4 + \frac{61}{720}x^6 + \dots$

9.4.83

a. The power series for $\cos x$ has only even powers of x, so that the power series has the same value evaluated at $-x$ as it does at x.

b. The power series for $\sin x$ has only odd powers of x, so that evaluating it at $-x$ gives the opposite of its value at x.

9.4.84 Long division gives $\csc x = \frac{1}{x} + \frac{1}{6}x + \frac{7}{360}x^3 + \dots$, so that $\csc x \approx \frac{1}{x} + \frac{1}{6}x$ as $x \to 0^+$.

9.4.85

a. Because $f(a) = g(a) = 0$, we use the Taylor series for $f(x)$ and $g(x)$ centered at a to compute that

$$
\begin{aligned}
\lim_{x \to a} \frac{f(x)}{g(x)} &= \lim_{x \to a} \frac{f(a) + f'(a)(x-a) + \frac{1}{2}f''(a)(x-a)^2 + \cdots}{g(a) + g'(a)(x-a) + \frac{1}{2}g''(a)(x-a)^2 + \cdots} \\
&= \lim_{x \to a} \frac{f'(a)(x-a) + \frac{1}{2}f''(a)(x-a)^2 + \cdots}{g'(a)(x-a) + \frac{1}{2}g''(a)(x-a)^2 + \cdots} \\
&= \lim_{x \to a} \frac{f'(a) + \frac{1}{2}f''(a)(x-a) + \cdots}{g'(a) + \frac{1}{2}g''(a)(x-a) + \cdots} = \frac{f'(a)}{g'(a)}.
\end{aligned}
$$

Because $f'(x)$ and $g'(x)$ are assumed to be continuous at a and $g'(a) \neq 0$,

$$
\frac{f'(a)}{g'(a)} = \lim_{x \to a} \frac{f'(x)}{g'(x)}
$$

and we have that

$$
\lim_{x \to a} \frac{f(x)}{g(x)} = \lim_{x \to a} \frac{f'(x)}{g'(x)}
$$

which is one form of L'Hôpital's Rule.

b. Because $f(a) = g(a) = f'(a) = g'(a) = 0$, we use the Taylor series for $f(x)$ and $g(x)$ centered at a to compute that

$$
\begin{aligned}
\lim_{x \to a} \frac{f(x)}{g(x)} &= \lim_{x \to a} \frac{f(a) + f'(a)(x-a) + \frac{1}{2}f''(a)(x-a)^2 + \frac{1}{6}f'''(a)(x-a)^3 + \cdots}{g(a) + g'(a)(x-a) + \frac{1}{2}g''(a)(x-a)^2 + \frac{1}{6}g'''(a)(x-a)^3 + \cdots} \\
&= \lim_{x \to a} \frac{\frac{1}{2}f''(a)(x-a)^2 + \frac{1}{6}f'''(a)(x-a)^3 + \cdots}{\frac{1}{2}g''(a)(x-a)^2 + \frac{1}{6}g'''(a)(x-a)^3 + \cdots} \\
&= \lim_{x \to a} \frac{\frac{1}{2}f''(a) + \frac{1}{6}f'''(a)(x-a) + \cdots}{\frac{1}{2}g''(a) + \frac{1}{6}g'''(a)(x-a) + \cdots} = \frac{f''(a)}{g''(a)}.
\end{aligned}
$$

Because $f''(x)$ and $g''(x)$ are assumed to be continuous at a and $g''(a) \neq 0$,

$$\frac{f''(a)}{g''(a)} = \lim_{x \to a} \frac{f''(x)}{g''(x)}$$

and we have that

$$\lim_{x \to a} \frac{f(x)}{g(x)} = \lim_{x \to a} \frac{f''(x)}{g''(x)}$$

which is consistent with two applications of L'Hôpital's Rule.

9.4.86

a. Clearly $x = \sin s$ because BE, of length x, is the side opposite the angle measured by s in a right triangle with unit length hypotenuse.

b. In the formula $\frac{1}{2}r^2\theta$ for the formula for the area of a circular sector, we have $r = 1$, and $\theta = s$, so that the area is in fact $\frac{s}{2}$. But the area can also be expressed as an integral as follows: the area of the sector is the area under the circle between P and F (i.e. the area of the region $PAEF$), minus the area of the right triangle PEF. The area of the right triangle is $\frac{1}{2}x\sqrt{1 - x^2}$ by the Pythagorean theorem and the formula for the area of a triangle. Equating these two formulae for the area of the sector, we have $\frac{s}{2} = \int_0^x \sqrt{1 - t^2}\,dt - \frac{1}{2}x\sqrt{1 - x^2}$, so $s = 2\int_0^x \sqrt{1 - t^2}\,dt - x\sqrt{1 - x^2}$.

c. The Taylor series for $\sqrt{1 - t^2}$ is $1 - \frac{1}{2}t^2 - \frac{1}{8}t^4 - \frac{1}{16}t^6 - \frac{5}{128}t^8 - \cdots$. Integrating and evaluating at x we have $s = \sin^{-1} x = 2\left(x - \frac{1}{6}x^3 - \frac{1}{40}x^5 - \frac{1}{112}x^7 - \frac{5}{1152}x^9\right) - x\left(1 - \frac{1}{2}x^2 - \frac{1}{8}x^4 - \frac{1}{16}x^6 - \frac{5}{128}x^8\right) + \cdots = x + \frac{1}{6}x^3 + \frac{3}{40}x^5 + \frac{5}{112}x^7 + \frac{35}{1152}x^9 + \cdots$.

d. Suppose $x = \sin s = a_0 + a_1 s + a_2 s^2 + \cdots$. Then $x = \sin(\sin^{-1}(x)) = a_0 + a_1(x + \frac{1}{6}x^3 + \frac{3}{40}x^5 + \dots) + a_2((x + \frac{1}{6}x^3 + \frac{3}{40}x^5 + \dots)^2 + \cdots$. Equating coefficients yields $a_0 = 0$, $a_1 = 1$, $a_2 = 0$, $a_3 = \frac{-1}{6}$, and so on.

Chapter Nine Review

1

a. True. The approximations tend to get better as n increases in size, and also when the value being approximated is closer to the center of the series. Because 2.1 is closer to 2 than 2.2 is, and because $3 > 2$, we should have $|p_3(2.1) - f(2.1)| < |p_2(2.2) - f(2.2)|$.

b. False. The interval of convergence may or may not include the endpoints.

c. True. The interval of convergence is an interval centered at 0, and the endpoints may or may not be included.

d. True. Because $f(x)$ is a polynomial, all its derivatives vanish after a certain point (in this case, $f^{(12)}(x)$ is the last nonzero derivative).

2 $p_3(x) = 2x - \frac{(2x)^3}{3!}$.

3 $p_2(x) = 1$.

4 $p_2(x) = 1 - x + \frac{x^2}{2}$.

5 $p_3(x) = x - \frac{x^2}{2} + \frac{x^3}{3}$.

6 $p_2(x) = \frac{\sqrt{2}}{2}\left(1 - (x - \pi/4) - \frac{1}{2}(x - \pi/4)^2\right)$.

7 $p_2(x) = x - 1 - \frac{1}{2}(x-1)^2$.

8 $p_4(x) = 8x^3/3! + 2x = 4x^3/3 + 2x$.

9 $p_3(x) = \frac{5}{4} + \frac{3(x - \ln 2)}{4} + \frac{5(x - \ln 2)^2}{8} + \frac{(x - \ln 2)^3}{8}$.

10

   a. $p_0(x) = p_1(x) = 1$, and $p_2(x) = 1 - \frac{x^2}{2}$.

   b.

n	$p_n(-0.08)$	$\|p_n(-0.08) - \cos(-0.08)\|$
0	1	3.2×10^{-3}
1	1	3.2×10^{-3}
2	0.997	1.7×10^{-6}

11

   a. $p_0(x) = 1$, $p_1(x) = 1 + x$, and $p_2(x) = 1 + x + \frac{x^2}{2}$.

   b.

n	$p_n(-0.08)$	$\|p_n(-0.08) - e^{-0.08}\|$
0	1	7.7×10^{-2}
1	0.92	3.1×10^{-3}
2	0.923	8.4×10^{-5}

12

   a. $p_0(x) = 1$, $p_1(x) = 1 + \frac{1}{2}x$, and $p_2(x) = 1 + \frac{1}{2}x - \frac{1}{8}x^2$.

   b.

n	$p_n(0.08)$	$\|p_n(0.08) - \sqrt{1 + 0.08}\|$
0	1	3.9×10^{-2}
1	1.04	7.7×10^{-4}
2	1.039	3.0×10^{-5}

13

   a. $p_0(x) = \frac{\sqrt{2}}{2}$, $p_1(x) = \frac{\sqrt{2}}{2}(1 + (x - \pi/4))$, and $p_2(x) = \frac{\sqrt{2}}{2}\left(1 + (x - \pi/4) - \frac{1}{2}(x - \pi/4)^2\right)$.

   b.

n	$p_n(\pi/5)$	$\|p_n(\pi/5) - \sin(\pi/5)\|$
0	0.707	1.2×10^{-1}
1	0.596	8.2×10^{-3}
2	0.587	4.7×10^{-4}

14 The bound is $|R_n(x)| \le M\frac{|x|^{n+1}}{(n+1)!}$, where M is a bound for $|e^x|$ (because e^x is its own derivative) on $[-1, 1]$. Thus take $M = 3$ so that $|R_3(x)| \le \frac{3x^4}{4!} = \frac{x^4}{8}$. But $|x| < 1$, so this is at most $\frac{1}{8}$.

15 The derivatives of $\sin x$ are bounded in magnitude by 1, so $|R_n(x)| \le M\frac{|x|^{n+1}}{(n+1)!} \le \frac{|x|^{n+1}}{(n+1)!}$. But $|x| < \pi$, so $|R_3(x)| \le \frac{\pi^4}{24}$.

16 The third derivative of $\ln(1-x)$ is $\frac{-2}{(x-1)^3}$, which is bounded in magnitude by 16 on $|x| < 1/2$ (at $x = 1/2$). Thus $|R_3(x)| \le 16\frac{|x|^4}{4!} \le 16\frac{1}{2^4 4!} = \frac{1}{4!}$.

17 Using the Ratio Test, $\lim\limits_{k \to \infty} \left| \frac{a_{k+1}}{a_k} \right| = \lim\limits_{k \to \infty} \left| \frac{(k+1)^2 x^{k+1}}{(k+1)!} \cdot \frac{k!}{k^2 x^k} \right| = \lim\limits_{k \to \infty} \left(\frac{k+1}{k} \right)^2 \frac{|x|}{k+1} = 0$, so the interval of convergence is $(-\infty, \infty)$.

18 Using the Ratio Test, $\lim\limits_{k \to \infty} \left| \frac{a_{k+1}}{a_k} \right| = \lim\limits_{k \to \infty} \left| \frac{x^{4k+4}}{(k+1)^2} \cdot \frac{k^2}{x^{4k}} \right| = \lim\limits_{k \to \infty} \left(\frac{k}{k+1} \right)^2 x^4 = x^4$, so that the radius of convergence is 1. Because $\sum \frac{1}{k^2}$ converges, the given power series converges at both endpoints, so its interval of convergence is $[-1, 1]$.

19 Using the Ratio Test, $\lim\limits_{k \to \infty} \frac{a_{k+1}}{a_k} = \lim\limits_{k \to \infty} \left| \frac{(x+1)^{2k+2}}{(k+1)!} \cdot \frac{k!}{(x+1)^{2k}} \right| = \lim\limits_{k \to \infty} \frac{1}{k+1}(x+1)^2 = 0$, so the interval of convergence is $(-\infty, \infty)$.

20 Using the Ratio Test, $\lim\limits_{k \to \infty} \left| \frac{a_{k+1}}{a_k} \right| = \lim\limits_{k \to \infty} \left| \frac{(x-1)^{k+1}}{(k+1)5^{k+1}} \cdot \frac{k5^k}{(x-1)^k} \right| = \lim\limits_{k \to \infty} \frac{k}{5k+5}|x-1| = \frac{1}{5}(|x-1|)$, so the series converges when $|1/5(x-1)| < 1$, or $-5 < x-1 < 5$, so that $-4 < x < 6$. At $x = -4$, the series is the alternating harmonic series. At $x = 6$, it is the harmonic series, so the interval of convergence is $[-4, 6)$.

21 By the Root Test, $\lim\limits_{k \to \infty} \sqrt[k]{|a_k|} = \lim\limits_{k \to \infty} \left(\frac{|x|}{9} \right)^3 = \frac{|x^3|}{729}$, so the series converges for $|x| < 9$. The series given by letting $x = \pm 9$ are both divergent by the Divergence Test. Thus, $(-9, 9)$ is the interval of convergence.

22 By the Ratio Test, $\lim\limits_{k \to \infty} \left| \frac{a_{k+1}}{a_k} \right| = \lim\limits_{k \to \infty} \left| \frac{(x+2)^{k+1}}{\sqrt{k+1}} \cdot \frac{\sqrt{k}}{(x+2)^k} \right| = \lim\limits_{k \to \infty} \sqrt{\frac{k}{k+1}}(|x+2|) = |x+2|$, so that the series converges for $|x+2| < 1$, so $-3 < x < -1$. At $x = -3$, we have a series which converges by the Alternating Series Test. At $x = -1$, we have the divergent p–series with $p = 1/2$. Thus, $[-3, -1)$ is the interval of convergence.

23 By the Ratio Test, $\lim\limits_{k \to \infty} \left| \frac{(x+2)^{k+1}}{2^{k+1}\ln(k+1)} \cdot \frac{2^k \ln k}{(x+2)^k} \right| = \lim\limits_{k \to \infty} \frac{\ln k}{2\ln(k+1)}|x+2| = \frac{|x+2|}{2}$. The radius of convergence is thus 2, and a check of the endpoints gives the divergent series $\sum \frac{1}{\ln k}$ at $x = 0$ and the convergent alternating series $\sum \frac{(-1)^k}{\ln k}$ at $x = -4$. The interval of convergence is therefore $[-4, 0)$.

24 By the Ratio Test, $\lim\limits_{k \to \infty} \left| \frac{x^{2k+3}}{2k+3} \cdot \frac{2k+1}{x^{2k+1}} \right| = x^2$. The radius of convergence is thus 1. At each endpoint we have a divergent series, so the interval of convergence is $(-1, 1)$.

25 The Maclaurin series for $f(x)$ is $\sum_{k=0}^\infty x^{2k}$. By the Root Test, this converges for $|x^2| < 1$, so $-1 < x < 1$. It diverges at both endpoints, so the interval of convergence is $(-1, 1)$.

26 The Maclaurin series for $f(x)$ is determined by replacing x by $(-x)^3$ in the power series for $\frac{1}{1-x}$, so it is $\sum_{k=0}^\infty (-1)^k x^{3k}$. The radius of convergence is still 1. The series diverges at both endpoints, so the interval of convergence is $(-1, 1)$.

27 The Maclaurin series for $f(x)$ is $\sum_{k=0}^\infty (-5x)^k = \sum_{k=0}^\infty (-5)^k x^k$. By the Root Test, this has radius of convergence $1/5$. Checking the endpoints, we obtain an interval of convergence of $(-1/5, 1/5)$.

28 Replace x by $-x$ in the original power series, and multiply the result by $10x$, to get the Maclaurin series for $f(x)$, which is $\sum_{k=0}^\infty (-1)^k 10 x^{k+1}$. By the Ratio Test, the radius of convergence is 1. Checking the endpoints, we obtain an interval of convergence of $(-1, 1)$.

29 Note that $\frac{1}{1-10x} = \sum_{k=0}^{\infty}(10x)^k$, so $\frac{1}{10} \cdot \frac{1}{1-10x} = \frac{1}{10}\sum_{k=0}^{\infty}(10x)^k$. Taking the derivative of $\frac{1}{10} \cdot \frac{1}{1-10x}$ gives $f(x)$. Thus, the Maclaurin series for $f(x)$ is $\frac{1}{10}\sum_{k=1}^{\infty}10k(10x)^{k-1} = \sum_{k=1}^{\infty}k(10x)^{k-1}$. Using the Ratio Test, we see that the radius of convergence is $1/10$, and checking endpoints we obtain an interval of convergence of $(-1/10, 1/10)$.

30 Integrating $\frac{1}{1-x}$ and then replacing x by $4x$ gives $-f(x)$, so the series for $f(x)$ is $-\sum_{k=0}^{\infty}\frac{1}{k+1}(4x)^{k+1}$. The Ratio Test shows that the series has a radius of convergence of $1/4$; checking the endpoints, we obtain an interval of convergence of $[-1/4, 1/4)$.

31 The first three terms are $1 + 3x + \frac{9x^2}{2}$. The series is $\sum_{k=0}^{\infty}\frac{(3x)^k}{k!}$.

32 The first three terms are $1 - (x-1) + (x-1)^2$. The series is $\sum_{k=0}^{\infty}(-1)^k(x-1)^k$.

33 The first three terms are $-(x - \pi/2) + \frac{1}{6}(x-\pi/2)^3 - \frac{1}{120}(x-\pi/2)^5$. The series is

$$\sum_{k=0}^{\infty}(-1)^{k+1}\frac{1}{(2k+1)!}\left(x - \frac{\pi}{2}\right)^{2k+1}.$$

34 The first three terms for $\frac{1}{1+x}$ are $1 - x + x^2$, so the first three terms of $x^2 \cdot \frac{1}{1+x}$ are $x^2 - x^3 + x^4$. The series is $\sum_{k=0}^{\infty}(-1)^k x^{k+2}$.

35 The first three terms are $4x - \frac{1}{3}(4x)^3 + \frac{1}{5}(4x)^5$. The series is $\sum_{k=0}^{\infty}(-1)^k\frac{(4x)^{2k+1}}{2k+1}$.

36 The nth derivative of $f(x) = \sin(2x)$ is $\pm 2^n$ times either $\sin 2x$ or $\cos 2x$. Evaluated at $-\frac{\pi}{2}$, the even derivatives are therefore zero, and the $(2n+1)^{\text{st}}$ derivative is $(-1)^{n+1}2^{2n+1}$. The Taylor series for $\sin 2x$ around $x = -\frac{\pi}{2}$ is thus $-2\left(x + \frac{\pi}{2}\right) + \frac{2^3}{3!}\left(x + \frac{\pi}{2}\right)^3 - \frac{2^5}{5!}\left(x + \frac{\pi}{2}\right)^5 + \cdots$, and the general series is $\sum_{k=0}^{\infty}(-1)^{k+1}\frac{2^{2k+1}}{(2k+1)!}\left(x + \frac{\pi}{2}\right)^{2k+1}$.

37 The nth derivative of $\cosh 3x$ at $x = 0$ is 0 if n is odd and is 3^n if n is even. The first 3 terms of the series are thus $1 + \frac{9x^2}{2!} + \frac{81x^4}{4!}$. The whole series can be written as $\sum_{k=0}^{\infty}\frac{(3x)^{2k}}{(2k)!}$.

38 $f(0) = \frac{1}{4}$, $f'(x) = \frac{-2x}{(x^2+4)^2}$, so $f'(0) = 0$. $f''(x) = \frac{6x^2-8}{(x^2+4)^3}$, so $f''(0) = -\frac{1}{8}$. $f'''(0) = 0$, and $f''''(0) = \frac{3}{8}$. The first three terms are $\frac{1}{4} - \frac{x^2}{16} + \frac{x^4}{64}$. The series is given by $\sum_{k=0}^{\infty}\frac{(-1)^k x^{2k}}{4^{k+1}}$.

39 $f(x) = \binom{1/3}{0} + \binom{1/3}{1}x + \binom{1/3}{2}x^2 + \cdots = 1 + \frac{1}{3}x - \frac{1}{9}x^2 + \cdots$.

40 $f(x) = \binom{-1/2}{0} + \binom{-1/2}{1}x + \binom{-1/2}{2}x^2 + \cdots = 1 - \frac{1}{2}x + \frac{3}{8}x^2 + \cdots$.

41 $f(x) = \binom{-3}{0} + \binom{-3}{1}\frac{x}{2} + \binom{-3}{2}\frac{x^2}{4} + \cdots = 1 - \frac{3}{2}x + \frac{3}{2}x^2 + \cdots$.

42 $f(x) = \binom{-5}{0} + \binom{-5}{1}(2x) + \binom{-5}{2}(2x)^2 + \cdots = 1 - 10x + 60x^2 + \cdots$.

43 $R_n(x) = \frac{(-1)^{n+1}e^{-c}}{(n+1)!}x^{n+1}$ for some c between 0 and x, and $\lim_{n\to\infty}|R_n(x)| \le e^{-|x|}\lim_{n\to\infty}\frac{|x|^{n+1}}{(n+1)!} = 0$, because $n!$ grows faster than $|x|^n$ as $n \to \infty$ for all x.

44 $R_n(x) = \frac{f^{(n+1)}(c)}{(n+1)!}x^{n+1}$ for some c between 0 and x. Because all derivatives of $\sin x$ are bounded in magnitude by 1, we have $\lim_{n\to\infty}|R_n(x)| \le \lim_{n\to\infty}\frac{|x|^{n+1}}{(n+1)!} = 0$ because $n!$ grows faster than $|x|^n$ as $n \to \infty$ for all x.

45 $R_n(x) = \frac{f^{(n+1)}(c)}{(n+1)!}x^{n+1}$ for some c in $(-1/2, 1/2)$. Now, $\left|f^{(n+1)}(c)\right| = \frac{n!}{(1+c)^{n+1}}$, so $\lim_{n\to\infty}|R_n(x)| \le \lim_{n\to\infty}(2|x|)^{n+1} \cdot \frac{1}{n+1} \le \lim_{n\to\infty}1^{n+1}\frac{1}{n+1} = 0$.

46 $R_n(x) = \frac{f^{(n+1)}(c)}{(n+1)!}x^{n+1}$ for some c in $(-1/2, 1/2)$. Now the $(n+1)^{\text{st}}$ derivative of $(\sqrt{1+x})$ is $\pm\frac{1\cdot 3\cdot 5\cdots(2n-1)}{2^{n+1}(1+x)^{(2n+1)/2}}$, so for c in $(-1/2, 1/2)$, this is bounded in magnitude by $\frac{1\cdot 3\cdot 5\cdots(2n-1)}{2^{n+1}(1/2)^{(2n+1)/2}} = \frac{1\cdot 3\cdot 5\cdots(2n-1)}{2^{1/2}}$, and thus

$$\lim_{n\to\infty}|R_n(x)| = \lim_{n\to\infty}\left|\frac{f^{(n+1)}(c)}{(n+1)!}x^{n+1}\right|$$

$$\leq \lim_{n\to\infty}\frac{1\cdot 3\cdot 5\cdot(2n-1)}{\sqrt{2}}\cdot\frac{1}{2^{n+1}\cdot(n+1)!}$$

$$= \lim_{n\to\infty}\frac{1\cdot 3\cdot 5\cdots(2n-1)}{\sqrt{2}}\cdot\frac{1}{2\cdot 4\cdot 6\cdots(2n+2)}$$

$$= \lim_{n\to\infty}\left(\frac{1}{\sqrt{2}}\cdot\frac{1}{2}\cdot\frac{3}{4}\cdots\frac{2n-1}{2n}\cdot\frac{1}{2n+2}\right) = 0.$$

for x in $(-1/2, 1/2)$.

47 The Taylor series for $\cos x$ centered at 0 is

$$\cos x = 1 - \frac{x^2}{2} + \frac{x^4}{24} - \frac{x^6}{720} + \cdots.$$

We compute that

$$\frac{x^2/2 - 1 + \cos x}{x^4} = \frac{1}{x^4}\left(x^2/2 - 1 + \left(1 - \frac{x^2}{2} + \frac{x^4}{24} - \frac{x^6}{720} + \cdots\right)\right)$$

$$= \frac{1}{x^4}\left(\frac{x^4}{24} - \frac{x^6}{720} + \cdots\right) = \frac{1}{24} - \frac{x^2}{720} + \cdots$$

so the limit of $\dfrac{x^2/2 - 1 + \cos x}{x^4}$ as $x \to 0$ is $\dfrac{1}{24}$.

48 The Taylor series for $\sin x$ centered at 0 is

$$\sin x = x - \frac{x^3}{6} + \frac{x^5}{120} - \frac{x^7}{5040} + \cdots$$

and the Taylor series for $\tan^{-1} x$ centered at 0 is

$$\tan^{-1} x = x - \frac{x^3}{3} + \frac{x^5}{5} - \frac{x^7}{7} + \cdots.$$

We compute that

$$\frac{2\sin x - \tan^{-1} x - x}{2x^5}$$

$$= \frac{1}{2x^5}\left(2\left(x - \frac{x^3}{6} + \frac{x^5}{120} - \frac{x^7}{5040} + \cdots\right) - \left(x - \frac{x^3}{3} + \frac{x^5}{5} - \frac{x^7}{7} + \cdots\right) - x\right)$$

$$= \frac{1}{2x^5}\left(\frac{11x^5}{60} + \frac{359x^7}{2520} - \cdots\right) = -\frac{11}{120} + \frac{359x^2}{5040} - \cdots$$

so the limit of $\dfrac{2\sin x - \tan^{-1} x - x}{2x^5}$ as $x \to 0$ is $-\dfrac{11}{120}$.

49 The Taylor series for $\ln(x-3)$ centered at 4 is

$$\ln(x-3) = (x-4) - \frac{1}{2}(x-4)^2 + \frac{1}{3}(x-4)^3 - \cdots.$$

We compute that

$$
\begin{aligned}
\frac{\ln(x-3)}{x^2-16} &= \frac{1}{(x-4)(x+4)}\left((x-4)-\frac{1}{2}(x-4)^2+\frac{1}{3}(x-4)^3-\cdots\right)\\
&= \frac{1}{(x-4)(x+4)}\left((x-4)\left(1-\frac{1}{2}(x-4)+\frac{1}{3}(x-4)^2-\cdots\right)\right)\\
&= \frac{1}{x+4}\left(1-\frac{1}{2}(x-4)+\frac{1}{3}(x-4)^2-\cdots\right)
\end{aligned}
$$

so the limit of $\dfrac{\ln(x-3)}{x^2-16}$ as $x\to 4$ is $\dfrac{1}{8}$.

50 The Taylor series for $\sqrt{1+2x}$ centered at 0 is

$$
\sqrt{1+2x}=1+x-\frac{x^2}{2}+\frac{x^3}{2}-\cdots.
$$

We compute that

$$
\begin{aligned}
\frac{\sqrt{1+2x}-1-x}{x^2} &= \frac{1}{x^2}\left(\left(1+x-\frac{x^2}{2}+\frac{x^3}{2}-\cdots\right)-1-x\right)\\
&= \frac{1}{x^2}\left(-\frac{x^2}{2}+\frac{x^3}{2}-\cdots\right)=-\frac{1}{2}+\frac{x}{2}-\cdots
\end{aligned}
$$

so the limit of $\dfrac{\sqrt{1+2x}-1-x}{x^2}$ as $x\to 0$ is $-\dfrac{1}{2}$.

51 The Taylor series for $\sec x$ centered at 0 is

$$
\sec x=1+\frac{x^2}{2}+\frac{5x^4}{24}+\frac{61x^6}{720}+\cdots
$$

and the Taylor series for $\cos x$ centered at 0 is

$$
\cos x=1-\frac{x^2}{2}+\frac{x^4}{24}-\frac{x^6}{720}+\cdots.
$$

We compute that

$$
\begin{aligned}
&\frac{\sec x-\cos x-x^2}{x^4}\\
&= \frac{1}{x^4}\left(\left(1+\frac{x^2}{2}+\frac{5x^4}{24}+\frac{61x^6}{720}+\cdots\right)-\left(1-\frac{x^2}{2}+\frac{x^4}{24}-\frac{x^6}{720}+\cdots\right)-x^2\right)\\
&= \frac{1}{x^4}\left(\frac{x^4}{6}+\frac{31x^6}{360}+\cdots\right)=\frac{1}{6}+\frac{31x^2}{360}+\cdots
\end{aligned}
$$

so the limit of $\dfrac{\sec x-\cos x-x^2}{x^4}$ as $x\to 0$ is $\dfrac{1}{6}$.

52 The Taylor series for $(1+x)^{-2}$ centered at 0 is

$$
(1+x)^{-2}=1-2x+3x^2-4x^3+\cdots
$$

and the Taylor series for $\sqrt[3]{1-6x}$ centered at 0 is

$$
\sqrt[3]{1-6x}=1-2x-4x^2-\frac{40x^3}{3}-\cdots.
$$

We compute that

$$\frac{(1+x)^{-2} - \sqrt[3]{1-6x}}{2x^2}$$

$$= \frac{1}{2x^2}\left(\left(1 - 2x + 3x^2 - 4x^3 + \cdots\right) - \left(1 - 2x - 4x^2 - \frac{40x^3}{3} - \cdots\right)\right)$$

$$= \frac{1}{2x^2}\left(7x^2 + \frac{28x^3}{3} + \cdots\right) = \frac{7}{2} + \frac{14x}{3} + \cdots$$

so the limit of $\dfrac{(1+x)^{-2} - \sqrt[3]{1-6x}}{2x^2}$ as $x \to 0$ is $\dfrac{7}{2}$.

53 We have $e^{-x^2} = 1 - x^2 + \frac{x^4}{2} - \frac{x^6}{6} + \frac{x^8}{24} - \cdots$, so $\int e^{-x^2}\,dx = \int(1 - x^2 + \frac{x^4}{2} - \frac{x^6}{6} + \frac{x^8}{24} - \cdots)\,dx = C + x - \frac{x^3}{3} + \frac{x^5}{10} - \frac{x^7}{42} + \cdots$. Thus, $\int_0^{1/2} e^{-x^2}\,dx = (0.5) - \frac{(0.5)^3}{3} + \frac{(0.5)^5}{10} - \frac{(0.5)^7}{42} + \cdots$. Because $(0.5)^7/42 < .001$, we can calculate the approximation using the first three numbers shown, arriving at approximately 0.461.

54 $\tan^{-1} x = x - x^3/3 + x^5/5 - x^7/7 + x^9/9 - \cdots$, so $\int \tan^{-1}(x)\,dx = \int(x - x^3/3 + x^5/5 - x^7/7 + x^9/9 - \cdots)\,dx = C + \frac{x^2}{2} - \frac{x^4}{12} + \frac{x^6}{30} - \frac{x^8}{56} + \cdots$. Thus, $\int_0^{0.5} \tan^{-1} x\,dx = \frac{(0.5)^2}{2} - \frac{(0.5)^4}{12} + \frac{(0.5)^6}{30} - \frac{(0.5)^8}{56} + \cdots$. Note that this series is alternating, and $\frac{(0.5)^6}{30} < .001$, so we add the first two terms showing to approximate the integral to the desired accuracy. Calculating gives approximately 0.120.

55 $x\cos x = x - \frac{x^3}{2} + \frac{x^5}{24} - \frac{x^7}{720} + \cdots$, so $\int x\cos x\,dx = \int(x - \frac{x^3}{2} + \frac{x^5}{24} - \frac{x^7}{720} + \cdots)\,dx = C + \frac{x^2}{2} - \frac{x^4}{8} + \frac{x^6}{144} - \frac{x^8}{5760} + \frac{x^{10}}{403200} - \cdots$. Thus $\int_0^1 x\cos x\,dx = \frac{1}{2} - \frac{1}{8} + \frac{1}{144} - \frac{1}{5760} + \cdots$. Because $\frac{1}{5760} < .001$, we add the first three terms to approximate to the desired accuracy. Calculating gives $\int_0^1 x\cos x\,dx \approx 0.382$.

56 $x^2\tan^{-1} x = x^3 - x^5/3 + x^7/5 - x^9/7 + x^{11}/9 + \cdots$, so $\int x^2\tan^{-1}(x)\,dx = \int(x^3 - x^5/3 + x^7/5 - x^9/7 + x^{11}/9 - \cdots)\,dx = C + \frac{x^4}{4} - \frac{x^6}{18} + \frac{x^8}{40} - \frac{x^{10}}{70} + \cdots$. Thus, $\int_0^{0.5} x^2\tan^{-1} x\,dx = \frac{(0.5)^4}{4} - \frac{(0.5)^6}{18} + \frac{(0.5)^8}{40} - \frac{(0.5)^{10}}{70} + \cdots$. Note that this series is alternating, and $\frac{(0.5)^6}{18} < .001$, so we use the first term showing to approximate the integral to the desired accuracy. Calculating gives approximately 0.015.

57 The series for $f(x) = \sqrt{x}$ centered at $a = 121$ is $11 + \frac{x-121}{22} - \frac{(x-121)^2}{10648} + \frac{(x-121)^3}{2576816} + \cdots$. Letting $x = 119$ gives $\sqrt{119} \approx 11 - \frac{1}{11} - \frac{1}{2\cdot 11^3} - \frac{1}{2\cdot 11^5}$.

58 Because 20 degrees corresponds to $\frac{\pi}{9}$ radians, we consider the series for $\sin x$ centered at 0. We have $\sin x \approx x - x^3/3! + x^5/5! - x^7/7! + \cdots$, so $\sin \pi/9 \approx \frac{\pi}{9} - \frac{(\pi/9)^3}{3!} + \frac{(\pi/9)^5}{5!} - \frac{(\pi/9)^7}{7!}$.

59 $\tan^{-1} x = x - x^3/3 + x^5/5 - x^7/7 + x^9/9 - \cdots$, so $\tan^{-1}(-1/3) \approx \frac{-1}{3} + \frac{1}{3\cdot 3^3} - \frac{1}{5\cdot 3^5} + \frac{1}{7\cdot 3^7}$.

60 $\sinh x = x + \frac{x^3}{6} + \frac{x^5}{120} + \frac{x^7}{5040} + \cdots$, so $\sinh(-1) \approx (-1) + \frac{(-1)^3}{6} + \frac{(-1)^5}{120} + \frac{(-1)^7}{5040}$.

61 Because $y(0) = 4$, we have $y'(0) - 16 + 12 = 0$, so $y'(0) = 4$. Differentiating the equation $n-1$ times and evaluating at 0 we obtain $y^{(n)}(0) = 4y^{(n-1)}(0)$, so that $y^{(n)}(0) = 4^n$. The Taylor series for $y(x)$ is thus $y(x) = 4 + 4x + \frac{4^2 x^2}{2!} + \frac{4^3 x^3}{3!} + \cdots$, or $y(x) = 3 + e^{4x}$.

62 We begin with $e^{-102x^2} = 1 - 102x^2 + \frac{102^2 x^4}{2!} + \cdots$. For $n = 2$, we have $11.4\int_0^{0.14}(1 - 102x^2)\,dx = 11.4(x - 34x^3)|_0^{0.14} = 0.5324256$. For $n = 3$, $11.4\int_0^{0.14}(1 - 102x^2 + 5202x^4)\,dx = 11.4(x - 34x^3 + 1040.4x^5)|_0^{0.14} \approx 1.170314983$. Clearly the second estimate is too high, because the true probability cannot exceed 1. The true value is approximately 0.9547855902.

63

a. The Taylor series for $\ln(1+x)$ is $\sum_{k=1}^{\infty}(-1)^{k+1}\frac{x^k}{k}$. Evaluating at $x = 1$ gives $\ln 2 = \sum_{k=1}^{\infty}(-1)^{k+1}\frac{1}{k}$.

b. The Taylor series for $\ln(1-x)$ is $-\sum_{k=1}^{\infty} \frac{x^k}{k}$. Evaluating at $x = 1/2$ gives $\ln(1/2) = -\sum_{k=1}^{\infty} \frac{1}{k2^k}$, so that $\ln 2 = \sum_{k=1}^{\infty} \frac{1}{k2^k}$.

c. $f(x) = \ln\left(\frac{1+x}{1-x}\right) = \ln(1+x) - \ln(1-x)$. Using the two Taylor series above we have $f(x) = \sum_{k=1}^{\infty} (-1)^{k+1} \frac{x^k}{k} - \left(-\sum_{k=1}^{\infty} \frac{x^k}{k}\right) = \sum_{k=1}^{\infty} (1 + (-1)^{k+1}) \frac{x^k}{k} = 2\sum_{k=0}^{\infty} \frac{x^{2k+1}}{2k+1}$.

d. Because $\frac{1+x}{1-x} = 2$ when $x = \frac{1}{3}$, the resulting infinite series for $\ln 2$ is $2\sum_{k=0}^{\infty} \frac{1}{3^{2k+1}(2k+1)}$.

e. The first four terms of each series are: $1 - \frac{1}{2} + \frac{1}{3} - \frac{1}{4} \approx 0.5833333333$, $\frac{1}{2} + \frac{1}{8} + \frac{1}{24} + \frac{1}{64} \approx 0.6822916667$, $\frac{2}{3} + \frac{2}{81} + \frac{2}{1215} + \frac{2}{15309} \approx 0.6931347573$ The true value is $\ln 2 \approx 0.6931471806$. The third series converges the fastest, because it has 3^{k+1} in the denominator as opposed to 2^k, so its terms get small faster.

64

a. $p_3(x) = 1 - 4x + 10x^2 - 20x^3$.

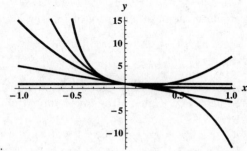

b.

c. The constant polynomial looks like $f(x)$ only at 0. The linear polynomial looks like $f(x)$ on about $(-.1, .1)$. The quadratic approximation looks like $f(x)$ on about $(-.1, .1)$ as well, and the cubic approximation looks like $f(x)$ on about $(-.2, .2)$.

Chapter 10

Parametric and Polar Curves

10.1   Parametric Equations

10.1.1 Given an input value of t, the point $(x(t), y(t))$ can be plotted in the xy-plane, generating a curve.

10.1.2 $x = 6\cos t$ and $y = 6\sin t$ for $0 \le t \le 2\pi$ generates the circle, because $x^2 + y^2 = 36\cos^2 t + 36\sin^2 t = 36$. Similarly, $x = 6\sin t$ and $y = 6\cos t$ for $0 \le t \le 2\pi$ generates the same curve.

10.1.3 Let $x = R\cos(\pi t/5)$ and $y = -R\sin(\pi t/5)$. Note that as t ranges from 0 to 10, $\pi t/5$ ranges from 0 to 2π. Because $x^2 + y^2 = R^2$, this curve represents a circle of radius R. Note also that for $t = 0$ the initial point is $(R, 0)$, and for small values of t the plotted points are in the third quadrant — so the curve is being traced with clockwise orientation.

10.1.4 Let $x = t$ and $y = -2t + 5$ for $t \in (-\infty, \infty)$.

10.1.5 Let $x = t$ and $y = t^2$ for $t \in (-\infty, \infty)$.

10.1.6 The former represents the part of the parabola $y = x^2$ lying in the first quadrant. The latter represents the part of that same parabola lying in the second quadrant.

10.1.7 Solving the first equation for t gives $t = \frac{1-x}{2}$. Substitute that value for t in the second equation to get $y = 3\left(\frac{1-x}{2}\right)^2$; simplifying gives $y = \frac{3}{4}x^2 - \frac{3}{2}x + \frac{3}{4}$.

10.1.8 With $t = 0$ the corresponding point on the curve is $(-2\sin 0, 2\cos 0) = (0, 2)$. As t increases from 0, the x-coordinate becomes negative, while the y coordinate decreases. Thus the curve is generated counterclockwise, running successively through $(0, 2)$, then $(-2, 0)$ for $t = \frac{\pi}{2}$, then $(0, -2)$ for $t = \pi$, then $(2, 0)$ for $t = \frac{3\pi}{2}$, and finally back to $(0, 2)$ for $t = 2\pi$. Then it repeats.

10.1.9 The slope of the tangent line is $\frac{dy}{dx} = \frac{dy/dt}{dx/dt}$, so at $t = a$ the slope is given by $\frac{g'(a)}{f'(a)}$, $f'(a) \ne 0$.

10.1.10 There is a horizontal tangent line at $t = a$ where $g'(a) = 0$, provided $f'(a) \ne 0$, so these points can be found by solving $g'(t) = 0$ and checking that any solution $t = a$ satisfies $f'(a) \ne 0$.

10.1.11

a.

b.

t	x	y
-10	-20	-34
-5	-10	-19
0	0	-4
5	10	11
10	20	26

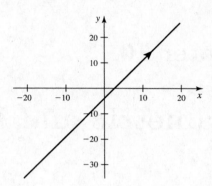

c. Solving $x = 2t$ for t yields $t = x/2$, so $y = 3t - 4 = 3x/2 - 4$.

d. The curve is the line segment from $(-20, -34)$ to $(20, 26)$.

10.1.12

a.

b.

t	x	y
-4	18	-16
-2	6	-8
0	2	0
2	6	8
4	18	16

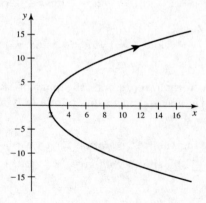

c. Solving $y = 4t$ for t yields $t = y/4$, so $x = t^2 + 2 = y^2/16 + 2$.

d. The curve is part of the parabola $x = y^2/16 + 2$ from $(18, -16)$ to $(18, 16)$.

10.1.13

b.

a.

t	x	y
-5	11	-18
-3	9	-12
0	6	-3
3	3	6
5	1	12

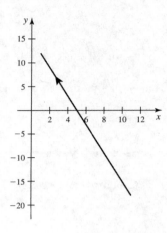

c. Solving $x = -t + 6$ for t yields $t = 6 - x$, so $y = 3t - 3 = 18 - 3x - 3 = 15 - 3x$.

d. The curve is the line segment from $(11, -18)$ to $(1, 12)$.

10.1.14

a.

t	x	y
-3	-28	-14
-2	-9	-9
-1	-2	-4
0	-1	1
1	0	6
2	7	11
3	26	16

b.

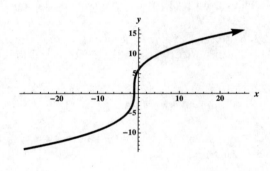

c. Because $t = \sqrt[3]{x + 1}$, we have $y = 5\sqrt[3]{x + 1} + 1$.

d. The curve is a shifted and scaled version of the cube root function.

10.1.15

a. Solving $x = \sqrt{t} + 4$ for t yields $t = (x - 4)^2$. Thus, $y = 3\sqrt{t} = 3(x - 4)$, where x ranges from 4 to 8. Note that all $t \geq 0$, $x > 0$, and $y > 0$.

b. The curve is the line segment from $(4, 0)$ to $(8, 12)$.

10.1.16

a. Solving $y = t + 2$ for t yields $t = y - 2$. Thus, $x = (t + 1)^2 = (y - 2 + 1)^2 = (y - 1)^2$, where $-8 \leq y \leq 12$.

b. The curve is the part of the parabola $x = (y - 1)^2$ from $(81, -8)$ to $(121, 12)$.

10.1.17

a. Because $\cos^2 t + \sin^2 t = 1$, we have $x^2 + y = 1$, so $y = 1 - x^2$, $-1 \leq x \leq 1$.

b. This is a parabola opening downward with a vertex at $(0,1)$, and starting at $(1,0)$ and ending at $(-1,0)$.

10.1.18

a. Note that $(1 - \sin^2 s) - \cos^2 s = 0$, so $x - y^2 = 0$, so $x = y^2$, $-1 \le y \le 1$.

b. This is a parabola opening to the right with a vertex at $(0,0)$, starting at $(1,-1)$ and ending at $(1,1)$.

10.1.19

a. Solving $x = r - 1$ for r yields $r = x + 1$. Thus, $y = r^3 = (x+1)^3$, where $-5 \le x \le 3$.

b. The curve is the part of the standard cubic curve, shifted one unit to the left, from $(-5, -64)$ to $(3, 64)$.

10.1.20

a. Solving $x = e^{2t}$ for t yields $t = \ln(\sqrt{x})$. Thus, $y = e^t + 1 = \sqrt{x} + 1$, where $1 \le x \le e^{50}$.

b. The curve is the part of the standard square root function, shifted one unit vertically, from the point $(1, 2)$ to $(e^{50}, e^{25} + 1)$.

10.1.21 Note that $x^2 + y^2 = 9\cos^2 t + 9\sin^2 t = 9$, so this represents an arc of the circle of radius 3 centered at the origin from $(-3, 0)$ to $(3, 0)$ traversed counterclockwise.

10.1.22 Note that $x^2 + y^2 = 9\cos^2 t + 9\sin^2 t = 9$, so this represents an arc of the circle of radius 3 centered at the origin from $(3, 0)$ to $(0, 3)$ traversed counterclockwise.

10.1.23 Note that $x^2 + (y - 1)^2 = \cos^2 t + \sin^2 t = 1$, so we have a circle of radius 1 centered at $(0, 1)$, traversed counterclockwise starting at $(1, 1)$.

10.1.24 Note that $(x + 3)^2 + (y - 5)^2 = 4$. This is a circle of radius 2 centered at $(-3, 5)$ and traversed clockwise starting at $(-3, 7)$.

10.1.25 Note that $x^2 + y^2 = 49\cos^2 2t + 49\sin^2 2t = 49$, so this represents an arc of the circle of radius 7 centered at the origin from $(-7, 0)$ to $(-7, 0)$ traversed counterclockwise. (So the whole circle is represented.)

10.1.26 Note that $(x - 1)^2 + (y - 2)^2 = 9\sin^2 4\pi t + 9\cos^2 4\pi t = 9$, so this represents the circle of radius 3 centered at $(1, 2)$ from $(1, 5)$ to $(1, 5)$ traversed counterclockwise.

10.1.27

Let $x = 4\cos t$ and $y = 4\sin t$ for $0 \le t \le 2\pi$.
Then $x^2 + y^2 = 16\cos^2 t + 16\sin^2 t = 16$.

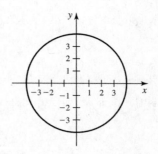

10.1.28

Let $x = 12\sin t$ and $y = 12\cos t$ for $0 \le t \le 2\pi$. Then $x^2 + y^2 = 144\cos^2 t + 144\sin^2 t = 144$, and for $t = 0$ the value of (x, y) is $(0, 12)$.

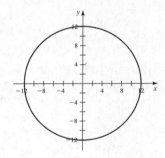

10.1.29

Let $x = \cos t + 2$ and $y = \sin t + 3$ for $0 \le t \le 2\pi$. Then $(x-2)^2 + (y-3)^2 = 1$, which is a circle with the desired center and radius and orientation.

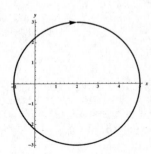

10.1.30

Let $x = 3\sin t + 2$ and $y = 3\cos t$ for $0 \le t \le 2\pi$. Then $(x-2)^2 + y^2 = 9$, which is a circle with the desired center and radius and orientation.

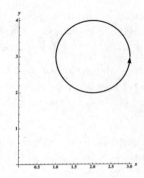

10.1.31

Let $x = -2 + 8\sin t$ and $y = -3 + 8\cos t$ for $0 \le t \le 2\pi$. Then $(x+2)^2 + (y+3)^2 = 64\sin^2 t + 64\cos^2 t = 64$.

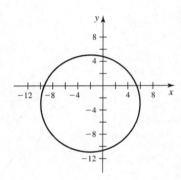

10.1.32

Let $x = 2-(3/2)\cos t$ and $y = -4+(3/2)\sin t$ for $\pi \le t \le 3\pi$. Then $(x-2)^2 + (y+4)^2 = \frac{9}{4}$. Note that for $t = \pi$, we have $x = 7/2$ and $y = -4$.

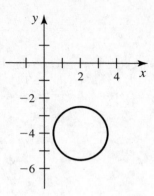

10.1.33 Let t be time in minutes, so $0 \le t \le 1.5$ Let $x = 400\cos(4\pi/3)t$ and $y = 400\sin(4\pi/3)t$. Then because $x^2 + y^2 = 400^2$, the path is a circle of radius 400. Note that the values of x and y are the same at $t = 0$ and $t = 1.5$, and that the circle is traversed counterclockwise.

10.1.34 Let t be time in seconds, so $0 \le t \le 60$ Let $x = 15\sin(\pi/30)t$ and $y = 15\cos(\pi/30)t$. Then because $x^2 + y^2 = 15^2$, the path is a circle of radius 15. Note that the values of x and y are the same at $t = 0$ and $t = 60$, and that the circle is traversed clockwise.

10.1.35 Let t be time in seconds, so $0 \le t \le 24$ Let $x = 50\cos(\pi/12)t$ and $y = 50\sin(\pi/12)t$. Then because $x^2 + y^2 = 50^2$, the path is a circle of radius 50. Note that the values of x and y are the same at $t = 0$ and $t = 24$, and that the circle is traversed counterclockwise.

10.1.36 Let t be time in minutes, so $0 \le t \le 3$. Because the low point is the origin, the circle we seek has its center at $(0, 20)$ and a radius of 20. Let $x = -20\sin(2\pi/3)t$ and $y = 20 - 20\cos(2\pi/3)t$. Then because $x^2 + (y-20)^2 = 20^2$, the path is a circle of radius 20. Note that the values of x and y are the same for $t = 0$ and $t = 3$.

10.1.37

Because $t = x - 3$, we have $y = 1 - (x - 3) = 4 - x$, so the line has slope -1. When $t = 0$, we have the point $(3, 1)$.

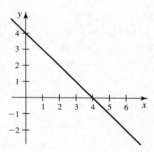

10.1.38

Because $t = \frac{4-x}{3}$, we have $y = -2+6\left(\frac{4-x}{3}\right) = 6 - 2x$, so the line has slope -2. When $t = 0$, we have the point $(4, -2)$.

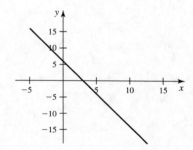

10.1.39

Because $y = 1$, this is a horizontal line with slope 0. When $t = 0$, we have the point $(8, 1)$.

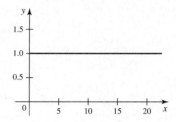

10.1.40

Because $t = \frac{3}{2}(x-1)$, we have $y = -\frac{1}{4} - \frac{15}{4}x$, so the line has slope $-\frac{15}{4}$. When $t = 0$, we have the point $(1, -4)$.

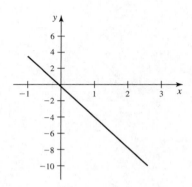

10.1.41 Let $x = x_0 + at$ and $y = y_0 + bt$. Letting $(x_0, y_0) = (0, 0)$, and then finding a and b so that the curve is at the point Q when $t = 1$ yields $x = 2t$, $y = 8t$ for $0 \leq t \leq 1$.

10.1.42 Let $x = x_0 + at$ and $y = y_0 + bt$. Letting $(x_0, y_0) = (1, 3)$, and then finding a and b so that the curve is at the point Q when $t = 1$ yields $x = 1 - 3t$, $y = 3 + 3t$ for $0 \leq t \leq 1$.

10.1.43 Let $x = x_0 + at$ and $y = y_0 + bt$. Letting $(x_0, y_0) = (-1, -3)$, and then finding a and b so that the curve is at the point Q when $t = 1$ yields $x = -1 + 7t$, $y = -3 - 13t$ for $0 \leq t \leq 1$.

10.1.44 Let $x = x_0 + at$ and $y = y_0 + bt$, and parametrize from $t = 0$ to $t = 1$. Because the point is at $(8, 2)$ when $t = 0$, we have $x_0 = 8$ and $y_0 = 2$. At $t = 1$, the point is at $(-2, -3)$, so that $-2 = 8 + a$ and $-3 = 2 + b$. Thus $a = -10$ and $b = -5$, and our equations are $x = 8 - 10t$ and $y = 2 - 5t$ for $0 \leq t \leq 1$.

10.1.45

Let $x = t$ and $y = 2t^2 - 4$, $-1 \leq t \leq 5$.

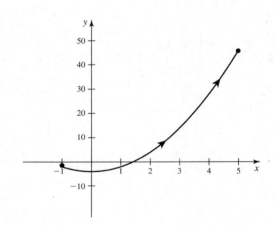

10.1.46

Let $x = t^3 - 3t$ and $y = t$, $-\infty < t < \infty$.

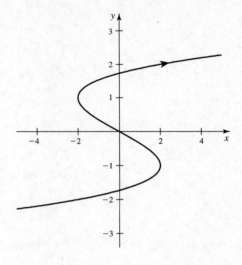

10.1.47

Let $x = -2 + 4t$ and $y = 3 - 6t$, $0 \le t \le 1$, and $x = t + 1$, $y = 8t - 11$ for $1 \le t \le 2$.

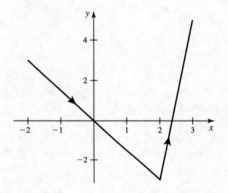

10.1.48

Let $x = -4 + 4t$ and $y = 4 + 4t$, $0 \le t \le 1$, and $x = t - 1$, $y = 8 - 2(t-1)^2$ for $1 \le t \le 3$.

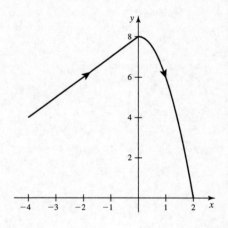

10.1.49

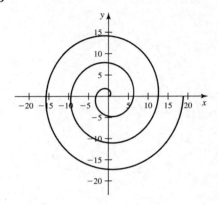

10.1.50

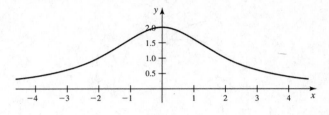

10.1.51

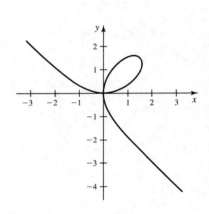

10.1.52

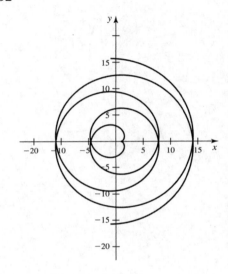

10.1.53

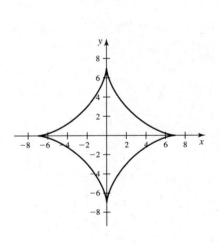

10.1.54

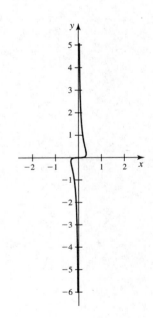

10.1.55

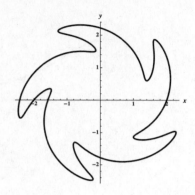

10.1.56

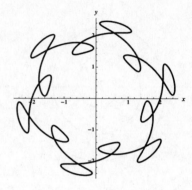

10.1.57

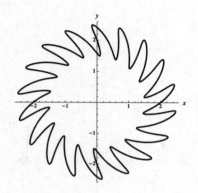

10.1.58

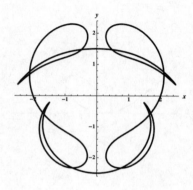

10.1.59

a. $\frac{dy}{dx} = \frac{dy/dt}{dx/dt} = -\frac{8}{4} = -2$ for all t. Because the curve is a line, the tangent line to the curve at the given point is the line itself.

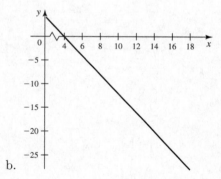

b.

10.1.60

a. $\frac{dy}{dx} = \frac{dy/dt}{dx/dt} = -\frac{3\sin t}{3\cos t} = -\tan t$. At the given value of t, the value of $\frac{dy}{dx}$ doesn't exist, and the tangent line is the vertical line $x = 3$.

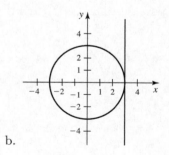

b.

10.1.61

a. $\frac{dy}{dx} = \frac{dy/dt}{dx/dt} = \frac{8\cos t}{-\sin t} = -8\cot t$. At the given value of t, the value of $\frac{dy}{dx}$ is $-8\cot\pi/2 = 0$. The tangent line at the point $(0,8)$ is thus the horizontal line $y = 8$.

b.

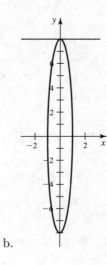

10.1.62

a. $\frac{dy}{dx} = \frac{dy/dt}{dx/dt} = \frac{3t^2}{2}$. At the given value of t, the value of $\frac{dy}{dx}$ is $\frac{3}{2}$, and the tangent line is $y = \frac{3}{2}x + 2$, tangent at the point $(-2,-1)$.

b.

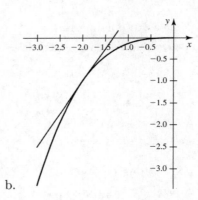

10.1.63

a. $\frac{dy}{dx} = \frac{dy/dt}{dx/dt} = \frac{1+\frac{1}{t^2}}{1-\frac{1}{t^2}} = \frac{t^2+1}{t^2-1}$. At the given value of t, the derivative doesn't exist, and the tangent line is the vertical line $x = 2$, tangent at the point $(2,0)$.

b.

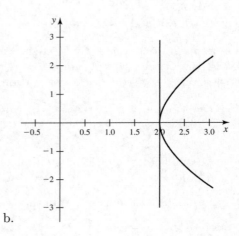

10.1.64

a. $\frac{dy}{dx} = \frac{dy/dt}{dx/dt} = \frac{2}{1/(2\sqrt{t})} = 4\sqrt{t}$. At the given value of t, the value of $\frac{dy}{dx}$ is 8. The equation of the tangent line is $y = 8x - 8$, tangent at the point $(2, 8)$.

b.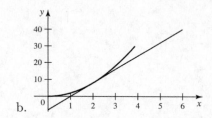

10.1.65

a. False. This generates a circle in the counterclockwise direction.

b. True. Note that when t is increased by one, the value of $2\pi t$ is increased by 2π, which is the period of both the sine and the cosine functions.

c. False. This generates only the portion of the parabola in the first quadrant, omitting the portion in the second quadrant.

d. True. They describe the portion of the unit circle in the 4th and 1st quadrants.

e. True. This ellipse has vertical tangents at $t = 0$ and $t = \pi$.

10.1.66 The point corresponding to $t = \pi/4$ is $(\sqrt{2}/2, \sqrt{2}/2)$. $\frac{dy}{dx} = \frac{dy/dt}{dx/dt} = \frac{-\sin t}{\cos t}$. At $t = \pi/4$, we have a slope of -1. The equation of the tangent line is thus $y - \sqrt{2}/2 = -1(x - \sqrt{2}/2)$, or $y = -x + \sqrt{2}$.

10.1.67 The point corresponding to $t = 2$ is $(3, 10)$. $\frac{dy}{dx} = \frac{dy/dt}{dx/dt} = \frac{3t^2+1}{2t}$, so the slope at $t = 2$ is $\frac{13}{4}$. The equation of the tangent line is therefore $y - 10 = \frac{13}{4}(x - 3)$, or $y = \frac{13}{4}x + \frac{1}{4}$.

10.1.68 The point corresponding to $t = 0$ is $(1, 0)$. $\frac{dy}{dx} = \frac{dy/dt}{dx/dt} = \frac{1}{(t+1)e^t}$, so the slope at $t = 0$ is 1. The equation of the tangent line is thus $y = x - 1$.

10.1.69 The point corresponding to $t = \pi/4$ is $\left(\frac{4\sqrt{2}+\pi\sqrt{2}}{8}, \frac{4\sqrt{2}-\pi\sqrt{2}}{8}\right)$. $\frac{dy}{dx} = \frac{dy/dt}{dx/dt} = \frac{\cos t - (\cos t - t \sin t)}{-\sin t + (\sin t + t \cos t)} = \tan t$. At $t = \pi/4$, we have a slope of 1. The equation of the tangent line is thus $y - \frac{4\sqrt{2}-\pi\sqrt{2}}{8} = 1\left(x - \frac{4\sqrt{2}+\pi\sqrt{2}}{8}\right)$, or $y = x - \frac{\pi\sqrt{2}}{4}$.

10.1.70 Let $x = -t$ and $y = t^2 + 1$, for $0 \le t < \infty$.

10.1.71 Let $x = 1 + 2t$ and $y = 1 + 4t$, for $-\infty < t < \infty$. Note that $y = 2(1 + 2t) - 1$, so $y = 2x - 1$.

10.1.72 Let $x = -2 - 6\cos t$ and $y = 2 - 6\sin t$, for $0 \le t \le \pi$. Then $(x + 2)^2 + (y - 2)^2 = 36$, so the curve represented is part of the circle of radius 6 centered at $(-2, 2)$. Note also that as t runs from 0 to π, the portion of the circle traversed is the lower portion, from $(-8, 2)$ to $(4, 2)$.

10.1.73 Let $x = t^2$ and $y = t$, for $0 \le t < \infty$. Note that $x = t^2 = y^2$, and that the starting point is $(0, 0)$.

10.1.74

a. This corresponds to graph (D). Note that $t = 0$ corresponds to the point $(-2, 0)$ and as $t \to \infty$, both $x \to \infty$ and $y \to \infty$.

b. This corresponds to graph (B). Note that $-1 \le x \le 1$ and $-1 \le y \le 1$ for all values of t.

c. This corresponds to graph (A). Note that as $t \to -\infty$, we have $x \to -\infty$ and $y \to -\infty$.

d. This corresponds to graph (C). Note that $-3 \le x \le 3$ and $-3 \le y \le 3$ for all values of t.

10.1.75

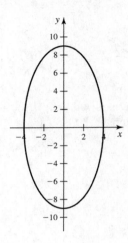

The entire curve is traversed for $0 \leq t \leq 2\pi$.

10.1.76

The entire curve is traversed for $0 \leq t \leq \pi$.

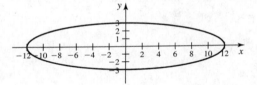

10.1.77

Let $x = 3\cos t$ and $y = \frac{3}{2}\sin t$ for $0 \leq t \leq 2\pi$. Then the major axis on the x-axis has length $2 \cdot 3 = 6$ and the minor axis on the y-axis has length $2 \cdot \frac{3}{2} = 3$. Note that $\left(\frac{x}{3}\right)^2 + \left(\frac{2y}{3}\right)^2 = \cos^2 t + \sin^2 t = 1$.

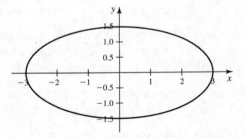

10.1.78

Let $x = 6\cos t$ and $y = -\sin t$ for $0 \leq t \leq 2\pi$. Then the major axis on the x-axis has length $2 \cdot 6 = 12$ and the minor axis on the y-axis has length $2 \cdot 1 = 2$. Note that $\left(\frac{x}{6}\right)^2 + (y)^2 = \cos^2 t + \sin^2 t = 1$.

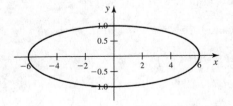

10.1.79

Let $x = 15\cos t - 2$ and $y = 10\sin t - 3$ for $0 \le t \le 2\pi$. Note that $\left(\frac{x+2}{15}\right)^2 + \left(\frac{y+3}{10}\right)^2 = \cos^2 t + \sin^2 t = 1$.

Then the major axis has length 30 and the minor axis has length 20.

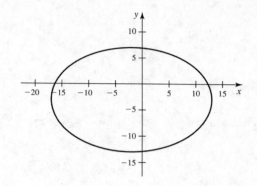

10.1.80

Let $x = 5\cos t$ and $y = -\frac{3}{2}\sin t - 4$ for $0 \le t \le 2\pi$. Note that $\left(\frac{x}{5}\right)^2 + \left(\frac{y+4}{3/2}\right)^2 = \cos^2 t + \sin^2 t = 1$.

Then the major axis has length 10 and the minor axis has length 3.

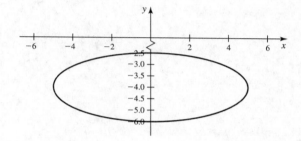

10.1.81

a. For $(1+s, 2s) = (1+2t, 3t)$, we must have $1 + s = 1 + 2t$ and $2s = 3t$, so that $s = 2t$ and $2s = 3t$. The only solution to this pair of equations is $s = t = 0$, so these two lines intersect when $s = t = 0$, at the point $(1, 0)$.

b. For $(2+5s, 1+s) = (4+10t, 3+2t)$, we must have $2 + 5s = 4 + 10t$ and $1 + s = 3 + 2t$, so that $s = 2 + 2t$ and $s = 2 + 2t$. This pair of equations has no solutions, so the lines are parallel.

c. For $(1+3s, 4+2s) = (4?3t, 6+4t)$, we must have $1 + 3s = 4?3t$ and $4 + 2s = 6 + 4t$, so that $s = 1?t$ and $s = 1 + 2t$. The only solution to this pair of equations is $s = 1$ and $t = 0$, so these two lines intersect for these values of s and t, at the point $(4, 6)$.

10.1.82 All three represent portions of the parabola $x = 2 \cdot (y-4)^2$ where x is between 0 and 32. However, the curve in part **b** only represents the portion of the parabola where $y \ge 4$, because for that curve, $y = 4 + t^2 \ge 4$.

10.1.83 Note that $x^2 + y^2 = 4\sin^2 8t + 4\cos^2 8t = 4$, so the curve is the circle $x^2 + y^2 = 4$.

10.1.84 Note that $4x^2 + y^2 = 4\sin^2 8t + 4\cos^2 8t = 4$, so the curve is the ellipse $4x^2 + y^2 = 4$.

10.1.85 Note that because $t = x$, we have $y = \sqrt{4 - t^2} = \sqrt{4 - x^2}$.

10.1.86 Note that $x^2 = t + 1$, so $y = \frac{1}{t+1} = \frac{1}{x^2}$.

10.1.87 Because $\sec^2 t - 1 = \tan^2 t$, we have $y = x^2$.

10.1.88 Note that $\left(\sqrt[n]{x/a}\right)^2 + \left(\sqrt[n]{y/b}\right)^2 = \sin^2 t + \cos^2 t$, so $\left(\sqrt[n]{x/a}\right)^2 + \left(\sqrt[n]{y/b}\right)^2 = 1$.

10.1.89 $\frac{dy}{dx} = \frac{dy/dt}{dx/dt} = \frac{4\cos t}{-4\sin t} = -\cot t$. We seek t so that $\cot t = -1/2$, so $t = \cot^{-1}(-1/2)$. The corresponding points on the curve are $\left(-\frac{4\sqrt{5}}{5}, \frac{8\sqrt{5}}{5}\right)$ and $\left(\frac{4\sqrt{5}}{5}, -\frac{8\sqrt{5}}{5}\right)$.

10.1.90 $\frac{dy}{dx} = \frac{dy/dt}{dx/dt} = \frac{8\cos t}{-2\sin t} = -4\cot t$. We seek t so that $\cot t = 1/4$, so $t = \cot^{-1}(1/4)$. The corresponding points on the curve are $\left(\frac{2\sqrt{17}}{17}, \frac{32\sqrt{17}}{17}\right)$ and $\left(-\frac{2\sqrt{17}}{17}, -\frac{32\sqrt{17}}{17}\right)$.

10.1.91 $\frac{dy}{dx} = \frac{dy/dt}{dx/dt} = \frac{1+(1/t^2)}{1-(1/t^2)} = \frac{t^2+1}{t^2-1}$. We seek t so that $\frac{t^2+1}{t^2-1} = 1$, which never occurs. Thus, there are no points on this curve with slope 1.

10.1.92 $\frac{dy}{dx} = \frac{dy/dt}{dx/dt} = -\frac{4}{(1/2\sqrt{t})} = -8\sqrt{t}$ for $t \neq 0$. Note that this isn't 0 for t on the interval $(0, \infty)$, but it is the case that $\lim_{t \to 0^+} \frac{dy}{dx} = 0$, so there is a flat tangent line at the point $(2, 2)$, as long as the point is approached from the right.

10.1.93 Note that in equation B, the parameter is scaled by a factor of 3. Thus, the curves are the same when the corresponding interval for t is scaled by a factor of $1/3$, so for $a = 0$ and $b = \frac{2\pi}{3}$. In fact, the same curve will be generated for $a = p$, $b = p + 2\pi/3$ where p is any real number.

10.1.94 Note that equation B can be obtained from A by replacing t by $t^{1/3}$. Thus, the curves are the same when $a = (-2)^3 = -8$ and $b = 2^3 = 8$.

10.1.95

a. $\frac{dy}{dx} = \frac{dy/dt}{dx/dt} = \frac{2\cos t}{2\cos 2t}$. This is zero when $\cos t = 0$ but $\cos 2t \neq 0$, which occurs for $t = \pi/2$ and $t = 3\pi/2$. The corresponding points on the graph are $(0, 2)$ and $(0, -2)$.

b. Using the derivative obtained above, we seek points where $\cos 2t = 0$ but $\cos t \neq 0$. This occurs for $t = \pi/4$, $3\pi/4$, $5\pi/4$, and $7\pi/4$. The corresponding points on the curve are $(1, \sqrt{2})$, $(-1, \sqrt{2})$, $(-1, -\sqrt{2})$, and $(1, -\sqrt{2})$.

10.1.96

a. $\frac{dy}{dx} = \frac{dy/dt}{dx/dt} = \frac{3\cos 3t}{4\cos 4t}$. This is zero when $\cos 3t = 0$ but $\cos 4t \neq 0$, which occurs for $t = \pi/6$, $\pi/2$, $5\pi/6$, $7\pi/6$, $3\pi/2$, and $t = 11\pi/6$. The corresponding points on the graph are the four points $\left(\pm\frac{\sqrt{3}}{2}, \pm 1\right)$ and the two points $(0, \pm 1)$.

b. Using the derivative obtained above, we seek points where $\cos 4t = 0$ but $\cos 3t \neq 0$. This occurs for $t = \frac{(2n+1)\pi}{8}$, $n = 0, 1, \ldots, 7$. The corresponding points on the curve are the four points $(\pm 1, \pm\sin(\pi/8))$ and $(\pm 1, \pm\sin(3\pi/8))$.

10.1.97

a. Let $\text{sgn}(x) = \begin{cases} 1 & \text{if } x \geq 0 \\ -1 & \text{if } x < 0. \end{cases}$ Let $x = a \cdot \text{sgn}(\cos t) \left|\cos(t)\right|^{2/n}$ and $y = b \cdot \text{sgn}(\sin(t)) \left|\sin(t)\right|^{2/n}$.

b.

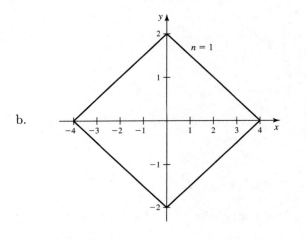

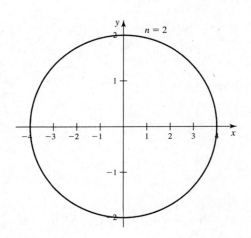

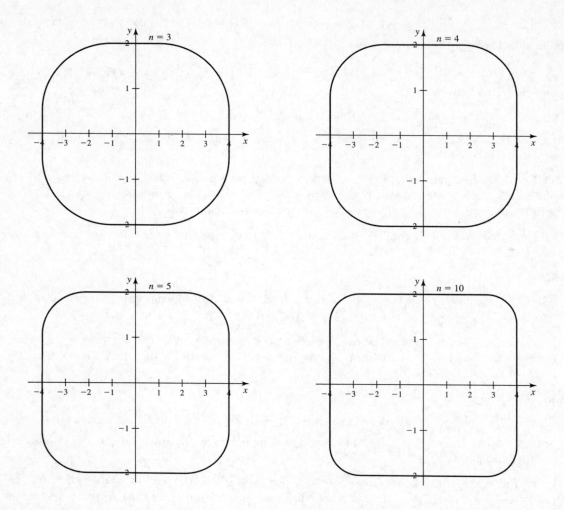

c. As n increases from near 0 to near 1, the curves change from star-shaped to a rectangular shape with corners at $(\pm a, 0)$ and $(0, \pm b)$. As n increases from 1 on, the curves become more rectangular with corners at $(\pm a, \pm b)$.

10.1.98

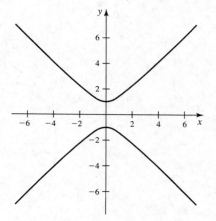

10.1.99 The first graphic shown is for $a = 1$ and $b = 1$. The second is for $a = 2$, $b = 1$, and the third is for $a = 1$, $b = 2$.

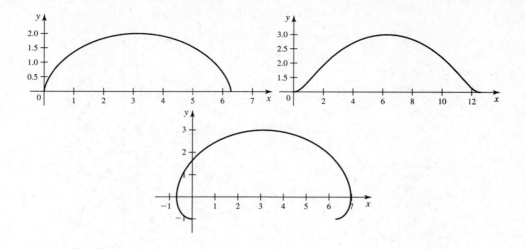

10.1.100

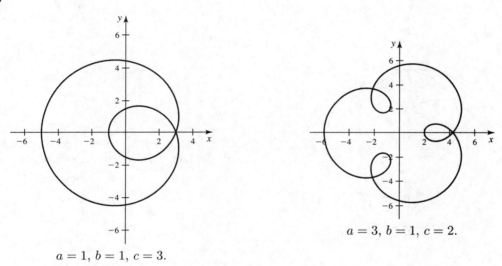

$a = 1, b = 1, c = 3.$

$a = 3, b = 1, c = 2.$

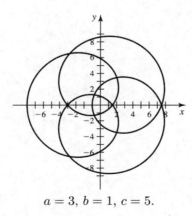

$a = 3, b = 1, c = 5.$

10.1.101

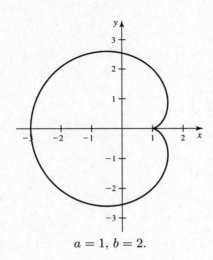

$a = 1, b = 2.$

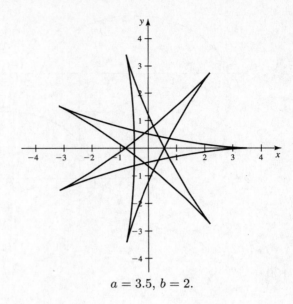

$a = 3.5, b = 2.$

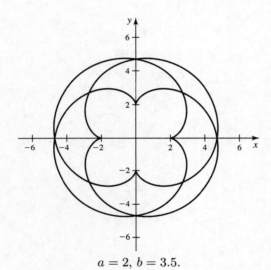

$a = 2, b = 3.5.$

Note that for $a < b$, we have cusps pointing inward, while for $a > b$, the cusps point outward.

10.1.102

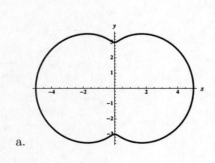

a.

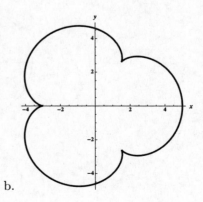

b.

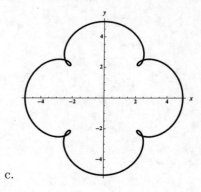

c.

For a fixed a, there appear to be loops when $n > a$.

10.1.103

a.

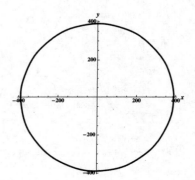

b.

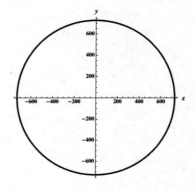

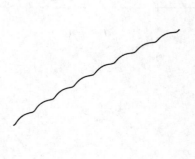

c.

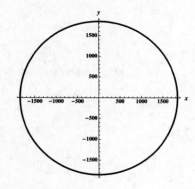

10.1.104 The packages lands when $y = 0$, so we seek a solution to $0 = -4.9t^2 + 3000$. So $t = \sqrt{\frac{3000}{4.9}} \approx 24.744$ seconds, at which point $x \approx 80 \cdot 24.744 \approx 1979.487$ meters.

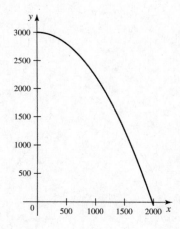

10.1.105 The package lands when $y = 0$, so when $-4.9t^2 + 4000 = 0$ for $t > 0$. This occurs when $t = \sqrt{\frac{4000}{4.9}} \approx 28.571$ seconds. At that time, $x \approx 100 \cdot 28.57 = 2857$ meters.

10.1.106

a.

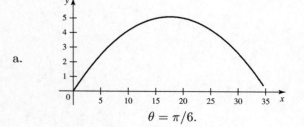

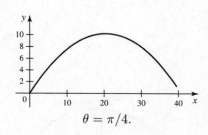

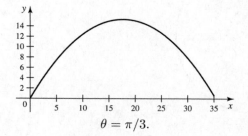

b. The maximum appears to be reached when $\theta = \pi/4$.

10.1.107 Let $x = 1 + \cos^2 t - \sin^2 t$ and $y = t$, for $-\infty < t < \infty$. Note that because $1 - \sin^2 t = \cos^2 t$, we have $x = 2\cos^2 t$, $y = t$.

10.1.108 Note that $\frac{dy}{dt} = \frac{dy}{dx} \cdot \frac{dx}{dt}$, so $\frac{d^2y}{dt^2} = \frac{d}{dt}\left(\frac{dy}{dx} \cdot \frac{dx}{dt}\right) = \frac{dy}{dx}\frac{d^2x}{dt^2} + \frac{dx}{dt} \cdot \frac{d}{dt}\left(\frac{dy}{dx}\right)$.

Also $\frac{d}{dt}\left(\frac{dy}{dx}\right) = \frac{d^2y}{dx^2} \cdot \frac{dx}{dt}$, and $\frac{dy}{dx} = \frac{dy/dt}{dx/dt}$. Thus,

$$\frac{d^2y}{dt^2} = \frac{dy}{dx} \cdot \frac{d^2x}{dt^2} + \frac{dx}{dt} \cdot \frac{d^2y}{dx^2} \cdot \frac{dx}{dt} = \frac{dy/dt}{dx/dt} \cdot \frac{d^2x}{dt^2} + \frac{d^2y}{dx^2} \cdot \left(\frac{dx}{dt}\right)^2.$$

Solving for $\frac{d^2y}{dx^2}$ yields $y'' = \frac{x'(t)y''(t) - x''(t)y'(t)}{(x'(t))^3} = \frac{f'(t)g''(t) - f''(t)g'(t)}{(f'(t))^3}$.

10.1.109 Suppose that $a^2 + c^2 = b^2 + d^2$, and that $ab + cd = 0$. Note that

$$x^2 + y^2 = a^2\cos^2 t + 2ab\sin t \cos t + b^2\sin^2 t + c^2\cos^2 t + 2cd\sin t \cos t + d^2\sin^2 t,$$

which can be rewritten as

$$(a^2 + c^2)\cos^2 t + (b^2 + d^2)\sin^2 t + (2ab + 2cd)\sin t \cos t.$$

Because $b^2 + d^2 = a^2 + c^2$ and because $2ab + 2cd = 0$, we can write this as

$$(a^2 + c^2)(\cos^2 t + \sin^2 t) = R^2,$$

so we have the circle $x^2 + y^2 = R^2$, as desired.

10.1.110 Note that if we let $x = t^{\frac{1}{t-1}}$ and $y = t^{\frac{t}{t-1}}$, $1 < t < \infty$, then we can see that $x\ln y = y\ln x$. Let L_1 represent this curve, and let L_2 be the curve with the same parametric equations but for $0 < t < 1$, and let L_3 be the line $y = x$. The region where $y^x > x^y$ is the region below L_1 and above L_3, and below L_3 but above L_2.

10.2 Polar Coordinates

10.2.1 The coordinates $(2, \pi/6)$, $(2, -11\pi/6)$, and $(-2, 7\pi/6)$ all give rise to the same point. Also, the coordinates $(-3, -\pi/2)$, $(3, \pi/2)$ and $(-3, 3\pi/2)$ give rise to the same point.

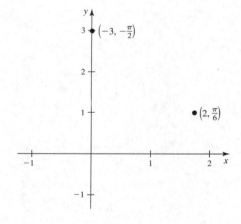

10.2.2 For a point with polar coordinates (r, θ), we have the Cartesian coordinates $x = r\cos\theta$ and $y = r\sin\theta$.

10.2.3 If a point has Cartesian coordinates (x, y) then $r^2 = x^2 + y^2$ and $\tan\theta = y/x$ for $x \neq 0$. If $x = 0$, then $\theta = \pi/2$ and $r = y$.

10.2.4 A cicle of radius $|a|$ centered at the origin has polar equation $r = |a|$.

10.2.5 Because $x = r\cos\theta$, we have that the vertical line $x = 5$ has polar equation $r = 5\sec\theta$.

10.2.6 Because $y = r\sin\theta$, the horizontal line $y = 5$ has polar equation $r = 5\csc\theta$.

10.2.7 x-axis symmetry occurs if (r,θ) on the graph implies $(r,-\theta)$ is on the graph. y-axis symmetry occurs if (r,θ) on the graph implies $(r,\pi-\theta) = (-r,-\theta)$ is on the graph. Symmetry about the origin occurs if (r,θ) on the graph implies $(-r,\theta) = (r,\theta+\pi)$ is on the graph.

10.2.8 Graph $r = f(\theta)$ as if r and θ were Cartesian coordinates with θ on the horizontal axis and r on the vertical axis. Choose an interval in θ on which the entire polar curve is produced. Then use this graph as a guide to sketch the points (r,θ) on the final polar curve.

10.2.9 The coordinates $(2,\pi/4)$, $(-2,5\pi/4)$, and $(2,9\pi/4)$ represent the same point.

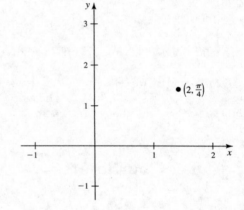

10.2.10 The coordinates $(3,2\pi/3)$, $(-3,5\pi/3)$ and $(3,8\pi/3)$ represent the same point.

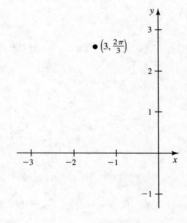

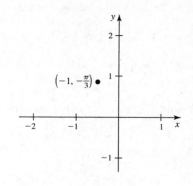

10.2.11 The coordinates $(-1, -\pi/3)$, $(1, 2\pi/3)$ and $(1, -4\pi/3)$ represent the same point.

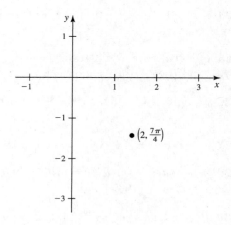

10.2.12 The coordinates $(2, 7\pi/4)$, $(-2, 3\pi/4)$ and $(2, -\pi/4)$ represent the same point.

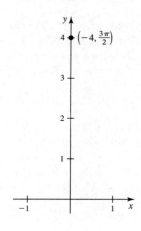

10.2.13 The coordinates $(-4, 3\pi/2)$, $(4, \pi/2)$ and $(-4, -\pi/2)$ represent the same point.

10.2.14 $A = (4, \pi/6) = (-4, 7\pi/6)$. $B = (3, \pi/4) = (-3, 5\pi/4)$. $C = (2, \pi/3) = (-2, 4\pi/3)$. $D = (4, \pi/2) = (-4, 3\pi/2)$. $E = (2, 4\pi/3) = (-2, \pi/3)$. $F = (4, -\pi/3) = (-4, 2\pi/3)$.

10.2.15 $x = 3\cos(\pi/4) = \frac{3\sqrt{2}}{2}$. $y = 3\sin(\pi/4) = \frac{3\sqrt{2}}{2}$.

10.2.16 $x = \cos(2\pi/3) = -1/2$. $y = \sin(2\pi/3) = \frac{\sqrt{3}}{2}$.

10.2.17 $x = \cos(-\pi/3) = \frac{1}{2}$. $y = \sin(-\pi/3) = -\frac{\sqrt{3}}{2}$.

10.2.18 $x = 2\cos(7\pi/4) = 2 \cdot \frac{\sqrt{2}}{2} = \sqrt{2}$. $y = 2\sin(7\pi/4) = -\sqrt{2}$.

10.2.19 $x = -4\cos(3\pi/4) = 2\sqrt{2}$. $y = -4\sin(3\pi/4) = -2\sqrt{2}$.

10.2.20 $x = 4\cos(5\pi) = -4$. $y = 4\sin(5\pi) = 0$.

10.2.21 $r^2 = x^2 + y^2 = 4 + 4 = 8$, so $r = \sqrt{8}$. $\tan\theta = 1$, so $\theta = \pi/4$, so $(2\sqrt{2}, \pi/4)$ is one representation of this point, and $(-2\sqrt{2}, -3\pi/4)$ is another.

10.2.22 $r^2 = x^2 + y^2 = 1 + 0$, so $r = \pm 1$. $\tan\theta = 0$, so $\theta = 0, \pi$. $(-1, 0)$ is one representation of this point, and $(1, \pi)$ is another.

10.2.23 $r^2 = x^2 + y^2 = 1 + 3 = 4$, so $r = \pm 2$. $\tan\theta = \sqrt{3}$, so $\theta = \pi/3, 4\pi/3$. $(2, \pi/3)$ is one representation of this point, and $(-2, -2\pi/3)$ is another.

10.2.24 $r^2 = 81$, so $r = \pm 9$. $\tan\theta = 0$, so $\theta = 0, \pi$. One representation of the given point is $(9, \pi)$, and $(-9, 0)$ is another.

10.2.25 $r^2 = 64$, so $r = \pm 8$. $\tan\theta = -\sqrt{3}$, so $\theta = -\pi/3, 2\pi/3$. One representation of the given point is $(8, 2\pi/3)$, and $(-8, -\pi/3)$ is another.

10.2.26 $r^2 = 16 + 48 = 64$, so $r = \pm 8$. $\tan\theta = \sqrt{3}$. One representation of the given point is $(8. \pi/3)$, and another is $(-8, 4\pi/3)$.

10.2.27 $x = r\cos\theta = -4$, so this is the vertical line $x = -4$ through $(-4, 0)$.

10.2.28 $y = r\sin\theta = \cot\theta\csc\theta\sin\theta = \cot\theta = \frac{x}{y}$. Thus, $y^2 = x$. This curve is a parabola with vertex at $(0, 0)$ which opens to the right.

10.2.29 Because $x^2 + y^2 = r^2 = 4$, this is a circle of radius 2 centered at the origin.

10.2.30 Because $y = r\sin\theta = 3\csc\theta\sin\theta = 3$, this is the horizontal line $y = 3$.

10.2.31 Note that $x^2 + y^2 = r^2 = 4\sin^2\theta + 8\sin\theta\cos\theta + 4\cos^2\theta = 4 + 8\sin\theta\cos\theta$. Also note that $x = r\cos\theta = 2\sin\theta\cos\theta + 2\cos^2\theta$ and $y = r\sin\theta = 2\sin^2\theta + 2\sin\theta\cos\theta$. Thus, $2x + 2y = 4 + 8\sin\theta\cos\theta$. If we combine these, we see that $x^2 + y^2 - (2x + 2y) = 0$. Thus $(x^2 - 2x + 1) + (y^2 - 2y + 1) = 2$, so we have the circle $(x - 1)^2 + (y - 1)^2 = 2$. This is a circle of radius $\sqrt{2}$ centered at $(1, 1)$.

10.2.32 We have $r\sin\theta = \pm r\cos\theta$, so $y = \pm x$. These are lines through the origin with slopes ± 1.

10.2.33 $r\cos\theta = \sin 2\theta = 2\sin\theta\cos\theta$. Note that if $\cos\theta = 0$, then r can be any real number, and the equation is satisfied. For $\cos\theta \neq 0$, we have $x = r\cos\theta = 2\sin\theta\cos\theta$, so $r = 2\sin\theta$, and thus $y = r\sin\theta = 2\sin^2\theta$. Thus $x^2 + y^2 - 2y = 4\sin^2\theta\cos^2\theta + 4\sin^2\theta\sin^2\theta - 4\sin^2\theta = 4\sin^2\theta(\sin^2\theta + \cos^2\theta) - 4\sin^2\theta = 4\sin^2\theta - 4\sin^2\theta = 0$. Note also that $x^2 + y^2 - 2y = 0$ is equivalent to $x^2 + (y - 1)^2 = 1$, so we have a circle of radius one centered at $(0, 1)$, as well as the line $x = 0$ which is the y-axis.

10.2.34 $r = \sin\theta\sec^2\theta$, so $x = r\cos\theta = \tan\theta = \frac{y}{x}$, so $y = x^2$, the standard parabola.

10.2.35 $r = 8\sin\theta$, so $r^2 = 8r\sin\theta$, so $x^2 + y^2 = 8y$. This can be written $x^2 + (y - 4)^2 = 16$, which represents a circle of radius 4 centered at $(0, 4)$.

10.2.36 The given equation implies that $2r\cos\theta + 3r\sin\theta = 1$, so $2x + 3y = 1$. This is a line with slope $-\frac{2}{3}$ and y-intercept $\frac{1}{3}$.

10.2.37

θ	0	$\pi/6$	$\pi/4$	$\pi/3$	$\pi/2$	$2\pi/3$	$3\pi/4$	$5\pi/6$	π
r	8	$4\sqrt{3}$	$4\sqrt{2}$	4	0	-4	$-4\sqrt{2}$	$-4\sqrt{3}$	-8

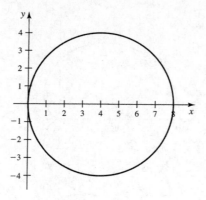

10.2.38

θ	0	$\pi/4$	$\pi/2$	$3\pi/4$	π	$5\pi/4$	$3\pi/2$	$7\pi/4$	2π
r	8	$4+2\sqrt{2}$	4	$4-2\sqrt{2}$	0	$4-2\sqrt{2}$	4	$4+2\sqrt{2}$	8

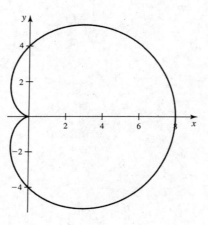

10.2.39 $r(\sin\theta - 2\cos\theta) = 0$ when $r = 0$ or when $\tan\theta = 2$, so the curve is a straight line through the origin of slope 2.

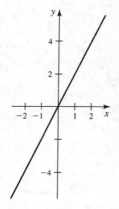

10.2.40

θ	0	$\pi/4$	$\pi/2$	$3\pi/4$	π	$5\pi/4$	$3\pi/2$	$7\pi/4$	2π
r	0	$\dfrac{\sqrt{2}-1}{\sqrt{2}}$	1	$\dfrac{\sqrt{2}+1}{\sqrt{2}}$	2	$\dfrac{\sqrt{2}+1}{\sqrt{2}}$	1	$\dfrac{\sqrt{2}-1}{\sqrt{2}}$	0

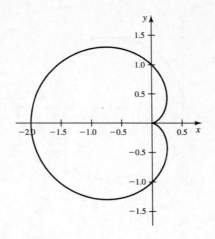

10.2.41

10.2.42

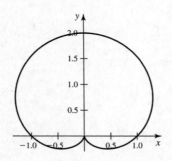

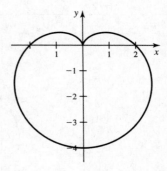

10.2.43

10.2.44

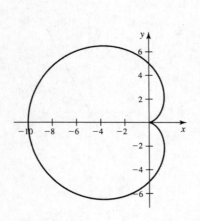

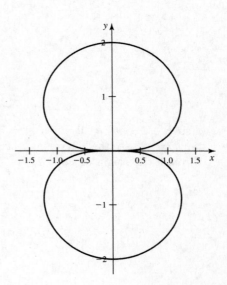

10.2.45

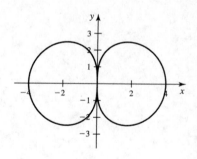

10.2.46

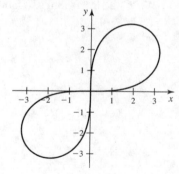

10.2.47

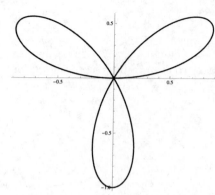

10.2.48

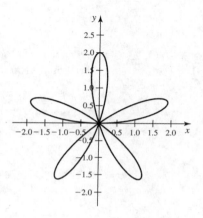

10.2.49 Points B, D, F, H, J and L have y-coordinate 0, so the graph is at the pole for each of these points. Points E, I, and M have maximal radius, so these correspond to the points at the tips of the outer loops. The points C, G and K correspond to the tips of the smaller loops. Point A corresponds to the polar point $(1, 0)$.

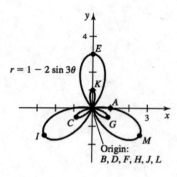

10.2.50 Points B, D, H and J have y-coordinate 0, so the graph is at the pole for each of these points. Points A and K lie where the graph intersects the negative x-axis. C and I are at the top of the two large loops, while F is is where the graph intersects the positive x-axis. E and G are the extreme points of the large wide loop.

10.2.51 Points B, D, F, H, J, L, N and P are at the origin. C, G, K and O are on the ends of the long loops, while A, E, I and M are at the ends of the smaller loops.

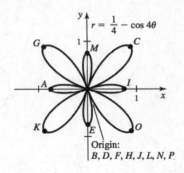

10.2.52 Points C, E, G and I are at the origin. B and D are at the ends of the two bigger loops, F and H are at ends of the two smaller loops. A and J are the points where the graph intersects the positive x-axis.

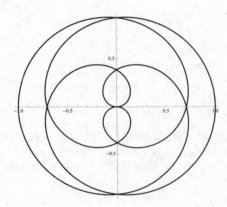

10.2.53   The interval $[0, 8\pi]$ generates the entire graph.

10.2.54   The interval $[0, 2\pi]$ generates the entire graph.

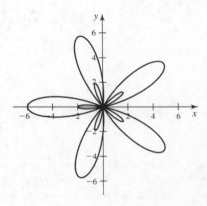

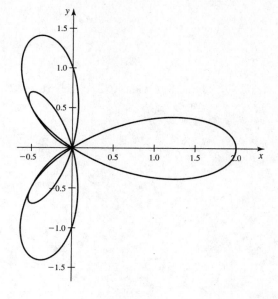

10.2.55 The interval $[0, 2\pi]$ generates the entire graph.

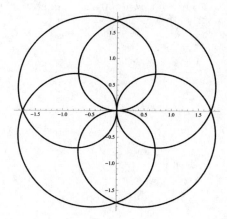

10.2.56 The interval $[0, 6\pi]$ generates the entire graph.

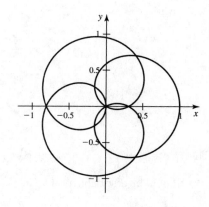

10.2.57 The interval $[0, 5\pi]$ generates the entire graph.

10.2.58 The interval $[0, 7\pi]$ generates the entire graph.

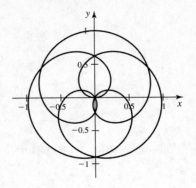

10.2.59 The interval $[0, 2\pi]$ generates the entire graph.

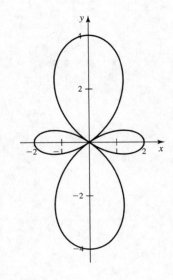

10.2.60 The interval $[0, 2\pi]$ generates the entire graph.

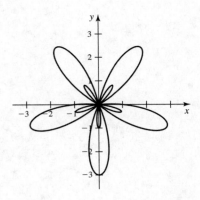

10.2.61

a. True. Note that $r^2 = 8$ and $\tan \theta = -1$.

b. True. Their intersection point (in Cartesian coordinates) is $(4, -2)$.

c. False. They intersect at the polar coordinates $(2, \pi/4)$ and $(2, 5\pi/4)$.

d. True. Note that for $\theta = \frac{3\pi}{2}$ we have $r = -3$. But the polar point $\left(-3, \frac{3\pi}{2}\right)$ is the same as the polar point $\left(3, \frac{\pi}{2}\right)$.

e. True. The first is the line $x = 2$ because $x = r\cos\theta = 2\sec\theta\cos\theta = 2$, and the second is $y = 3$ because $y = r\sin\theta = 3\csc\theta\sin\theta = 3$.

10.2.62 We have $y = r\sin\theta = 3$, so $r = \frac{3}{\sin\theta} = 3\csc\theta$.

10.2.63 We have $r\sin\theta = r^2\cos^2\theta$, so $r = \frac{\sin\theta}{\cos^2\theta} = \tan\theta\sec\theta$.

10.2.64 We have $(r\cos\theta - 1)^2 + r^2\sin^2\theta = 1$, so $r^2\cos^2\theta - 2r\cos\theta + 1 + r^2\sin^2\theta = 1$, and thus $2r\cos\theta = r^2$. Thus $r = 2\cos\theta$.

10.2.65 We have $r\sin\theta = \frac{1}{r\cos\theta}$, so $r^2 = \sec\theta\csc\theta$.

10.2.66

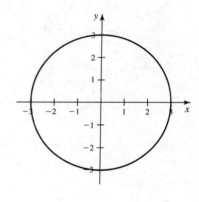

10.2.67

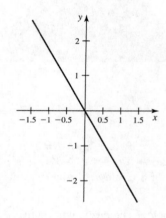

10.2.68

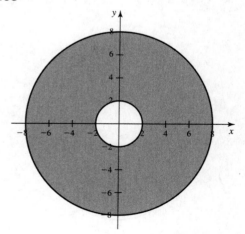

10.2.69

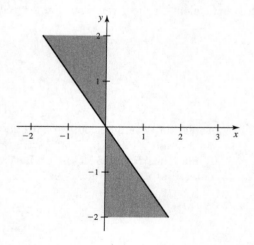

10.2.70

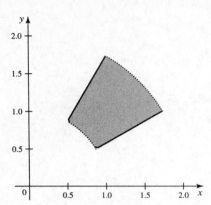

10.2.71

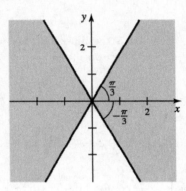

10.2.72

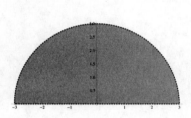

10.2.73

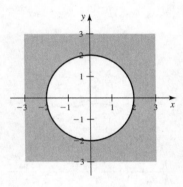

10.2.74 Let $x = r\cos\theta$ and $y = r\sin\theta$, so that $r^2 = x^2 + y^2$. Then the given equation can be written $(x^2 + y^2) - 2ax - 2by + (a^2 + b^2) = R^2$, which in turn can be written as $(x - a)^2 + (y - b)^2 = R^2$, which is the equation of a circle of radius R centered at (a, b).

10.2.75 Consider the circle with center $C(r_0, \theta_0)$, and let A be the origin and $B(r, \theta)$ be a point on the circle not collinear with A and C. Note that the length of side BC is R, and that the angle CAB has measure $\theta - \theta_0$. Applying the law of cosines to triangle CAB yields the equation $R^2 = r^2 + r_0^2 - 2rr_0\cos(\theta - \theta_0)$, which is equivalent to the given equation.

10.2.76 In relation to number 66, we have $2a = 6$, so $a = 3$ and $b = 0$. So $R^2 - a^2 - b^2 = R^2 - 9 = 16$, and thus $R^2 = 25$. Thus we have a circle centered at $(3, 0)$ with radius 5.

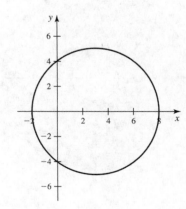

10.2.77 In relation to number 75, we have $r_0 = 2$ and $\theta_0 = \pi/3$, and $R^2 - 4 = 12$, so $R^2 = 16$. Thus this is a circle with polar center $(2, \pi/3)$ and radius 4.

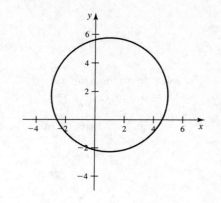

10.2.78 In relation to number 75, we have $r_0 = 4$ and $\theta_0 = \pi/2$, and $R^2 - 16 = 9$, so $R^2 = 25$. Thus this is a circle with polar center $(4, \pi/2)$ and radius 5.

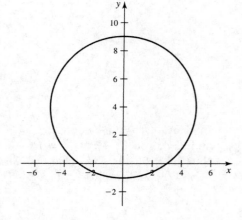

10.2.79 In relation to number 66, we have $a = 2$ and $b = 3$. So $R^2 - a^2 - b^2 = R^2 - 13 = 3$, and thus $R^2 = 16$. Thus we have a circle centered at $(2, 3)$ with radius 4.

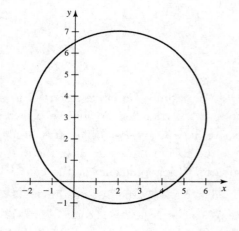

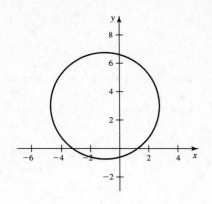

10.2.80 In relation to number 66, we have $a = -1$ and $b = 3$. So $R^2 - a^2 - b^2 = R^2 - 10 = 4$, and thus $R^2 = 14$. Thus we have a circle centered at $(-1, 3)$ with radius $\sqrt{14}$.

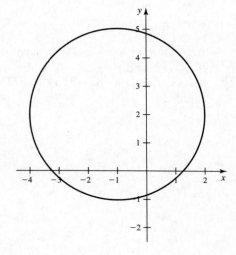

10.2.81 In relation to number 66, we have $a = -1$ and $b = 2$. So $R^2 - a^2 - b^2 = R^2 - 5 = 4$, and thus $R^2 = 9$. Thus we have a circle centered at $(-1, 2)$ with radius 3.

10.2.82 The radius of a circle inscribed in a triangle with side lengths a, b, and c is $\frac{2A}{a+b+c}$ where A is the area of the triangle. So for the bigger circle, $R = r_0 = \frac{2}{2+2\sqrt{2}} = \frac{1}{1+\sqrt{2}}$. For each of the smaller circles, we have $R = \frac{1}{2+\sqrt{2}}$. The area inside the three circles is thus $2\pi \cdot \frac{1}{(2+\sqrt{2})^2} + \pi \cdot \frac{1}{(1+\sqrt{2})^2} \approx 1.078$. Because the area of the square is 2, there is more area inside the circles than outside the circles but inside the square. Using problem 75, the equation of the largest circle is $r^2 - 2r\left(\frac{1}{1+\sqrt{2}}\right)\cos(\theta - \pi/2) = 0$. The smaller circle in the 3rd quadrant has center with polar radius $r_0 = \frac{\sqrt{2}}{2} - \frac{1}{2+\sqrt{2}} = \sqrt{2} - 1$, so its equation is $r^2 - 2r\left(\sqrt{2} - 1\right)\cos(\theta - 5\pi/4) = R^2 - r_0^2 = \sqrt{2} - 3/2$, and the other circle has equation $r^2 - 2r\left(\sqrt{2} - 1\right)\cos(\theta + \pi/4) = \sqrt{2} - 3/2$.

10.2.83

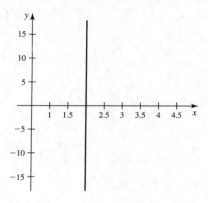

a. On all three intervals, the graph is the same vertical line, oriented upward.

b. For $\theta \neq \frac{2m+1}{2}\pi$ where m is an integer, we have $\cos\theta \neq 0$, so the equation is equivalent to $x = r\cos\theta = 2$. So the graph is a vertical line.

10.2.84

a. Given $y = mx + b$, let $x = r\cos\theta$ and $y = r\sin\theta$. Then $r\sin\theta = m(r\cos\theta) + b$, so $r\sin\theta - mr\cos\theta = b$, and thus $r(\sin\theta - m\cos\theta) = b$, and $r = \frac{b}{\sin\theta - m\cos\theta}$, provided $\sin\theta - m\cos\theta \neq 0$.

b. Using the right triangle shown, we see that $\frac{r_0}{r} = \cos(\theta_0 - \theta)$, so $r_0 = r\cos(\theta_0 - \theta)$.

10.2.85 Using problem 84b, this is the line with $r_0 = 3$ and $\theta_0 = \frac{\pi}{3}$. So it is the line through the polar point $(3, \pi/3)$ in the direction of angle $\pi/3 + \pi/2 = 5\pi/6$. The Cartesian equation is $y = -\frac{x}{\sqrt{3}} + 2\sqrt{3}$.

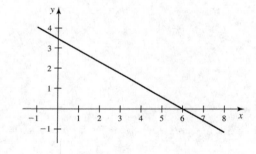

10.2.86 Using problem 84b, this is the line with $r_0 = 4$ and $\theta_0 = -\frac{\pi}{6}$. So it is the line through the polar point $(4, -\pi/6)$ in the direction of angle $-\pi/6 + \pi/2 = \pi/3$. The Cartesian equation is $y = \sqrt{3}x - 8$.

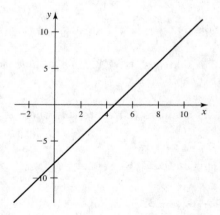

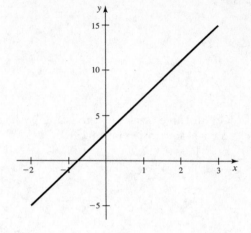

10.2.87   Using problem 84a, this is the line with $b = 3$ and $m = 4$, so $y = 4x + 3$.

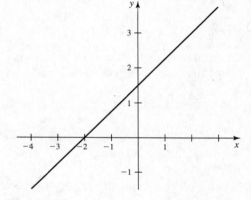

10.2.88   Using problem 84a, this is the line with $b = 3/2$ and $m = 3/4$, so $y = \frac{3}{4}x + \frac{3}{2}$.

10.2.89

  a. This matches (A), because we have $|a| = 1 = |b|$, and the graph is a cardioid.

  b. This matches (C). This has an inner loop because $|a| = 1 < 2 = |b|$. Note that $r = 1$ when $\theta = 0$, so it can't be (D).

  c. This matches (B). This has $|a| = 2 > 1 = |b|$, so it has an oval-like shape.

  d. This matches (D). This has an inner loop because $|a| = 1 < 2 = |b|$. Note that $r = -1$ when $\theta = 0$, so this can't be (C).

  e. This matches (E). Note that there is an inner loop because $|a| = 1 < 2 = |b|$, and that $r = 3$ when $\theta = \pi/2$.

  f. This matches (F).

10.2.90 As $b \to \infty$, the inner loop approaches the outer loop, so that for large b the graph appears to be a single circle with diameter b. Thus, there is no limiting curve as $b \to \infty$.

10.2.91

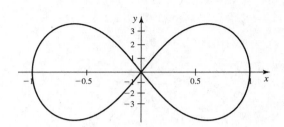

10.2.92

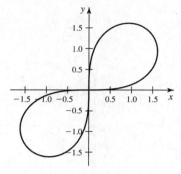

10.2.93

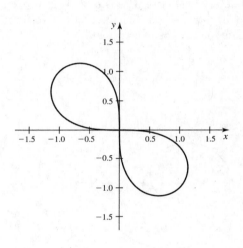

10.2.94

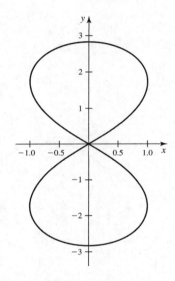

10.2.95

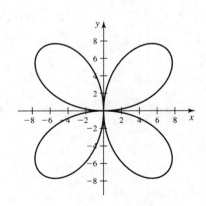

10.2.96

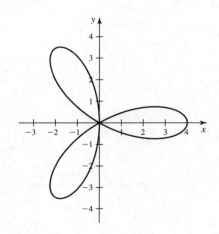

10.2.97

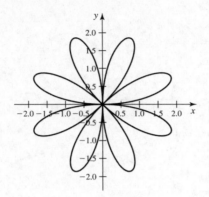

10.2.98

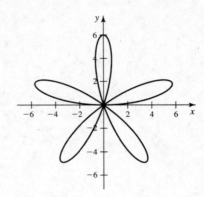

10.2.99 Note that $a\sin m\theta = 0$ for $\theta = \frac{k\pi}{m}$, $k = 1, 2, \ldots, 2m$. Thus the graph is back at the pole $r = 0$ for each of these values, and each of these gives rise to a distinct petal of the rose if m is odd. If m is even, then by symmetry, each petal for $k = 1, 2, \ldots \frac{m}{2}$ is equivalent to one for $k = \frac{m}{2} + 1, \frac{m}{2} + 2, \ldots, m$. (Note that this follows because the sine function is odd.) A similar result holds for the rose $r = a\cos\theta$.

10.2.100 The spirals wind outward counterclockwise.

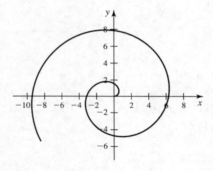
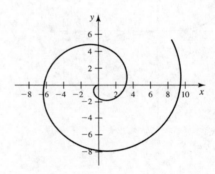

10.2.101 For $a = 1$, the spiral winds outward counterclockwise. For $a = -1$, the spiral winds inward counterclockwise.

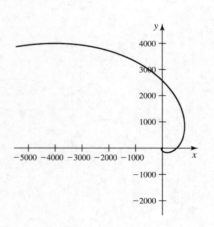
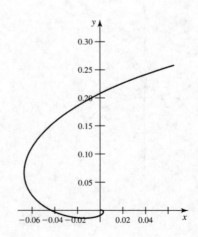

10.2.102 The spirals wind inward counterclockwise for $a = 1$ and outward clockwise for $a = -1$.

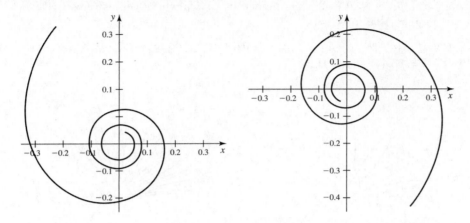

10.2.103 Suppose $2\cos\theta = 1 + \cos\theta$. Then $\cos\theta = 1$, so this occurs for $\theta = 0$ and $\theta = 2\pi$. At those values, $r = 2$, so the curves intersect at the polar point $(2, 0)$. The curves also intersect when $r = 0$, which occurs for $\theta = \pi/2$ and $\theta = 3\pi/2$ for the first curve and $\theta = \pi$ for the second.

10.2.104 Suppose $4\cos\theta = 1 + 2\cos\theta + \cos^2\theta$. Then $(\cos\theta - 1)^2 = 0$, so $\theta = 0$. At that value, $r = 2$, so the curves intersect at the polar point $(2, 0)$. The curves also intersect when $r = 0$, which occurs for the first curve at $\pi/2$ and $3\pi/2$, and for the second curve at π. Also, the curves intersect when $4\cos\theta = -1 - 2\cos\theta - \cos^2\theta$, which occurs for $\cos^2\theta + 6\cos\theta + 1 = 0$, or (using the quadratic formula) $\theta = \cos^{-1}(-3 + 2\sqrt{2}) \approx 1.743$. This leads to the polar intersection points at approximately $(0.828, \pm 1.743)$.

10.2.105 Suppose $1 - \sin\theta = 1 + \cos\theta$, or $\tan\theta = -1$. Then $\theta = 3\pi/4$ or $\theta = 7\pi/4$. So the curves intersect at the polar points $(1 + \sqrt{2}/2, 7\pi/4)$ and $(1 - \sqrt{2}/2, 3\pi/4)$. They also intersect at the pole $(0, 0)$, which occurs for the first curve at $\pi/2$ and for the second curve at π.

10.2.106 Suppose $\cos 2\theta = \sin 2\theta \geq 0$. Then $2\theta = \frac{\pi}{4}$, so $\theta = \frac{\pi}{8}, \frac{9\pi}{8}$. The curves intersect at $\pi/8$ and $9\pi/8$ where both $\cos 2\theta$ and $\sin 2\theta$ have value $\frac{\sqrt{2}}{2}$. The curves also intersect at the pole, which occurs for the first curve at $\pi/4$, and $3\pi/4$, $5\pi/4$ and $7\pi/4$, and for the second curve at 0, $\pi/2$, π, and $3\pi/2$. Thus the intersection points are $(0, 0)$, and approximately $(0.841, 0.393)$ and $(-0.841, 0.393)$.

10.2.107

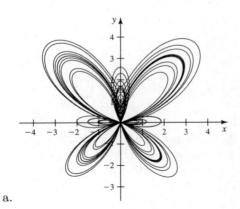

a.

b. It adds multiple layers of the same type of curve as $\sin^5\theta/12$ oscillates between -1 and 1 for $0 \leq \theta \leq 24\pi$.

10.2.108

a. $f(0) = \cos(1) - 1.5$, and $f(2\pi) = \cos(((1 + 12\pi)^{1/2\pi})^{2\pi}) - 1.5 = \cos(1 + 12\pi) - 1.5 = \cos(1) - 1.5 = f(0)$. The points correspond to the polar points $(-0.960, 0)$.

b. No. The curve for $-\pi \le \theta \le 0$ has nowhere where the absolute value of the radius is equal to 1, whereas the curve for $\pi \le \theta \le 2\pi$ has numerous places where this is true, because a^x has a much bigger range on $[0, \pi]$ than on $[-\pi, 0]$.

c. Because $((1 + 2k\pi)^{1/2\pi})^0 = 1$ and $((1 + 2k\pi)^{1/2\pi})^{2\pi} = 1 + 2k\pi$, we have that $f(0) = \cos(1) - b = \cos(1 + 2k\pi) - b = \cos(1) - b = f(2\pi)$.

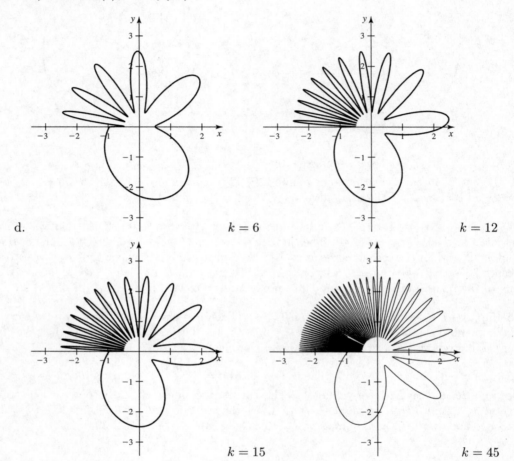

d.

$k = 6$

$k = 12$

$k = 15$

$k = 45$

10.2.109

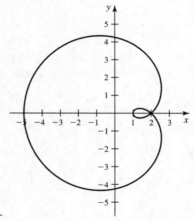

a.

b. $r = 3 - 4\cos \pi t$ is a limaçon, and $x - 2 = r\cos \pi t$ and $y = r\sin \pi t$ is a circle, and the composition of a limaçon and a circle is a limaçon.

10.2.110

a. The region is given by $\{(r, \theta) : 1 \le r \le 2, 0 \le \theta \le \pi\}$.

b. The inflow is given by $\{(r, \theta) : 1 \le r \le 2, \theta = 0\}$. The outflow is given by $\{(r, \theta) : 1 \le r \le 2, \theta = \pi\}$.

c. The tangential velocity at $(1.5, \pi/4)$ is $v(1.5) = 10 \cdot 1.5 = 15$ meters per second. At $(1.2, 3\pi/4)$ it is $v(1.2) = 10 \cdot 1.2 = 12$ meters per second, so it is greater at 1.5.

d. The velocity is greater at $r = 1.3$, because $\frac{20}{1.3} > \frac{20}{1.8}$.

e. $\int_1^2 10r \, dr = 5r^2 \big|_1^2 = 15$, while $\int_1^2 \frac{20}{r} \, dr = 20 \ln r \big|_1^2 \approx 13.86$, so the flow is greater in part c).

10.2.111 With $r = a\cos\theta + b\sin\theta$, we have $r^2 = ar\cos\theta + br\sin\theta$, or $x^2 + y^2 = ax + by$, so $\left(x - \frac{a}{2}\right)^2 + \left(y - \frac{b}{2}\right)^2 = \frac{a^2 + b^2}{4}$. Thus, the center is $(a/2, b/2)$ and $r = \frac{\sqrt{a^2 + b^2}}{2}$.

10.2.112 Note that $\cos(2\theta) = \cos^2\theta - \sin^2\theta$, so $r^2 = a^2(\cos^2\theta - \sin^2\theta)$, so $r^4 = a^2(r^2\cos^2\theta - r^2\sin^2\theta)$, so $(x^2 + y^2)^2 = a^2(x^2 - y^2)$.

10.2.113 Because $\sin(\theta/2) = \sin(\pi - \theta/2) = \sin((2\pi - \theta)/2)$, we have that the graph is symmetric with respect to the x-axis.

10.2.114

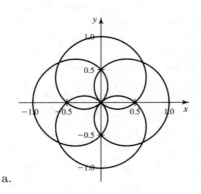

a.

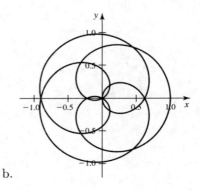

b.

c. If n is even, then the whole curve is generated for $0 \le \theta \le 2m\pi$. If n is odd, then the whole curve is generated for $0 \le \theta \le m\pi$.

10.3 Calculus in Polar Coordinates

10.3.1 Because $x = r\cos\theta$ and $y = r\sin\theta$, we have $x = f(\theta)\cos\theta$ and $y = f(\theta)\sin(\theta)$.

10.3.2 We need $\frac{dy}{dx}$, which can be computed using the formula $\frac{dy}{dx} = \frac{dy/d\theta}{dx/d\theta} = \frac{f'(\theta)\sin\theta + f(\theta)\cos\theta}{f'(\theta)\cos\theta - f(\theta)\sin\theta}$, which will then need to be evaluated at $\theta = \theta_0$.

10.3.3 Because slope is given relative to the horizontal and vertical coordinates, it is given by $\frac{dy}{dx}$, not by $\frac{dr}{d\theta}$.

10.3.4 This would be given by $\frac{1}{2}\int_\alpha^\beta (f(\theta)^2 - g(\theta)^2) \, d\theta$.

10.3.5 $\frac{dy}{dx} = \frac{-\cos\theta\sin\theta + (1 - \sin\theta)\cos\theta}{-\cos^2\theta - (1 - \sin\theta)\sin\theta}$. At $(1/2, \pi/6)$, we have $\frac{dy}{dx} = \frac{0}{-1} = 0$. The given curve intersects the origin $r = 0$ for $\theta = \pi/2$. At this point, $\frac{dy}{dx}$ does not exist, and the tangent line is vertical. (It is the line $\theta = \pi/2$.)

10.3.6 $\frac{dy}{dx} = \frac{-4\sin^2\theta + 4\cos^2\theta}{-8\cos\theta\sin\theta}$. At $(2, \pi/3)$ we have $\frac{dy}{dx} = \frac{-2}{-2\sqrt{3}} = \frac{\sqrt{3}}{3}$. The given curve intersects the origin $r = 0$ for $\theta = \pi/2$ and $\theta = 3\pi/2$. At these points, the derivative does not exist, and the tangent line is vertical, so $\theta = \pi/2$ is the tangent line.

10.3.7 $\frac{dy}{dx} = \frac{16\cos\theta\sin\theta}{-8\sin^2\theta + 8\cos^2\theta}$. At $(4, 5\pi/6)$ we have $\frac{dy}{dx} = \frac{-4\sqrt{3}}{4} = -\sqrt{3}$. The given curve intersects the origin $r = 0$ for $\theta = 0$ and $\theta = \pi$. At these points, the derivative is 0, and the tangent line is horizontal, so $\theta = 0$ is the tangent line.

10.3.8 $\frac{dy}{dx} = \frac{\cos\theta\sin\theta + (4+\sin\theta)\cos\theta}{\cos^2\theta - (4+\sin\theta)\sin\theta}$. At $(4,0)$ we have $\frac{dy}{dx} = \frac{4}{1} = 4$. At $(3, 3\pi/2)$ we have $\frac{dy}{dx} = \frac{0}{3} = 0$. The given curve does not intersect the origin, because $r \geq 3$ for all θ.

10.3.9 $\frac{dy}{dx} = \frac{-3\sin^2\theta + (6+3\cos\theta)\cos\theta}{-3\cos\theta\sin\theta - (6+3\cos\theta)\sin\theta}$. At both $(3, \pi)$ and $(9, 0)$, this doesn't exist. The given curve does not intersect the origin, because $r \geq 3$ for all θ.

10.3.10 $\frac{dy}{dx} = \frac{6\cos(3\theta)\sin\theta + 2\sin(3\theta)\cos\theta}{6\cos(3\theta)\cos\theta - 2\sin(3\theta)\sin\theta}$. The tips of the leaves occur at $\theta = \pi/6$, $\pi/2$ and $5\pi/6$. At $\pi/6$, we have $\frac{dy}{dx} = \frac{\sqrt{3}}{-1} = -\sqrt{3}$. At $\pi/2$ we have $\frac{dy}{dx} = \frac{0}{2} = 0$. At $5\pi/6$ we have $\frac{dy}{dx} = \frac{-\sqrt{3}}{-1} = \sqrt{3}$. The graph intersects the origin for $\theta = 0$, $\theta = \pi/3$, $\theta = 2\pi/3$ and $\theta = \pi$, and these are the corresponding equations of the tangent lines. (Note that the lines $\theta = 0$ and $\theta = \pi$ are the same.)

10.3.11 $\frac{dy}{dx} = \frac{-8\sin(2\theta)\sin\theta + 4\cos(2\theta)\cos\theta}{-8\sin(2\theta)\cos\theta - 4\cos(2\theta)\sin\theta}$. The tips of the leaves occur at $\theta = 0$, $\pi/2$, π and $3\pi/2$. At 0 and at π, we have that $\frac{dy}{dx}$ doesn't exist. At $\pi/2$ and $3\pi/2$ we have $\frac{dy}{dx} = 0$. The graph intersects the origin for $\theta = \pi/4$, $\theta = 3\pi/4$, $\theta = 5\pi/4$ and $\theta = 7\pi/4$, and thus the two distinct tangent lines are $\theta = \pi/4$ and $\theta = 3\pi/4$.

10.3.12 $\frac{dy}{dx} = \frac{0 + 3(\sqrt{2}/2)}{0 - 3(\sqrt{2}/2)} = -1$. The curve is at the origin when $\sin 2\theta = -\frac{1}{2}$, which occurs when $2\theta = 7\pi/6, 11\pi/6, 19\pi/6$, and $23\pi/6$, or $\theta = 7\pi/12, 11\pi/12, 19\pi/12$, and $23\pi/12$.

10.3.13 The curve hits the origin at $\pm\pi/4$, where the tangent lines are given by $\theta = \pi/4$ and $\theta = -\pi/4$. The slopes of those lines are given by $\tan(\pi/4) = 1$ and $\tan(-\pi/4) = -1$.

10.3.14 $\frac{dy}{dx} = \frac{2\sin\theta + 2\theta\cos\theta}{2\cos\theta - 2\theta\sin\theta}$. At $(\pi/2, \pi/4)$ this is $\frac{\sqrt{2} + \pi\sqrt{2}/4}{\sqrt{2} - \pi\sqrt{2}/4} \approx 8.32$. The graph intersects the origin at $\theta = 0$, where there is a horizontal tangent.

10.3.15 Note that the curve is at the origin at $\pi/2$, so there is vertical tangent at $(0, \pi/2)$. Also, $\frac{dy}{dx} = \frac{-4\sin^2\theta + 4\cos^2\theta}{-8\sin\theta\cos\theta} = \frac{1 - 2\sin^2\theta}{\sin(2\theta)}$. Thus, there are horizontal tangents at $\pi/4$ and $3\pi/4$ (at the polar points $(2\sqrt{2}, \pi/4)$ and $(-2\sqrt{2}, 3\pi/4)$). There is also a vertical tangent where $\theta = 0$, at the point $(4, 0)$.

10.3.16 Note that the curve is at the origin at $3\pi/2$, so there is vertical tangent at $(0, 3\pi/2)$. Also, $\frac{dy}{dx} = \frac{2\cos\theta\sin\theta + (2+2\sin\theta)\cos\theta}{2\cos^2\theta - (2+2\sin\theta)\sin\theta} = \frac{\cos\theta(2+4\sin\theta)}{(2-4\sin^2\theta) - 2\sin\theta}$. Thus, the are horizontal tangents where this expression is 0 at $\pi/2$ and $7\pi/6$ and $(11\pi/6)$ (at the polar points $(4, \pi/2)$ and $(1, 7\pi/6)$ and $(1, 11\pi/6)$). There are also vertical tangents where the denominator is 0 and the numerator isn't, which occurs at the point $(3, \pi/6)$ and at $(3, 5\pi/6)$.

10.3.17 Using the double angle identities somewhat liberally:

$$\frac{dy}{dx} = \frac{2\cos(2\theta)\sin\theta + \sin(2\theta)\cos\theta}{2\cos(2\theta)\cos\theta - \sin(2\theta)\sin\theta} = \frac{\sin\theta(\cos 2\theta + \cos^2\theta)}{\cos\theta(\cos(2\theta) - \sin^2\theta)} = \frac{\sin\theta(3\cos^2\theta - 1)}{\cos\theta(1 - 3\sin^2\theta)} = \frac{\sin\theta(3\cos^2\theta - 1)}{\cos\theta(3\cos^2\theta - 2)}.$$

The numerator is 0 for $\theta = 0$ and for $\theta = \pm\cos^{-1}(\pm\sqrt{3}/3)$, so there are horizontal tangents at the corresponding points $(0, 0)$, $(0.943, 0.955)$, $(-0.943, 2.186)$, $(0.943, 4.097)$, and $(-0.943, 5.328)$. The denominator is 0 for $\theta = \pi/2$ and $3\pi/2$, and for $\theta = \pm\cos^{-1}(\pm\sqrt{6}/3)$, so there are vertical tangents at $(0, 0)$, $(0.943, 0.615)$, $(-0.943, 2.526)$, $(0.943, 3.757)$, and $(-0.943, 5.668)$.

10.3.18 The curve intersects the origin at $\theta = 7\pi/6$ and $\theta = 11\pi/6$, so those don't give rise to vertical or horizontal tangents. We have $\frac{dy}{dx} = \frac{6\cos\theta\sin\theta + (3+6\sin\theta)\cos\theta}{6\cos\theta\cos\theta - (3+6\sin\theta)\sin\theta} = \frac{\cos\theta(1+4\sin\theta)}{(2-\sin\theta-4\sin^2\theta)}$. Thus there are horizontal tangents for $\theta = \pi/2$ and $3\pi/2$, at the corresponding points $(9, \pi/2)$ and $(-3, 3\pi/2)$, and at the points where $\sin(\theta) = -1/4$, which are $(3/2, 3.394)$ and $(3/2, 6.031)$. There are vertical tangents where the denominator is 0, which occurs for $\theta = \sin^{-1}\left(-\frac{1}{8} \pm \frac{\sqrt{33}}{8}\right)$, so the corresponding points are $(-2.06, 5.28)$, and $(6.56, .634)$.

10.3.19 The curve intersects the origin at $\theta = \pi/2$, and there is a vertical tangent at $(0, \pi/2)$. $\frac{dy}{dx} = \frac{-\cos\theta\sin\theta + (1-\sin\theta)\cos\theta}{-\cos^2\theta - (1-\sin\theta)\sin\theta} = \frac{\cos\theta(1-2\sin\theta)}{\sin^2\theta - \cos^2\theta - \sin\theta} = \frac{\cos\theta(1-2\sin\theta)}{2\sin^2\theta - \sin\theta - 1}$. There are horizontal tangents when $\sin\theta = 1/2$, which occurs for $\theta = \pi/6, 5\pi/6$, and when $\cos\theta = 0$ (but not $\sin\theta = 1$) which occurs at $\theta = 3\pi/2$. So the horizontal tangents are at $(1/2, \pi/6)$, $((1/2, 5\pi/6)$, and $(2, 3\pi/2)$. There are vertical tangents when $2\sin^2\theta - \sin\theta - 1 = (2\sin\theta + 1)(\sin\theta - 1) = 0$, or $\theta = 7\pi/6$ and $\theta = 11\pi/6$. The vertical tangents are thus at $(3/2, 7\pi/6)$, $(3/2, 11\pi/6)$, and $(0, \pi/2)$, as well as the aforementioned $(0, \pi/2)$.

10.3.20 Note that this curve is actually the vertical line $x = 1$, so it has no horizontal tangents, and a vertical tangent at every θ, so at $(\sec\theta, \theta)$ for every θ.

10.3.21 $A = 2 \cdot \frac{1}{2} \int_0^{\pi/2} \cos\theta \, d\theta = \sin\theta \Big|_0^{\pi/2} = 1.$

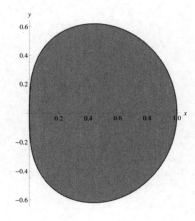

10.3.22 $A = 2 \cdot \frac{1}{2} \int_0^{\pi/4} \cos 2\theta \, d\theta = \frac{1}{2}(\sin 2\theta) \Big|_0^{\pi/4} = \frac{1}{2}.$

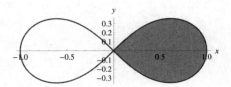

10.3.23
$A = \frac{1}{2} \int_0^\pi (8 \sin\theta)^2 \, d\theta = 32 \int_0^\pi \sin^2\theta \, d\theta = 32 \int_0^\pi \frac{1-\cos 2\theta}{2} \, d\theta = 32 \left(\frac{1}{2}\theta - \frac{\sin\theta\cos\theta}{2} \right) \Big|_0^\pi = 16\pi.$

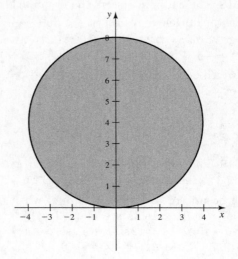

10.3.24
$A = \frac{1}{2} \int_0^{2\pi} (4 + 4\sin\theta)^2 \, d\theta$
$= 8 \int_0^{2\pi} (1 + 2\sin\theta + \sin^2\theta) \, d\theta$
$= 8 \left(\theta - 2\cos\theta + \frac{1}{2}\theta - \frac{\sin\theta\cos\theta}{2} \right) \Big|_0^{2\pi} = 24\pi.$

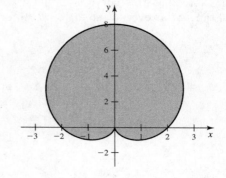

10.3.25
Using symmetry, we have $\frac{1}{2} \cdot 2 \int_0^\pi (2 + \cos\theta)^2 \, d\theta = \int_0^\pi (4 + 4\cos\theta + \cos^2\theta) \, d\theta = \left(4\theta + 4\sin\theta + \frac{1}{2}\theta + \frac{\sin\theta\cos\theta}{2} \right) \Big|_0^\pi = \frac{9\pi}{2}.$

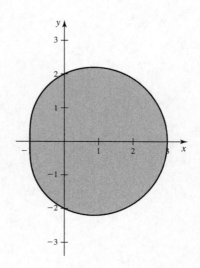

Because there are 4 symmetric leaves, we compute the area of 1/2 of one of the leaves, and then multiply by 8 to get the total area. We have

10.3.26
$\frac{1}{2} \int_0^{\pi/4} 9 \sin^2(2\theta)\, d\theta = \frac{9}{2} \int_0^{\pi/4} \sin^2(2\theta)\, d\theta = \frac{9}{4} \left(\theta - \frac{\sin 2\theta \cos 2\theta}{2} \right) \Big|_0^{\pi/4} = \frac{9\pi}{16}$. So the total area is $8 \cdot \frac{9\pi}{16} = \frac{9\pi}{2}$.

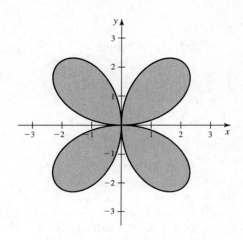

10.3.27
$2 \cdot \frac{1}{2} \int_0^{\pi/6} \cos^2 3\theta\, d\theta = \int_0^{\pi/6} \frac{1 + \cos 6\theta}{2}\, d\theta = \left(\theta/2 + \frac{\sin 6\theta}{6} \right) \Big|_0^{\pi/6} = \frac{\pi}{12}$.

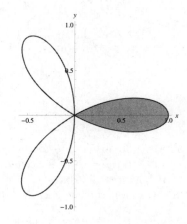

10.3.28
$2 \cdot \frac{1}{2} \int_0^{\pi/3} (\cos\theta - 1/2)^2\, d\theta = \int_0^{\pi/3} (\cos^2\theta - \cos\theta + 1/4)\, d\theta = \int_0^{\pi/3} (\cos(2\theta)/2 - \cos\theta + 3/4)\, d\theta = (\sin(2\theta)/4 - \sin\theta + 3\theta/4) \Big|_0^{\pi/3} = \sqrt{3}/8 - \sqrt{3}/2 + \pi/4 = \pi/4 - \frac{3\sqrt{3}}{8}$.

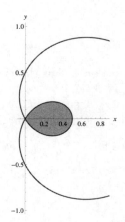

10.3.29

The area is given by $2 \cdot \frac{1}{2} \int_0^{\pi/3} (\cos^2\theta - (1/2)^2) \, d\theta = \int_0^{\pi/3} (\cos(2\theta)/2 + \frac{1}{4}) \, d\theta = (\sin(2\theta)/4 + \theta/4) \Big|_0^{\pi/3} = \frac{\sqrt{3}}{8} + \frac{\pi}{12}.$

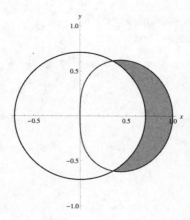

10.3.30

We have already computed the area inside $\sqrt{\cos\theta}$ to be 1. Now we must take away the portion of the circle with radius $1/\sqrt{2}$ between $\theta = -\pi/3$ and $\theta = \pi/3$. This is $1/3$ of a circle, so the area being removed is $(1/3)\pi(1/2) = \pi/6$. We must also remove the area of the regions inside $\sqrt{\cos\theta}$ between $-\pi/2$ and $-\pi/3$ and $\pi/3$ and $\pi/2$. These have area $2 \cdot \frac{1}{2} \int_{\pi/3}^{\pi/2} \cos\theta \, d\theta = (\sin\theta) \Big|_{\pi/3}^{\pi/2} = 1 - \sqrt{3}/2$. So the area is $1 - (\pi/6 + (1 - \sqrt{3}/2)) = \sqrt{3}/2 - \pi/6$.

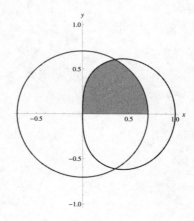

10.3.31

The region inside the circle between 0 and $\pi/3$ is $1/6$ the area of a circle of radius $1/\sqrt{2}$ so it has area $(1/6)\pi(1/2) = \pi/12$. The rest of the area is represented by $\frac{1}{2} \int_{\pi/3}^{\pi} \cos\theta \, d\theta = \frac{1}{2} (\sin\theta) \Big|_{\pi/3}^{\pi} = \frac{1}{2} (1 - \sqrt{3}/2)$. The total area is therefore $\frac{\pi}{12} + \frac{1}{2} - \frac{\sqrt{3}}{4}$.

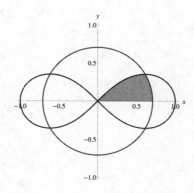

10.3.32

The region inside the circle between 0 and $\pi/6$ is $1/12$ the area of a circle of radius $1/\sqrt{2}$ so it has area $(1/12)\pi(1/2) = \pi/24$. The rest of the area is represented by $\frac{1}{2} \int_{\pi/6}^{\pi/4} \cos 2\theta \, d\theta = \frac{1}{4} (\sin 2\theta) \Big|_{\pi/6}^{\pi/4} = \frac{1}{4} (1 - \sqrt{3}/2)$. The total area is thus $\frac{\pi}{24} + \frac{1}{4} - \frac{\sqrt{3}}{8}$.

10.3.33 Using symmetry, we compute the area of 1/2 of one leaf, and then double it. We have $A = \frac{1}{2}\int_0^{\pi/10}\cos^2(5\theta)\,d\theta = \frac{1}{10}\int_0^{\pi/2}\cos^2 u\,du = \frac{1}{10}\left(\frac{1}{2}u + \frac{\cos u \sin u}{2}\right)\Big|_0^{\pi/2} = \frac{\pi}{40}$. So the area of one leaf is $2 \cdot \frac{\pi}{40} = \frac{\pi}{20}$.

10.3.34 The curves intersect where $4\cos 2\theta = 2$, or $\theta = \pi/6$. By symmetry, we can compute the area of 1/2 of the tip of one leaf, and then multiply by 8. The area of 1/2 of the tip of one leaf is given by $\frac{1}{2}\int_0^{\pi/6}(4\cos(2\theta)^2 - 4)\,d\theta = \int_0^{\pi/6}(8\cos^2(2\theta) - 2)\,d\theta = (4\theta + \sin(4\theta) - 2\theta)\Big|_0^{\pi/6} = \frac{\pi}{3} + \frac{\sqrt{3}}{2}$. Thus the total area desired is $8\left(\frac{\pi}{3} + \frac{\sqrt{3}}{2}\right) = \frac{8\pi}{3} + 4\sqrt{3}$.

10.3.35 Note that the area inside one leaf of the rose but outside the circle is given by $\frac{1}{2}\int_{\pi/12}^{5\pi/12}(16\sin^2(2\theta) - 4)\,d\theta = (2\theta - \sin(4\theta))\Big|_{\pi/12}^{5\pi/2} = \sqrt{3} + \frac{2\pi}{3}$. Also, the area inside one leaf of the rose is $\frac{1}{2}\int_0^{\pi/2}16\sin^2(2\theta)\,d\theta = (4\theta - \sin(4\theta))\Big|_0^{\pi/2} = 2\pi$. Thus the area inside one leaf of the rose and inside the circle must be $2\pi - (\sqrt{3} + \frac{2\pi}{3}) = \frac{4\pi}{3} - \sqrt{3}$, and the total area inside the rose and inside the circle must be $4(\frac{4\pi}{3} - \sqrt{3}) = \frac{16\pi}{3} - 4\sqrt{3}$.

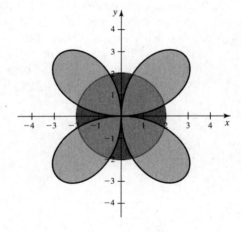

10.3.36 The curves intersect for $2\sin(2\theta) = 1$, which occurs in the first quadrant at $\theta = \pi/12$ and $\theta = 5\pi/12$. So one half of the total desired area is given by $\frac{1}{2}\int_{\pi/12}^{5\pi/12}(2\sin(2\theta) - 1)\,d\theta = \frac{1}{2}\left(-\cos(2\theta) - \theta\right)\Big|_{\pi/12}^{5\pi/12} = -\frac{1}{2}\left(-\sqrt{3} + \frac{\pi}{3}\right) = \frac{\sqrt{3}}{2} - \frac{\pi}{6}$. So the total desired area is $\sqrt{3} - \frac{\pi}{3}$.

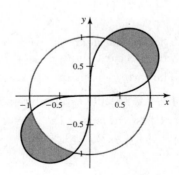

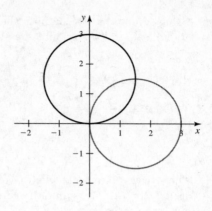

10.3.37   These curves intersect when $\sin\theta = \cos\theta$, which occurs at $\theta = \pi/4$ and $\theta = 5\pi/4$, and when $r = 0$ which occurs for $\theta = 0$ and $\theta = \pi$ for the first curve and $\theta = \pi/2$ and $\theta = 3\pi/2$ for the second curve. Only two of these intersection points are unique: the origin and the point $(3\sqrt{2}/2, \pi/4) = (-3\sqrt{2}/2, 5\pi/4)$.

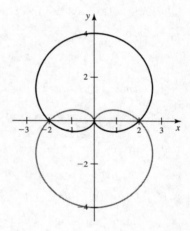

10.3.38   The curves intersect where $2 + 2\sin\theta = 2 - 2\sin\theta$, which occurs when $\sin\theta = 0$. The curves also intersect at the origin, which occurs for the first curve at $\theta = 3\pi/2$ and for the second curve at $\pi/2$. The only points of intersection are the origin, $(2,0)$ and $(2,\pi)$.

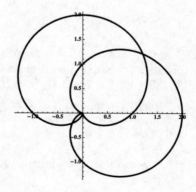

10.3.39   The curves intersect when $\sin\theta = \cos\theta$, which occurs for $\theta = \pi/4$ and $\theta = 5\pi/4$. The corresponding points are $\left(\frac{2+\sqrt{2}}{2}, \frac{\pi}{4}\right)$ and $\left(\frac{2-\sqrt{2}}{2}, \frac{5\pi}{4}\right)$. They also intersect at the pole: the first curve is at the pole at $(0,\pi)$ and the other at $(0, 3\pi/2)$.

10.3.40 These curves intersect when $\cos(2\theta) = \frac{\sqrt{2}}{2}$, which occurs when $2\theta = \pi/4, 7\pi/4, \ldots,$ so for $\theta = \pi/8, 7\pi/8, \ldots.$ The intersection points are thus $(1, \pi/8), (1, 7\pi/8), (1, 9\pi/8), (1, 15\pi/8), (1, 17\pi/8), (1, 23\pi/8), (1, 25\pi/8),$ and $((1, 31\pi/8).$

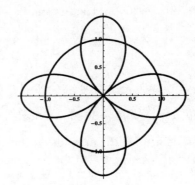

10.3.41 By symmetry, we need to compute the area inside $r = 3\sin\theta$ between 0 and $\pi/4$ and then double that result. We have $2 \cdot \frac{1}{2} \int_0^{\pi/4} 9\sin^2\theta \, d\theta = \frac{9}{2} \int_0^{\pi/4} (1 - \cos(2\theta)) \, d\theta = \frac{9}{2} \left. (\theta - (1/2)\sin(2\theta)) \right|_0^{\pi/4} = \frac{9}{2} \left(\frac{\pi}{4} - \frac{1}{2} \right) = \frac{9}{8}(\pi - 2).$

10.3.42 By symmetry, we need to compute the area of the region inside $r = 2 - 2\sin\theta$ between 0 and $\pi/2$ and then quadruple it. We have $4 \cdot \frac{1}{2} \int_0^{\pi/2} (2 - 2\sin\theta)^2 \, d\theta = 8 \int_0^{\pi/2} (1 - 2\sin\theta + \sin^2\theta) \, d\theta = 8 \int_0^{\pi/2} ((3/2) - 2\sin\theta - (1/2)\cos 2\theta) \, d\theta = \left. (12\theta + 16\cos\theta - 2\sin(2\theta)) \right|_0^{\pi/2} = 6\pi + 0 - 0 - (0 + 16 - 0) = 6\pi - 16.$

10.3.43 By symmetry, we can compute the area between $\pi/4$ and $5\pi/4$ inside $r = 1 + \cos\theta$ and then double it. This will include both the bigger and smaller enclosed regions. We have $2 \cdot \frac{1}{2} \int_{\pi/4}^{5\pi/4} (1 + \cos\theta)^2 \, d\theta = \int_{\pi/4}^{5\pi/4} (1 + 2\cos\theta + (1/2)(1 + \cos(2\theta))) \, d\theta = \int_{\pi/4}^{5\pi/4} ((3/2) + 2\cos\theta + (1/2)(\cos 2\theta)) \, d\theta = \left. (3\theta/2 + 2\sin\theta + (1/4)\sin 2\theta) \right|_{\pi/4}^{5\pi/4} = \left(\frac{15\pi}{8} - \sqrt{2} + \frac{1}{4} \right) - \left(\frac{3\pi}{8} + \sqrt{2} + \frac{1}{4} \right) = \frac{3\pi}{2} - 2\sqrt{2}.$

10.3.44 By symmetry, we can compute the area between 0 and $\pi/8$ within the circle $r = 1$ and add it to the area between $\pi/8$ and $\pi/4$ within the curve $\sqrt{2}\cos 2\theta$ and then multiply this by 8. The area within the circle between 0 and $\pi/8$ is $(1/16)$th the area of the circle, so this area is $\frac{\pi}{16}$. The area between $\pi/8$ and $\pi/4$ within $\sqrt{2}\cos 2\theta$ is given by $\frac{1}{2} \int_{\pi/8}^{\pi/4} 2\cos^2 2\theta \, d\theta = \frac{1}{2} \int_{\pi/8}^{\pi/4} (1 + \cos 4\theta) \, d\theta = \frac{1}{2} \left. (\theta + (1/4)\sin 4\theta) \right|_{\pi/8}^{\pi/4} = \frac{1}{2} \left(\frac{\pi}{4} + 0 - \left(\frac{\pi}{8} + \frac{1}{4} \right) \right) = \frac{\pi}{16} - \frac{1}{8}.$ Adding this to the previously computed area gives that $1/8$ of the total area is $\frac{\pi}{16} - \frac{1}{8} + \frac{\pi}{16} = \frac{\pi}{8} - \frac{1}{8}.$ Thus the total area we are seeking is $\pi - 1.$

10.3.45

a. False. The area is given by $\frac{1}{2} \int_\alpha^\beta f(\theta)^2 \, d\theta.$

b. False. The slope is given by $\frac{dy}{dx}$, which can be computed using the formula

$$\frac{dy}{dx} = \frac{dy/d\theta}{dx/d\theta} = \frac{f'(\theta)\sin\theta + f(\theta)\cos\theta}{f'(\theta)\cos\theta - f(\theta)\sin\theta}.$$

10.3.46 The polar point $(-1, 3\pi/2)$ is equivalent to the polar point $(1, \pi/2)$ which does satisfy the equation.

10.3.47 The circles intersect for $\theta = \pi/6$ and $\theta = 5\pi/6.$

The area inside $r = 2\sin\theta$ but outside of $r = 1$ would be given by $\frac{1}{2} \int_{\pi/6}^{5\pi/6} (4\sin^2\theta - 1) \, d\theta = \frac{1}{2} \left. (x - \sin(2x)) \right|_{\pi/6}^{5\pi/6} = \frac{\pi}{3} + \frac{\sqrt{3}}{2}.$ The total area of $r = 2\sin\theta$ is $\pi.$ Thus, the area inside both circles is $\pi - \left(\frac{\pi}{3} + \frac{\sqrt{3}}{2} \right) = \frac{2\pi}{3} - \frac{\sqrt{3}}{2}.$

10.3.48 The inner loop is traced from $\theta = 2\pi/3$ to $\theta = 4\pi/3$. So the area is given by $\frac{1}{2} \int_{2\pi/3}^{4\pi/3} (2 + 4\cos\theta)^2 \, d\theta =$
$\int_{2\pi/3}^{4\pi/3} (2 + 8\cos\theta + 8\cos^2\theta) \, d\theta = \left(2\theta + 8\sin\theta + 4\theta + 2\sin(2\theta)\right) \Big|_{2\pi/3}^{4\pi/3} = 4\pi - 6\sqrt{3}$.

10.3.49 The inner loop is traced out between $\theta = \pi/6$ and $\theta = 5\pi/6$, so its area is given by $\frac{1}{2} \int_{\pi/6}^{5\pi/6} (3 -$
$6\sin\theta)^2 \, d\theta = \frac{1}{2} \int_{\pi/6}^{5\pi/6} (9 - 36\sin\theta + 36\sin^2\theta) \, d\theta = \frac{3}{2} \left(3\theta + 12\cos\theta + 6\theta - 3\sin(2\theta)\right) \Big|_{\pi/6}^{5\pi/6} = 9\pi - \frac{27\sqrt{3}}{2}$.

We can determine the area inside the outer loop by using symmetry and doubling the area of the region traced out between $5\pi/6$ and $3\pi/2$. Thus the area inside the outer region is $2 \cdot \frac{1}{2} \int_{5\pi/6}^{3\pi/2} (3 - 6\sin\theta)^2 \, d\theta =$
$3 \left(3\theta + 12\cos\theta + 6\theta - 3\sin(2\theta)\right) \Big|_{5\pi/6}^{3\pi/2} = 18\pi + \frac{27\sqrt{3}}{2}$. So the area outside the inner loop and inside the outer loop is $18\pi + \frac{27\sqrt{3}}{2} - \left(9\pi - \frac{27\sqrt{3}}{2}\right) = 9\pi + 27\sqrt{3}$.

10.3.50 The curves intersect at $\theta = \pi/3$, and using symmetry, the area we seek is $2 \cdot \frac{1}{2} \int_0^{\pi/3} (1 + \cos\theta)^2 \, d\theta +$
$2 \cdot \frac{1}{2} \int_{\pi/3}^{\pi/2} (3\cos\theta)^2 \, d\theta = \int_0^{\pi/3} (1 + 2\cos\theta + \cos^2\theta) \, d\theta + \int_{\pi/3}^{\pi/2} 9\cos^2\theta \, d\theta = \left(\theta + 2\sin\theta + \frac{\theta}{2} + \frac{\sin 2\theta}{4}\right) \Big|_0^{\pi/3} +$
$\left(\frac{9\theta}{2} + \frac{9\sin 2\theta}{4}\right) \Big|_{\pi/3}^{\pi/2} = \frac{\pi}{2} + 2 \cdot \frac{\sqrt{3}}{2} + \frac{\sqrt{3}}{8} + \frac{9\pi}{4} - \left(\frac{3\pi}{2} + \frac{9\sqrt{3}}{8}\right) = \frac{5\pi}{4}$.

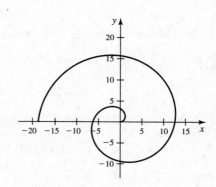

10.3.51 The first horizontal tangent line is at the origin. The next is at approximately $(4.0576, 2.0288)$, and the third at approximately $(9.8262, 4.9131)$. The first vertical tangent line is at approximately $(1.7206, 0.8603)$, the next is at about $(6.8512, 3.4256)$, and the next at approximately $(12.8746, 6.4373)$.

10.3.52

a. The area of one half of one leaf is $\frac{1}{2} \int_0^{\pi/(4m)} \cos^2(2m\theta) \, d\theta = \left(\frac{\theta}{4} + \frac{\sin(4m\theta)}{16m}\right) \Big|_0^{\pi/(4m)} = \frac{\pi}{16m}$. So the area of all $8m$ half-leaves is $\frac{\pi}{2}$.

b. The area of one half of one leaf is $\frac{1}{2} \int_0^{\pi/(4m+2)} \cos^2((2m+1)\theta) \, d\theta = \left(\frac{\theta}{4} + \frac{\sin(2(2m+1)\theta)}{4(4m+2)}\right) \Big|_0^{\pi/(4m+2)} =$
$\frac{\pi}{8 \cdot (2m+1)}$. So the area of all $2(2m+1)$ half-leaves is $\frac{\pi}{4}$.

10.3.53

a. $A_n = \frac{1}{2} \int_{(2n-2)\pi}^{(2n-1)\pi} e^{-2\theta} \, d\theta - \frac{1}{2} \int_{2n\pi}^{(2n+1)\pi} e^{-2\theta} \, d\theta = -\frac{1}{4} e^{-(4n-2)\pi} + \frac{1}{4} e^{-(4n-4)\pi} + \frac{1}{4} e^{-(4n+2)\pi} - \frac{1}{4} e^{-4n\pi}$.

b. Each term tends to 0 as $n \to \infty$ so $\lim_{n\to\infty} A_n = 0$.

c. $\dfrac{A_{n+1}}{A_n} = \dfrac{e^{-(4n+2)\pi} + e^{-(4n)\pi} + e^{-(4n+6)\pi} - e^{-(4n+4)\pi}}{e^{-(4n-2)\pi} + e^{-(4n-4)\pi} + e^{-(4n+2)\pi} - e^{-4n\pi}} = e^{-4\pi}$, so $\lim_{n\to\infty} \dfrac{A_{n+1}}{A_n} = e^{-4\pi}$.

10.3.54 The area of one half of one leaf is $\frac{1}{2}\int_0^{\pi/6} 4 \cdot \cos^2(3\theta)\, d\theta = \left(\theta + \frac{\sin(6\theta)}{6}\right)\Big|_0^{\pi/6} = \frac{\pi}{6}$. So the area of all 6 half-leaves is π.

10.3.55 One half of the area is given by $\frac{1}{2}\int_0^{\pi/2} 6\sin 2\theta\, d\theta = -\frac{3}{2}\cos 2\theta \Big|_0^{\pi/2} = 3$, so the total area is 6.

10.3.56 By symmetry, we can compute the area between $\theta = 5\pi/6$ and $\theta = 3\pi/2$ and double it. Thus, the total area we seek is given by $\int_{5\pi/6}^{3\pi/2}(2 - 4\sin\theta)^2\, d\theta = \int_{5\pi/6}^{3\pi/2}(4 - 16\sin\theta + 16\sin^2\theta)\, d\theta =$
$\left(4\theta + 16\cos\theta + 8\theta - 4\sin(2\theta)\right)\Big|_{5\pi/6}^{3\pi/2} = 6\sqrt{3} + 8\pi$.

10.3.57 The area is given by

$$\frac{1}{2}\int_0^{2\pi}(4 - 2\cos\theta)^2\, d\theta = \int_0^{2\pi}(8 - 8\cos\theta + 2\cos^2\theta)\, d\theta = \left(8\theta - 8\sin\theta + \theta + \frac{1}{2}\sin(2\theta)\right)\Big|_0^{2\pi} = 18\pi.$$

10.3.58

a. Because V and R are constants, the function is a parabola which opens downward with vertex at $(0, V)$, so the velocity is maximal when $r = 0$.

b. The average velocity is $\frac{1}{\pi R^2} \cdot 2\pi \cdot \int_0^R V \cdot \left(1 - \frac{r^2}{R^2}\right) r\, dr = \frac{2\pi}{\pi R^2} V \left(-\frac{r^4}{4R^2} + \frac{r^2}{2}\right)\Big|_0^R = \frac{2}{R^2} \cdot \frac{VR^2}{4} = \frac{V}{2}$.

c. The average velocity is $\frac{1}{\pi R^2} \cdot 2\pi \cdot \int_0^R V \cdot \left(1 - \frac{r^2}{R^2}\right)^{1/p} r\, dr = \frac{2V}{R^2} \cdot \frac{1}{R^{2/p}}\int_0^R (R^2 - r^2)^{1/p} \cdot r\, dr = \frac{2V}{R^2} \cdot$
$\frac{1}{R^{1/p}}\left(-\frac{p\left(R^2 - r^2\right)^{\frac{1}{p}+1}}{2p+2}\right)\Big|_0^R = \frac{2V}{R^2} \cdot \frac{1}{R^{2/p}} \cdot \frac{p(R^2)^{(p+1)/p}}{2p+2} = \frac{2pV}{2p+2}$.

c. $\lim_{p\to\infty} V_{\text{avg}} = V \cdot \lim_{p\to\infty} \frac{2p}{2p+2} = V$.

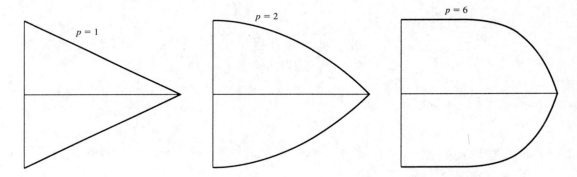

10.3.59 Suppose that the goat is tethered at the origin, and that the center of the corral is $(1, \pi)$. The circle that the goat can graze is $r = a$, and the corral is given by $r = -2\cos\theta$. The intersection occurs for $\theta = \cos^{-1}(-a/2)$.

The area grazed by the goat is twice the area of the sector of the circle $r = a$ between $\cos^{-1}(-a/2)$ and π, plus twice the area of the circle $r = -2\cos\theta$ between $\pi/2$ and $\cos^{-1}(-a/2)$. Thus we need to compute

$A = \int_{\cos^{-1}(-a/2)}^{\pi} a^2\, d\theta + \int_{\pi/2}^{\cos^{-1}(-a/2)} 4\cos^2\theta\, d\theta = a^2\pi - a^2\cos^{-1}(-a/2) + \left(2\cos\theta\sin\theta + 2\theta\right)\Big|_{\pi/2}^{\cos^{-1}(-a/2)} =$

$a^2(\pi - \cos^{-1}(-a/2)) - \pi - \frac{1}{2}a\sqrt{4 - a^2} + 2\cos^{-1}(-a/2)$. Note that $\pi - \cos^{-1}(-a/2) = \cos^{-1}(a/2)$, so this can be written as $(a^2 - 2)\cos^{-1}(a/2) + \pi - \frac{1}{2}a\sqrt{4 - a^2}$. Note that for $a = 0$ this is 0, and for $a = 2$, this is π, as desired.

10.3.60 Imagine that the boundary of the concrete slab is the fence from the previous problem Then the area the goat could graze in the previous problem becomes the area it can't graze in this problem. If the slab weren't there, the goat could graze a region of area πa^2. Thus, the goat can graze a region of area $\pi a^2 - \left((a^2 - 2)\cos^{-1}(a/2) + \pi - \frac{1}{2}a\sqrt{4 - a^2}\right) = \pi(a^2 - 1) + \frac{1}{2}a\sqrt{4 - a^2} + (2 - a^2)\cos^{-1}(a/2)$. If $a = 0$, this quantity is 0, while if $a = 2$, this quantity is 3π.

10.3.61 Again, suppose that the goat is tethered at the origin, and that the center of the corral is $(1, \pi)$. The equation of the corral fence is given by $r = -2\cos\theta$. Note that to the right of the vertical line $\theta = \pi/2$, the goat can graze a half-circle of area $\pi a^2/2$. Also, there is a region in the 2nd quadrant and one in the 3rd quadrant of equal size that can also be grazed. Let this region have area A, so that the total area grazed will then be $\frac{\pi a^2}{2} + 2A$.

Imagine that the goat is walking "west" from the polar point $(a, \pi/2)$, and is keeping the rope taut until his whole rope is along the fence in the third quadrant. Let ϕ be the central angle angle from the origin to the polar point $(1, \pi)$ to the point on the fence that the goat's rope is touching as he makes this walk. When the goat is at $(a, \pi/2)$, we have $\phi = 0$. When the goat is all the way to the fence, we have $\phi = a$. Then length of the rope not along the fence is $a - \phi$. Thus, the value of A is $\frac{1}{2}\int_0^a (a - \phi)^2 d\phi = \frac{1}{2}\left(a^2\phi - a\phi^2 + \frac{\phi^3}{3}\right)\Big|_0^a = \frac{a^3}{6}$.

Thus, the goat can graze a region of area $\frac{\pi a^2}{2} + \frac{a^3}{3}$.

10.3.62

a. The slope of the line tangent to $r = f(\theta)$ at P is $\frac{dy}{dx}\Big|_P$. Also, the slope of a line intersecting the x-axis at an angle α is $\tan\alpha$. (Note that in the picture, $\tan(\pi - \alpha) = -\tan(\alpha) = \frac{\text{rise}}{-\text{run}} = -\text{slope of the tangent line.})$

b. Draw a vertical line through P and let Q be the point where this line intersects the x-axis. Then in triangle OPQ we see $\tan\theta = \frac{y}{x}$.

c. Note that

$$\frac{dy}{dx} = \frac{f'(\theta)\sin\theta + f(\theta)\cos\theta}{f'(\theta)\cos\theta - f(\theta)\sin\theta} = \frac{\tan\theta + \frac{f(\theta)}{f'(\theta)}}{1 - \frac{f(\theta)}{f'(\theta)}\tan\theta} = \tan\alpha.$$

Because $\alpha = \phi + \theta$ and $\tan(\phi + \theta) = \frac{\tan\theta + \tan\phi}{1 - \tan\phi\tan\theta}$, we see that $\tan\phi = \frac{f(\theta)}{f'(\theta)}$.

d. l is parallel to the x-axis when $\frac{dy}{dx} = 0$, or when $f'(\theta)\sin\theta + f(\theta)\cos\theta = 0$, hence if $\tan\theta = -\frac{f(\theta)}{f'(\theta)}$.

e. l is parallel to the y-axis when $\frac{dx}{dy} = 0$, which occurs when $f'(\theta)\cos\theta - f(\theta)\sin\theta = 0$, hence if $\tan\theta = \frac{f(\theta)}{f'(\theta)}$.

10.3.63

a. If $\cot\phi = \frac{f'(\theta)}{f(\theta)}$ is constant for all θ, then $\phi = \cot^{-1}\left(\frac{f'(\theta)}{f(\theta)}\right)$ is constant. Then $\frac{d}{d\theta}\ln(f(\theta)) = \frac{1}{f(\theta)} \cdot f'(\theta) = \cot\phi$ is constant.

b. If $f(\theta) = Ce^{k\theta}$, then $\cot\phi = \frac{f'(\theta)}{f(\theta)} = \frac{kCe^{k\theta}}{Ce^{k\theta}} = k$.

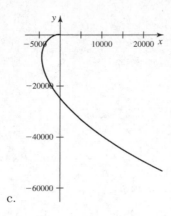

c.

10.4   Conic Sections

10.4.1 A parabola is the set of points in the plane which are equidistant from a given fixed point and a given fixed line.

10.4.2 An ellipse is the set of points in the plane with the property that the sum of the distances from the point to two given fixed points is a given constant.

10.4.3 A hyperbola is the set of points in the plane with the property that the difference of the distances from the point to two given fixed points is a given constant.

10.4.4

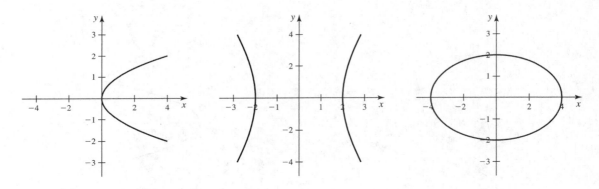

10.4.5

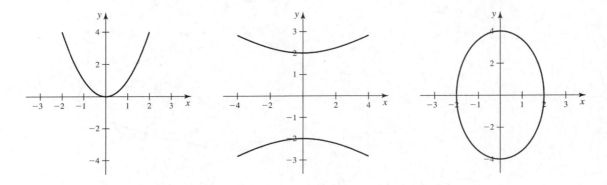

10.4.6 $x^2 = 4py$, where $p < 0$.

10.4.7 $\left(\dfrac{x}{a}\right)^2 + \dfrac{y^2}{a^2 - c^2} = 1$.

10.4.8 $\left(\dfrac{y}{a}\right)^2 - \dfrac{x^2}{c^2 - a^2} = 1$.

10.4.9 The foci for both are $(\pm ae, 0)$.

10.4.10 By theorem 11.4, this is given by $r = \frac{ed}{1 + e\cos\theta}$, $-\pi < \theta < \pi$.

10.4.11 The asymptotes are $y = -\frac{b}{a} \cdot x$ and $y = \frac{b}{a} \cdot x$.

10.4.12 If $e = 1$, the conic section is a parabola. If $e > 1$, it is a hyperbola. If $0 < e < 1$, it is an ellipse.

10.4.13   Directrix: $y = -3$. Focus: $(0, 3)$.

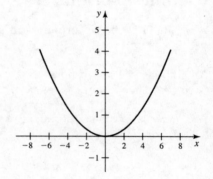

10.4.14   Directrix: $x = -5$. Focus: $(5, 0)$.

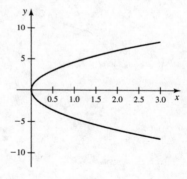

10.4.15   Directrix: $x = 4$. Focus: $(-4, 0)$.

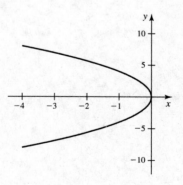

10.4.16 Directrix: $x = 1$. Focus: $(-1, 0)$.

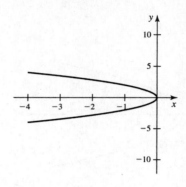

10.4.17 Directrix: $y = \frac{2}{3}$. Focus: $\left(0, -\frac{2}{3}\right)$.

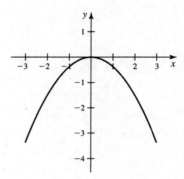

10.4.18 Directrix: $x = -\frac{3}{5}$. Focus: $\left(\frac{3}{5}, 0\right)$.

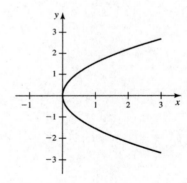

10.4.19

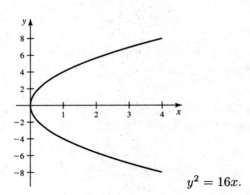

$y^2 = 16x$.

10.4.20

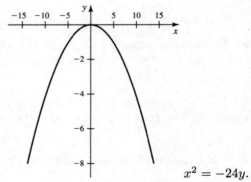

$x^2 = -24y$.

10.4.21   **10.4.22**

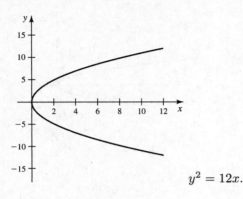

$$y^2 = 12x.$$

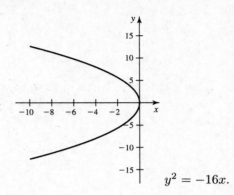

$$y^2 = -16x.$$

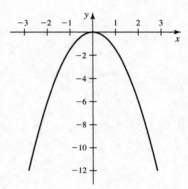

10.4.23 $x^2 = 4py$ and $4 = 4p(-6)$, so $p = -\frac{1}{6}$ and
$x^2 = -\frac{2}{3} \cdot y$.

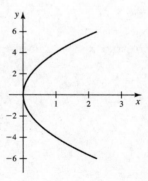

10.4.24 $y^2 = 4px$ and $(-4)^2 = 4p(1)$, so $p = 4$ and
$y^2 = 16x$.

10.4.25 Because the vertex is $(-1, 0)$ and the parabola is symmetric about the x-axis, we have $y^2 = 4p(x+1)$ and because the directrix is one unit left of the vertex, we obtain $p = 1$ and $y^2 = 4(x + 1)$.

10.4.26 Because the vertex is $(0, 4)$ and the parabola is symmetric about the y-axis, we have $x^2 = 4p(y - 2)$ and because the directrix is 2 units above the vertex, we obtain $p = -2$ and $x^2 = -8(y - 2)$.

10.4.27 Vertices are $(\pm 2, 0)$, and the foci are $(\pm\sqrt{3}, 0)$. The major axis has length 4 and the minor axis has length 2.

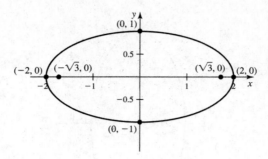

10.4.28 Vertices are $(\pm 3, 0)$, and the foci are $(\pm\sqrt{5}, 0)$. The major axis has length 6 and the minor axis has length 4.

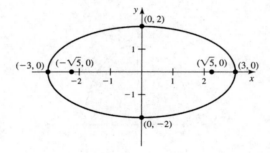

10.4.29 Vertices are $(0, \pm 4)$, and the foci are $(0, \pm 2\sqrt{3})$. The major axis has length 8 and the minor axis has length 4.

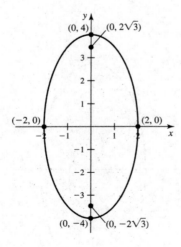

10.4.30 Vertices are $(0, \pm 3)$, and the foci are $(0, \pm 2\sqrt{2})$. The major axis has length 6 and the minor axis has length 2.

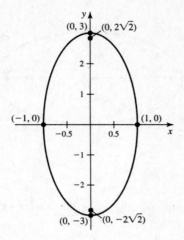

10.4.31 Vertices are $(0, \pm\sqrt{7})$, and the foci are $(0, \pm\sqrt{2})$. The major axis has length $2\sqrt{7}$ and the minor axis has length $2\sqrt{5}$.

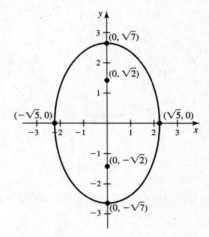

10.4.32 Vertices are $(0, \pm 2\sqrt{3})$, and the foci are $(0, \pm\sqrt{7})$. The major axis has length $4\sqrt{3}$ and the minor axis has length $2\sqrt{5}$.

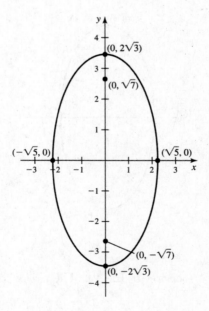

10.4.33 $a = 4$, and $b = 3$, so the equation is $\frac{x^2}{16} + \frac{y^2}{9} = 1$.

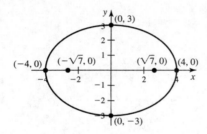

10.4.34 $a = 6$, and $a^2 = b^2 + c^2$ where $c = 4$, so $b^2 = 36 - 16 = 20$, and the equation is $\frac{x^2}{36} + \frac{y^2}{20} = 1$.

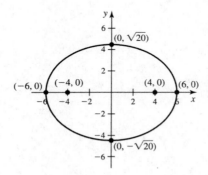

10.4.35 $a = 5$, and the equation is of the form $\frac{x^2}{25} + \frac{y^2}{b^2} = 1$. Because $(4, \frac{3}{5})$ is on the curve, we have $\frac{16}{25} + \frac{9}{25b^2} = 1$, so $b = 1$. The equation is $\frac{x^2}{25} + y^2 = 1$.

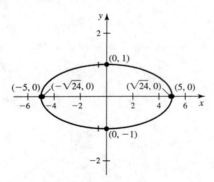

10.4.36 $a = 10$, and the equation is of the form $\frac{y^2}{100} + \frac{x^2}{b^2} = 1$, and because $(\sqrt{3}/2, 5)$ is on the curve, we have $\frac{1}{4} + \frac{3}{4b^2} = 1$, so $b = 1$. The equation is $x^2 + \frac{y^2}{100} = 1$.

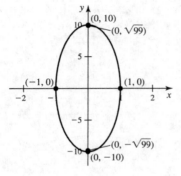

10.4.37 $a = 3$ and $b = 2$, so the equation is $\frac{x^2}{4} + \frac{y^2}{9} = 1$.

10.4.38 $a = 10$ and $b = 8$, so $\frac{x^2}{100} + \frac{y^2}{64} = 1$.

10.4.39 The vertices are $(\pm 2, 0)$, and the foci are $(\pm\sqrt{5}, 0)$. The asymptotes are $y = \frac{\pm 1}{2} \cdot x$.

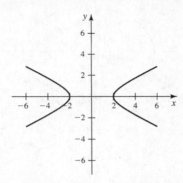

10.4.40 The vertices are $(0, \pm 4)$, and the foci are $(0, \pm 5)$. The asymptotes are $y = \frac{\pm 4}{3} \cdot x$.

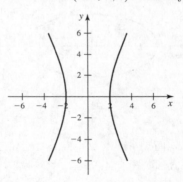

10.4.41 The vertices are $(\pm 2, 0)$, and the foci are $(\pm 2\sqrt{5}, 0)$. The asymptotes are $y = \pm 2x$.

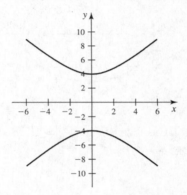

10.4.42 The vertices are $(0, \pm 2)$, and the foci are $(0, \pm 29)$. The asymptotes are $y = \frac{\pm 2}{5} \cdot x$.

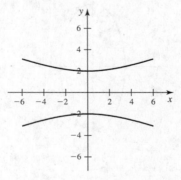

10.4.43 The vertices are $(\pm\sqrt{3}, 0)$, and the foci are $(\pm 2\sqrt{2}, 0)$. The asymptotes are $y = \pm\sqrt{\frac{5}{3}} \cdot x$.

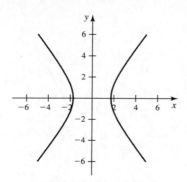

10.4.44 The vertices are $(\pm\sqrt{14}, 0)$, and the foci are $(\pm\sqrt{34}, 0)$. The asymptotes are $y = \pm\sqrt{\frac{10}{7}} \cdot x$.

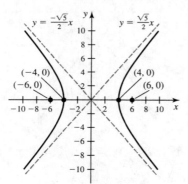

10.4.45 We have $a = 4$ and $c = 6$, so $b^2 = c^2 - a^2 = 20$, so the equation is $\frac{x^2}{16} - \frac{y^2}{20} = 1$.

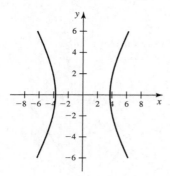

10.4.46 We have $a = 1$, so the equation is of the form $x^2 - \frac{y^2}{b^2} = 1$. Because $(5/3, 8)$ is on the curve, we have $\frac{25}{9} - \frac{64}{b^2} = 1$, so $b = 6$. The equation is $x^2 - \frac{y^2}{36} = 1$.

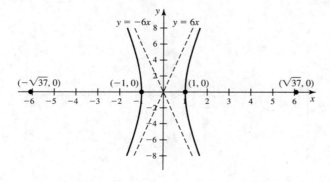

10.4.47 We have $a = 2$, and because the asymptoes are $y = \frac{\pm bx}{a}$, we have that $b = 3$, so the equation is $\frac{x^2}{4} - \frac{y^2}{9} = 1$.

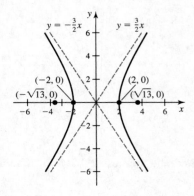

10.4.48 We have $a = 2$ and because the asymptotes are $y = \frac{\pm a}{b} \cdot x$, we have $b = 1$, and the equation is $\frac{y^2}{4} - x^2 = 1$.

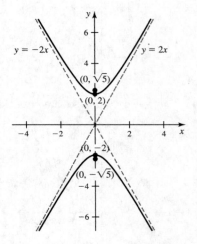

10.4.49 We have $a = 4$ and $c = 5$, so $b^2 = 25 - 16 = 9$, so $b = 3$ and the equation is $\frac{x^2}{16} - \frac{y^2}{9} = 1$.

10.4.50 We have $a = 6$ and $c = 10$, and $b^2 = 100 - 36 = 64$, so $b = 8$, and the equation is $\frac{y^2}{36} - \frac{x^2}{64} = 1$.

10.4.51 We have $a = 9$ and $e = \frac{1}{3}$, so $c = ae = 3$, and $b^2 = a^2 - c^2 = 72$, so the equation is $\frac{x^2}{81} + \frac{y^2}{72} = 1$.

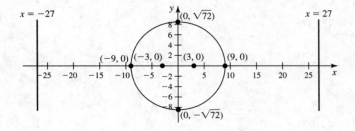

10.4.52 We have $a = 9$ and $e = \frac{1}{4}$, so $c = ae = \frac{9}{4}$, and $b^2 = a^2 - c^2 = 81 - \frac{81}{16} = \frac{1215}{16}$. Thus the equation is $\frac{16x^2}{1215} + \frac{y^2}{81} = 1$.

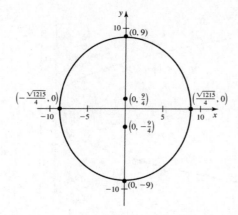

10.4.53 We have $a = 1$ and $e = 3$, so $c = ae = 3$ and $b^2 = c^2 - a^2 = 9 - 1 = 8$. Thus, the equation is $x^2 - \frac{y^2}{8} = 1$.

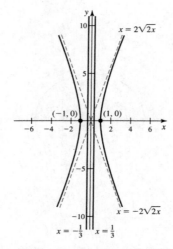

10.4.54 We have $a = 4$ and $e = 2$, so $c = ae = 8$ and $b^2 = c^2 - a^2 = 64 - 16 = 48$. Thus, the equation is $\frac{y^2}{16} - \frac{x^2}{48} = 1$.

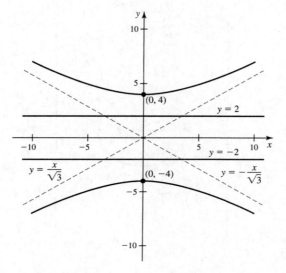

10.4.55 The vertex is $(2,0)$. The focus is $(0,0)$, and the directrix is the line $x = 4$.

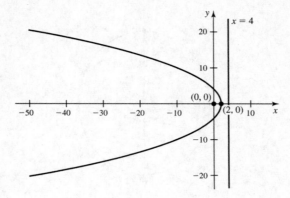

10.4.56 The vertices are $(4/3,0)$ and $(-4,0)$. The center is $(-4/3,0)$. The foci are $(0,0)$ and $(-8/3,0)$.

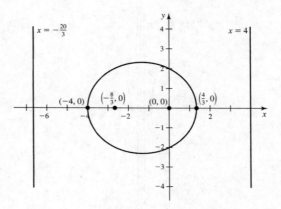

10.4.57 The vertices are $(1,0)$ and $(-1/3,0)$. The center is $(1/3,0)$. The directrices are $x = -1$ and $x = 5/3$.

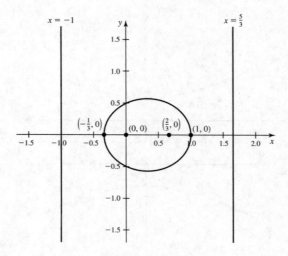

10.4.58 The vertices are $(0, 6/5)$ and $(0, -6)$. The center is $(0, -12/5)$. The foci are $(0, 0)$ and $(-24/5, 0)$.

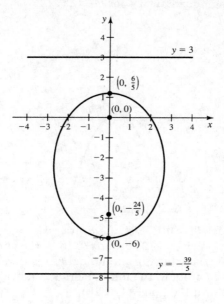

10.4.59 The vertex is $(0, -1/4)$, and the focus is $(0, 0)$. The directrix is the line $y = -\frac{1}{2}$.

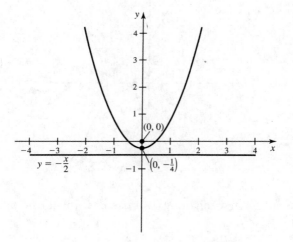

10.4.60 The vertices are $(6, 0)$ and $(-3, 0)$. The center is $(3/2, 0)$. The foci are $(0, 0)$ and $(3, 0)$.

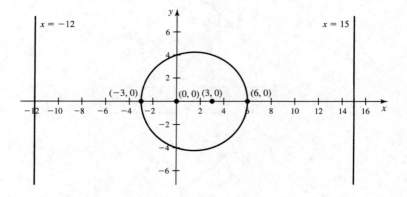

10.4.61 The parabola starts at $(1, 0)$ and goes through quadrants I, II, and III for $\theta \in [0, 3\pi/2]$. It then approaches $(1, 0)$ by traveling through quadrant IV for $\theta \in (3\pi/2, 2\pi)$.

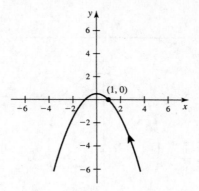

10.4.62 Note that the value of r for $\theta = 0$ is $1/3$. As θ proceeds to $\pi/2$, the curve is traced in the first quadrant and approaches the polar point $(1, \pi/2)$ From $\pi/2$ to π, the curve approaches the asymptote, and then appears along the asymptote in the fourth quadrant and heads toward the polar point $(-1, \pi)$. From π to 2π, the curve approaches the asymptote in the first quadrant, and then reappears in the third quadrant along the asymptote, and heads toward the point $(1/3, 2\pi)$.

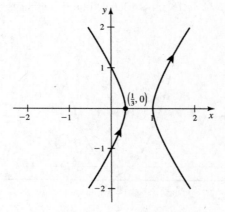

10.4.63 The parabola begins in the first quadrant and passes through the points $(0, 3)$ and then $(-3/2, 0)$ and $(0 - 3)$ as θ ranges from 0 to 2π.

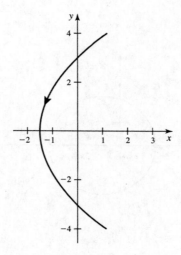

10.4.64 As θ ranges from 0 to $\pi/3$, the branch of the hyperbola in quadrant III starts at the point $(-1,0)$, and approaches the asymptote (note that $r \to \infty$ as $\theta \to \pi/3^-$.) As θ takes on the values from $\pi/3$ to $\pi/2$, the portion of the parabola in quadrant I appears and heads toward the point $(0,1)$. For θ ranging from $\pi/2$ to $3\pi/2$, the curve ranges from $(0,1)$ to $(-1/3,0)$ to $(0,-1)$. From $\theta = 3\pi/2$ to $\theta = 5\pi/3$, the curve approaches the asymptote in quadrant IV. From $5\pi/3$ to 2π, the curve reappears along the asymptote in quadrant II, and approaches the point $(-1,0)$.

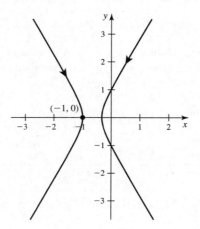

10.4.65 For negative p, the parabola opens to the left and for positive p it opens to the right. As p increases to 0, the parabola opens wider and as p decreases (for $p > 0$), it gets narrower.

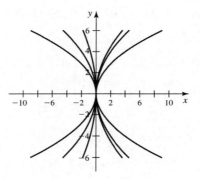

10.4.66 As e gets larger, the vertices move closer to each other.

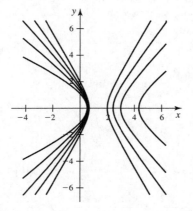

10.4.67

a. True. Note that if $x = 0$, the equation becomes $-y^2 = 9$, which has no solution.

b. True. The slopes of the tangent lines range continuously from $-\infty$ to 0 to ∞ and then back through 0 to $-\infty$ again.

c. True. Given c and d, one can compute a, b, and e. See the summary after Theorem 10.3.

d. True. The vertex is exactly halfway between the focus and the directrix.

10.4.68 Using implicit differentiation, we have $2yy' = 8$, and at the point $(8, -8)$, we have $y' = -\frac{1}{2}$. So $y - (-8) = -\frac{1}{2}(x - 8)$, or $y = -\frac{1}{2}x - 4$ is the equation of the tangent line.

10.4.69 Differentiating gives $2x = -6y'$, so at $(-6, -6)$ we obtain $-12 = -6y'$, so $y' = 2$. Thus $y - (-6) = 2(x - (-6))$, or $y = 2x + 6$ is the equation of the tangent line.

10.4.70 We have

$$\frac{dy}{dx} = \frac{-\frac{\cos\theta\sin\theta}{(1+\sin\theta)^2} + \frac{\cos\theta}{1+\sin\theta}}{-\frac{\cos^2\theta}{(1+\sin\theta)^2} - \frac{\sin\theta}{1+\sin\theta}} = \frac{\sin\theta - 1}{\cos\theta}.$$

At $\theta = \frac{\pi}{6}$ we have $y' = \frac{(1/2)-1}{\sqrt{3}/2} = -\frac{\sqrt{3}}{3}$. The equation of the tangent line is therefore $y - \frac{1}{3} = -\frac{\sqrt{3}}{3}(x - \frac{\sqrt{3}}{3})$, or $y = -\frac{\sqrt{3}}{3}x + \frac{2}{3}$.

10.4.71 Differentiating implicitly, we have $2yy' - \frac{x}{32} = 0$, so at $(6, -5/4)$ we have $-\frac{5}{2}y' - \frac{3}{16} = 0$, so $y' = -\frac{3}{40}$. The equation of the tangent line is $y + \frac{5}{4} = -\frac{3}{40}(x - 6)$, or $y = -\frac{3x}{40} - \frac{4}{5}$.

10.4.72 We have an ellipse with focus at the origin and directrix $x = 2$. Because $(2/3, 0)$ is a vertex, $e = \frac{|PF|}{|PL|} = \frac{2/3}{4/3} = \frac{1}{2}$ and $r(\theta) = \frac{\frac{1}{2}\cdot 2}{1 + \frac{1}{2}\cos\theta} = \frac{2}{2+\cos\theta}$.

10.4.73 We have a hyperbola with focal point at the origin and directrix $y = -2$. Furthermore $P = (0, -4/3)$ is a vertex. Thus, $e = \frac{|PF|}{|PL|} = \frac{4/3}{2/3} = 2$, and $r(\theta) = \frac{2(2)}{1-2\sin\theta} = \frac{4}{1-2\sin\theta}$.

10.4.74

a. $e = \frac{|PF|}{|PL|}$, so $r = |PF| = e|PL| = e|-d - r\cos\theta|$, or $r = e(d + r\cos\theta)$. Solving for r yields $r = \frac{ed}{1-e\cos\theta}$.

b. $r = |PF| = e|PL|$, or $r = e(d - r\sin\theta)$. Solving for r yields $r = \frac{ed}{1+e\sin\theta}$.

c. $r = |PF| = e|PL|$, or $r = e(-d - r\sin\theta)$. So $r = e(d + r\sin\theta)$, and solving for r yields $r = \frac{ed}{1-e\sin\theta}$.

10.4.75 The points on the intersection of the two circles are a distance of $2a + r$ from F_1 and a distance of r from F_2. So for P an intersection point, we have $|PF_1| - |PF_2| = 2a$ for all r, and the set of all such points form a hyperbola with foci F_1 and F_2.

10.4.76

a. Making use of the substitution $\frac{x}{\sqrt{2}} = \sin t$, we have

$$A = \int_0^1 \left(\sqrt{1 - \frac{x^2}{2}} - \frac{x^2}{\sqrt{2}} \right) dx = \int_0^{\pi/4} \sqrt{1 - \sin^2 t}\sqrt{2}\cos t\, dt - \frac{1}{\sqrt{2}}\int_0^1 x^2\, dx$$

$$= \sqrt{2}\cdot\frac{1}{2}\left(\cos x\sin x + x \right)\Big|_0^{\pi/4} - \frac{1}{3\sqrt{2}} = \frac{\sqrt{2}}{2}\left(\sin(\pi/4)\cos(\pi/4) + \frac{\pi}{4} \right) - \frac{1}{3\sqrt{2}}$$

$$= \frac{\sqrt{2}}{2}\cdot\left(\frac{1}{2} + \frac{\pi}{4} \right) - \frac{\sqrt{2}}{6} = \frac{\sqrt{2}}{12} + \frac{\sqrt{2}\pi}{8}.$$

b. About the x-axis, we obtain $\pi \int_0^1 \left(1 - \frac{x^2}{2} - \frac{x^4}{2}\right) dx = \pi \left(x - \frac{x^3}{6} - \frac{x^5}{10}\right)\Big|_0^1 = \frac{11\pi}{15} \approx 2.304$.

About the y-axis, we obtain

$$2\pi \int_0^1 \left(x\sqrt{1 - \frac{x^2}{2}} - \frac{x^2}{\sqrt{2}}\right) dx = 2\pi \int_{1/2}^1 u^{1/2} \, du - \frac{1}{\sqrt{2}} \int_0^1 x^3 \, dx$$

$$= 2\pi \left(\frac{2}{3} u^{3/2}\right)\Big|_{1/2}^1 - \left(\frac{1}{4\sqrt{2}} x^4\right)\Big|_0^1 = 2\pi \left(\frac{2}{3} - \frac{2}{6\sqrt{2}} - \frac{1}{4\sqrt{2}}\right) \approx 1.597.$$

So the volume about the x-axis is greater.

10.4.77 Using implicit differentiation, we have $\frac{2x}{a^2} + \frac{2yy'}{b^2} = 0$, or $y' = -\frac{b^2 x}{a^2 y}$. If (x_0, y_0) is the point of tangency, then $-\frac{b^2 x_0}{a^2 y_0} = \frac{y - y_0}{x - x_0}$, so $\frac{x_0(x - x_0)}{a^2} = -\frac{y_0(y - y_0)}{b^2}$, so $\frac{x_0 x}{a^2} + \frac{y_0 y}{b^2} = \frac{x_0^2}{a^2} + \frac{y_0^2}{b^2} = 1$.

10.4.78 Using implicit differentiation, we have $\frac{2x}{a^2} - \frac{2yy'}{b^2} = 0$, so $y' = \frac{b^2 x}{a^2 y}$. At (x_0, y_0), we have $y' = \frac{b^2 x_0}{a^2 y_0}$, so the tangent line is given by $y - y_0 = \frac{b^2 x_0}{a^2 y_0}(x - x_0)$, or $\frac{y(y - y_0)}{b^2} = \frac{x_0(x - x_0)}{a^2}$, or $\frac{y_0 y}{b^2} - \frac{x_0 x}{a^2} = \frac{y_0^2}{b^2} - \frac{x_0^2}{a^2} = -1$, so $\frac{x x_0}{a^2} - \frac{y y_0}{b^2} = 1$.

10.4.79 $V_x = \pi \int_{-a}^a \left(b^2 - \frac{b^2 x^2}{a^2}\right) dx = \pi b^2 \int_{-a}^a \left(1 - \frac{x^2}{a^2}\right) dx = \pi b^2 \left(x - \frac{x^3}{3a^2}\right)\Big|_{-a}^a = \frac{4\pi b^2 a}{3}$.

$V_y = \pi \int_{-b}^b \left(a^2 - \frac{a^2 y^2}{b^2}\right) dy = \pi a^2 \int_{-b}^b \left(1 - \frac{y^2}{b^2}\right) dy = \pi a^2 \left(y - \frac{y^3}{3b^2}\right)\Big|_{-b}^b = \frac{4\pi a^2 b}{3}$.

These are different if $a \neq b$. In the case $a = b$, both volumes give $\frac{4\pi a^3}{3}$, the volume of a sphere.

10.4.80

a. The focus is at $c = \sqrt{a^2 + b^2}$. We have $A = 2b \int_a^c \sqrt{\frac{x^2}{a^2} - 1} \, dx = \frac{2b}{a} \int_a^c \sqrt{x^2 - a^2} \, dx$. Using either the substitution $x = a \sec \theta$ (or a table of integrals), we have

$$A = \frac{2b}{a} \cdot \left(\frac{1}{2} x \sqrt{x^2 - a^2} - \frac{1}{2} a^2 \ln\left(2\left(\sqrt{x^2 - a^2} + x\right)\right)\right)\Big|_a^c$$

so

$$A = ab\ln(a) - ab\ln(\sqrt{a^2 + b^2} + b) + \frac{\sqrt{a^2 + b^2}}{a} \cdot b^2.$$

b.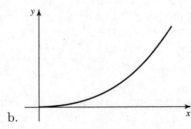

10.4.81

a. $V_x = \pi \int_a^c \left(\sqrt{\frac{b^2 x^2}{a^2} - b^2}\right)^2 dx = \pi \int_a^c \left(\frac{b^2 x^2}{a^2} - b^2\right) dx = \pi b^2 \left(\frac{x^3}{3a^2} - x\right)\Big|_a^c = \pi b^2 \left(\frac{c^3}{3a^2} - c - \frac{a}{3} + a\right) = \frac{\pi b^2}{3a^2}(c^3 - 3ca^2 + 2a^3) = \frac{\pi b^2}{3a^2}(a - c)^2(2a + c)$.

b. $V_y = 2 \cdot 2\pi \int_a^c a^2 b \sqrt{\frac{x^2}{a^2} - 1} \, dx = 2\pi \int_0^{b^2/a^2} a^2 b \sqrt{u} \, du = 2\pi a^2 b \left(\frac{2}{3} u^{3/2}\right)\Big|_0^{b^2/a^2} = 2\pi a^2 b \frac{2b^3}{3a^3} = \frac{4\pi b^4}{3a}$.

10.4.82 $V_R = 2\pi \int_0^{\sqrt{h/a}} x(h - ax^2) \, dx = 2\pi \int_0^{\sqrt{h/a}} (xh - ax^3) \, dx = 2\pi \left(\frac{hx^2}{2} - \frac{ax^4}{4}\right)\Big|_0^{\sqrt{h/a}} = 2\pi \left(\frac{h^2}{2a} - \frac{h^2}{4a}\right) = \frac{\pi h^2}{2a}$. The cone has height h and radius $\sqrt{h/a}$, so $V_c = \frac{1}{3}\pi \left(\sqrt{\frac{h}{a}}\right)^2 \cdot h = \frac{\pi h^2}{3a}$, and $V_R = \frac{3}{2} \cdot \frac{\pi h^2}{3a} = \frac{\pi h^2}{2a}$.

10.4.83

a. The slope of a line making an angle θ with the horizontal is $\tan\theta$. The slope of the tangent line at (x_0, y_0) is $y' = \frac{x}{2p}$, so $y' = \frac{x_0}{2p}$, so $\tan\theta = \frac{x_0}{2p}$.

b. The distance from $(0, y_0)$ to $(0, p)$ is $p - y_0$, and $\tan\phi = \frac{\text{opposite}}{\text{adjacent}} = \frac{p - y_0}{x_0}$.

c. Because l is perpendicular to $y = y_0$, we have $\alpha + \theta = \pi/2$, or $\alpha = \frac{\pi}{2} - \theta$, so $\tan\alpha = \cot\theta = \frac{2p}{x_0}$.

d. $\tan\beta = \tan(\theta + \phi) = \frac{\frac{x_0}{wp} + \frac{p - y_0}{x_0}}{1 - \frac{p - y_0}{2p}} = \frac{x_0^2 + 2p^2 - 2py_0}{x_0(p + y_0)}$. Now because $x_0^2 = 4py_0$, we obtain $\tan\beta = \frac{4py_0 + 2p^2 - 2py_0}{x_0(p + y_0)}$
$= \frac{2p(p + y_0)}{x_0(p + y_0)} = \frac{2p}{x_0}$.

e. Because α and β are acute, we have that $\tan\alpha = \tan\beta$, so $\alpha = \beta$.

10.4.84 We have a vertex at $(0,0)$ and the parabola passes through $(640, 152)$, so $152 = a(640)^2$, so $a = \frac{19}{51200} \approx 0.000371$. Thus, $y = \frac{19}{51200}x^2$, and the guy wire has length $L = \frac{19}{51200}(500^2) = \frac{11875}{128} \approx 92.77$ meters.

10.4.85 Assume the two fixed points are at $(c, 0)$ and $(-c, 0)$. Let P be the point $(0, b)$, and note that P is equidistant from the two given points, so we must have $b^2 + c^2 = a^2$ by the Pythagorean theorem. Now let $Q = (u, 0)$ be on the ellipse for $u > c$. Then $u - c + (c + u) = 2a$, so $u = a$. Now let $R = (x, y)$ be an arbitrary point on the ellipse (assume $x > 0$ and $y > 0$ – the other cases are similar.) Using the triangles formed between the foci, R, and the projection of R onto the x-axis, we have $\sqrt{(x + c)^2 + y^2} = 2a - \sqrt{(c - x)^2 + y^2}$. Squaring both sides gives $(x + c)^2 + y^2 = 4a^2 - 4a\sqrt{(c - x)^2 + y^2} + (c - x)^2 + y^2$. Isolating the root gives $\sqrt{(c - x)^2 + y^2} = \frac{1}{4a}\left((c - x)^2 + y^2 - (c + x)^2 - y^2 + 4a^2\right)$, so $\sqrt{(c - x)^2 + y^2} = a - \frac{c}{a}x$. Squaring again yields $(c - x)^2 + y^2 = a^2 - 2xc + \frac{c^2}{a^2}x^2$, so $c^2 - 2cx + x^2 + y^2 = a^2 - 2cx + \frac{c^2}{a^2}x^2$, or $x^2\left(1 - \frac{c^2}{a^2}\right) + y^2 = a^2 - c^2$. Thus $\frac{x^2}{a^2} + \frac{y^2}{a^2 - c^2} = 1$, which can be written $\frac{x^2}{a^2} + \frac{y^2}{b^2} = 1$, because $b^2 = a^2 - c^2$.

10.4.86 The intersection points of the branches with the x-axis are at $(-a, 0)$ and $(a, 0)$ because the distances to $(c, 0)$ and $(-c, 0)$ are $c + a$ and $c - a$, so the difference is $\pm 2a$. Consider one point on the right branch (the left branch will follow by a similar argument.) Let the distance from $(-c, 0)$ to (x, y) be u and the distance from $(c, 0)$ to (x, y) be v. Then $u = \sqrt{(c + x)^2 + y^2}$ and $v = \sqrt{(c - x)^2 + y^2}$, and because $u - v = 2a$, we have $\sqrt{(c + x)^2 + y^2} = 2a + \sqrt{(c - x)^2 + y^2}$. Squaring gives $(c + x)^2 + y^2 = 4a^2 + 4a\sqrt{(c - x)^2 + y^2} + (c - x)^2 + y^2$. Isolating the root gives $\sqrt{(c - x)^2 + y^2} = \frac{1}{4a}\left((c + x)^2 + y^2 - (c - x)^2 - y^2 - 4a^2\right)$, so $\sqrt{(c - x)^2 + y^2} = -a + \frac{c}{a}x$.

Squaring again yields $(c - x)^2 + y^2 = a^2 - 2xc + \frac{c^2}{a^2}x^2$, so $c^2 - 2cx + x^2 + y^2 = a^2 - 2cx + \frac{c^2}{a^2}x^2$, or $x^2\left(1 - \frac{c^2}{a^2}\right) + y^2 = a^2 - c^2$. Thus $\frac{x^2}{a^2} + \frac{y^2}{a^2 - c^2} = 1$, which can be written $\frac{x^2}{a^2} - \frac{y^2}{b^2} = 1$, where $b^2 = c^2 - a^2$.

10.4.87 Let the parabola be symmetric about the y-axis with vertex at the origin. Let the circle have radius r and be centered at $(r + a, 0)$, and let the line be $y = -a$. The distance form the point $P(x, y)$ to the line is $u = y + a$. The distance from the point P to the circle is $v = \sqrt{x^2 + (r + a - y)^2} - r$. Setting $u = v$ yields $y + a = \sqrt{x^2 + (r + a - y)^2} - r$, so $y + r + a = \sqrt{x^2 + (r + a - y)^2}$, and squaring gives $y^2 + 2(r + a)y + (r + a)^2 = x^2 + (r + a - y)^2$, so $y^2 + 2(r + a)y + (r + a)^2 = x^2 + (r + a)^2 - 2(r + a)y + y^2$, and thus $4(r + a)y = x^2$, so $y = \frac{1}{4(r + a)}x^2$, the equation of a parabola.

10.4.88 With focus at the origin, the cartesian equation of an ellipse with the second focus at $(-2c, 0)$ and major axis length $2a$, minor axis length $2b$ is $\frac{(x + c)^2}{a^2} + \frac{y^2}{b^2} = 1$. Using $c = ae$ and polar coordinates yields $\frac{(r\cos\theta + ae)^2}{a^2} + \frac{r^2\sin^2\theta}{a^2(1 - e^2)} = 1$. Thus, $(1 - e^2)(r^2\cos^2\theta + 2aer\cos\theta + a^2e^2) + r^2\sin^2\theta = a^2(1 - e^2)$, so $r^2 - e^2r^2\cos^2\theta + 2ae(1 - e^2)r\cos\theta + (1 - e^2)a^2e^2 = a^2(1 - e^2)$. Gathering like terms gives $(1 - e^2\cos^2\theta)r^2 + 2ae(1 - e^2)\cos\theta \cdot r - a^2(1 - e^2)^2 = 0$. Using the quadratic formula, we have

$$r = \frac{-2ae(1 - e^2)\cos\theta + \sqrt{4a^2e^2(1 - e^2)^2\cos^2\theta + 4a^2(1 - e^2)^2(1 - e^2\cos^2\theta)}}{2(1 - e^2\cos^2\theta)}.$$

This can be written as

$$r = \frac{-2ae(1-e^2)\cos\theta + 2a(1-e^2)}{2(1-e^2\cos^2\theta)} = \frac{a(1-e^2)(-e\cos\theta+1)}{(1-e\cos\theta)(1+e\cos\theta)} = \frac{a(1-e^2)}{1+e\cos\theta}.$$

10.4.89 Let the hyperbolas be centered at the origin with equations $\frac{x^2}{a^2} - \frac{y^2}{b^2} = 1$ and $\frac{y^2}{B^2} - \frac{x^2}{A^2} = 1$ and eccentricities $e = \frac{c}{a}$ and $E = \frac{C}{B}$, respectively. Because the hyperbolas share a set of asymptotes $A = ra$ and $B = rb$ fro some $r > 0$, and

$$C^2 = A^2 + B^2 = (ra)^2 + (rb)^2$$
$$= r^2(a^2 + b^2) = r^2 c^2.$$

Then we have

$$e^{-2} + E^{-2} = \left(\frac{c}{a}\right)^{-2} + \left(\frac{C}{B}\right)^{-2} = \frac{a^2}{c^2} + \frac{B^2}{C^2}$$
$$= \frac{a^2}{c^2} + \frac{r^2 b^2}{r^2 c^2} = \frac{a^2 + b^2}{c^2} = \frac{c^2}{c^2} = 1.$$

10.4.90 The focal chord of slope $m \neq 0$ has equation $y = m(x-p)$. Because $y^2 = 4px$, the focal chord and the parabola intersect for $(mx - mp)^2 = 4px$, which occurs (via the quadratic formula) at $x = \frac{(m^2 + 2 \pm 2\sqrt{m^2+1})p}{m^2}$. The corresponding y-values are $\frac{(m^2 + 2 \pm 2\sqrt{m^2+1})p}{m} - mp$. Now $y' = \frac{2p}{y}$, so $y' = \frac{m}{1 \pm \sqrt{m^2+1}}$ at the two points. The product of these two values of y' is -1, so the two lines are perpendicular. If we call the intersection points found above (x_0, y_0) and (x_1, y_1), then the two lines intersect for

$$\frac{m}{1 + \sqrt{m^2+1}}(x - x_0) + y_0 = \frac{m}{1 - \sqrt{m^2+1}}(x - x_1) + y_1,$$

which when solved for x gives $x = -p$, so the two lines meet on the directrix.

   Note that in the case of a vertical chord, we have $(x_0, y_0) = (p, 2p)$ and $(x_1, y_1) = (p, -2p)$, and thus the slopes of the tangent lines are 1 and -1, so their product is still -1 and thus they are perpendicular. Then the tangent lines meet when $1(x - p) + 2p = -1(x - p) - 2p$, which occurs when $x = -p$, so they still meet on the directrix.

10.4.91 The latus rectum L intersects the parabola at $x = p$, $y = \pm 2p$. The distance between any point $P(x, y)$ on the parabola to the left of L and L is $p - x$. The distance from F to P is $\sqrt{(x-p)^2 + y^2} = \sqrt{x^2 - 2px + p^2 + 4px} = \sqrt{x^2 + 2px + p^2} = x + p$ (because both x and p are positive.) Thus $D + |FP| = p - x + x + p = 2p$.

10.4.92 Because the latus rectum intersects the parabola at $(p, 2p)$ and $(p, -2p)$, its length is $4|p|$.

10.4.93 Let P be a point on the intersection of the latus rectum and the ellipse. The length of the latus rectum is twice the distance from P to the focus. Let l be the length from P to the focus, and let L be the distance from P to the other focal point. Then $l + L = 2a$, so $L^2 = 4c^2 + l^2$, and thus $(2a - l)^2 = 4c^2 + l^2$, and solving for l yields $l = a - \frac{c^2}{a}$. Because $c^2 = a^2 - b^2$, this can be written as $l = a - \frac{a^2 - b^2}{a} = a - (a - \frac{b^2}{a}) = \frac{b^2}{a}$. The length of the latus rectum is therefore $\frac{2b^2}{a}$. Now because $e = \frac{c}{a}$, we have $\sqrt{1 - e^2} = \sqrt{1 - \frac{a^2 - b^2}{a^2}} = \sqrt{\frac{b^2}{a^2}} = \frac{b}{a}$. The length of the latus rectum can thus also be written as $2b \cdot \frac{b}{a} = 2b\sqrt{1 - e^2}$.

10.4.94 Let P be a point on the intersection of the latus rectum and the hyperbola. The length of the latus rectum is twice the distance from P to the focus. Let l be the length from P to the focus, and let L be the distance from P to the other focal point. Then $L - l = 2a$, so $L^2 = 4c^2 + l^2$, and thus $(2a + l)^2 = 4c^2 + l^2$, and solving for l yields $l = \frac{c^2}{a} - a$. Because $c^2 = a^2 + b^2$, this can be written as $l = \frac{a^2 + b^2}{a} - a = \frac{b^2}{a}$. The length of the latus rectum is therefore $\frac{2b^2}{a}$. Now because $e = \frac{c}{a}$, we have $\sqrt{e^2 - 1} = \sqrt{\frac{a^2 + b^2}{a^2} - 1} = \sqrt{\frac{b^2}{a^2}} = \frac{b}{a}$. The length of the latus rectum can thus also be written as $2b \cdot \frac{b}{a} = 2b\sqrt{e^2 - 1}$.

10.4.95 Let the equation of the ellipse be $\frac{x^2}{a^2}+\frac{y^2}{a^2-c^2}=1$ and let the equation of the hyperbola be $\frac{x^2}{r^2}-\frac{y^2}{c^2-r^2}=1$. Let (x_0,y_0) be a point of intersection. By evaluating both equations at the point of intersection and subtracting, we obtain the result

$$\frac{x_0^2}{a^2}-\frac{x_0^2}{r^2}+\frac{y_0^2}{a^2-c^2}+\frac{y_0^2}{c^2-r^2}=0,$$

which can be written

$$\frac{r_0^2 x_0^2 - a^2 x_0^2}{a^2 r^2}+\frac{(c^2-r^2)y_0^2+(a^2-c^2)y_0^2}{(a^2-c^2)(c^2-r^2)}=0.$$

This equation can be rewritten in the form $\frac{x_0^2}{y_0^2}=\frac{a^2 r^2}{(a^2-c^2)(c^2-r^2)}$, which we will use later.

Now implicitly differentiating the equation for the ellipse yields $\frac{2x}{a^2}+\frac{2yy'}{a^2-c^2}=0$, and thus the slope of the tangent line to the ellipse at (x_0,y_0) is $y'_e=-\frac{x_0}{y_o}\cdot\frac{a^2-c^2}{a^2}$. Differentiating the equation of the hyperbola gives $\frac{2x}{r^2}-\frac{2yy'}{c^2-r^2}=0$, so the slope of the tangent line to the hyperbola at the point of intersection is $y'_h=\frac{x_0}{y_0}\cdot\frac{c^2-r^2}{r^2}$.

Now consider the product

$$-1\cdot y'_e\cdot y'_h=\frac{x_0^2}{y_0^2}\cdot\frac{(a^2-c^2)(c^2-r^2)}{a^2 r^2}.$$

By the result of the first paragraph, this is equal to 1, and thus the two curves are perpendicular at the point of intersection.

10.4.96 The vertical distance at x_0 is given by $d(x_0)=\frac{bx_0}{a}-\sqrt{\frac{x_0^2 b^2}{a^2}-a^2}=\frac{b}{a}\left(x_0-\sqrt{x_0^2-\frac{a^4}{b^2}}\right)$. We have

$$\lim_{x_0\to\infty}d(x_0)=\frac{b}{a}\lim_{x_0\to\infty}\left(x_0-\sqrt{x_0^2-\frac{a^4}{b^2}}\right)=\frac{b}{a}\lim_{x_0\to\infty}\left(\frac{x_0^2-\left(x_0^2-\frac{a^4}{b^2}\right)}{x_0+\sqrt{x_0^2-\frac{a^4}{b^2}}}\right)=0.$$

10.4.97

a. The curve and the line intersect when $x^2-m^2(x^2-4x+4)-1=0$, which occurs for $\frac{2m^2\pm\sqrt{1+3m^2}}{m^2-1}$, assuming $m\neq\pm1$. So there are two solutions in this case – but if $-1<m<1$, one of the solutions is negative (the intersection lies on the other branch of the hyperbola.) If $m^2=1$, then the equation becomes $4x-5=0$, and there is only the solution $x=\frac{5}{4}$. So there are two intersection points on the right branch exactly for $|m|>1$. We have $v(m)=\frac{2m^2+\sqrt{1+3m^2}}{m^2-1}$ and $u(m)=\frac{2m^2-\sqrt{1+3m^2}}{m^2-1}$.

b. $\displaystyle\lim_{m\to 1^+}u(m)=\lim_{m\to 1^+}u(m)\cdot\frac{2m^2+\sqrt{1+3m^2}}{2m^2+\sqrt{1+3m^2}}=\lim_{m\to 1^+}\frac{4m^4-3m^2-1}{(m^2-1)(2m^2+\sqrt{1+3m^2})}=$
$\displaystyle\lim_{m\to 1^+}\frac{(m^2-1)(4m^2+1)}{(m^2-1)(2m^2+\sqrt{1+3m^2})}=\frac{5}{4}$.

$\displaystyle\lim_{m\to 1^+}v(m)=\lim_{m\to 1^+}v(m)\cdot\frac{2m^2-\sqrt{1+3m^2}}{2m^2-\sqrt{1+3m^2}}=\lim_{m\to 1^+}\frac{4m^4-3m^2-1}{(m^2-1)(2m^2-\sqrt{1+3m^2})}=$
$\displaystyle\lim_{m\to 1^+}\frac{(m^2-1)(4m^2+1)}{(m^2-1)(2m^2-\sqrt{1+3m^2})}=\lim_{m\to 1^+}\frac{(4m^2+1)}{(2m^2-\sqrt{1+3m^2})}=\infty$.

c. $\displaystyle\lim_{m\to\infty}u(m)=\lim_{m\to\infty}\frac{2-\sqrt{\frac{1}{m^4}+\frac{3}{m^2}}}{1-\frac{1}{m^2}}=2$.

$\displaystyle\lim_{m\to\infty}v(m)=\lim_{m\to\infty}\frac{2+\sqrt{\frac{1}{m^4}+\frac{3}{m^2}}}{1-\frac{1}{m^2}}=2$.

d. The expression $\lim_{m\to\infty}A(m)$ represents the area of the region bounded by the hyperbola and the line $x=2$. It is given by $2\int_1^2\sqrt{x^2-1}\,dx=2\left(\frac{x}{2}\sqrt{x^2-1}-\frac{1}{2}\ln(x+\sqrt{x^2-1})\right)\Big|_1^2=2\sqrt{3}-\ln(2+\sqrt{3})$.

10.4.98

a. The area of the anvil is $A = 4 \int_0^p \sqrt{1+y^2}\, dy = 4 \int_0^{\tan^{-1}(p)} \sec^3 t\, dt = 2p\sqrt{1+p^2} + 2\ln(\sqrt{1+p^2}+p)$, where this last integral can be evaluated using the techniques of chapter 7 (or a table of integrals.)

The area of R is equal to the area of S when $2 = p\sqrt{1+p^2} + \ln(\sqrt{1+p^2}+p)$. Using a CAS, the result is $p \approx 0.8927$.

b. For R to have twice the area of S, we need $4 = p\sqrt{1+p^2} + \ln(\sqrt{1+p^2}+p)$, which occurs for $p \approx 1.5279$.

10.4.99

a. With $x^2 = a^2\cos^2 t + 2ab\sin t\cos t + b^2\sin^2 t$, $y^2 = c^2\cos^2 t + 2cd\sin t\cos t + d^2\sin^2 t$, and $xy = ac\cos^2 t + (ad+bc)\sin t\cos t + bd\sin^2 t$, we have $Ax^2 + Bxy + Cy^2 = (Aa^2 + Bac + Cc^2)\cos^2 t + (2Aab + B(ad+bc) + 2Ccd)\sin t\cos t + (Ab^2 + Bbd + Cd^2)\sin^2 t = K$. Thus we have an equation of the desired form as long as there exist A, B, C, and K so that $A(a^2 - b^2) + B(ac - bd) + C(c^2 - d^2) = 0$ and $2Aab + B(ad+bc) + 2Ccd = 0$. This turns out to be the case when $ad - bc \neq 0$. Note that the value of K is $Aa^2 + Bac + Cc^2$.

b. Suppose that $ad - bc \neq 0$, but $ac + bd = 0$. Then $\frac{b}{a} = -\frac{c}{d}$, and $\tan^{-1}(b/a) = \tan^{-1}(-c/d)$.

Note that $x = \sqrt{a^2+b^2}\cos(t + \tan^{-1}(-b/a))$, $y = \sqrt{c^2+d^2}\sin(t + \tan^{-1}(c/d))$. This can be seen by applying the trigonometric identities for the sum of two angles. Then $\frac{x^2}{a^2+b^2} + \frac{y^2}{c^2+d^2} = \cos^2(t + \tan^1(b/a)) + \sin^2(\tan^{-1}(-c/d)) = 1$.

c. Using the work in part b), we see that the equation is $\frac{x^2}{a^2+b^2} + \frac{y^2}{c^2+d^2} = 1$, or $x^2 + y^2 = r^2$, where $r^2 = a^2 + b^2 = c^2 + d^2$.

Chapter Ten Review

1

a. False. For example, $x = r\cos t$, $y = r\sin t$ for $0 \leq t \leq 2\pi$ and $x = r\sin t$, $y = r\cos t$ for $0 \leq t \leq 2\pi$ generate the same circle.

b. False. Because $e^t > 0$ for all t, this only describes the portion of that line where $x > 0$.

c. True. They both describe the point whose cartesian coordinates are $(3\cos(-3\pi/4), 3\sin(-3\pi/4)) = (-3\cos(\pi/4), -3\sin(\pi/4)) = (-3/\sqrt{2}, -3/\sqrt{2})$.

d. False. The given integral counts the inner loop twice.

e. True. This follows because the equation $0 - x^2/4 = 1$ has no real solutions.

f. True. Note that the given equation can be written as $(x-1)^2 + 4y^2 = 4$, or $\frac{(x-1)^2}{4} + y^2 = 1$.

2

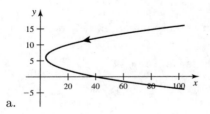

a.

b. $x = t^2 + 4 = (6-y)^2 + 4$.

c. The curve is a parabola which opens in the positive x-direction, with vertex at $(4, 6)$.

d. $\frac{dy}{dx} = -\frac{1}{2t}$. At the point $(5, 5)$ we have $t = 1$, so $\frac{dy}{dx} = -\frac{1}{2}$.

3

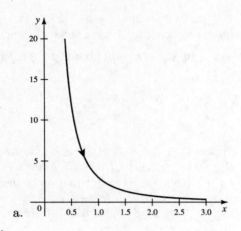

a.

b. $y = 3(e^t)^{-2} = \frac{3}{x^2}$.

c. The curve represents the portion of $\frac{3}{x^2}$ for $x > 0$.

d. $\frac{dy}{dx} = -\frac{6}{x^3}$, so at $(1, 3)$ we have $\frac{dy}{dx} = -6$.

4

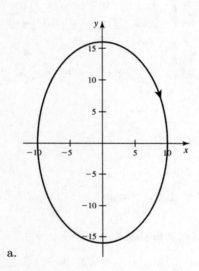

a.

b. $\left(\frac{x}{10}\right)^2 + \left(\frac{y}{16}\right)^2 = \sin^2 2t + \cos^2 2t = 1$.

c. The curve represents an ellipse traced clockwise.

d. $\frac{dy}{dx} = -\frac{32 \sin 2t}{20 \cos 2t}$, and at $t = \pi/6$ this is equal to $-\frac{16\sqrt{3}}{10}$.

5

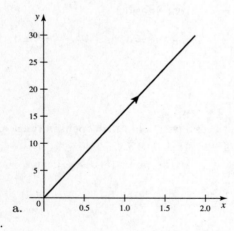

a.

b. Because $\ln t^2 = 2 \ln t$ for $t > 0$, we have $y = 16x$ for $0 \le x \le 2$.

c. The curve represents a line segment from $(0, 0)$ to $(2, 32)$.

d. $\frac{dy}{dx} = 16$ for all value of x.

6 As derived in the last problem in section 10.4, this describes a circle provided $ad - bc \neq 0$, but $ac + bd = 0$, and $a^2 + b^2 = c^2 + d^2$. In this case, the circle has radius $r = \sqrt{a^2 + b^2}$.

7 Note that $\left(\frac{x}{4}\right)^2 + \left(\frac{y}{3}\right)^2 = 1$. This represents an ellipse generated counterclockwise.

8 Note that $\left(\frac{x+1}{4}\right)^2 + \left(\frac{y-2}{4}\right)^2 = 1$, so $(x+1)^2 + (y-2)^2 = 16$. This is a circle of radius 4 centered at $(-1, 2)$ generated counterclockwise.

9 Note that $(x+3)^2 + (y-6)^2 = 1$. This is the right half of a circle of radius 1 centered at $(-3, 6)$. It is generated clockwise.

10 If we let $r = 1 + \cos t$, then $x = r \cos t$ and $y = r \sin t$. The curve $r = 1 + \cos t$ is a cardioid.

11 $x = 3 \sin t$, $y = 3 \cos t$, $0 \le t \le 2\pi$.

12 $x = 3 \cos t$, $y = 2 \sin t$, $0 \le t \le \pi$.

13 $x = 3 \cos t$, $y = 2 \sin t$, $-\pi/2 \le t \le \pi/2$.

14 $x = t$, $y = 4t + 11$, $-\infty \le t \le \infty$.

15 From P to Q, we use $(x(t), y(t)) = tQ + (1-t)P = (t, t) + (t-1, 0) = (2t-1, t)$. So $x(t) = 2t - 1$, $y(t) = t$, $0 \le t \le 1$.
　　From Q to P, we use $(x(t), y(t)) = tP + (1-t)Q = (-t, 0) + (1-t, 1-t) = (1-2t, 1-t)$, for $0 \le t \le 1$. Thus $x(t) = 1 - 2t$, $y(t) = 1 - t$, $0 \le t \le 1$.

16 $x = t$, $y = t^3 + 2t$, $0 \le t \le 2$.

17 $\frac{dy}{dx} = \frac{dy/dt}{dx/dt} = \frac{\sin t}{1 - \cos t}$. At $t = \pi/6$, the slope of the tangent line is $\frac{1}{2 - \sqrt{3}} = 2 + \sqrt{3}$. So the equation of the tangent line is $y - (1 - \sqrt{3}/2) = (2 + \sqrt{3})(x - (\pi/6 - 1/2))$, or $y = (2 + \sqrt{3})x + (2 - \frac{\pi}{3} - \frac{\pi\sqrt{3}}{6})$.
　　At $t = 2\pi/3$, the slope of the tangent line is $\frac{\sqrt{3}}{3}$, so the equation of the tangent line is $y - \frac{3}{2} = \frac{\sqrt{3}}{3}(x - (\frac{2\pi}{3} - \frac{\sqrt{3}}{2}))$, or $y = \frac{x}{\sqrt{3}} + 2 - \frac{2\pi}{3\sqrt{3}}$.

18   **19**

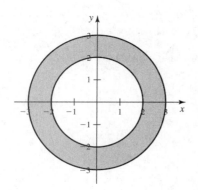   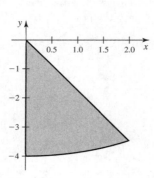

20

　　a. This matches (F). Note that there are 8 solutions to the equation $3 \sin 4\theta = 3$ for $0 \le t \le 2\pi$, corresponding to the tips of the petals.

　　b. This matches (D). Note that for every value of θ for $-\pi/2 < \theta < \pi/2$, there are two symmetric values for r.

　　c. This matches (B). Note that this limaçon has its largest value for r at $\theta = 3\pi/2$.

d. This matches (E). Note that this limaçon has its largest value for r at $\theta = 0$.

e. This matches (C). Note that there are 3 unique solutions to $r = 3\cos\theta = 3$ for $0 \le \theta \le \pi$ that correspond to the tips of the petals. Note that the curve is generated for $0 \le \theta \le \pi$.

f. This matches (A). Note that $r \to 0$ as $\theta \to \infty$, and $r \to \infty$ as $\theta \to -\infty$.

21 Liz should choose the cardioid, which is $r = 1 - \sin\theta$.

22 Jake should send $r^2 = \cos 2\theta$.

23 Letting $x = r\cos\theta$, $y = r\sin\theta$, and $r^2 = x^2 + y^2$, we have $x^2 + y^2 + 2y - 6x = 0$, which can be written as $x^2 - 6x + 9 + y^2 + 2y + 1 = 10$, or $(x - 3)^2 + (y + 1)^2 = 10$, so this is a circle of radius $\sqrt{10}$ centered at $(3, -1)$.

24

a. We can write the equation as $r\sin\theta - 6r\cos\theta = 4$, or $y - 6x = 4$. This is a straight line with slope 6 and y-intercept 4.

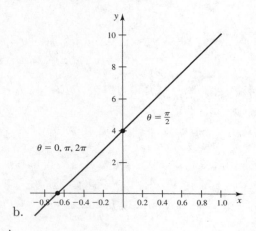

b.

c. Note that $\sin\theta - 6\cos\theta = 0$ for $\theta = \tan^{-1}(6)$. The whole curve can be generated for $\tan^{-1}(6) - \pi < \theta < \tan^{-1}(6) + \pi$.

25 If $x = r\cos\theta$ and $y = r\sin\theta$, then $(r\cos\theta - 4)^2 + r^2\sin^2\theta = 16$, so $r^2\cos^2\theta - 8r\cos\theta + 16 + r^2\sin^2\theta = 16$, so $r^2 = 8r\cos\theta$, and thus $r = 8\cos\theta$. The complete circle can be described by $-\pi/2 \le \theta \le \pi/2$.

26 We have $r\cos\theta = r^2\sin^2\theta$, so $r = \cot\theta\csc\theta$. The whole parabola is described by $0 < \theta < \pi$.

27

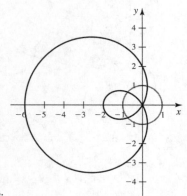

a.

There are 4 intersection points.

b. Note that $2 - 4\cos\theta = 1$ for $\theta = \cos^{-1}(1/4) \approx 1.32$, and $2 - 4\cos\theta = -1$ for $\theta = \cos^{-1}(3/4) \approx .73$. The points of intersection (in polar form) are approximately $(1, 1.32)$, $(1, 2\pi - 1.32) \approx (1, 4.96)$, $(-1, .73)$, and $(-1, 2\pi - .73) \approx (-1, 5.56)$.

28

a. $\dfrac{dy}{dx} = \dfrac{dy/d\theta}{dx/d\theta} = \dfrac{-4\sin(2\theta)\sin\theta + 2\cos(2\theta)\cos\theta}{-4\sin(2\theta)\cos\theta - 2\cos(2\theta)\sin\theta}$. This is 0 when $-4\sin(2\theta)\sin\theta + 2\cos(2\theta)\cos\theta = -8\sin^2\theta\cos\theta + 2\cos^3\theta - 2\sin^2\theta\cos\theta = 0$, which occurs for $\cos\theta = 0$, and for $2\cos^2\theta - 10\sin^2\theta = 0$, or $\tan^2\theta = \frac{1}{5}$. So there are 6 places with horizontal tangent lines: at $\theta = \pm\pi/2$, $\theta = \pm\tan^{-1}(\sqrt{1/5})$, and $\theta = \pi \pm \tan^{-1}(\sqrt{1/5})$.

Vertical tangent lines occur when $-4\sin(2\theta)\cos\theta - 2\cos(2\theta)\sin\theta = -8\sin\theta\cos^2\theta - 2\cos^2\theta\sin\theta + 2\sin^3\theta = 0$. Thus occurs when $\sin\theta = 0$, and when $-8\cos^2\theta - 2\cos^2\theta + 2\sin^2\theta = 0$, which can be written as $\tan^2\theta = 5$. So the vertical tangent lines occur at $\theta = 0$, $\theta = \pi$ and $\theta = \pm\tan^{-1}(\sqrt{5})$ and $\theta = \pi \pm \tan^{-1}(\sqrt{5})$.

b. The curve is at the origin for $\theta = \frac{\pi}{4}, \frac{3\pi}{4}, \frac{5\pi}{4}$, and $\frac{7\pi}{4}$. At these values, $\frac{dy}{dx} = \pm 1$, so the tangent lines have the equation $y = x$ or $y = -x$.

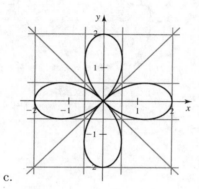

c.

29

a. $\dfrac{dy}{dx} = \dfrac{dy/d\theta}{dx/d\theta} = \dfrac{2\cos\theta\sin\theta + (4 + 2\sin\theta)\cos\theta}{2\cos\theta\cos\theta - (4 + 2\sin\theta)\sin\theta} = \dfrac{4\cos\theta + 4\sin\theta\cos\theta}{2\cos^2\theta - 2\sin^2\theta - 4\sin\theta}$.

This is 0 when $\cos\theta = 0$, and when $4\sin\theta = -4$, so the only solutions are $\theta = \pi/2, 3\pi/2$.

The denominator is 0 when $2 - 4\sin^2\theta - 4\sin\theta = 0$ which occurs (using the quadratic formula) for $\sin\theta = -\frac{1}{2} + \frac{\sqrt{3}}{2}$, so there are vertical tangent lines at $\theta = \sin^{-1}(-\frac{1}{2} + \frac{\sqrt{3}}{2})$ and $\theta = \pi - \sin^{-1}(-\frac{1}{2} + \frac{\sqrt{3}}{2})$.

b. The curve is never at the origin.

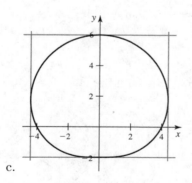

c.

30

a. $\dfrac{dy}{dx} = \dfrac{dy/d\theta}{dx/d\theta} = \dfrac{6\sin\theta\cdot\sin\theta + (3 - 6\cos\theta)\cos\theta}{6\sin\theta\cos\theta - (3 - 6\cos\theta)\sin\theta} = \dfrac{6 - 12\cos^2\theta + 3\cos\theta}{12\sin\theta\cos\theta - 3\sin\theta}$.

This is 0 when $\cos^2 \theta - \frac{1}{4} \cos \theta - \frac{1}{2} = 0$, which (by the quadratic formula) occurs where $\cos \theta = \frac{1}{8} \pm \frac{\sqrt{33}}{8}$, so for $\theta \approx .568, 2.206, 4.078,$ and 5.715.

The denominator is 0 when $\sin \theta = 0$ and when $12 \cos \theta - 3 = 0$, or $\theta = \pm \cos^{-1}(1/4)$.

b. The curve is at the origin for $\theta = \pm\pi/3$, and because $\tan \pi/3 = \sqrt{3}$, the tangent lines have the equations $y = \pm\sqrt{3}x$.

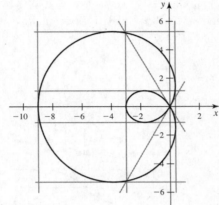

c.

31

a. Note that the whole curve is generated for $-\pi/4 \le \theta \le \pi/4$, so we restrict ourselves to that domain. Write the equations as $r = \sqrt{2 \cos 2\theta}$. Then

$$\frac{dy}{d\theta} = \sqrt{2 \cos 2\theta} \cos \theta - \sin \theta \frac{2 \sin 2\theta}{\sqrt{2 \cos 2\theta}} = \frac{\cos \theta}{\sqrt{2 \cos 2\theta}} \left(2 \cos 2\theta - 4 \sin^2 \theta\right) = \frac{\cos \theta}{\sqrt{2 \cos 2\theta}} \left(2 - 8 \sin^2 \theta\right).$$

Also, $\frac{dx}{d\theta} = -\sqrt{2 \cos 2\theta} \sin \theta + \cos \theta \frac{2 \sin 2\theta}{\sqrt{2 \cos 2\theta}} = \frac{\sin \theta}{\sqrt{2 \cos 2\theta}} \left(-4 \cos^2 \theta - 2(\cos 2\theta)\right) = \frac{(2 - 8 \cos^2 \theta) \sin \theta}{\sqrt{2 \cos(2\theta)}}$. Thus $\frac{dy}{dx} = \frac{dy/d\theta}{dx/d\theta} = \cot \theta \left(\frac{1 - 4 \sin^2 \theta}{1 - 4 \cos^2 \theta}\right)$.

This expression is 0 on the given domain only for $\sin^2 \theta = \frac{1}{4}$, so there are horizontal tangent lines at $\theta = \pm \frac{\pi}{6}$. There are vertical tangent lines on the given domain only for $\theta = 0$ In cartesian coordinates, the lines are $x = \pm\sqrt{2}$.

b. The curve is at the origin for $\theta = \pm\pi/4$, and because $\tan \pi/4 = 1$, the tangent lines have the equations $y = \pm x$.

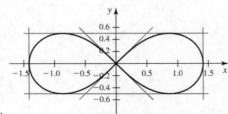

c.

32 One leaf is traced for $0 \le \theta \le \pi/4$, so $A = 8 \cdot \frac{1}{2} \int_0^{\pi/4} (3\sin(4\theta))^2 \, d\theta = 36 \int_0^{\pi/4} \sin^2 4\theta \, d\theta = 36 \left(-\frac{1}{8}\sin(4\theta)\cos(4\theta) + \frac{\theta}{2} \right) \Big|_0^{\pi/4} = 36 \left(\frac{\pi}{8} \right) = \frac{9\pi}{2}$.

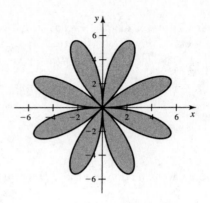

33 The area is given by $A = \frac{1}{2} \int_0^{2\pi} (3 - \cos\theta)^2 \, d\theta = \frac{1}{2} \int_0^{2\pi} (9 - 6\cos\theta + \cos^2\theta) \, d\theta = \frac{1}{2} \left(9\theta - 6\sin\theta + \frac{1}{2}(\cos\theta\sin\theta + \theta) \right) \Big|_0^{2\pi} = \frac{1}{2}(18\pi + \pi) = \frac{19\pi}{2}$.

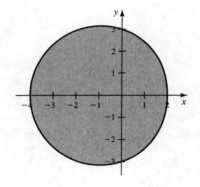

34 The curves intersect at $\theta = \pm\pi/2$. By symmetry, the area is twice the area outside the circle and inside the limaçon between 0 and $\pi/2$. We have $A = 2 \cdot \frac{1}{2} \int_0^{\pi/2} ((2 + \cos\theta)^2 - 2^2) \, d\theta = \int_0^{\pi/2} (4\cos\theta + \cos^2\theta) \, d\theta = \left(4\sin\theta + \frac{1}{2}(\cos\theta\sin\theta + \theta) \right) \Big|_0^{\pi/2} = 4 + \frac{\pi}{4}$.

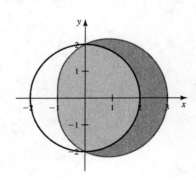

The curves intersect at $\theta = \pm\frac{1}{2}\cos^{-1}(1/16)$.
By symmetry the total desired area is
$A = 4 \cdot \frac{1}{2}\int_0^{\cos^{-1}(1/16)/2}(4\cos 2\theta - \frac{1}{4})\,d\theta =$

35

$2\left(2\sin 2\theta - \frac{\theta}{4}\right)\Big|_0^{\cos^{-1}(1/16)/2} \quad = \quad \frac{1}{4}\sqrt{255} -$

$\frac{\cos^{-1}(1/16)}{4}.$

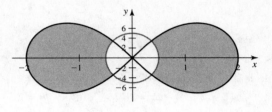

36 By symmetry, we can compute the area within the curve $r = 1 - \cos\theta$ for $0 \le \theta \le \pi/2$ and then quadruple it. We have

$$4 \cdot \frac{1}{2}\int_0^{\pi/2}(1 - \cos\theta)^2\,d\theta = 2\int_0^{\pi/2}(1 - 2\cos\theta + (1/2) + (1/2)\cos 2\theta)\,d\theta$$

$$= (3\theta - 4\sin\theta + (1/2)\sin 2\theta)\Big|_0^{\pi/2} = \frac{3\pi}{2} - 4 + 0 - (0 - 0 + 0) = \frac{3\pi}{2} - 4.$$

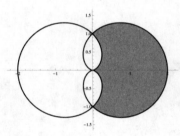

37 Note that we can compute the area within $1 + \cos\theta$ between 0 and $\pi/2$ and then subtract 1/4 of the area from the previous problem, and then double this difference. If we compute $\frac{1}{2}\int_0^{\pi/2}(1 + \cos\theta)^2\,d\theta =$

$\frac{1}{2}\int_0^{\pi/2}(1 + 2\cos\theta + \cos^2\theta)\,d\theta = \int_0^{\pi/2}(3/4 + \cos\theta + (1/4)\cos 2\theta)\,d\theta = (3\theta/4 + \sin\theta + (1/8)\sin 2\theta)\Big|_0^{\pi/2} =$

$3\pi/8 + 1 + 0 - (0 + 0 + 0) = 3\pi/8 + 1.$

If we subtract 1/4 of the previous result, we have $3\pi/8 + 1 - (3\pi/8 - 1) = 2$. Doubling this gives a final result of 4.

38

a. This represents a parabola.

b. We can write $y^2 = \frac{1}{16}x = 4 \cdot \frac{1}{64}x$, so $(p, 0) = (\frac{1}{64}, 0)$ is the focus, and the directrix is $x = -\frac{1}{64}$. The vertex is $(0, 0)$.

c. $e = 1$, because that is the case for all parabolas.

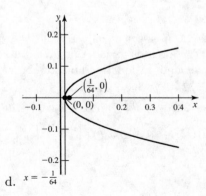

d.

39

   a. This represents a hyperbola with $a = 1$ and $b = \sqrt{2}$.

   b. The vertices are $(\pm 1, 0)$, the foci are $(\pm c, 0)$ where $c^2 = a^2 + b^2 = 3$, so they are $(\pm\sqrt{3}, 0)$. The directrices are $x = \frac{\pm a^2}{c} = \frac{\pm 1}{\sqrt{3}}$.

   c. The eccentricity is $e = \frac{c}{a} = \sqrt{3}$.

   d.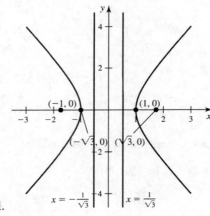

40

   a. This represents an ellipse with $a = 5$ and $b = 2$.

   b. The vertices are $(0, \pm 5)$. The foci are $(0, \pm c)$ where $c^2 = a^2 - b^2 = 25 - 4 = 21$, so they are $(0, \pm\sqrt{21})$. The directrices are $y = \frac{\pm a^2}{c} = \frac{\pm 25}{\sqrt{21}}$.

   c. The eccentricity is $e = \frac{c}{a} = \frac{\sqrt{21}}{5}$.

   d.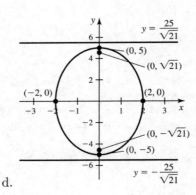

41

   a. This can be written as $\frac{y^2}{16} - \frac{x^2}{4} = 1$. It is a hyperbola with $a = 4$ and $b = 2$.

   b. The vertices are $(0, \pm 4)$. The foci are $(0, \pm c)$ where $c^2 = a^2 + b^2 = 16 + 4 = 20$, so they are $(0, \pm\sqrt{20})$. The directrices are $y = \frac{\pm a^2}{c} = \frac{\pm 16}{\sqrt{20}} = \frac{\pm 8}{\sqrt{5}}$.

c. The eccentricity is $e = \frac{c}{a} = \frac{\sqrt{20}}{4} = \frac{\sqrt{5}}{2}$.

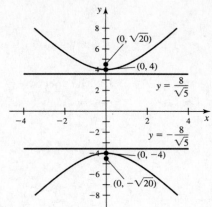

d.

42

a. This can be written in the form $y = 8(x+1)^2$, so it is a parabola opening upward.

b. The vertex is $(-1, 0)$, and because $\frac{1}{8}y = (x+1)^2$, we have $p = \frac{1}{32}$ and the focus is $(-1, \frac{1}{32})$. The directrix is $y = -\frac{1}{32}$.

c. The eccentricity is $e = 1$, as it is for all parabolas.

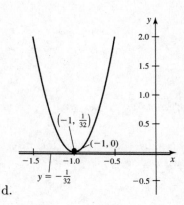

d.

43

a. This can be written as $\frac{x^2}{4} + \frac{y^2}{2} = 1$, so it is an ellipse with $a = 2$ and $b = \sqrt{2}$.

b. The vertices are $(\pm 2, 0)$. The foci are $(\pm c, 0)$ where $c^2 = a^2 - b^2 = 4 - 2 = 2$, so they are $(\pm \sqrt{2}, 0)$. The directrices are $x = \frac{\pm a^2}{c} = \frac{\pm 4}{\sqrt{2}} = \pm 2\sqrt{2}$.

c. The eccentricity is $e = \frac{c}{a} = \frac{\sqrt{2}}{2}$.

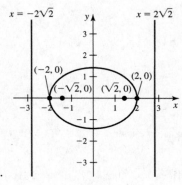

d.

44

   a. This matches graph (E).

   b. This matches graph (D).

   c. This matches graph (B).

   d. This matches graph (F).

   e. This matches graph (C).

   f. This matches graph (A).

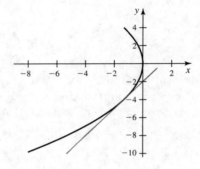

45 $2y\frac{dy}{dx} = -12$, so at the point in question, $\frac{dy}{dx} = 3/2$. So the equation of the tangent line is $y + 4 = \frac{3}{2}\left(x + \frac{4}{3}\right)$, or $y = \frac{3}{2}x - 2$.

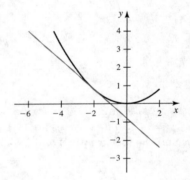

46 $2x = 5\frac{dy}{dx}$, so at the given point, we have $\frac{dy}{dx} = -\frac{4}{5}$. So the equation of the tangent line is $y - \frac{4}{5} = -\frac{4}{5}(x + 2)$, or $y = -\frac{4}{5}x - \frac{4}{5}$.

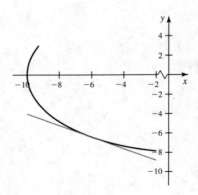

47 $\frac{x}{50} + \frac{y}{32} \cdot \frac{dy}{dx} = 0$, so at the given point, $\frac{dy}{dx} = -\frac{6}{10} = -\frac{3}{5}$. So the equation of the tangent line is $y + \frac{32}{5} = -\frac{3}{5}(x + 6)$, or $y = -\frac{3}{5}x - 10$.

48 $\frac{x}{8} - \frac{2y}{9} \cdot \frac{dy}{dx} = 0$, so at the given point, $\frac{dy}{dx} = -\frac{15}{16}$. The equation of the tangent line is therefore $y + 4 = -\frac{15}{16}\left(x - \frac{20}{3}\right)$, or $y = -\frac{15}{16}x + \frac{9}{4}$.

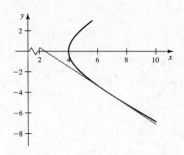

49 The eccentricity is 1, and the directrix is $y = 2$. The vertex is $(0, 1)$ and the focus is $(0, 0)$.

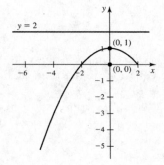

50 The eccentricity is 2, and the directrices are $x = -\frac{3}{2}$ and $x = -\frac{5}{2}$. The vertices are $(-1, 0)$ and $(-3, 0)$ and the foci are $(0, 0)$ and $(-4, 0)$.

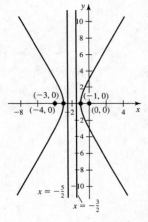

51 The eccentricity is $\frac{1}{2}$, and the directrices are $x = 4$ and $x = -\frac{20}{3}$. The vertices are $\left(\frac{4}{3}, 0\right)$ and $(-4, 0)$ and the foci are $(0, 0)$ and $\left(-\frac{8}{3}, 0\right)$.

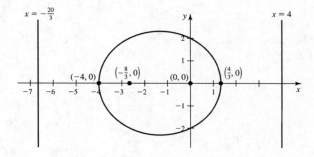

52 The eccentricity is $\frac{2}{5}$. The vertices are $(10/7, 0)$ and $(-10/3, 0)$, so the center is $(-20/21, 0)$. The foci are $(0, 0)$ and $(-40/21, 0)$. The directrices are $x = -\frac{145}{21}$ and $x = 5$.

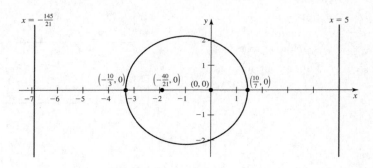

53

   a. Recall that $\cos 2\theta = \cos^2 \theta - \sin^2 \theta$, so $r^2 \cos(2\theta) = 1$ becomes $r^2(\cos^2 \theta - \sin^2 \theta) = x^2 - y^2 = 1$. The curve is a hyperbola.

   b. With $a = b = 1$, we have $c^2 = 2$, so the vertices are $(\pm 1, 0)$ and the foci are $(\pm\sqrt{2}, 0)$. The directrices are $x = \pm\frac{a^2}{c} = \pm\frac{1}{\sqrt{2}}$. The eccentricity is $e = \frac{c}{a} = \sqrt{2}$.

   c. It does not have the form as in Theorem 11.4 because it does not have a focus at the origin.

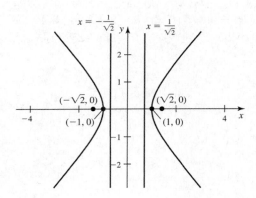

54 Because the center is halfway between the foci, it is $(0, 0)$. We must have $c = 4$ and because $\frac{a^2}{c} = d = 8$, we have $a^2 = 32$. So $b^2 = a^2 - c^2 = 32 - 16 = 16$. The ellipse has equation $\frac{x^2}{32} + \frac{y^2}{16} = 1$. The eccentricity is $\frac{c}{a} = \frac{4}{4\sqrt{2}} = \frac{\sqrt{2}}{2}$.

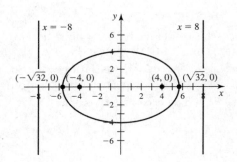

55 Because the center is halfway between the vertices, it is $(0,0)$. We must have $a = 4$ and because $\frac{a^2}{c} = d = 10$, we have $c = \frac{8}{5}$. So $b^2 = a^2 - c^2 = 16 - \frac{64}{25} = \frac{336}{25}$. The ellipse has equation $\frac{25x^2}{336} + \frac{y^2}{16} = 1$. The eccentricity is $\frac{c}{a} = \frac{8/5}{4} = \frac{2}{5}$.

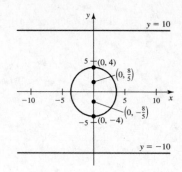

56 Because the center is halfway between the vertices, it is $(0,0)$. We must have $a = 4$ and because $\frac{a^2}{c} = d = 2$, we have $c = 8$. So $b^2 = 64 - 16 = 48$. The hyperbola has equation $\frac{x^2}{16} - \frac{y^2}{48} = 1$. The eccentricity is $\frac{c}{a} = \frac{8}{4} = 2$.

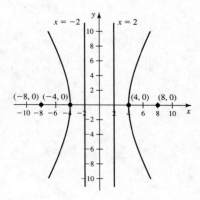

57 Because the center is halfway between the vertices, it is $(0,0)$. We must have $a = 2$ and because $\frac{a^2}{c} = d = 1$, we have $c = 4$. So $b^2 = 16 - 4 = 12$. The hyperbola has equation $\frac{y^2}{4} - \frac{x^2}{12} = 1$. The eccentricity is $\frac{c}{a} = \frac{4}{2} = 2$.

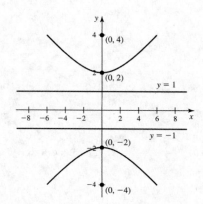

58 We have $c = 2$, $e = \frac{c}{a} = 2$, so $a = 1$. Also, $b^2 = c^2 - a^2 = 3$, so the equation is $\frac{y^2}{1} - \frac{x^2}{3} = 1$. We have $d = \frac{a^2}{c} = \frac{1}{2}$. The vertices are $(0, \pm 1)$ and the directrices are $y = \pm\frac{1}{2}$.

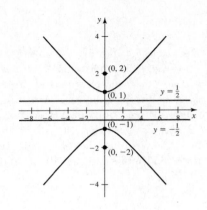

59 We have $a = 6$, $c = 4$ and $e = \frac{c}{a} = \frac{4}{6} = \frac{2}{3}$. Also, $b^2 = a^2 - c^2 = 36 - 16 = 20$, and the equation is $\frac{y^2}{36} + \frac{x^2}{20} = 1$. The vertices are $(\pm 2\sqrt{5}, 0)$. The directrices are $y = \pm\frac{a^2}{c} = \pm 9$.

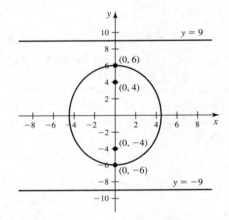

60 $1 - \cos\theta = \theta$, so $\theta = 0$ is a solution. Note that if $f(\theta) = 1 - \cos\theta - \theta$, then $f'(\theta) = \sin\theta - 1 \leq 0$ for all θ. Thus this function is non-decreasing and the only solution is the one already found.

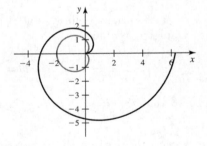

61 $\sin 2\theta = \theta^2$ when $\theta = 0$. Graphing the functions reveals a root near $\theta = 1$. A CAS reveals the intersection point to be $\theta \approx .9669$. In polar coordinates, the intersection points are $(0, 0)$ and $(.9669, .9669)$.

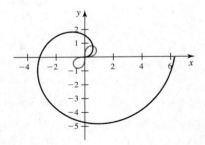

62 $\sin 2\theta = 2\sin\theta\cos\theta$, and $(1 - 2\sin\theta)^2 = 1-4\sin\theta+4\sin^2\theta$. The equation $1-4\sin\theta+4\sin^2\theta = 2\sin\theta\cos\theta$ does not lend itself to an analytic solution, however. A graphing utility shows three points of intersection, and a CAS reveals the origin as an intersection point, as well as the approximate polar intersection points $(.6148, .1938)$ and $(-.8445, 1.1738)$.

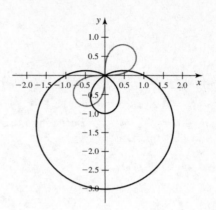

63 The curves intersect for $\theta = 0$. Note also that when $\theta = k\pi$ for k an odd integer, the curve $r = -\theta$ is at the polar point $(-k\pi, k\pi) = (k\pi, 0)$. And for $\theta = 2k\pi$, the curve $r = \frac{\theta}{2}$ is at the point $(k\pi, 0)$. So the curves intersect at these points.

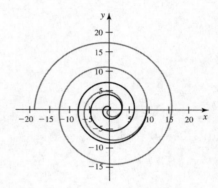

64 Note that $a = ed$ and $b = a\sqrt{1 - e^2}$, so the ellipse given by

$$r = \frac{ab}{\sqrt{a^2\sin^2\theta + b^2\cos^2\theta}}$$

has the same area as the original ellipse, but is centered at the origin. We compute the area of this ellipse instead. Using symmetry, we have

$$A = 4 \cdot \frac{1}{2}\int_0^{\pi/2} \frac{ab}{\sqrt{a^2\sin^2\theta + b^2\cos^2\theta}}\, d\theta = 2\int_0^{\pi/2} \frac{a^2 b^2 \sec^2\theta}{a^2\tan^2\theta + b^2}\, d\theta = 2a^2\int_0^{\pi/2} \frac{\sec^2\theta}{\frac{a^2}{b^2}\tan^2\theta + 1}\, d\theta.$$

Let $u = \frac{a}{b}\tan\theta$ so that $du = \frac{a}{b}\sec^2\theta\, d\theta$. Then we have $A = 2ab\int_0^\infty \frac{1}{1+u^2}\, du = 2ab \cdot \lim_{z\to\infty}\tan^{-1} z = \frac{2ab\pi}{2} = \pi ab$.

65 By symmetry, we can focus on the region in the first quadrant. That area is given by $A = xy$ where $y = \sqrt{b^2 - \frac{b^2}{a^2}x^2}$. So

$$A(x) = x\sqrt{b^2 - \frac{b^2}{a^2}x^2},$$

so

$$A'(x) = \sqrt{b^2 - \frac{b^2}{a^2}x^2} - \frac{b^2 x^2}{a^2\sqrt{b^2 - \frac{b^2}{a^2}x^2}}.$$

Setting the derivative equal to 0 and clearing denominators yields $\left(b^2 - \frac{b^2}{a^2}x^2\right)a^2 - b^2 x^2 = 0$, and solving for x gives the critical point $x = \frac{\sqrt{2}}{2}a$. Because this is the only critical point and it clearly does not give a minimum (because $A(0) = A(a) = 0$), it must yield a maximum. The whole rectangle has dimensions $\sqrt{2}a \times \sqrt{2}b$, and area $2ab$.

We focus on the first quadrant and then use symmetry for the rest. Consider points within the triangle with vertices $(0,0)$, $(a,0)$ and (a,a). Any point (x,y) within this triangle is closer to the line $x = a$ than any other side of the square, so the distance from this point to the square is $a - x$. The distance from (x,y) to the origin is $\sqrt{x^2 + y^2}$. So we have $x^2 + y^2 = x^2 - 2ax + a^2$, or the parabola $y^2 = -2ax + a^2$.

66 In the triangle with vertices $(0,0)$, $(0,a)$ and (a,a), the point (x,y) is closer to the line $y = a$, so the distance from that point to the line is $a - y$. Therefore, the points we are seeking lie along a curve where $x^2 + y^2 = y^2 - 2ay + a^2$, or the parabola $x^2 = -2ay + a^2$. Note that the two curves mentioned intersect intersect along the line $y = x$ at the point $(a(\sqrt{2} - 1), a(\sqrt{2} - 1))$. The curve desired is thus the union of portions of 4 parabolas.

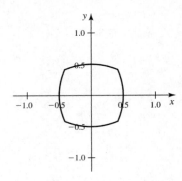

67 The area of the ellipse in the first quadrant is $\frac{\pi ab}{4}$, so we are seeking θ_0 so that

$$\frac{\pi ab}{8} = \frac{1}{2} \int_0^{\theta_0} \frac{a^2 b^2}{a^2 \sin^2 \theta + b^2 \cos^2 \theta} \, d\theta = \frac{a^2}{2} \int_0^{\theta_0} \frac{\sec^2 \theta}{\frac{a^2}{b^2} \tan^2 \theta + 1} \, d\theta.$$

Let $u = \frac{a}{b} \tan \theta$ so that $du = \frac{a}{b} \sec^2 \theta \, d\theta$. Then we have $\frac{\pi ab}{8} = \frac{ab}{2} \int_0^{\frac{a}{b} \tan \theta_0} \frac{1}{1 + u^2} \, du = \frac{ab}{2} \tan^{-1}(\frac{a}{b} \tan(\theta_0))$. Note that this equation is satisfied when $\tan(\theta_0) = \frac{b}{a}$, because then the expression on the right-hand side of that equation is $\frac{ab}{2} \cdot \frac{\pi}{4} = \frac{\pi ab}{8}$. So the desired value of m is $\tan(\theta_0) = \frac{b}{a}$.

68

  a. The curves are tangent when there is only one point of intersection in the first quadrant. This occurs when $x^2 - p^2 x^4 = 1$ has only one solution. This quadratic-type equation $-p^2 (x^2)^2 + (x^2) - 1 = 0$ has solution $x^2 = \frac{1 \pm \sqrt{1 - 4p^2}}{2p^2}$, and the discriminant $1 - 4p^2$ is 0 for $p = 1/2$.

  b. The two curves intersect for $x^2 = \frac{1 \pm 0}{2p^2} = 2$, so for $x = \sqrt{2}$. The corresponding value for y is $\frac{1}{2}(\sqrt{2})^2 = 1$.

  c. Using the same line of reasoning, we seek the value of p so that $\frac{x^2}{a^2} - \frac{p^2 x^4}{b^2} = 1$, which yields the quadratic-type equation $p^2 a^2 (x^2)^2 - b^2 (x^2) + a^2 b^2 = 0$. The discriminant is 0 when $b^4 - 4p^2 a^4 b^2 = 0$, which occurs when $p = \frac{b}{2a^2}$. The point of intersection is $x = \sqrt{2}a$. The corresponding value of y is $px^2 = b$.

69 Note that $Q = (a \cos \theta, a \sin \theta)$ and $R = (b \cos \theta, b \sin \theta)$, where θ is the angle formed by l and the x-axis. Then $P = (a \sin \theta, b \cos \theta)$ is a point on the ellipse $\frac{x^2}{a^2} + \frac{y^2}{b^2} = 1$, because it satisfies that equation.

70 The focal point is at the origin, the directrix is $x = -\frac{3}{2}$, so $d = \frac{3}{2}$, and $r = \frac{ed}{1 - e \cos \theta}$ where $e = \frac{c}{a}$. Because c is the distance from the center to the focal point, we have $c = 2$, and because a is the distance from the center to a vertex, we have $a = 1$. Thus $e = 2$ and $r = \frac{3}{1 - 2 \cos \theta}$.

71 The focal point is at the origin, the directrix is $y = -d$, so we have an equation of the form $r = \frac{ed}{1 - e \sin \theta}$. Because c is the distance from the center to the focal point, we have $c = 3/8$, and because a is the distance from the center to a vertex, we have $a = 9/8$. Then we have $e = \frac{c}{a} = \frac{3/8}{9/8} = \frac{1}{3}$, and $d = \frac{a^2}{c} - \frac{3}{8} = 3$. Thus $r = \frac{1}{1 - \frac{1}{3} \sin \theta} = \frac{3}{3 - \sin \theta}$.

Appendix A

A.1.1 This is the set of real numbers greater than -4 and less than or equal to 10; $(-4, 10]$.

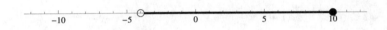

A.1.2 This set can be written as $\{x : x < 2\}$.

A.1.3 The absolute value function is defined as a piecewise function in this manner: $|x| = \begin{cases} x & \text{if } x \geq 0 \\ -x & \text{if } x < 0. \end{cases}$

A.1.4 In order for $|x - 2| \leq 3$ we must have both $x - 2 \leq 3$ and $x - 2 \geq -3$.

A.1.5 In order for $|2x - 4| \geq 3$ we must have either $2x - 4 \geq 3$ or $2x - 4 \leq -3$.

A.1.6 If the point (x, y) is to be 5 units away from $(2, 3)$, then $\sqrt{(x - 2)^2 + (y - 3)^2} = 5$, so $(x - 2)^2 + (y - 3)^2 = 25$. This is the circle with center $(2, 3)$ and radius 5.

A.1.7 If (x_1, y_1) and (x_2, y_2) are two known points, then the distance between them is given by the expression $\sqrt{(x_2 - x_1)^2 + (y_2 - y_1)^2}$.

A.1.8 The expression $\sqrt{(x - 0)^2 + (y - 2)^2}$ represents the distance between (x, y) and $(0, 2)$. Thus $\sqrt{(x - 0)^2 + (y - 2)^2} > 4$ represents the set of points whose distance from $(0, 2)$ is greater than 4, and this is equivalent to the expression $x^2 + (y - 2)^2 > 16$. Thus we have the points outside the circle of radius 4 centered at $(0, 2)$.

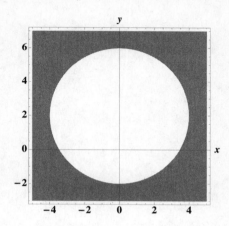

A.1.9 The set of points (x, y) whose distance from the origin is 6 is given by $x^2 + y^2 = 36$. Solving for y gives $|y| = \sqrt{36 - x^2}$. Note that $y = \sqrt{36 - x^2}$ represents the upper half of the circle while $y = -\sqrt{36 - x^2}$ represents the bottom half.

A.1.10 The solution set could be the empty set (for example if we have $x^2 + y^2 + 1 = 0$), it could be a single point (for example if we have $x^2 + y^2 = 0$), or it could be a circle (for example, if we have $x^2 + y^2 - 9 = 0$).

A.1.11 Using the point-slope form of the equation of a line, we write $y - (-2) = m(x - 4)$ or $y = -2 + m(x - 4)$.

A.1.12 Using the slope-intercept form of the equation of a line, we write $y = mx + 6$.

A.1.13 If two lines are parallel, then either their slopes are equal (in the case of non vertical lines) or they both have slopes which are undefined (in the case of vertical lines).

A.1.14 For nonvertical/horizontal pairs, the lines have slopes which are negative reciprocals of each other. So if one line has slope m_1 and the other m_2, then $m_1 = -\frac{1}{m_2}$. In the case of vertical/horizontal pairs, the horizontal line has slope 0 while the vertical line has undefined slope.

A.1.15 $\left(\frac{1}{8}\right)^{-2/3} = 8^{2/3} = \sqrt[3]{8}^2 = 2^2 = 4$.

A.1.16 $\sqrt[3]{-125} + \sqrt{1/25} = -5 + \frac{1}{5} = -\frac{25}{5} + \frac{1}{5} = -\frac{24}{5}$.

A.1.17 $(u + v)^2 - (u - v)^2 = u^2 + 2uv + v^2 - (u^2 - 2uv + v^2) = u^2 + 2uv + v^2 - u^2 + 2uv - v^2 = 4uv$.

A.1.18 $\frac{(a+h)^2 - a^2}{h} = \frac{a^2 + 2ah + h^2 - a^2}{h} = \frac{h(2a + h)}{h} = 2a + h$ for $h \neq 0$.

A.1.19 $\frac{1}{x+h} - \frac{1}{x} = \frac{1}{x+h} \cdot \frac{x}{x} - \frac{1}{x} \cdot \frac{x+h}{x+h} = \frac{x - (x+h)}{x(x+h)} = -\frac{h}{x(x+h)}$.

A.1.20 $\frac{2}{x+3} - \frac{2}{x-3} = \frac{2}{x+3} \cdot \frac{x-3}{x-3} - \frac{2}{x-3} \cdot \frac{x+3}{x+3} = \frac{2x - 6 - (2x + 6)}{(x-3)(x+3)} = -\frac{12}{(x-3)(x+3)}$.

A.1.21 $y^2 - y^{-2} = y^2 - (y^{-1})^2 = (y - y^{-1})(y + y^{-1})$.

A.1.22 $x^3 - 9x = 0$, so $x(x^2 - 9) = x(x - 3)(x + 3) = 0$, so $x = 0$ or $x = 3$ or $x = -3$.

A.1.23 Note that $u^4 - 11u^2 + 18 = (u^2 - 9)(u^2 - 2) = (u - 3)(u + 3)(u - \sqrt{2})(u + \sqrt{2})$, so this equation is equal to 0 when $u = 3$, $u = -3$, $u = \sqrt{2}$ or $u = -\sqrt{2}$.

A.1.24 Note that $4^x = (2^2)^x = 2^{2x} = (2^x)^2$. Thus we can write the given equation as $(2^x)^2 - 6(2^x) + 8 = 0$. Let $2^x = u$. Then we have $u^2 - 6u + 8 = (u - 4)(u - 2) = 0$, so the solutions in terms of u are $u = 4$ and $u = 2$. Thus in terms of x we have $2^x = 4$ and $2^x = 2$, so the solutions are $x = 2$ and $x = 1$.

A.1.25 $\frac{(x+h)^3 - x^3}{h} = \frac{x^3 + 3x^2h + 3xh^2 + h^3 - x^3}{h} = \frac{h(3x^2 + 3xh + h^2)}{h} = 3x^2 + 3xh + h^2$.

A.1.26 $\frac{\sqrt{x+h}-\sqrt{x}}{h} = \frac{\sqrt{x+h}-\sqrt{x}}{h} \cdot \frac{\sqrt{x+h}+\sqrt{x}}{\sqrt{x+h}+\sqrt{x}} = \frac{x+h-x}{h(\sqrt{x+h}+\sqrt{x})} = \frac{h}{h(\sqrt{x+h}+\sqrt{x})} = \frac{1}{\sqrt{x+h}+\sqrt{x}}$.

A.1.27 $x^2 - 6x + 5 < 0$ can be written as $(x-5)(x-1) < 0$. The product of two numbers is negative when one is positive and the other is negative, so we have either $x - 5 < 0$ and $x - 1 > 0$ or $x - 5 > 0$ and $x - 1 < 0$. The first case occurs when both $x < 5$ and $x > 1$, so for $1 < x < 5$. The second case occurs when $x > 5$ and $x < 1$ simultaneously, which isn't possible. So the solution set consists of the interval $(1, 5)$.

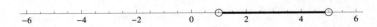

A.1.28 Note that we can write $\frac{x+1}{x+2} - 6 = \frac{x+1-6(x+2)}{x+2} = \frac{-5x-11}{x+2}$. This expression is negative when either $-5x - 11 < 0$ while $x + 2 > 0$, or when $-5x - 11 > 0$ while $x + 2 < 0$. In the first case we have both $x > -\frac{11}{5}$ and $x > -2$ which occurs for $x > -2$. In the second case we have both $x < -\frac{11}{5}$ and $x < -2$ which occurs for $x < -\frac{11}{5}$. The solution set is thus $(-\infty, -\frac{11}{5}) \cup (-2, \infty)$.

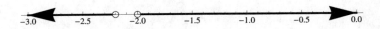

A.1.29 This can be written as $\frac{(x-5)(x-4)}{x-6} \le 0$. The expression on the left is zero for $x = 5$ and $x = 4$, while the expression is undefined for $x = 6$. These numbers partition the number line into the intervals $(-\infty, 4)$, $(4, 5)$, $(5, 6)$ and $(6, \infty)$. Using test values, we see that the expression is negative on the interval $(-\infty, 4)$ and on $(5, 6)$ while it is positive on the other intervals. Thus the given expression is less than or equal to 0 on $(-\infty, 4] \cup [5, 6)$.

A.1.30 Note that expression $x\sqrt{x-1}$ is only defined for $x \ge 1$. Also, it is equal to 0 only for $x = 1$. On the interval $(1, \infty)$ both $x > 0$ and $\sqrt{x-1} > 0$, so their product is positive as well. The solution set is $(1, \infty)$.

A.1.31 In order for $|3x - 4| > 8$ we must have either $3x - 4 > 8$ or $3x - 4 < -8$. Thus we either have $3x > 12$ and thus $x > 4$, or we have $3x < -4$ or $x < -\frac{4}{3}$. The solution set is $\left(-\infty, -\frac{4}{3}\right) \cup (4, \infty)$.

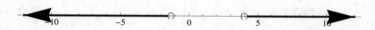

A.1.32 For $x > 0$ this inequality can be written $1 \leq x \leq 10$. For $x < 0$, this can be written as $1 \leq -x \leq 10$, or multiplying through by -1 we have $-10 \leq x \leq -1$. The solution set is $[-10, -1] \cup [1, 10]$.

A.1.33 If $2x - 1 > 0$ (which occurs for $x > \frac{1}{2}$), we have $3 < 2x - 1 < 5$ or $2 < x < 3$. If $2x - 1 < 0$ (which occurs for $x < \frac{1}{2}$), we have $3 < 1 - 2x < 5$ or $2 < -2x < 4$, or dividing through by -2 we have $-2 < x < -1$. The solution set is thus $(-2, -1) \cup (2, 3)$.

A.1.34 If $\frac{x}{2} - 5 > 0$ (which occurs for $x > 10$), we have $2 < \frac{x}{2} - 5 < 6$, or $7 < \frac{x}{2} < 11$, or $14 < x < 22$. If $\frac{x}{2} - 5 < 0$ (which occurs for $x < 10$) we have $2 < 5 - \frac{x}{2} < 6$, or $-3 < -\frac{x}{2} < 1$. Multiplying through by -2 yields $-2 < x < 6$. The solution set is $(-2, 6) \cup (14, 22)$.

A.1.35 The circle centered at $(-1, 2)$ with radius 3 is given by $(x + 1)^2 + (y - 2)^2 = 9$. This can be written as $(y - 2)^2 = 9 - (x + 1)^2$, and taking square roots of both sides gives $|y - 2| = \sqrt{9 - (x + 1)^2}$, so $y = 2 \pm \sqrt{9 - (x + 1)^2}$. The lower half of the circle is described by $y = 2 - \sqrt{9 - (x + 1)^2}$.

A.1.36 Completing the squares, we write this expression as

$$x^2 + 6x + 9 + y^2 + 8y + 16 \geq 25 + 9 + 16,$$

which can be written as $(x + 3)^2 + (y + 4)^2 \geq 50$. This is the set of points on or outside of the circle centered at $(-3, -4)$ with radius $\sqrt{50} = 5\sqrt{2}$.

A.1.37 Using the slope-intercept form of the equation of a line we have $y = \frac{5}{3}x + 4$.

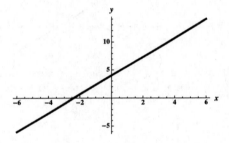

A.1.38 ℓ must be a vertical line, so its equation is $x = 0$.

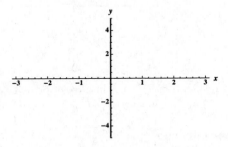

A.1.39 The slope of ℓ must be $\frac{-4-0}{0-5} = \frac{4}{5}$. Then using the slope-intercept form of the equation of a line, we have $y = \frac{4}{5}x - 4$.

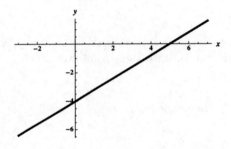

A.1.40 If ℓ is parallel to the x-axis, then it must be horizontal and have slope 0. The equation must therefore be $y = 3$.

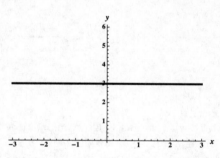

A.1.41 The line we are seeking must have the same slope as $x + 2y = 8$, which can be written as $y = -\frac{1}{2}x + 4$, so the slope must be $-\frac{1}{2}$. Using the slope-intercept form of the equation of a line, the line we are seeking must have equation $y = -\frac{1}{2}x + 12$.

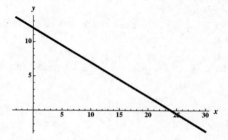

A.1.42 The line $2x - 5 = 0$ can be written $x = \frac{5}{2}$; this is a vertical line. The line we are seeking must be vertical and contain the point $(-6, 0)$, so it must be the vertical line $x = -6$.

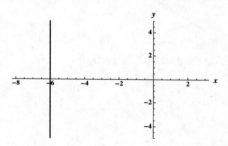

A.1.43 The line we are seeking is perpendicular to a line of slope -3, so it must have slope $\frac{1}{3}$. Using the point-slope form of the equation of a line, we have $y - (-6) = \frac{1}{3}(x - 3)$, or $y = -6 + \frac{1}{3}x - 1$, or $y = \frac{1}{3}x - 7$.

A.1.44 The line joining the given points has slope $\frac{2-(-5)}{-9-3} = -\frac{7}{12}$. So the perpendicular bisector must have slope $\frac{12}{7}$. The midpoint of the line segment between the given points is $\left(\frac{-9+3}{2}, \frac{2-5}{2}\right) = (-3, -3/2)$. Using the point-slope form of the equation of a line we have $y - (-3/2) = \frac{12}{7}(x - (-3))$ or $y = -\frac{3}{2} + \frac{12}{7}x + \frac{36}{7}$ or $y = \frac{12}{7}x + \frac{33}{2}$.

A.1.45

a. False. $\sqrt{16} = 4$, not -4. Note that the equation $x^2 = 16$ does have two solutions, but this is solved properly by taking the square root of both sides to obtain $|x| = 4$, which then yields $x = \pm 4$.

b. True. Both sides are equal to 4.

c. False. No real numbers satisfy this equation as $|x| > 0$ for all x.

d. False. $|x| \geq 0$ for all x.

e. False. The distance from the point $(1,1)$ to the origin is $\sqrt{(1-0)^2 + (1-0)^2} = \sqrt{2} > 1$, so the point $(1,1)$ is outside the circle of radius 1 centered at the origin.

f. True. Note that $x^4 = (x^2)^2$, so $\sqrt{x^4} = |x^2| = x^2$ for all x.

g. False. For example, consider the case $a = 2$ and $b = -3$. Then $\sqrt{a^2} = 2$ and $\sqrt{b^2} = 3$, so $\sqrt{a^2} < \sqrt{b^2}$, but it isn't true that $a < b$.

A.1.46 This is the set of numbers less than 12, which can be written as $\{x : x < 12\}$.

A.1.47 The complement of this set is the interval $(-2, 4)$ which is the set of numbers within 3 units of the number 1. This can be written as $\{x : |x - 1| < 3\}$. The set we are seeking is the complement of this, so it can be written as $\{x : |x - 1| \geq 3\}$.

A.1.48 Note that the interval $(2, 5)$ can be thought of as the set of numbers that are within 1.5 units of the midpoint, 3.5. Also, the interval $(3, 4)$ can be thought of as the set of numbers that are within 0.5 units of the midpoint 3.5. So the set we are seeking is $\{x : 0.5 \leq |x - 3.5| < 1.5\}$.

A.1.49 Because the absolute value function is only 0 at 0, we must have $x - y = 0$, or $y = x$, which is the line through the origin with slope 1.

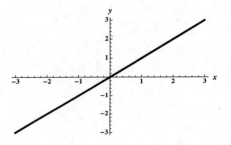

A.1.50 This equation is satisfied for either $y = x$ or $y = -x$, so we have both the line through the origin with slope 1 and the line through the origin with slope -1.

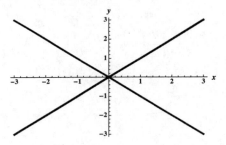